A Gui
Majo

2001/2002 edition

Volume 1
The top 300 trusts

Luke FitzHerbert
Gavin Richards

DIRECTORY OF SOCIAL CHANGE

A Guide to the Major Trusts
Volume 1
2001/2002 edition

Published by
The Directory of Social Change
24 Stephenson Way
London NW1 2DP
Tel: 020 7209 5151, fax: 020 7209 5049
e-mail: info@dsc.org.uk
from whom further copies and a full publications list are available

The Directory of Social Change is a Registered Charity no. 800517

First published 1986
Second edition 1989
Third edition 1991
Fourth edition 1993
Fifth edition 1995
Sixth edition 1997
Seventh edition 1999
Eighth edition 2001

ISBN 1 900360 80 2

British Library Cataloguing in Publication data

A catalogue record for this book is available from the British Library

Cover design by Keith Shaw
Designed and typeset by Linda Parker
Printed and bound by Page Bros, Norwich

Contents

Introduction **v**

Dates for your diary **xv**

The major trusts ranked by grant total **xviii**

Trust descriptions in alphabetical sequence **1**

Subject index **337**

Geographical index **349**

Alphabetical index **355**

Introduction

This is the eighth edition of this book, which is researched from scratch and rewritten every two years.

The book follows the format of previous editions except for the following changes:

- Text which quotes from a trust's own material is now in a separate typeface, rather than being identified only by repeated quotation marks. We hope this will make some of the longer entries more accessible to our readers.
- The beneficial area of each trust is not listed unless it is restricted either legally or as a matter of policy.
- There are now full subject and regional indices (previously these appeared in Volume 2 of this series, though covering the entries in both books).
- We have included, in the accompanying box, a listing of some of the main sources of small grants (generally, for less than £5,000). Readers may be encouraged by the relatively high success rates for such applications; they are also urged by these editors to encourage other small charities that they may know to apply for such grants.

Entries are drafted from public information. The basic documents are the legally required annual report and accounts; where these are unsatisfactory, we say so. For many trusts there are also guidelines for applicants; for some there are non-statutory 'annual reviews'. Occasionally there are also press cuttings about the trust or about individual trustees or members of staff.

The entries try to be descriptive and informal and they include editorial comment where this seems called for – these trusts are public institutions and are therefore, in the Charity Commission's words, subject to 'the beneficial light of public scrutiny'.

All trusts are sent draft copies of their entries, with an invitation to comment, correct or protest if they feel subjected to unfair criticism. Very often, we are able to make changes that bring some satisfaction to both parties, especially when the problem arises from our having insufficient information.

We try hard not to be influenced by the amount of co-operation we ourselves receive in writing this book; even the most enlightened trust may reasonably see our enquiries as an interruption to more important work. In practice, we are again very pleased to thank all those trusts, the overwhelming majority, which go out of their way to co-operate with us.

We do not normally ask for information beyond what is routinely available (though we ask for clarification when we do not understand what is given to us). We think that trusts should provide full information about their work as a basic part of their accountability to society. The trusts that did not meet their obligation to send copies of their annual report and accounts on request will be seen listed below.

So far as is reasonable, we repeat the language used by the trust being described, in order to help readers appreciate the style of the organisation concerned. If a trust categorises some grants as going to 'the elderly', for example, we will accept that usage, even if we would try not to do so when writing our own material.

Figures are normally rounded up; this may lead to apparent inconsistencies. In some cases there are also internal inconsistencies in the material provided, which we have not been able to resolve. We do not mask such difficulties. Often they are caused by a lack of clarity in the distinction between 'grants awarded' and 'payments made'.

The geographical distribution of grants

The complaints we have made in successive editions of this book about the unfair geographical distribution of trust grants left us feeling rather exposed as our evidence was largely impressionistic. It was a relief to have these hostages to fortune redeemed by the publication in early 2000 of the Charities Aid Foundation's *Patterns of Independent Grant-Making in the UK*. This study demonstrated comprehensively that in fact we had been too cautious in attacking the bias in trust expenditure towards support for work in London (despite some people's assumption to the contrary, we had always excluded, as does CAF, the influence of grants to national charities based in the capital).

The big surprise was that Scotland does quite well; the losers are elsewhere. The CAF figures are as follows, in terms of the value of grants per head:

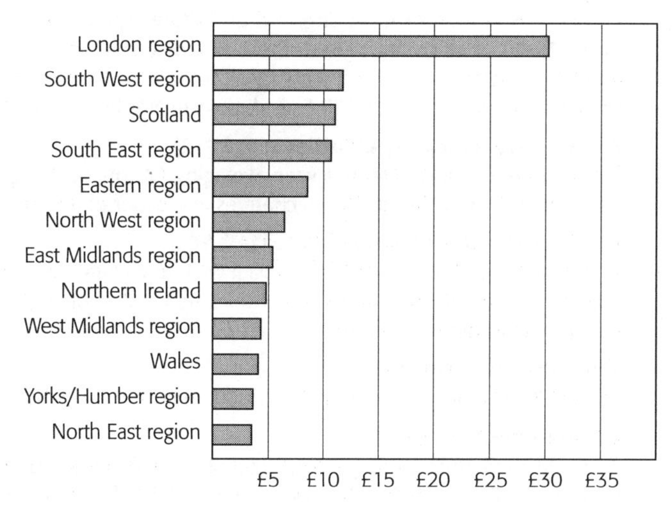

We welcome the fact that, in recognition of this situation, trusts such as Tudor and Lankelly have for some years taken positive steps to counter this flow, and that others, such as Henry Smith's Charity, have now moved actively towards a less uneven distribution. We believe that more trusts should follow their examples. The onus lies, in our view, with the trusts that have no policy restrictions on their giving but nevertheless concentrate the distribution of their money in London or the southern counties. Where we have found such situations, they are described in the text.

In order to achieve a fair distribution, trusts must be able to measure where their money is going. At present, some do list their grants according to the country or region concerned, but almost always as total sums of money rather than in terms of their value per head of population, which is the relevant measure – the countries and regions concerned have wildly varying

Small grants from trusts and foundations

This listing is to help charities who want small grants, usually for amounts of less than £5,000. There are many other trusts making grants of this sort. This is intended just a starting point.

The 'success rates' for applications given below are a guide, rather than precise figures.

The list excludes trusts with a narrow field of interest (such as the Elton John AIDS Foundation, which has a 'rapid response fund' for HIV/AIDS charities; or the Clore Foundation, which runs a small grants programme for museum and gallery education) and most of those whose grantmaking is restricted to a particular local area or region.

Awards for All Lottery grants (see National Lottery entry, page 221)
Over 15,000 small grants, but only to organisations with incomes of less than £15,000 a year. Response within 12 weeks. Success rates: nearly 50% in England, 63% in Scotland. Covers art, sport and heritage as well as charity. Different arrangements in Wales and N Ireland.

The BBC Children in Need Appeal (page 19)
Over 1,000 small grants, starting at hundreds of pounds, to projects for disadvantaged children and young people (up to age 18). Success rate over 50%.

The Esmée Fairbairn Charitable Trust (page 93)
New small grants scheme, up to £5,000, for local and small national organisations. Success rate close to 50% for 'eligible' applicants.

The Paul Hamlyn Foundation (page 125)
Small grants programme for local projects. About 150 grants a year of up to £3,000 each. Priority for the arts, education and 'publishing, books and reading'. Awarded monthly, with 66% success rate.

Help the Aged (page 138)
Large numbers of small grants to community and voluntary groups helping older people and their carers, including start-up grants of up to £1,000, and grants of up to £4,000 to develop and expand forums in local areas.

Laing's Charitable Trust (page 172)
Several hundred grants a year, typically for less than £1,000 each, in a very broad field. Roughly 33% success rate.

Laing Family Foundations (page 167)
At least 200 new grants a year, many for less than £1,000 each, in a broad field, but local branches of large networks are not normally funded. Roughly 25% success rate.

Lloyds TSB Foundation for England and Wales (page 191)
About 2,000 small grants a year for 'social and community needs' and 'education and training' for disabled and disadvantaged people in England and Wales, with a success rate of 70% for eligible applications. Preliminary discussion welcomed. There are similar schemes for Lloyd's TSB Foundations in Northern Ireland and Scotland.

The Mercers' Company Charities (page 212)
Several hundred small grants a year, averaging £2,700, covering a wide range of causes, including arts, heritage and the environment. Small locally based charities are favoured for grants under £5,000. About 66% success rate.

The Northern Rock Foundation (page 226)
Grants from £1,000 to £10,000 for social welfare charities with an annual expenditure of less than £25,000, in the north of England (especially the north east) and Scotland. 60% of eligible applications succeed (around half of all those received). Aims to respond within two months.

The Robertson Trust (page 257)
At least 200 grants a year for up to £3,000, mainly in Scotland. Probably around one in three applications successful.

Smith's Charity (page 284)
A new fast-response small grants programme (with decisions every two weeks) gives awards of up to £10,000 (normally £1,000–£3,000) to organisations with an income of less than £250,000. An alternative scheme operates in selected counties in southern England.

Foundation for Sport and the Arts (page 294)
Over 1,000 grants for sport and over 400 for the arts, mainly for capital costs of up to £5,000. Both areas of funding focus on community-based activities. About 33% success rate.

The Sir Jules Thorn Charitable Trust (page 307)
A Small Donations Fund, distributing over 500 new grants a year, for charities providing relief to sick or disabled people and other disadvantaged groups. Most grants are for less than £1,000, for core funding. About two in three appeals succeed.

The Tudor Trust (page 311)
A large number of small grants (from £500 upwards) for a wide range of causes, particularly social welfare. Continuous assessment process, with a response normally in eight weeks. Overall success rate 29%.

The Variety Club of Great Britain (page 317)
Several hundred small one-off grants (averaging about £1,000) for children and young people.

The Garfield Weston Foundation (page 324)
Several hundred small grants a year, from £500 to £5,000, covering most fields of work. Probable success rate of over 50%.

populations and £1 million for one may represent a lower sum per head than £2 million for another.

To make it easier for grantmakers to express their results in these terms, the editors of this book will be happy to e-mail to any trust, free of charge, a copy of their 'Word' listing of the population for each country, region and local authority in the UK.

Some recent developments

Access by telephone

Most trusts with their own staff now welcome preliminary telephone calls. It seems to have been realised that this can actually help both sides by reducing the number of inappropriate applications.

This information is noted prominently in all relevant entries, but readers are warned that, for many other, smaller trusts, there is no 'office'. Calls to them will therefore go through to someone's home, where they may not be welcome.

Some trusts give, as an address, that of their lawyers or accountants. Often this is just an accommodation address; if so, there may be no point in ringing for information about the trust.

Websites

As everywhere, trust websites are sprouting all over. They are listed with each entry, and many of the longer entries in this book have taken material extensively from them. However, many sites are still 'under development' and some are already out of date. A reference list is printed below.

The H B Allen Charitable Trust	http://members.nbci.com/hballenchtrust
The Architectural Heritage Fund	www.ahfund.org.uk
Awards for All (the National Lottery)	www.awardsforall.org.uk
The Baring Foundation	www.baringfoundation.org.uk
The BBC Children in Need Appeal	www.bbc.co.uk/cin
The Bridge House Estates Trust Fund	www.bridgehousegrants.org.uk
The William A Cadbury Charitable Trust	www.wa-cadbury.org.uk
The Campden Charities	www.campdencharities.org.uk
The Charities Aid Foundation	www.CAFonline.org/caf
Charity Know How	www.charityknowhow.org
The Church Urban Fund	www.cuf.org.uk
City Parochial Foundation, Trust for London	www.cityparochial.org.uk
Comic Relief	www.comicrelief.org.uk
The Community Foundation	www.communityfoundation.org.uk
The Community Foundation in Wales	www.communityfoundationwales.freeserve.co.uk
Community Foundation Network	www.communityfoundations.org.uk
The Roald Dahl Foundation	www.roalddahl.org
The Diana, Princess of Wales Memorial Fund	www.theworkcontinues.org
The John Ellerman Foundation	www.ncvo-vol.org.uk/jef.html
The Esmée Fairbairn Charitable Trust	www.efct.org.uk
The Gatsby Charitable Foundation	www.gatsby.org.uk
The Great Britain Sasakawa Foundation	www.gbsf.org.uk
Greater Bristol Foundation	www.gbf.org.uk
Hact (The Housing Associations Charitable Trust)	www.hact.org.uk
The Paul Hamlyn Foundation	www.phf.org.uk
Peter Harrison Foundation	www.peterharrisonfoundation.org
Help a London Child	www.capitalfm.com
Help the Aged	www.helptheaged.org.uk
Hospital Saving Association Charitable Trust	www.hsa.co.uk
Isle of Dogs Community Foundation	www.idcf.org
The Jerwood Charitable Foundation	www.jerwood.org.uk
The Elton John AIDS Foundation	www.eltonjohn.com
The King's Fund	www.kingsfund.org.uk
Landfill Tax Credit Scheme and ENTRUST	www.entrust.org.uk
The Allen Lane Foundation	www.allenlane.demon.co.uk
The Leverhulme Trust	www.leverhulme.org.uk
Lloyds TSB Foundations	www.lloydstsbfoundations.org.uk
The Lord's Taverners	www.lordstaverners.org
The Mental Health Foundation	www.mentalhealth.org.uk
The Mercers' Company Charities	www.mercers.co.uk
The Metropolitan Hospital–Sunday Fund	www.mhsf.org.uk
The Henry Moore Foundation	www.henry-moore-fdn.co.uk/hmf
The National Art Collections Fund	www.art-fund.org

The National Lottery (see Awards for All)	www.awardsforall.org.uk
The National Lottery Charities Board	www.nlcb.org.uk
The Northern Ireland Voluntary Trust	www.nivt.org
The Northern Rock Foundation	www.nr-foundation.org.uk
The Nuffield Foundation	www.nuffieldfoundation.org
The Nuffield Trust	www.nuffieldtrust.org.uk
The Peabody Community Fund	www.peabody.org.uk
Jack Petchey Foundation	www.jackpetcheyfoundation.org.uk
PPP Healthcare Medical Trust	www.ppptrust.org.uk
The Joseph Rowntree Charitable Trust	www.jrct.org.uk
The Joseph Rowntree Foundation	www.jrf.org.uk
The Rufford Foundation	www.rufford.org
The Francis C Scott Charitable Trust	www.fcsct.org.uk
SHINE (Support and Help In Education)	www.shinetrust.org.uk
South Yorkshire Community Foundation	www.sycf.org
The Sir Halley Stewart Trust	www.sirhalleystewart.org
The Sutton Trust	www.suttontrust.com
The Sir Jules Thorn Charitable Trust	www.julesthorntrust.org.uk
The Tudor Trust	www.tudortrust.org.uk
The Variety Club of Great Britain	www.varietyclub.org.uk
The Wellcome Trust	www.wellcome.ac.uk
Westminster Foundation for Democracy	www.wfd.org
The Woodward Charitable Trust	www.woodwardcharitabletrust.org.uk

A common application form?

Would a single application form, to be used by many or all funders, be oppressive or helpful? The London Funders Group, a body combining both statutory and trust funders, is developing a 'single application form'. The group says:

'*Funders in Good Form*', the London Funders Group report on the development of a Single Application Form, was launched in July 2000. Around 35 funders from across the UK are using the form during its first phase. The evaluation of the form's usage is currently being discussed with funders, and it will be carefully developed to cover the appropriate range of organisations, and enable grant cycles and assessments to be robust and credible. Initial evaluation findings will be emerging around May 2001.'

For further information, contact Margaret Doherty, Development Manager, London Funders Group, on 020 8831 6941.

How much should trusts pay out?

Trusts must spend their income on charitable purposes, rather than simply accumulate it for the future, but there is little guidance on the details of this. For example, can a trust invest all its money in shares that pay few dividends but offer substantial capital growth?

In the USA, following years of controversy on the subject, foundations are normally required to pay out five per cent of their net worth each year – an admirable provision but one that in recent years has still allowed for substantial capital growth. In 1999 there was pressure to raise the figure to six per cent.

In these editors' view, five per cent is a good benchmark, sustainable over the long term so far as history is a guide, but one that is met only by a small minority of the trusts in this book. For an example of very low grant levels, see the box in the entry for the Garfield Weston Foundation.

In our view, the Charity Commission should accept the five per cent level as a norm, and ask trusts that spend less on charitable activities to justify their restraint.

Seals of respectability

Is this quote from the annual report of the Wates Foundation a straw in the wind? 'I would imagine that the time is not far off when only charities with some outside accreditation like PQASSO or Investors in People will get grants from the Wates Foundation.'

The payment of trustees

After extensive consultations, the Charity Commission has published an admirably forthright reaffirmation of its opposition in principle to the payment of trustees: 'The principle of unpaid trusteeship has been one of the defining characteristics of the charitable sector' (leaflet CC 11). The new leaflet says that the first consideration a charity should take into account, even where a power to pay trustees already exists, is whether there is 'any realistic alternative' to such an arrangement.

In the case of trusts, the issue normally arises where professional accounting, administrative or legal services are provided to the charity by the businesses of which individual trustees, or those connected with them, are directors or partners. These are circumstances in which there must normally be ample 'realistic alternatives'.

Previous editions of this book have always criticised such practices, even when the services supplied were cheap and effective (which is not always the case). In our view the principle of unpaid trusteeship, and the consequent avoidance of the possibility of a conflict of interest, should be given precedence. Though there has been no change in the legal position, now that the Commission has spoken out so publicly, perhaps the trusts concerned will change their arrangements. They include, from among the trusts listed in this book:

The Lord Ashdown Charitable Settlement
The Band Trust
The Ernest Cook Trust
The Dunhill Medical Trust
The E B M Charitable Trust

How to use this guide

The trusts are listed alphabetically, with indexes at the back of the book.

At the front of the book (from page xviii) we have ranked the trusts by the amount of money they give. This list also shows their main areas of interest. If looking for grants for your charity, we recommend that you start with this listing and tick the boxes of those trusts which *might* be relevant – starting with the biggest.

When you have ticked enough to be getting on with, read each trust entry carefully before deciding to apply. Very often a trust's interest in your field will be limited and precise, and may demand an application specifically tailored to its requirements – or, often, no application at all.

Remember to cover *all parts of the guide*; do not just start at the beginning of the alphabet. It is surprising, but true, that trusts near the end of the alphabet receive fewer applications.

It is particularly important to show awareness of all the information available from the trust, to acquire up to date guidelines where possible, and to target your applications with respect to each trust's published wishes. Inappropriate and ill-considered approaches, especially those that show that you have not read the published guidelines, antagonise trusts and damage your organisation's reputation. Of course, many trusts publish nothing useful; here, you are on your own.

This edition includes a chart to help with the timing of your applications (see page xv). It shows, for over 130 trusts, the months when trustee meetings are usually held, and when applications need to be submitted.

For those new to raising money from trusts, the box on page xii containing advice from the Association of Charitable Foundations is recommended as a starting point.

Classification

Serious applicants who will be fundraising from trusts in the long term do best, we believe, if they go to the most promising entries in this book and try to establish specific links between what the trust seems to be interested in and what their organisation is trying to do. Trusts want partners in whose work they too can take both pride and satisfaction. This is usually a personal rather than a technical process, particularly if there is a substantial sum of money involved. The subject and geographical indexes on pages 337–53 are best seen as aiding this process, rather than substituting for it.

Notes on the entries

Total grant-aid and financial year

The most up to date available information is given. In a few cases the financial information in the main text is for preceding year/s. This is the result of 'last minute' information from the trust.

The main areas of funding

These categories have been chosen by the editors from an analysis of the trusts' funding. They are indicative rather than definitive, and useful in a preliminary trawl through the guide. They are no substitute for a close reading of each entry.

The correspondent

The lead person nominated by the trust. (Sometimes they are solicitors or accountants handling trust affairs solely on a 'postbox' basis.) Other useful administrative contacts may also be given in the 'Applications' section, or within the main body of text.

Beneficial area

The area/s within which the trust operates, when this is restricted, either legally or as a matter of policy or practice. When a trust with a UK-wide remit shows an interest in a particular locality, this is noted. While this information usually comes from the trust itself, it may also arise from a pattern of grantmaking seen by the editors. Where this heading does not appear, the area of benefit is unrestricted.

Information available

Published reports, application guidelines or other leaflets available directly from the trust are noted. The basic information source about a trust is its annual report and accounts. These should be available from the trust, but sometimes they are not. A copy should always be on the public file at the Charity Commission. We give the dates for the most recent accounts available at the time of our research, and note the extent, if any, to which they fall short of the requirements laid down.

The main body of the entry

A summary of the trust's grantmaking usually prefaces the text. Trusts' policy notes and guidelines for applicants, where these exist, are normally reprinted in full. For the first time, however, there are a few instances in which these have become so lengthy that there has had to be some abridgement. This is always made clear in the text.

More trusts now analyse their own funding in their annual reports and this material also will usually be quoted in full. More often, any analysis has been carried out by the editors based on grants lists accompanying the accounts.

Exclusions and Applications sections

These reproduce, where possible, the trusts' own information or comments, though edited to suit the format of this book.

The Constance Green Foundation
The Dowager Countess Eleanor Peel Trust
The Porter Foundation
The Robertson Trust
The Baily Thomas Charitable Fund
The Will Charitable Trust
The Charles Wolfson Charitable Trust

The revised SORP

A revised version of the SORP (Statement of Recommended Practice for charity accounts) was published by the Charity Commission in October 2000 (although it had been around as a recommended draft for some time). The provisions on the disclosure of grants are lengthened rather than strengthened.

The requirements for the narrative report, on the other hand, have been reduced even from their previously inadequate coverage in what seems to us a misjudged attempt 'to encourage charities to expand on their activities'. Our experience is that accountants, who appear to draft most of these documents as far as grant-making trusts are concerned, are professionally conditioned by commercial practice to seek to disclose as little as possible without clearly breaking the rules. So we may get less rather than more in future.

Good grantmaking

In 1999 the *Harvard Business Review* published a substantial analysis of how trusts can best make good grants: 'Philanthropy's New Agenda: Creating Value', by Michael E. Porter and Mark R. Kramer.

In this lengthy article, the authors note that although trusts purchase social benefits, the same benefits could be purchased by individual donors, and trusts only create any added value when their activities generate social benefits beyond the mere purchasing power of their grants. They suggest that the creation of added value requires a positive strategy.

Such a strategy for a trust would need four elements:

- setting the goal of achieving superior performance in a chosen arena;
- choosing a particular position on where and how it will make its impact;
- developing its own activities to achieve this;
- accepting that this means saying 'no' to other attractive opportunities.

Although written against a US background, these are principles that, in our opinion, are equally characteristic of the most effective trusts in Britain. It was encouraging to have them set out and explained more fully than has previously been the case.

The article is illuminated by telling examples. Most striking is the Philanthropic Ventures Association of California, which offers grants (to teachers, for small, urgent expenditures in their schools) within one hour of receiving a faxed request on the appropriately headed paper. Would that we had more examples of such tailored grantmaking to write about in this book.

The article was described and reviewed in *Trust Monitor*, spring 2000 edition (published by the Directory of Social Change). Further information is available from these editors on 020 7209 4422.

Failure to supply accounts

Every charity is required by law to supply, on request, a copy of its most recent annual report and accounts. Of the trusts in this volume, 85% did so, the best result ever (half a dozen requested payment, occasionally of exorbitant amounts, which is noted in the relevant entries). Failing a response from the trust concerned, we used the information available on the public file at the Charity Commission, to whose helpful staff we again offer our thanks.

The following 41 trusts did not respond to our initial request for copies of their reports and accounts:

The Boltons Trust
The Booth Charities
The Cadogan Charity
Charity Association Manchester Ltd
CHK Charities Limited
The Donald Forrester Trust
The Gosling Foundation
The M & R Gross Charities
The Gur Trust
Alan Edward Higgs Charity
The Reta Lila Howard Foundation
The Albert Hunt Trust
The Huntingdon Foundation
The Jordan Charitable Foundation
The Kennedy Charitable Foundation
The Graham Kirkham Foundation
Ernest Kleinwort Charitable Trust
The John and Rosemary Lancaster Charitable Foundation
The Leathersellers' Company Charitable Fund
The Kennedy Leigh Charitable Trust
Enid Linder Foundation
The Lolev Charitable Trust
The Jim Marshall Charitable Trust
Mayfair Charities
The M K Charitable Trust
The Network Foundation
The Pet Plan Charitable Trust
The Rothschild Foundation
The Rowlands Trust
The J B Rubens Charitable Foundation
The Rubin Foundation
The Samuel Sebba Charitable Trust
The Ayrton Senna Foundation
The Archie Sherman Charitable Trust
Shlomo Memorial Fund
The Steel Charitable Trust
Stevenson Family's Charitable Trust
The W O Street Charitable Foundation
The Tompkins Foundation
The Weinstock Fund
The Will Charitable Trust

How trust information could be improved

In summer 2000 the QUEST team at the Department of Culture, Media and Sport looked at the information that potential applicants wanted from funders, beyond the usual data about the scheme concerned, and came out with the following consensus list:

- how much money there was available for a particular scheme;
- the number of eligible applications;
- their success rates;
- the profile of successful and unsuccessful applicants;
- the actual processing times;
- the size of the grants.

At present, only a tiny proportion of trusts meet these suggestions in full. In particular, many funders described here do not say how many applications they receive, nor what proportion of these are eligible (essential information given the high and varying proportions of ineligible applications that are reported). Few of the trusts with a range of programmes separate these out as far as applications and success rates are concerned.

What are the main reasons for the failure of eligible applications? What are the characteristics of success? Most trusts say nothing. Some say merely that they get more good applications than they are able to fund. Though doubtless true, this leaves open the question of what is the difference between those that succeed and those that do not. A useful example of how this can be tackled can be seen in the entry for the Lloyds TSB Foundation for Scotland.

'Project' or 'core' funding?

Trustees are aware that core funding is becoming increasingly difficult to obtain and they are open to receiving applications for this purpose. (Ellerman Foundation)

We suggest that the distinction between 'project' and 'core' funding can be misleading. A bigger divide is between funding for present expenditure or for long-term investment. By and large, trusts cannot let themselves get tied down too far in long-term support for particular organisations. On the other hand, most of their applicants are trying to meet ongoing needs.

A requirement that these needs must be put in 'project' form is often to demand a distortion; the National Lottery Charities Board is the leader in this unhappy practice. But to offer to fund core costs instead of projects does not necessarily help, if these costs are simply the running costs of the organisation for a few years; at the end of this period the problems remain unchanged.

What is needed most is a willingness to fund investment in future financial stability. This can either be in the development of an organisation's earning power in the new welfare market, or in increasing its regular donated income.

It is therefore surprising and unfortunate that so few trusts, even those which cite sustainability as a key criterion in deciding which organisations to support, will actually invest in the development of sustainable funding. The Charities Aid Foundation is a noticeable and long-standing exception, but its resources are modest. On the other hand, many trusts, such as the Ellerman Foundation quoted above, do give short-term contributions to core costs. While an advance on refusing any help with core costs at all, this seems likely, in many cases, to postpone rather than address the problem.

Why this reluctance to invest in long-term sustainability? It is probably because of a disinclination by trustees to pay for fundraising, which is often seen as an undesirable overhead rather than an essential pre-condition to the independent long-term delivery of effective services. And there can be few better achievements for a trust than to enable a charity it supports to achieve long-term and sustainable independence.

Note that in the entries about individual trusts, text that is quoted from their own material is printed in a visibly different sans-serif typeface, but does not have quote marks. The following excerpt is an example:

The foundation publishes the following guidelines for applicants (to be slightly revised in February 2001):

Trustees will be looking for applications which reflect the use of education programmes to enhance the capabilities and enjoyment of the public, whether in formal or informal educational groups or as individual or family learners. ...

Which trusts are in this guide?

About 300 of the top grant-making trusts in the UK are described, each normally with a grant-making capacity of at least £350,000. The vagueness is because some trusts come in groups within a single entry; others appear individually as well as in a group entry.

Smaller trusts will be found in the companion *A Guide to the Major Trusts, Volumes 2 or 3,* or in the DSC's regional trust guides, or in specialist books such as the *Environment* or *Arts Funding Guides.* Over 3,500 trusts can be found on the DSC's *Grant-making Trusts CD-ROM*, available in spring 2001.

Where a trust has been wound up or merged, we have provided an entry noting the fact; otherwise readers might wonder about the unexplained disappearance of a familiar name.

Not included are ...

Company charitable trusts, dependent on annual allocations from, and operated by, the company. For full details see *The Guide to UK Company Giving,* also published by the Directory of Social Change. Marginal cases, included here, include the Lloyds TSB foundations.

'Single issue' grantmakers, i.e. those which support one clearly defined and limited cause, such as Help the Hospices or the medical research charities with specified and limited remits – such as, say, the Arthritis Research Council.

Trusts which only fund overseas activities (see *The International Directory,* published by the Directory of Social Change in summer 2001).

Grantmakers funded from the public purse (even though they may have charitable status). Examples include the Arts Councils and regional arts boards, English Heritage and the Countryside Commission, or Community Relations Councils.

But ...

Brief information about the National Lottery Charities Board and the cross-distributor Awards for All small grants scheme has been included. Is the Lottery a part of the public purse?

Other marginal cases, to be found in this book, include those community foundations, such as those in South Yorkshire or Northern Ireland, which combine revenue from both statutory and independent sources.

Applying to a charitable trust or foundation

The following note has been written and published by the Association for Charitable Foundations, to which we are grateful for permission to reproduce it here.

There are about 8,800 grant-making trusts and foundations in the UK. They give in total about £1.25 billion per year to charitable causes. To this might be added £320 million given by the National Lottery Charities Board and £280 million by a dozen large operating charities which make grants in the course of their work (e.g. Cancer Research, Oxfam), making £1.85 billion in all.

Total grant-giving to the voluntary sector by trusts is about the same as that of central or local government (apart from government grants to housing associations and employment schemes), and larger than that of the corporate sector. The figures are, however, notoriously difficult to analyse, and are complicated by the 'contract culture', so comparisons can be misleading. For example, although government gives little aid to voluntary organisations in the educational field, its total spending on education is about £31 billion, whereas trust spending is about one-hundredth of this: £320 million. Similar comparisons emerge in social welfare. This is why trusts fight shy of long-term funding of services, especially services which could reasonably be part of state provision. In particular fields, however, trust funding can be significant, e.g. research in medicine and housing.

Trusts can only preserve their distinctive role by doing special things. They therefore like to concentrate their funding on:

- new methods of tackling problems;
- disadvantaged and minority groups that have trouble using ordinary services, or which are inadequately served by them;
- responses to new or newly discovered needs and problems;
- work which is hard to finance through conventional fundraising;
- one-off purchases or projects, including research;
- short and medium-term work which is likely to bring long-term benefit and/or to attract long-term funding from elsewhere.

Core funding is not ruled out for work which falls into one or more of these categories.

Trusts vary enormously in their policies, styles of working, and administrative capacities. So three golden rules are:

- *Do your homework beforehand;*
- *Prepare your application carefully;*
- *Leave plenty of time.*

Selecting trusts

Use the various directories to locate trusts which may be able to help – and to rule out those which will *not* be interested. Draw up a short list of possible trusts. Your list should include:

- Trusts which operate in your geographical area. Look especially for any trusts which can *only* fund in your area or which express a preference for it. Don't approach a trust which *cannot* fund in your area, nor ask for funding for a *national* project from a trust which is limited to a particular locality. A trust which funds nationally *may* be interested in a local project if it particularly matches the trust's interests and/or is of national significance; i.e. it would make a grant because of the pioneering nature of the project's work rather than because of the needs of the area. Only the very largest national trusts (the top 50 or so) are able to fund local projects more widely than this.

- Trusts which are interested in your field of work and the sort of people who will benefit from it. If a trust says that it makes grants only in a particular field or to benefit a particular age group, it means it. Likewise, if a trust says that it does not fund general appeals or that projects of a particular type are excluded, don't try and persuade it that you are the exception.

- Trusts which make (and have sufficient funds to make) grants of the size you need. Don't ask a small trust for too much (or a large one for too little).

Many trusts publish information leaflets for applicants. (The same information is often reproduced in various directories.) Write off for these details if necessary, and use them to refine your shortlist, which will usually be quite short – perhaps only three or four trusts, and probably not more than twenty. Where a trust's information says that it has an application form, obtain this before proceeding any further; don't waste time drafting a letter until you have completed the form. Most trusts, however, do *not* use an application form.

If you can't find any trusts that seem likely to be interested, think again about how to present your work. Can you describe it in a different way, emphasising different (and preferably unusual) aspects that may attract different groups of funders? If the amount you need is too large, can you sub-divide the proposal into smaller projects?

Writing your application

Remember to include the following points:

- The purpose of the work to be funded – who it will help and how, what is distinctive about it, what will be achieved if a grant is given (and perhaps what will *not* be achieved if the grant is *not* given).
- A budget for the project. Work out your needs carefully. Don't economise on essentials, such as training or unavoidable overhead costs.
- Ask for a specific sums of money. If necessary, say that you are seeking a contribution of £X towards a budget of £Y, and that you hope to raise the remainder from other sources which you specify. Do not simply say that you are a very worthwhile organisation and desperately need funds.
- Your name, address, and phone number – oh yes, people *do* forget!

Make the application long enough to describe what you want properly, but short enough to be easy to take in the first reading – usually no more than two pages for your main letter.

Don't overload the application with attachments. A trust which is seriously interested will ask for information it hasn't got. You should, however, always include your most recent annual report and accounts. (If your accounts show apparently large reserves, attach a note explaining why you hold them and why they cannot be used to fund the project for which you are seeking funds. If you cannot explain the size of your reserves, consider *spending* them instead of applying for grants!)

If your organisation does not have charitable status, explain why the work funded is charitable, and if possible name a registered charity that will take responsibility on your behalf (providing written confirmation from that charity). You *must* identify such a charity when applying to a trust that has a policy of only funding registered charities.

Connecting with trusts

Apply well before you need the money. Trusts generally make decisions through trustees' meetings which take place every two or three months. Some meet only two or three times a year. While a few trusts have a small grants programme where a fast response can be given, most are unable to deal quickly with even the very best applications.

Trusts generally have quite a limited administration capacity. Although the largest trusts are quite substantial organisations, only the top 300 or so employ any staff at all. The vast majority of trusts are run on a part-time or voluntary basis, and are themselves very small organisations. Don't try and expect too much of them. The sheer volume of applications means that most trusts do not normally acknowledge applications, and many are unable to reply to applicants who are ultimately unsuccessful. If you want to be sure of an acknowledgement, send a reply-paid postcard addressed to yourself.

Many trusts visit at least the larger applications they are considering and if you receive a visit it is usually a sign that you have got over the first hurdle. Try to establish what the funder wishes to see and who he or she wishes to meet. It is useful to identify how long the funder can spend with you. Are they hoping to see your project in action as well as discuss the organisation's work? Are they interested in the whole organisation or just this particular project? The answers to these questions will help you decide [who in your organisation] should be there.

What trusts look for

Trust usually make visits in order to assess the *need* for the project and the extent to which the applicants have come up with a good solution. They will also be looking for reassurance that the applicants have the ability to deliver what they promise. This is your chance to bring the project to life so try to ensure that the person meeting the funder both knows about the project and is enthusiastic about it.

While some trusts will want to visit you, others will deal with your application entirely by letter. Some will be willing to discuss the application (or a prospective application) over the phone, while others will not. (If a trust's entry does not include a phone number, this means that calls are unwelcome. It will not help to trace the number through Directory Enquiries.)

If you happen to know a trustee of a trust, tell him or her that you are applying, but in general it won't help you to approach trustees direct; deal with a trust through its designated secretary or correspondent.

Remember that trusts may get more applications than they can fund. A typical trust, if there is such a thing, may be able to fund only one in four of the eligible applications received, and half or more enquiries it receives may be ineligible. So if you don't succeed, it may not reflect on the quality of your application. The reasons that applications are ineligible are that they are outside the trust's stated guidelines, or lack obvious details such as a return address.

A continuing relationship?

If you are lucky enough to receive a grant, ensure first of all that you acknowledge receipt of the cheque and thank the funder – it is surprising how many applicants do not do this. Thereafter try to keep in touch in *whatever way the funder suggests*. If the funder wants frequent reports then make sure you supply them but if the funder only wants a report once a year do not bombard them with information in between times.

Do let your funder know if there are problems. It is far better to be alerted at an early stage to any difficulties – when a funder may be able to help, for example, by varying the times at which the grant is paid, or helping you to identify other funders who might be able to make up a shortfall or offering advice if similar problems occurred in other organisations. Don't wait until there is a real crisis before letting the funder know what is happening.

On the positive side, if you receive any particular significant good news, such as increased funding, good publicity or the achievement of a particular objective, do let your funders know. Finally it is worth checking, perhaps six months before your current funding runs out, whether that particular funder is willing to consider further applications!

Dates for your diary

A = the last month for the receipt of applications

X = the usual month of trustees' or grant allocation meetings

Please note that these dates are provisional, and that the fact of an application being received does not necessarily mean that it will be considered at the next meeting.

	Jan	*Feb*	*Mar*	*Apr*	*May*	*Jun*	*Jul*	*Aug*	*Sep*	*Oct*	*Nov*	*Dec*
The 29th May 1961 Charitable Trust		X			X			X			X	
The H B Allen Charitable Trust										A		X
The Architectural Heritage Fund		A	X		A	X		A	X		A	X
The Baily Thomas Charitable Fund				A		X			A			X
The Baring Foundation	X	X		X	X		X		X	X		X
The BBC Children in Need Appeal	X		A				X			X	A	
The Bedford Charity	X		A	X		A	X		A	X		A
The Percy Bilton Charity			X			X			X			X
Burdens Charitable Foundation	A		X	A		X	A		X	A		X
The A & S Burton Charitable Trust	X	X	X	X	X	X	X	X	X	X	X	X
The W A Cadbury Charitable Trust					X						X	
The Barrow Cadbury Trust	A		X		A		X		A		X	
The Campden Charities	X	X	X	X	X	X	X		X	X	X	X
The Carnegie United Kingdom Trust	A		X	A		X			A		X	
Sir John Cass's Foundation			X			X			X			X
The Charities Aid Foundation		X	A		XA		X		A		X	A
Charity Know How	A		X	A		X	A		X	A		X
The Childwick Trust				A	X				A	X		
The Church Urban Fund	A		X	A		X	A		X	A		X
The City Parochial Foundation	X			A			X	A		X	A	
Cleveland Community Foundation			X	A			X	A			X	A
The Clothworkers' Foundation	XA	A	XA	A	XA	A	XA	A	A	XA	XA	A
Richard Cloudesley's Charity				X							X	
Sir James Colyer-Fergusson's CT			X			X			X			X
The Ernest Cook Trust	A		X					A		X		
The Cripplegate Foundation		X		X		X			X	X		X
The D'Oyly Carte Charitable Trust					A	X					A	X
Baron Davenport's Charity			A		X				A		X	
The Diana, Princess of Wales Fund			A				X	A				X
The Dulverton Trust	X				X		X			X		
The Dunhill Medical Trust			X		X				X			X
The Eveson Charitable Trust	X	A	X		A		X	A		X	A	
The Esmée Fairbairn Charitable Trust		X	A		A		X	A			X	
Fishmongers' Company's CT		A	X			A	X			A	X	
The Donald Forrester Trust		X							X			
The Hugh Fraser Foundation	X		A	X		A	X		A	X		A
The Gannochy Trust	X	X	X	X	X	X	X		X	X	X	X
J Paul Getty Jr Charitable Trust			X			X			X			X

	Jan	*Feb*	*Mar*	*Apr*	*May*	*Jun*	*Jul*	*Aug*	*Sep*	*Oct*	*Nov*	*Dec*
The G C Gibson Charitable Trust										A		X
Gloucestershire Environmental Trust	X	A	X	A	X	A	X	A	X	A	X	A
Goldsmiths' Company's Charities	X	X	X	X	X	X	X			X	X	X
The Grand Charity of Freemasons	XA	A	A	XA	A	A	XA	A	A	XA	A	A
Great Britain Sasakawa Foundation			A		X				A		X	
The Constance Green Foundation	A		X		A	X			A		X	
Greggs Trust			A		X				A		X	
The Gulbenkian Foundation		X		X			X				X	
Hact		X		X		X	A		X	X		X
The Paul Hamlyn Foundation	X		A	X	A	X			A	X		A
The Hampton Fuel Allotment Charity	A	X	A	X	A	X	A	X	A	X	A	X
The Charles Hayward Foundation	X			X			X			X		
The Hedley Foundation	X		X	X	X	X		X	X	X		X
Help a London Child					A							
Help the Aged	X	X	X	X	X	X	X	X	X	X	X	X
Alan Edward Higgs Charity	X	A	X	A	X	A	X	A	X	A	X	A
The Jane Hodge Foundation	X	X	X	X	X	X	X	X	X	X	X	X
The Hospital Saving Association CTt	X			X			X			X		
The Albert Hunt Trust					A	X					A	X
John James Bristol Foundation	A	X		A	X		A	X		A	X	
King George's Fund for Sailors							X				X	
The King's Fund		X		X			X		X		X	
Ernest Kleinwort Charitable Trust			X							X		
The Sir James Knott Trust		X		A		X		A		X		A
J W Laing Biblical Scholarship Trust	X	X	X	X	X	X	X		X	X	X	X
The J W Laing Trust	X	X	X	X	X	X	X		X	X	X	X
Lambeth Endowed Charities	A		X	A		X		A		X	A	X
The Allen Lane Foundation		X		A		X		A		X		A
The Lankelly Foundation	X			X			X			X		
The Law Society Charity				X			X		X			X
The William Leech Charity	X		X		X		X		X		X	
Leeds Hospital Fund Charitable Trust		X			X		X				X	
The Levy Foundation		X			X					X		
Lloyds TSB Foundation for N. Ireland		A	X		A	X		A	X		A	X
Lloyds TSB Foundation for Scotland	A	X	A	X	A	X	A	X	A	X	A	X
The Lord's Taverners	A	X		A	X				A	X		
John Lyon's Charity	A		X	A		X			A			X
The Mackintosh Foundation					X						X	
The MacRobert Trusts			X			A				AX		
The Medlock Charitable Trust			X			X			X			X
The Mercers' Company Charities	X	X	X	X	X	X	X	X	X	X	X	X
Metropolitan Hospital–Sunday Fund			A									X
The Henry Moore Foundation	X		A	X		A	X		A	X		A
The National Art Collections Fund		X	X	X	X	X	X		X	X	X	X
F and A Newman Foundation				A		X	A		X			
The Nuffield Foundation		X		X			X			X		
The Nuffield Trust	A		X		A		X		A		X	
The P F Charitable Trust	X	X	X	X	X	X	X	X	X	X	X	X
The Peabody Community Fund			X			X					X	
The Pilgrim Trust	X		A	X		A	X		A	X		A
The Pilkington Charities Fund			X							X		
The Porter Foundation			X				X				X	

	Jan	Feb	Mar	Apr	May	Jun	Jul	Aug	Sep	Oct	Nov	Dec
Mr and Mrs J A Pye's C. Settlement		A	X		A	X		A	X		A	X
Queen Mary's Roehampton Trust				A		X			A		X	
The Joseph Rank Benevolent Trust	A			X			A			X		
The Rank Foundation			A			A			A			A
The Sir James Reckitt Charity				A	X					A	X	
The Richmond Parish Lands Charity	X	X	X	X	X	X	X	X	X	X	X	X
The Robertson Trust	X	A	X	A	X	A	X	A	X	A	X	A
The Rose Foundation					X					X		
The Rowan Charitable Trust		X				A		X				A
Joseph Rowntree Charitable Trust	A		X	A		X	A		X	A		X
The Joseph Rowntree Foundation			X			X			X			X
Joseph Rowntree Reform Trust		A	X		A	X		A	X		A	X
The Rufford Foundation		A		X				A		X		
The Save & Prosper Charities		A	X	A	X	A	X	A	X		A	X
The Francis C Scott Charitable Trust		A	X			A	X			A	X	
Sir Samuel Scott of Yews Trust		A		X				A		X		
The Archie Sherman Charitable Trust	X	X	X	X	X	X	X		X	X	X	
Smith's Charity	A		X	A		X	A		X	A		X
The Souter Foundation	X		X	X		X			X	X	X	
South Yorkshire Comm. Foundation		A						A			A	
Southover Manor Education Trust		X		X		X		X		X		X
Spitalfields Market Community Trust	X	X	X	X	X	X	X		X	X	X	
Foundation for Sport and the Arts	A	A	A	A	A	A	A	A	A	A	A	A
The Steel Charitable Trust	X			X			X			X		
The Sir Halley Stewart Trust		X		A		X		A		X		A
The W O Street Charitable Foundation	X			X			X			X		
Bernard Sunley Charitable Foundation	X			A	X				A	X		A
Sutton Coldfield Municipal Charities	X	X	X		X	X	X		X	X	X	
The Talbot Village Trust		A		X				A		X		
The Sir Jules Thorn Charitable Trust				X							X	
The Triangle Trust	A	X			A	X		A	X	A	X	
The Trust for London	A		X	A		X	A		X	A		X
The Variety Club of Great Britain	A	A	A	A	A	A	A	A	A	A	A	A
Sir Siegmund Warburg's Settlement	A	X				A	X		A	X		
The Waterside Trust	A	A	A	A	A	A	A	A	A	A	A	A
The Welton Foundation	A	X				A	X		A	X		
The Westminster Foundation		X	A		X		A		XA		X	A
Westminster Fdn for Democracy	X	A		X	A		X	A		X	A	
The Will Charitable Trust	A		X					A		X		
The Wolfson Family Charitable Trust			A			X			A			X
The Wolfson Foundation			A			X			A			X
The Woodward Charitable Trust	X						X					

The major trusts ranked by grant total

Trust	*Grants*	*Main grant areas*
☐ **Wellcome Trust**	**£392,000,000**	Biomedical research, history of medicine, biomedical ethics, public engagement with science
☐ **National Lottery Charities Board**	**£360,000,000**	Those at greatest disadvantage in society
☐ **Landfill Tax Credit Scheme and ENTRUST**	**£183,000,000**	Environmental improvement
☐ **Sainsbury Family Charitable Trusts**	**(£50,000,000)**	See the entries for the individual trusts
☐ **Wolfson Foundation**	**£36,480,000**	Medical and scientific research, education, health and welfare, heritage, arts
☐ **Garfield Weston Foundation**	**£31,550,000**	Arts, education, health, general
☐ **Tudor Trust**	**£24,851,000**	Social welfare, general
☐ **Smith's Charity**	**£22,400,000**	Social welfare, older people, disability, health, medical research
☐ **Community Foundation Network**	**(£21,987,000)**	See entries for the individual foundations
☐ **Esmée Fairbairn Charitable Trust**	**£19,865,000**	Social welfare, arts and heritage, education, environment
☐ **Gatsby Charitable Foundation**	**£17,997,000**	General
☐ **BBC Children in Need Appeal**	**£17,711,000**	Welfare of disadvantaged children
☐ **Lloyds TSB Foundation for England and Wales**	**£17,311,000**	Social and community needs, education and training
☐ **PPP Healthcare Medical Trust**	**£17,000,000**	Healthcare and public health research, training and development
☐ **Comic Relief**	**£16,514,000**	Community based UK charities, Africa
☐ **Bridge House Estates Trust Fund**	**£16,000,000**	Welfare in London
☐ **Leverhulme Trust**	**£14,827,000**	Research
☐ **Northern Ireland Voluntary Trust**	**£11,654,000**	Community development, social welfare
☐ **Laing Family Foundations**	**(£10,366,000)**	See the entries for the individual trusts
☐ **Diana, Princess of Wales Memorial Fund**	**£9,584,000**	Children and young people in the UK, overseas
☐ **Northern Rock Foundation**	**£9,200,000**	Disadvantaged people in northern England and Scotland
☐ **Rank Foundation**	**£8,483,000**	Christian communication, youth, education, general
☐ **Foundation for Sport and the Arts**	**£8,242,000**	Sport, the arts
☐ **Shetland Islands Council Charitable Trust**	**£7,956,000**	General, in Shetland
☐ **Linbury Trust**	**£7,068,000**	General
☐ **Clore and Duffield Foundations**	**£6,984,000**	Arts/museums, Jewish charities, education
☐ **Joseph Rowntree Foundation**	**£6,964,000**	Research and development in social policy
☐ **Charles Wolfson Charitable Trust**	**£6,588,000**	Medical research, health, education, Jewish charities, general
☐ **City Parochial Foundation and the Trust for London**	**£6,115,000**	Social welfare in London
☐ **Headley Trust**	**£6,014,000**	Arts, environment, health, education, development
☐ **Nuffield Foundation**	**£5,541,000**	Education, child protection, family law and justice, access to justice, mental health, ageing
☐ **Jerwood Charitable Foundation/Jerwood Foundation**	**£5,000,000**	Education, arts, medicine, conservation
☐ **Lankelly Foundation**	**£4,912,000**	Social welfare, disability
☐ **Lloyds TSB Foundation for Scotland**	**£4,808,000**	Social and community needs, education and training, scientific, medical and social research
☐ **Monument Trust**	**£4,807,000**	Arts, health and welfare (especially AIDS), environment
☐ **Parthenon Trust**	**£4,601,000**	Third world, general
☐ **Variety Club of Great Britain**	**£4,476,000**	Children's charities, 'Sunshine Coaches'
☐ **J W Laing Trust**	**£4,405,000**	Christian evangelism, general
☐ **John Ellerman Foundation**	**£4,350,000**	Health, welfare, art and conservation, for national organisations

Trust	Grant total	Main areas
☐ **Robertson Trust**	**£4,344,000**	General, mainly in Scotland
☐ **Robert and Lisa Sainsbury Trust**	**£4,331,000**	See entry
☐ **Architectural Heritage Fund**	**£4,283,000**	Loans and grants for building preservation
☐ **Joseph Rowntree Charitable Trust**	**£4,242,000**	Poverty, economic and racial justice, peace, democratic process, corporate responsibility, Ireland, South Africa
☐ **National Art Collections Fund**	**£4,220,000**	Acquisition of works of art by museums and galleries
☐ **Church Urban Fund**	**£4,208,000**	Welfare, Christian development in disadvantaged urban areas in England
☐ **Dunhill Medical Trust**	**£4,183,000**	Medical research, elderly
☐ **Allchurches Trust**	**£4,014,000**	Churches, general
☐ **Ruben and Elisabeth Rausing Trust**	**£4,010,000**	Human rights, self-reliance and sustainability, art and culture
☐ **Peter Moores Foundation**	**£4,007,000**	The arts, particularly opera, social welfare
☐ **Westminster Foundation for Democracy**	**£4,000,000**	Strengthening democracy overseas
☐ **Sobell Foundation**	**£3,672,000**	Jewish charities, health and welfare
☐ **Lord Ashdown Charitable Settlement**	**£3,611,000**	Jewish education, inter-faith and racial harmony, community development
☐ **Clothworkers' Foundation**	**£3,452,000**	Clothworking, general
☐ **Barrow Cadbury Trust/Barrow Cadbury Fund**	**£3,306,000**	Immigration and resettlement, justice and peace, disability, gender, penal affairs, racial justice
☐ **Baily Thomas Charitable Fund**	**£3,245,000**	Mental illness, mental disability
☐ **Sir Jules Thorn Charitable Trust**	**£3,209,000**	Medical research, medicine, welfare
☐ **Bernard Sunley Charitable Foundation**	**£3,205,000**	General
☐ **King George's Fund for Sailors**	**£3,193,000**	The welfare of seafarers
☐ **Jerusalem Trust**	**£3,151,000**	Promotion of Christianity
☐ **Gannochy Trust**	**£3,140,000**	General, in Scotland, especially Perthshire
☐ **Dulverton Trust**	**£3,137,000**	Youth and education, welfare, conservation, general
☐ **Wolfson Family Charitable Trust**	**£3,062,000**	Jewish charities
☐ **Grand Charity of Freemasons**	**£3,029,000**	Health, hospices and welfare
☐ **Kirby Laing Foundation**	**£2,890,000**	Health, welfare, Christian religion, general
☐ **Pilgrim Trust**	**£2,865,000**	Social welfare, art and learning, preservation of buildings
☐ **Rank Benevolent Trust**	**£2,863,000**	The Methodist Church, Christian-based social work
☐ **Baring Foundation**	**£2,800,000**	Strengthening the voluntary sector, arts in education and in the community, international
☐ **Childwick Trust**	**£2,763,000**	Health and medical research in the UK, health and education in South Africa, Jewish charities, equestrianism
☐ **Maurice and Hilda Laing Charitable Trust**	**£2,745,000**	Promotion of Christianity, relief of need, in the UK and overseas
☐ **29th May 1961 Charitable Trust**	**£2,712,000**	Social welfare, general
☐ **Balcraig Foundation**	**£2,500,000**	Relief of suffering, particularly by children
☐ **Mayfair Charities**	**£2,481,000**	Orthodox Judaism
☐ **Equitable Charitable Trust**	**£2,453,000**	Education of disabled/disadvantaged children
☐ **Eveson Charitable Trust**	**£2,416,000**	Health, welfare in the west midlands area
☐ **Ian Karten Charitable Trust**	**£2,300,000**	Computer technology centres for disabled people, postgraduate education
☐ **Mercers' Company Charities**	**£2,278,000**	Independent schools, almshouses, general
☐ **Paul Hamlyn Foundation**	**£2,209,000**	Arts, education, overseas, publishing
☐ **Vardy Foundation**	**£2,200,000**	Christian, education in the north east of England, general
☐ **Arbib Foundation**	**£2,190,000**	General
☐ **Waterside Trust**	**£2,121,000**	Christian, welfare
☐ **Gulbenkian Foundation**	**£2,092,000**	Education, arts, welfare
☐ **Kay Kendall Leukaemia Fund**	**£2,085,000**	Research into leukaemia
☐ **John Lyon's Charity**	**£2,082,000**	Children and young people in north and west London

Trust	Grant total	Main areas
☐ **King's Fund**	**£2,070,000**	Health and healthcare in London
☐ **John and Rosemary Lancaster Charitable Foundation**	**£2,061,000**	Christian causes
☐ **Charles Hayward Foundation**	**£2,009,000**	Welfare and health, medical research, overseas
☐ **Trusthouse Charitable Foundation**	**£2,000,000**	General
☐ **Sutton Trust**	**£2,000,000**	Education
☐ **Peacock Charitable Trust**	**£1,943,000**	Medical research, disability, general
☐ **Rufford Foundation**	**£1,922,000**	Nature conservation, sustainable development, environment, general
☐ **Ernest Kleinwort Charitable Trust**	**£1,860,000**	General
☐ **Community Foundation (serving Tyne & Wear and Northumberland)**	**£1,758,000**	Social welfare, general
☐ **Goldsmiths' Company's Charities**	**£1,736,000**	General, London charities, the precious metals craft
☐ **Rayne Foundation**	**£1,695,000**	Arts, medicine, higher education, social welfare, general
☐ **Sutton Coldfield Municipal Charities**	**£1,668,000**	Relief of need, education and general in Sutton Coldfield
☐ **Balint Family Charitable Trusts**	**£1,653,000**	Jewish charities, medicine, children and general
☐ **Hugh Fraser Foundation**	**£1,640,000**	General, mainly in Scotland
☐ **CHK Charities Limited**	**£1,627,000**	General
☐ **Souter Foundation**	**£1,626,000**	Social welfare, Christianity, especially in Scotland; third world
☐ **AIM Foundation**	**£1,609,000**	Integrated preventative medicine, community development, environment, general
☐ **Lloyds TSB Foundation for Northern Ireland**	**£1,600,000**	Social and community need, education and training, scientific and medical research
☐ **Wates Foundation**	**£1,586,000**	Social welfare, especially in south London
☐ **Elton John AIDS Foundation**	**£1,574,000**	HIV/AIDS welfare and research
☐ **Mackintosh Foundation**	**£1,546,000**	Performing arts, general
☐ **Lord's Taverners**	**£1,544,000**	Minibuses and sports equipment for people with disabilities, cricket
☐ **J Paul Getty Jr Charitable Trust**	**£1,527,000**	Social welfare, conservation
☐ **Jack Petchey Foundation**	**£1,500,000**	Young people in east London and west Essex
☐ **Peter Harrison Foundation**	**£1,500,000**	Sport for disabled or disadvantaged people, welfare of children and young people
☐ **D'Oyly Carte Charitable Trust**	**£1,491,000**	Arts, medical welfare, environment
☐ **Historic Churches Preservation Trust**	**£1,490,000**	Historic churches
☐ **Eranda Foundation**	**£1,467,000**	Research into education and medicine, the arts, social welfare
☐ **John James Bristol Foundation**	**£1,458,000**	Education, health, general in Bristol
☐ **Drapers' Company Charities**	**£1,451,000**	General
☐ **P F Charitable Trust**	**£1,415,000**	General
☐ **Francis C Scott Charitable Trust**	**£1,335,000**	Disadvantaged people in Cumbria and Lancashire
☐ **Sir James Knott Trust**	**£1,312,000**	General, in the north east of England
☐ **Djanogly Foundation**	**£1,309,000**	Education, arts, Jewish charities, general
☐ **Help the Aged**	**£1,301,000**	Day centres, lunch clubs, hospices, general, for older people
☐ **Maurice Hatter Foundation**	**£1,300,000**	Education, health, Jewish, general
☐ **Rubin Foundation**	**£1,293,000**	Jewish charities, general
☐ **Achisomoch Aid Company**	**£1,242,000**	Jewish religious charities
☐ **Campden Charities**	**£1,232,000**	Welfare and education in Kensington, London
☐ **Glencore Foundation for Education & Welfare**	**£1,225,000**	Jewish charities, health
☐ **Horne Foundation**	**£1,200,000**	Education, arts, youth, in or near Northampton
☐ **Law Society Charity**	**£1,200,000**	Law and justice, worldwide
☐ **Westminster Foundation**	**£1,172,000**	General
☐ **Maurice Laing Foundation**	**£1,162,000**	Environment, medicine (often complementary), overseas, general
☐ **Archie Sherman Charitable Trust**	**£1,147,000**	Jewish charities, arts, welfare

Trust	Grant total	Main areas
☐ **Kennedy Leigh Charitable Trust**	**£1,142,000**	Jewish charities, medical research, general
☐ **Booth Charities**	**£1,137,000**	Welfare, health, education, in Salford
☐ **Spitalfields Market Community Trust**	**£1,130,000**	Education, employment, welfare in Tower Hamlets
☐ **Edward Cadbury Charitable Trust**	**£1,129,000**	Religion, general
☐ **Medlock Charitable Trust**	**£1,121,000**	Education, health, welfare, mainly in Bath and Boston
☐ **Al Fayed Charitable Foundation**	**£1,103,000**	Children, health and general
☐ **A W Charitable Trust**	**£1,100,000**	Jewish, general
☐ **Barnwood House Trust**	**£1,088,000**	Disability charities in Gloucestershire, medical research
☐ **Leathersellers' Company Charitable Fund**	**£1,072,000**	General
☐ **Jane Hodge Foundation**	**£1,069,000**	Medicine, education, religion, mainly in Wales
☐ **Save & Prosper Charities**	**£1,054,000**	Education
☐ **J W Laing Biblical Scholarship Trust**	**£1,051,000**	Christian evangelism
☐ **Jones 1986 Charitable Trust**	**£1,037,000**	General, especially in Nottinghamshire
☐ **Levy Foundation**	**£1,014,000**	Young people, elderly, health, medical research, Jewish charities
☐ **Zochonis Charitable Trust**	**£1,007,000**	General, especially Greater Manchester
☐ **Cripplegate Foundation**	**£1,000,000**	General, in Cripplegate/Islington, London
☐ **Bradbury Foundation**	**£1,000,000**	Welfare
☐ **Hedley Foundation**	**£996,000**	Youth, health, welfare
☐ **Tedworth Trust**	**£996,000**	Parenting, child welfare and development, general
☐ **Charities Aid Foundation**	**£995,000**	Charity management and finance
☐ **Carnegie United Kingdom Trust**	**£991,000**	Community service, arts, heritage
☐ **Huntingdon Foundation**	**£974,000**	Jewish causes
☐ **Sir John Cass's Foundation**	**£973,000**	Education in inner London
☐ **Will Charitable Trust**	**£967,000**	Environment/conservation, cancer care, blindness, mental handicap
☐ **Kennedy Charitable Foundation**	**£952,000**	Roman Catholic ministries, general, especially in the west of Ireland
☐ **Steel Charitable Trust**	**£950,000**	Social welfare, health, medical research, general
☐ **Rose Foundation**	**£942,000**	Building projects for charities, general
☐ **E B M Charitable Trust**	**£933,000**	Health, welfare, bloodstock
☐ **Hadley Trust**	**£925,000**	Social welfare
☐ **Alglen Ltd**	**£917,000**	Jewish causes
☐ **Itzchok Meyer Cymerman Trust**	**£907,000**	Jewish Orthodox education, other Jewish organisations
☐ **Metropolitan Hospital–Sunday Fund**	**£883,000**	Sick and disabled people in London
☐ **David and Frederick Barclay Foundation**	**£882,000**	Medical research, welfare
☐ **Ashden Charitable Trust**	**£879,000**	Environment, homelessness, urban rejuvenation, arts
☐ **George John Livanos Charitable Trust**	**£877,000**	Health, maritime charities, general
☐ **John Moores Foundation**	**£867,000**	Social welfare in Merseyside and Northern Ireland, emergency relief overseas
☐ **Stevenson Family's Charitable Trust**	**£865,000**	Museums, health, general
☐ **Staples Trust**	**£862,000**	Development, environment, women's issues
☐ **Henry Moore Foundation**	**£856,000**	Visual art, particularly sculpture
☐ **Manifold Trust**	**£855,000**	Historic buildings, environmental conservation, general
☐ **Samuel Sebba Charitable Trust**	**£854,000**	Jewish charities in Israel and Britain
☐ **Gosling Foundation**	**£848,000**	Naval charities, general
☐ **Lolev Charitable Trust**	**£846,000**	See entry
☐ **Help a London Child**	**£844,000**	Children in London
☐ **John and Lucille van Geest Foundation**	**£841,000**	Medical research, healthcare, general
☐ **H B Allen Charitable Trust**	**£838,000**	General
☐ **Sir Halley Stewart Trust**	**£834,000**	Medical, social and religious research
☐ **Pilkington Charities Fund**	**£829,000**	General

☐ **Glass-House Trust**	**£818,000**	Parenting, child development and family welfare, art, general
☐ **Camelia Botnar Foundation**	**£815,000**	Disadvantaged young people
☐ **Alchemy Foundation**	**£812,000**	Health and welfare, famine relief overseas
☐ **H C D Memorial Fund**	**£807,000**	See entry
☐ **Richard Cloudesley's Charity**	**£800,000**	Churches, health and welfare in Islington, London.
☐ **Northwood Charitable Trust**	**£800,000**	Probably local causes in Dundee, health
☐ **Laing's Charitable Trust**	**£797,000**	General
☐ **Hact (The Housing Associations Charitable Trust)**	**£796,000**	Housing and related social need
☐ **Kreitman Foundation**	**£791,000**	Jewish charities, the arts, general
☐ **Sir James Colyer-Fergusson's Charitable Trust**	**£790,000**	Church buildings, general, in Kent and Suffolk
☐ **Beatrice Laing Trust**	**£789,000**	Health, welfare, in the UK and overseas
☐ **Reta Lila Howard Foundation**	**£760,000**	Children
☐ **Hampton Fuel Allotment Charity**	**£757,000**	General, in Twickenham and Richmond
☐ **Leeds Hospital Fund Charitable Trust**	**£751,000**	Hospitals in Yorkshire, charities in Leeds
☐ **Joseph Rowntree Reform Trust**	**£750,000**	Innovative and reforming work, ineligible for charitable status
☐ **Gloucestershire Environmental Trust Company**	**£750,000**	Environmental improvements
☐ **Stobart Newlands Charitable Trust**	**£744,000**	Christian causes
☐ **Lambeth Endowed Charities**	**£725,000**	Education, general social needs in Lambeth, London
☐ **J J Charitable Trust**	**£722,000**	Environment, in UK and overseas, literacy
☐ **Artemis Charitable Trust**	**£719,000**	Psychotherapy, parent education, and related activities
☐ **South Yorkshire Community Foundation**	**£712,000**	General, in South Yorkshire
☐ **Donald Forrester Trust**	**£709,000**	Disability, general
☐ **Entindale Ltd**	**£708,000**	Orthodox Jewish charities
☐ **Band Trust**	**£707,000**	Health, disability, elderly, children, art
☐ **Charities Advisory Trust**	**£702,000**	See entry
☐ **Isle of Dogs Community Foundation**	**£695,000**	Social regeneration on the Isle of Dogs, London
☐ **Wills 1965 Charitable Trust**	**£691,000**	General (particularly preservation of wildlife, 2001–03)
☐ **Shlomo Memorial Fund**	**£679,000**	Jewish causes
☐ **MacRobert Trusts**	**£678,000**	General, mainly in Scotland
☐ **Sir Samuel Scott of Yews Trust**	**£667,000**	Medical research
☐ **Woodward Charitable Trust**	**£660,000**	General
☐ **Great Britain Sasakawa Foundation**	**£653,000**	Links between Great Britain and Japan
☐ **Ernest Cook Trust**	**£651,000**	Rural conservation and environmental research, youth, arts and crafts
☐ **Cleveland Community Foundation**	**£649,000**	General, in Cleveland
☐ **Hospital Saving Association Charitable Trust**	**£643,000**	Healthcare, medical research
☐ **Dowager Countess Eleanor Peel Trust**	**£642,000**	Medical research, general
☐ **Boltons Trust**	**£632,000**	Social welfare, medicine, education
☐ **Mrs L D Rope Third Charitable Settlement**	**£618,000**	General, particularly in south east Suffolk
☐ **Robert Gavron Charitable Trust**	**£614,000**	Arts, policy research, disability, education
☐ **Percy Bilton Charity**	**£613,000**	Disabled, young or older people, health
☐ **Sir James Reckitt Charity**	**£602,000**	Society of Friends, general
☐ **SHINE (Support and Help In Education)**	**£600,000**	Education in London and south east England
☐ **Talbot Village Trust**	**£598,000**	General, in east Dorset
☐ **John Beckwith Charitable Settlement**	**£596,000**	Youth, general
☐ **Gur Trust**	**£591,000**	Jewish causes
☐ **10th Duke of Devonshire's Charitable Trust**	**£573,000**	General, especially in Derbyshire
☐ **Rowan Charitable Trust**	**£571,000**	Overseas aid, social welfare, general
☐ **Weinstock Fund**	**£569,000**	General
☐ **Pet Plan Charitable Trust**	**£569,000**	Animals
☐ **Underwood Trust**	**£564,000**	General

Trust	Grant total	Causes
☐ G C Gibson Charitable Trust	£562,000	Churches, health, welfare, general
☐ Charitworth Limited	£562,000	Jewish causes
☐ Network Foundation	£556,000	Third world debt, environment, human rights, peace, arts
☐ NiKeNo Trust	£550,000	Local in Sussex, medical research
☐ Rothschild Foundation	£540,000	Heritage, Jewish charities, general

Trust	Grant total	Causes
☐ Mr and Mrs J A Pye's Charitable Settlement	£537,000	Environment, mental health, general
☐ Frances and Augustus Newman Foundation	£537,000	Medical research and equipment
☐ Triangle Trust	£536,000	Carers, elderly, homeless, disabled, regeneration
☐ M & R Gross Charities	£534,000	Jewish causes
☐ Richmond Parish Lands Charity	£533,000	General, in Richmond
☐ Sir Siegmund Warburg's Voluntary Settlement	£531,000	Medicine and education
☐ Tompkins Foundation	£525,000	Health, welfare
☐ Mary Kinross Charitable Trust	£516,000	Mental health, penal affairs, youth
☐ Isle of Anglesey Charitable Trust	£516,000	General, in Anglesey
☐ Fishmongers' Company's Charitable Trust	£515,000	Relief of hardship and disability, education

Trust	Grant total	Causes
☐ William Adlington Cadbury Charitable Trust	£513,000	Birmingham area, Quaker churches, overseas
☐ Baron Davenport's Charity	£509,000	Almshouses, hospices, residential homes, children, in the West Midlands
☐ Allen Lane Foundation	£505,000	Disadvantaged minorities, unpopular causes
☐ Charity Association Manchester Ltd	£500,000	Jewish charities
☐ Mental Health Foundation	£500,000	Mental health & learning disability research, community work
☐ J G Joffe Charitable Trust	£497,000	Development policy, projects in developing countries.
☐ Southover Manor General Education Trust	£496,000	Education, youth, in Sussex
☐ Alan Edward Higgs Charity	£492,000	Child welfare, in the Coventry area
☐ Queen Mary's Roehampton Trust	£492,000	War disabled ex-service people and their dependants
☐ Sir John Eastwood Foundation	£491,000	Social welfare, education, health, in Nottinghamshire

Trust	Grant total	Causes
☐ Welton Foundation	£491,000	Medical research, music, general
☐ William Leech Charity	£491,000	Health and welfare in the north east of England, overseas aid
☐ Greater Bristol Foundation	£481,000	General, in Bristol
☐ Enid Linder Foundation	£477,000	Health, welfare
☐ Basil Samuel Charitable Trust	£473,000	General
☐ Bedford Charity (also known as the Harpur Trust)	£472,000	Education, welfare and recreation in and around Bedford
☐ Porter Foundation	£467,000	Education, environment, general
☐ Jim Marshall Charitable Trust	£466,000	General
☐ Jordan Charitable Foundation	£462,000	General, especially in Herefordshire
☐ Anglian Water Trust Fund	£459,000	Money advice provision, individuals in need

Trust	Grant total	Causes
☐ Graham Kirkham Foundation	£455,000	General
☐ Albert Hunt Trust	£451,000	Welfare
☐ Lord Leverhulme's Charitable Trust	£450,000	Education, welfare, arts, general
☐ North British Hotel Trust	£450,000	Welfare, health, mainly in Scotland
☐ Audrey & Stanley Burton Charitable Trust	£444,000	Health, arts, Jewish charities, welfare and general
☐ Leverhulme Trade Charities Trust	£443,000	Charities benefiting commercial travellers, grocers or chemists
☐ Hilden Charitable Fund	£441,000	Minorities, overseas, penal, homelessness, general
☐ Maud Elkington Charitable Trust	£428,000	Social welfare, general, in Northamptonshire and Leicestershire
☐ Greggs Trust	£425,000	Social welfare in the north east of England
☐ Roald Dahl Foundation	£419,000	Haematology, neurology, literacy

Trust	Grant total	Causes
☐ Constance Green Foundation	£417,000	Medicine, health, social welfare, general
☐ Alan & Babette Sainsbury Charitable Fund	£416,000	General

☐ **Charity Know How**	**£415,000**	Central and Eastern Europe and the former Soviet Union
☐ **M K Charitable Trust**	**£412,000**	Jewish charities
☐ **Raymond & Beverley Sackler Foundation**	**£410,000**	Cambridge University, the British Museum
☐ **Peabody Community Fund**	**£405,000**	Social welfare in London
☐ **Burdens Charitable Foundation**	**£400,000**	General
☐ **Lewis Family Charitable Trust**	**£399,000**	Medical research, health, education, Jewish charities
☐ **Van Leer Foundation (UK) Trust**	**£395,000**	Childhood development
☐ **W O Street Charitable Foundation**	**£394,000**	Education, disability, young people, welfare

---

☐ **Spring Harvest Charitable Trust**	**£361,000**	The promotion of Christianity
☐ **J B Rubens Charitable Foundation**	**£351,000**	Mainly Jewish causes
☐ **Ayrton Senna Foundation**	**£345,000**	Children's health and education
☐ **Philip & Pauline Harris Charitable Trust**	**£313,000**	General
☐ **Three Guineas Trust**	**£284,000**	Autism, women's issues, poverty/homelessness
☐ **Cripps Foundation**	**£162,000**	Education, healthcare and churches in Northamptonshire, Cambridge University

The 29th May 1961 Charitable Trust

Social welfare, general

£2,712,000 (1998/99)

Beneficial area UK, with a special interest in the Warwickshire/Birmingham/Coventry area.

c/o Macfarlanes, 10 Norwich Street, London EC4A 1BD

Tel. 020 7831 9222 **Fax** 020 7831 9607

Correspondent The Secretary

Information available Report and accounts available. Grants list but no narrative.

Summary

Over 300 grants are made a year, ranging in size from hundreds to hundreds of thousands of pounds; most are between £1,000 and £5,000. About half appear to be for work in the Warwickshire area. Most grants are repeated from year to year. Perhaps less than 20% of the grant total is available for reallocation in a given year.

General

This is a large trust, with reserves of nearly £86 million generating £3.5 million of income in 1999. It is named after the date on which it was established by the late Helen Martin of Kenilworth, Warwickshire. The pattern of grantmaking suggests that it is the old (pre-1974) county of Warwickshire, which includes Birmingham and Coventry, that remains the priority area of benefit. Little explanation of grants policy is provided except for the following summary from the trustees' report:

The policy of the trustees is to support a wide range of charitable organisations across a broad spectrum with grants for both capital and revenue purposes. Some grants are one-off, some recurring and others spread over two or three years. The majority of grants are made to organisations within the UK and preference is given, where possible, to charities operating in the Midlands area.

About 40% of the funds in each year goes to the Midlands, and 20% to London and the south. Most of the remainder is given to UK-wide charities, with a small proportion going overseas.

In 1998/99 over £2.5 million was donated to 301 organisations, which the trust categorises as follows:

	1998/99	*(1997/98)*
Art, leisure and youth projects	£804,000	(£1,078,000)
Social welfare	£601,000	(£617,000)
Health	£474,000	(£555,000)
Education and training	£336,000	(£340,000)
Homelessness and housing	£323,000	(£338,000)
Offenders	£137,000	(£128,000)
Conservation and protection	£37,000	(£69,000)
Total	£2,712,000	(£3,125,000)

The list of grant recipients appears to change very little from year to year. Out of the top 25 grant recipients in 1999, 23 had received similar grants in the previous year. At least 90% of the organisations even at the lower end of the list, who got £1,000 in 1999, had received the same amount in 1998.

Four grants were for six-figure sums: University of Warwick (£307,000); NSPCC (£110,000); Federation of London Youth Clubs (£101,000), and Coventry & Warwickshire Award Trust (£100,000).

Large grants also went to Cancer Bacup (£77,000); Prince's Youth Business Trust (£75,000); Coventry Day Care Fund for the Mentally Handicapped (£65,000); Crisis (£50,000); Sadler's Wells Trust (£50,000), and St Basil's Centre (£50,000).

Others included Amnesty International (£30,000); Birmingham Settlement (£25,000); St Edmundsbury Cathedral (£15,000); Life Education Centres (£10,000); National Federation of Young Farmers Clubs (£7,000); Drugline (£5,000); North Devon Community Transport Association (£3,000); London Business School (£2,000); Castle Bromwich Hall Gardens Trust (£1,000), and Nuneaton Area Hospital Broadcasting (£1,000).

Exclusions

Grants only to registered charities. No grants to individuals.

Applications

To the secretary in writing. Applicants must enclose a copy of their most recent accounts. Trustees meet in February, May, August and November.

The A W Charitable Trust

Jewish, general

£1,100,000 (1998/99)

Messrs B Olsber & Co., Barclay House, 35 Whitworth Street West, Manchester M1 5NG

Correspondent The Trustees

Information available Accounts on file at the Charity Commission, but without a list of grants since 1991/92.

General

In 1997/98 the trust had assets of £3.4 million and an income of £1.4 million. Management and administration costs were very low, at £12,000. The trust gave grants totalling £1.1 million.

Disappointingly, there has been no information on the work of this trust, or details of the grants made, since 1991/92. During that year £55,000 was given in grants, all to Jewish organisations.

The trustees' report contained only empty statements, like the following: the trust supports 'all causes which are considered charitable according to the law of England'. The description of its 'developments, activities and achievements' was similarly void of information, stating only that the performance of the charity that year was 'satisfactory'.

Applications

In writing to the correspondent.

Achisomoch Aid Company

Jewish religious charities

£1,242,000 (1998/99)

26 Hoop Lane, London NW11 8BU

Tel. 020 8455 7132

Correspondent I M Katz, Secretary

Information available Annual report and accounts, but no grants list.

General

The address above is taken from the previous edition of this book. We wrote asking for new information, but there was no response. An alternative address, the company's registered office, may be:

c/o Cohen, Arnold and Co., 13–17 New Burlington Place, London W1X 2JP.

The trust has never included a list of grants with its accounts, but one was supplied for the entry in the last edition, which is reprinted here:

The trust seeks to advance religion in accordance with the Jewish faith.

In 1997/98 income derived mainly from donations to the charity, there being no permanent endowment.

Almost 500 grants were made to Jewish charities, mostly for hundreds rather than thousands of pounds, and many for smaller sums still – such as Beth Hayaled, £59, or I Kohn Char, £55.

The largest single grant was to another grantmaker, itself featured in this book, the Lolev Charitable Trust (£103,000). The other major awards were to Marbeh Torah Trust (£63,000), WSRT (£30,000), Achiezer (£32,000), Gateshead Talmudical College (£33,000) and the Jewish Secondary Schools Mov. (£21,000).

The AIM Foundation

Integrated preventative medicine, community development, environment, general

£1,609,000 (1998/99)

Beneficial area UK, with an apparent local interest in Essex, and overseas.

Farrer & Co., 66 Lincoln's Inn Fields, London WC2A 3LH

Tel. 020 7242 2022

Correspondent Charles Woodhouse, Trustee

Trustees *Ian Roy Marks; Angela Marks; Charles Woodhouse.*

Information available Annual report and accounts lacking the required explanation of grants.

Summary

A small number of grants, some for very large amounts, and most as part of on-going support or for long-term projects. The organisations supported typically offer alternative and radical solutions to social, environmental and health problems. (See also the Network Foundation, whose policy seems to run along similar lines.)

The foundation says that it is entirely proactive, spending about £30,000 a year on research into how it can best make a difference in its grantmaking in its areas of interest, so unsolicited applications will fail.

General

Set up in 1971 as the Ian Roy Marks Charitable Trust, this trust changed its name to The AIM Foundation in 1993.

The charity said in October 2000 that it had more recent accounts than those used in preparing this entry, but 'was not inclined to help' by sending a copy to these editors, despite the statutory requirement to the contrary. This was a surprising refusal from a firm of solicitors.

The information on policy given in the 1998/99 trustees' report was as follows:

> The Trustees' grant-making policy is to be highly proactive in seeking out potential partners to initiate and promote charitable projects principally in the fields of healthcare, community development and environmental matters both in the UK and overseas; they have a clear policy of not supporting individuals and they do not under any circumstances respond to unsolicited applications.
>
> The Trustees employ three professional fund managers to invest the capital of the Trust on the world's stock markets with a social, ethical and environmental emphasis. …

In 1998/99 a Gift Aid donation of £1,350,000 and a gift of £457,000 in shares contributed to a nearly tenfold rise in the trust's total income, to over £2 million (compared to £265,000 in 1997/98). Assets stood at £7.2 million (up from £6.4 million in 1997/98). Total grantmaking subsequently increased from half a million pounds in 1997/98 to over £1.6 million in the following year.

Grants of over £1,000 were made to 21 organisations, with 13 of them, including most of the larger recipients, having received support in the previous year.

These payments were led by a £1 million endowment of the Foundation for Integrated Medicine, which was supplemented by a repeat grant of £100,000. The foundation also made a commitment to the Essex Community Foundation of £750,000 in endowment funding backed up by further payments of £40,000 annually for three years.

Other major beneficiaries were the Ripple Effect Foundation, which received a new grant of £200,000, and Sustrans (£100,000, following a £90,000 grant in 1997/98).

These four organisations together accounted for about 90% of the grant expenditure. The trust's annual report for 1998/99 provided the following examples of other grants.

Healthcare (8 grants, £1,140,000)

Aside from the £1.1 million for the Foundation for Integrated Medicine, other grants included £10,000 to Natural Justice and £5,000, repeated, to the Foundation for Traditional Chinese Medicines. Local beneficiaries included £5,500 to Chelmsford and District MIND (repeat) and £2,250 to Princess Alice Hospice in Surrey.

Environment (3 grants, £137,000)

In addition to Sustrans, grants were made to the Gaia Foundation (£35,000; £5,000 in 1997/98) and Saferworld (£2,000).

Community development including homelessness (4 grants, £82,500)

A total of £65,000 was paid to Essex Community Foundation. Other grants included £10,000 to NSPCC Tilbury Project and £5,000 to the New Economics Foundation, both repeats.

Miscellaneous, including youth development (6 grants, £227,000)

Most money under this heading went to the Ripple Effect Foundation. Previously supported beneficiaries were the Network Foundation (£10,000) and Ashoka (£6,000). A new grant went to Tools for Self Reliance (£2,000). A grant of £28,000 was listed as 'Material grant not disclosed', and grants of £1,000 and below during the year totalled £22,000.

Exclusions

No grants to individuals.

Applications

It cannot be stressed enough that this foundation does not wish to receive applications.

The Al Fayed Charitable Foundation

Children, health and general

£1,103,000 (to institutions, 1999)

5th Floor, c/o 87–135 Brompton Road, Knightsbridge, London SW1X 7XL

Tel. 020 7225 6673 **Fax** 020 7225 6872

Correspondent Belinda White

Trustees *Mohammed Al Fayed; A Fayed; S Fayed.*

Information available Annual report and accounts.

General

Most of the foundation's income (£793,000 in 1999) is covenanted from Harrods Holdings plc, but in recent years it has also been channelling money coming in from the Dodi International Foundation to West Heath School in Sevenoaks, Kent (an initial £3 million in 1998 was followed by £515,000 in 1999). The foundation plans to turn the school, once attended by Princess Diana, into a home for the Beth Marie Centre for educating abused children.

Other grants totalled £638,000, including £51,000 used to assist eight individuals. The beneficiaries were a fairly varied group. Two small grants went to charities in a part of west London where Mohammed Al Fayed owns the local football club.

The accounts listed 31 recipients of £1,000 or more, adding up to £539,000. Of this total 45% went in grants of £50,000 or more to Building Conservation Trust (£70,000); Mary Hare Grammar School (£62,000); Zoe's Place – Baby Hospital (£60,000) and RADA (£50,000).

Twelve further grants ranged from £10,000 to £32,000, the recipients including the Lufti Foundation (£32,000); Rainbow Family Trust (£30,000); Thailand Orphanage (£26,000); Children of Egypt (£25,000); Muslim Council of Great Britain (£25,000); Royal Cornwall Hospital (£24,000); The Children's Centre Fund (£22,000), and Oxted Hockey Club (£18,500).

Recipients of grants under £10,000 included the Soul Intention Childline Tour; Eating Disorders Association; Rhys Daniels Trust; Arab Women's Association; Clifton Hill Pool Fund; Craven Cottage Social Club; and Barnes Community Association.

Donations under £1,000 totalled £48,453.

Applications

In writing to the correspondent.

The Alchemy Foundation

Health and welfare, famine relief overseas

£812,000 (to organisations, 1998/99)

Trevereux Manor, Limpsfield Chart, Oxted, Surrey RH8 0TL

Tel. 01883 730600 **Fax** 01883 730800

Correspondent Richard Stilgoe, Trustee

Trustees *Alex Armitage; Andrew Murison; Esther Rantzen; Revd Donald Reeves; Annabel Stilgoe; Holly Stilgoe; Jack Stilgoe; Dr Jemima Stilgoe; Joseph Stilgoe; Richard Stilgoe; Rufus Stilgoe.*

Information available Report and accounts with list of grants of £2,000 or over.

Summary

Several hundred small donations are made a year, averaging £1,500, to charities supporting people in need, including children and young adults, older people and those with an illness or disability. About £200,000 a year is reserved for international relief organisations working in developing countries. Larger grants, for tens of thousands of pounds, up to a maximum of £100,000, go almost exclusively to this type of beneficiary.

In most years, the largest donation is for a sister organisation, the Orpheus Trust, that shares the same trustees and whose work supports music projects for people with disabilities.

General

The foundation was established as the 'Starlight Foundation' in 1985 by Richard and Annabel Stilgoe. Two years later its name was changed to the Alchemy Foundation to avoid confusion with an American charity, recently arrived in the UK, also called Starlight. A remarkably steady income, of over £1 million a year, is provided by the royalties from the musicals *Starlight Express* and *The Phantom of the Opera.*

Income for 1998/99 was £1,159,000, the same as in the previous year. Direct charitable expenditure was £860,000, with management and administration costs adding just £1,864 to the expenses.

In addition to £127,000 for the Orpheus Trust, the foundation made 454 grants to institutions totalling £685,000 and 213 grants to individuals worth £48,000. The accounts listed 82 recipients of grants for £2,000 or more. These were headed by Water Aid and Oxfam, which received £100,000 each.

The only other grants in excess of £10,000 were £18,500 to Bridget's Home for the Disabled of Cambridge University, and £10,500 each to VSO and the Centre for the Rehabilitation of the Paralysed in Bangladesh, all having been supported in previous years.

A further 23 grants ranged from £3,000 to £6,000 and the remaining 54 were for £2,000.

A sample of grants for £2,000 reads as follows: Cambodia Trust; Disabled Living Foundation, Emmaus Cambridge Appeal; Fairbridge; Good Shepherd Trust; Housing Associations Charitable Trust; IPSEA; John Grooms Association; Koestler Award Trust; Listening Books; Mansfield Settlement; New Horizon Youth Centre; Oasis; Prison Reform Trust; Quaker Social Action; Research into Ageing.

Applications

In writing to the correspondent, although applicants should know that the foundation felt that a wide spread of applicants was already being addressed without the additional load that inclusion in this guide might produce.

Alglen Ltd

Jewish causes

£917,000 (1998/99)

Felds, Trustees' Accountants, 5 North End Road, London NW11 7RJ

Tel. 020 8455 6789 **Fax** 020 8455 2277

Correspondent Mrs R Lipschitz, Secretary

Trustees *Mrs E Stieglitz; D Schreiber; Mrs R Lipschitz; J A Brunner.*

Information available Annual report and accounts.

General

The trust supports Jewish organisations only. In 1998/99, it had an income of £291,000 and gave grants totalling

£917,000, a dramatic increase from £248,000 in the previous year. The assets of the trust therefore decreased over the year from £1.4 million to £730,000.

All the grants in previous years have been to Jewish organisations. No grants list was included with the accounts for this year, as 'The governors consider that disclosure of the recipients' names may prejudice the furtherance of the purposes of the recipient institutions.'

Applications

In writing to the correspondent.

Allchurches Trust

Churches, general

£4,014,000 (1999)

Beneficial area UK.

Beaufort House, Brunswick Road, Gloucester GL1 1JZ

Tel. 01452 528533

Correspondent R W Clayton, Secretary

Trustees *Sir Alan McLintock, Chair; Viscount Churchill; M R Cornwall-Jones; B V Day; Mrs S Homersham; Revd D G Snelgrove; W H Yates.*

Information available A copy of the report and accounts, statement of policy and guidelines, and application forms are available on request from the correspondent.

Summary

A large number of small grants is awarded mainly to Anglican churches and cathedrals. A very small part of the trust's funds is given to other organisations, many also having Christian associations, particularly in the health and welfare field.

General

The company was established in 1972 to promote Christian religion and to contribute to the funds of charitable institutions.

Available funding is derived from its wholly owned subsidiary company Ecclesiastical Insurance Office plc. The trustees make grants to the Church and Christian community, usually in support of Churches, Church establishments, religious charities, charities preserving UK heritage, theological colleges, schools promoting Christian religion, charities recommended by the Church, the local community and those concerned with the welfare of the disadvantaged and disabled.

Grants range from £100 to £5,000, in the form of a single one-off payment. The trustees prefer to support a specific project rather than contribute to running costs or salaries.

Annual income from the Ecclesiastical Insurance Office now stands at £4 million a year.

Grants in 1999

Over £3.5 million was disbursed in diocesan grants (£3.27 million, or 93%, to Church of England dioceses and parishes) and a further £243,000 in grants to cathedrals.

A total of 374 churches and 12 cathedrals were specifically named in the grants list, the largest beneficiaries being Chalford Tabernacle Baptist Church in Gloucestershire, Westminster Abbey, York Minster and five English cathedrals, each receiving £5,000.

Aside from the support given to churches and cathedrals, further grants were categorised as follows:

	No.	*Amount*
Other religious institutions	44	£102,000
Hospitals, hospices and care centres	58	£34,000
Community appeals	97	£18,000
Overseas	2	£6,000
'Charities'	22	£3,000
Colleges and other	15	£24,000

The following five beneficiaries received grants for more than £5,000: Clergy Pensions Board, £50,000; Council for the Care of Churches, £25,000; Worshipful Company of Coopers Quincentenary Appeal, £20,000; Ridley Hall, Cambridgeshire, £10,000; Lambeth Palace (String of Pearls Millennium Festival), £10,000.

Examples of the larger grants made under the above categories were as follows:

Hospices, hospitals and care centres

Princess Royal Trust for Carers; Yeldall Christian Centres, Reading; St Luke's Hospital for the Clergy (£2,000 each); Help the Hospices (£1,000).

Community appeals

Herefordshire MIND (£2,000); Cardinal Hume Centre, London (£1,500); Michael House Centre, Cambridgeshire (£1,000); Radicle, London (£1,000).

Overseas

TB Alert (£5,000); Anglican Centre in Rome (£1,000).

Charities

There were 18 grants of £100, plus four more for amounts up to £250. Beneficiaries included 12 local YMCAs, the Salvation Army, Prince's Trust, Arthritis Research Campaign and Deafblind UK.

Colleges and other

University of York Department of Archaeology (£5,000); Stained Glass Museum, Cambridgeshire (£4,000); The Landmark Trust, Berkshire (£2,500); Nadfas, London (£1,000).

Exclusions

The trustees do not make grants to charities with political associations. They do not generally make grants to national charities, or respond to appeals from individuals.

Applications

Applications should be submitted in writing to the correspondent, detailing charity number, the objectives of the charity, the appeal target, how the funds are to be utilised, funds raised to date and previous support received from the trust. If available, the application should be accompanied by supporting literature and annual report. Trustees meet quarterly.

The H B Allen Charitable Trust

General

£838,000 (2000)

Beneficial area UK.

Teigncombe Barn, Chagford, Devon TQ13 8ET

Tel. 01647 433235

e-mail hballen.charitabletrust@btinternet.com

website http://members.nbci.com/hballenchtrust

Correspondent Peter Shone, Trustee

Trustees *Heather Allen; Peter Shone.*

Information available Annual report and accounts, extracts of which can be found on the trust's website.

Summary

Grants, usually between £5,000 and £25,000, to a wide range of charities, national and local, usually including at least a scattering of grants for

- nautical charities, both welfare and environmental
- child health and welfare
- hospices
- third world development

There are few or no grants for the arts, or for education, other than for those with disabilities.

General

The grants list for 2000 shows 78 grants, all but two for amounts between £5,000 and £30,000. All are in round figures, suggesting that they may be contributions to the general work of the charities involved, rather than grants to pay for individually costed projects. The trust describes its work as follows:

The Trustees have no restrictions on them ... and are generally prepared to consider any field. There is no typical grant size, though the Trustees make a large number at £5,000. Grants can be recurring or one-off, and for revenue or capital purposes. They have tended to make (without commitment) recurring grants to several charities as well as one-off grants to some charities newly selected each year.

The Trustees receive a ... rising number of appeals each year – some 720 in 1996, over 950 in 1997 and almost 1,200 in 1999. In view of the number, it is not their practice to acknowledge appeals.

The major grants in 2000 were as follows:

Royal Naval Museum	£100,000
Wildlife Conservation Research Unit	£30,000
The Rowans, Portsmouth Area Hospice	£25,000
Crisis	£25,000
The Falkland Islands Memorial Chapel	£25,000

The Royal Naval Museum and The Rowans received the same amount in the previous year, being among those charities getting recurrent funding.

Among the 10 beneficiaries of grants for £20,000 were the Children's Society, Dermatrust, Intermediate Technology, The Hebridean Trust, Save the Children and Calvert Trust Kielder.

Of the remaining grants, 24 were for £10,000, 38 for £5,000 and 1 for £3,000.

These included Mount's Bay Lugger Association; Body Positive; Lupus UK; Tools for Self Reliance; The Hawk and Owl Trust; Camphill Village Trust (Croft Community, Malton); Contact the Elderly; The Cassel Hospital Families Centre Appeal; and the Fishermen's Mission.

Exclusions

No grants to individuals, or to organisations which are not registered charities.

Applications

In writing to the correspondent.

The Anglian Water Trust Fund

Money advice provision/ individuals in need

£459,000 (to organisations, 1999/2000)

Beneficial area Anglian Water region, i.e. Cambridgeshire, Lincolnshire, Norfolk and Suffolk plus parts of Bedfordshire, Buckinghamshire, Essex, Leicestershire, Northamptonshire, Rutland and Hartlepool.

PO Box 42, Peterborough PE3 8XH

Tel. 01733 331177 **Fax** 01733 334344

Correspondent Ed Hickman

Trustees *Barbara Ruffell, Chair; Graham Blagden; Norman Guffick; Stephen Harrap; Elizabeth Ingram; Stuart de Prochnow; John Sansby.*

Information available Full annual report and accounts, including guidelines, were provided by the trust.

Summary

The trust's main activity, worth about £1.3 million a year, is to help individuals and families in hardship who are customers of Anglian Water plc with their water and sewerage debts, and to assist with general welfare support, such as help with other priority debts or the purchase of essential household equipment.

A secondary programme aims to improve and increase the provision of independent money advice services in the Anglian Water region, typically by paying for the salaries, over three years, of advice workers at citizens advice bureaux.

General

The trust fund receives an income of £2 million a year from Anglian Water plc. The trust primarily assists individuals and families in need. In addition, a relatively small proportion is left over for grants to organisations (£459,000 in 1999/2000). Grants are given to voluntary organisations to enable them to:

- establish or extend debt counselling services;
- provide education in the prevention of debt.

The annual report for 1998/99 says:

The Trust offers organisational grants for either capital or revenue expenditure. Projects can seek assistance with revenue expenditure for up to three years but assistance from the Trust will be tapered after the first year. Such continuing funding beyond the first year is also conditional on the project raising funding from another source to meet the withdrawal of Trust funding.

During its first year, the Trust made awards to 36 organisations; in its second year, the Trust made awards to 22 organisations. The majority of these awards were for revenue expenditure over three years for the employment of money advice workers and support staff. ... in its third year (1998/99) the Trust was faced with a significant commitment in continuing to fund a number of these organisations albeit on a reduced basis. This therefore necessarily lessened the amount of funding available for new projects for that year. The Trust therefore determined to fund only a small number of projects which would significantly enhance the availability of money advice in areas poorly resourced in such provision.

In 1998/99, 25 organisations benefited from continuing support totalling £242,000, ranging from about £2,000 to £23,000.

Grants approved for new projects amounted to £175,000, the largest being £41,000 to Castle Point CAB, £31,000 to Brandon and Mildenhall CAB and £28,000 to Norfolk Rural Advice and Information Project. Six other CABs received grants ranging from £5,000 to £20,000. An award of just under £5,000 was also made to Peterborough Diocesan Family Care to enable it to extend its debt counselling work with young families in need.

To support its work with voluntary organisations, in 1998/99 the trust gave a grant to the Money Advice Trust for the appointment of a Money Advice Development Officer for Eastern England, based at the NACAB regional office in Cambridge.

Applications

Organisational grants: please contact the trust in writing to obtain information on the next grants programme (there is normally one grants round a year).

Individual grants: applications can be submitted throughout the year (except during pre-notified closure periods). Applications must be made on a standard application form which can be obtained from local advice centres such as citizens advice bureaux or by writing to the trust.

The Arbib Foundation

General

£2,190,000 (1999/2000)

Beneficial area Unrestricted, but with a special interest in the Henley area.

The Old Rectory, 17 Thameside, Henley-on-Thames, Oxon RG9 1LH

Tel. 01491 417128 **Fax** 01491 416050

Correspondent Linda Sanderson

Trustees *Martyn Arbib; A H Arbib; J S Kirkwood.*

Information available Inadequate annual report and accounts, without the required list of grant recipients or analysis of grantmaking.

Summary

The foundation's main commitment in recent years has been to support the development of the excellent River and Rowing Museum in Henley-on-Thames. In 1997/98 a grant of £1.8 million was made for this purpose, and in the following year the same amount was transferred to the foundation's capital account to fund future donations to the museum.

Other grants, ranging from £100 to £100,000, have been made in a wide variety of fields. These change from year to year, but have recently included organisations involved with conservation, medical research and social welfare.

General

Following a request in May 2000, the foundation provided the following information about its activities:

The Arbib Foundation supports the philanthropy of Mr Arbib. Income for 1999/2000 totalled £1.3 million, made up entirely from donations to the foundation. Grants of about £2.2 million were made.

The charity has supported a wide range of general causes, but most grants are to organisations with which the foundation or the trustees have an established connection. Other beneficiaries are usually local charities in the Henley area.

The trust's objectives specify, among other things, that 'the foundation's aim is to support the establishment of a museum in the Thames Valley for the education of the general public in the history, geography and ecology of the Thames Valley and the River Thames'. The museum has been completed and opened in summer 1998 to critical acclaim and has since received many awards. It is possible that further grants will be required for its on-going development.

Grants range in size from as little as £100 to as much as £1,000,000.

The trust's capital funds decreased by £1 million in 1999/2000, suggesting that a further substantial donation was made to the River and Rowing Museum. As no further information about grantmaking was available this entry must reprint that used in the previous edition of this book, when recipients of larger grants in 1997/98 were as follows:

Animal welfare: Animal Health Trust (£100,000), Thames Salmon Trust (£20,000), Tuskforce Wild at Heart (£15,000), Wildlife Trust (£10,000) and the Tiger Trust (£2,500).

Medical research: Institute of Cancer Research (£75,000) and the Leukaemia Research Fund (£5,000).

Social and community work: Barbados Children's Trust (£25,000), Help the Hospices (£20,000), Almshouse Association (£20,000), Wiltshire Community Fund (£5,000) and NSPCC (£4,000).

Applications

To the correspondent, but 'most grants are to organisations with which the foundation or the trustees have an established connection'. The trust regrets that it cannot respond to unsolicited applications, except in the case of charities local to its address.

The Architectural Heritage Fund

Loans and grants for building preservation

£4,283,000 (for new loan offers, 1999/2000)

Beneficial area UK.

Clareville House, 26–27 Oxendon Street, London SW1Y 4EL

Tel. 020 7925 0199 **Fax** 020 7930 0295

e-mail ahf@ahfund.org.uk

website www.ahfund.org.uk

Correspondent Jonathan Thompson, Director

Trustees *Sir John James, Chair; David Adams; Colin Amery; Nicholas Baring; William Cadell; Robert Clow; Malcolm Crowder; Fionnuala Jay-O'Boyle; John Pavitt; Jane Sharman; Merlin Waterson; Dr Roger Wools.*

Information available Extremely thorough and informative annual report and accounts (in return for a donation sufficient to cover costs); notes for applicants and detailed application forms; book on forming a buildings preservation trust; directory of funding sources for historic buildings in England and Wales; information sheets.

Summary

The fund makes low-interest loans to building preservation trusts, and gives advice and information to encourage and assist the preservation and rehabilitation of old buildings by preservation trusts and other charities. Loans supplement funds which groups raise themselves. Grants are also made, to building preservation trusts only, for feasibility studies on potential projects and to assist with administrative and development costs of projects.

General

The Architectural Heritage Fund (AHF), an independent charity, was established in 1976 to encourage and support the work of organisations dedicated to the preservation and renewal of buildings of architectural and historic significance which have failed to find a viable reuse on the open market.

The AHF is controlled by a Council of Management, half of whose members are appointed by the Department for Culture, Media and Sport. Its principal source of working capital over the years has been government grants supplemented by donations from companies, charitable trusts and individuals.

The fund provides financial assistance in the following ways:

Loans

Loans are available to Building Preservation Trusts (BPTs) and other organisations with charitable status for repair projects that involve a change in the use and/or the ownership of historic buildings (normally through their acquisition by the borrower). Only buildings which enjoy the statutory protection of being listed, scheduled or in a conservation area are eligible. Loans are usually for a period of up to two years and for up to 75% of the estimated cost of a qualifying project, subject to a ceiling of £500,000 per loan. Every borrower must provide adequate security. The AHF charges simple interest at 4% for the agreed loan period.

Grants (available to Building Preservation Trusts only)

- Feasibility Study Grants
- Project Administration Grants
- Project organiser grants
- Refundable project development grants
- Other forms of assistance

Loans and grants in 1999/2000

During the year to 31 March 2000 the fund contracted 18 new loans, worth £2,156,000. It received and approved 23 applications for loans, amounting to over £4 million. In addition, £46,000 was awarded in grants for 14 new feasibility studies. In response to 23 eligible applications in the year, 20 offers were made.

Exclusions

Applications from private individuals and non-charitable organisations. Applications for projects not involving a change of ownership or of use, or for a building not on a statutory list or in a conservation area.

Applications

Detailed notes for applicants for loans and feasibility studies are supplied with the application forms. Trustees meet in March, June, September and December. Applications must be received six weeks before meetings.

The Artemis Charitable Trust

Psychotherapy, parent education, and related activities

£719,000 (1999)

Beneficial area UK.

Brook House, Quay Meadow, Old Bosham, West Sussex PO18 8LY

Correspondent Richard Evans

Information available Annual report and accounts.

Summary

Only two or three new grants are awarded each year, usually for less than £5,000, but they can be for more than £200,000 if made to an organisation working in the trust's specialised field of counselling, psychotherapy or parenting. The bulk of the trust's funds, typically over 90% in a given year, is tied up in ongoing commitments to around six such organisations.

General

The trust was set up in 1985 by Richard and Gai Evans to make 'grants to aid the provision of counselling, psychotherapy, parenting, human relationship training and related activities'. They do this, on the whole, proactively, seeking out organisations and programmes to which they give long-term support – a model of grantmaking strongly encouraged by these editors.

The 1999 annual report says:

It is the policy of trustees to make grants on the basis of the current needs of grantees, utilising both the capital and income of the trust, and not to restrict grants to the level of the trust's income for the year.

As a result of this policy, the trust's capital base continued to decrease, to £2.5 million in 1999, when £719,000 was disbursed in ten grants.

In addition to these grants, during the year the trust continued to provide resources for the Parenting Education and Support Forum which arose out of the International Year of the Family. The Parenting Education and Support Forum is a body established to co-ordinate the various bodies concerned with parenting.

In 1998 and 1999, the five organisations receiving most of the money were as follows:

	1999	*1998*
Counselling in Primary Care Trust	£282,000	£266,000
The Metanoia Institute	£219,000	£201,000
PIPPIN	£111,000	£111,000
Parent Network	£40,000	£60,000
National Association for Staff Support	£36,000	£40,000

Two other grants to previously supported organisations went to the National Children's Bureau (£10,000) and Relate National Marriage Guidance (£3,000).

Two of the three new grants went to local beneficiaries: Chichester Counselling Services (£4,000) and the South Downs Planetarium Trust (£1,000). The third went to the Parenting Education and Support Forum (£13,000).

Applications

The trust can only give grants to registered charities. 'We cannot entertain applications either from individuals or from organisations which are not registered charities. Applicants should also be aware that most of the trust's funds are committed to a number of major on-going projects and that spare funds available to meet new applications are very limited.'

The Ashden Charitable Trust

Environment, homelessness, urban rejuvenation, arts

£879,000 (approved, 1998/99)

See entry for the Sainsbury Family Charitable Trusts

Tel. 020 7410 0330

Correspondent Michael Pattison, Director

Information available Good annual report and accounts, with full grants listing.

Summary

This is one of the Sainsbury Family Charitable Trusts, which share a joint administration. Its areas of interest are:

- (in the UK) transport, pollution and energy issues;
- (overseas) the application of renewable or sustainable energy to poverty reduction;
- homelessness and associated support needs;
- national and local work for urban rejuvenation;
- grassroots special needs or inner-city arts activities, with a developing interest in environmental drama.

General

Sarah Butler-Sloss (née Sainsbury) is the settlor of this trust. Its asset value was nearly £20 million in April 1999 and it was continuing to receive further donations from her, valued at more than £1.5 million in each of the two most recent years.

Staff include Michael Pattison, director of all the trusts in the group, and Jane Shepherd, executive.

Making less than 100 grants a year, in clearly defined and limited fields, this is one of the Sainsbury family trusts that probably approaches most completely their ideal of wholly proactive grantmaking. Its most direct activity has been the publication of the fine *Ashden Directory of Environment and Drama* (also available on its ashdendirectory.org website).

Grants approved during 1998/99 were analysed as follows:

	Approvals	*Value*
Environmental projects UK	36	£424,000
Environmental projects overseas	16	£152,000
Homelessness	10	£85,000
Urban rejuvenation	6	£101,000
Community arts	13	£74,000
General	9	£42,000
Total	90	£879,000

Out of 38 identifiably local projects in the UK, 23 were in London or the southern half of England and 15 in the northern half, a fairer distribution for such grants than is found for the Sainsbury trusts as a whole. There were, however, no such UK grants outside England.

Grantmaking 1998/99

The following information is taken from the annual report.

Environmental projects UK: 36 awards worth £423,700

The Trust continues to initiate and support work in the areas of

- transport policy
- pollution
- energy efficiency
- renewable energy technology.

The Trust has made grants for projects that seek to demonstrate alternative transport schemes, such as car-sharing, and for objective research to inform both transport policy makers and the general public, for example the research into aviation and the environment, due to be published early next year [2001]. The Trust is particularly interested in the contribution that non-motorised transport, and in particular cycling, can make towards improving health and the environment. Cycling has been a major focus during the year, and in partnership with others, the Trust has initiated projects at three levels:

- local authority cycling policy
- cycling at the community level
- cycling within the business sector.

Demonstration projects are under way and this work will continue at least into the next year. For this reason, cycling will be less of a priority as far as new grants are concerned.

In addition to cycling, during the year the Trust has also supported work on energy efficiency, including two projects working at the domestic level, and a grant to support a London-wide initiative aimed at coordinating energy-efficiency projects more effectively and reducing duplication. The Trust has also made a grant for the development of renewable energy on Lundy Island.

The largest award was to the Cyclist Touring Club (£86,000 over three years) to support the work of local authorities in increasing levels of cycling. A further £69,000 was to support work by the London School of Economics, at both policy and local project levels, to promote cycling. A large non-cycling grant was the £60,000 for the Hackney Building Exploratory.

Environmental projects overseas: 16 awards worth £151,885

The Trust continues to support community-based renewable energy projects that aim to help people to help themselves in an environmentally sustainable way. These projects often combine solar, biogas and micro-hydro technologies with income generation and agricultural activities and the Trust is particularly interested in the contribution that renewable energy can make to the alleviation of poverty. ...

While support has continued to focus largely (though not exclusively) on east Africa, clearer criteria will be used in the future against which to judge new project proposals. The proposed criteria are included in the [report of the recent jointly promoted seminar in Tanzania – copies available from the address above]. The aim is to support community-based projects that are innovative, meet a clearly demonstrated need (rather than being technology-led), can have an impact on poverty alleviation and can act as a model for others. Within this context, the Trust is considering setting up a modest award scheme.

The Trust has continued to focus on the need to disseminate examples of renewable energy best practice to policy makers, donors and NGOs, and has continued to support Solarnet in Kenya to carry out this role ... The aim is to show others how renewable energy can contribute to their own aims and objectives.

The Trust has also continued to focus on training through support for Energy Alternatives Africa, ITDG [Intermediate Technology Development Group] and the Commonwealth Science Council. The Tanzanian seminar highlighted the need for more high quality training (both technical and in project management) and this will continue to be an area of Trust support.

The largest awards were to Surude, Tanzania (£36,000), Energy Alternatives Africa (£30,000) and ITDG (£22,000). There was a handful of smaller grants, such as the £200 for an independent assessment of a SIATRA biogas proposal and £1,000 for training in solar drying in Zambia.

Homelessness: 10 awards worth £85,400

Grants are made to organisations that help homeless people to secure permanent accommodation and to regain economic independence. The Trust recognises that providing housing alone is only part of the equation and is therefore interested in projects that provide a range of support needs (social, educational and economic) to help people once they move into independent accommodation. The Trust has also supported the prevention of homelessness through a grant to the national Shelterline project.

The major awards were to Luton Day Centre for the Homeless (£22,000 for building works) and Southern Focus Trust, Portsmouth (£17,000 for a project for ex-offenders).

Urban rejuvenation: 6 awards worth £101,475

Funding in this category is aimed at schemes that help people develop skills, improve self-esteem and increase employment prospects in areas of urban deprivation. This also included projects concerning drug misuse and offending. The Trust continues to be interested in both high-profile national projects seeking to influence policy, such as Crime Concern's Neighbourhood Safety Programme, as well as funding local self- help community groups implementing smaller-scale initiatives to improve the local quality of life.

The two major awards were to the Furniture Resource Centre (£50,000 for salary costs) and Crime Concern (£49,000 for ten demonstration projects in Wolverhampton).

Community arts: 13 awards worth £74,450

The trust continues to support a number of grass-roots arts activities, and in particular those groups for which relatively modest grants can have a considerable impact. Support covers a range of organisations, from special needs to inner city.

The trust continues to develop its interest in environmental drama. Following earlier work commissioned by the trust to establish comparative information on environmental drama companies throughout the UK, the trust has initiated and is funding the development of an internet-based *Directory of Environment and Drama*, and a newsletter on the same theme. The aim will be to provide a practical resource that can stimulate greater interest and high quality work in an area that, research suggests, remains relatively underdeveloped. The major awards were to Death by Theatre (£15,000), Environmental Drama

(£11,000), ADiTi (the National Organisation of South Asian Dance) and North Kensington Arts (£10,000 each).

Applications

See the guidance for applicants in the entry for the Sainsbury Family Charitable Trusts. A single application will be considered for support by all the trusts in the group. However, for this as for many of the trusts, 'proposals are generally invited by the Trustees or initiated at their request. Unsolicited applications are discouraged and are unlikely to be successful, even if they fall within an area in which the Trustees are interested.'

The Lord Ashdown Charitable Settlement

Jewish education, inter-faith and racial harmony, community development

£3,611,000 (1998/99)

Beneficial area UK.

44a New Cavendish Street, London W1M 7LG

Tel. 020 7486 4663 **Fax** 020 7224 3942

Correspondent Clive Marks

Trustees *Clive Marks; J M Silver; Dr Richard Stone.*

Information available Excellent report and accounts.

General

The annual report of this charity says that it receives the startling total of about 7,000 applications a year, far more than would be expected for a trust of its size, especially one with a limited range of interests. Cynics suggest that an early placing in alphabetically organised directories may play a part in this. Whatever the reason for this deluge, the trust is 'no longer likely to respond to unsolicited applications'. In 1998/99 only five per cent of applicants received substantial grants. A further 1.5%, many of whom were applicants for larger amounts, received grants of £250 or less.

Almost a third of the likely sum to be available for the next two years had already been committed by April 1999.

In the annual report for 1998/99, the trustees say that they will be concentrating principally on four areas (which were indeed already the focus of most grantmaking):

- Jewish education
- inter-faith activities and racial harmony
- sustaining many existing beneficiaries
- grassroots community development

Many of the causes supported would be called, broadly speaking, 'progressive'. Examples include support for the Maimonides Foundation, seeking increased Jewish/Muslim dialogue; the Charta Mede Trust for its anti-discrimination work, or the Society of Black Lawyers in its work for racial justice.

Most of the money is given in grants of £10,000 or more. Six grants of between £100,000 and £470,000 accounted for about 40% of the total. And 109 small grants of £250 or less accounted for £22,000 of the grant total.

In a practice always regretted by these editors (though there is no suggestion of impropriety), much of the administration of the charity was carried out by organisations with which two of the three trustees are connected.

C M Marks was a consultant with Morley and Scott during the year. This firm provided bookkeeping and financial research relating to all major grants and for the renewal of funding; preparation of monthly management statements; and financial services to the charity during the year. The total fees were £55,750 (1998 – £53,315).

R M Stone is a consultant to the Paddington Consultancy partnership, which provided the charity with advice on medical and health promotion grants during the year. The total fees (excluding VAT) paid to the partnership ... were £14,000 (1998 – £14,000).

These editors welcome the recent advice by the Charity Commission that such payments should only take place if there is no realistic alternative – they are not justified, it says, simply by the existence of a 'power' to make such payments in a trust deed. The issue is not one of whether the services being purchased are effective and low cost (and there is no reason in the present instance to doubt that they are), but of 'the principle that a trustee cannot receive any benefit'. In these editors' view, other arrangements should be made.

Grants in 1998/99

The annual report lists only the 50 largest grants. These account for £2.7 million out of the total £3.6 million awarded. Over two thirds of these grants, by value, went to Jewish charities in a number of fields. They are classified as follows:

Arts	£91,000
Children and youth	£15,000
Community	£1,321,000
Education	£1,184,000
Inter-faith/race	£25,000
Medical	£24,000

These figures do not reflect ongoing long-term support, where there is, for instance, a further £100,000 a year under the Inter-faith/race heading.

Under the major headings the largest grants were to Jewish organisations. The six new awards of £100,000 or more were as follows:

Joint Jewish Charitable Trust	£350,000
London School of Jewish Studies	£470,000
Jewish Educational Development Trust (Immanuel College)	£307,000
Spiro Institute	£185,000
Yakar Educational Foundation	£171,000
Manor House Trust	£100,000

The smaller grants are more widely spread, with a continued scattering of support for projects in the Paddington area of London, such as the Bayswater Homeless Families Project (£76,000) and Paddington Development Trust (£20,000).

The report notes that the trust is ensuring the growth of the oldest surviving Jewish theological seminary in the world – the London School of Jewish Studies – formerly Jews' College. It also notes that the trustees continue to have a deep commitment to addressing racism and anti-semitism, a field in which at least one trustee, Richard Stone, is publicly very active.

Exclusions

The trust does not, save in exceptional cases, fund the mainstream arts, large well-established national charities, exploration or adventure projects, purely academic research (although it does assist in medical research with practical objectives); nor does it give grants to enable students to study overseas, support elective periods of medical students, or assist with fees at private schools.

Applications

Due to the commitment of nearly all the funds available, the trustees are no longer likely to respond to unsolicited applications.

Awards for All small grants

See entry for the National Lottery (not that for the National Lottery Charities Board) on page 221.

The Baily Thomas Charitable Fund

Mental illness, mental disability

£3,245,000 (1998/99)

Beneficial area UK.

Ernst & Young, 400 Capability Green, Luton LU1 3LU

Tel. 01582 643125

Correspondent G R Mean, Senior Trust Manager

Information available Report and accounts listing the largest 50 grants only, and with no analysis of grantmaking. Over £1 million of undisclosed new grant awards.

Summary

Grants are made to organisations in the fields of mental disability/illness care or research, with an apparent and welcome special interest in respite care. Large commitments can be made, approaching half a million pounds in at least one case. Capital works, projects and core costs are all supported. However, £50,000 or £25,000 is a more common figure for even the larger grants.

Over £1 million is given in awards of £20,000 or less, down to a minimum of £250. The size distribution of the few disclosed awards suggests that there may be several hundred smaller grants. The disclosed awards in 1998/99 were spread around a wide variety of institutions, for national programmes, local projects of national bodies and solely local organisations.

There is a separate and recently introduced application process for medical research projects, in which full peer review is appropriately required. The limited information divulged suggests that less than 10% of the grants by value have been for this kind of work, but it may be the intention for this proportion to be increased.

The fund says its previously noted special interest in the Nottingham area no longer exists. The absence of a full grants list means that this cannot be confirmed.

General

This is a trust of great importance and interest, as it concentrates on a field which generally lacks specialist grant-making attention. It is unfortunate therefore that the Baily Thomas Fund should use the small print of the SORP as an excuse to keep unreported much of its charitable activity. The £1,286,000 of undisclosed awards made in 1998/99 would be enough on its own to justify a separate entry in this book. The SORP allows disclosure to be limited to the largest 50 grants only provided that all material grants are disclosed, and even then those not disclosed must be suitably analysed and explained. It is offensive to the taxpayers who support this programme to find these trustees defining such a large programme as 'not material'. It is also unkind to the memory of Mr Baily Thomas to refuse to divulge the work being done with the funds settled in his name.

In the year ending October 1999 assets had risen to £62 million, held almost entirely in a single investment as the trustees were not to dispose of their Mansfield Brewery shares unless there were special circumstances which made this desirable. These circumstances arose in 1999 when the brewery was taken over. This charity was to receive £75 million for its holding. This should generate an income of over £3 million a year, an improvement on the less than £2 million received from the brewery shares in 1998/99, which will replace the extra income still being received in that year from the estate of Mr Baily Thomas.

These editors always regret payments by trusts to trustees or to organisations connected to trustees, unless there are exceptional reasons that make this necessary, and these reasons are explained fully in the charity's annual reports. In this case payments were made to organisations with which three of the present trustees have connections. However, some or all of the three trustees concerned may have had a personal connection with Mr Baily Thomas during his lifetime and may have played a part in establishing this charity in his name, but, if so, this is not reported.

Grant-making policy

The charity issued the following revised and useful guidelines for its main grant-making programme in July 2000.

The ... Fund was established to aid the research into the causes of mental disability and mental illness and to aid the care and relief of those affected by mental illness and disability ...

Mental disability: We consider under mental disability the conditions generally referred to as severe learning disabilities, together with autism. In this area we consider projects concerning children or adults. Mental disability, thus defined, is our priority for funding.

Mental illness: We consider under mental illness the various mental disorders affecting adults. Within this field we focus on disorders causing severe and lasting disablement. Though we recognise the value of preventive work and early intervention for people who are vulnerable but not currently suffering from mental disorder, our funds are limited and we do not normally support projects concerned with these activities. For the same reason, while recognising the importance of the problems, we do not normally support projects concerned with the abuse of alcohol or drugs, or with homelessness.

- Funding is normally considered for capital and revenue costs and for both specific projects and for general running/core costs.
- Grants are awarded for amounts from £250 and depend on a number of factors including the purpose, the total funding requirement and the potential sources of other funds including, in some cases, matching funding.
- Normally one-off grants are awarded but exceptionally a new project may be funded over two or three years, subject to satisfactory reports of progress.
- The following areas of work normally fall within the Fund's policy:
  Capital building/renovation/refurbishment works for residential, nursing and respite care, and schools;
  Employment schemes including woodwork, crafts, printing and horticulture;
  Play schemes and play therapy schemes;
  Day and social activities centres including building costs and running costs;
  Support for families, including respite schemes;
  Independent living schemes and support in the community schemes;
  Swimming and hydro-therapy pools and snoezelen rooms.

For areas unlikely to receive funding, see under 'Exclusions' below.

Research grants

The description of the fields of mental disability and mental illness that are supported by the charity still apply. Then:

- We generally direct our limited funds towards the initiation of research so that it can

progress to the point at which there is sufficient data to support an application to one of the major funding bodies.
- Applications will only be considered from established research workers and will be subject to normal professional peer review procedures.

All grants, not just those for research projects, are subject to independent review. The specific application procedures will be found under 'Applications' below.

Grants in 1998/99

There is the following description in the annual report for 1998/99:

The largest grant made this year was one of £230,000 to the Development Trust (for the Mentally Handicapped). This was for two projects, a grant of £80,000 being made towards the building and equipping of the Osbourne Court Respite Home for Children in Malvern. A further £150,000 was committed to a Respite Care Home to be built in Newport. Other grants were made to a wide variety of projects including the construction of residential homes, telephone information and helplines, employment schemes, nurseries and after school clubs.

The Trustees were pleased and encouraged by the publication during the year of the Mental Health Foundation's report on their Bright Futures Initiative, promoting children and young people's mental health, which was supported by the ... Fund. Support is continuing for the Foundation's programme, Growing Older with Learning Disabilities, towards which £400,000 has been committed over two years.

Apart from projects described above, five further beneficiaries received amounts of more than £50,000:

- National Autistic Society: £130,000 for its Wellingborough Outreach Project and for an extension to Helen Allison School.
- Norah Fry Research Centre: £100,000 for the Directorship.
- MENCAP City Foundation: £85,000 for its special projects fund for learning disabilities.
- White Lodge Children's Centre: £75,000 for rebuilding.
- Zito Trust: £60,000 for a research project on neural imaging in the field of mental disorder and violence.

As the best indication of the destination of the undisclosed smaller grants, those receiving £20,000 included the following: Wednesday Club – manager's salary; Wandsworth Rathbone – over 25s project; Sunny Mount, Knowle – Paddock View Appeal; Style Acre Friends – skill centre; St Matthew Society – for move-on flats; St Bartholomew's Church Centre – development worker post; Spastics Society [SCOPE], Sale – Stockdales refurbishment; SIRI for mental health users – counselling and psychotherapy project; Side by Side (Kids) Ltd — expansion of nursery.

Exclusions

Grants are not normally awarded to individuals. The following areas are unlikely to receive funding:

- Hospices.
- Minibuses, except where used for residential and/or day care services for the mentally disabled or elderly people with senile dementia or Alzheimer's Disease.
- Advocacy projects.
- Arts and theatre projects, unless participants include the mentally ill (projects for the mentally disabled will be referred to the MENCAP City Foundation).
- Physical disabilities unless accompanied by significant mental disabilities.

Applications

Applications, only from voluntary organisations which are registered charities or are associated with a registered charity, should be made on the forms available from the correspondent.

Annual report and accounts must be sent.

Do not send architectural drawings, plans or photographs. These are seldom necessary, but will be asked for if required.

A second application from an organisation will not normally be considered for a period of at least one year after completion of an initial grant or notification of an unsuccessful application.

Trustees' meetings are usually held in June and December each year and applications should therefore be submitted not later than 1 May or 1 October for consideration at the next meeting.

The Balcraig Foundation

Relief of suffering, particularly children

£2,500,000 (1995/96)

Beneficial area Scotland, Africa.

Balcraig House, Scone, Perth PH2 7PG

Tel. 01738 552303 **Fax** 01738 552101

Correspondent David McCleary, Secretary

Trustees *Ann Gloag; David McCleary; Jonathan Scott.*

Information available The trust did not reply to a written request for copies of its report and accounts, despite its statutory obligation to do so.

General

In the absence of further information, this entry repeats that which was printed in *A Guide to the Major Trusts, volume 2* (1999/2000 edition):

In 1995/96, grants were made totalling £2.5 million. No further information was available for this year, but we were informed that this level of grantmaking has continued.

This trust's income increased dramatically in March 1993 with a gift of 500,000 ordinary shares in Stagecoach Holdings plc from Mrs Ann Gloag, one of the trustees. The foundation sold some of its shares for a net cash amount of £879,000 and its income totalled £1,619,000 that year. The following year income was £322,000 and after charitable donations a surplus of £249,000 was carried over. The foundation purchased a residential property in Blantyre, Malawi, for £62,000 and intends to use rental income from the property to fund charitable projects in Malawi.

In 1993/94, the trust made donations totalling £73,000, including those to a hospital project in Malawi (£24,300), an orphanage project in Kenya (£7,850), and five awards for the benefit of individuals (£8,683 in all).

The endowment had risen in value to £8 million by 1996.

Exclusions

Applications from individuals are not generally accepted.

Applications

Applicants should apply in writing, setting out a brief outline of the project for which funding is sought. Trustees meet quarterly.

The Andrew Balint Charitable Trust

See the entry for the Balint Family Charitable Trusts.

The George Balint Charitable Trust

See the entry for the Balint Family Charitable Trusts.

The Balint Family Charitable Trusts

Jewish charities, medicine, children and general

£1,653,000 (1999/2000)

Beneficial area UK and overseas, especially Israel.

Suite A, 4–6 Canfield Place, London NW6 3BT

Tel. 020 7624 2098 **Fax** 020 7624 2076

Correspondent J K Olver, Administrator

Trustees *See below.*

Information available Annual reports and accounts. The grants lists, where available, do not include details of the size of the grants concerned.

Summary

The trusts are jointly administered, and grants are directed to similar, if not the same, beneficiaries. Grant totals from 1998 to 2000 were as follows:

	1999/2000	*1998/99*
George Balint Charitable Trust	£1,027,000	£1,403,000
Paul Balint Charitable Trust	£383,000	£386,000
Andrew Balint Charitable Trust	£243,000	£226,000

'The three trusts are not looking for new grant areas as their current commitments more than account for the income received.'

General

The Paul Balint Charitable Trust is connected through common trustees to both the George Balint Charitable Trust and the Andrew Balint Charitable Trust, and 'the charities sometimes work together to advance their mutual objectives'. The full trustee bodies are as follows:

Andrew Balint CT
Agnes Balint
Dr Gabriel Balint-Kurti
Roy David Balint-Kurti

George Balint CT
Dr Andrew Balint
George Balint
George Rothschild
Marion Farkas-Balint

Paul Balint CT
Dr Andrew Balint
Dr Gabriel Balint-Kurti
Paul Balint
Marc Balint

Grants in the UK were made in the following categories:

	1999/2000	*1998/99*
Education	£411,000	£388,000
Welfare	£373,000	£488,000
Medical	£103,000	£151,000
Children	£62,000	£35,000
Religion	£61,000	£63,000
Old age	£58,000	£30,000
Benevolent	£48,000	£9,000
Individual	£9,000	£17,000
Refugee	£1,000	£2,000
UK total	£1,126,000	£1,182,000

In 1999/2000 a further £526,000 was donated to other countries (85% in the Middle East, frequently to causes in Israel).

The following organisations received grants for over £5,000 from both the George Balint and Andrew Balint trusts: Nightingale House; Galil Education Centre; Institute for the Advancement of Education, Jaffa; Joint Jewish Charitable Trust; United Jewish Israel Appeal; Hungarian Senior Citizens; Shalva, and the Charitable Trust for Former Employees of Balint Companies.

In 1997/98, the latest year for which specific figures were available for the size of grants, Nightingale House received £900,000 in total (two thirds from the George Balint Trust, a third from the Andrew Balint). Also well supported that year was the Jaffa Institute (£75,000 divided in the same way). In their report, the trustees of the Paul Balint Trust said simply that they 'receive applications for donations from a wide variety of charitable institutions, including those engaged in medical and ancillary services (including medical research), education, helping the aged and infirm and relieving poverty. The trustees consider all requests which they receive and make such donations as they feel appropriate.'

Exclusions

No grants for religious purposes or to individuals.

Applications

To the correspondent in writing, but funds are fully committed.

The Band Trust

Health, disability, elderly, children, art

£707,000 (1998/99)

Beneficial area UK.

Macnair Mason, Chartered Accountants, St Clare House, 31–33 Minories, London EC3N 1BU

Tel. 020 7481 3022

Correspondent R J S Mason, Trustee

Trustees *The Hon. Mrs Nicholas Wallop; The Hon. Nicholas Wallop; R J S Mason; B G Streather.*

Information available Annual reports and accounts.

Summary

The trust makes over 100 grants a year, about half of them for amounts of £1,000 or less, and seldom for more than £30,000, though exceptional grants up to £100,000 can be made. About half the recipients in 1998/99 were also supported in the previous year. Grants can be made for up to three years.

General

The trust is a new entry in this book; it has been building up its grantmaking as money from its testator has become available. Its 1998/99 annual report states that all the trust's income is committed for the immediate future to projects with which it is already involved. The trust presents its work as if it were a commercial organisation rather than a charity, referring to its Income and

Expenditure account (SOFA) as its 'results'.

A feature of the charity (one always regretted by these editors) is that some of its administration is carried out, on a relatively modest scale, by businesses with which trustees are connected. The work of the charity is concentrated in or around London, as the trustees like to be within a reasonable distance of potential or actual beneficiaries. Grants are categorised as follows:

	1998/99	*1997/98*
Children	£205,000	£35,000
Disabled	£170,000	£139,000
Medical	£136,000	£150,000
Arts	£84,000	£44,000
Educational	£45,000	£7,000
Elderly	£37,000	£27,000
Miscellaneous (up to £1,000)	£13,000	£13,000
Ex-employees	£13,000	£12,000
Church	£5,000	£15,000
Legal	£1,000	£1,000
Total	£707,000	£443,000

There is no information beyond the following about the charitable purposes of the trust.

The Trustees' prime objective is to aid residents of the United Kingdom who are in need of care, whether wholly or partially, including those who are ill, disabled or injured, old and infirm or children with special needs. Such aid includes the providers such as Institutions, homes and equipment and the carers themselves, in particular the nursing profession.

The Trustees' policy is to devote the greater part of their available income to the foregoing needs and such as remains to particular charitable objectives chosen by the Settlors personally during their lifetime or known to meet their wishes, including certain scholarships.

Income net of expenses was less than grants and donations in the year by £113,022. It is anticipated that the income for the current year will match the total of grants, donations and expenses. In these circumstances, the Trustees regrettably find it impossible in the immediate future to support projects other than those in which they are already involved.

There is expected to be a further receipt from the legacy but due to the testator being a Member of Lloyds, the precise amount cannot be ascertained until the liabilities in that area are finalised.

There is a full categorised listing of grants; the awards of £20,000 or more were as follows:

	1998/99	*1997/98*
Children and Young People		
NSPCC	£108,000	£6,200
Christopher's Children's Hospice, Loseley Park	£20,000	–
National Playing Fields Association	£25,000	–
Disabled		
Raynauld's and Scleroderma Association	£25,000	–
Friends of Boveridge House	£20,000	–
The Development Trust	£20,000	–
SIGN	£20,000	–
Medical		
Macmillan Nurses	£27,000	£27,000
Blond McIndoe Research Centre	£30,000	£25,000
Nicol Cross Brown Leukaemia Fund	£25,000	–
Arts		
Royal Opera House	£75,000	£25,000
Educational		
The Treehouse Trust	£20,000	–
Elderly		
Friends of the Elderly	£22,000	£1,500

Applications

In writing to the correspondent, for consideration at trustees' meetings at least twice a year. However, unsolicited applications will not normally be considered.

David and Frederick Barclay Foundation

Medical research, welfare

£882,000 (1999)

Beneficial area UK.

3rd Floor, 20 St James's Street, London SW1A 1ES

Tel. 020 7915 0915

Correspondent Lord Peyton, Chairman

Trustees *Lord Peyton, Chair; Lord McAlpine; Sir David Barclay; Sir Frederick Barclay.*

Information available Inadequate report and accounts, without a proper grants list or explanation of policy.

Summary

The main area of interest is said to be in funding medical research, through donations to relevant institutions or to individual researchers. The foundation has said that the aim is to 'make possible or accelerate research projects which seem valuable, but which for one reason or another are unable to get off the ground'. However, a significant number of major donations in a given year are apparently broader in scope. It seems that the foundation's policy also extends to supporting the general welfare of a range of disadvantaged groups, particularly older people, disabled people and children.

General

Donations from Sir David and Sir Frederick Barclay in 1999 amounted to £793,000. Grantmaking totalled £882,000, up from £546,000 the year before.

In that year the chairman said:

As usual, the number of applications has continued to increase. It is now beyond previous years and far beyond the resources available to meet them. It has been my aim that our grants should stay at a level where they are likely to make some notable difference to the recipient.

It has previously been reported that the foundation funds no more than 10 to 15 major projects a year out of over 1,000 applications, though the number of projects approved may now have increased slightly.

The report no longer gives information on either the amount awarded or the purpose of each grant, but previously the foundation has funded both capital and, less frequently, revenue costs, including salaries.

In 1999 there were 65 grants for £1,000 or more, averaging about £13,000 (61 averaging £8,500 in 1998). Grants under £1,000 totalled £10,498 and nine grants made to individuals totalled £37,000.

The following 18 organisations were listed as receiving the 'principal donations' (only the NSPCC had appeared in the equivalent list in the previous year): Abbeyfield Reading Society; The Bromley by Bow Centre; The Chain of Hope; Drug Concern Guernsey; Fund for Osteopathic Research into ME; Glasgow University; Institute of Cancer Research; London School of Hygiene and Tropical Medicine; Make-a-Wish Charity; NSPCC Justice for Children Appeal; Parkinson's Disease Society; Queen Elizabeth's Foundation for Disabled People; Royal College of Surgeons of Edinburgh; Royal Free Hospital School of Medicine; Sherwood Coalfield Community Association; St Luke's Hospital for the Clergy; Stoke Mandeville Scanner Appeal; University of Newcastle Institute for the Health of the Elderly Appeal.

Applications

Applications should be in writing, clearly outlining the details of the proposed project (in lay terms if the application is for medical research) and giving detailed costings. When the applications are received, 10–15 major projects are picked out from over 1,000 in all. When this process of narrowing down has been completed the organisations that remain are visited, and a report put together for the benefit of the trustees. The trustees will only make decisions on the basis of these reports at full trustee meetings, of which there is at least one a year. The trustees require written reports at the end of projects, but they also keep in touch throughout the life of a grant and are keen to find out how projects are progressing.

The Baring Foundation

Strengthening the voluntary sector, arts in education and in the community, international

£2,800,000 (1999)

Beneficial area England and Wales, with a special interest in London, Merseyside, Cornwall and Devon; also UK charities working with NGO partners in developing countries.

60 London Wall, London EC2M 5TQ

Tel. 020 7767 1348 **Fax** 020 7767 7121

e-mail baring.foundation@ing-barings.com

website www.baringfoundation.org.uk

Correspondent Toby Johns, Director

Trustees *Nicholas Baring, Chairman; Tessa Baring; R D Broadley; Dr Ann Buchanan; Martin Findlay; Janet Lewis-Jones; Lady Lloyd; Anthony Loehnis; Sir Crispin Tickell; J R Peers.*

Information available Exemplary annual report and guidelines for individual programmes are available from the foundation.

Summary

The foundation has three grant programmes (with their value in 1999):

- strengthening the voluntary sector (£1,600,000)
- arts in education and in the community (£625,000)
- international (£578,000)

Within each programme there are a number of different schemes, as set out below, only some of them open to direct application. Within each programme the foundation makes a number of grants for core costs, to selected organisations that it invites to apply.

The foundation has stopped funding in Scotland. Funding for Northern Ireland will continue but is unlikely to be by direct application.

The Strengthening the Voluntary Sector Programme through local projects has been extended to Cornwall and Devon (in addition to Merseyside and London) but has been withdrawn from the north east.

General

Though no longer one of the largest, this has become one of the most interesting grantmakers in Britain. In particular it specifically addresses the key issue of 'core' versus 'project' funding with experimental programmes, carefully applied, which are being properly evaluated as a guide to future grantmaking.

The foundation has also established an impressive system of seeking out its own beneficiaries for its proactive programmes and has unusually thorough and careful processes for evaluating the 'open' applications it receives.

The arts programme is particularly welcome, as it focuses on community arts, a sector where the need for modest financial assistance was so powerfully demonstrated, and then left unmet, by the runaway success of the not to be repeated Arts Council A4E Express lottery grant programme.

The foundation relies in the first instance on part time advisers, some of them regional and some of them specialist. Most of them are already widely experienced in the voluntary sector and their other activities keep them in touch with ongoing work in their areas or fields of interest. They are listed below, with their particular fields noted:

Strengthening the Voluntary Sector:
Ms L Ball (mergers and joint working)
Ms J Brooker (Wales)
Nicky Eastwood (Merseyside)
Terence Finley (North East)
Ms B Rance
Barbara Riddell
Mrs J Thompson (Cornwall, Devon)
Claire Walters
Ms E Salamon

Arts: Phyllida Shaw

International: B Twigg

In addition, the foundation obtains policy advice from Julia Unwin. Two external advisers, currently Ms E Salamon and Ms D Sathe, sit on the arts committee but do not assess applications.

Strengthening the voluntary sector

The objective of this programme is to improve the organisational effectiveness of voluntary organisations. There are four schemes:

- core costs grants available to UK and national organisations and local ones in London, Merseyside, Cornwall and Devon which are invited to apply by the foundation;
- skills and effectiveness grants available by open application to national and

THE BARING FOUNDATION – EXCERPTS FROM THE DIRECTOR'S REPORT, 1999

During 1999, the Council reviewed the Foundation's strategy... It decided ... to move to a total return strategy for distribution with effect from 1 January 2000. This will have the objective of maximising the level of distribution while maintaining the capital value of the portfolio in real terms. It was decided that initially the annual level of distribution should be fixed at 4.5% of the capital value of the fund averaged over the previous three years...

The least welcome conclusion for Council members was that the Foundation could no longer realistically fund across the United Kingdom. ... The strength of the sector in Scotland and the level of other independent funding available there led Council members to conclude that the least bad option would be to stop funding in Scotland entirely while maintaining support for the sector in Wales and possibly Northern Ireland which have much lower levels of independent funding. The more autonomous and different nature of the sector in Northern Ireland has also led the Foundation to conclude that it should find ways to support it other than by inviting direct application for project grants.

The Council also decided with regret that the Foundation had done as much as it could to help organisations in North East England under the Strengthening the Voluntary Sector Programme ... In future, the Foundation will support local projects under this programme in Cornwall and Devon (in addition to Merseyside and London) reflecting a wish to take a greater interest in rural issues. The Arts Programme is open to application for local projects across England and Wales.

local organisations in the same geographical areas as above;
- knowledge and skills exchange grants available to members of eight national network organisations which administer the grants on the foundation's behalf;
- mergers and joint structures grants available to all UK voluntary organisations.

Only the second and fourth are given by open application; the foundation's guidelines covering application for skills and effectiveness grants are reprinted at the end of this section. Those interested in the possibility of a 'merger' grant should contact the foundation's staff in the first instance.

The programme has been developing and the guidelines below are the proper guide to its present nature. The following section reviews the programme as it was described in the 1999 annual report. Expenditure on the schemes is shown in the table below and this is followed by relevant excerpts from that report.

	1999	*1998*	*1997*
Core costs	£951,000	£878,000	£893,000
Skills and effectiveness	£536,000	£400,000	£495,000
Knowledge and skills exchange	£62,000	£83,000	£54,000
Mergers and joint structures	£73,000	£75,000	£199,000

Core costs grants

Thirteen new grants [*of between £50,000 and £75,000 over three years. Ed.*] were made to a range of national and local organisations, and second and third instalments were paid to the 25 organisations which were awarded grants in 1997 and 1998.

The core costs grants formed the majority of the Foundation's expenditure on strengthening the voluntary sector (59%). As in previous years, the grants are concentrated on medium sized organisations.

The organisations which received grants ... are: Age Concern London, Black Training and Enterprise Group, British Association of Settlements & Social Action Centres, Care & Repair, Sefton Council for Voluntary Service, Council of Ethnic Minority Voluntary Sector Organisations, Dial UK, Evelyn Oldfield Unit, Hartlepool Voluntary Development Agency, Justice, London Voluntary Sector Training Consortium, Voluntary Arts Network and Women's Aid Federation of England.

The core costs grants differ from the majority of funding schemes open to the voluntary sector because they are unrestricted grants for organisational development, rather than being tied to a specific project. The Foundation ... has commissioned an ongoing evaluation of the scheme. To date, this has shown that the grants are being used in four main ways:
- strengthening the organisation by improving functions such as fundraising, marketing, administration and financial systems
- providing the means to meet new challenges and demands for service
- supporting a move towards self-sufficiency
- general running costs.

	1999	*1998*	*1997*
Number of applications invited	16	13	13
Number of grants available	13	12	13
Total value of grants	£951,000	£877,500	£892,500
Largest grant	£75,000	£75,000	£75,000
Smallest grant	£51,000	£60,000	£37,000

Skills and effectiveness

In 1999, the Foundation made 60 grants to support the development of the management or organisational effectiveness of voluntary organisations. Awards were made for a number of activities:
- consultancies covered financial reviews, marketing and fundraising, strategic planning, increasing user involvement in decision-making and management reviews
- training activities included work on managing and recruiting volunteers, increasing the skills of management committees and supporting the courses that are provided by voluntary sector umbrella organisations
- start-up funding was given to establish new networks and alliances
- dissemination grants supported good practice publications and conferences
- feasibility studies looked at the potential for new activities and partnerships.

... As in previous years, most grants (57%) benefited more than one organisation and national organisations were more successful than local organisations. The average size of grant was about 50% higher in 1999 compared to 1998 reflecting the intention of trustees to award larger grants although regrettably this also means fewer grants.

Knowledge and skills exchange

In 1999 the Foundation gave funds to eight umbrella organisations [*average, about £7,000. Ed.*] for distribution in the form of 110 small grants to enable their members to learn from each other through exchange visits [*the average final grant was about £500. Ed.*] The umbrella organisations were BASSAC, Community Matters, Contact a Family, Development Trusts Association, Dial UK, Mind Cymru, Scottish Council for Voluntary Organisations, and Sia.

Mergers and joint structures

In 1999, the Foundation made 15 grants to help organisations consider or undertake major structural change. The value of the grants awarded was £73,375.

Most of the grants were given for consultancy work or other professional assistance associated with the preparation and setting up of new mergers and joint structures. However, this programme is also available for organisations that want to investigate the potential for new formal partnerships and that is why grants are given for feasibility studies ... The Foundation has commissioned Bill Mather to write Merging Interests, a guide for decision-makers in the voluntary sector who are considering a merger... [to] be available from the Baring Foundation in 2000.

Guidelines for applicants

Skills and effectiveness programme

Who may apply?

Constituted not-for-profit voluntary organisations working:
- nationally across England and/or Wales
- across the whole of London or in more than one borough or providing services to other voluntary organisations in one borough
- on Merseyside (i.e. in the districts of Liverpool, Knowsley, Sefton, St Helens and Wirral)
- in Devon or Cornwall
- UK organisations working with partner organisations and community groups in developing countries.

What may we apply for?

The Foundation wishes to fund work which will lead to a significant and lasting change in the effectiveness of an organisation by improvements to its strategy, structure, systems or skills. For example,
- the introduction of organisational strategy and business planning or fundamental reviews of existing strategies and plans
- a new, more effective organisational or management structure
- introducing co-ordination and collaboration between organisations
- formal combined working or mergers
- improvements to essential systems such as information technology, finance, personnel and training
- the introduction of appropriate ways of assessing and improving the overall quality and effectiveness of an organisation
- introducing new skills or knowledge to organisations
- supporting the dissemination or replication of effective practice
- involving users or beneficiaries in planning and management for the first time or in a significantly better way
- making organisations more responsive to the needs of their users or potential users

- umbrella organisations can apply to administer a block grant that is used to enable exchanges of knowledge and skills between its members.

This list is not definitive: other work which is important to improving the effectiveness of an organisation will be considered. However, the Foundation does not support the introduction of new or the expansion of existing services simply to increase the amount of work undertaken by organisations. The Foundation is flexible about how its money is used to achieve these sort of improvements. The ways in which its grants have been used include:

- freeing up the time of existing staff to undertake the work
- feasibility studies
- pilot schemes
- training
- buying in external advice and expertise
- meeting the costs of seminars or conferences
- exchanging skills and knowledge between individual organisations

Specific and absolute exclusions are listed below.

What will not be funded?

- continuing running costs of an organisation
- cost of existing or increased services
- work already completed or currently taking place or due to start while the application is being considered
- repeat of an activity that took place in a previous year
- routine staff training
- costs of employing fundraisers
- general fundraising appeals
- purchase, conversion, refurbishment of buildings, gardens or playgrounds
- general office equipment including IT hardware
- vehicles
- medical research or equipment
- bursaries or scholarships
- expeditions
- religious activity

How much can we apply for?

The Foundation is prepared to consider applications for grants for up to £30,000 for work spanning up to two years. However, the great majority of grants will be for much less; the Foundation's average grant is £8,710 and only 23% of grants are for more than £10,000. The Foundation is willing to fund a piece of work in its entirety or with a number of other funders.

Arts in education and in the community

The Arts Programme has three objectives:

- to support access to the arts for their own sake, and in particular to create opportunities for people whose access is limited for whatever reason;
- to support organisations which use the arts for community benefit;
- to support education in and through the arts for people of any age, ability or educational background.

The aim of the programme is to support the provision of opportunities to participate in the arts in educational and community settings and to recognise and encourage good practice.

There are three components to the programme (with the value of grants in 1999):

- core costs grants, available to arts organisations which are invited to apply by the Foundation (£375,000);
- the Small Projects scheme, open to UK-based arts organisations working across the full range of art forms (£178,000);
- the Knowledge and Skills Exchange scheme, also open to UK-based arts organisations working across the full range of art forms (£72,000).

The chairman's introduction to the 1999 annual report notes that the arts adviser, Phyllida Shaw, dealt with over 400 applications in the year (which led to 80 grants). A brief account of the programmes, from the annual report for 1999, is followed by the guidelines for applicants for the Small Projects scheme and, in much abbreviated form, for the smaller Knowledge and Skills Exchange scheme.

Core costs grants

Six new grants were awarded to organisations working in Northern Ireland, Wales, southern England, south west England and London.

The new grants [*average £63,000. Ed.*] were awarded to Artswork Southampton, Crescent Arts Centre, Exeter Phoenix, Ffotogallery Wales, Lyric Theatre Hammersmith, and the Oily Cart Company.

Small projects scheme

In 1999, 56 new Small Projects grants were made to support small scale arts activities (projects costing less than £20,000 in all) in educational or community settings [*the average grant was £3,000. Ed.*]. The number of grants and success rates of applications has remained largely unchanged since 1998 [*when the success rate of eligible applications was about 16%. Ed*].

Knowledge and Skills Exchange

In 1999, 24 grants were made to allow artists, arts managers and animateurs working in educational or community settings to learn from each other. The majority of grants were given for exchange visits, conferences or seminars and training. The grants covered work in a range of artforms, and again activities in combined artforms were most successful. Grants were distributed throughout the UK and the London region, which generates the greatest number of applications, received the most grants.

Guidelines for applicants

Small Projects Fund

The Small Projects Fund contributes to the cost of small-scale arts projects taking place in an educational or community context. A 'small project' might be a one-off activity, an event or the development of an idea.

The Fund supports a wide range of creative activities across all artforms in England and Wales. Please note that the Small Projects Fund is not available to applicants based in or working in Scotland or Northern Ireland.

How much can we apply for?

Every year the Small Projects Fund makes around 40 grants worth between £1,000 and £7,000. The total amount available for distribution in 2000 is £150,000.

Who may apply?

The Small Projects Fund is only open to constituted, not-for-profit arts organisations based in England or Wales.

The applicant organisation may be of any size and working in any artform.

The Foundation actively welcomes applications from arts organisations wishing to work with partners in other sectors (e.g. youth service, educational establishments, probation service, social services, community development etc.) but the application must be made by the arts organisation.

The Foundation will not consider applications made by unconstituted or commercial arts organisations, individual artists, local authority departments, local authority-run arts organisations and museums, schools, colleges, universities or youth clubs.

What may we apply for?

A 'small project' might be a one-off activity, an event or the development of an idea. The small project must fulfil one or more of the objectives of the Arts Programme set out above.

The small project may be in any artform, for people of any age, in any part of England or Wales. The total budget of the small project for which funding is sought must not exceed £25,000.

Priority will be given to applicants who can demonstrate that the proposed project has been properly planned and prepared for. Evidence of this from the applicant and from any partners in the project will be helpful...

Exclusions

- Applications from anyone other than a constituted, not-for-profit arts organisation based in England and Wales.
- Projects with a total budget in excess of £25,000.
- Projects that will take place outside England or Wales.
- Projects scheduled to start before a decision can be made ...

- The running costs/overheads of an existing project, event or organisation.
- Capital costs (e.g. the refurbishment of a building, the purchase of a computer).
- General fundraising appeals.

An organisation may only make one application to this fund within a 12 month period.

How do we apply?
All applications must be made on a Baring Foundation Arts Programme application form. Applications are considered three times a year.

Knowledge and Skills Exchange Fund
The Fund supports exchanges involving arts organisations, artists, arts managers, arts teachers and trainee teachers. The application for funding must be made by a constituted, not-for-profit arts organisation based in England or Wales. While the proposed exchange may be with organisations outside these boundaries, the application must come from within England or Wales.

Applications involving self-employed arts practitioners, teachers or trainee teachers must also be made by a constituted, not-for-profit arts organisation.

How much can we apply for?
The Knowledge and Skills Exchange Fund usually makes grants of between £500 and £3,000. An exceptional proposal requiring a larger amount may be considered. The total amount available for distribution in 2000 is £40,000.

Who may apply?
The ... Fund is only open to constituted, not-for-profit arts organisations in England or Wales. The application may be made on behalf of the organisation as a whole or on behalf of an individual or individuals working for or with the organisation. The applicant organisation may be of any size and working in any artform.

The Foundation will not consider applications made by unconstituted or commercial arts organisations, individual artists, local authority departments, local authority-run arts organisations and museums, schools, colleges, universities or youth clubs.

What may we apply for?
The emphasis of this fund is on individual and/or organisational development. The 'exchange' might take the form of a one-off visit to an individual or organisation from whom the applicant would like to learn; it might be a two-way exchange with colleagues spending time in each other's organisation; it might be an exchange of ideas in writing, or a mentoring or shadowing project. The Fund will also consider exchanges involving trainee teachers outside their course curriculum and exchanges involving qualified teachers other than formal INSET provision.

The exchange may involve any artform and participants at any stage of their careers. Priority will be given to applicants who can demonstrate that the proposed exchange has been properly planned and prepared for. Evidence of this from the partners in the exchange will be helpful.

Exclusions
- Applications from anyone other than a constituted, not-for-profit arts organisation based in England or Wales.
- Any part of an academic or vocational training course. (N.B. Applications by arts organisations to work with trainee teachers outside their mainstream college curriculum will be considered.)
- Participation in a course, conference, seminar, festival or competition.
- The organisation of a course, conference, seminar, festival or competition.
- The development or publication of websites, handbooks, documentation etc.
- Research trips to develop a creative product, e.g. an exhibition, play, film, composition etc.
- The continuation of a well established link with an individual or organisation in the UK or abroad.
- Activity scheduled to start before a decision can be made...
- General fundraising appeals.

An organisation may only make one application to this fund within a 12 month period.

How do we apply?
All applications must be made on a Baring Foundation Arts Programme application form. Applications are considered three times a year.

International grants

In October 2000 the foundation announced the end of its then International Programme. There will be a new programme for UK NGOs to help them develop the effectiveness of NGOs and community organisations in Latin America and sub-Saharan Africa. Existing project grants will cease and the new programme, for which details were still awaited, will

- be focused on organisations in the field of the long-term migration and displacement of people;
- provide core and block grants for up to three years for re-granting to southern organisations.

The foundation made 23 international grants totalling £577,780 in 1999. Beneficiaries included World University Service, Tree Aid, Plan International UK, Central America Women's Aid and Africa Educational Trust. All received amounts between £10,000 and £15,000.

Exclusions

See guidelines for specific programmes. More generally:

- appeals or charities set up to support statutory organisations;
- animal welfare charities;
- grant-maintained, private, or local education authority schools or their Parent Teachers Associations;
- individuals.

Applications

See the guidelines above. Note that there is no provision for 'general' applications that lie outside the foundation's specific programmes.

The Barnwood House Trust

Disability charities in Gloucestershire, medical research

£1,088,000 (to institutions, 1999)

Beneficial area Gloucestershire.

The Manor House, 162 Barnwood Road, Gloucester GL4 7JX

Tel. 01452 614429 **Fax** 01452 372594

Correspondent Paul Guy, Director

Trustees *The trust is controlled by a board of trustees (total 12) which is responsible for the day to day running of the trust, chosen from an elected governing council.*

Information available Excellent report and accounts. Four information leaflets are available: 'Grants to Organisations, Notes for Guidance'; 'For Your Information'; 'Grants to Individuals, Notes for Guidance'; 'Grants for Course Fees, Notes for Guidance'.

Summary

This admirable trust helps people in Gloucestershire with serious mental and physical disabilities or disorders by making grants to both organisations and individuals. It also supports related medical research. There are three grant programmes for organisations (with 1999 totals in brackets):

- Research budget: research into the causes and treatment of disability (£300,000).
- Strategic grants budget: '... the capacity to make very large grants for worthwhile capital projects and to support selected service organisations with revenue grants'. These grants can be either one-off or recurrent (£437,000).
- Small grants budget: responds rapidly to small one-off appeals from organisations (£351,000).

A total of 168 grants were made to organisations in 1999, 118 of them for amounts of less than £7,000. The largest single continuing programme has been supporting the research of Dr Raisman, through the British Neurological Research Trust, into repairing the spinal cord, with £100,000 being given. Only three other grants were for £50,000 or more.

General

This entry reprints much of the excellent and detailed information given by the trust in its 1999 annual report, a model of a trust accounting for its activities to the wider public. In particular, the description of the policy formation process is as unusual as it is welcome. So is the trust's practice of involving large numbers of voluntary supporters in its grant-making activities.

Readers should note, to better understand what follows, that the trust also has an extensive programme of grants for individuals facing problems with their physical or mental health.

Barnwood House Trust, established in its original form in 1792, is Gloucestershire's largest Charity aiming to assist people with disabilities, including those with mental disorders who live in the County. Its current endowment arises principally from the sale of the land upon which Barnwood House Hospital stood until 1966. From then it has developed as a provider of facilities for the disabled and of grants and loans to alleviate their problems.

Objects

The relief of sickness, infirmity, poverty and distress among persons suffering from mental or nervous disorders or from serious physical infirmity or disability ... The promotion of research into any matters relating to the causation, prevention and treatment of sickness and the publication of the results of such research.

Chairman's introduction

As can be seen throughout this report, 1999 was another exciting year for the Trust. ... As forecast, our income is now declining which has caused us to consider our future priorities with great care. Grant commitments were, accordingly, reduced in 1999 but it is hoped that, with careful husbandry of our resources, no further reduction will be necessary. ...

Policy sub-committee

The Policy Sub-Committee seeks information from all relevant sources in order to recommend changes in policy, to keep client needs and the development of policy and priorities under continuous review, and to undertake monitoring and evaluation of the effectiveness of the Trust's funding to other organisations.

The County Director of Social Services, Andrew Cozens and Jeff James, Chief Executive of the Health Authority again made an excellent joint presentation in February, 1999. It was especially encouraging to hear of the ways in which their respective organisations are working closer together which has made it easier to identify areas where we can be of supplementary assistance.

Monitoring and Evaluation reports showed once again that the great majority of our grant expenditure is being well utilised by the recipients. Our relationship encourages beneficiaries to tell us when the requirement reduces or is delayed, possibly resulting in a refund of the grant. ...

Review of grant-making activity

Overall, the aim of grant-making continues to be meeting special needs that Gloucestershire people with serious physical or mental disabilities cannot afford.

Essential healthcare is provided by the NHS so grants for individual health care are not made. However, the Trust does support health care strategically through medical research grants and support for the NHS in Gloucestershire in ways that add value to its work with our beneficial groups.

In the social welfare field, emphasis has been given to helping those in need who are not eligible for assistance from the State and by less underwriting of charity services purchased by government on behalf of people for whom it has retained responsibility. ...

There has been no change to the nature of existing grant budgets which are:

- medical research budget into the causes and treatment of disability
- strategic grants budget which has the capacity to respond to and seek out larger worthwhile projects to support
- grants budget which responds rapidly to smaller appeals from organisations
- individual welfare fund which helps meet individual exceptional needs arising from having a disability

New grant commitments totalled £1,436,699 in 1999. This figure represents a 13% reduction in grant-making when compared to 1998 and is largely accounted for by less spent on medical research and a drop in requests from individuals in need. Grants Committee's decision last year not to send small Christmas donations to over 100 Gloucestershire disability organisations is the principal reason for a drop in the total number of grants made, from 1,608 in 1998 to 1,468 in 1999. No new loans to organisations were agreed in 1999. The table below gives the net grant commitments in 1999 after adjustment for cancelled grants:

Committee	*1999*	*1998*
Strategic grants (organisations)	£437,000	£659,000
Strategic grants (med. research)	£300,000	£382,000
Grants committee	£351,000	£344,000
Individual grants	£283,000	£329,000
Total	£1,371,000	£1,714,000

For the second year running, the Trust committed a larger share of its grants budget to revenue grants than to capital schemes. Strategic Grants Committee carried most of the revenue commitments which accounted for 55% of its spend last year. This type of support is structured for a fixed time period to avoid silting up the grant-making budgets with long term commitments. Strategic Grants Committee distributed 57% of the total grants budget, making 49 grants (including grants made under the Cheltenham Award 2000) compared to 119 made by Grants Committee.

85% of Grants Committee's grants were for sums of £5,000 and under. While most of the grants under £5,000 are described as 'revenue' they are really 'added-value' grants for recurring activities such as client holidays and outings.

Appeals received cover a wide range and many small grants, which do not appear in this report, were made to organisations to help make holidays, activities, outings, art classes and other forms of occupational therapy more affordable for the Trust's beneficial groups. ...

The changing needs of learning disabled adults growing older and changing expectations of younger learning disabled adults made building adaptations and refurbishment necessary at the Old Quarries Avening, run by the Home Farm Trust [£30,000]. The Trust was pleased to contribute towards this and, for similar reasons, to the expansion at the Salter's Hill Charity home in Gorsley. ...

The everyday work of transporting people with disabilities continues to be an essential service and grants to Gloucester City Dial-a-Ride [£16,000], Lydney Dial-a-Ride [£15,000], Newton House in Gloucester, Gloucestershire Red Cross Tewkesbury Service [£12,000] and the Leonard Cheshire Home [£10,000] enabled each to purchase a new vehicle. Financial backing for the Forest Transport Broker [£12,500] through Forest Voluntary Action Forum is enabling FVAF to encourage more effective use of existing vehicles and resources.

Training for work for people recovering from an acute mental illness is the remit of Gloucester Clubhouse which was again supported by the Trust. Artspace in the Forest, Artshape in Cheltenham [£10,500] and a variety of health and social services day centres throughout the county also received grant aid from the Trust to enhance their work with the mentally ill.

Funding for disabled access to a number of community venues enabled the Gloucestershire Neighbourhood Projects Network [£11,200] to implement new learning zones at neighbourhood level for people with varying types of disability.

Support for the League of Friends of Gloucestershire Royal Hospital scanners appeal was agreed [£50,000]. These two machines will enhance diagnostic facilities for people with life threatening gastro-intestinal disorders. …

There are about 300 refugees from the Balkans living in Gloucester City. Their plight is placing much strain on local services and so a grant to the Gloucester & South Tewkesbury Primary Care Group [£7,000] was agreed to help meet the medical interpretation needs of the refugees as their serious physical and mental disabilities begin to emerge. …

The amount spent on research was less than in the previous year. As some long standing commitments draw to a close, future priorities for medical research are under consideration by both Strategic Grants Committee and the Policy Review Group.

In the meantime, the Trust is particularly pleased to continue its support for the work of Dr Geoffrey Raisman on repair of the spinal cord [£100,000].

Members took the opportunity to visit Dr Dawn Skelton's project in London where she is assessing the progress of elderly people recovering from serious falls and the benefit they derive from a specially designed exercise regime.

A grant to the Hearing Research Trust [£18,000] enabled Dr Ling Yui to continue his valued research into hearing aid implantation. Grants were also made to Action Research [£20,000], the Mental Health Foundation [£21,000], the Institute of Psychiatry and Severn NHS Trust R & D Fund for projects that are still underway and have yet to report.

Exclusions

Other than for selected clinical research projects, referred by co-ordinating organisations which have undertaken peer review, GRANTS ARE RESTRICTED TO GLOUCESTERSHIRE.

Applications

On trust application forms obtainable from Mrs Christine Ellson, Assistant Director (Grants), or Mrs Gail Rodway, Grants Administrator, at the address above (Tel: 01452 611292). Applications from organisations are investigated by representatives of the trust who then make recommendations to the trustees. Trustees meet every other month. Grant-making committees meet quarterly.

For information about grants for individuals, contact the trust.

The BBC Children in Need Appeal

Welfare of disadvantaged children

£17,711,000 (1998/99)

Beneficial area UK.

PO Box 76, London W3 6FS

Tel. 020 8576 7788 **Fax** 020 8576 8887

website www.bbc.co.uk/cin

Correspondent Martina Milburn, Director

Trustees *Roger Jones, Chair; Tim Cook; Colin Browne; Will Day; Diane Louise Jordan; Michelle Kershaw; Neena Mahal; Simon Milner; Liz Rylatt; Angela Sarkis; Peter Salmon; Pippa Wicks; Terry Wogan.*

Information available Excellent annual reports, guidelines and application forms, all informative and accessible, are available from the four UK national offices (listed under 'Applications' below).

Summary

Thousands of grants ranging from a few hundred pounds to a normal maximum of about £75,000 are made twice a year for specific projects which directly help disadvantaged children and young people (aged 18 and under). About half of all applications result in a grant. Most of the money goes to pay for a couple of hundred grants worth between £30,000 and £100,000, usually payable over three years. However, most grants, by number of awards, are for less than £5,000. Grants in 1998/99 were categorised according to the following areas of need for children:

- living in poverty and deprivation, £9.3 million;
- suffering from illness, distress, abuse or neglect, £5.7 million;
- with mental or physical disabilities, £4.1 million;
- with behavioural and psychological disorders, £0.9 million.

The entry below starts with a general description of the charity's work. This is followed by a reprint of the Appeal's excellent grant guidelines (except that a couple of the administrative sections will be found at the end of the entry, under the heading 'Applications'). Then we give further information from the trustees' report of 1998/99. Finally we describe some of the larger grants (and just a few of the smaller ones) from that year.

Background

This charity was set up by the BBC to distribute the proceeds of its annual appeal of the same name. It aims to make a positive difference to the lives of disadvantaged children throughout the UK.

The charity is almost completely dependent on this single source of income, and on the interest earned on the sum raised in the interval before it is distributed in grants. In case the income flow should stop, the charity has set up a continuity fund that would still enable it to meet its multi-year forward commitments to grant recipients.

Although the charity does no fundraising itself, it does benefit from substantial legacy income – £500,000 in 1998/99 and £800,000 in the previous year.

There is a rapid turnover on the trustee body, as they are limited to a three-year term of office. Of the 12 trustees named two years ago in the previous edition of this book, only three remain in the list above. During the same period, Julia Kaufman, the very widely respected and long-serving director, has also retired (her successor, Martina Milburn, comes from the directorship of ASPIRE, the spinal injuries charity). These arrangements must be some challenge to the continuity of the charity's experience at trustee level. However, it is refreshing to find the opposite pattern to that more generally found in grant-making trusts where the turnover of trustees is often glacial.

A remarkable feature for such a well-established grantmaker is that very many of its small grants go to first-time applicants, suggesting that a more active marketing programme might be appropriate.

Grantmaking

The charity received 4,002 applications in 1998/99, a reduction on the previous year once again, this time of 10%. A total of 2,178 grants were made, meaning a success ratio of 54% (52% in the previous year). However, the donations comprised only 20% of the total amount requested, so either there was a higher rejection rate for large applications, or many grants were not for the full amount requested, or both.

The four main categories of children being helped are described more fully, and movingly, as follows:

- Children living in poverty and deprivation. These children live in families for whom life is a struggle; many spend their childhood in rundown homes, in drab and hopeless

environments. Some experience temporary homelessness.
- Children suffering from illness, distress, abuse or neglect. Many of these children are 'invisible'. They may be confined to home or hospital through illness; they may be in care; or they may have become quiet and withdrawn through grief, neglect or abuse.
- Children with mental or physical disabilities. Children with disabilities need extra help to join in with chosen activities. Some are profoundly disabled from birth or from an accident and are totally dependent on constant care from others.
- Children with behavioural and psychological disorders. These children are often labelled 'difficult'. Their behaviour makes it difficult to fit in; they are often rejected and desperately unhappy.

The work of the charity in 1998/99 was also classified by the kind of activity supported:

- £4.1 million: to provide family support, welfare and care for children suffering through illness, distress, abuse or neglect.
- £3.8 million: to provide family support, welfare and care for children living in poverty and deprivation.
- £3.8 million: to involve children, many with physical and mental disabilities, in activities such as sport, drama, music and play.
- £2.7 million: to provide support and therapeutic services for disabled children and advice or counselling services for children with special needs.
- £2.2 million: to playgroups, nurseries and other services for disadvantaged children aged under five.
- £2.1 million: to help young people in trouble because of homelessness, drugs or solvent abuse, alcohol problems or eating disorders.
- £1.0 million: to provide safe outdoor play facilities and holidays in the UK for children who need them.
- £0.3 million: to schools, hospitals and social services for activities and equipment for children.

The size of grants

The table to the right shows the number of grants, and their total value in £ million, for 1998/99, 1997/98 and for the two years together.

These figures are slightly affected by a single large grant of £500,000 in 1998/99 made annually for some years to the Family Welfare Association to enable it to provide emergency grants for individual children in need.

Applications and grant policy

The number of applications to BBC Children in Need has been declining for some years. This is probably due partly to the welcome arrival of a number of other small grants schemes, such as Awards for All from the National Lottery, Bridge House in London and Northern Rock in the north of England. However, those applications that do arrive are increasingly for help with salary costs, which now account for more than half of the value of grants. It may be that the problems of meeting long-term needs with salaried staff reliant on short-term project funding are becoming so great as to deter some applicants – a successful three-year salary application can just increase an organisation's long-term problems.

With effectively both a new management and a new trustee body in place, it may be time for a review of overall funding policy to address this issue.

Applications are assessed by a team of freelance assessors. Most of them are then considered, and grant decisions recommended, by advisory committees and staff at country or regional level.

The assessment reports cover five main areas:

- The eligibility of the application: Are the children disadvantaged? Is the organisation charitable?
- The acceptability of the project: Is it well organised? Does it take child protection into account? Does it involve children, where relevant?
- The organisation's ability to carry out the project: What is the organisation's capacity? What is its track record? What are its linkages with others, especially the local authority?
- The organisation's finances: Is the organisation adequately managed financially? Are the project finances sensible?
- The mission: What differences will be achieved for the children? How will this be monitored/evaluated?

The advisory committee chairs and regional co-ordinators are as follows:

- *Scotland* Robin Lingard, Fraser Falconer
- *Wales* Steve Wood, Jenny Lewis
- *Northern Ireland* William Odling-Smee, Sheila Jane Malley
- *North West England* John Kealey, Joan Langford
- *North East England* Minna Ireland, Rosemary Vincent
- *Midlands and East* Kathleen Curnock, Jenny Whately
- *South West England* Shaheen Chaudhry, Jane Lewthwaite
- *South East England* Atul Patel, Pat Fox

There is also an All-UK advisory committee chaired by Will Day and Angela Sarkis.

Geographical distribution

The charity notes that it aims to provide a service to the entire country – 'we target our grants on the areas of greatest need'. Because the charity uses its own regional classification, with unknown populations, it is only possible to see the value per head of its grants on a country by country basis. The 1998/99 figures were as follows:

- England: £0.22
- Scotland: £0.56
- Wales: £0.54
- Northern Ireland: £1.07
- All-UK grants: £0.50

These figures need further explanation. Although successive editions of this book have criticised the excessive concentration of trust grants in London and the south of England, and it is a welcome change to find an apparent example of the opposite, nevertheless the differences between countries seem to be greater than would result simply from a weighting of the budgets based on published indices of deprivation.

Grant guidelines

We welcome applications for good quality projects which show a clear focus on children and careful planning in order to bring a positive difference or change to their lives. The children we help are aged 18 years and under in the United Kingdom. Their disadvantages include:
- any kind of disability
- behavioural or psychological problems

THE BBC CHILDREN IN NEED APPEAL – THE SIZE OF GRANTS

Number of grants, and value in £ million (1998/99, 1997/98 and the two years together)

	1998/99		*1997/98*		*Total*	
£1–£1,000	542	£0.4	732	£0.5	1,274	£0.9
£1,001–£5,000	916	£2.5	963	£2.5	1,879	£5.0
£5,001–£10,000	281	£2.1	231	£1.7	512	£1.7
£10,001–£25,000	215	£3.5	186	£3.2	401	£6.7
£25,001–£100,000	217	£10.4	180	£8.4	397	£18.8
Over £100,000	7	£1.2	10	£1.8	17	£3.0

- living in poverty or situations of deprivation
- illness, distress, abuse or neglect

Please do not apply for a grant to benefit children who do not fall within the above categories. We appreciate the good work which is done for the average child or young person in average circumstances but we are unable to make a financial contribution.

When to apply

[See under 'Applications' below.]

How we work

BBC Children in Need is a national grant-making trust which distributes between £10–£20 million a year to help children in need in the UK.

The Trustees, appointed by the BBC's Board of Governors, are advised by regional committees whose members have knowledge of child welfare issues and the voluntary sector.

We receive around 6,000 applications each year [*the annual report says 4,000 for 1998/99. Ed.*] and most applicants are contacted by our freelance assessors who work from home. An assessor may phone you or your referee to clarify the information provided on your application or to ask you to send additional information. If they cannot reach you during normal working hours they may phone in the evening. Assessors report to our advisory committees but have no decision-making powers.

Equality of opportunity

We want to ensure that our grants are used to benefit children in need and that none are overlooked because of prejudice.

The BBC Children in Need Appeal is committed to taking positive steps to ensure continuing fairness in its grant-making processes and practices.

Who can apply

We welcome applications from properly constituted not for profit groups. These may be:

- self help groups
- voluntary organisations
- registered charities

We give low priority to applications from statutory (public) bodies and local authorities for schools, hospitals, social services, etc. Such grants are rarely over a few thousand pounds and most are for much smaller amounts.

We regret that we cannot accept applications from private individuals or parents, nor from social workers or other welfare professionals on behalf of their clients.

However, we do allocate funds to the Family Welfare Association to make grants to individual children on our behalf. Applications must be made by a qualified social worker or other welfare professional and forms can be obtained from the FWA at 501–505 Kingsland Road, Dalston, London E8 4AU.

One, two or three year funding?

We give salary and revenue grants for up to 3 years at a time but rarely for amounts over £25,000. For the following, we only give one year grants:

- Capital projects
- Seasonal projects eg. holiday playschemes
- Holidays & outings
- Equipment & welfare funds

Organisations may hold only one grant at a time from the BBC Children in Need Appeal.

Salaries

If you are applying for staff salaries we will be looking at your experience as an employer or your plans to acquire the management skills you need. In the interests of equal opportunities all new posts funded by BBC Children in Need should be publicly advertised, unless for short term or sessional staff. Please would you:

- State whether a salary is for a new post or an existing one.
- Make sure your costs include all the extras involved in employing staff (for example: recruitment costs, inflation and increments, employers costs and any other on-costs).
- Enclose a job description, person specification and a first year work plan with your application form.

Monitoring & evaluation

When we give grants to support salaried staff we ask organisations to take responsibility for monitoring and evaluating their work. This is particularly important when organisations want us to fund their work for more than one year.

Monitoring and evaluating is about measuring what you have achieved, and comparing it to what you hoped to achieve. So you need to set clear and realistic targets before you write your application. …

The kind of answers we are looking for here are to do with keeping records, doing surveys, getting feedback from your users, or anything else you think gives us an indication of your progress.

We ask for this type of information so we can spend our money as wisely as possible, but we do understand that progress isn't problem free, so please be as clear and honest as you can. …

Children with disabilities

We wish to use our funds appropriately to help children with physical, sensory and/or learning disabilities. We recognise that each child with a disability is an individual to be considered as a child first, sharing the same needs and aspirations as all children and equally entitled to respect and dignity.

Children with disabilities are disadvantaged not only by the effect of their disabilities but also by the attitudes of others towards them and towards their participation in society. They may also experience other disadvantages such as poverty, isolation, illness and restricted opportunities.

We require applicants to demonstrate a sensitive appreciation of the needs and aspirations of the children to benefit from a grant and we want our funds to support children with disabilities in ways that:

- Improve their choice and opportunity
- Enhance their abilities
- Encourage independence
- Build their confidence and self esteem
- Involve disabled young people and adults as role models
- Counter negative attitudes and barriers to participation
- Recognise the needs of families and carers

We do not normally provide capital or revenue funding which is within statutory responsibilities.

We will not fund projects that reinforce negative stereotypes of children and young people with disabilities.

Child protection

We expect applicant organisations to take appropriate steps to keep children safe from harm, including the possibility of abuse, while in their care. We may ask you about this.

What we are looking for

A focus on children and quality

We are looking for quality work and projects which show a clear focus on children.

- Your project should be about changing the lives of children for the better.
- It should be for children (rather than their parents or for the needs of your organisation).
- Where possible and appropriate it should take account of children's views and involve them in decision-making.

A thoughtful and honest application

A thoughtful and honest application always stands out in the crowd! Tell us clearly what the problem is, and how your project will do something about it. Give us relevant facts and figures, please don't use jargon, and don't be vague. You don't need to promise the moon, just tell us what you can realistically achieve.

Your budget should show that you've done your homework and know what things cost. A thoughtful and honest application isn't a hurried and last minute dash to meet our deadlines with something dreamed up overnight. It is a serious and sincere attempt by your organisation to use its experience and skill to make a positive difference where it is needed.

Grants in 1998/99

There were six grants of over £100,000 (apart from the £500,000 for the Family Welfare Association noted above):

- ChildLine: £130,000 over three years for its telephone counselling service in Northern Ireland.
- Children's Legal Centre: £127,000 over three years for the running costs of its advice service.
- National Pyramid Trust: £120,000 over three years for work with disadvantaged children in Cornwall schools.

- NCH Action for Children: £112,000 to support child carers.
- Valley House Association, Coventry: £108,000 over three years for running costs.
- Enable: £101,000 over three years to develop local support groups for families in Scotland.

Of the 50 largest grant payments, only eight were for capital purposes, including minibuses (two grants) and building refurbishment.

The medium-sized grants, of a few thousand pounds, are usually for the running costs of play or group activities, or for equipment for meeting places, toy libraries and the like, although there are also grants to welfare funds such as the £2,700 to WRVS Cumbernauld, in Scotland, to enable it to make small individual grants to deprived children.

There are many grants for hundreds rather than thousands of pounds, such as the £250 to the Lenadon Community Festival so it could have arts workshops for children.

Exclusions

The appeal does not consider applications from private individuals or the friends or families of individual children. In addition, grants will not be given for:

- trips and projects abroad;
- medical treatment or medical research;
- unspecified expenditure;
- deficit funding or repayment of loans;
- projects which take place before applications can be processed (this takes up to five months from the closing dates);
- projects which are unable to start within 12 months;
- distribution to another/other organisation(s);
- general appeals and endowment funds;
- the relief of statutory responsibilities.

Applications

Straightforward and excellent application forms and guidelines are available from the appeal at the following addresses:

England: PO Box 76, London W3 6FS. Tel: 020 8576 7788

Scotland: Broadcasting House, Queen Street, Edinburgh EH2 1JF. Tel: 0131 248 4225

Wales: Broadcasting House, Llandaff, Cardiff CF5 2YQ. Tel: 029 2032 2383

Northern Ireland: Broadcasting House, Ormeau Avenue, Belfast BT2 8HQ. Tel: 028 9033 8221

There are two closing dates for applications – 30 November and 30 March. Organisations may submit only one application and may apply to only one of these dates. Applicants should allow up to five months after each closing date for notification of a decision. (For summer projects applications must be submitted by the November closing date or be rejected because they cannot be processed in time.)

The John Beckwith Charitable Settlement

Youth, general

£596,000 (1998/99)

124 Sloane Street, London SW1X 9BW

Tel. 020 8941 7896 **Fax** 020 8941 7896

Correspondent Irene Crapnell

Trustees *J L Beckwith; H M Beckwith; C M Meech.*

Information available Information supplied by the trust.

General

Most of the trust's funds are set aside for regular support to the Youth Sports Trust, which was founded by John Beckwith with the aim of improving sporting provision for children. Smaller amounts are available for educational charities, the underprivileged, charities covering overseas aid and the young, and for medical research, although not all of these areas appear to be supported in each year.

Net assets stood at £1.5 million in 1999.

A total of 32 grants were made in 1998/99. The largest grant was for £253,000 to the Youth Sports Trust (£188,000 in 1995/96), which accounted for three quarters of the total expenditure.

Other grants for £5,000 or more were as follows: St Edwards School (£100,000); Royal Opera House (£74,000); Institute of Sport, Loughborough University (£88,000); King's College, London (£37,000); The Enham Trust (£6,000); Macmillan Cancer Relief (£5,000).

Applications

To the correspondent in writing.

The Bedford Charity (also known as the Harpur Trust)

Education, welfare and recreation in and around Bedford

£472,000 (to organisations, 1998/99)

Beneficial area Bedford and its neighbourhood.

Princeton Court, Pilgrim Centre, Brickhill Drive, Bedford MK41 7PZ

Tel. 01234 369500 **Fax** 01234 369505

e-mail info@harpur-trust.org.uk

Correspondent Desmond Wigan, Clerk

Trustees *The governing body consists of four university nominations; the nominees of the teaching staff and parents of the trust's four schools; ten co-opted trustees; two nominees each of Bedford Borough Council and Bedfordshire County Council.*

Information available Comprehensive annual report and accounts and an annual narrative booklet.

Summary

Up to 100 grants a year, averaging about £6,000, are made to charities and other institutions in the area of benefit. Normally, £100,000 a year is set aside for a substantial contribution (in excess of £100,000) to a 'major project' with a value of £500,000 or more.

General

Established in 1566 by Sir William Harpur and his wife, the objectives of the trust are:

- the promotion of education
- relief of the aged, sick and poor
- provision of recreational and leisure facilities in the interests of social welfare.

Although only the last two are specifically aimed at the 'area of Bedford and the neighbourhood thereof in the County of Bedfordshire', the restriction effectively applies also to education. The charity owns and administers four schools and 65 almshouse properties.

Total assets of the trust amount to £158 million, held mainly as school and almshouse property but with endowment producing assets of £60 million. At present, 8/11ths of the endowment income is devoted to the welfare of pupils at its four main schools. The remaining 3/11ths are at the disposal of the grants committee for the maintenance of almshouses and for financial grants to individuals and projects in north Bedfordshire.

Up to 100 grants a year are made to charities and other institutions in the area of benefit. In 1998/99 these averaged around £6,200. Also, up to 400 grants are made annually to individuals.

In 1998/99, 525 grants were made from 716 applications, a 73% success rate (though not necessarily all for the full amount requested). Of these grants, 76 went to organisations and amounted to £472,000.

The largest 50 grants listed with the accounts were from £1,500 upwards, and totalled about £450,000. The top three, worth 43% of the total donated to organisations, were partnership projects for the following purposes: £130,000 for the Bedford Foyer project, offering accommodation and training to young people; £50,000 for an Out of School Learning Project centred around a summer 'children's university', and £25,000 in support of a bid for an Education Action Zone.

Ten further grants ranging from £10,000 to £21,000 accounted for another 26% of the total. The recipients included Youth Action Bedford (for a co-ordinator's salary); Furniture-Link Bedford (box-van purchase/running); Goldington Middle School (refurbishment of the youth centre), and the Prince's Trust (study clubs project).

Exclusions

No grants to organisations or individuals outside the borough of Bedford, unless the organisation supports a significant proportion of residents of the borough.

Applications

In writing to the correspondent.

Benesco Charity Limited

See the entry for the Charles Wolfson Charitable Trust on page 330.

General

As previously reported, this charity, funded by active and strikingly successful property investment, transfers almost all its income to the Charles Wolfson Charitable Trust, with which it is formally connected. The exception is that some of its properties, shown in the accounts as investment properties, have long been let to charities. If at less than market rates, this would have represented support, of a previously unknown extent, for these organisations. Hence the interest of these editors.

This position is now recognised in the accounts and the element of subsidy is shown as donations, an improved form of presentation. These totalled £194,000 in 1998/99, too low an amount to justify an entry in future editions of this book.

The rest of the income, over £5 million, was transferred to the associated Charles Wolfson Trust, which is the grant-making body.

Applications

No applications: see the entry for the Charles Wolfson Charitable Trust.

The Percy Bilton Charity

Disabled, young or older people, health

£613,000 (to organisations, 1999/2000)

Beneficial area UK (though very occasional response to overseas disaster appeals).

Bilton House, 58 Uxbridge Road, London W5 2TL

Tel. 020 8579 2829 **Fax** 020 8567 5459

Correspondent Mrs Wendy Fuller, Administrator

Trustees *R W Groom, Chair; M Bilton; Mrs M Loxton; W Moberley.*

Information available Excellent annual reports and accounts. Guidance notes for applicants, largely reprinted under 'Applications' below.

Summary

Main grants, from £2,000 up to a usual maximum of £20,000, but generally for less than £5,000, are made to organisations working with

- disabled people
- youth
- older people

Grants are normally only for building projects or for items of capital expenditure. Small grants of £500 or less are made for similar purposes.

General

Since the previous edition of this book was written, the charity has sold its shares in the Percy Bilton property and construction company and re-invested the proceeds in a diversified portfolio. This has led to some reduction in revenue, though hopefully this will now be more securely based for the long term.

This trust is a representative of a type once much more commonly found. It gives money for individuals in need as well as to organisations, gives very many small grants to the latter, and no very large grants to anyone. Virtually all its awards are one-off and for building or equipment costs. Because, no doubt, of the large number of grants (over 1,000 in all each year) the administrative costs are high, at 26% of the value of grants. Being well resourced, the charity is able to answer telephone enquiries about the eligibility of an intended application, a most welcome service. The staff (or at least one of them) are well paid: the highest earning member received a salary of over £50,000, a high figure for a charity with an income of less than £1 million.

Recently the trustees have begun to seek out funding opportunities, as well as reacting to applications received. In 1999/2000, following the swing of fashion that has happily and belatedly brought the issue to the fore, they settled on a Young Carers Project in Harrow which has been offered £40,000 over two years.

The trust seems most comfortable when it is asked to pay for a specific item of capital expenditure. Though it will make a contribution to larger appeals, it requires that 75% of the other funding for the project be in place already. It will not pay for office furniture or equipment, only for items that will be of direct assistance to beneficiaries. Grants for the last two years have been categorised as follows:

	1999/2000	*1998/99*
Disabled people	£340,000	£416,000
Youth	£150,000	£202,000
Elderly	£82,000	£161,000
Miscellaneous	£42,000	£28,000

A second categorisation of all except the small grants, for 1999/2000, is by their purpose:

Facilities for physically disabled people	38%
Facilities for people with learning disabilities	17%
Youth recreational projects	17%
Projects for the elderly	12%
Youth educational projects	5%

Other youth projects	9%
Other	2%

The main grants programme accounted for over £500,000 of the 1999/2000 grant expenditure.

There were about 65 awards, almost all for equipment or building projects. There were three beneficiaries who received amounts around the normal maximum of £20,000:

- National Playing Fields Association, for a multi-games wall in Cornwall.
- Lincolnshire House, Scunthorpe, for a contribution to a new building for people with cerebral palsy.
- The Royal British Legion, for specialist baths in a residential care home in Kent.

There were many more awards for £15,000 or £10,000, including unusual support for Youth at Risk in London for training for two residential volunteers, a non-capital item. More typical were the awards for carpets and equipment in the Radlett Lodge special school of the National Autistic Society or that to provide Cairngorm ski-lift facilities for people with special needs.

There are no grants between £500 and £2,000, but there is a separate small grants programme for amounts of £500 or less. In 1999/2000 there were over 100 such grants to organisations. Typical were the £435 for coarse fishing equipment and a pool table for St Mary's Community Project in Kent, and the £435 for a talking microwave for Merthyr Tydfil Institute for the Blind.

Exclusions

The charity will not consider:

- donations for general funding/ circularised appeals
- the arts (theatre, dance groups, etc.)
- running expenses (for the whole organisation or for projects)
- salaries or office equipment/furniture
- minibuses and motor vehicles
- playschemes/summer schemes
- holidays/residentials or expeditions for individuals or groups
- trips, activities or events
- centres or village halls predominantly for wider community use
- community sports/play area facilities
- pre-schools or playgroups (other than for special needs groups)
- church/church hall refurbishment or repair (including disabled access)
- schools, colleges and universities (other than special schools)
- welfare funds for the distribution of grants to individuals
- hospital equipment
- projects which have already been completed.
- research of any kind
- minor building/conversion works

Applications

Applications for small grants to be addressed to Miss Tara Smith, all other correspondence to Mrs Wendy Fuller, the charity administrator. If in doubt regarding the suitability of an appeal, contact the charity either in writing, giving a brief outline, or by telephone.

How to apply for main funding

The charity does not provide application forms. Kindly incorporate the following in your appeal:

1. A brief history and outline of your charity.

2. A description of the project and its principal aims.

3. Details of funding:

i. For equipment appeals, provide a list of items required with costs.
ii. Provide a budget for the project, including details of funds already raised and other sources being approached.
iii. State cost or costs involved for building/refurbishment projects – please itemise major items and professional fees (if any).

4. Submit building or other plans. Does the project have all relevant planning consents?

5. Dates when construction/ refurbishment is to commence and be completed.

6. State whether the project has ongoing revenue funding.

7. Plans for monitoring and evaluating the project.

8. Enclose a copy of your latest annual report and accounts.

For a small grant (£500 or less)

Please supply the following:

1. Brief details of your organisation.

2. Outline of the project and its principal aims.

3. Cost of the item/s required. Reference from one organisation you work with or Youth Service/Voluntary Service Council.

4. A copy of your latest audited accounts.

The board meets quarterly to consider applications. It may take up to three months for your application to be considered. Since the charity receives more applications than it can fund, inevitably some will be unsuccessful. However, you may reapply after 12 months.

If you have received a grant please allow at least one year from the date of payment before reapplying.

On-site visits or meetings may be required for larger applications.

A report must be submitted within one year after the grant is paid describing the activities resulting from the project, if required. If requested, photographs must be supplied free of charge to the charity.

The Boltons Trust

Social welfare, medicine, education

£632,000 (1998/99)

44a New Cavendish Street, London W1M 7LG

Tel. 020 7486 4663

Correspondent Clive Marks, Trustee

Trustees *Clive Marks; B Levin; Mrs C Albuquerque.*

Information available Report and accounts on file at the Charity Commission.

Summary

The main aims of the trust are:

- the pursuit of peace and understanding throughout the world, and the reduction of innocent suffering
- to support education

The policy of the trust is to select and support a strictly limited number of projects, and it is at pains to deter unsolicited applications, emphasising its request for 'absolutely no personal callers or telephone enquiries', and stating that 'unsolicited applications are unlikely to be successful'.

General

The trust did not respond to a request for a copy of its annual report and accounts, despite the statutory requirement to the contrary, but they were on file, in good order, at the Charity Commission.

The trust was set up in 1967 by Charlotte Bernstein, and until 1973 it bore her name. Her endowment was 83,000 shares in Granada plc, and shares in the company still make up over a quarter of the trust's assets of £3.4 million. It is a 'sister trust' to the Lord Ashdown Charitable Trust (see separate entry) and Leigh Trust, with whom it shares the same offices and correspondent.

The trust notes that 'all funds have been fully committed' (and figures are given below to show the extent of these commitments). Its grants are generally single, 'but not more than three years'.

In 1998/99, the trust had an income of £104,000 and grants totalled £632,000. Some recipients have received grants from the trust over a number of years. Several of the organisations reflect the trust's concern with family life. A grant of £100,000 was given to the Council of Christians and Jews, and grants of £50,000 each to: Conciliation Resources; Jewish Care; Jewish Child's Day; Norwood Ravenswood, and Yakar Educational Foundation, Jerusalem. Ongoing support continued to Power (Prosthetics and Orthotics World Education Relief, for mine victims, £40,000) and Henry Doubleday Research Association (£40,000 for organic produce research). New recipients included Thames Valley University (£20,000 for student bursaries); Mine Victims Fund (£10,000); Chai-Lifeline (£10,000 for cancer support and healthcare) and Kopple Goodman Family Support Project (£2,000). The trust had commitments at the year end in the following categories:

	1999	*2000*	*2001*
Aged	£80,000	£50,000	£50,000
Children	£100,000	£100,000	£50,000
International peace	£50,000	£100,000	£50,000
Education	£150,000	£50,000	£50,000
Interfaith	£110,000	£20,000	£20,000
Medical	£90,000	£50,000	–
Miscellaneous	£52,000	–	–

Applications

'Sadly, the trust can no longer respond to unsolicited applications.'

The Booth Charities

Welfare, health, education, in Salford

£1,137,000 (1999/2000)

Beneficial area Salford.

205 Moss Lane, Bramhall, Stockport, Cheshire SK7 1BA

Tel. 0161 736 2989

Correspondent J M Shelmerdine, Clerk to the Trustees

Trustees *M C Mowat, Chair; R P Kershaw; W Jones; E S Tudor-Evans; R J Weston; E W Hunt; R C Rees; W T Whittle; D J Tully; R J Christmas; J M Shelmerdine.*

Information available Annual report and accounts on file at the Charity Commission.

Summary

The Booth Charities are a group of at least 10 local trusts supporting disadvantaged people in Salford. Together they provide a wide range of support, including pension payments to individuals, grants to local charities and facilities such as almshouses, day centres and holiday camps for children from poor families.

This entry is concerned with Humphrey Booth the Elder's and Grandson's Charities, whose main activity is to maintain and repair the Sacred Trinity Church in Salford, but also makes grants ranging from hundreds to tens of thousands of pounds. Most grants appear to be for capital purposes, but revenue funding is also provided, including core running costs and salaries and bursaries for health and youth workers.

The largest amounts apparently go to projects where the charity's contribution is directly recognised and to some with which individual trustees have personal connections. In 1999 the charities had several commitments to local capital projects, the major one being £1.5 million to build and equip the Humphrey Booth Clinical Research Centre at Hope Hospital.

General

Income in 1998/99 amounted to £1,146,000 and grantmaking totalled £778,000. Grants to long-standing beneficiaries included £20,000 for Sacred Trinity Church and £147,000 for a refurbishment programme at Kirkdale Holiday House, which provides subsidised holidays for older people.

Further grantmaking was categorised as follows (with grant totals for the two most recent years for which information is available):

	1998/99	*1997/98*
Relief of aged, impotent or poor	£90,000	£96,000
Relief of distress and sickness	£95,000	£210,000
Recreation and leisure facilities	£244,000	£77,000
Educational facilities	£59,000	£585,000
Other	£65,000	£77,000
Total	£553,000	£1,045,000

The annual report for 1998/99 included a full review of the year's grantmaking, although amounts for specific grants were not given, other than those to related parties, despite the SORP requirement to the contrary.

A major beneficiary during the year was Salford Children's Holiday Camp, which received £141,000 for a building at the camp in Prestatyn, Wales.

The report also made reference to grants for research fellowships in geriatric medicine and a stroke development nurse post at Hope Hospital, and a new 'Humphrey Booth Bursary Award' for staff employed in care for older people at Salford Royal Hospitals NHS Trust.

Other grants included those to St Paul's Church, Swinton, for the building of a community facility; Elizabeth Prout Group (a religious organisation providing day activities for older people), a grant for the purchase of a minibus; YMCA, to fund a specialist instructor working with physically disabled children; St Ambrose Family Project, for a church community worker to work with single parents and toddler groups; Salford Education Department, towards the costs of running and maintaining Lledr Hall – an outdoor activities centre in north Wales; and Fairbridge in Salford, for bursaries for youth training courses.

Applications

In writing to the correspondent.

The Camelia Botnar Foundation

Disadvantaged young people

£815,000 (1999)

Beneficial area UK.

Maplehurst Road, Cowfold, Horsham, West Sussex RH13 8DQ

Tel. 01403 864556 **Fax** 01403 865041

Correspondent Stephen Hibbin

Trustees *Miss D P Lawson; J S H North; Mrs M C Botnar; B A Groves.*

Information available Accounts available at the Charity Commission, but without a full list of grants.

General

This foundation's work is much wider than just grantmaking, with direct charitable expenditure of £2.5 million (all its income). Its assets were £51 million in 1999.

The overall objects of the foundation are 'to assist disadvantaged young people under 21, who are in need of help due to family, social and other circumstances beyond their control'. The trust does this mainly through running a residential training and working estate in Cowfold, West Sussex, where young people are encouraged to stay and receive training and encouragement in a number of disciplines, such as carpentry, cabinet-making, catering, painting and horticulture. The foundation also funds the Camelia Botnar Children's Centre, which received £469,000 in 1999 (£484,000 in 1998), and works towards helping children with disabilities and their families.

A smaller proportion of the trust's income is donated in grants to organisations which share the same objects. In 1999 one grant of £200,000 was given to Charity Challenge Heritage. There were 19 other donations, totalling £146,000. Information on beneficiaries was not available, but in 1997 grants were given to Barnardos and Cystic Fibrosis Holiday Fund for Children.

Applications

In writing to the correspondent.

The Bradbury Foundation

Welfare

Probably over £1,000,000 a year

Beneficial area Hong Kong and UK.

Highlands, 2a Warren Lane, Friston, Eastbourne BN20 0HD

Correspondent D B Minns, UK Representative

Trustees *No information.*

Information available As this is not a UK charity, its reports and accounts are not filed with the Charity Commission. The foundation has supplied information for this entry.

General

This trust, highly regarded by organisations that it has supported, is based in Hong Kong.

Grants are usually between £250,000 and £350,000 and are for building projects. These must bear the name of Bradbury in recognition of any donation made.

The main areas of interest are:

- British Red Cross
- Salvation Army
- older people
- blind people
- charities helping the 'disadvantaged and unfortunate'

For 20 years, up to the 1990s, only Hong Kong charities were supported, but recently, and especially since 1997, UK charities have been the main beneficiaries.

Applications from the UK are processed through the correspondent above and normally involve going on to a waiting list before formal applications are agreed and submitted to an advisory board, which meets in Hong Kong three times a year.

Beneficiaries in the past have included day hospices, multiple sclerosis centres, Cheshire homes, projects for people with disabilities, Barnardos and similar organisations.

Exclusions

Support for building projects only.

Applications

In writing to the correspondent.

The Bridge House Estates Trust Fund

Welfare in London

£16,000,000 (1999/2000)

Beneficial area Greater London.

PO Box 270, Guildhall, London EC2P 2EJ

Tel. 020 7332 3710 **Fax** 020 7332 3720

e-mail bridgehousetrust@corpoflondon.gov.uk

website www.bridgehousegrants.org.uk

Correspondent Clare Thomas, Chief Grants Officer

Trustees *The Corporation of the City of London.*

Grants committee: John Leslie Bird, Chair; Peter Rigby; Sir Alan Traill, Robert Finch; Wilfred Archibald; William Fraser; Geoffrey Lawson; Joyce Nash; Barbara Newman; Joseph Reed; John Holland; Esmond Roney; Michael Cassidy; Richard Scriven.

Information available Detailed guidelines and application forms available from the fund, and also on its website. Full report and accounts available.

Summary

The trust is a grant-making arm of the Corporation of London and since 1995 has become a major source of funding for the city's voluntary sector. It concentrates its giving in five broad areas, set out below (with grants by number and value in 1999/2000):

1. Transport and access for older and disabled people (109 grants, £6.2 million).

2. Environmental conservation (24 grants, £1.7 million).

3. Children and young people (60 grants, £3.2 million).

4. The provision of technical assistance to voluntary organisations (35 grants, £2.2 million).

5. Assistance to older people to stay within the community (37 grants, £1.9 million).

In all cases priority is given to projects in areas of deprivation.

In exceptional cases the trust may fund outside these priority areas – during 1999/2000 it made four such 'exceptional' grants worth £759,000, including £500,000 for London's new Millennium Bridge.

The trust has also started a pilot small grants programme applicable to all the London boroughs, but on a three year cycle, 11 of them each year. (See the box opposite and the annual report, below.) In 2000, there were 24 grants, ranging from £500 to £5,000 and totalling £83,000.

The trust received 469 applications to its main grants programme during 1999/2000, the total amount requested being nearly £20.2 million. Of these applications, 53% were successful and grants worth £14.2 million were awarded. The average grant was £57,000, as against an average request of £84,000. Of these grants:

- 59% were for revenue over two or three years;
- 18% were for revenue for one year;
- 22% were one-off capital donations.

An overview of the fund's grantmaking as a whole can be read in the accompanying box. The fund's guidelines are reprinted here, followed by extracts from the annual report which give more detailed descriptions of specific grants.

Background

The trust's origins can be traced back to 1097 when William Rufus, second son of William the Norman, raised a special tax to help repair London Bridge. By the end of the twelfth century, the shops and houses adorning Peter de Colechurch's new stone London Bridge were beginning to generate not only increased cross-river trade, but also increased taxes, rents and bequests. A significant fund began to accumulate and it was administered from a building on the south side of the bridge called Bridge House.

Over succeeding centuries this fund has been administered by the Corporation of London. In 1995 the accumulated fund being so large, and the need, or space, for further City bridges being reduced, the objectives of the fund were widened to allow the surplus money to be used to support charitable activities across London.

Guidelines

Timetable

Trustees meet regularly and applications are accepted throughout the year. It takes about four months from receiving your application until a final decision is reached.

What type of grants do we give?

We give grants for both running costs and capital costs. Grants for running costs are usually for projects rather than core costs and can be from one to three years.

When can you reapply?

Normally we would make only one grant to an organisation at a time. If you receive a grant then you can reapply for a different purpose at the end of the period of the grant when the work has been evaluated. In the case of capital grants a year must have elapsed since payment

How much do we give?

We have no minimum amount but applications over £25,000 need to be accompanied by a detailed proposal. Large grants to small organisations are unlikely to be made. We expect organisations to have some other revenue funding before making a grant.

Priority 1. Transport and access for older and disabled people

The Trust supports initiatives which give older people and disabled people access to

- transport
- buildings
- opportunities

Older people are generally defined as those over 60 years. We support disabled people of all ages and our definition of disability is that contained in the Disability Discrimination Act.

Aims

This programme aims to improve services and opportunities to older people and disabled people and to encourage their active participation in the planning and management of services.

Priorities

Access to transport

We welcome applications from

- community transport schemes
- projects demonstrating maximum or shared usage of vehicles
- schemes improving transport services through better co-ordination

Access to buildings

We want to encourage

- projects improving access to buildings in the voluntary and community sectors
- schemes improving access to the built environment
- schemes increasing access awareness, information and design

Access to opportunities

We invite applications from organisations providing:

- training, employment, arts, sports and leisure activities
- information, advocacy and community support
- training for independent living
- disability equality training
- increased social participation and integration

BRIDGE HOUSE ESTATES TRUST FUND

The grant-making activity: an overview

To award over £16 million carries great responsibilities and it is not enough to be a mere 'conduit' for money, however worthy the recipient organisations. This year we increased the impact of our grant-making through a strategic partnership with the London Voluntary Services Council (LVSC). The Greater London Authority Liaison Project is helping the Voluntary Sector prepare for and participate in policy development for the emerging Greater London Authority. Charities have a vital role to play in the economic regeneration of London, promoting social inclusion and encouraging the involvement of minority ethnic communities in that process. In February 2000, in partnership with LVSC, we hosted an exciting hustings style conference at the Guildhall. Mayoral candidates presented their policies for London and how these would impact the voluntary sector. It was a rare opportunity for a whole range of different organisations to speak directly to those with potential power and influence.

A nine month research and consultation exercise into the need for a new kind of centre to help make London more sustainable was undertaken by URBED (Urban and Economic Development Group) for the Trust. Put simply, sustainability protects and enhances the environment, meets social needs and promotes economic success. Ten thousand organisations were asked if London needed a centre dedicated to the promotion and understanding of sustainability. Responses from the public, private and voluntary sectors were overwhelmingly supportive and the feasibility study has established conclusively the need for a new project. The Trust is, therefore, inviting applications from leading charities to develop a pilot initiative, the London Sustainability Exchange. Its strategic importance for London should not be underestimated.

At the other end of the scale, the Trust has increased its support of local charities, reaching out to hundreds of small organisations, many of which lack any stable funding. In February 2000, the Rt Hon Paul Boateng MP, Minister of State at the Home Office, with responsibility for the voluntary sector, launched our Small Grants Scheme at the Guildhall. The scheme is supporting local groups doing vital work in their communities with grants of £500–£5,000. It has been particularly effective at reaching minority ethnic communities in the 11 London boroughs where it is being piloted. Next year we are bringing the programme to other boroughs. At the end of the three-year experiment all London boroughs will have had an equal opportunity to access funds. We have adopted this intensive approach, working closely with leading voluntary sector development agencies and umbrella bodies, so that we can reach hundreds of small groups, many of which normally have limited access to funding. ...

In all our funding, we strive to be fair, assessing applications against our published criteria. Unusually for a grant-making trust, the Grants Committee meets in public, safeguarding the transparency of our grantmaking. In 1999/2000 the Trust awarded over £16 million to 293 London projects.

Principles of good practice
We wish to encourage user involvement in the planning and delivery of services. When the request is for vehicle purchase groups need to demonstrate
- appropriate garaging and security arrangements
- evidence of planning for insurance and running costs
- commitment to safety and driver training
- that there is no existing community or specialist transport service which can provide the level or nature of the required service

When the request is for access to buildings groups must show that they have taken expert advice from an Access Officer or equivalent specialist.

Exclusions
Not included is access to churches and large, national public buildings such as museums, galleries and arts venues. However, local and community resources can be supported.

Priority 2. Environmental conservation

The Trust supports projects which will sustain, protect and improve London's environment and create a better environmental future for London.

Aims
We aim to help:
- maintain, protect and enhance the natural environment
- maintain London's biodiversity

Priorities
We welcome applications from organisations which are working to
- develop environmental education work
- protect and improve the natural environment
- maintain London's 'biodiversity' or variety of life
- raise awareness and knowledge of environmental issues within the wider community
- ensure that resources are used in the least harmful and most efficient way

Principles of good practice
The Trust particularly wishes to support projects which
- enable other organisations to benefit and learn from successful initiatives
- encourage the involvement of all sections of the community, particularly marginalised or disadvantaged groups
- demonstrate innovative approaches to address environmental issues
- show a commitment to 'sustainability' or minimising the drain on the world's resources
- encourage the involvement of volunteers

Areas of interest
We are interested in supporting smaller organisations and organisations which do not have the environment as their main focus. The Trust will therefore support
- local development agencies and larger environmental organisations to provide help in kind, resources, staff time and technical assistance to smaller organisations
- consortium bids under which a number of smaller groups could form partnerships with a well established charitable organisation when applying for funding. The Trust will also allow community organisations which do not have environment as their main focus to make a separate application for an environmental project in addition to a proposal addressing another of the Trust's categories.

Priority 3. Children and young people

The Trust views young people as a major resource, whose potential can be wasted if not nurtured and supported.

Aims
We aim to
- support children and young people to develop their potential
- encourage the active involvement of young people in society
- support young people in crisis to re-establish their lives positively

Priorities
We have identified three themes

Preventative work with children and young people (aged 5–16)
This includes work with families, individuals and groups, particularly
- work preventing homelessness or drug and alcohol misuse
- advice, counselling and information services
- life skills and personal development projects
- work breaking cycles of violence, abuse, crime and mental illness

Work promoting active involvement of young people (aged 11–18)
We want to encourage work
- enabling young people to realise their potential
- encouraging young people to take responsibility
- involving young people actively in their communities, including inter-generational work
- grantmaking bodies to make grants on its behalf
- developing personal and emotional skills, especially in the areas of parenting, lifeskills and relationships

Young people in crisis (aged 16--21)
Applications are welcome from
- projects tackling drug and alcohol problems and homelessness
- groups supporting young parents, young carers or those with mental health problems
- projects offering fresh opportunities to those who are living in poverty or deprivation

Principles of good practice
We wish to encourage:
- the principle of involving young people in the planning and delivery of services
- projects aiming to give young people the opportunity to participate actively in society

Applications addressing the needs of marginalised or disaffected young people are particularly welcome.

Exclusions
The Trust does not usually fund under-5s work, play provision, playschemes or after-school care.

Priority 4. Technical assistance to voluntary organisations

The Trust recognises technical assistance is important for a healthy voluntary sector. We define 'technical assistance' as the provision of information, advice, training and consultancy to help voluntary organisations to develop.

Aims
The programme aims to
- strengthen the voluntary sector
- assist voluntary organisations in long term development and financial planning

Priorities
The Trust welcomes applications from groups which are working to
- improve the delivery of services by second tier organisations to other voluntary organisations, especially smaller voluntary organisations
- assist voluntary organisations with their organisational development, for example, training for management committees or volunteers, advice on funding matters and legal advice
- provide specialist training and information to non-specialist organisations, for example, training and information on disability equality, HIV/Aids or substance misuse
- develop councils for voluntary services in boroughs which lack co-ordinating bodies
- support organisations which promote volunteering

Principles of good practice
We want to encourage applications that will
- encourage collaboration amongst organisations and better co-ordination of services
- promote the sharing of best practice
- minimise unnecessary duplication.

Priority 5. Assistance to older people to remain within the community

The Trust supports a range of services which improve the lives of older people (defined as those aged 60 and over).

Aims
We aim to
- support older people to remain in their own homes

- improve the care and support of older people
- promote the health and well-being of older people
- give older people greater choice and control over services they receive
- focus on those in greatest need particularly disadvantaged or marginalised groups

Priorities

The Trust welcomes applications from organisations which are working to

- represent and empower older people without a strong or clear voice
- enable older people to make informed choices
- address the needs of older people with dementia and their carers
- support older people affected by depression and other mental health problems
- enable older people in residential or nursing home care to maintain their involvement in the wider community

Principles of good practice

The Trust wants to encourage applications from organisations demonstrating a commitment to the following principles of good practice

- respect for privacy and dignity
- maintenance of self-esteem
- fostering of independence
- choice and control (including the involvement of older people in the management and planning of services where possible)
- recognition of diversity (including ethnic, cultural, religious and social diversity) and individuality
- older people who use services should be kept safe and feel safe
- responsible risk taking
- citizens' rights
- sustaining relationships with friends and relatives
- opportunities for leisure activities

Exclusions

The Trust does not usually support applications for the capital costs of sheltered housing schemes or residential care costs.

Annual report 1999/2000

Small Grants Scheme 2000

(24 grants totalling £82,840)
Our new programme, Small Grants Scheme 2000, was launched during the year. Applications were received from January 2000 and the first awards were made in March 2000. Its principal aim is to broaden our giving to include small local organisations doing grassroots work, which have previously not had access to our funds.

Volunteers

Volunteer-led local projects are a vital element of vibrant and healthy communities. A small amount of money can go a very long way in the hands of committed volunteers. Grants of £500–£5,000 have now been made available to small, registered charities.

Benefit

The scheme will run for three years, covering eleven boroughs of Greater London each year. It supports projects for:

- people with disabilities
- environmental conservation
- children and young people
- older people

The experience so far

The new scheme is running for three consecutive calendar years and the very first awards were agreed by the Committee in March 2000. Hence only these few appear in this year's report. Of the first 24 grants approved, 20 were for projects benefiting children and young people, reflecting need. Awards were made in all eleven boroughs targeted by the scheme. Nine of the grants were specifically for the benefit of minority ethnic communities and were for capital and revenue purposes.

Review

Partners from both voluntary and statutory agencies have helped promote the scheme in their areas. Many have given us feedback regarding strengths and shortcomings, which we welcome. The Trust is committed to consultation and continuous review. Following the pilot year, amendments will be made to improve the scheme for the remainder of the three years.

Transport and access for older and disabled people

(109 grants totalling £6.2 million)
Improving access to transport, buildings and opportunities for older and disabled Londoners continues to be a cornerstone of the Trust's grant-making. This programme remains the Trust's largest, both in terms of number of grants approved and total funds awarded this year.

Access to transport

(15 grants totalling £0.5 million)
London has yet to offer a fully accessible, efficient and affordable transport system to enable older and disabled people to play a full part in the community. We support charities which are using resources strategically to address vital transport needs.

Community transport schemes provide co-ordinated and professional services making a big difference in the lives of older and disabled people. For example, Community Transport Hillingdon and Hackney Community Transport received £73,400 and £129,392 respectively, to increase the availability and effectiveness of their schemes.

Access to buildings

(26 grants totalling £2.1 million)
The mark of the Millennium has enriched London's architectural landscape. Whilst new buildings provide improved access to those with mobility difficulties, much of the Capital's built environment dates back to a time when little or no consideration was given to access needs. Greater awareness, coupled with the provisions of the Disability Discrimination Act 1995, are creating a new and welcomed urgency to improve accessibility to buildings and the Trust is responding increasingly to approaches from organisations seeking to enhance access to services and resources. Several groups have also benefited from expert advice from the Corporation's Access Officer.

A grant of £100,000 will enable St Paul's in Bow to provide full access to its new, multi-purpose community centre. Similarly, a grant of £148,600 awarded to the Voluntary Sector Trust in Bromley will provide a new borough-wide resource accessible to everyone.

Grants to the Horniman Museum and Gardens £200,000, Dulwich Picture Gallery £89,000, and Lambeth Fund (at Lambeth Palace) £30,000 are increasing access to arts, culture, recreation and leisure for many older and disabled Londoners. A grant of £32,000 will assist the Bangladesh Women's Association in Haringey in installing an accessible lift for its members who have mobility difficulties.

Other large grants included £400,000 to the John Grooms Association, towards making new homes fully accessible, and £106,500 to the new Fawcett Library, the National Library of Women, for access costs.

Access to opportunities

(68 grants totalling £3.6 million)
Disabled people of all ages and older people sometimes have to contend with limited choices and the statutory services and equipment which are provided are mainly for strictly functional purposes. For many disabled people specially adapted aids or equipment can enrich their quality of life. Whizz Kidz was awarded a grant of £84,000 to assess and provide disabled children with leisure equipment such as adapted tricycles and sports wheelchairs. North Kensington Canalside Trust's grant of £21,000 will enable children with learning disabilities to participate in exciting activities such as canoeing and water sports alongside their disabled and non-disabled peers. PALACE's grant of £42,300 is for a play worker for children with disabilities. Norwood Ravenswood's grant of £139,000 is opening up more recreational opportunity for learning disabled young adults.

Other awards included:

- £210,000 over three years to the National Schizophrenia Fellowship, for an advocacy service;
- £95,000 over three years to the Pedestrians Association for Road Safety, for a project to improve access for people on London's streets;

- £13,000 over two years to Kenya Community Support Network, for a volunteer programme assisting people with HIV/AIDS.

Environmental conservation

(24 grants totalling £1.7 million)

Education

Environmental education in schools and youth and community centres continues to interest us and 5 grants are supporting environmental education centres.

The largest grant of £175,000 to the Wildfowl and Wetlands Trust goes towards developing the world's first urban wetland conservation centre at Barn Elms, just 5 miles from the heart of London. The centre will play a key role in monitoring and expanding London's biodiversity and in developing the school curriculum on themes like mankind's effect upon the natural world, the importance of water and natural resources and social topics such as recycling, energy conservation and waste management.

Grants of £110,000 to Creekside Education Trust, £75,000 to Painshill Park Trust and £13,250 to Sunnyside Community Gardens Association are all enriching the environmental education of London school children.

Think globally – act locally

The 1992 Earth Summit in Rio de Janeiro highlighted the desperate need for a world-wide programme of action for sustainable development. Agenda 21 is translating this into a reality in London in a number of ways. The Agenda 21 Environmental Forum in Harrow is using its grant of £30,000 to co-ordinate local environmental networks, whilst the grant of £13,000 is enabling the Centre for Environmental Initiatives to review Agenda 21 in Sutton.

Involving the community

Groundwork Southwark's grant of £58,000 is encouraging the local community to engage in the redevelopment of Burgess Park. The grant of £119,000 enables Going for Green to work in Merton on projects promoting organic vegetable nurseries, a garden tools recycling scheme and 'Action at Home' explains to local residents where to buy low energy light bulbs, how to implement waste reduction and in general to be more energy efficient.

Practical solutions

The Pesticides Trust's grant of £21,000 is contributing to the reduction in use of harmful pesticide chemicals in the Capital by advising on sustainable alternatives.

Hundreds of empty houses in public or social ownership stand empty and deteriorate rapidly but the Empty Homes Agency's grant of £20,000 to establish a hotline is bringing them back into use and encouraging London boroughs to adopt empty property strategies.

Children and young people's programme

(60 grants totalling £3.2 million)

Many of London's children live in poverty, lack opportunities or suffer abuse or disadvantage. The Trust's support for children and young people is an investment in all our futures. Work seeking to improve their prospects and quality of life is funded through our three programme themes:

Preventative work

(28 grants totalling £1.5 million)

Quality of life is about emotional well-being and safety from harm. Grants in this category help avoid crises later in life. A significant proportion of grants this year are for counselling projects both in schools and communities. Brent Bereavement Services received £14,960 to counsel bereaved children while the Willow Tree Project will use a grant of £38,400 for a therapy project in East London schools. Preventative support for children in stressful family circumstances is vitally important; Kiran Asian Women's Aid's grant of £79,500 will pay for a child development post while £50,000 to Clouds will support the families of people with addictions.

The largest amounts donated in this category were:

- £152,000 over three years to the Caldecott Foundation, for a service for young care leavers;
- £113,000 over three years to Tower Hamlets Association of Alcohol Services and Problems, for a worker to work with children affected by parental alcohol abuse;
- £100,000 to the Salvation Army, for extending an alcohol and drug detoxification centre.

Active involvement

(8 grants totalling £0.5 million)

Increasing the involvement of young people in civic society is one of our key aims. Grants both large and small will support projects in which young people themselves are the driving force, gaining experience in both planning and decision making. Greenwich Arts Education Forum was awarded £16,000 to produce a local arts newsletter while ex-offenders at Clean Break Theatre were awarded £50,000 to run drama workshops for other vulnerable young people. The grant of £146,000 to the National Children's Bureau is helping young people participate in public decision making.

Young people in crisis

(24 grants totalling £1.2 million)

The transition to adulthood is hazardous for some. Projects providing a safety net for young people who find themselves in crisis are supported, together with those offering fresh opportunities to those most marginalised. For example, a modest grant of £10,000 to African Healthcare and Counselling Services will assist young people with HIV/AIDS, Kidscape's grant of £24,000 will pay for practical workshops for bullied children and a significant grant of £300,000 will help Sign build a unique residential centre for deaf young people with serious mental health problems.

Technical assistance

(35 grants totalling £2.2 million)

This programme strengthens London's charities by funding organisations that provide advice, information and training to smaller charities so that they can build up their organisations, improving the quality of their services to the community.

Keeping up with change

The Government's policies on social inclusion and 'New Deal' programmes have presented new challenges for London's voluntary sector. A grant of £10,500 to the National Council for Voluntary Organisations is to evaluate the experiences of young people involved in London's voluntary sector through the Government's New Deal training initiative, while £11,750 to London Voluntary Service Council contributed to a best practice guide promoting the role of voluntary and community organisations in London's economic development.

The social economy

The Charity Commission is now prepared in certain circumstances to consider economic regeneration as a charitable activity and the voluntary sector is playing an increasing role in the regeneration of disadvantaged areas. Terms like 'Social Enterprise', 'Social Capital' and 'Social Entrepreneur' are gaining wider currency to describe the galvanisation of the talents and resources of local people in the economic and social regeneration of their communities. A grant of £60,000 to The Civic Trust will provide technical support to London charities delivering sustainable regeneration projects, while £11,650 has helped Social Enterprise London develop a Social Economy Framework for London. A grant of £50,000 over 3 years to Bright Red Dot Foundation is supporting its work with 'Social Entrepreneurs' – individuals whose energy and charismatic leadership enable them to work effectively with the most marginalised communities where more mainstream initiatives have failed.

Volunteering

Volunteers give a tremendous amount of time for the benefit of their communities. Without their efforts there would be no voluntary sector. Without the right support, their experiences can be poor and their volunteering unsustained. Charities need to recruit, train, support and endorse their volunteers appropriately. A number of grants went to sustaining or improving volunteering. £120,000 is helping the National Centre for Student Volunteering to promote volunteering in 30 higher and further education establishments, Victim Support London's grant of £50,000 is extending good practice training to 2000 volunteers across London.

Older people in the community

(37 grants totalling £1.9 million)
We have maintained our support for work assisting older people to live independently within their local community helping them to enjoy a good quality of life. Sometimes, an individual may require access to a complex range of care and support services to help them achieve at least a degree of independence and these facilities need to be flexible enough to respond to changing needs. For others who are more active, recreational, welfare and advice services can be vital in helping to relieve social isolation and to improve an individual's living conditions.

Additionality
One of our largest grants this year was an award of £220,000 to the Brendoncare Foundation, assisting in the redevelopment of its day care and rehabilitation centres in south London for older mentally frail people. Such respite facilities can provide the specialist help necessary to assist an older person and their immediate family to maintain their chosen lifestyle. A grant of £88,500 over three years is helping the Dutch Pot Lunch and Social Club improve the lives of local African Caribbean elders through the provision of individual advice on housing, welfare and financial issues. Evidence shows that many older people do not claim their full income entitlement and schemes such as this can make a real difference in encouraging benefit take-up.

Empowerment
Smaller scale intervention can be equally effective in making life easier for older people. A grant of £10,000 over two years to St Peter's Community Centre in Bethnal Green is helping older Bangladeshi residents in one of the most deprived corners of London. Here, the elders are very much involved in the running of their own support services, which we see as a most positive aspect of the work. A grant of £33,000 over three years will allow Islington Carers Forum to increase its services to people in the borough, many themselves elderly, who have a caring responsibility for an older relative or companion. Despite recent legislative changes, the social, welfare and information needs of carers remains an important and under-resourced area.

Among the other recipients were St Francis Hospice, which was granted £130,000 over three years for a hospice at home service, and The Passage, £100,000 for the refurbishment of a day centre for homeless people.

Exceptional grants

(4 grants totalling £0.8 million)
Some grants were awarded outside our 5 programme areas. These 'exceptional grants' were for projects of great merit, two of which are celebrating the Millennium.

£500,000 has helped the London Millennium Bridge Trust complete the first pedestrian-only bridge crossing the Thames. The bridge's striking, innovative and stylish design is both a physical and a symbolic link between Bankside and the City, bringing together the two communities. Radical design, however, is not without problems and some initial difficulties including bridge movement are now being addressed.

JC 2000 received £50,000 for its work with London school children of all faiths exploring the origins of the Millennium as the anniversary of the life of Jesus Christ. The project involved thousands of schools in the United Kingdom, all exploring the relevance of moral and spiritual values in today's world through the medium of contemporary arts. The project culminated in a spectacular Arts Festival at the Albert Hall.

Occasionally, applications address a number of our interests. Radicle's grant of £141,000 is for its work with older people living in the community and its support of lone parents and younger people. Similarly, Education Extra received £68,000 in recognition of its work in developing extra curricular opportunities in both the arts and the environment for school children in London. Education Extra also provides practical advice to over 200 London schools on a whole range of issues connected with out-of-school activities from building management to health and safety.

Exclusions

- political parties;
- political lobbying;
- non-charitable activities;
- statutory or corporate bodies where the body involved is under a statutory or legal duty to incur the expenditure in question;
- grants which do not benefit the inhabitants of Greater London;
- individuals;
- grant-making bodies to make grants on its behalf;
- schools, universities or other educational establishments except where they are undertaking ancillary charitable activities specifically directed towards one of the agreed priority areas;
- medical or academic research;
- churches or other religious bodies where the monies will be used for the construction, maintenance and repair of religious buildings and for other religious purposes;
- hospitals.

Grants will not usually be given to:

- organisations seeking funding to replace cuts by statutory authorities
- organisations seeking funding to top up on under-priced contracts

Applications

Applications must be submitted on an application form (which are available from the trust, or can be downloaded from the website) with accompanying documentation. Applications sent by fax or e-mail will not be considered. The form is a substantial eight page document. It includes a full page summary 'request for funding' which will be copied to trustees.

Applications from unincorporated bodies, unless they are registered charities, will not be considered unless a registered charity has agreed to receive and account for any grant that may be awarded.

Your application will be considered by the trust fund committee and your form may be included in the papers for a committee meeting. You should ensure that the completed form provides a sufficient summary of what is proposed without the need for any other information to be attached. All applications will be acknowledged. Before the application is considered by the committee it will have been assessed – the assessor may need to visit the applicant organisation.

The trust says, 'If you need someone to talk to about your application, please get in touch with the Grants Unit. We will be happy to discuss it with you.'

Burdens Charitable Foundation

General

£400,000 (planned for 2000/01)

Beneficial area UK and overseas, with a special interest in Powys, Bristol, Midlands and the north west.

St George's House, 215–219 Chester Road, Manchester M15 4JE

Tel. 0161 832 4901 **Fax** 0161 835 3668

Correspondent Pam Maddocks, Secretary

Trustees *Arthur Burden; Roland Evans; Godfrey Burden; Hilary Perkins; Sally Schofield.*

Information available Report and accounts with list of top 50 grants, without the required analysis of donations, but see below.

Summary

A very large number of small grants are made, mostly to small charities, and divided between overseas aid organisations and welfare charities in the UK. Few local charities are supported outside the Manchester area.

General

The foundation was created in 1977 by Mr and Mrs W T Burden, who endowed it with shares in the business Mr Burden had created in 1929, WTB Group Ltd. This is a private company which employs about 600 people, many of whom also own shares in the company.

The foundation expects to be able to give about £400,000 a year in grants, the total being maintained in real terms over time.

Grant-making policy is described as follows:

The present aim is to allocate about half the income to the UK and half to less privileged countries overseas. The grants are intended to be of a size and duration sufficient to make a significant difference to the causes aided. Priority is given

- to the relief of human suffering, impairment and economic deprivation
- to small, highly focused and local community groups rather than large national/ international charities
- where volunteers play a key role in the service being delivered
- to social outreach projects based on local churches and established faith groups
- to low-cost umbrella agencies acting as monitoring conduits of similar criteria to the above.

Grants, mostly small – i.e. generally less than £1,000 in the UK – may be one-off or recurring over two or more years. They can relate to core costs, salaries, capital assets etc. without any exclusions in principle, save only that they really do make a difference. So large charities/projects and causes using professional fundraising costs to any substantial extent do not score particularly well as a generality.

Causes which rarely or never benefit include animal welfare (except in less developed countries), the arts and museums, political activities, most medical research, preservation etc. of historic buildings and monuments and sport.

In keeping with the present policy regarding less privileged parts of the world, this tenet also applies within the UK. For instance the Trustees perceive the South to be economically better placed than the North, and London to have a resource of charitable grantmaking trusts well out of line per capita than elsewhere. Whilst not always readily capable of precise measurement, the Trustees endeavour to assist where the need is greatest and alternative resources are the least.

The grants list for 1999/2000 was headed by just three grants for five figure sums, to the Community Foundation for Greater Manchester (£25,000), Easton Christian Family Centre (£14,000), and William Hulme Grammar School (£10,000). For the first of these the charity retained disbursement rights. The second two had been similarly supported in the previous year.

The total number of grants was 361, and the average amount necessarily very small. There were over 50 grants for amounts between £2,500 and £8,000, and a further £190,000 was given in smaller awards.

Exclusions

No grants to individuals.

Applications

In writing to the correspondent, accompanied by recent, audited accounts and statutory reports, coupled with at least outline business plans where relevant.

The Audrey & Stanley Burton Charitable Trust

Health, arts, Jewish charities, welfare and general

£444,000 (1998/99)

Beneficial area Unrestricted, with a special interest in Yorkshire.

Trustee Management Ltd, 19 Cookridge Street, Leeds LS2 3AG

Tel. 0113 243 6466 **Fax** 0113 243 6566

Correspondent The Secretary

Information available Annual reports and accounts available for a fee of £5 a copy.

Summary

Over 100 grants a year, seldom for more than £50,000 and about half for less than £1,000, for a wide range of causes.

General

The trust says that 'grants are normally made to cover health, arts, education and social needs. Preference will be given to charities in Yorkshire which have a specific aim or purpose.'

In 1998/99 the trust had assets worth a little over £1.5 million. Income, at £399,000, came mostly from Gift Aid donations and from the Stanley Howard Burton 1956 Charitable Trust, whose income the trust now receives. A total of 85 grants of £1,000 or more were awarded, 7 of them for over £10,000. Grants under £1,000, amounting to £30,000, were undisclosed.

About two thirds of the beneficiaries were healthcare or medical research charities. The largest grant in the year was for £74,000, to the Mental Health Foundation, which had received a similar amount two years previously. The major new beneficiary was Harrogate Families Housing Association, which received a grant of £50,000.

Further substantial awards in the field of health were given to Yorkshire Kidney Research Fund (£19,000); Alzheimer's Research Trust (£18,000); SENSE (£13,000; £5,000 in 1997/98) and the Manic Depression Fellowship (£10,000, repeat). Smaller grants in this category included those to Scope, The Partially Sighted Society, and the Multiple Sclerosis Centre, Sheffield (£1,000 each).

Arts beneficiaries included Opera North (£20,000; £5,000 in 1997/98); Leeds Art Collection Fund (£10,000; £1,000 in 1997/98); Harrogate International Festival (£10,000); Yorkshire Sculpture Park (£2,500), and the National Youth Orchestra of Great Britain (£1,000).

Jewish charities featured prominently among the other beneficiaries, which included Leeds Jewish Welfare Board (£10,000); The Jerusalem Foundation (£6,000; £5,000 in 1997/98); University of Newcastle (£5,000, repeat); Chabad's Charity Trust (£5,000); Antislavery International (£2,500; £5,000 in 1997/98); the Home for Aged Jews (£2,000); Community Shop Trust (£1,000); Friends of the Earth (£1,000, repeat), and Voluntary Action, Leeds (£1,000, repeat).

Fewer grants were made for work overseas than in the previous year, though Oxfam received a grant for £20,000.

The trust's policy appears to have changed somewhat since 1997/98, when considerable support was given to charities working overseas. In that year about 170 grants totalling £540,000 were made. Of this total, 58% went to the following five major beneficiaries:

- Oxfam (£83,000)
- Joint Jewish Charitable Trust (£74,000)
- Action Aid (£61,000)
- Save the Children (£50,000)
- Children's Aid Direct (£50,000)

About half the grants are probably for under £1,000, usually for £250 or £500. In 1997/98 (the last year for which these grants were listed in the annual report) the recipients included Mission Romania, West Yorkshire Police, Batley Culture Trust, World Vision, British Diabetic Association, MENCAP Nottingham, Wireless for the Bedridden, The Brontë Society, North Derbyshire Childcare Clubs Network, Israel Folk Dance Institute, Yorkshire Museum of Farming, and the Sue Ryder Foundation.

Exclusions

No grants to individuals.

Applications

In writing only to the trust. Unsuccessful applicants will not necessarily be notified.

The William Adlington Cadbury Charitable Trust

Birmingham area, Quaker churches, overseas

£513,000 (1999/2000)

Beneficial area Mainly West Midlands; some UK and Ireland, and overseas.

2 College Walk, Selly Oak, Birmingham B29 6LQ

Tel. 0121 472 1464 (a.m. only)

e-mail christine@stober.freeserve.co.uk

website www.wa-cadbury.org.uk

Correspondent Mrs Christine Stober

Trustees *Brandon Cadbury; James Taylor; Rupert Cadbury; Katherine van Hagen Cadbury; Margaret Salmon; Sarah Stafford; Adrian Thomas; John Penny.*

Information available Full report and accounts. Guidelines for applicants.

Summary

The trust makes a large number of modest grants, with very few for more than £5,000. About half the awards are to new applicants. The trust has five areas of grantmaking, as follows (with details of grants in 1999/2000):

- organisations serving Birmingham and the West Midlands (148 grants):
- UK based charities working overseas (41 grants worth £186,000)
- organisations whose work has a national significance*
- organisations outside the West Midlands where the trust has well-established links*
- organisations in Ireland*

* 70 grants under the last three headings.

Grant-making policy

This is described as follows:

Types of grant

Trustees favour specific grant applications. They do not usually award grants on an annual basis, except to a small number of charities for revenue costs.

Applications are encouraged from ethnic minority groups and women-led initiatives.

Grants, which are made only to, or through, registered charities, range from £100 to £5000. Larger grants are seldom awarded. Major appeals are considered by Trustees at meetings in May and November each year. Small grants of up to £1,000 are made on a continuing basis under the Trust's small grants programme.

Grant programmes

West Midlands

- Churches – The Religious Society Of Friends (Quakers) and other Churches
- Medical – Hospitals & Nursing Homes; Health Care projects; Medical Research
- Social Welfare – community groups; children and young people; the elderly; people with disabilities; the homeless; housing initiatives; counselling and mediation agencies
- Education & Training – Schools and Universities; Adult Literacy Schemes; Employment Training
- The Environment & Conservation Work
- Preservation – Museums & Art Galleries
- The Arts – Music, Drama & Visual Arts
- Penal Affairs – work with offenders and ex-offenders; Police projects

UK and Ireland

- The Religious Society of Friends (Quakers)
- Education projects which have a national significance
- UK environmental education programmes
- Preservation of listed buildings & monuments
- Penal Affairs – penal reform; work with offenders/ex-offenders
- Ireland – Cross community health and social welfare projects

International

- UK charities working overseas on long-term development projects

General

For a modestly sized organisation, with no full time staff, the trust is enterprisingly run. It produces a very full annual report and its website allows applications to be made on-line. The administrator notes that many applicants, after an initial telephone discussion, choose to send in their applications in this form – a model that may well become more general, and more satisfactory, than the paper based alternatives. In autumn 2000 the trust was planning a visit to west Africa to identify suitable new projects for support.

In 1999/2000, 1,080 appeals were received, as against 1,056 in the previous year. A total of 259 grants were made, giving a success rate of 24%. More detailed figures, broken down by category over two years, show surprisingly modest variations on this overall rate. One in ten applications were for individuals or expeditions, which the trust does not fund.

The largest grants were both to overseas aid charities – £20,000 each to the British Red Cross and to Oxfam (for its Orissa cyclone appeal). Otherwise £10,000 was the maximum, with three such beneficiaries being Sunfield Children's Home near Birmingham, the Birmingham Bond Scheme and Amnesty International. Most grants, though, were for hundreds rather than thousands of pounds and the trust's figure of £5,000 as its maximum normal grant is borne out by the grants list.

Although Ireland is an area of benefit, the nine grants in 1999/2000 all appeared to be for cross-community work in Northern Ireland.

Exclusions

The trust does not fund:

- individuals (whether for research, expeditions, educational purposes, etc.);
- projects concerned with travel or adventure;
- local projects or groups outside the West Midlands.

Applications

Applicants should in the first instance write to the secretary, giving the charity's registration number, a brief description of the charity's activities, and details of the specific project for which a grant is being sought.

Applications should also include a budget of the proposed work, together with a copy of the charity's most recent accounts. Trustees will also wish to know what funds have already been raised for the project and how any shortfall is to be met.

Alternatively you may fill in and submit a copy of the on-line application form.

The trust receives more applications than it can support. Even if your work falls within its policy, it may not be able to help, particularly if your project is outside the West Midlands.

Applications are not acknowledged unless the charity provides a stamped addressed envelope.

The Edward Cadbury Charitable Trust

Religion, general

£1,129,000 (1999/2000)

Beneficial area UK, with a special interest in West Midlands, overseas.

Elmfield, College Walk, Selly Oak, Birmingham B29 6LE

Tel. 0121 472 1838

Correspondent Mrs M Walton, Secretary

Trustees *Charles E Gillett, Chair; Christopher Littleboy; Charles R Gillett; Andrew Littleboy; Nigel Cadbury.*

Information available Report and accounts with full grants list; information sheets.

Summary

After major donations to the Quakers' Selly Oak complex of charities and buildings, with which the foundation has a close connection, and to other Quaker causes, about 150 further grants are made, ranging from £25 to around £60,000 but typically for between £500 and £5,000. Beneficiaries are varied but are generally either local West Midlands charities or, less often, national organisations. A few grants are awarded to UK groups working overseas and to overseas charities. There are virtually no grants for local charities outside the West Midlands.

General

In 1999/2000 the trust generated income of £893,000. About 150 charities received grants but a single large grant dominated the list of beneficiaries:

Our trustees have for some years sought large projects where a significant grant from us can make a real impact, where the project is needed, is cost-effective and well managed amongst the main criteria. Just such a project has come up this year and we have been happy to make a grant of £500,000 to the Ironbridge Gorge Museum Trust for their £5.9 million Coalbrookdale Project. Our grant completes the funding requirement and enables the project to proceed.

The trust's policies are stated as follows:

Policy of trustees: To continue to support, where appropriate, the charitable interests of the founder and of the trustees. [This means] the voluntary sector in the West Midlands, including education, Christian mission, the ecumenical mission and inter-faith relations.

Type of grants: The size of grant varies, but most are between £250 and £2,500 and are usually one-off, for a specific purpose or part of a project. Ongoing funding commitments are rarely considered.

Type of beneficiary: Registered charities working within the areas outlined under policy. Preference to the newly established.

There were 13 other grants in 1999/2000 for sums of over £10,000. They were led by two grants totalling £143,000 for Selly Oak Colleges, a Quaker cause that has been the leading beneficiary of the trust for many years. Other major beneficiaries were Christian Aid (£40,000), the Birmingham Hippodrome project (£25,000), Birmingham Scout Association (£16,000) and the Jubilee 2000 Coalition (£30,000). More typical grants were those to Gaines Christian Youth Centre (£500), Abbeyfield Society, Hagley (£1,000), Maldon (Quaker) Meeting (£1,000) and Friends for the Young Deaf (£600).

Exclusions

Registered charities only. No student grants or support for individuals. The trust is unlikely to fund projects which have popular appeal or fund areas which are normally publicly funded.

Applications

At any time, but allow three months for a response. Applications that do not come within the trust's policy as stated above will not be considered or acknowledged.

The trust does not have an application form. Applications should be made in writing to the correspondent. They should clearly and concisely give relevant information concerning the project and its benefits, an outline budget and how the project is to be funded initially and in the future. Up to date accounts and the organisation's latest annual report are also required.

The Barrow Cadbury Trust, and the Barrow Cadbury Fund

Immigration and resettlement, justice and peace, disability, gender, penal affairs, racial justice

£3,306,000 (1999/2000)

Beneficial area Unrestricted, but mainly UK.

2 College Walk, Selly Oak, Birmingham B29 6LQ

Tel. 0121 472 0417 **Fax** 0121 471 3130

Correspondent Eric Adams, Director

Trustees *Anna Southall, Chair; James Cadbury; Catherine Hickinbotham; Roger Hickinbotham; Richard Cadbury; Erica Cadbury; Ruth Cadbury; Candia Compton; Thomas Cadbury; Helen Cadbury; Nicola Cadbury.*

Information available Guidelines for applicants. Excellent report and accounts.

Summary

Grants are made to support marginalised, discriminated against groups in society such as ethnic minorities, women, prisoners and refugees. A typical grant would be for £15,000, but the trust is beginning to support a few major programmes on a larger scale.

Most grants are given towards salaries and running costs, often on an ongoing basis. Donations are made throughout the UK and, in rare instances, abroad. Grantmaking is no longer focused on Birmingham and the West Midlands, although a substantial number of grants continue to be made in the area, as well as in Northern Ireland where the trust has small programmes in defined geographical areas.

The Barrow Cadbury Fund supports work which is not charitable but which meets the other criteria of the trust.

Guidelines

The guidelines read as follows:

Trustees and directors:

- seek to support projects of an innovatory nature and national significance which aim to realise a more just and democratic society. Grants may be for capital or revenue purposes.
- have no deadlines for relevant applications and no application form, in the belief that applicants can best express their needs in their own ways.
- rarely respond to general appeals, or applications to local projects.
- do not acknowledge unsolicited approaches unrelated to published criteria.
- like to receive copies of minutes, accounts, budgets and working papers which indicate the thinking which has gone into making the application.
- aim for a mutual trust and respect between the recipient and the trust so that there can be a sharing of the ideas and aspirations associated with the project.
- require adherence to a formal set of terms during the period grants are made and expect to receive regular copies of minutes, reports and accounts.
- are concerned that all sections of the population should benefit through the effective application of equal opportunities policies.

Programmes

The trust makes grants of over £3 million a year in the following programmes:

Asylum, Immigration and Resettlement – support for the settlement needs of refugees and the rights of asylum seekers and immigrants.

Disability – national projects promoting inclusive education for those with learning difficulties.

Gender – women-led initiatives enabling women to take a full part in creating a just, equal and democratic society.

Justice and Peace – the promotion of a just and peaceful society.

Penal affairs – promotion of a humane and just prison and remand service and an equitable system of justice.

Racial justice – support for black and multi-racial projects fostering self advocacy and inter-ethnic and religious understanding.

The Barrow Cadbury Fund Limited is a registered company and is not restricted to grantmaking for charitable purposes. Its annual income after tax is about £450,000. Grants are made in the same fields as the Trust if there are grounds for assuming that the activity would not be deemed charitable in the legal sense.

Annual report 1999/2000

The general nature of this trust's grantmaking has remained substantially unchanged for a number of years. However, there are now a number of new trustees, of a new generation of the founding Cadbury family, and the long-serving director, Eric Adams, is approaching retirement. It is likely that there will be substantial new developments, probably affecting most programmes. Those most recently developed, Asylum, Immigration and Resettlement, and Racial Justice, are least likely to see major changes.

The excellent annual report for 1999/2000 describes the different programmes, and the grants made within them. An unusual and welcome feature is that each programme is reported on by a named trustee.

Potential applicants should note that most grants are recurrent. The trust gives ongoing support to numerous organisations in its specialist fields.

Asylum, immigration and resettlement programme

[Total: £314,000 in 28 grants]

The programme encompasses the following main areas of concern:

1. the rights of asylum seekers, refugees and immigrants;
2. the settlement needs of refugees, where initiatives can effect change in policy and practice.

Within the portfolio the Trust endeavours to support asylum seekers and immigrants in Britain and to influence policy both in the UK and Europe. A new Immigration and Asylum Act received Royal Assent in November 1999 and has far reaching implications for the treatment of asylum seekers and immigrants. The forced dispersal of asylum seekers to towns and cities across Britain, and the introduction of a voucher system have serious implications for the large London-based organisations in terms of the service they provide and for smaller regional organisations who may well be called upon to provide services on a much greater scale.

We hope that our support for both the large campaigning organisations such as the Refugee Council and the National Coalition of Anti-Deportation Campaigns, and smaller ones such as the Detention Advice Service and Asylum Aid, will enable them to support their clients and change government policy so that the basic human rights of refugees and asylum seekers are protected.

1999 saw a major emergency initiative by the government for Kosovan refugees in conjunction with other European governments. The advent of the Amsterdam Treaty offers some opportunities for a more humane and principled approach to the global changes in refugee and migratory movements. Future UK legislation will increasingly be influenced by European policy development. The importance of groups such as the European Council for Refugees and Exiles, the Migration Policy Group and the Immigration Law Practitioners' Association's work in monitoring and influencing politicians, policy-makers and the press in a fast changing situation will be critical.

We have also sought to encourage grant-making trusts to work together in this field, through our active membership of the Association of Charitable Foundations and its Racial Equality Interest Group. (Erica Cadbury)

Grants included the following:

- Asylum Aid, London: asylum appeals work and rent costs, £15,000.
- Black Women's Rape Action Project, London: service to refugee women, £22,000.
- Electronic Immigration Network, Manchester: running costs, £10,000.
- Independent Immigration Support Agency, West Midlands: asylum and detention project, £22,000.
- Refugee Council, London: parliamentary liaison and advocacy service, £16,000.
- West Midlands Anti-Deportation Campaign: salary and running costs, £4,000.
- Small grants (six), £10,000.

Community organising programme

[Total: £688,000 in 27 grants]

The Citizen Organising Foundation and its associated Broad-Based Organisations and selected Northern Ireland community initiatives.

Trustees maintain their view of the importance for communities to build and maintain their own value base. In the last year they have continued their support for projects with a focus on developing their own strategies and community plans in order to build a shared sense of community identity and a spirit which can be both optimistic and realistic in the face of the political, economic and social pressures of the day.

The basis of these ventures has varied. In some it has been issues of school performance and exclusion; in another community/public health. Underlying all the initiatives which Trustees have supported, however, has been the principle of people taking charge of their lives and in association with their fellow citizens striving to realise a more just and inclusive society.

By far the biggest contribution Trustees make to this end continues to be their support for Community Organising and we await the results of the Citizen Organising Foundation's move to foster independent broad-based organisations as charitable organisations with great interest. During the year the Trust has also been glad to offer modest support, through their new Berlin budget, to the fledgling community organising project there.

We do not envisage any changes in the direction of this programme in the year ahead nor any significant increase in funding. (Jim Cadbury)

Grants included the following:

- Citizen Organising Foundation: core funding and local organisation training, £166,000.
- Eureka! Co-operation Works!, Birmingham: training course, £10,000.
- Father Hudson's Society, Six Ways Initiative, Smethwick: running costs, £8,500.
- Industrial Areas Foundation, Chicago: bursaries, £6,000.
- PressWise, Bristol: running costs, £10,000.
- Scarman Trust, Birmingham: administration and project costs, £48,900.
- Trillick Enterprise Group, Co. Tyrone: salary, £15,000.
- Small grants (six), £11,480.

Justice & peace programme

[Total: £573,000 in 29 grants]

This programme focuses on the promotion of a just and peaceful civil society, with particular concern for Northern Ireland.

The justice, peace and reconciliation portfolio of the Trust endeavours to realise a deeply held Quaker testimony of its founders. At least the drive for the peaceful resolution of conflicts is no longer a minority pursuit. The Trust, however, continues to look for innovative approaches to peace making. These are often within small organisations or small-scale initiatives within larger institutions. The Jerusalem Studies Scholarship at Exeter University is one such, enabling as it does talented postgraduate students from Palestine to spend time studying in the UK and reflecting on their experience and hope for the future. Within the UK, Trustees have renewed their support for the Alternatives to Violence Project which is pioneering new approaches to conflict resolution both in the community and in prisons. The latter dimension links well with the Trust concern for a humane prison service.

We remain convinced that institutions of higher education need to reach out to the wider community. We hope our sponsorship of Bradford University's Department of Peace Studies' move into distance learning using e-mail will do just this, with students and participating institutions all over the world.

Northern Ireland retains a certain priority in our grantmaking. We recognise that much work remains to be done. Although we share in the joy of all communities in Northern Ireland when public steps are made towards peace, we also admire the vitality and importance of smaller scale community projects, particularly those which work across the fault lines of the different communities. It was such thinking that encouraged Trustees to offer significant funding this year to Forth Spring in Belfast and lies behind continuing grants to the Ulster Quaker Service Committee and Restoration Ministries. (Erica Cadbury)

Grants included the following:

- Fermanagh Trust: endowment and grants programme, £150,000.
- Northern Ireland Children's Holiday Scheme, Belfast: salary, £10,000
- Trust for Early Childhood, Family & Community Education, Jerusalem: running costs, £20,000
- Ulster Quaker Service Committee: running costs, £10,000.
- Small grants (three), £9,000.

Disability programme

[Total: £400,000 in 25 grants]

National projects promoting inclusive education for those with learning difficulties.

Themes of inclusion have been maintained and developed during this year. The overall focus has been the support of individuals and organisations campaigning for the civil rights of people with learning difficulties and their families. This has centred upon the issue of mainstream education, but it encompasses support and care services to enable the families to function in an ordinary fashion.

The cluster of projects brought together under the Circles Network banner has been instrumental in this way. The Bristol Crowley House project similarly exemplifies this approach; positive news has been that the work is gaining ground with some statutory agencies which are contributing funding now. This has enabled understanding to permeate through the system. Partners in Policymaking and the leadership training courses which continue to receive Trust funds are available for disabled people and parents of disabled children. The course fast-tracks people through the most advanced learning systems around inclusion.

The second major strand has encompassed support for projects developed by the Alliance for Inclusive Education. They recently invited members to offer a definition of inclusion. One example was 'Disabled children having exactly the same opportunities as their non-disabled next door neighbours'. Trustees have been pleased to receive news of the increasing collaboration between the Alliance, Parents for Inclusion and Disability Equality in Education; Trust support for the latter will enable disabled people to become advisers on inclusion in schools. Their collaboration will strengthen the movement and the message.

A Barrow Cadbury Fund grant to Independent Living Services based in Blackpool is intended to promote more awareness of independent living and the opportunities of Direct Payments. The aim of the initiative is to enable disabled people to have a choice, to take more control of their own lives and be able to purchase their own community care support. The venture offers training opportunities in terms of workshops as well as individual support. (Jim Cadbury)

Grants included the following:

- Circles Network, Bristol: salary and running costs, £75,000.
- Network 81, Stansted: salaries, £15,000.
- Ravenswood, Berkshire: facilitated communication project, £25,000.
- South Cumbria Care At Home Service: running costs, £10,000.
- Small grants (six), £11,000.

Gender programme

[Total: £331,000 in 29 grants]

1. Women-led initiatives which enable women to take a full part in the creation of a more equal, just and democratic society. Priority is given to West Midlands based initiatives.

2. Applications which can effect change in policy, practice, attitudes and opinions on gender equality and women's rights at a national level.

3. In Northern Ireland priority is given to women-led rural-based projects and Trustees are keen to enable women to raise the profile of gender inequality on the public and political agenda.

The Programme continues to be driven by the recognition of the important role women play in effecting social change. Support for development posts in community-based organisations engaged in local women's development remains central to current Trust interests. A further grant was given to the Birmingham Women's Advice and Information Centre. The West Midlands-based schemes giving grants to self-help women's groups continue. Locally managed and administered, the schemes have encouraged local women to become more aware of the dynamics of grant making. The schemes have also highlighted the richness of voluntary activity led by local women.

Nationally, Trustees agreed to provide continued support to the Fawcett Society, recognising the importance of maintaining a strong voice on how changes in legislation and policy affect women's equality and rights. To date there has been no substantive study of the role of women's organisations in British society. The Trust continues its support to the Centre for Institutional Studies, University of East London on their project to examine the issues that affect the development of women's organisations. It is also hoped that the Women's Communication Centre's publication – The Sexual Renaissance – will inform current debate on gender issues in the twenty-first century.

The women's sector in Northern Ireland has developed considerably. However, it recognises that the growth has occurred in the absence of a clear strategic or coherent approach. With the demise of the Peace and Reconciliation

Programme, questions are being raised about the sustainability of the sector. For the present, Trustees remain committed to their current priorities and to maintaining their involvement for the immediate future. Further grants were provided to the Women's Support Network, Fermanagh Women's Support Network and the Derry Women's Centre. (Ruth Cadbury)

Grants included the following:

- All Saints Women's Resource Centre, Wolverhampton: salary and running costs, £25,000.
- Barnardos, Harmara Project, Sandwell: salary and running costs, £16,500.
- University of East London: research on women's sector, £15,000.
- Small grants (six), £12,500.

Northern Ireland:

- Derry Women's Centre: administration costs, £10,000.
- Fermanagh Women's Network: salaries and running costs, £20,000.
- Women's News Collective, Belfast: media outreach project, £7,500.

Penal affairs

[Total: £197,000 in 12 grants]

Promotion of a humane and just prison and remand service and an equitable system of justice.

As a matter of policy, Trustees have essentially confined the Penal Affairs Programme to continuing support for organisations to which they have recently been committed. Thus grants have again been made to the Prison Reform Trust (core funding); the Institute of Criminology at Cambridge (Cropwood Fellowships and Prison Studies course); NACRO (for the Parliamentary All-Party Penal Affairs Group, the Penal Affairs Consortium and NACRO's own new Social Crime Prevention programme of publications); to the Prisoners' Advice Service (core funding); to the Trust for the Study of Adolescence (for their Youth Justice Fellowship scheme); to the Dawn Project in Sheffield (for their Surviving Separation and Divorce Programme); and to Voluntary Service Overseas (for the second term of their volunteer placement with the Zimbabwean Community Service Scheme). Only two new grants of significance were made during the year – that to the Galleries of Justice Museum in Nottingham for their exciting programme of preventive work with youngsters at risk on local housing estates, and to the Faculty of Law at Sheffield University for their study of Communities and Crime.

Trustees do not envisage any significant change in this programme in the year ahead.

Grants included the following:

- Institute of Criminology, Cambridge: Cropwood Fellowships and Conferences, £32,000.
- Penal Affairs Parliamentary All-Party Group, London: running costs, £12,000.
- Trust for the Study of Adolescence, Brighton: Youth Justice Fellowship, £10,000.
- Small grants (two), £6,000.

Racial justice programme

[Total: £437,000 in 38 grants]

Trustees seek to enable black and minority ethnic communities to address their needs and concerns; enable the wider society to address its racism, and religious and cultural prejudices; and foster a better inter-ethnic and religious understanding. The programme gives priority to work which addresses overt racism and fascism, and institutionalised racism, as well as education, training and employment issues facing black and minority ethnic communities.

Britain has seen a lot of activity on the race relations front over the last year. Central to this activity has been the Stephen Lawrence Inquiry. The determination and resilience of the Lawrence family and their supporters have led to a watershed in British race relations. The Stephen Lawrence Inquiry highlighted the deep mistrust between black communities and the police, and placed institutional racism in the public domain. Many in the African Caribbean and Asian communities have felt for a long time that radical change has been long overdue, not only within the criminal justice system but in other public authorities. Trustees provided support to two local racial harassment monitoring projects in Birmingham and Sandwell, as well as a further grant to the network of community-based racial harassment monitoring projects, now known as BRAIN. Such agencies will be critical in ensuring improved policy and practice. Those who work in the field of racial justice welcome the good intentions of government, but many remain uncertain about the commitment to prioritising and integrating racial equality in public policy-making in Britain.

Government is also looking to reform the Race Relations Act. The Commission for Racial Equality with other national black organisations has presented proposals for strengthening the Act. Trustees maintained their grants to several black-led organisations operating at a national level in their pursuit of greater racial justice. Renewed support was provided to the National Assembly against Racism. The Stephen Lawrence Inquiry has set the immediate tone for these organisations on work on racial equality issues. However only time will tell if any real difference will be made. Never has their work been more necessary than now.

The introduction of the Human Rights Act 1998 may offer opportunities to address racial discrimination within public bodies. To this end Trustees provided a grant to the Civil Liberties Trust to bring forward cases, and a small grant to the 1990 Trust to promote public awareness of the Act.

Through support for Operation Black Vote, Trustees hope its pilot project will enable greater participation of black people in public and political life. (Ruth Cadbury)

Grants included the following:

- Bangladesh Community Development, Birmingham: outreach education project, £7,000.
- Black Racial Attacks Independent Network, London: salary and running costs, £13,500.
- Commission on Islamophobia/ Runnymede Trust, London: consultant's fee and supervisory costs, £10,000.
- Northern Ireland Council for Ethnic Minorities, Belfast: administration costs, £10,000.
- Society of Black Lawyers, London: core costs, £18,250.
- UNITED, Amsterdam: information service, £9,000.

Barrow Cadbury Fund Ltd

The Fund's primary purpose remains the support of non-charitable projects which are considered important within the programme areas of the Trust. It is intended that any income not committed under this criterion will be devoted to issues of Community Democracy.

Grants to organisations (24 totalling £212,000) included:

Community organising

- Communities Organised for a Greater Bristol: local organisation training, £10,000.
- Merseyside Broad Based Organisation, Liverpool: local organisation training, £10,000.
- Süd Ost Europa Kultur, Berlin: education and training, £10,000.
- Trefnu Cymunedol Cymru, Wrexham: local organisation training, £10,000.
- Trillick Enterprise Group, Co. Tyrone: building costs, £20,000.
- Small grants (10), £16,250.

Justice and peace

- International Democracy: running costs, £20,000.
- Youth Sport Omagh, County Tyrone: running costs, £20,000.
- Small grants (three), £7,000.

Disability

- Action for Inclusion, Bolton: bursaries, £6,000.
- Parents with Attitude, Sheffield: publications, £6,000.

Exclusions

The trustees rarely respond to general appeals or applications from local projects except, as indicated, in the Racial Justice and Gender programmes.

Applications

Informal enquiry by telephone is encouraged before formal application is made.

Applications relevant to the Justice and Peace, Disability and Penal Affairs programmes of the trust should be discussed with the director, Eric Adams.

Applications relevant to the Immigration, Gender and Racial Justice programmes of the trust should be discussed with the assistant director, Dipali Chandra.

Trustees meet in March, July and November. Applications have to be received at least two months before the meeting.

The Campden Charities

Welfare and education in Kensington, London

£1,232,000 (to organisations, 1998/99)

Beneficial area The former parish of Kensington, London; a north–south corridor, roughly from Earl's Court to the north of Ladbroke Grove.

27a Pembridge Villas, London W11 3EP

Tel. 020 7243 0551 **Fax** 020 7229 4920

e-mail chris-stannard@campdencharities.org.uk

website www.campdencharities.org.uk

Correspondent A Cornick, Clerk

Trustees *Revd Tim Thornton, Chair; Lady Astor; D Banks; Miss E Christmas; S Dehn; Dr A Hamilton; M Heald; S Hoier; Mrs A Law; S Lockhart; J Madge; C Marr-Johnson; C McLaren; Mrs C Porteous; E Tomlin; R Tuck; I Weekes; N Wickham-Irving.*

Information available Annual report and accounts.

Summary

The charities divide their grantmaking into two main areas, the 'relief of need' and education, in a very limited area of west London. In 1998/99, nearly £1.25 million was given to organisations in 226 grants. Of this, roughly 55% was for the relief of need, mainly to social welfare organisations, and 45% for education, in its broadest sense. Grants are normally between £1,000 and £10,000, with an average of about £5,000, but many far exceed this, as shown below. Over 1,000 grants to individuals were also made.

General

The charities have their origin in the first half of the seventeenth century, when the first Viscount and Viscountess Campden each left £200 in their wills to the residents of Kensington. All the money was invested in land locally and some of this land is still owned today. In 1998/99 the organisation had over £54 million worth of assets, and an income of over £2 million, making it one of the wealthiest local trusts in the UK.

The trust aims to divide its resources roughly equally between 'relief of need' and education. In 1998/99, overall grantmaking to organisations increased by 25% from 1997/98. The charities have reclassified many 'relief of need' causes into education, so comparisons of sector totals in previous years are not relevant. Funds were provided for a range of projects, including equipment, appeals and running costs. Most grants, perhaps inevitably in a small area, go to organisations previously supported. However, amounts usually change from year to year and the grants do not have the appearance of regular, repeat subventions.

Relief of need

The greatest beneficiaries were Action Disability Kensington and Chelsea (£54,000 on holidays for disabled people and running costs); London Lighthouse (£50,000 towards its capital appeal, supporting HIV and AIDS sufferers); Venture Community Centre (£37,000 for an extended care scheme, adventure playground and running costs); Staying Put Kensington and Chelsea (£28,000 for decorating services and running costs), and Notting Hill Housing Trust (£21,000 on a joint project for funding a furniture store).

Education

The largest share of the funds went to organisations involved with pre-school or primary school age children. The largest grant in this category was to the Kensington and Chelsea Pre School Alliance (£29,000 towards the running costs for eight playgroups). Other recipients included Bevington School, which received £16,500 for computers, and £15,000 to The Making Place, a science, design and technology resource centre. Training projects for adults also featured significantly, such as a £15,000 grant for equipment and running costs at a music technology training project for unemployed youth, and £5,000 in each year to North Kensington Arts for its Portobello Festival work experience programme in 1998 and 1999. A substantial grant of £27,000 was also made to the Community Language Centre for emergency deficit funding and running costs.

Individuals

Part of the charities' expenditure for the relief of need consists of the payment of regular pensions to a large number of sick, older and frail people living in Kensington who are in financial need. Assistance is given also to other individuals in need, of any age, who are referred by the Social Services or other agencies.

Grants are also made to individuals for a variety of educational purposes. Again, beneficiaries must be residents of Kensington and in financial need.

Exclusions

- national charities or charities outside Kensington, unless they are of significant benefit to Kensington residents;
- schemes or activities which are generally regarded as the responsibility of the statutory authorities;
- national fundraising appeals;
- environmental projects unless connected with education or social need;
- medical research or equipment;
- animal welfare;
- advancement of religion or religious groups, unless they offer non-religious services to the community;
- commercial and business activities;
- endowment appeals;
- projects of a political nature;
- retrospective capital grants.

Applications

Organisations

Initial enquiries from organisations should be made in writing or by telephone to the grants officer for advice and an application form which must be completed and returned with supporting information as required. Office visits are also encouraged to discuss complex applications, or staff may visit organisations.

The organisations committee, which meets 11 times a year, first considers applications and trustees may decide to visit organisations or invite them to present their requests in person. The committee's recommendations are subsequently approved by the board of trustees. This process can take up to two months.

Trustees' decisions are imparted to the applicant by letter, which stipulates the nature and size of the grant, date of payment and follow-up reports required from beneficiaries. Beneficiaries must ensure monies are spent only as intended. The charities' staff monitor grants made by studying annual or follow-up reports and by visits.

Individuals, welfare

Applications must be made through social workers in the borough of Kensington and Chelsea, or local welfare organisations, on an application form obtainable from the assistant clerk. Telephone enquiries can be made to establish eligibility.

Individuals, pensions

Applications may be made to the assistant clerk directly by individuals either by telephone or in writing. Applicants will be visited by a pensioner visitor and, if eligible, their names will be placed on the waiting list for eventual consideration for a pension.

Education grants to individuals

Applications should be submitted as early as possible in the calendar year and be addressed to the education assistant by telephone or in writing. After a preliminary interview by the education assistant, completion of an application form and submission of references, eligible applicants will be called for interview with the education committee, which meets monthly.

The Carnegie United Kingdom Trust

Community service, arts, heritage

£991,000 (1999)

Beneficial area UK and Eire.

Comely Park House, Dunfermline, Fife KY12 7EJ

Tel. 01383 721445 **Fax** 01383 620682

Correspondent John Naylor, Secretary

Trustees *William Thomson, Chair; Dr Alexander Lawson; George Adamson; George Atkinson; Linda Brown; The Countess of Albemarle; Sir Timothy Colman; Sheriff John Stuart Forbes; Lady Anthony Hamilton; Walter Hutchison; Prof. David Ingram; Joy Kinna; Janet Lewis-Jones; L E Linaker; Anthony Mould; Lord Murray; David Tudway Quilter; Arthur Robertson; Sandy Saddler; James Scott; Jessie Spittal; David Stobie; Sir Kenneth Stowe; Dame Gillian Wagner; C Roy Woodrow.*

Information available Policy guidelines are available free on receipt of an A5 sae. A copy of the annual report will be supplied for £6 including postage. The annual report (ISBN prefix 0 900259) is lodged in all main public and reference libraries and with major voluntary organisations. Intending applicants are advised to read a recent report to gain a better idea of the aims and work of the trust.

Summary

The trust makes grants of usually £1,000 to £50,000 for up to three years in a limited number of fields. For the period 1996–2000 these covered aspects of the fields listed below. However, a new quinquennial policy is due to be launched in April 2001, and much may change.

Arts
- Young people
- Multi-media
- Voluntary arts

Heritage
- Independent museums
- Village halls

Community service
- Young people
- Parenting
- Third age

Unusual initiatives

The trust also funds programmes of work of its own instigation and grantmaking is but part of its activity. Unlike most trusts in this book it sets out to achieve specific changes in British society and, given its relatively modest resources, has been strikingly successful.

General

The Carnegie United Kingdom Trust was founded in 1913 with a $10 million endowment from US industrialist Andrew Carnegie, who divided his philanthropy between the USA and his native Britain, and especially Scotland.

The trust has carried out an energetic restructuring of its trustee body. The number of trustees has been reduced, from 18 to 14, their period in office has been limited to 5 years and vacant positions are now being advertised. The standard and excellent American practice of a nominations committee has been adopted, the committee being responsible for writing appropriate job specifications and for the recruitment and vetting of trustees.

The trust has for years carried an influence far beyond its apparent weight. This is due to its welcome practice of taking up particular limited causes and supporting them consistently over a number of years, with direct campaigning and by encouraging other funders to join in the enterprise, as well as by its own grantmaking. Past examples are its campaigns to make arts venues accessible to people with disabilities, to get the features of heritage locations clearly explained to visitors or, in the still current Carnegie Third Age programme, to see extended opportunities of all kinds for people in their 'third age'.

As an example, the results of the latter programme are to be seen no doubt by every reader, but the trust notes rather its failure, so far, to have discrimination against people on the grounds of their age made unlawful: 'Age is the one major cause of discrimination not regulated by law – with the inevitable consequence that it is seen as being of less importance than other causes.'

Other current policy programmes are for the development of voluntary arts through the Voluntary Arts Network, for Volunteer Development in Independent Museums and the major Carnegie Young People Initiative. The latter, now approaching its end, aims to improve young people's ability to manage their many transitions between the ages of 11 and 25. It is notable that the present chairman of the initiative is himself under 25.

The combination of policy development and grantmaking, by which these editors are strongly impressed, is described as follows in the 1999 annual report:

> Very few, if any, other trusts follow the pattern which Carnegie has now developed across almost all its grant policies of combining social policy development and action.
>
> Whenever possible, the two elements reinforce and complement one another. Policy development is enriched by action on the ground through grant-giving. The impact of each pound spent by the Trust is, thereby, increased. Personnel involved in major initiatives can provide informed comment on grant applications while, as a result of the in-depth understanding of a field gained during a major

initiative, grant-giving can be more effective and have a wider impact.

The way in which the inter-relationship between policy analysis and grant-giving develops is not always the same. With the Carnegie Third Age Inquiry and Programme and the Young People Initiative, the starting point has been policy analysis: for other areas of Trust interest the grass-roots need has been the starting point. For instance, the Trust's grants for new activities in village halls has led to the Trust funding separate studies of the wider needs of village halls in England, Wales and most recently Scotland.

In a final example of the unusual enterprise of this trust, and setting a precedent that could again be usefully followed by many others, it is seeking to increase its endowment with further gifts and legacies.

Current grant programmes (1996–2000)

Readers should note these are likely to change, to a greater or lesser extent, in April 2001. The resources of the trust are small in relation to its reputation. As a result, it gets many applications of which only about one in ten can, at present, be successful.

Arts

Young people

Open to local, regional and national voluntary arts bodies to help young people participate in the arts outside and beyond formal education.

Priority will be given to projects which develop links between voluntary arts bodies and educational establishments … to encourage a smooth transition for young people (aged 14–25) to enjoy continued development in the arts. Funding comes with stringent guidelines for expenditure.

Multi-media

Open to national, regional and significant local groups which work with electronic multi-media and the arts for creative purposes, ie, not for management information. Priority will be given to initiatives outside the formal educational system for young people without other access to multi-media. Consideration will also be given to cross generational applications. Proposals with a wider community dimension or which link with libraries will be of particular interest. …

Voluntary arts – electronic information

Open to national and regional umbrella bodies for the voluntary arts.

Hardware, software and training to electronically link with the Voluntary Arts Network information service, to access CD based reference material and to offer on-line information services to groups will be considered. …

Voluntary arts – training

Open to national, regional and other major local voluntary arts organisations, eg those with buildings or undergoing major developments. Training should be for key paid staff and volunteers and their co-operation to strengthen the management and administration of the arts organisation. Special consideration will be given to training which has a cascade effect, ie those who receive the initial training passing it on to others.

Heritage

Independent museums

Open to members of AIM (Association of Independent Museums) and registered with the Museums and Galleries Commission.

A) Innovation in the use of information technology. Special consideration will be given to those who are prepared to share their success or difficulties with others and indicate how they will do it. In 1999 the guidelines were widened to include University Museums and feasibility/pilot schemes for major IT projects.

B) Volunteer Development. Limited funding is available to enable volunteers to undertake structured training, preferably leading to a recognised qualification and for initiatives which improve volunteer management.

Village halls

Open to village hall committees where the population is below 5,000.

Grants of up to £5,000 are available to develop a new activity for equipment and relevant building alterations but not for general repairs and access.

Between 1930 and 1949, the trustees assisted with the early development of village halls. Now, they wish to support halls' development and growth by encouraging their use as multi-purpose village centres.

These grants are administered in conjunction with ACRE (England), WCVA (Wales), SCVO (Scotland) and Foras Eireann (Ireland).

Community

Young people

During this quinquennium (1996–2000) the Carnegie UK Trust, in collaboration with others, will be initiating a project to: examine the social, economic and personal issues affecting young people, drawing mainly on existing knowledge but with some capacity for original research. Its purpose will be to improve the prospects for young people by influencing public policy, agency and professional practice, and adult attitudes, so as to secure the practical application of current and new knowledge.

An information leaflet giving more details about the project will be available.

The trust will await the conclusions before considering specific policies. In the meantime, the trust retains its interest in young people from the previous quinquennium. It will consider exceptional proposals which broaden constructive experience by involving disadvantaged young people in the community in ways that develop responsibility and possibly leadership potential. Preference will be given to proposals involving young people in the management.

Parenting

For national and regional voluntary agencies which support local development. Priority will be given to proposals which focus on fathers, couples, parents of teenage children and grandparents and which encourage the improvement of parental care through practical support services and informal education projects.

Other parenting projects may be considered but lower priority will be given to applications which focus on mothers of young children as these were the main beneficiary in the previous quinquennium. Schemes mainly for counselling, crisis intervention, conciliation and child development are excluded.

Third age

Open to national and regional organisations and those local organisations developing initiatives which could spread regionally or nationally. Designed to make the third age 'vastly more rewarding', this Carnegie driven initiative is now in its final stages.

The trust will support selected proposals which have emerged from Carnegie Third Age Programme thinking and are focused on those who have completed their main career and child rearing.

Priorities will include projects which introduce or re-introduce people after a long absence to volunteering.

Unusual initiatives

Open to national, regional or local organisations.

Creative initiatives which pioneer new ways forward across traditional boundaries will be considered by the trust. These may involve unusual collaborations, completely new ideas or the identification of gaps in provision which have emerged because they do not fit present institutional frameworks. The proposal should have significant ramifications, indicate what its wider impact might be and show how findings, approaches or ideas will be disseminated if the initiative is successful.

Grants in 1999

The Carnegie does not have fixed budgets for its different areas of grantmaking, though there seems to be considerable consistency between headings from year to year. It does seek, however, to distribute its money over time around the four countries it serves pro rata to the population concerned. In the 1999 report it notes that it has been finding it hard to ensure that Wales is fully represented, presumably because of a shortage of applications of suitable quality.

Grants were categorised as follows:

Arts	23	£271,000
Community service	17	£460,000
Heritage	78	£260,000

Apart from support of its own programmes, no grants were for more than the £32,000 to Youth Clubs UK (to extend its Youth FM radio station run by and for young people). Other awards of £30,000 were to Jubilee Arts in Sandwell, Leicester Education Action Zone, Children in Scotland, the Spare Tyre Theatre Company in London and the SeaChange Trust in Great Yarmouth (for an arts centre).

Many of the heritage grants were for village halls.

Exclusions

Grants are not made in response to:

- general appeals;
- closed societies;
- endowment funds;
- debt clearance;
- individuals;
- replacement of statutory funding.

The following are specifically excluded during the quinquennium, 1996–2000:

- restoration, conversion, repair and purchase of buildings;
- formal education – schools, colleges and universities;
- sports;
- research or publications, conferences and exhibitions (except in special circumstances where trustees wish to initiate certain work);
- community business initiatives;
- animal welfare;
- medical or related healthcare purposes;
- holidays, adventure centres and youth hostels;
- residential care, day-care centres and housing;
- conciliation and counselling services;
- care in the community;
- pre-school groups and playschemes;
- arts centres, professional arts companies and festivals, including performances and workshops;
- pipe organs in churches and other buildings;
- environmental matters, including displays and trails;
- libraries.

The trust does not usually accept another application from the same organisation within 12 months from the date of the decision in the case of a rejection, or completion in the case of a grant receipt.

Applications

Application is usually by letter, except for proposals to the Voluntary Arts – information network, Independent Museums – volunteer development and Village Halls programmes. All applications should be directed to the secretary. Applicants should not approach individual trustees. All applications need to include the information listed below:

- Brief description of the organisation – its history, work budget, management and staffing.
- Last annual report, audited accounts, the main part of the constitution, charity registration number and committee membership.
- Description of the project including its purpose; time scales incorporating any milestones during the programme; expected outcomes; number of people who will benefit; and how the project will be managed.
- Amount requested from the Carnegie UK Trust.
- Budget for the project, including details of funds already raised and other sources being approached.
- How the work will continue after the trust's grant has been completed – plans for monitoring and evaluating the project: the trust attaches great importance to this.
- How information about the project and what has been learnt from it will be shared with others in the field.
- Contact name, address, telephone and fax numbers. These should normally be for the person directly responsible for the work, not the fundraiser. The application letter should be signed by the senior person responsible, such as the chairman or the director.
- Deadlines for applications are 30 January for the March trustees' meeting, 30 April for the June meeting and 30 September for the November meeting. Applications can be submitted at any time. Early preliminary submissions are particularly welcome so that a comprehensive application can be presented to the trustees. The trust aims to inform applicants of trustees' decisions by the end of the month in which the meeting is held. However, the volume of applications received and the need for assessment may mean consideration is delayed.
- Applications are acknowledged on receipt.

Inquiries about trust policy and a possible application are invited by telephone to the secretary or administrator. Applications within guidelines and being considered for a grant may be followed up with enquiries for further information and by a visit from a trust representative.

Sir John Cass's Foundation

Education in inner London

£973,000 to organisations, but see below (1999/2000)

Beneficial area The inner London boroughs – Kensington & Chelsea, Camden, City of London, Greenwich, Hackney, Hammersmith & Fulham, Islington, Lambeth, Lewisham, Newham, Southwark, Tower Hamlets, Wandsworth, Westminster.

31 Jewry Street, Aldgate, London EC3N 2EY

Tel. 020 7480 5884 **Fax** 020 7488 2519

Correspondent Colin Wright, Clerk to the Governors

Trustees *18 in all, of whom the following are members of the grants committee: Revd B J Lee; M Venn; K M Everett.*

Information available Guidelines for applicants. Good annual report and accounts.

Summary

Grants, usually for amounts between £5,000 and £40,000, to organisations, be they schools, organisations working with schools, or those with educational programmes outside school, for educational work with children and young people in London. Most support goes to areas near the foundation's base in east London.

The foundation owns a primary school and a secondary school in Tower Hamlets, which receive regular support (£137,000 in 1999/2000) and also gives priority to funding various projects at London Guildhall University (£57,000).

General

The foundation's guidelines read as follows:

The Sir John Cass's Foundation was established in 1748 to educate 'poor but worthy' children of the Portsoken ward of the City of London. Since that time the Foundation's beneficial area has been extended to include the City of London, the City of Westminster, the Royal Borough of Kensington & Chelsea, and the London

Boroughs of Camden, Greenwich, Hackney, Hammersmith and Fulham, Islington, Lambeth, Lewisham, Newham, Southwark, Tower Hamlets, and Wandsworth.

The Foundation can only consider proposals from schools and organisations that will benefit young people under the age of 25, who are permanently residents of inner London.

The Foundation will consider applications for time-limited projects where it is clear for what purpose and activities grant assistance is being sought. In 1998/9 the Foundation made grants totalling £1.3 million, the value of which ranged from £830 to £60,000. [*These figures include grants to individuals, the smallest grant to an organisation being £2,000. Ed.*]

Foundation Governors wish to encourage and, where appropriate, support applications which:

- incorporate structured educational content related, where appropriate, to the teaching and learning of the relevant key stage(s) of the National Curriculum.
- demonstrate a realistic likelihood of continuing after the expiry of the Foundation's grant.
- are innovative, in the sense of identifying and meeting educational needs not met by other grant-giving bodies.

Within these parameters, Governors particularly favour applications which:

- promote the teaching of science, maths, engineering and technology.
- develop programmes that improve access to the curriculum and prepare beneficiaries for the world of work.
- develop curricula or activities outside the normal school day.

Preference is given to original developments, not yet part of the regular activities of an organisation; to developments that are either strategic, such as practical initiatives directed toward addressing the root causes of problems; or seminal, because they seek to influence policy and practice elsewhere.

Due to the large number of applications in relation to the limited funds available, many good projects still have to be refused – even though they fit within the Foundation's general guidelines. The Foundation may also, from time to time, initiate new projects that do not fall into the priority areas for grant; in this fashion the Governors explore potential areas for involvement in the future.

Grants in 1999/2000

	No.	*Amount*
Literacy and numeracy	7	£174,000
Employment training	4	£46,000
Arts activities	7	£122,000
Environmental education	2	£40,000
Science and technology	2	£40,000
Social science and humanities	2	£28,000
Miscellaneous	5	£109,000
Grants to Church of England schools	4	£220,000
Grants to London Guildhall University	3	£57,000
Grants to Cass schools	2	£137,000
Total	38	£973,000

An additional £144,000 was donated to individuals.

The year's largest grants, of £100,000 each, were to sponsor the creation of an Education Action Zone in Hackney, and to provide additional classrooms at St Leonard's Primary School in Streatham (through Southwark Diocesan Board for Education).

Four grants made under the 'arts activities' and 'science and technology' headings were match-funding grants for four schools, to help them bid for arts college or technology college status.

Other beneficiaries included:

- National Literacy Trust – £27,000, final year's support for 12 'Reading is Fundamental' groups in primary schools across inner London.
- The Margaret McMillan Field Studies Centre – £25,000, school journey grants for children from low income families.
- Leyton Orient Community Sports Programme – £25,000, 'Football as a Curriculum Topic' programme in Hackney and Newham primary schools.
- Chelsea Children's Hospital School – £15,000, careers counselling for young adults with chronic illnesses.
- Youth At Risk Impact Centre – £15,000, youth disaffection programme in two secondary schools.
- The Horniman Public Museum and Park Trust – £20,000, salary costs for two education staff over three years.

Exclusions

The governors will not normally fund:

- basic equipment or teachers' salaries that are the responsibility of the education authorities;
- the purchase, repair or furnishing of buildings;
- stage, film or video production costs;
- performances, exhibitions or festivals;
- independent schools;
- local youth and community projects;
- conferences or seminars;
- university or medical research;
- establishing funds for bursary or loan schemes;
- supplementary schools or mother tongue teaching;
- retrospective grants to help pay off overdrafts or loans (nor will the foundation remedy the withdrawal or reduction of statutory funds);
- the purchase of vehicles, computers or sports equipment;
- research or publication costs;
- one-off music, drama, dance or similar productions, or the tours of such productions (nor does the foundation support ticket subsidy schemes);
- holiday projects, school journeys, trips abroad or exchange visits;
- school ground improvements;
- general fundraising campaigns and appeals.

Applications

1. To apply for a grant you should send an initial letter outlining your application to the clerk to the governors. The letter should include some basic costings for your project and background details on your organisation.

2. If your proposal falls within the current policy and the foundation's basic criteria are satisfied, you will be invited to submit an application under headings that the foundation will provide, together with an annual report and audited accounts.

3. Upon receipt of the completed application, foundation staff will discuss your proposal with you and may arrange to visit.

4. Completed applications are then considered by governors, who meet quarterly.

5. Decisions are conveyed to applicants within seven days of a meeting.

6. Throughout the process, the foundation's staff will be happy to clear up any questions you might have and are available to receive initial telephone enquiries.

Applicants should note that an application is only finalised when all documentation has been received, a meeting has taken place and there are no further questions to raise. All this takes time and it is the applicant's responsibility to allow a reasonable length of time for this process.

Successful projects will include appropriate measures of performance, as the foundation is interested in evaluating the results of funded activities.

The Charities Advisory Trust

See below

£702,000 (1998/99)

Radius Works, Back Lane, London NW3 1HL

Tel. 020 7794 9835 **Fax** 020 7431 3739

e-mail charities.advisory.trust@ukonline.co.uk

Correspondent Hilary Blume, Director

Trustees *Dr Cornelia Navari; Dr Carolyne Dennis; Prof. Bob Holman; Ms Dawn Penso.*

Information available Annual report and accounts.

General

A principal activity of this charity is running the Card Aid operation which raises substantial sums for charities participating in its annual Christmas card operation – whose shops across London each year will have been seen by many readers. However, the operation also raises a surplus which is given out in the form of grants to other charities – typically about £300,000 annually. The year 1998/99 was exceptional because of one massive grant.

Grantmaking is not pre-planned. As the trustees and director are active in the voluntary sector, most issues arise outside any application process, but

> we do get unsolicited applications as a result of our appearance in the directories. We probably respond to five per cent in any positive way – and often this may be a token £100.
>
> We give very substantial grants – say two a year at around the £100,000 level. ... Smaller amounts, say up to £20,000, may be given on a long-term or one-off basis in the categories for which we have a special interest, or have a special relationship with a charity.
>
> Other grants may be because we have an interest at a particular time, or want to meet a particular need.

The trust notes some of its present areas of interest as:

- income generation projects
- homelessness
- museums
- cancer research and treatment
- peace and reconciliation
- refugees

However, grants are wide-ranging, and no area of work is excluded if a sufficiently interesting or unusual project comes along.

As an example of this, 1998/99 grants were dominated by an exceptionally large grant of £340,000 to enable an indigenous group in south India to buy back a tea plantation (visited by this editor on a memorable and inspiring expedition) that had been created from the forests where the people concerned had previously lived. Two earlier grants of £100,000 were for the planting of trees in London and for the British Museum's educational work in primary schools.

Other 1998/99 grants went to providing travel and telephone cards for refugees (£15,000, via the Refugee Council); to a local project for school books and uniforms in Grenada, West Indies (£5,000); to the Aston Settlement in Birmingham (£20,000 for a re-mortgaging scheme for homeless people) and to the Royal Free Hospital in London (£5,000 for equipment for treating diabetics).

The interest in peace and reconciliation was represented by £5,000 to KOLOT in Israel and £6,000 for Religious Women for the Sanctity of Life.

As well as the British Museum grant mentioned above, a grant of £3,000 was made to the South Bank Centre for its education programme. The former museum also received a further £20,000 to support its campaign against the introduction of admission charges.

There is a special interest in the odd, unusual or unforeseeable situation that falls outside normal funding categories. For example, a recent grant was to help a small charity that had received a large but complex legacy, and lacked the resources to pay for the necessary legal fees, to realise its benefaction in a tax-effective way. Applications for the mainstream work or projects of established charities seem, to this editor, to be unlikely to be successful.

Exclusions

Expeditions, scholarships, missionary activities (of any religions), private education or healthcare where state provision exists. Grants are very rarely made to individuals (and then only if the application comes from a charity).

Applications

In writing to the correspondent, but see above.

The Charities Aid Foundation

Charity management and finance

£995,000 (1999/2000)

Kings Hill, West Malling, Kent ME19 4TA

Tel. 01732 520031 **Fax** 01732 520001

e-mail enquiries@caf.charitynet.org

website www.CAFonline.org/caf

Correspondent Judith McQuillan, Grants Administrator

Trustees *Grants Council: David Carrington, Chair; John Bateman (young people); Susan Cordingley (voluntary action in general); Babu Bhattacherjee (voluntary action in general); Yogesh Chauhan (black & ethnic minorities); Gillian Crosby (elderly people); David Eggleston (children); Revd John Kennedy (religious matters); Jane Lewis (science and education); Gary McKeone (cultural activities); Dorothy McGahan (people with physical disabilities); Prof. David Landon (medicine and health); Ceridwen Roberts (family matters); Miranda Spitteler (aid to developing countries); Peter Woodward (environmental issues).*

Information available Guidelines for applicants (largely reprinted below), annual report and accounts and exemplary further information about the charity's grantmaking are available from the foundation.

Summary

Grants of up to £10,000, but averaging half that, are made to help all except very large charities secure their financial and managerial viability. More than half the expenditure is to enable charities to obtain the consultancy or fundraising help they need.

There is an additional and important ethnic minorities fund, described below, and a new budget for helping 'second tier' or umbrella organisations. There are also smaller funds administered by the grants council for neurological research, welfare charities and for the support, directly or through intermediary charities, of needy Scottish or French individuals.

General

The Charities Aid Foundation's main activities lie in providing financial services, some of them invaluable, to the voluntary sector. Grantmaking is a relatively minor part of its work, and is conducted by a separate grants council. It is a model programme, focused, important and effective.

Guidelines for applicants

The foundation's guidelines for its main programmes describe its grantmaking as follows:

The Charities Aid Foundation makes grants to enable charities to improve their management and effectiveness. Grants are made to assist a charity

- to improve its effectiveness in meeting its objectives;
- to improve its use of financial resources, facilities, members, staff or volunteers;
- to improve its strength or sustainability;
- to research or move into new areas of need;
- in exceptional and unforeseen circumstances, to meet an emergency financial setback or to provide a single injection of funds to maintain the viability of the charitable organisation;
- training needed to achieve the above objectives (not routine staff training);
- staff funding only in fulfilling the above (not regular/core costs).

The CAF Grants Council are particularly interested in funding applications with a wide and lasting benefit and work which will improve the capacity, strength and sustainability of a charitable organisation. For example, if the charitable organisation seeks a grant for funding a consultant (fundraising or strategic review), the Council are keen to see how lasting benefit and transfer of knowledge to in-house staff or volunteers will be achieved.

Grants are for

- small and medium charitable organisations, with a maximum total income of £1 million; (Preference is given to those with limited freely available funds or insufficient reserves to meet the need themselves.)
- any registered (or Inland Revenue approved) organisation anywhere in the UK;
- charitable organisations of all types of organisation and beneficiary group (bar exceptions below, under Exclusions);
- a maximum of £10,000 (the average grant in 1999/2000 was £4,400).

Grants council annual review 1999/2000

The programme is described below in the words of the grant council's annual review for 1999/2000, somewhat abbreviated. Among other things, this comprehensive account demonstrates the difficulty of achieving an equitable distribution across England, even by an energetic and enlightened grantmaker, and one which is particularly well known throughout the voluntary sector.

London, South West and South East England received 45% of the regionally distributed money (national organisations excluded) and the rest of England received 17%. The population figures of the two halves of the country are similar. In these editors' view the continuing scale of this problem calls for funders to take proactive steps to change the common pattern, especially those such as CAF whose example is most likely to be followed by others.

Introduction

In 1999/2000 a total of 246 applications were considered by the Grants Council and 182 grants were made. The grants made using CAF's criteria, from the Foundation's own funds, special donor funds and from funds distributed on behalf of trust or company clients totalled £802,000. This compares with 136 grants made in the period 1998/99 that totalled £564,000, an increase of 34% on the number of grants and 42% on the amount distributed. The average grant amount has increased from £4,100 (1998/99) to £4,400 (1999/2000).

Of the £802,000 distributed, £60,000 went towards supporting second tier groups such as councils for voluntary service and other umbrella organisations in the UK.

In addition to the £802,000, £130,000 was allocated under a second initiative to assist black and ethnic minority groups. The Ethnic Minorities Fund distributed 66 grants ... under the guidance of a separate advisory group which made recommendations to the Grants Council based on different criteria to the main grants programme.

Range and level of grants

The majority of grants awarded in 1999/2000 were for £5,000 or less (62%) as was the case in 1998/99. However in money terms £453,000 (56%) of the total given was in grants of over £5,000. In 1998/99 only 38% of the total grants given were for more than £5,000. Five of the grants were below £1,000, three less than last year, and five were at the maximum level of £10,000, one more than last year.

	No. of grants	*Total*
Up to £3,000	40	£70,000
£3,001–£5,000	73	£279,000
£5,001–£8,000	53	£308,500
£8,001–£10,000	16	£144,100
Totals	182	£801,600

The greatest number of grants, 61 (34%), was made to charities with an income of between £100,000 and £250,000. Only 3% of grants went to charities with incomes above £1 million. The average income was £219,000.

The purpose of grants

As in previous years the largest proportion of grant money was made to assist with fundraising (40%), followed by funds for organisational reviews, business planning and general consultancy fees (16%).

The recently included IT grant details have changed little since their introduction last year; they again represent 12 of the grants although the amount of these grants has increased slightly from £39k to £43,000.

The amount granted towards staff training has increased by 210% since 1998/99 and now represents £69,000 (9%) of the total compared to the previous £22,000 (4%).

	No. of grants	*Amount*	
Staff fundraiser	28	£161,000	20%
Fundraising consultant	38	£161,000	20%
Org. review/business planning consultant	33	£127,000	16%
Other consultant	13	£45,000	6%
IT (software, consultancy, training)	12	£43,000	5%
Staff training	20	£69,000	9%
Provision of training	5	£18,000	2%
Financial setback	11	£68,000	8%
Pilot project/ feasibility study	13	£62,000	8%
Other	9	£50,000	6%

Second tier initiative

Almost 700 (25%) of the total number of application packs requested during 1999/2000 were in response to the introduction of the second tier initiative which was launched in June and distributed at the September and November meetings. Seventeen grants were made under the initiative and a total of £60,000 was distributed to groups such as councils for voluntary service and other umbrella organisations in the UK.

These second tier organisations are essential to the voluntary sector, however, due to their nature, often struggle to attract funding. The money was used to maintain the development of these organisations and to address particular areas of need. In addition £1,300 was set aside to provide two days initial diagnostic consultancy to two applicants.

Ten councils for voluntary service were given a total of £34,000 and five other umbrella organisations were given £25,000. Several of these grants can be seen to have had a multiplier effect as the second tier organisations used them to help the smaller groups affiliated to them. For example, four grants given under the initiative for the provision of training programmes for member groups, the creation of a website and development of a brokerage scheme between local businesses and voluntary groups meant almost 300 smaller affiliated groups have benefited.

In addition to the funds that were distributed to CAF's criteria, which included the Second Tier Initiative, the Grants Council oversaw the distribution of a further £399,000 usually with the assistance of specialist advisory groups.

CAF ethnic minorities fund

During 1999/2000 the Ethnic Minorities Fund was allocated £130,000 for the purpose of making grants to black and ethnic minority groups and organisations. 1,698 application packs were requested. 265 completed applications were returned.

The Ethnic Minorities Fund Advisory Group met to consider applications in September 1999 and in January and March 2000; they considered 100 applications for grant aid over the three meetings. The amount requested was £344,000, almost three times the amount available for distribution. 66 grants were made, a total of £129,000.

Four applications to the Ethnic Minorities Fund were transferred at the Advisory Group's meetings for consideration in the main grants programme. These were the Consortium of Bengali Associations, The Chara Trust, Southampton Voluntary Services and Race on the Agenda. The first three of these were awarded grants for the training of local groups and Race on the Agenda was awarded a grant for business planning.

Three of the organisations that received grants from the Ethnic Minorities Fund had originally applied to CAF's main grants programme. The Advisory Group thought that the proposals from the Confederation of Indian Organisations, London African Volunteers Network and NMP Anti-Racist Trust would be more suitably considered by the Ethnic Minorities Fund Advisory Group than by the main Grants Council.

Sixty-six grants totalling £129,000 were made. The range of the grants was from £400 to £4,000, the average being £1,952. Eight of the grants were for £1,000 or less while only two were at the maximum level of £4,000.

The Ethnic Minorities Fund has focused on 'visible' minorities, i.e. those communities that have experienced racism and discrimination on account of the colour of their skin and particular country of origin. The following figures come from self-definitions made by the organisations with regards to which ethnic minority groups they mainly support.

Groups run by or for the black community received the most support with 28 grants (42%) amounting to £53,000 (41%) of the total grants awarded, as was the case in 1998/99. Twenty-two grants totalling £40,000 (32%) of the funds available were given to groups working with the Asian community, either Pakistani, Indian, Bangladeshi or a combination.

Other funds administered by the CAF grants council

Patrick Berthoud Charitable Trust

During the year 1999/2000 £184,000 was spent on grants to charities under the Small Grants Programme and in continuing support to five Patrick Berthoud Fellows. During the year two of the Fellows completed their fellowships and have taken up posts in the UK. At its yearly meeting the Advisory Group recommended four grants totalling £24,000 to neurological research charities under the Small Grants Programme for consumables and to purchase equipment. However it was not possible to recommend the award of any fellowships.

Betard Bequest

Thirty-seven grants totalling £33,000 were made during 1999/2000 to assist arthritis sufferers or to elderly and needy Scottish and French individuals through this trust. Twenty-two of these went to individuals and 15 to charities to distribute to eligible individuals.

Frognal Trust

Seventy-eight grants were distributed on behalf of the Trustees of the Frognal Trust, a total of £63,000. These grants were made to assist charities for the benefit of the elderly, children, blind, handicapped, medical research and environmental heritage.

Grants in 1999/2000

The following is just a short section of the overall grants list, to give readers a flavour of the work being supported:

SHAD Haringey – £6,000, to make good the deficit caused by the unforeseen loss of a major care package being provided by the charity to a disabled person.

Shankill Women's Centre – £4,000, towards the costs of a residential strategic planning exercise.

Sheffield Law Centre – £7,000, to conduct a feasibility study on a project on family friendly working, with the aim of improving and safeguarding working conditions and employment opportunities for women with family commitments.

Soho Family Centre Trust – £3,000, to cover the fees of a consultant to develop a fundraising strategy.

Southampton Voluntary Services – £3,000 to cover the fees of a consultant to deliver a training programme to local black and ethnic minority groups.

South Sudanese Community Association – £4,500, to cover consultancy fees to assist in the production and implementation of a business plan and to develop operational systems and plans.

Southwark Festival Association – £6,000, towards the salary of a fundraiser and development officer.

South Yorkshire Funding Advice Bureau – £5,000, to cover the fees of a consultant to carry out an evaluation of the information service.

Spadework – £6,000, towards the cost of carrying out a review of services and developing a strategic plan.

Suffolk Association of Voluntary Organisations – £6,000, towards the cost of developing West Suffolk Connect, a brokerage scheme between local businesses and voluntary groups.

Surrey Voluntary Service Council – £7,000, to cover the fees of consultants to carry out a review of the current status and operation of the CVS network in Surrey.

Survivors – £2,600, to cover the fees of consultants to assist in the development and implementation of a fundraising strategy.

Exclusions

Grants will not be given for:

- capital items, buildings, vehicles, maintenance costs;
- core, routine or continuation costs of running or expanding the charitable organisation and associated charitable appeals;
- start-up costs of a new charitable organisation;
- academic or scientific research projects;
- debt, deficit or loan funding;
- funding that should properly be the responsibility of statutory agencies;
- support or services to individuals or other beneficiaries;
- schools, universities or NHS trusts;
- work already completed or currently taking place or due to start before the application has been considered.

Applications

In writing to the correspondent. Grants are decided four times a year, in February, May, August and November, and applications should be received two months in advance.

Charitworth Limited

Jewish causes

£562,000 (1998/99)

Beneficial area UK.

13–17 New Burlington Place, London W1X 1FA

Correspondent D Halpern, Trustee

Trustees *D M Halpern; Mrs R Halpern; S Halpern; S J Halpern.*

Information available Accounts on file at the Charity Commission, but without a grants list or a narrative report.

General

This trust was set up in 1983 and its objects are the advancement of the Jewish religion, relief of poverty and general charitable purposes. It is particularly interested in supporting religious and educational charities.

In 1998/99, the trust had assets of £7.3 million and an income of £2.3 million, mostly from donations. This figure has risen greatly in recent years (in 1996/97, assets were £146,000 and income £338,000). The trust gave grants totalling £562,000, and paid administration and management costs of just £7,000.

No grant information is available for the last couple of years but in 1996/97, when the grant total was just £109,000, one large grant of £100,000 was given to Torah V'chessed Lezra Vesaad, and a number of one-off grants of between £1,000 and £5,000 to Cosman Belz, Finchley Road Synagogue and Pardes House School.

This entry was not confirmed by the trust but was correct according to information at the Charity Commission.

Applications

In writing to the correspondent.

Charity Association Manchester Ltd

Jewish charities

About £500,000 annually

Beneficial area UK and Israel.

134 Leicester Road, Salford, Manchester M7 4GB

Tel. 0161 740 1960

Correspondent J Freedman

Information available Basic accounts only for 1992/93, and even then without a list of grants, available on file at the Charity Commission.

General

In June 2000 this trust had still not filed any accounts with the Charity Commission since 1992/93. The previous edition of this book reprinted the information available that year, but it seems ridiculous to continue doing so.

The Charity Commission should not allow the trust to continue in this way without some explanation of what is happening.

Applications

In writing to the correspondent.

Charity Know How

Central and Eastern Europe and the former Soviet Union

£415,000 (1998/99)

Beneficial area Central and Eastern Europe and the former Soviet Union.

114–118 Southampton Row, London WC1B 5AA

Tel. 020 7400 2315 **Fax** 020 7404 1331

e-mail ckh@caf.charitynet.org

website www.charityknowhow.org

Correspondent Andrew Kingman, Director

Trustees *Trustees of the Charities Aid Foundation (see separate entry).*
Grants Committee: representatives from the fund's contributors.

Information available The fund publishes a clear and informative annual report, applicant guidelines and an application form.

Summary

Grants, seldom for more than £10,000, are made to pairs of organisations seeking to work in partnership for the development of NGO activity in the areas stated above. About a third of the expenditure is for proactive programmes by CKH and a selected local partner.

General

Charity Know How is a joint initiative of a group of grant-making trusts and of the Department for International Development. It is a grant-making organisation established in 1991 to assist the revitalisation of the voluntary sector in Central and Eastern Europe and the republics of the former Soviet Union.

The aim of CKH funding is to enhance the transfer of skills and know how and to form productive and supportive links between NGOs in the region and the UK.

The following list of the grants made in 1998 for work in Latvia will give a feel for the kind of project that is supported:

Applicant: The Latvian Portage Association

Partner: Friends of North Kent Portage

The project builds on previous work conducted between the partners. Three trainers conducted training courses in the Portage method, with approximately 60 participants. The Portage method is developed to assist the development of children with disabilities.

Project total: £7,478

Applicant: NGO Centre – Riga

Partner: Upside Down Trust

This project will see three Latvian NGO trainers:

- undertake an adult education training course in the UK;
- develop individual evaluations of the NGO Centre-Riga's training programme;
- lead follow-up training workshops for NGO personnel in Riga.

Project total: £3,950

Applicant: Powerful Information

Partner: Information Centre – Green Library

Participant: Environmental Protection Club (VAK)

The project involves an intensive five-day training programme to improve the effectiveness and efficiency of Green Library's information provision. An Information Outreach Programme will also be developed, with implementation to be monitored over nine months.

Project total: £4,783.

The charity offers full information about its work. Main points include the following:

Countries covered at present ... are: Albania, Belarus, Bosnia-Herzegovina, Croatia, Czech Republic, Estonia, Former Republic of Yugoslavia, Hungary, Kazakhstan, Kyrgyzstan, Latvia, Lithuania, Macedonia (FYROM), Moldova, Poland, Russia, Slovakia, Tadjikistan, Turkmenistan, and Uzbekistan.

Applications must include at least two organisations *from different countries* working in partnership.

The transfer of skills between NGOs known to CKH in countries of Central & Eastern Europe and the Newly Independent States is also eligible for support and therefore both applicant and partner can be from these countries without the involvement of a UK charity.

State-run organisations and institutions, professional associations, private schools, universities and organisations aimed primarily at promoting a specific religion are not themselves eligible for funding, although NGOs using their facilities may still apply.

What kinds of activity do we fund?

- Exploratory work aimed at further activity which includes a significant element of the transfer of know-how

- Visits to any eligible countries or to the UK to enable NGO sectoral and organisational learning and development
- Training programmes for NGO staff and volunteers, usually in areas such as financial management, strategic planning, lobbying, volunteer management, governance, fundraising, public relations etc, rather than in specific professional skills such as nursing techniques, artistic skills or journalism, although all capacity-building initiatives will be considered. Training programmes funded tend to be workshops and seminars (and very occasionally conferences) or short-term placements within organisations.
- Professional advice visits from charity or NGO representatives to assist with organisational aspects of an individual NGO, co-ordinating bodies or the sector as a whole
- Translation and adaptation of training or information materials for NGOs.

Exclusions

Grants are not normally available for the following:

- The teaching of English as a foreign language.
- The costs of offices, salaries or equipment (including fax machines and other communications equipment).
- Any building or capital cost.
- The costs of transporting humanitarian aid or medical equipment.
- Attendance at conferences where the benefit to NGO development is not clearly demonstrated.
- The administration of schemes for UK volunteers (e.g. working holidays).
- Core funding in the region or the UK.
- Full professional fees for any consultancy (although some replacement costs may be considered).
- Activities considered by the grants committee to be for personal rather than institutional development.
- Youth, artistic or cultural exchanges.
- The promotion of a specific religion or sectarian belief.
- Applications from individuals.
- Student programmes or scholarships.
- Retrospective grants.

Applications

There is a clear application form to which other material can be attached, together with comprehensive guidance notes for applicants. The grants committee meets four times a year, in March, June, September and December, and there is a published deadline for receipt of applications for grants about six weeks in advance of these meetings. Potential applicants should first read the 'Guidelines for Applicants' available from CKH.

The Childwick Trust

Health and medical research in the UK, health and education in South Africa, Jewish charities, equestrianism

£2,763,000 (1998/99)

Beneficial area UK, especially the south east of England, and with a local interest in the area around the trust offices; South Africa.

9 The Green, Childwick Bury, St Albans AL3 6JJ

Tel. 01727 812486 **Fax** 01727 844666

Correspondent Peter Doyle, Land Agent & Administrator

Information available Guidelines for applicants. Full accounts with a list of beneficiaries of £5,000 or more, and a limited trustees' report.

Summary

Up to 300 grants are made a year, sometimes for £100,000 or more, mostly in the UK but some in South Africa. Many grants are one-off capital donations, for no more than £15,000, but larger recurrent grants are given to regularly supported medical research and equine beneficiaries.

General

The trust's funding policies are closely tied to the interests of the late settlor, Mr H J Joel, a bloodstock breeder who had business interests in South Africa. Large grants primarily go to

- hospitals, for medical research;
- Africa, especially educational institutions;
- racing charities.

Smaller grants are disbursed more widely, with Jewish charities and healthcare featuring prominently. The trust says:

> The bulk of the grants awarded each year are made to charities that promote the health and relief of the disabled in the UK. The next largest proportion of grants goes to charities in South Africa due to the links that Mr Joel had there. For similar reasons, charities connected with thoroughbred racing and breeding are next in line and Jewish charities follow close behind.

Part of the trust's guidelines say:

- Preferential consideration is given to appeals received from self-help organisations and charities. The trust does not consider requests for major building works, nor for running costs, administration and salaries.
- The trust does not involve itself in annual subscriptions or recurring grants to charities. [*Nevertheless, of the top six recipients in 1995/96, four also received major grants in 1998/99. Ed.*]
- In general the trust does not involve itself in directly financing research for which very substantial government funding and/or grants from a number of trusts are available. However, limited financial support is given for small specific projects (particularly those involving the provision of equipment undertaken in various institutions and by certain specialist charitable organisations.)
- Normally, the trust does not support charities whose accounts disclose substantial financial resources and which have well established and ample fundraising capabilities.
- No support is given to any political, industrial or commercial appeal.

Grantmaking in South Africa is administered through the Jim Joel Education and Training Fund, which was set up to evaluate beneficiaries on behalf of the trust. A sum of £800,000 was transferred to that fund in 1998/99.

The trust's net assets and investment income both decreased in value over the year to April 1999, to £57,705,000 and £2,249,000 respectively (£58,097,000 and £2,308,000 in 1997/98). At the same time, administration and staff costs increased by half, although they remained very low at £26,000.

Grants in 1998/99

A total of 42 grants and 38% of expenditure went to South Africa, with the balance being spent in the UK. The report lists the top 150 grants. Beneficiaries include many hospitals, medical research institutes, national charities for disabled and older people, and Jewish organisations. Beneficiaries in the UK, where the locality was identified, were predominantly based in south eastern England, particularly Hertfordshire, Hampshire and Suffolk.

The top 15 grants, for £50,000 or more, accounted for 40% of the total expenditure. Four of these were made to organisations in South Africa:

- African Self Help Association (£112,000)

- Khululeka Community Education Development Centre (£82,000)
- West Rand Educare Project (£72,000)
- Early Learning Resource Unit (SA) (£70,000)

In addition, Ntataise Rural Pre-school Development Trust received £46,000 and Sekukhune Educare Project £41,000.

Three UK beneficiaries received grants of £100,000, as follows: Cambridge University, Professorship of Equine Reproduction; Guy's, King's and St Thomas' School of Medicine; Racing Welfare Charities, Suffolk.

Other UK grants included those to Northwick Park Institute for Research (£75,000); Animal Health Trust (£50,000); Great Ormond Street Hospital (£30,000); New West End Synagogue (£25,000), and the Imperial Cancer Research Fund (£12,000 to Clare Hall Laboratories, Herts.).

In all, 110 of the beneficiaries received grants in the range £5,000 to £15,000. Recipients outside London and the south east are more likely to get grants at the lower end of this range, such as the Hospice of the Marches in Wales, Percy Hedley Centre, Newcastle, and the Hospital Heartbeat Appeal, Leeds (each received £5,000).

The beneficiaries of 148 further grants for under £5,000, averaging £1,850, were not disclosed.

Applications

The trust does not issue application forms but the guidelines provide the following information:

- Applications should be made in writing on the registered charity's official headed notepaper. Ideally, the appeal letter should be not longer than two pages of A4.
- Detailed costings or a budget for the project or projects referred to in the appeal letter should form a separate appendix or appendices to the appeal letter and should provide the fullest possible financial detail.
- The latest annual report of the applicant charity, together with the latest available full audited accounts, including a full balance sheet, should also accompany the written application.

During the course of the written application letter, applicants should endeavour to:

- Introduce the work of the applicant charity; state when the charity was established; describe its aims and objectives; and define precisely what the applicant charity does and who benefits from its activities.
- Comment upon the applicant charity's track record since its inception and refer to its notable achievements and successes to date. Endeavour to provide an interesting synopsis of the organisation.
- Describe the project for which a grant is being sought fully, clearly and concisely and comment on the charity's plans for the future.
- Provide full costings or a budget for the project/projects, to include a detailed breakdown of the costs involved.
- Give details of all other applications which the applicant charity has made to other sources of funding, and indicate precisely what funds have already been raised from other sources for the project.
- It can be beneficial for the applicant charity to concentrate on providing accurate and detailed costings of the project concerned, thereby enabling the trust to make its own judgement as to the level of financial support to be considered.

Applicants can greatly help their cause by concentrating on clarity of presentation and by providing detailed factual information. The trust will then do its utmost to ensure that the application receives the fullest and most careful consideration.

Acknowledgement of the trust's benefactions by means of loud publicity is discouraged, but publication of details of any benefaction is permitted if carried out in a discreet and unobtrusive way.

CHK Charities Limited

General

£1,627,000 (1998/99)

Beneficial area UK, especially Gloucestershire and Oxfordshire, with few or no grants for the north of England.

PO Box 191, 10 Fenchurch Street, London EC3M 3LB

Tel. 020 7475 6246

Correspondent N R Kerr-Sheppard Esq., Administrator

Trustees *David Peake, Chair; D A Acland; Mrs S E Acland; Mrs K S Assheton; Mrs C S Heber Percy; Mrs L H Morris; Mrs S Peake; Mrs J A Prest*

Information available Incomplete and inadequate annual report, not sent on request but seen at the Charity Commission.

Summary

At least 200 donations are made a year, and perhaps many more, most of them for amounts between £2,000 and £5,000. The lists of grants suggest interests, not disclosed in the most recent annual report (1998/99), in Gloucestershire, Oxford and Oxfordshire, probably accounting for about 20% of the grants by value. There are also clusters of grants suggesting interests in environmentalism, in agriculture, in riding and other rural activities, including blood sports, and in (conservative) economics and business education. There is a reference in the annual report to small local charities needing 'a specific connection' if they are to be supported, but there is no indication of who or what needs to be connected with.

Large grants are also made (up to £105,000 in 1998/99) to a very wide variety of causes.

General

These charities, which operate as a single unit, have been endowed by members of the Kleinwort family, formerly connected with the Kleinwort Benson bank, and incorporate the former Sir Cyril Kleinwort Charitable Trust.

In 1998/99 the charities had an 'unusually high' income of £2,508,000 but only £1,627,000 was given in grants.

The 1998/99 annual report gives the following account of the charities' policies:

> The trustees' current policy is to consider all written appeals, but only successful applications are notified of the trustees' decision. During the year under review (1999) the trustees made a total of 212 donations ... and showed particular interest in charities working in the fields of education, job creation, conservation, arts, population control, crime prevention and youth development.
>
> In approved cases, the trustees will provide assistance towards start-up or capital costs and ongoing expenses. This may take the form of a grant for say three to five years following which support may be withdrawn to enable the resources to be applied to other projects.
>
> The trustees do not normally respond favourably to appeals from individuals, nor to those from small local charities, e.g. individual churches, village halls, etc. where there is no specific connection [*but see below. Ed.*].

The large grants in the year are a surprisingly mixed bunch. The lists supplied to the Charity Commission merely name the recipient organisation and give no indication of the purpose of the grant or, often, the location or nature of the organisation (despite the requirement in the SORP that they be 'appropriately analysed'), which makes them hard to describe – for example, a grant is described simply as 'Rudolf Steiner School – £2,000'. The largest grant went to The Amber Foundation in Wiltshire, which takes in young people in danger of wrecking their lives with drugs and crime to give them another chance to find a more positive life plan.

The largest grants were as follows:

- Amber Foundation, £105,000;
- Life Education Centre, £100,000;
- Oxford University, £85,000;
- Durrell Trust for Conservation Biology, £63,000;
- Health Unlimited, £55,000.

The list of grants is strikingly varied and names a number of organisations, often with sporting connections, that do not often feature in this book. They include Cambridge Female Education Trust (£5,000); Handicapped Anglers Trust (£5,000); the Shrievalty Association (£2,000), and the Uphill Ski Club (£5,000).

However, there are also many of the more familiar names of national charities, large and small. They include Youth Clubs UK, Who Cares? Trust, Transport 2000 Trust, the Royal Academy of Arts and the National Portrait Gallery, each receiving £5,000.

The annual report says that 212 grants were made, but these include a payment of £63,000 to the Charities Aid Foundation. Though it is possible that this grant was for the work of that foundation, it is more likely that it was made in order to enable CHK to make a large number of small grants using the convenient CAF charity voucher system. No grant for less than £2,000 is shown in the grants list; if the voucher system is indeed being used for the payment of smaller awards, there must be at least 30 of these and could be several hundred. The annual report should make clear the nature of this transfer to CAF because otherwise the statement that 212 donations were made, while technically true, might also mislead its readers.

The grants list is, despite the statement in the annual report, replete with grants, large and small, to small local charities, but only in Gloucestershire or to a lesser extent in Oxfordshire, which presumably is what constitutes a 'specific connection'. Two of the three Oxfordshire grants are to apparently county-wide bodies, the Oxfordshire Association for the Blind (£2,500) and Oxfordshire MIND (£3,000), but many of the more frequent Gloucestershire and Cotswold awards seem more narrowly focused. First, there were a number of grants for Gloucestershire generally, such as those for Gloucestershire Playing Fields Association (£2,500) or Gloucestershire Young Carers Project (£1,500). Secondly, there was a group of beneficiaries centred in Gloucester itself, including Gloucester Cathedral (£15,000), Gloucester Family Support (£3,000) and Gloucester Dial A Ride (£5,000). Finally, though there are occasional grants for other towns in the county, such as Cheltenham (£5,000 for the Association for the Transport of the Disabled) or Tewkesbury (£5,000 for the Abbeyfield Society), there is a distinct group of grants, some of them large, in one area in the Cotswolds. Beneficiaries include Badminton Conservation Trust (£31,000), Chipping Norton Theatre Trust (£10,000), Dormer House School in Moreton-in-Marsh (£20,000), the Heythrop Hunt Charitable Trust (£1,000) and St James's Church, Upper Slaughter (£1,500).

Exclusions

No grants to individuals, nor to small local charities, such as individual churches or village halls, where there is no special connection to the trust. Appeals from local branches or offshoots of national charitable bodies are normally not considered.

Applications

To the correspondent. CHK charities say: 'Appeals will usually be considered within three months, but may be referred for further consideration at board meetings which are held twice a year, normally in March and October.'

The Church Urban Fund

Welfare, Christian development in disadvantaged urban areas in England

£4,208,000 (1999)

Beneficial area Urban priority areas in England.

1 Millbank, London SW1P 3JZ

Tel. 020 7898 1729 **Fax** 020 7898 1601

e-mail enquiries@cuf.org.uk

website www.cuf.org.uk

Correspondent Angela Sarkis, Chief Executive

Trustees *The Archbishop of Canterbury, Dr George Carey, Chair; Stephen O'Brien; Vice-Chair; Michael Mockridge, Chair of Grants Committee; The Right Revd John Austin; Patrick Coldstream; Mark Cornwall-Jones; Richard Farnell; The Ven. Granville Gibson; Revd Eileen Lake; Revd Canon John Stanley; Dorothy Stewart.*

Information available Full information available from the fund. A general advice leaflet for applicants. The list of grants in the accounts covers less than half of the total value. Good website including application details.

Summary

The fund makes grants to community based projects that tackle issues of disadvantage, poverty and marginalisation in Urban Priority Areas throughout England. Its projects fall into seven key areas:

- community work
- opening up church and community buildings
- youth/children
- social welfare
- homeless/housing
- employment
- interfaith

Grants are normally to a maximum of £30,000, but most are for less than £10,000.

General

CUF was established in 1988 following the publication of the report 'Faith in the City', commissioned by the Church of England. The report suggested that the Church should 'set up a fund to help churches work more closely with their local communities to help people tackle poor housing, poor education, unemployment and poverty'. The fund describes its purposes and grants as follows:

- to assist Urban Priority Areas (the poorest areas of England) with grants, advice and schemes which directly benefit the local community
- to enable the Church to understand the needs and gifts of people living in UPAs and develop practical responses in partnership with others
- to influence national and local government regeneration policy through the experience of CUF-funded projects

- to bring in money that will allow our work to continue and develop
- operate efficiently and accountably, upholding the principal of equal opportunity.

Types of grant

There are three types of grant: project grants, development grants and small grants. For grants in Scotland, apply to Iain Johnston of the Church of Scotland Priority Areas Fund on 0131 225 5722.

Project grants

[These] are made in four grants rounds each year specifically to projects in Urban Priority Areas (UPAs) – the poorest areas of England – with the aim of helping specific communities face their challenges. Any project with a charitable purpose that is able to raise part of the required money from other sources and is linked to the Anglican Church may apply for a grant. Grants can be one-off payments covering building expenses or may be paid over several years to cover the salary of a worker. To apply for a grant, contact your diocesan CUF coordinator (see diocesan list for details). Guidelines for completing the application form are available online (see website above).

Development grants

The Development Programme works in partnership with faith communities, statutory and voluntary projects. It supports effective and radical thinking, within the Church and outside it, on tackling powerlessness, racial discrimination, physical decay, social disintegration and poverty. Seven substantial grants were made through the Development Programme in 1999.

To apply for a Development Fund grant, please read all the guidance, including the guiding principles, themes and the application procedure.

Guiding principles

- Proposals must clearly demonstrate benefits to communities experiencing urban deprivation.
- Proposals should involve partnerships with other agencies. These may be of other faith communities, statutory or voluntary bodies.
- There should be a strategic dimension which seeks to have an impact on the Church and the wider community, alongside a theological dimension which seeks to increase the prophetic impact of the Church.
- There should be a clear evaluative element, an intention to produce outcomes that can be models for others, and a process for disseminating insights and experience.
- Proposals should demonstrate the distinctive contribution of faith communities to urban community development and regeneration.

Small grants

[These] enable specific pieces of work to go ahead. The small grants programme has two components: small initiatives and project support. Awards range up to £2,000 and you may apply at any time, receiving an answer as soon as the request is processed. For more information, see the guidelines.

Small grants are divided into small initiative grants and project support grants. To be eligible for these grants, a project must demonstrate church involvement, be serving an urban priority area and be engaged in urban regeneration.

All applications must be made on the appropriate form and submitted via your diocese along with relevant documentation and the recommendation of the diocesan bishop. For more information, contact your diocesan coordinator or contact the Grants Unit.

Small initiative grants

Specific work: maximum £2,000

These grants assist communities, particularly the most disadvantaged, that do not feel ready or able to take on full-scale projects but nevertheless want to engage in work on a smaller scale that involves urban regeneration. This could include pilot work to test the need and the community's wish to become involved, or specific short term work such as youth and children's initiatives.

Credit Union start-up: maximum £1,000

The purpose of these grants is to enable the growth of credit unions in the most disadvantaged areas of England by covering their start-up costs.

Evangelical Urban Training Programme: maximum £500

The awards enable parishes to strengthen their Christian witness by taking part in the Evangelical Urban Training Programme.

Project support grants

Grants are available for social audit/architect fees, project development, and project evaluation.

Social audit grants

Stage 1: Social audit. Maximum £2,000. Research into the social need of the area, including consultation with the church and wider community.

Stage 2: Architect study. Maximum £1,500 (or 50 per cent of total costs) towards architect's fees, with evidence of match funding.

Project development grants: maximum £2,000

The involvement of local people and project users is fundamental to CUF's aims. These grants could be used for committee participation, project start-ups, brainstorming etc. Part of the grant may be used to provide childcare facilities during training.

Project evaluation: maximum £500

Grants are available for independent, external evaluations of projects that have been supported by CUF for three years and wish to apply for a continuation of their grant.

The fund profiles the following schemes in its 1999 annual review. Further information on grants over £25,000 made in the year is taken from the trustees' report.

Examples of project grants

Church/community buildings

St Mary's 2000, Sheffield: A £40,000 capital grant was awarded to ensure the continued use of this inner city church as a focal point for the community. The grant helped to unlock other major funding sources such as the European Regional Development Fund. Eighteen further grants of £25,000 or more were listed in the trustees' report.

Young people and children

St Paul's Family Support Project, Liverpool: An 'Out of School Care' scheme, started in 1999, was the latest addition to the project. Seven other beneficiaries included the Pathways for Young People, Newton (£35,000) and SPACE Project, Grimsby (£30,000).

Community work

Brixwork, London: A partnership with Christ Church North Brixton, running since 1989, has helped establish a range of community projects focused on the church, including a foyer providing training and support for young people.

THE CHURCH URBAN FUND – GRANTS IN 1999

Grants were categorised as follows:

	Amount	*No.*
Opening up church and other buildings for community use	£987,000	68
Young people and children	£742,000	64
Community (development) work	£732,000	59
Community (centre based) work	£642,000	61
Social welfare	£486,000	37
Housing and homeless	£411,000	24
Other (employment, interfaith)	£208,000	18
Total	£4,208,000	331

Social welfare
Dutch Pot, Paddington, London: £21,000 was given for salary costs to this club providing a range of services for elderly people. Five more beneficiaries were listed, including Churches Commission for Racial Justice (£80,000) and Christians in Hackney AIDS Initiative (£30,000).

Housing and homeless
York Nightstop, an initiative providing support for young homeless people, received £12,000 towards the salary costs of a part-time project co-ordinator. Four other listed grants ranged from £26,000 for the ROC Drop-in Centre, St Helens, to £36,000 for Crisis Fareshare South Yorkshire, Doncaster.

Employment
The Silai Project, Bristol: This project helps women from ethnic minority communities develop sewing skills. £24,000 was given towards the salaries of three key workers.

Interfaith
The Melting Pot, Bolton: A £30,000 capital grant went to this 'state-of-the-art' community centre, due for completion in 2001.

Development grants

Seven grants totalling £292,000 were made in 1999, the programme's second year. Projects included:

- a partnership with the Coalfields Regeneration Trust aiming to increase the church's role in reviving communities in former coalfield areas;
- a series of 'Taking Part' workshops, begun in partnership with the New Economics Foundation, to help local people to participate more effectively in regeneration;
- the 'Flourishing Communities' research initiative, which aims to assist churches in making a contribution to the government's New Deal for Communities;
- SEARCH (Social and Economic Action Resource of Churches in Hull & District) received £29,000 to pay for a part-time worker.

Small grants

Beneficiaries included Pan London Unit for Ministry on Estates (PLUME), Southwark Bereavement Care, Black Christian Civic Forum and the Inter Faith Network.

Exclusions

Payments for stipendiary clergy; projects and activities for which full funding is normally available from the Church Commissioners, dioceses, local authorities, statutory bodies or organisations for the conservation of historical buildings; charitable grants to individuals; direct support of other grant-making institutions. Capital support for voluntary aided schools eligible for statutory funding. Individuals.

Applications

Check with the fund whether a project falls into one of the supported areas, and request a formal application form. All applications for grants are first of all sent to the diocesan bishop, who will help put forward applications. They must be approved by the bishop before being sent to the trustees. The bishop is also requested to indicate the priority of projects in relation to the long-term plan for the diocese. Projects which survive this procedure will go to the trustees of the fund who may sanction assistance. Field officers also visit every applicant to help with applications.

The grants committee meets in March, June, September and December; applications have to be sent over two months in advance. Contact the fund for details of exact dates and of the relevant diocese contacts.

The City Parochial Foundation and the Trust for London

Social welfare in London

£6,115,000 (1999)

Beneficial area The Metropolitan Police District of London and the City of London.

6 Middle Street, London EC1A 7PH

Tel. 020 7606 6145 **Fax** 020 7600 1866

e-mail info@cityparochial.org.uk

website www.cityparochial.org.uk

Correspondent Bharat Mehta, Clerk

Trustees *Prof. Gerald Manners, Chair; Maggie Baxter; John Barnes; John Barker; The Ven. Pete Broadbent; Peter Dale; William Dove; Prof. Julian Franks; Patrick Haynes; The Earl of Limerick; Ian Luder; John Muir; Miss Jyoti Munsiff; Nigel Pantling; Roger Payton; Gillian Roberts; Robin Sherlock; Lynda Stevens; Albert Tucker; Lady Tumin; Jane Wilmot.*

Information available Leaflet on policies and procedures, annual report, a review of policy for the years 1997–2001 and an annual grants review, the whole being an example of good practice.

Summary

The foundation makes grants to organisations working for the benefit of poor people within the 32 London boroughs and the City of London. They are usually for development, project or running costs, with only a few small few awards for capital expenditure. Grants may represent a continuation of existing support. Amounts are normally between £5,000 and £50,000, spread over up to three years. Over 200 new grants are awarded each year. A further 100 or so smaller grants, averaging about £5,000 and for not more than £10,000 in any one year, are made through the Trust for London, also covered by this entry (and which accounts for £580,000 of the grant total above). The recipients are small – entirely voluntary, or with no more than two full time staff – locally based community organisations, independent of larger bodies. In recent years, four fifths of City Parochial money has gone to inner city based organisations. The foundation has, at present, two priority concerns:

- the need to tackle social isolation, injustice and exclusion;
- the need to provide help for young people (aged 10 to 25 years) experiencing poverty.

The foundation has noted that 'there has been significant underfunding of local initiatives to combat racial harassment and crime. In addition, few applications have been received from organisations working to alleviate poverty through advocacy for policy change. Clearly work has to be done to stimulate applications as both are major areas of concern.'

A range of new activities are being developed, and further initiatives are now being planned for the next quinquennium, from 2002 to 2006. The possibilities for these are discussed in the annual review for 1999, largely reprinted in the box on page 54.

The Trust for London

This trust works in an unusual way in that its field officers search out small groups and help them develop their applications. Indeed they will not even be sent an application form until such a discussion has taken place. For most applicants the

Trust for London grants will be the first funding that they have received.

As the trust correctly reports, because of its focus on small groups and particularly women's groups and black and ethnic minority groups, it has established extensive links with refugee and migrant communities and has built up a reputation with them as a sympathetic and approachable funder, adopting what it calls a 'funding-plus' approach.

Background and administration

The City Parochial Foundation was established in 1891 as an amalgamation of the charities of most of the 112 parishes of the City of London (though the five largest, such as the Cripplegate, also featured in this book, were spared).

The trustees are appointed by various other bodies such as the Corporation of London, the Crown and London University. In 1986 the foundation also undertook the administration of the Trust for London.

Throughout its history the foundation has been guided by two major principles:

- An awareness of, and a need to guard against, the tendency for benefactions intended for the poor to fall into the hands of a somewhat higher income class.
- A concern not to finance schemes which can be financed by local or central government so that charitable funds are, in effect, used to subsidise the statutory authorities.

The Foundation is in a period of some financial decline: 'over the past decade, the monies available to the Foundation for grantmaking have dropped in real terms, from a peak of just over £8 million in 1989 to just under £5 million in 1998'. It is to the foundation's credit that it has been spending its income, rather than attempting to accumulate further capital – many trusts appear to regard the capital growth of their investments as one of their charitable objectives, which it cannot be. Nevertheless the foundation might consider using its position as the leading charity for the poorest citizens of one of the world's richest and presently booming cities, for a fundraising campaign to rebuild and increase its endowment.

The possibility of doing this appears to be hinted at in the 1999 annual review which talks of bringing people together to promote the foundation's mission.

The foundation is energetic, thoughtful and carefully focused on the very poorest residents of London.

As this book went to press, the foundation announced the appointment of Martin Jones, formerly with the Camelot Foundation, as its director of grants and programmes.

Grant guidelines – City Parochial: priorities, policies and procedures 1997–2001

[This guidance is unchanged from the previous edition of this book.]

Basic requirements

The following will apply to all work funded during the Quinquennium:

- Applicants must demonstrate that their organisation is open to all wishing to join or make use of the services offered.
- All applicants seeking to work directly to alleviate poverty must show how the work to be funded will benefit the poor of London and how their active involvement will be achieved.
- The Foundation requires that monitoring and reporting procedures are built into the funded work from the outset. Emphasis will be placed on recording the way work is undertaken, as well as its outcomes.

Grant-making strategy: 1997–2001

Direct work to alleviate poverty

During the preparations for the quinquennium the Trustees were struck forcibly by the way in which poverty can lead to social isolation, injustice and exclusion in all sections of the community and by the effect of poverty on young people.

In consequence the Foundation has decided to focus a significant part of its resources upon what it regards as two priority concerns. These are:

- The need to tackle social isolation, injustice and exclusion as they affect individuals in any section of the community.
- The need to provide help for young people (aged 10 to 25 years) experiencing poverty.

The particular way in which these two concerns will be addressed is through grants to assist direct work only by means of:

- The provision of advice, information and assistance with individual advocacy.
- Local initiatives to combat racial harassment and crime.
- Support for education and training initiatives and schemes.

Indirect and strategic work to alleviate poverty

The Trustees also appreciate the importance of back-up and development work for the voluntary sector and will be prepared to consider applications to assist work in the following areas;

Infrastructure support for the voluntary sector

Experience has repeatedly shown that in the individual boroughs and across London there is a need for infrastructure support for voluntary organisations, and that service providers need to have the best advice, information and training to develop high quality services for the poor of London.

Advocacy for policy change

Work in the voluntary sector can highlight the need for policy change, and arguments need to be constructed and presented to the appropriate authorities for improvements. This is a legitimate part of charitable activity, provided it falls within the Charity Commissioners' published Guidelines on Campaigning by Charities. Within these the trustees will consider applications which aim to bring about changes in policy or service provision for the benefit of the poor of London. Such proposals must clearly arise from the applicant's current work.

Collaborative responses

The Trustees wish to encourage applications from organisations working together within one borough or across several boroughs to meet the needs of the poor.

Continuation grants, small grants and unexpected needs

In addition the Foundation will consider applications, which are for:

Continuation grants

It is recognised that some work does not easily attract new funding and a continuation grant for work previously funded by the Foundation may be appropriate for a limited period.

Small grants

Any organisation working directly to benefit the poor of London, except those listed below as exclusions, may apply for a one-off grant of up to £10,000.

Unexpected needs

The Trustees are always ready to consider proposals to address new or emerging needs.

Dissemination

In certain cases the Foundation will consider with the beneficiary how best to disseminate the experience or the lessons learned from the work it has funded either through local workshops, individual reports, seminars, or a publication.

Foundation's initiatives

During the Quinquennium the Foundation will continue to take its own initiatives. These are likely to include:

- special funding programmes for which applications will be invited
- local area based work
- alliances with other funders to deal with certain complex issues.

Details of the above will be publicised as and when initiatives are launched.

Grant guidelines – Trust for London 1997–2001

General policy and approach

The Trust targets small locally based community organisations with charitable purposes, which are independent of larger bodies. 'Small' is defined as being entirely volunteer or membership based, or with no more than the equivalent of two full-time paid staff.

The Trust particularly welcomes proposals from women's groups, black and minority ethnic women's groups and black and minority ethnic organisations. The Trust seeks:

- to have an initiating and pro-active role, rather than to wait for applications
- to ensure that its grants have a distinctive and particular impact
- to be accessible to small groups.

Funding priorities

The Trust will not make grants above £10,000 a year [*now reduced to £7,000. Ed.*] for capital costs or revenue costs. Revenue costs may be given over a two or three year period though normally with a reducing level of grant. Applications will be considered from small groups in any London borough as follows:

- any self-help group particularly women's groups and young and elderly people's groups
- supplementary and mother tongue schools
- organisations working with people with disabilities
- refugee and migrant groups.

In addition

- any small charitable group can apply for a start-up grants of no more than £500
- any small charitable group can apply for a grant of up to £1,500 for training costs.

Continuation grants

The Trustees will consider applications from some of the organisations previously grant-aided for revenue costs by the Trust. Further grants will not be given automatically but field officers will discuss with organisations what they require to continue effective work.

New initiatives

There have been two successful proactive initiatives by the foundation, through the Trust for London: the Small Groups Worker Scheme, and the Resource Unit for Supplementary and Mother Tongue Schools. The City Parochial guidelines above refer to the possibility of further initiatives during the five year period concerned.

These are now in hand, but potential applicants should note that they are generally proactive developments, rather than grant-making programmes.

Local area initiatives

There are now four of these. Two are based on foundation-led projects based on playing field sites that have been owned by the City Parochial Foundation for many years (in Greenford, Ealing and Bellingham, Lewisham). The other two are in the form of alliances with other organisations. In Kilburn a new youth resource centre has been set up with a group of local agencies and in St Peter's ward in Tower Hamlets there is a five year regeneration project in partnership with the Peabody Trust (which has its own entry in this book).

School exclusion

The foundation has put £100,000 into a project in Merton with the Bridge House Estates Trust.

Disability

£277,000 over three years has been contributed to the 'Count us in' strategic initiative led by GLAD.

Employability

In a fine example of the 'gap filling' role of trusts, the foundation has taken a lead in the establishment of 'Employability', through which 13 organisations are jointly working to ease the problem of employability for highly qualified and experienced refugees who are nevertheless finding it hard to get work.

The foundation funds activities across the whole of London. The annual review lists the number and value of grants in each borough. While useful, this information would be better expressed in terms of grant value per head; few people are able to compare in their heads a figure for, say, Croydon, which has a very large population, with ones for the smaller boroughs. Nevertheless it is clear from the figures that the most heavily funded boroughs have all been in the inner ring, such as Southwark and Newham.

The size of grants in 1999 was as follows (the percentage referring, it appears, to the value rather than the number of the grants concerned):

Up to £9,999	7%
£10,000–£24,999	29%
£25,000–£49,999	43%
More than £50,000	21%

New initiative grants

There were six six-figure grants, all to support the foundation's own initiatives, as follows:

- Greater London Association for the Disabled (GLAD): £277,000 over three years.
- People First: £264,000 over three years to support the foundation's disability programme.
- Bellingham Community Recreation Project, Lewisham: £186,000 in three grants for a project to develop an existing centre on playing fields owned by the foundation.
- Praxis: £180,000 in three grants to support the education of refugees.
- Council of Ethnic Minority Voluntary Organisations: £120,000 over three years for the salary for a London regional manager.
- Merton Education Business Partnership: £100,000 over three years for work to support children excluded from school.

Major grants

Organisations receiving the usual maximum of £50,000 or thereabouts included the following:

- Newham Council for Racial Equality, for a salary.
- Harrow Club, towards a café training manager.

THE CITY PAROCHIAL FOUNDATION – GRANTS IN 1999

Grants in 1999 were categorised as follows, by number and value:

	Number	*Value*
Social isolation, injustice and exclusion	93	£2,287,000
Young people 10–25 experiencing poverty	37	£599,000
Indirect and strategic work to alleviate poverty	33	£955,000
Foundation's initiatives	16	£1,165,000
Continuation grants	23	£376,000
Small grants	21	£154,000

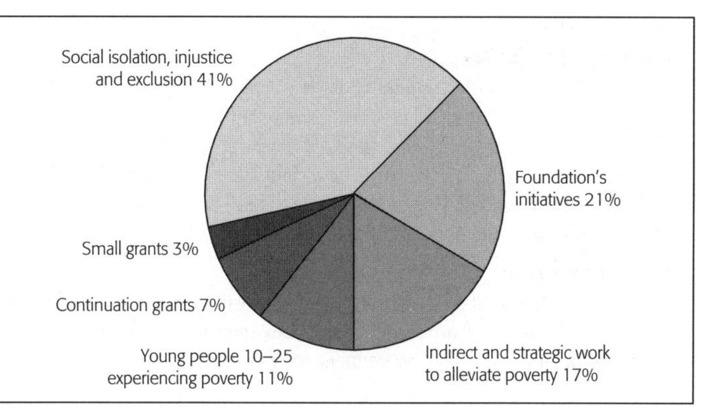

The City Parochial Foundation – Annual review 1999 (excerpts only)

Over the next two years, Trustees will be actively planning for the next five year period starting in 2002. Amongst other preparations, we shall be consulting widely to hear the views of others on the priorities that we might adopt.

Reviewing progress

The City Parochial Foundation and Trust for London operate in an environment where there are still high levels of social deprivation. Indicators show that the gap between the rich and poor is wider in the Capital than in the rest of the country, unemployment is twice the national average and thirteen of the most deprived local authorities are in London. In housing, 94% of the poorest council estates are in London – homelessness, overcrowding and temporary accommodation levels are well above national averages. Statistics for education and children reinforce this picture of high deprivation.

Over the past decade, the monies available to the Foundation for grant making have dropped in real terms, from a peak of just over £8 million in 1989 to just under £5 million in 1998. At the same time there has been no diminution in the number of applicants securing grants – thus smaller grants are being agreed for shorter terms.

While the Foundation retains a powerful influence both in London and nationally it has now dropped into fourth place in terms of pure financial philanthropy within the Capital with the arrival in recent years of the National Lottery Charities Board and Bridge House Estates Trust Fund ...

During the 1997–2001 period it is likely that the Foundation will distribute £25 million in grants to about 1,200 organisations, a small rise from the previous five year period. To date, expenditure on direct work to alleviate poverty accounts for almost half of the funds available. This amounts to three times the money provided for indirect and strategic purposes. Funding to continue work already grant aided stands at less than a fifth of the total spent.

Since 1997, four-fifths of the money available has gone to inner city based organisations, reflecting the greater level of deprivation in these areas.

Overall there has been a drop in capital funding. However, grants have been slightly larger on average but more of them are for shorter periods (that is less than three years). While targets have been achieved in funding some of the main areas of concern – notably combating exclusion and providing help for young people, and for education and training initiatives – there has been significant under funding of local initiatives to combat racial harassment and crime. In addition, few applications have been received from organisations working to alleviate poverty through advocacy for policy change. Clearly work has to be done to stimulate applications as both are major areas of concern ...

Another significant aspect of the work over the last decade has been the special programmes. These tackle complex issues where a multi-faceted approach is needed if an impact is to be made. The special programmes have included the Trust for London's Small Groups Worker scheme, the Resource Unit for Supplementary and Mother Tongue Schools, and the Foundation's London Voluntary Sector Resource Centre, local areas work, the Refugee Education Unit, the Financial Monitoring project, and, most recently, Employability to assist displaced professionals to access appropriate work.

The common feature of these initiatives is that they have required more than simple funding. They have grown naturally out of the grants work and have required active input from staff, Trustees and external advisors. As a by-product, they have also resulted in the Foundation and Trust acquiring a higher profile ...

Looking ahead

... There are a number of strategies which will be considered:

- To bring together all the individuals involved to enhance 'corporateness', and promote the Foundation's mission and values to benefit the poor of London
- To consider alternative approaches to grant funding, possibly through fewer, larger grants, or funding in tightly defined areas, or even a combination of these
- To develop more special funding initiatives
- To continue and to enhance the 'funding plus' approach including providing training, advice, possibly consultancy and thereby to influence other funders and policy makers
- To encourage advisors to help voluntary and charitable organisations by increasing their 'pro-bono' work with Foundation-funded organisations
- To encourage loan applications particularly from those seeking to establish independence, and move towards contractual arrangements
- A greater role might be taken by the Foundation – perhaps involving voluntary organisations with direct experience – in speaking out on poverty issues through adopting a higher public and media profile, and by meetings with policy makers to achieve direct influence. This approach would mean adherence to the Foundation's long held stance that voluntary bodies and charities are the most direct conduit through which to benefit the poor of London.

Trust for London

Over the first years of the current quinquennium there has been a fairly even spread of grants across the boroughs, though Hackney and Newham feature prominently – unsurprisingly given their ranking among the four poorest boroughs. Other features have been a low take up in the number of continuation grants while no small grants (of up to £500) have been made.

The Trust for London has maintained a number of distinctive approaches to grant making. In particular it has sought out small groups, many of which are not linked into existing funding networks. The 1998 study 'Trusting in the Community' showed that the Trust for London has been central in assisting a hidden and often neglected segment of the voluntary sector.

Moving ahead

Local area initiatives

As part of the 1997–2001 quinquennial planning, the Trustees commissioned a review of needs in London boroughs. One particular interest was to undertake work in quite small areas which may not have benefited from large scale government initiatives. Another aspect was to work in alliance with other funders, local agencies and statutory organisations.

Since then projects have been set up in four areas – Kilburn; St Peter's Ward in Tower Hamlets; Bellingham, in Lewisham; and Greenford. The last two are based around playing field sites which have been owned by the Foundation for many years, from the time when the Trustees recognised the need to provide leisure and sporting facilities for poor communities ...

School exclusion

In 1999 a mapping exercise involving five trusts was carried out to establish what was being done around London to tackle this issue. Subsequently, after meeting a range of academic researchers, agencies and the DfEE, a number of boroughs were invited to make submissions about what they were hoping to do and how they saw partnerships working.

As a result of this Merton was selected as an area where charitable trust input could strengthen the local authority and voluntary sector to make a real impact on school exclusion and develop and disseminate good practice. The Foundation and Bridge House Estates Trust Fund are directly funding the Merton Education Business Partnership while the Equitable Charitable Trust is supporting a project known as Jigsaw.

- Hamden Trust, towards staffing the new Resource Centre in Hampstead Old Town Hall.
- Federation of Independent Advice Centres, for the 'Kitemark for Advice' project.
- Ethnic Alcohol Couselling in Hounslow, for a salary.
- Enfield Voluntary Action, for the salary of a children's officer.
- Children's Discovery Centre, Newham, for the Director's salary.
- Bromley User Group, for a salary.
- Barking and Dagenham DIAL, for a welfare benefits officer salary.

Other grants

Few grants were for less than £10,000. Typical beneficiaries included the following: Havering CAB (£5,500); Hornsey Management Agency (£25,000 for money advice); Iranian Community Centre (£20,000 over two years for interpreting); Lambeth ACCORD (£40,000 over two years); Little Sisters of the Poor (£10,000 for water tanks and radiators); Midi Music Company (£20,000); Refugee Action, Kingston (£18,000 over two years).

Trust for London grants

These were categorised by number and value, as follows:

Working with people with disabilities	10	£53,000	9%
Supplementary and mother tongue schools	25	£89,000	15%
Refugee and migrant groups	35	£144,000	25%
Self-help groups	33	£111,000	19%
Continuation grants	5	£25,000	4%
Training grants	1	£1,000	1%
The Resource Unit for Supplementary Schools	1	£156,000	27%

A selection from the end of the grants list will give a feel for the kind of organisations being supported: Waaberi Cultural Association (£2,000); Wandsworth MENCAP (£12,000 over two years); Western Kurdish Association (£5,000 for rent and volunteers' expenses); Winchmore Hill Meet A Mum Association (£2,340); Women's Music Workshop, Lambeth (£3,500 for tutors' fees); Wooden Spanner Club (£4,000 for a motorbike ramp).

Exclusions

No grants for

- community business initiatives;
- medical research and equipment;
- individuals;
- fee paying schools;
- trips abroad;
- general holiday playschemes;
- one-off events;
- publications;
- sports;
- major capital appeals;
- the direct replacement of public funds;
- endowment appeals.

Applications

(For the Trust for London, see section below.) There are no application forms. Prior to submitting a detailed application, it is advisable to discuss the proposed application with one of the staff. It is required that all applicants adopt the following basic format:

- statement about the organisation: legal status, aims, brief history, staffing and management committee details, and current activities (reference should be made to any previous grants from the foundation or Trust for London).
- detailed financial position of the organisation, listing main sources of income;
- statement on the particular need for which funding is being sought;
- full costing of the proposal;
- details of other funding sources, especially applications to other trusts;
- details of the monitoring to be carried out on the scheme for which funding is being requested.

The above should be accompanied (where available) by a copy of the constitution; most recent annual report; most recent audited accounts; budget for the current financial year; the job description, if the application concerns a post; equal opportunities policy; list of names and addresses of office holders.

The application should not exceed three sides of A4 plus necessary appendices.

During 2000, all applications had to be finalised by:

- 30 April for July meeting
- 15 August for October meeting
- 15 November for January meeting

Applicants are advised to phone in to find out the new deadlines.

An application is only finalised when all documentation has been received, staff have no further questions to raise, and where, if necessary, a meeting has taken place between the applicant and a member of the foundation's staff.

In 2000 there were two field officers helping the clerk in the foundation's grant-making work, Ann Curno and Helal Uddin Abbas. Two new appointments were made during the year: Martin Jones (Director of Grants & Programmes) and Sara Bennett (Field Officer with responsibility for monitoring and evaluation).

Trust for London

As part of the applications procedure, organisations are required to fill in an application form and provide the documents requested on it. Application forms are not issued on request. Organisations are encouraged to discuss a potential application with the relevant field officer as a first step. If they are eligible to apply, the field officer will arrange a meeting.

Only when the field officer regards the process as complete will the application be eligible to be considered. All applicants must indicate what monitoring they will carry out of the work funded. Successful applicants will be required to cooperate with the trust's monitoring procedures.

The trust requires accounts for the previous year and the year in which the grant is provided. A period of at least 12 months must elapse between the trust making a grant and any fresh application. The decision of the grants committee is final.

The grants committee meets four times a year, in March, June, September and December. In 2000, the deadlines for completed applications were:

- 31 January for March meeting
- 15 April for June meeting
- 31 July for September meeting
- 15 October for December meeting

Again, applicants are advised to contact the trust to find out the new deadlines.

'Completed' means that all documentation has been received, staff have no further questions to raise, and a meeting has taken place between the applicant and a member of the staff.

Cleveland Community Foundation

General, in Cleveland

£649,000 (1999/2000)

Beneficial area The old county of Cleveland, being the local authority areas of Hartlepool, Middlesbrough, Redcar and Cleveland, and Stockton-on-Tees.

Southlands Business Centre, Ormesby Road, Middlesbrough TS3 0HB

Tel. 01642 314200 **Fax** 01642 313700

e-mail ccftrust@yahoo.com

Correspondent Kevin Ryan, Director

Trustees *Ken Kime, Founder; Sir Ronald Norman, President; Dr Tony Gillham, Chair; Michael Stewart; Robert Sale; John Bloom; John Foster; Chris Hope; Marjory Houseman; Alan Kitching; Kate Macnaught; Jack Ord; Mike Scott; Pat Sole; Simon Still; Bernard Storey.*

Information available Full and excellent information available from the foundation.

Summary

This growing community foundation distributes over 150 small grants each year, through a variety of funds, to benefit people in Cleveland. Grants usually peak at a few thousand pounds, though amounts of up to £50,000 are awarded from the largest fund, for education and training projects.

General

Like other community foundations, this charity is both building up an endowment, from it which it generates an income for grantmaking, and acting as an expert conduit for the charitable giving of others, both companies and individuals.

In 1999/2000 grants totalling £649,000 were disbursed through six grant-making programmes. Descriptions of these programmes, along with details of individual grants, were provided by the annual review for 1998/99 and used for this entry. Grants made in that year totalled £510,000.

Tees Valley TEC Distribution Fund

A total of £321,000 was awarded to 41 organisations 'for the advancement of education and training'.

The largest grants went to the borough councils of Middlesbrough (£50,000) and Redcar and Cleveland (£21,000); Branksome School (£25,000) and the Workers' Educational Association (£23,000). Others, mostly for between £1,000 and £10,000, went to various schools, colleges and other training providers.

Teesside Youth Development Programme

Funds are available to groups in Cleveland which seek to address the needs of young persons in the age group 8 to 25 who suffer from some form of disadvantage.

TYDP allocates its grants in three ways:

- Reactive – responding to requests.
- Proactive – researching areas of need and finding ways of meeting them.
- Competitive – funding the winners of competitions for the best youth projects.

In all, 44 grants were made, totalling £47,000, ranging from £180, to Sacred Heart Youth Club, to £3,500 for Belle Vue Youth and Sports Centre.

The Cleveland Fund

A general fund, giving 48 grants to a value of £56,000. The three largest went to the following: FRADE (£5,000 towards the cost of recycling surplus furniture to people in need); Teesside Common Purpose (£4,000 on bursaries for voluntary sector workers to go on courses); Teesside Homeless Action Group (£3,000 towards training and volunteers' expenses).

Teesside Power Fund

Grants up to £2,000, totalling £18,000, were awarded to groups in the nine wards adjacent to the Teesside Power Station.

Prince's Trust/CCF Partnership Fund

Grants comprised £14,000 to individuals and a further £5,000 to 10 organisations assisting people 'who are suffering some form of disadvantage'.

Voluntary Sector Management Training Fund

Awards totalled £4,000 in 10 small grants, led by £800 to the Voluntary Sector Training Unit, for bursaries.

Exclusions

Major fundraising appeals; sponsored events; the promotion of religion; holidays or social outings, and individuals.

Applications

Through the correspondent.

The Clore and Duffield Foundations

Arts/museums, Jewish charities, education

£6,984,000 (1999)

Beneficial area UK, but most money goes to London-based institutions.

Studio 3, Chelsea Manor Studios, Flood Street, London SW3 5SR

Tel. 020 7351 6061 **Fax** 020 7351 5308

e-mail clorefoun@aol.com

Correspondent Sally Bacon, Executive Director

Trustees *The Clore Foundation: Dame Vivien Duffield, Chair; David Harrel; Sir Mark Weinberg.*
The Vivien Duffield Foundation: Dame Vivien Duffield; David Harrel; Sir Jocelyn Stevens; Caroline Deletra; Michael Trask.

Information available Excellent annual reports and accounts. Guidelines for the Clore Small Grants Scheme for museums and galleries.

Summary

These two foundations, which are operated together, have overlapping trustees and derive their endowments from the same fortune, are seeking to amalgamate to become the Clore Duffield Foundation and an application to one can be taken as an application to both. '1999 saw the emergence of a new, strategic focus on museum and gallery education, through both a new small grants funding initiative and major donations to large museums in the capital.' In 1999 £3.8 million or 61% of the value of disclosed grants of the combined foundations was for major national museums and galleries in London. £688,000 or 11% was given for charities with specifically Jewish connections, including £338,000 for Britain's first non-Orthodox state Jewish primary school.

General

These foundations, in whose activities Vivien Duffield is usually assumed to play a dominant role, are increasingly focused on a magnificent programme of support for London's major museums and galleries, especially on the new world class educational centres within the British Museum, the Tate Modern and the Natural History Museum.

It is unfortunate that this is not balanced by a comparable level of support for similar work outside London, as the projects are being subsidised by taxpayers throughout the country. This would matter less if there were other foundations whose grants elsewhere might balance this London-centred programme – but, overall, this is not the case and these are leading examples of the way in which the major trusts as a whole are sucking money into London from the rest of the country.

The trusts point out that, because of the excellent new Small Grants Programme, grants by number are becoming well spread through the country. However, just because they are small, the overall distribution of the money is not significantly affected, and this is always the measure first used by these editors. Readers interested in the Clore Small Grants Programme for Museum and Gallery Education should see the accompanying box.

Annual reports

The annual reports for 1999 give an excellent account of the work of the charities. Where individual beneficiaries are mentioned in the following text, which has amalgamated parts of the reports of both charities, these editors have added the value of the grant concerned.

Whilst the [Clore] Foundation's interests have been wide-ranging, certain priorities have remained particularly constant over the years. These can be summarised as education, museums and galleries (and museum and gallery education), the performing arts, health, social welfare and disability. The Foundation has a particular interest in children and young people and all of society's more vulnerable individuals and maintains a balance between Jewish and secular causes.

The [Duffield] Foundation's interests can be summarised in three main categories: museums and galleries (and museum and gallery education), the performing arts (and performing arts education), and health, social welfare & disability. The Foundation is particularly interested in helping children and young people and society's more vulnerable individuals.

Although the Foundations have clear priorities, they are not bound by a rigid approach. They do not fund individuals, but they have matched lottery funding, funded capital re-developments and provided project, programme and revenue funding. Application procedures are flexible and the Foundations maintain a balance between supporting large-scale projects with far-reaching effects and small-scale local community endeavours, particularly in the arts and museums sectors.

1999 saw the emergence of a new, strategic focus on museum and gallery education, through both a new small grants funding initiative and major donations to large museums in the capital.

At the end of 1998 the Trustees of the Clore Foundation and the Trustees of the Vivien Duffield Foundation announced that they would be making donations totalling £7 million to establish Clore Centres for Education at the British Museum, the new Tate Gallery, Tate Modern, at Bankside, and the Natural History Museum, and to launch the Clore Small Grants Programme [£200,000 a year] for education work at regional museums and galleries. This announcement built on over twenty years of support for museums and galleries by the Foundations and marked a clear strategic focus for the Clore Foundation for the next five years.

The Clore Small Grants Programme

The first Clore Small Grants were awarded during 1999 when a total of thirteen grants were made (and a further eighteen announced) to museums and galleries throughout the UK.

In the first round of the Programme, eighty institutions submitted applications, requesting a total of £1,338,000. In July, in consultation with the Programme's Specialist Advisors, the Foundation's Trustees allocated grants totalling almost £100,000 to thirteen projects. The majority of grants in the first round were awarded to institutions in the North of England and the East Midlands, reflecting the high level of applications from these parts of Britain.

Other Clore donations

During 1999, major donations were made to both the British Museum [£1 million] and Tate Modern [£550,000] to fund Clore Education Centres within the Museum's Great Court Development and the new Tate's Turbine Hall respectively. The Trustees hope that this combination of large- and small-scale funding for museum and gallery education will enable many more children and families to explore their cultural heritage in exciting and imaginative ways and within purpose-built spaces.

The Foundation's first significant steps into the world of state-funded Jewish primary schools came with donations to Simon Marks School in Hackney in 1998. 1999 saw the opening of the Clore Shalom School in Hertfordshire, Britain's first non-orthodox state Jewish primary school. The Foundation's donations to the new school [£338,000] represented a major contribution to the world of state-funded and non-orthodox Jewish education.

A continuing concern for the quality of life for Britain's elderly population was reflected in continued support for the work of the Elderly Accommodation Counsel (£10,000), the only national body offering counselling and advice on housing and residential care for the elderly, and in a further donation to Nightingale House [£200,000], the largest nursing and residential home for elderly people in Britain.

The Trustees continued their support for the construction of the new Royal Opera House [£550,000], with donations reflecting the need for an international house in London which could present world-class opera and ballet to the widest possible audiences.

Other donations from the Duffield Foundation

1999 saw a number of donations to arts organisations to fund their work with young people, and particularly those who could only participate with financial support, such as participants in the Yorkshire Ballet Summer School [£5,000]. The Foundation continued its support for the Chicken Shed Theatre [£5,000], a London-based company which produces original participatory theatre through a way of working which includes everyone who wants to get involved, particularly those who might otherwise have been excluded from the opportunity of participating. The Trustees also provided support for YCTV [£8,000], a charity which provides disadvantaged young people with education, training and employment opportunities in TV, film and the communications industries.

The Trustees were particularly happy to be supporting Polka Theatre for Children in Wimbledon [£17,000]. Having funded a First Timers Scheme at the theatre in 1994, aimed at children who had never visited the theatre for financial reasons, the Foundation funded a second, and larger, scheme through 1999, involving five productions and 16,000 children. The Foundation also made a contribution [£10,000] towards the involvement of talented young musicians in the International Academy of String Quartets at the Britten-Pears School at Aldeburgh.

The Trustees continued their support for the construction of the new Royal Opera House [£505,000]. Other donations to the performing arts world included a contribution to the redevelopment of the new Sadler's Wells [£100,000].

Children and young people remained high on the Foundation's agenda beyond the sphere of the performing arts. The Trustees confirmed their commitment to the work of the NSPCC with a final donation [£50,000] to an NSPCC Family Centre in Bransholme, Hull. Bransholme is believed to be the largest housing estate in Western Europe and the Centre provides preventative family support. [*The estate contains the family home of one of the editors of this book. He notes that this is the only reference to support for its residents that he*

The Clore Small Grants Programme for Museum and Gallery Education

This programme, worth over £200,000 a year, has the following aims:

- To offer support to institutions which are striving to set in place successful education projects; in these cases, to raise the level of education work through support for new programmes and the development of good practice.
- To develop and extend excellence and innovation on education work in those institutions where successful education programmes are already in place.

The foundation publishes the following 'Guidelines for Applicants' (to be slightly revised in February 2001).

What will the programme fund?

Trustees will be looking for applications which reflect the following:

- the use of education programmes to enhance the capabilities and enjoyment of the public, whether in formal or informal educational groups or as individual or family learners;
- high-quality proposals which serve to create and/or develop meaningful access to, and use of, collections for enjoyment and understanding, and which serve to extend access to new users/audiences where possible.

The Programme will fund such initiatives as:

- imaginative education programmes;
- education outreach work;
- the refurbishment and creation of education spaces;
- handling or loan collections and associated learning materials;
- materials or learning resources if none exist and if they do not represent a significant part of the cost of the project;
- pilot projects for hitherto untried and untested programmes;
- initiatives to develop new audiences;
- INSET provision, if it represents part of a larger project;
- development of education volunteer training.

However other imaginative projects will be considered.

Value of grants

The minimum annual amount available for distribution, until 2003, will be £200,000. Institutions are invited to submit applications for sums between £2,000 and £20,000.

Who is eligible to apply?

Grants are available for all museums and galleries in the UK. Institutions may be local authority-managed, independent, university, non-national, non-designated, national etc. but all institutions submitting applications MUST have charitable status (with the exception of local authority museums). The Foundation particularly encourages applications from non-designated local and regional institutions. If in doubt, please telephone the Foundation's office to discuss your eligibility.

Points to note

Although there are some exclusions for funding (see below), the Foundation does not intend to be heavily prescriptive in terms of criteria as it is seeking applications which are needs-led, not criteria-led, and assessors will wish museums and galleries to approach this funding opportunity in creative and imaginative ways. However the following points should be noted:

- for the purposes of this programme, education provision can be defined as provision for school groups (and after-school groups), families, community groups, adult learners, those in continuing education and individual learners of all ages;
- there will be no requirement to seek matching funding;
- the majority of grants will be made available for finite periods of one to two years;
- Trustees will wish to see education policy documents where they are already in place. Where they are not, assessors will wish to see evidence of clear education objectives and plans;
- Trustees will wish to see that target audiences have been clearly identified;
- applications should reflect an institution-wide commitment to expand the educational role of the institution. Trustees will wish to see evidence that the institution applying for funding is also making or proposing to make an internal financial commitment to funding education work within the institution, and that the governing body has a commitment to the strategic development of education within the institution. Completed application forms must be signed by the head of the project, the head of the institution and one trustee;
- Trustees will wish to see an annual report, together with a separate breakdown of education visit/participation numbers and funding (i.e. the education budget figures);
- Trustees will wish to see provision for monitoring progress and for internal evaluation of the proposed programmes. Applicants may wish to allocate a small portion of the project's funding towards their own evaluation;
- Trustees will take account of plans for sustaining the benefits of the activity supported by the Foundation after its funding has come to an end;
- the assessment process will take into account the cost-effectiveness of the project;
- Trustees will be interested in the potential for projects to serve as models of good practice for other museums or galleries;
- grants will be made to single institutions, but Trustees will also consider funding partnership applications from two or more linked institutions;
- recipients will be unable to re-apply for further funding within two years of the completion of their grant.

Exclusions

Grants will not be made for the following:

- matching funding for successful lottery or any other funding applications;
- up and running, successful, well-tried and well-funded projects;

- post-funding, unless specialist museum educator costs form a part of a larger project;
- school transport costs unless they form part of a specific education project for which a grant application is made;
- research, unless it is an essential but minor element of the project;
- individuals, grants will only be available for institutions;
- academic research, academic publications and exhibition catalogues;
- exhibitions, unless they are a small component of a larger project;
- conferences or seminars (unless part of INSET provision);
- general appeals or endowments;
- the purchase of property or heritage assets.

Application procedures

Application forms are available from the Foundation and applications will be considered twice a year, in April and October. The closing date for applications will be the second week of March and September respectively – please check the precise dates with the Foundation. Applicants will be notified within six weeks of the Trustees' meeting.

has seen while reading several hundred grants lists. Ed.]

1999 also saw the launch of a major new visual arts education project for the Foundation. Artworks: The National Children's Art Awards. The scheme, worth a total of £250,000 a year, is an annual initiative supported by the Arts Councils and QCA, and still developing.

This foundation's contribution to the British Museum project was £1.5 million, and the Natural History Museum £200,000.

Throughout 1999 the Clore Foundation and the Vivien Duffield Foundation received a combined total of over 1,800 applications and the Clore Foundation donated a total of £4,002,926 to fifty charities.

Other examples of grants in 1999

C stands for the Clore, D for the Duffield foundation. An asterisk indicates that the organisation had not been previously funded.

Education

(C) Oxford Institute for Yiddish Studies:* £2,600 towards an annual Yiddish Programme.

(C) Farms for City Children:* £14,000 towards a 'First-timers Scheme' for Birmingham schools.

(C) Lady Margaret Hall: £9,000 for a feasibility study for a new library.

(C) University of Oxford Development Trust:* £10,000 towards the Vice-Chancellor's Fund.

Performing arts

(C) Broomhill Opera: £20,000 towards a production of *Der Silbersee.*

(C) British Friends of the Israel Philharmonic Orchestra: £33,000 in two general donations.

(D) Aldeburgh Foundation: £10,000 towards International Academy of String Quartet and Education space.

(D) Festival of Music:* £25,000, the first instalment of three donations towards a production of *Jane Eyre.*

(D) Yorkshire Ballet: £5,000 towards a Summer School.

(D) Philharmonia Trust: £10,000 general donation.

Museums, galleries and education

(C) Archaeological Resource Centre (York Archaeological Trust):* £10,000 towards an archaeological sensory garden.

(C) Brantwood (Coniston, Cumbria):* £10,000 towards the creation of an education programme at the former Lakeland home of John Ruskin.

(C) Burton Constable Foundation (Skirlaugh, East Yorkshire):* £12,000 to refurbish the old Brewhouse as an education room for school and student groups.

(C) Captain Cook Birthplace Museum (Middlesbrough):* £15,000 towards the creation of a Discovery Centre (decked out as a ship's living quarters, with handling objects etc.).

(C) Sittingbourne Heritage Museum (Kent):* £2,500 towards an Outreach Project in the form of themed loan resource boxes.

Social welfare, health and disability

(C) Ability Net:* £10,000 towards core services; 1st of 3 annual instalments.

(C) Marie Stopes International: £33,000 towards programmes in Albania.

(C) Manchester Jewish Federation: £21,000 towards 'Project Smile' and Children's Social Work programme.

(C) Passage House Appeal:* £250,000 towards a permanent night shelter.

(D) Help the Hospices: £50,000 towards Hospice House.

(D) Motivation: £20,000 for staff costs for special seating provision and a parent support centre in Russia.

(D) SeeAbility:* £100,000 as a general donation towards the cost of a new centre for young people suffering from Batten's disease.

Exclusions

No donations or grants to individuals, whether for education or any other purpose.

Applications

Applicants whose proposals fall within the foundation's defined areas of interest are advised to submit first-stage letters of application, on no more than two sides of A4. Institutions wishing to apply to the Clore Small Grants Programme for museum and gallery education should contact the foundation to request an application form.

The Clothworkers' Foundation

Clothworking, general

£3,452,000 (1999)

Clothworkers' Hall, Dunster Court, Mincing Lane, London EC3R 7AH

Tel. 020 7623 7041

Correspondent Michael Harris, Secretary

Trustees *37 Governors of the Foundation, including: Peter Rawson, Chairman of the Trusts and Grants Committee; Richard Jones, Deputy Chairman.*

Information available Accounts; annual review with full grants list, analysis of grants/grantmaking, policy and guidelines.

Summary

Grants are seldom for more than £50,000 and always for more than £1,000, generally for capital expenditure and in a wide range of fields. There is little support for major national charities or for their local branches.

Successful applicants are normally barred from reapplying for the next five years.

The foundation is notably accessible to applicants. Because of this, and because of the breadth of the fields of charity it covers, the foundation receives many applications and the success rate, even for those that fully meet its requirements, may not be more than about one in six.

General

The foundation, with associated trusts whose activities are also covered by this entry, is a charitable arm of The Clothworkers' Company, one of the largest of the livery companies of the City of London, a group of grant-making bodies often found remote and inaccessible by charities that lack personal contacts in this specialised corner of British society. The Clothworkers' Foundation is not like this; 'The Foundation takes great pride in the fact that it welcomes telephone discussions between the Foundation's staff and appeal officers when friendly, positive and helpful advice can be given as to what the Foundation will or will not support. ... Experience has shown that providing help and guidance over the telephone is a highly cost-effective, efficient and helpful service to our applicants.'

As this quotation suggests, the foundation sees itself as responding to 'appeals'. Although large grants may be spread over a number of years, they are still usually awards for single time-limited, discrete projects; the foundation seems most wary of getting involved with the support of ongoing work. It prefers to contribute to projects with a number of sources of support, rather than being the sole funder.

The foundation produces excellent reports and guidelines. Much of the rest of this entry reprints the bulk of this material, as it was available in summer 2000. However, the material does not specifically address the geographical pattern of the trust's grantmaking.

The geographical distribution of grants

The foundation is not restricted in its giving and, to its credit, appears to recognise its responsibilities to Scotland, Wales and Northern Ireland – a sizeable grant was made to each of these areas in 1999.

However, in common with most of the London-based trusts described in this book, there is a strong bias in practice towards the south of England, with the northern half of the country being ill served. For this entry, the editors analysed all 1999 grants of £20,000 or more (other than those for clothworking) that were for work in a specific UK locality. These amounted to nearly half of all non-clothworking grants by value. As usual in this book, England was then divided for this purpose into two halves of equal population:

Grants	*No.*	*Amount*	*Per 1,000 people*
South of England	19	£740,000	£30.26
North of England	5	£135,000	£5.52

The needs of other parts of the UK are fully recognised, and the charity would welcome more good applications from the north of England that would enable this situation to be changed. It may be that a vicious cycle has been set up in which the relative lack of grants in the area dissuades others from applying. Or it may be that the members of the company responsible for grantmaking have consciously recognised the needs of the most distant parts of the country but are unaware of the necessity for equivalent recognition of other parts of England. In the absence of a deliberate policy to seek a fair distribution, grants will naturally tend to go those areas with which those involved are most familiar – often those that are already most prosperous.

Grant-making policy

Introduction

All appeals received from registered charities, if specifically addressed to The Clothworkers' Foundation or The Clothworkers' Company, are considered and, in so far as these are refused without direct reference to the Trusts and Grants Committee, lists are circulated to the Committee and the Governors on a quarterly basis in case any Governor may wish to request that an appeal be referred back for further consideration.

General information

It is normally expected that a period of at least five years will elapse before consideration is given to further grants to the same charitable organisation.

Grants are made by means of single payments, except in the case of the more substantial grants, which may be made in up to five annual instalments.

Acknowledgement of the Foundation's benefactions by means of loud publicity is discouraged, but publication of details of any benefaction is permitted if carried out in a discreet and unobtrusive way.

In general the Foundation does not involve itself in directly financing research for which very substantial Government funding and/or grants from a number of Trusts are available. However, limited financial support is given for small specific projects (particularly those involving the provision of equipment) undertaken in various institutions and by certain specialist charitable organisations.

Preferential consideration is given to appeals received from self-help organisations and to charities requiring support to 'prime the pumps' for development and more extensive fundraising initiatives. Also to appeals to Textiles and kindred activities.

Normally the Foundation does not support charities whose Accounts disclose substantial financial resources and which have well established and ample fundraising capabilities.

Occasional support is given towards the relief of world-wide natural disasters, such as earthquakes, floods, etc., but such support is normally channelled through the charity known as ECHO International Health Services.

With certain limited exceptions the Foundation does not involve itself in annual subscriptions or recurring grants to charities.

The Governors of the Foundation, through their Trusts and Grants Committee, studiously avoid the introduction of inflexible policy decisions in order to preserve the breadth of charitable endeavour which the Foundation is enabled to support.

Grant-making practice

Introduction

The Clothworkers' Foundation continues to provide a clear message about itself and its activities with full entries in both the Directory of Grant-Making Trusts, published by the Charities Aid Foundation, and A Guide to The Major Trusts (Volume 1), published by the Directory of Social Change. The depth and quality of information included in these directories reflects the Foundation's willingness to give the fullest possible help to potential applicants.

The Foundation takes great pride in the fact that it welcomes telephone discussions between the Foundation's staff and appeal officers when friendly, positive and helpful advice can be given as to what the Foundation will or will not support, and as to how an application should be submitted to the Foundation. Advice can also be given on the likely scale of competition for funds; how an application will be dealt with and approximately how long it will take for a decision to be reached. Experience has shown that providing help and guidance over the telephone is a highly cost-effective, efficient and helpful service to our applicants. As a matter of policy, grant interviews are rarely given in connection with fundraising since there would be insufficient time for all such interviews during each working day.

Application forms are not issued but Guidelines for Grant Applicants are available [*see below. Ed.*]. All applicants must complete a Data Information Sheet which should accompany the written application/appeal.

The Foundation's Trusts and Grants Committee meets on six occasions each year, usually in October, December, January, February, May and July. The Committee's recommendations are then placed before a subsequent meeting of the Governors. Accordingly, there is a rolling programme of dealing with and processing applications and the Foundation prides itself on its flexibility. All applications receive the fullest and most careful consideration and are judged on merit and substance. Clarity of presentation and the provision of detailed factual information continues to be of the utmost importance. All grant applicants are encouraged to seek funding from a wide range of sources and will be required to provide details of funds already raised in support of the applicant's appeal. Each year, in September, the Governors of the Foundation meet for an annual Seminar when they have an opportunity, inter alia, to review the benefactions of the past year and consider the areas of need where their help might most usefully be given in the year to come.

Distribution of funds in 1999

During 1999 the Governors disbursed a total sum of £3,451,555 in the payment of grants to no less than 176 charitable organisations and objects. Unfortunately the number of applications, from registered charities, to which we were unable to respond in 1999 numbered 846. Each of these unsuccessful applications received full and careful consideration and each received a reply, even though we could not help them. The majority of these appeals did not fully comply with the Foundation's current Grant Making Policy. The total distribution of £3,451,555 was divided among our nine established categories in the following ways:

Relief in need & welfare	£859,106	25%
Clothworking	£683,650	20%
Education/the sciences	£503,940	15%
Children/youth	£434,570	13%
Medicine/health	£345,000	10%
Overseas	£257,250	7%
The arts	£192,150	6%
Heritage/environment	£140,500	4%
The church	£35,389	1%

The major new awards under these headings were as follows:

Relief in need and welfare: £150,000 for rebuilding at Toynbee Hall in London; £52,000 for a kitchen for the Bethshan Nursing Home for the elderly in Montgomeryshire.

Clothworking: £70,000 for textile conservation by the Victoria and Albert Museum (there is also ongoing support for the Department of Colour Chemistry in Leeds).

Education and the sciences: £100,000 for a project to develop SKILLS projects in schools.

Children and youth: £50,000 towards ships for the Sail Training Association; £44,000 for the Children's Trust at Tadworth, Surrey, for building.

Medicine and health: £60,000 each for a scanner for the Institute of Cancer Research and for equipment for work with deaf children by the Mary Hare Centre in Newbury.

Overseas: £40,000 to Motivation Charitable Trust for its wheelchair project in Africa; £33,000 to Action Health for a self-help project in the Nilgiri Hills, south India.

The arts: £66,000 for the National Theatre to replace its equipment to help deaf people.

Heritage and environment: £25,000 to extend Marks Hall Arboretum in Essex.

Compared to many of their applicants, whose work is often dominated by short-term funding needs, trusts can and often do seek a longer-term view. An illuminating example is printed as follows in the 1999 annual review of the charitable work of the Clothworkers' Foundation:

The amazing story of ECHO International Health Services is the realisation of the unique vision of Dr James and Mrs Peggy Burton who went to the Congo (now Zaire) in 1948 as medical missionaries and spent 8 years providing medical services and establishing a hospital in a remote area with limited resources. The Burtons returned to the United Kingdom in 1956 and Dr James Burton was appointed Medical Director of the Baptist Missionary Society in 1963 and, in 1964, launched a medical appeal to raise funds to repair and re-equip African mission hospitals. At this time many UK hospitals were being refurbished and offers of unwanted medical equipment and instruments were received.

In 1966, under his direction, a self-supporting agency, The Joint Mission Hospital Equipment Board Limited (JMHEB) began the supply of low cost medical equipment. The name of ECHO (Equipment for Charity Hospitals Overseas) was [later] chosen.

Soon customers from all denominations, nationalities and societies associated with medical work were buying supplies from ECHO. The scope of products expanded to include pharmaceuticals and an appropriate technology programme, under the supervision of a medical physics technician, produced a range of low-tech equipment products.

In 1999 ECHO celebrated its 33rd birthday. During the last year alone they have supplied more than £5 million worth of medicines and equipment to 130 countries. Some of these have gone to well known disaster situations around the world, but a great deal of their work has also focused on helping equally vital services in other areas which rarely make the media headlines.

The Clothworkers' Foundation have been long-standing supporters of ECHO, with a record of a pump-priming grant of £3,000 from the Clothworkers' Company as long ago as 1973. The Clothworkers' Company paid a further £2,000 in 1974 to meet the cost of a study by professional consultants into the trading activities and fundraising potential of the organisation and to finance its publicity and growth.

It was in 1983 that The Clothworkers' Foundation paid £25,000 towards the purchase of the then new premises at Coulsdon, Surrey, followed by £25,000 in 1988 to enable the charity to set up a Pharmaceutical Advisory Service. In 1989 the Governors of The Clothworkers' Foundation commenced the first grant of £25,000 for ECHO's Disaster Fund, and support on an annually reviewed and renewal basis has continued each year since 1989. The Governors of The Clothworkers' Foundation have chosen to support the ECHO Disaster Fund as an effective method of responding to world-wide disasters, and the Foundation accordingly does not normally make grants to disaster appeals on an ad hoc basis.

The Governors of The Clothworkers' Foundation are very proud of their association with ECHO.

Exclusions

Charitable support is not given:

- If it may go in direct relief of state aid or in the reduction of financial support from public funds.
- Directly to organisations or groups which are not registered charities.
- In response to applications by, or for the benefit of, individuals.
- By means of sponsorship for individuals undertaking fundraising activities on behalf of any charity.
- Towards the general maintenance, repair or restoration of cathedrals, abbeys, churches or other ecclesiastical buildings, unless they have an existing and long-standing connection with The Clothworkers' Company, or unless they

are appealing for a specific purpose which is considered to be of outstanding importance in relation to the national heritage.

- To schools/colleges in the primary or secondary sector of education (whether public or private), unless they have an existing and long-standing connection with The Clothworkers' Company.
- To organisations or groups whose main objects are to fund or support other charitable bodies. Assistance to individuals for educational purposes is limited; in London such grants are made through the associated Mary Datchelor Trust, details of which can be found in the companion *Educational Grants Directory*.

Applications

The Clothworkers' Foundation does not issue application forms. However, all applicants must complete a data information sheet, which should accompany the written application/ appeal.

(a) Applications from registered charities should be made in writing on the applicant charity's official headed notepaper. Ideally, the appeal letter itself should be no longer than two and a half pages of A4.

(b) Detailed costings or a budget for the project or projects referred to in the appeal letter should form a separate appendix or appendices to the appeal letter and should provide the fullest possible financial details.

(c) The latest annual report of the applicant charity, together with the latest available full audited accounts, including a full balance sheet should also accompany the written application. During the course of the written application letter, applicants should endeavour to:

- Introduce the work of the applicant charity; state when the charity was established; describe its aims and objectives; and define precisely what the applicant charity does and who benefits from its activities.
- Comment upon the applicant charity's track record since its inception and refer to its notable achievements and successes to date. Endeavour to provide an interesting synopsis of the organisation.
- Describe the project requiring funding fully, clearly and concisely and comment on the charity's plans for the future.
- Provide full costings or a budget for the project/projects to include a detailed breakdown of the costs involved.
- Give details of all other applications which the applicant charity has made to other sources of funding, and indicate precisely what funds have already been raised from other sources for the project.
- All applicants are, of course, perfectly at liberty to request a precise sum of money by way of grant. However, it can be more beneficial for the applicant charity to concentrate on providing accurate and detailed costings of the project concerned, thereby enabling the foundation to make its own judgement as to the level of financial support to be considered.

Applicants can greatly help their cause by concentrating on clarity of presentation and by providing detailed factual information. The foundation will then do its utmost to ensure that the application receives the fullest and most careful consideration.

Trustees meet regularly in January, February, May, July, October and December. The committees' recommendations are then placed before a subsequent meeting of the governors. Accordingly, there is a rolling programme of dealing with and processing applications and the foundation prides itself on flexibility.

All unsuccessful applicants receive a written refusal letter.

Richard Cloudesley's Charity

Churches, health and welfare in Islington, London

£800,000 (1999/2000)

Beneficial area North Islington only – map included with guidelines.

Beaufort House, 15 St Botolph Street, London EC3A 7EE

Tel. 020 7247 6555 **Fax** 020 7247 5091

Correspondent Keith Wallace, Clerk to the Trustees

Trustees *Appointed by the local council, the local Church of England churches, and co-options by the trustees. The Mayor of Islington and the Vicar of St Mary's, Upper Street are also trustees.*
Grants Committee: J Durdin, Chair; the Mayor of Islington; Revd G Claydon; Mrs P Bradbury; W Carter; Mrs S Clark; R Collier; Councillor P Haynes; R Turner.

Information available Comprehensive guidelines entitled 'Help for Islington Charities. How to apply for a block grant'. Annual report and accounts.

Summary

Grants ranging from £100 to £20,000 are disbursed twice a year to Church of England churches and charities benefiting the 'sick poor' in the ancient parish of Islington. The charity also has a welfare fund to support individuals in need of financial and medical help in the area. There are perhaps only half a dozen new beneficiaries in a year, with most grants, although referred to as 'one-off', repeatedly given to a largely unchanging list of beneficiaries.

General

In 1998/99 the charity's assets stood at £18,671,000. Income was low at £611,000. Grants expenditure, at £750,000, deliberately exceeded income.

The trustees aim for a 'smooth and rising trend' in grants distribution in order to assist the long-term planning of the churches and medical causes served.

In many cases, Cloudesley money supports a salary structure for a worker, or provides a worker with essential facilities. 'Stop-go' funding would jeopardise these essential, but inelastic, commitments.

About 300 enquiries were received in 1998/99, but it is difficult to know how many of these resulted in grants being made.

The charity's background is described as follows:

Richard Cloudesley's Charity is Islington's oldest and largest endowed charity.

It was founded in 1517 by the will of a pious Islington resident, Richard Cloudesley. He left the rent from a 14 acre field in Islington to be used for the benefit of residents of Islington parish.

The field was in Barnsbury and its centre was Cloudesley Square. During the Depression in the 1930s about two thirds of the land and buildings were sold, mostly to residents, and the proceeds were invested.

Guidelines

Geographic scope

Cloudesley money can only assist in activities in the 'Ancient Parish' of Islington. This is the northern part of the modern London Borough of Islington – roughly everything north of Chapel Market and City Road.

Obviously enough there are few bodies that confine their work to a small area like the Ancient Parish of Islington. We are quite used to helping charities in Islington as a whole, or Islington and nearby London Boroughs. What we ask is that you give us an assessment of the proportion of what you do that can be said to be related to people living in the Ancient Parish of Islington.

The geographic scope makes for difficulties in grant funds to nationally organised charities. Some of these have locally accounted branches – and others have locally identifiable projects – but without some restriction like this, we will be unable to assist.

Purpose scope

Grants can only be made to benefit the 'sick poor'. This means that both a medical and a financial need must be shown.

Medical need

The Cloudesley trustees take a generous view on what is a medical need. As well as supporting bodies working with conventional medical conditions – strokes, arthritis, mental handicap, for example – grants have been made recently to charities dealing with –

- drugs
- alcohol abuse
- sex problems
- victim support
- bereavement counselling

Financial need

The Cloudesley charities take the view that charities working in the 'medical field' – in its wider interpretation – are supporting those in financial need. Pure medical research, though, would be outside the permitted ambit.

Can other causes be helped?
Often charities whose work is outside the medical field may be able to identify some aspect of what they do which can be viewed as medical.

Example 1. Cloudesley money can't be used for prisoners' welfare but it is given for facilities in Pentonville Prison hospital wing. Inmates in the wing are seen as falling within the 'sick poor' test.

Example 2. Charities helping the homeless are outside the scope but any medical or health services made available to homeless people can be the subject of grant assistance.

Grants in 1999/2000

Full accounts for the year were not available at the time of writing, but the charity provided a grants list from which the following information was taken.

The largest amount, £158,000, was set aside for the charity's welfare fund, as is the norm, which made emergency grants to over 900 individuals.

A further 91 grants amounted to £642,000, divided between churches and medical/welfare charities.

In addition, 23 churches received grants ranging from £4,000 to £30,000, typically worth about £15,000 for the year.

Another 68 organisations got a total of £242,000 during the year. Single grants are seldom for more than £5,000, but about £100,000 went to six charities which each received £10,000 or more. They were the Assisted Living Foundation (formerly Islington Crossroads, £32,000); Islington MIND (£22,000); Positively Women (£14,000); CARIS (Islington) Churches Bereavement Service (£11,000); St Mary's Neighbourhood Centre, Upper Street (£10,000), and In Touch – Islington (£10,000).

Other beneficiaries included The Angel Drug Project (£7,000); Islington People's Rights, which helps disabled people obtain benefits (£4,000); Turkish Cypriot Elderly Group (£2,500 for equipment and transport); Finsbury Park Homeless Families Project (£2,000 for health related services); The Cot Death Society (£1,600 for alarms), and Islington Dyslexia (£500 for computer equipment).

Exclusions

Applicants must fall within the geographic and purposes scope of the charity.

Applications

The guidelines say:

If you think your charity is going to be able to qualify for consideration of a grant, write first to the Clerk to the Charity. You will than get an application form. Applications should be:

- timely
- in writing
- supported by accounts

If you would like us to acknowledge your application, please send a self-addressed envelope. Otherwise, to save expense, we will not confirm safe receipt.

Block grants are considered twice a year, around late April, and early November at a Grants Committee meeting.

Recommendations are made by the Grants Committee at these meetings and are reviewed and authorised by the Cloudesley trustees as a whole two weeks later. The trustees normally adopt all the recommendations.

We need to know what work your charity does, how it fits within [our] geographical scope and purpose scope and the purpose for which you are seeking a grant. So long as this is clearly set out, we do not need a great deal of detail.

We place a great deal of importance on receiving the accounts of the charities we fund so please be sure to send these each time you apply.

We will give brief reasons with any application that is not successful.

The John S Cohen Foundation

The foundation is in the process of being wound up and its remaining assets are being transferred to the David Cohen Family Charitable Trust (see *A Guide to the Major Trusts Volume 2*).

Sir James Colyer-Fergusson's Charitable Trust

Church buildings, general, in Kent and Suffolk

£790,000 (1999/2000)

Beneficial area UK, but Kent and Suffolk for all except the largest grants.

Suite 232–233, Friars House, 157–168 Blackfriars Road, London SE1 8EZ

Tel. 020 7242 2022

Correspondent Jacqueline Rae, Clerk to the Trustees

Information available Application form with a guidance note for applicants. Accounts with only a spartan report.

Summary

The trust makes grants ranging from £500 up to around £20,000, with occasional exceptional awards for larger amounts. Many donations are for Anglican churches' capital costs, but a variety of other causes are also supported.

General

The trust's endowment is mainly in the form of property, which made a loss of £6 million on revaluation in 1999/2000, bringing its assets down to £17 million from £23 million the year before.

Incoming resources totalled £748,000, and £790,000 was spent on donations.

The trust's guidance for applicants reads as follows:

The Colyer-Fergusson Charitable Trust makes grants to charities and churches in Kent and Suffolk aiming to improve quality of life, tackle poverty, social isolation or exclusion and protect the natural resources and heritage of the local areas for their inhabitants.

Who can apply?

Churches and registered charities (or those with registration pending) working or based in Kent and Suffolk.

Trust priorities

The trust currently has the following priority areas:
(a) Projects that involve the utilisation of church buildings or other church resources to the wider community and can demonstrate a practical need.
(b) Projects that involve the preservation of the natural environment and promote community access to these resources.
(c) Projects that are innovative or developmental and aim to tackle social isolation, exclusion or poverty as they affect the community.
(d) Projects that will use the arts to provide the community with a new creative experience or increase access to the arts in locations where access is limited. Extra consideration will be given to projects that encourage self-help; involve users in their management; have built-in evaluation procedures; will use funds to lever funding from other sources.

[*Information on how to apply and exclusions is reprinted under the relevant sections below. Ed.*]

Exceptional grants

Very occasionally the trust will make grants outside of Kent or Suffolk for projects of major national or international significance. However, these are exceptional and are not part of the application form process. Only six such grants have been made over the last ten years. If you would like to be considered for one of these grants please write to the Clerk explaining briefly (on one side of A4) the nature of your project. Please indicate clearly that you are applying for an Exceptional Grant. You will be asked to supply detailed information if the Trustees wish to take your application further.

By far the largest donation in 1999/2000 was of £400,000, to Balliol College, Oxford. The year also saw a final payment of £64,000 to the Tureck Bach Research Foundation, which had been funded since 1995. 'Innovative grants' totalling £130,000 were made to three churches.

There were 72 further grants, of which 33 were to churches. The charities supported included the Gingerbread Foundation for Lone Parent Families (£10,000); Holiday Explorers, Bury St Edmunds, and Ickworth Primary School (£5,000 each); Ipswich YMCA (£3,000); Dover Bronze Age Boat Trust, and Romney Marsh Research Trust (£2,500 each). Grants for £1,000 were made to national charities such as Scope, Cruse Bereavement Care and British Trust for Conservation Volunteers, and to local causes including Kent River Walk, Maidstone Citizens Advice Bureau, the Faversham Society and DIAL Kent (Disability Information Advice Line).

Exclusions

No grants to churches and charities outside Kent or Suffolk, other than small grants made from covenanted donations. No grants to:

- animal welfare charities;
- individuals directly;
- research (except practical research designed to benefit the local community directly);
- hospitals or schools;
- political activities;
- commercial ventures or publications;
- the purchase of vehicles including minibuses;
- overseas travel or holidays;
- retrospective grants or loans;
- direct replacement of statutory funding or activities that are primarily the responsibility of central or local government;
- large capital, endowment or widely distributed appeals.

Applications

All applicants must complete an application form and send it by post to the trust's office. There is no deadline for applications and all applications will be acknowledged. Trustees meet regularly during the year and decisions are usually processed within four to six weeks. All applicants will be notified in writing.

For exceptional grants, see above.

Comic Relief

(the operating name for Charity Projects)

Community-based UK charities, Africa

£11,505,000 in Africa; £5,010,000 in UK (1998/99)

Beneficial area UK and Africa.

5th Floor, 89 Albert Embankment, London SE1 7TP

Tel. 020 7820 5555 **Fax** 020 7820 5500

minicom 020 7820 5570

e-mail red@comicrelief.org.uk

website www.comicrelief.org.uk

Correspondent UK Grants Department; Africa Grants Department

Trustees *Peter Benett-Jones, Chair; Bisi Adeleye-Fayemi; Richard Curtis; Colin Howes; Mike Harris; Emma Freud; Matthew Freud; Lenny Henry; Melinda Letts; Claudia Lloyd; Eric Nicoll; Laurence Newman; Nalini Varma.*
UK Grants Committee: Nalini Varma, Chair; Dr Dorothy Black; Sheron Carter; Louise Casey; Jim Deery; Merav Dover; Fiona Ellis; Nikhil Gomes; Frances Hasler; David Johnson; Anthony Kendall; Nic Millington; Jane Minter; Hannah-May Murdock; Alison Norman; Saverimuthi Stanislaus; Brian Thirsk; Richard Wood; Zaya Yeebo.

Information available Excellent grant guidelines available from the charity from May 2001 for the next cycle of grants; available in big print, audiotape and Braille. Financial statements with a brief report of the trustees. Annual review concerned primarily with fundraising, and a list of recipient organisations and their locations, but with no information about the purposes of the grants. The SORP requirement that grants should be analysed and explained is not adequately met.

Summary

Comic Relief runs two grants programmes, one aimed at the UK and the other, the larger, towards Africa. This entry is concerned only with the UK grants as this book does not cover overseas grant programmes, except when they might otherwise go unreported. Full details of Comic Relief's Africa programme are available from the charity.

Programmes operate on a two year cycle, each with five 'rounds' of applications. The extent of grantmaking depends entirely on the fundraising success of each

Red Nose day. Policies for 2001 to 2003 were under review when this book went to press and new guidelines were due to be published in May 2001, but precedent suggests that the general direction of grantmaking may remain substantially unchanged.

Over 300 grants are currently made in a full two year cycle of the UK programme, with an average size of over £20,000, and with few grants being for less than £2,000. However 10% of the money is allocated for grants of less than £5,000.

Awards are made towards capital or revenue costs and may be single payments or spread across up to three years. 'Comic Relief aims to reach the poorest and most disadvantaged communities to help them take control of their lives and find solutions to the problems they face.'

The UK grant priorities from April 1999 until the guidelines for the next cycle are available in May 2001 (with the total of 1999 allocations) were:

- young people (£2,235,000)
- disabled people's rights (£1,218,000)
- older people's rights (£900,000)
- refugee programme (£70,000)
- domestic violence programme (no grants in 1999)

There is also occasional funding for other specific issues. There was no information available in the summer of 2000 about any such current programmes, but in 1999 they had included:

- rural development project (£475,000)
- special initiatives (support for 'umbrella' organisations) (£115,000)

Until August 2000 there was a separate programme with its own application form for grants up to £3,000, though there were only 29 such grants in 1999.

General

Comic Relief derives its revenue from the Red Nose day fundraising event that it organises with BBC television every two years. In March 1999 over £35 million was raised, a 30% increase on 1997. The charity does not have a separate endowment, but spends what it raises over each two-year cycle so its grantmaking is wholly dependent on the success of each event. Because of the unknown levels of future income, applications usually close about six months before the next Red Nose day (due, when this book went to print, in spring 2001).

Grant-making policy is revised on a similar cycle, so the information in this entry about past practice is not necessarily a secure guide to future activity, but the charity has maintained consistent general policies for a number of years.

Comic Relief has developed a superb reputation for intelligent and sensitive funding of some of the most difficult areas of social need, though the information publicly available to support this is unfortunately weak. There is a review of the effectiveness of grantmaking at the end of every two-year cycle, but the charity does not publish, and was reluctant to disclose, information from these reviews to help in writing this commentary. Some information was finally received on the very day this entry went to press.

Instead the charity talks about the number of 'case studies' that it publicises. These are doubtless valuable, but a charity taking this much money from the public should be willing to share its more substantial analysis of the effectiveness of its work.

The aims of the UK grants programme are to

- reach the poorest and most disadvantaged people
- support people in finding solutions to the problems they face
- give a voice to groups who face discrimination so that their views and voices are heard
- support groups who encourage users to take part in developing and running their services, or who can show they want to move towards users controlling the service
- increase public awareness of the needs, hopes and rights of the disadvantaged people we support
- support work which influences policy at national, regional and local levels.

This is expanded on in the Comic Relief website (which unfortunately does not yet include the guidelines for applicants):

What do we fund in the UK?

Comic Relief aims to reach the poorest and most disadvantaged communities to help them take control of their lives and find solutions to the problems they face.

We want to give voices to those who are denied them, and encourage disadvantaged people to be involved in developing and running the services and projects they use. We also want to increase public awareness of the needs, hopes and rights of the disadvantaged people we support, and to influence policy locally, regionally and nationally.

Comic Relief money is targeted towards the needs of the most disadvantaged, to projects that find it hard to attract funding, and to new and innovative ways to tackle some of the most entrenched problems in our society. We do this through five funding programmes:

- Young People
- Disabled People's Rights
- Older People's Rights
- Refugees
- Domestic violence

Earlier this year [1999], the UK Grants Team also developed Special Grants Initiatives, now closed, working with Travellers and Self Organised Drug and Alcohol User Groups.

The 1999/2000 guidelines summarised above show detailed sub-headings within the five stated priorities. It is not clear whether these were indications of particular interests, or whether projects within the general headings will only be considered if they also fall into one of the sub-categories.

The grant lists suggest that the grants are indeed rigorously directed to organisations working towards the general ends stated, and there are no grants listed to organisations clearly outside the guidance given. The following figures, by value, are available for the 1997/98 cycle of grants:

- black and ethnic minorities 23%
- rural 21%
- women 14%
- lesbians and gay men 2%

There is no analysis of the size of grants. For an examination of a sample of 100 awards in 1999, see the box below.

It appears that most of the money is spent in grants of between £20,000 and £50,000, and the charity says that 'the majority of larger grants are made for a period of three years'. No doubt many of these are paid over a period of up to three years, but there is no information on what proportion is for one-off expenditures rather than for on-going work. The decision to concentrate funding on a relatively narrow range of grant

COMIC RELIEF – THE SIZE OF GRANTS

(from a sample of 100 awards in 1999)

	Grants	*Value*	*%*
Up to £5,000	37	£168,000	7%
From £5,001 to £20,000	12	£158,000	7%
From £20,001 to £50,000	38	£1,223,000	52%
More than £50,000	13	£788,000	34%

allocations is unusual, but there is no analytical information about the charity's grant-making activity.

The high average size of grants suggests that much of the money may go to the 'salaried' voluntary sector and relatively little to the 'self-help' part of the sector. Though this is where most of the voluntary activity takes place in the fields described, the organisations concerned are usually operating on an altogether smaller scale than that implied by the size of these grants. It is surprising that 'small grants' seem to account for such a minor part of the charity's funding, though the lack of information makes it hard to come to any firm opinions on this.

The largest grant in the sample was for £75,000 (to the Bias Irish Travellers Project). Grants of £60,000 or more were made to the Scottish Drugs Forum, Women's Aid, Swansea and Brent Carers Centre, among others.

There is a two stage application process, with the cycle taking up to six months to complete. There is an excellent four page Summary Form for Stage 1 and presumably a more extensive one for Stage 2, but this has not been seen by these editors.

A very large number of applications is received, with only about 10% resulting in a grant. It is not known whether the charity makes reduced or partial offers in response to applications received. However potential applicants are invited to contact the charity in advance, when some guidance on such matters may, perhaps, be made available.

Reapplication is possible 'in the last nine months of your funding from us', but there is no information on the extent to which grants are the result of such reapplications. The charity lists six UK grants staff, headed by Gilly Green, and an overall Grants Director, Liz Firth. The charity also use outside assessors. The guidelines for the 1999/2000 cycle, however, give information on the criteria applied in the past to applications at the summary Stage 1. It is likely that these considerations also applied at Stage 2.

The charity notes that in the 1997/98 cycle 26% of the money was spent on activities in London, which has 12% of the UK population (the figures do not include grants to national charities based in London). The charity allocates 15% of its money to fund activities in rural areas. Scotland, Wales and Northern Ireland were supported at or above the levels appropriate to their populations, so areas faring worst, in relative terms, were English regions away from London.

Guidelines for applicants

This section summarises the guidelines for applicants for the 1999/2001 cycle (due to be replaced in May 2001). Applications under these guidelines are likely to have closed by the time this book is in print; they are reproduced solely as the best available guide to the policies of the charity. Under each heading, these editors have added examples of major beneficiaries in 1999.

UK grants programme – priorities for grantmaking 1999–2001

The grants we make in the UK support the work of voluntary organisations to tackle poverty and promote social justice. Our aims are to

- reach the poorest and most disadvantaged people
- support people in finding solutions to the problems they face
- give a voice to groups who face discrimination so that their views and voices are heard
- support groups who encourage users to take part in developing and running their services, or who can show they want to move towards users controlling the service
- increase public awareness of the needs, hopes and rights of the disadvantaged people we support
- support work which influences policy at national, regional and local levels.

What do we fund?

We know that there is enormous need and that our resources are limited. In order to be as effective as possible, we direct our funding to five specific areas. As a result we can only consider applications under the following five programmes.

- Young people's programme
- Disabled people's rights programme
- Older people's rights programme
- Domestic violence programme
- Refugee programme.

During 1999–2001 we will also be funding projects on specific issues which we have identified through our work over the last two years [*this appears to have covered, by the end of June 1999, a rural development project and support for 'umbrella' organisations. Ed.*].

Who can apply?

We make grants to voluntary organisations and self-help groups throughout the UK. We give particular attention to parts of the UK which often miss out on funding, especially towns and cities outside London, and rural areas. We welcome applications from both small local grassroots projects as well as larger organisations.

Any work we fund must be charitable. If your group is not a registered charity, but the work you are planning to do has charitable aims, we can pay funds through a registered charity. They will then pass on the grant to you.

Equal opportunities

... we are especially keen to hear from groups, in the areas that we support, who are very disadvantaged or find it particularly hard to get funding. So we welcome applications that specifically benefit the following:

- people from Black and ethnic minority groups
- women
- lesbians and gay men
- people who live in rural areas, and towns and cities outside London.

To apply, these groups must fall within one or more of our grant-making programmes

What type of grants do we give?

We give grants for both running costs and capital costs. ... We give building costs a very low priority.

How much do we give?

Small Grants Programme

The Small Grants Programme is only open to small, local organisations with a turnover of up to £50,000 or with no more than two full-time (or equivalent) staff. [*This is an odd sentence: a charity with £50,000 or two staff is one of the 20% largest registered charities in the country. Ed.*] The most you can apply for is £3,000, and we will give priority to applications for core and equipment costs. [*Note that there were only 29 grants in this category in 1999. Ed.*]

Large Grants Programme

The Large Grants Programme is open to any voluntary organisation that works within our grant-making programmes. We can make grants for running costs for up to three years. Grants will not usually be for more than £25,000 each year. However the trustees might give more to projects which show new ideas or will make a major impact. If you would like to talk to someone before you apply, please get in touch with our UK Grants Team [*seven staff led by Gilly Green. Ed.*]

Young People's Grants Programme

Our Young People's Grants Programme supports work with people aged 14–25. Within this age group we have identified a number of areas in this programme where young people are particularly disadvantaged and where there are gaps in services.

We have identified the following groups as those we want to fund:

- people abused through prostitution;
- young people involved with the criminal justice system;
- young people affected by drugs and alcohol; and
- work which is run by young people themselves.

There were 104 new grant allocations in 1999, totalling £2,235,000. Beneficiaries included:

- Awaz Utoah, Avon £63,000
- Drugs Action, Grampian £60,000
- Leeds Racial Harassment Project £60,000

- Spare Tyre Theatre Company, London £25,000
- Exeter Rape Support Service £4,600
- Mission in Hounslow Trust £1,000

Older People's Rights Programme
The aims of the Older People's Rights Programme are to support older people:
- to make their voices heard;
- to obtain their rights; and
- to be actively involved in running organisations which meet their needs.

We will only fund projects which are run by older people or which can show that they consult or involve users. Due to limited funds we are not able to fund social activities or lunch clubs.

There were 41 new grant allocations in 1999, totalling £900,000. Beneficiaries included:

- Dumfries and Galloway Elderly Forum £76,000
- Alzheimer's Concern, Ealing £55,000
- Hackney Chinese Community Services £15,000
- Age Concern, Gateshead £4,000

Disabled People's Rights Programme
Mental health and HIV and AIDS groups are also included under this programme. Types of work we will fund
- The development and support of local and regional forums of disabled people, especially those that improve communication between service 'users' and those that provide services.
- Peer and self-advocacy.
- Campaigning for better services.
- Networking and co-ordination.

We particularly welcome applications from:
- organisations run by people with learning disabilities;
- organisations working with disabled people aged 14–25; and
- organisations that are run by, or moving towards being run by, disabled people from Black and minority ethnic communities, or disabled lesbians and gay men.

There were 68 new grant allocations in 1999, totalling £1,218,000. Beneficiaries included:

- Disability Awareness in Action £68,000
- MIND in Brighton and Hove £56,000
- Harrow Association of Disabled People £15,000
- Disability Doncaster £1,500

Domestic Violence Programme
There were no grant allocations under this heading, or payments from earlier allocations, in 1999.

Refugee Programme
There were just three new grant allocations in 1999, totalling £70,000. Beneficiaries were:
- Somali Welfare Association £40,000
- Barbara Melunsky Fund £15,000
- Pilotlight £15,000

Exclusions

(For UK grants.) In general, the charity does not fund the following:

- academic research
- general appeals
- schools, colleges and hospitals
- individual people
- promoting religion
- trips abroad, holidays and outings
- services run by statutory or public authorities
- medical research or equipment
- minibuses
- sporting activities

The charity also notes that it does not fund social clubs or activities for the elderly.

Applications

(For UK grants only.)

Small Grants Programme

Applications, through the small grants application form, had closed for the 1999/2000 cycle when this book went to press. A new cycle was expected to start in summer 2001.

Large Grants Programme

Applications had closed for the 1999/2000 cycle when this book went to press. A new grant-making schedule was expected in spring 2001.

Previously there had been a two stage application process:

At Stage 1 you fill in the summary form, giving basic details about your work. This will give us enough information to decide whether you should send us a full application or not ... As well as assessing your application against the requirements of the individual programme, we will take the following into account.
- the size of your organisation – we want to fund both small and larger organisations.
- the ages of people who will benefit from our funding.
- the benefit to groups who face particular disadvantage (women, people from Black and minority ethnic communities, lesbians and gay men, and people living in rural areas).
- how involved the project users are in the planning and management of the organisation.
- how the work influences policy or changes the lives of disadvantaged people.
- how we are spreading our funding throughout the UK.'

Once we have received all the summary forms we will draw up a shortlist of applications for Stage 2. If your application qualifies, we will send you our full application pack [*not seen by these editors*] ... We cannot consider another application until you are in the last nine months of your funding from us.

Community Foundation Network

£21,987,000 (1999/2000)

2 Plough Yard, Shoreditch High Street, London EC2A 3LP

Tel. 020 7422 8611 **Fax** 020 7422 8616

e-mail network@communityfoundations.org.uk

website www.communityfoundations.org.uk

Correspondent Gaynor Humphreys, Director

General

This is the national association for local community foundations in the UK. These bodies are independent charities but collectively represent an energetic movement. They seek, by calling on local loyalties, to build up a grant-making capacity in their area, based on the accumulation of a permanent endowment.

A list of the most established community foundations follows, with their grant totals for 1999/2000. Collectively they are growing fast and some of the largest, marked with an asterisk in the list below, are already big enough to have their own entries in this book.

Some of the figures below include statutory or European grant programmes, not covered by this book.

Berkshire Community Foundation Tel. 01189 303021	£142,000
The Birmingham Foundation Tel. 0121 326 6886	£142,000
Calderdale Community Foundation Tel. 01422 349700	£147,000
*Cleveland Community Foundation Tel. 01642 314200	£649,000
County Durham Foundation Tel. 0191 383 0055	£166,000
The Craven Trust Tel. 01756 793333	£6,000
Cumbria Community Foundation Tel. 01900 325801	£24,000

Dacorum Community Trust Tel. 01442 231396	£8,000
Derbyshire Community Foundation Tel. 01332 621348	£58,000
Devon Community Foundation Tel. 01392 252252	£34,000
Essex Community Foundation Tel. 01245 355947	£167,000
The Fermanagh Trust Tel. 028 6632 0210	£50,000
County of Gloucestershire Community Foundation Tel. 01452 522006	£49,000
*Greater Bristol Foundation Tel. 0117 989 7700	£481,000
Community Foundation for Greater Manchester Tel. 0161 828 8725	£48,000
Heart of England Community Foundation Tel. 024 7688 4386	£84,000
Hertfordshire Community Foundation Tel. 01707 251351	£175,000
*Isle of Dogs Community Foundation Tel. 020 7345 4444	£695,000
Milton Keynes Community Foundation Tel. 01908 690276	£293,000
*Northern Ireland Voluntary Trust Tel. 028 9024 5927	£13,796,000
Oxfordshire Community Foundation Tel. 01865 798666	£91,000
Royal Docks Trust (London) Tel. 020 7474 7484	£182,000
St Katharine & Shadwell Trust Tel. 020 7782 6962	£232,000
The Scottish Community Foundation Tel. 0131 225 9804	£273,000
*South Yorkshire Community Foundation Tel. 0114 273 1765	£712,000
Stevenage Community Trust Tel. 01438 773368	£65,000
Telford and Wrekin Community Trust Tel. 01952 201858	n/a
*Community Foundation serving Tyne & Wear and Northumberland Tel. 0191 222 0945	£2,611,000
The Community Foundation in Wales Tel. 029 2052 0250	£236,000
Wiltshire Community Foundation Tel. 01380 729284	£283,000

The Community Foundation (serving Tyne & Wear and Northumberland)

Social welfare, general

£1,758,000 (1999/2000)

Beneficial area Tyne & Wear and Northumberland.

Cale Cross House, 156 Pilgrim Street, Newcastle upon Tyne NE1 6SU

Tel. 0191 222 0945 **Fax** 0191 230 0689

e-mail general@cftwn.co.uk

website www.community foundation.org.uk

Correspondent Maureen High, Grants Administrator

Trustees *Board Members: Nigel Smith, Chair; Sally Black; Barbara Dennis; Cllr George Gill; John Hamilton; Joy Higginson; Robert Hollinshead; Brian Latham; Roy McLachlan; The Duke of Northumberland; Guy Readman; Brian Roycroft; Derek Smail; Derek Tait Walker; Paul Walker; Tricia Webb.*

Information available Excellent grant guidelines. Comprehensive yearbook incorporating an annual review with financial information.

Summary

Managing over 70 different funds, the foundation is an important supporter of community development in the region. Donations vary according to the funds they come from. Most of them have specific criteria and small one-off grants are much more common than large multi-year awards.

General

Set up in 1988 as the Tyne & Wear Foundation, this is the largest community foundation in Britain. In October 1999 the name was changed to reflect its expanded area of benefit and to link in with other (domestic and overseas) organisations increasingly known as community foundations – an aim it has failed to achieve with these editors.

It describes its role as follows:

The Community Foundation provides a service to families and companies who want to help the local community. Funds set up by our donors at the Community Foundation are invested to produce an annual income to support a wide range of carefully chosen voluntary groups in Tyne & Wear and Northumberland. Our aim is to make it easier and more rewarding for successful people and organisations to serve the community.

Despite the large number of funds, only one grant application need be made, as projects are matched by the foundation to the most appropriate source. Major grants of £2,500 or over are said to be awarded every three months and smaller grants every two months. Applications are acknowledged within two weeks and considered by an advisory panel of staff and committee members. Those short-listed are contacted by staff for further information or to arrange a meeting. The staff report is then considered at the committee meeting and applicants are informed of the final decision within the following week. The whole process should be completed in three to six months. Those not awarded a grant will normally be sent a standard letter and invited to ring and discuss possible further applications.

About one fifth of applications received get funding and not all of those receive the full amount requested. The grant guidelines say: 'The larger the application, the less likely it is to succeed.'

Grant guidelines 2000

The Community Foundation awards grants to voluntary organisations in Tyne & Wear and Northumberland. Grants range from a few pounds to £100,000 but most are of £1,000 and less. Many of our grants are recommended directly by our donors from funds they have set up at the foundation.

We support causes from the cradle to the grave but we particularly value applications in the following areas:

The third age

Thanks to a legacy from the late Douglas Kellett of £5 million, we award grants once a year to organisations working with people in the third age – the period from retirement onwards when older people can contribute actively to the community. We want to make sure that the skills and experiences of people in the third age are used to the full.

Helping young people help themselves

Through the Readman Foundation, grants are awarded to individual young people and to voluntary organisations that give young people the opportunity to help themselves. The Readman Foundation is especially keen to back groups undertaking projects that will make a difference and encourage talents of young people in ways that would help their future careers.

Developing voluntary organisations

We believe that local charities can make a creative difference to our communities and want to make grants that will place them on a firmer footing and enable them to give an even better service in future. We will also want to help develop skills of staff and management committees to run voluntary groups better through training and consultancy. We make a few larger grants each year for capacity building that will give outstanding groups a chance to raise more funds and develop their activities in a time limited period.

Expect the unexpected

We are always keen to respond to new issues as they arise and to listen to unusual requests. Don't be afraid to ring and ask if we can help you with an unusual and innovative new idea. We may occasionally consider bridging genuine emergencies and respond quickly if necessary.

General criteria

In assessing applications for a grant we always give priority to projects which:

- help people in greatest need
- involve minority and disadvantaged groups
- are locally run and led
- use volunteers fully
- demonstrate good practice and management

We like to be a significant funder in any project and don't normally make small contributions to major appeals that are regrettably beyond our reach. ...

What we fund

- The vast majority of our grants are under £2,500
- We also make a number of grants each year of up to £20,000
- We recommend a few proposals to a national grant-making trust, Henry Smith's Charity, which may fund at an even higher level and covers the whole of the northern region.
- We make a small number of grants for several years
- We are keen to work with other funding partners but will consider 100% funding if there are no other options available
- We make grants to villages and neighbourhoods as well as supporting projects that work across our whole area. We take account of the different needs of urban and rural areas.
- Many of our grants are made at the request of people who have set up their own funds at the Foundation.

What we do not fund

[See under 'Exclusions' below.]

Grantmaking

In 1998/99, the foundation's assets were £19 million and its income was £3 million. From this 628 grants were made totalling almost £2 million, including £998,000 on behalf of Henry Smith's Charity and £23,000 for the Joseph Brough Charitable Trust. In addition, 128 grants worth £445,000 were made from the Millennium Commission's funds, which brought the total donated up to nearly £2.5 million.

The largest funds (£25,000 and over) in 1998/99

- Kellett Fund – 26 grants totalling £254,000 for people in the 'third age'.
  Largest grant: Age Concern Newcastle, £50,000.
- Readman Foundation – 72 grants totalling £125,000 supporting self-help for young people.
  Largest grant: Choysez Project, £15,000.
- Tyne & Wear Foundation General Grants – 22 grants totalling £107,000.
  Largest grant: Royal Quays Community Centre, £10,000.
- Sir Tom Cowie Fund – 24 grants totalling £46,000 for projects in Sunderland.
  Largest grant: Sunderland Sports Centre, £5,000.
- Gregg Charitable Trust Fund – one grant of £30,000 to the Choysez Project.
- Chapman Fund – 44 grants totalling £28,000 for equipment and building maintenance for youth projects in Tyne & Wear.
  Largest grants: Balliol Youth Centre and Durham Scout Association, £2,000 each.
- William Leech Fund – five grants totalling £26,000 for general charitable work in the region.
  Largest grant: Northern Initiative on Women and Eating, £7,000.
- Evening Chronicle Sunshine Fund – 29 grants totalling £25,000 to disabled children.

These eight largest funds accounted for one third of the total awarded.

New funds in 1998/99

The Heyman Scholarship Fund for Nursing Personnel was set up after the deaths of Sir Horace and Lady Heyman to help nurses broaden their experience and skills or facilitate research through overseas travel.

The South Tyne Valley Fund, established with an anonymous donation to benefit Haltwhistle and the surrounding rural areas, had assets of over £500,000 by summer 1999.

The FARNE Fund and the Baines Fund, which fund research into arthritis and rheumatology, had their combined value of £500,000 transferred to the Community Foundation.

The Women's Fund was established with a donation of over £250,000 from Margaret Barbour of J Barbour & Sons. At the time of the launch the foundation was seeking to double this sum through further contributions.

'The aim of the Women's Fund is to offer more choices and opportunities to women in order that they can gain confidence and play a more active and fulfilling role in the community. It will help women of all backgrounds to achieve their full potential.'

The following projects, supported before the Women's Fund was launched, are cited as typical recipients:

- Apna Ghar – helps Asian women in South Tyneside gain skills and confidence to seek employment.
- Northern Initiative on Women and Eating (NIWE) – has developed innovative ways of supporting women with eating disorders in the community.
- Them Wifies – helps disadvantaged women express themselves through the arts.

Examples of major grants in 1998/99

- Choysez Project, Ashington (£270,000, consortium of Gregg Charitable Trust, Northumberland TEC, Readman Foundation and Save & Prosper Educational Trust) – a major initiative to help young people excluded from school.
- Alzheimer's Disease Society of North Tyneside (£75,000 over three years, Kellett Fund) – for 'Voices for Choices', a volunteer befriending programme for people with dementia.
- Wayout in Gateshead (£2,500, Readman Foundation) – full funding of a programme to take women and young people on team and confidence-building skiing expeditions in Scotland.
- Ferguson Lane Action Group (£1,000, Jackie Haq Fund) – enabling local people to paint a mural about the regeneration of Scotswood, Newcastle.

Exclusions

The foundation does not normally make grants for the following purposes:

- sponsorship and fundraising events
- small contributions to major appeals
- large capital projects
- endowments
- political or religious groups
- work which should be funded by health and local authorities
- projects outside its area

unless funding is made available by one of its supporters from funds they have contributed to the foundation.

Applications

Applicants should obtain a set of the latest guidelines, which includes an application cover sheet and notes on how to apply.

We recommend that you plan your application well in advance. It can be made at any time, as committees, donors and advisory panels award grants at varying times and frequencies. You only need to make one application, which we will match to the appropriate fund or funds. You are welcome to phone to discuss your application at any stage.

Applicants are encouraged to contact Jane Shewell or Lesley Spuhler on 0191 222 0945 for advice on fulfilling the Community Foundation's funding criteria.

Your application will be acknowledged within 2 weeks and we will let you know when you will get a decision. In most cases, this will be within three months and often sooner, depending on committee agendas.

One of the staff, usually Jane Shewell or Karen Griffiths, will contact you for further information or ask to meet you. The staff report on your application is then considered by the committee and you will be informed of the decision within a week of the committee meeting.

The Ernest Cook Trust

Rural conservation and environmental research, youth, arts and crafts

£651,000 (1999/2000)

Beneficial area UK, but with a special interest in Gloucestershire and in other areas where the trust owns land (Buckinghamshire, Leicestershire and Dorset).

The Estate Office, Fairford Park, Fairford, Gloucestershire GL7 4JH

Tel. 01285 713273 **Fax** 01285 713417

Correspondent Mrs Judy Malleson, Grants Administrator

Information available Policy and guidelines leaflet; annual review with an explanatory paragraph for each grant. Report and accounts with full grants list.

Summary

A large number of small grants are made within the following categories (with totals for 1999/2000):

Countryside and environment	£292,000
Youth	£187,000
The arts, crafts and architecture	£91,000
Environmental research	£70,000
Other	£11,000

Grantmaking is sometimes more 'urban' than these categories might suggest, with youth work grants in particular often being for projects in areas of urban deprivation.

Of the more than 150 grants, only 16 were for £10,000 or more, and none for more than £16,000. Many were for less than £1,000.

Small grants can go to substantial organisations, with, for example, awards of £1,000 to Book Aid and Understanding Industry.

General

The trust was founded in 1952 by the late Ernest Cook, a grandson of Thomas Cook, who had pioneered the package holiday over 100 years earlier with a temperance day out in Loughborough by train from Leicester. The sale of the family travel business in 1928 generated enough wealth for the founder to direct his energies into the purchase and conservation of great houses and estates and the art works they contained.

The trust had assets of £43 million in 1998/99, and an income of £1.7 million, including an exceptional £386,000 in the form of a donation of some buildings. The assets are largely in the form of agricultural estates, managed by the charity.

The trustees are chosen to bring a wide range of experience in both education and rural land management, and each received remuneration of £4,000 in 1998/99, a practice always regretted by these editors who believe, like the Charity Commission, that the principle of unpaid trusteeship 'is one of the defining characteristics of the charitable sector'. The Commission's recent guidance saying that a mere legal power to pay trustees is not in itself a sufficient justification for payment, and calling for the demonstration that there is 'no realistic alternative', may lead to a reconsideration in cases such as this.

In 2000 the trust described its work as follows:

Educational schemes which relate to rural conservation form the major part of the trust's work, and the trustees' support for work in this field and for education and training in the arts, architecture and architectural crafts forms, as it were, an extension of their work in conservation. Also, but not least in importance, support is given to a few of the many projects submitted which have no rural bent, but which seem to the trustees to be particularly effective in their use of education as a catalyst to help alleviate hardship, handicap or social ills. It is a small way in which they feel that a country based organisation, which has many pressing concerns of its own, can look outside and give a little help to the towns and cities.

Countryside and environment

In view of the trust's association with land, emphasis is placed on the schemes which benefit rural areas. Grants in this category are made for educational work concerning conservation of the ecology of the countryside and for schemes which lead to a greater understanding of the countryside and rural life generally. Support is also given to responsible projects designed to increase an intelligent concern for the environment as a whole.

Other projects

A number of projects which lie outside the immediate areas of ECT concern are supported simply upon their merits as outstanding schemes or because they show potential for small amounts of money to have maximum impact on worthwhile activities. Among these, consideration is given to particularly innovative schemes providing a combination of housing, education and training for homeless and unemployed young people. Exceptional grants are also made for educational projects which have a geographic connection or close link with the trust.

Arts, crafts and architecture

While it is not the policy of this trust to fund work connected with building or structural conservation, trustees encourage appreciation of architecture and support organisations providing training in practical conservation skills. Support is also given to rural craft training schemes. Funding is rarely given to community arts projects, concerts, festivals, theatre, dance and sculpture projects.

Environmental research

Grants for research are made to universities or other relevant institutions. Projects supported reflect the trust's concern for the rural environment.

Grants in 1998/99

The trust's accounts and grants lists for 1999/2000 were not yet available at the time of going to press, so the following descriptions of grants come from the previous year's material.

In 1998/99, the trust made 177 grants totalling £632,000. Of these, 16 grants ranging from £10,000 to £15,500 accounted for 28% of the grant total. The trust gave the following examples of the purposes of its grants, to which examples of other typical beneficiaries have been added.

Countryside and environment

Shared Earth Trust – £12,000 for the work of a centre in west Wales comprising a nature reserve, demonstration site and research, training and education centre.

Centre for Alternative Technology – £10,000 towards the director's salary.

Other beneficiaries for lesser amounts included the Soil Association, Somerset Wildlife Trust, South Devon Resource Centre, Working Woodlands Trust and World Land Trust.

Environmental research

Allerton Research Trust – £12,000.

Rothamsted International – £13,000 towards the cost of a 12-month fellowship.

Other beneficiaries for lesser amounts included Manchester University and the Institute for Economic Affairs.

Arts, crafts and architecture

St Mary's Cathedral Workshops (Edinburgh) – £15,500 towards the costs of training an apprentice.

Other beneficiaries for lesser amounts included Lincoln Cathedral, Llandaff Summer Music School and the Farriery Training Service.

Youth

Newbury Motor Project – £15,000 for three years' support for a scheme of courses for children aimed at reducing juvenile motor-related criminal activity.

Lawlor Foundation – £10,000 for further development of a grammar school bursary scheme for children from low income families in the Greater Shankill area of Belfast.

Other beneficiaries for lesser amounts included Safe in the City, Cathedral Camps, Understanding Industry and the Shaw Trust.

Other grants lying outside specified categories

Disability Employment Enterprise Workshops, Weston-super-Mare – £12,000 to fund the part-time appointment of a qualified IT instructor.

Coventry Cathedral Development Trust – £10,000 towards developing the work of the International Ministry, which promotes inter-cultural understanding and reconciliation.

Exclusions

Grants are not awarded for charitable purposes which are not educational, to organisations that do not hold charitable status or for work overseas. Projects allied to medicine, health or social work are not supported. Awards are not made retrospectively, or for the following:

- general appeals
- building and restoration work
- sports and recreational activities

Funds are rarely committed for:

- community projects
- performing arts
- publications

Support for wildlife trusts and for farming and wildlife advisory groups is largely restricted to those based in counties in which ECT owns land (Gloucestershire, Buckinghamshire, Leicestershire and Dorset).

Awards are not made to individuals or to agricultural colleges.

Applications

Trustees meet in the spring and autumn to consider applications and additional meetings are held at three-monthly intervals to consider requests under £2,000. Proposals are welcome throughout the year; there is no set form for these but applicants are asked to focus their request on a specific educational need, to avoid jargon and repetition, and to present clear and concise proposals on a maximum of four sides of A4 paper. The enclosure of a self-addressed envelope will ensure acknowledgement of an application.

The majority of grants are paid within one to four months of commitment. Recipients of conditional grants are usually given up to 12 months to meet the provisos. Reports are requested on all work supported by grants of over £5,000 and payment of annual grant instalments is dependent upon a satisfactory report on work undertaken in the previous year.

The Cripplegate Foundation

General, in Cripplegate/ Islington, London

£1,000,000 (to organisations, 1999)

Beneficial area The ancient parish of St Giles, Cripplegate, London, the former parish of St Luke Old Street as constituted in 1732 (broadly speaking, the southern part of Islington and the north of the City of London), and now extended to include the Islington Council wards of Barnsbury, Bunhill, Clerkenwell, Canonbury East, Canonbury West, St Mary, St Peter and Thornhill.

76 Central Street, London EC1V 8AG

Tel. 020 7336 8062 **Fax** 020 7336 8201

e-mail kristina@cripplegate.org.uk

Correspondent David Green, Clerk

Trustees *Grants Committee: John Broadbent, Chair; Angela Agard-Brennan; Rosemary Boyes-Watson; Roger Daily-Hunt; Paula Kahn; Councillor Carol Powell; Barbara Riddell; Maxine Roberts; Jack Sheehan; Rachel Stewart.*

Information available Guidelines and application forms, including detailed map of the area of benefit. Ten-year review of grantmaking. Excellent reports and accounts.

Summary

The foundation donates £1 million a year to a wide range of organisations in the City and Islington areas of London. Grants are usually for revenue purposes in the range £1,000 to £10,000. A substantial number of grants over £25,000 are also made, going up to £150,000. Funding for projects over more than one year has become more common, with multi-year awards accounting for 43% of the expenditure in 1999.

General

Although the foundation was established in 1891, its origins lie in gifts and donations for the poor and needy made to the Church of St Giles-without-Cripplegate, which now stands in the heart of the modern Barbican estate in

London. The year 2000 marked the 500th anniversary of the first recorded gift to the church, by the will of a city goldsmith called John Sworder.

In September 1998 the foundation enlarged its area of benefit, as above, and the population served has consequently increased, from 11,000 to 68,000. The 1998/99 guidelines for applicants say that grants are made for the following purposes:

- the relief of need, hardship and distress of residents of the area of benefit
- to provide facilities for recreation or leisure-time occupations that promote social welfare
- for other charitable purposes which are for the general benefit of the inhabitants of the area.

The foundation emphasises that grants must be for people, services or work in the area of benefit:

The area of benefit connection is an essential criterion that all applicants must meet. Where an application is for a project covering a wider area it is important that the application should show what proportion of those benefiting from the project live or work in the area of benefit.

The foundation will consider applications for many different purposes, including providing core funding, as its grant-giving powers are very wide. Under the heading 'general benefit' of the community, most charitable activities are eligible. The governors are particularly looking for projects:

- addressing an identified need in the main area of benefit
- addressing a need not covered by other local projects
- which draw funds and resources from other sources
- which provide a benefit at a reasonable cost per head.

Current priorities

Young people

The governors have identified the needs of young people, from the earliest years to age 25, as a high priority. Applications are sought from schools and from organisations working with young people, whether within formal education or outside it.

Schools

The foundation has adopted clear guidelines for the funding of the 30 schools in the extended area of benefit. The objective is to assist in raising the levels of achievement and to enrich pupils' experience of the curriculum, for example through projects in art or music. The foundation also provides grants to assist schools in addressing social issues such as bullying, racism or awareness of drugs. Projects which will work in more than one school will be especially welcome.

Mental health

The foundation has funded a number of counselling projects and wishes to fund more projects working with people with mental health problems in the community, for whom there is little provision from statutory sources. A new programme is being developed to establish mental health services for young people aged 15–25.

Strategy

The foundation has become increasingly proactive in grantmaking and has commissioned a number of surveys and conferences to assess the needs of different groups in the area of benefit. Consultation with, and input from, community groups appears to be an important part of the foundation's strategy. A conference in 1999, 'Growing Up in Islington – Strategies to Meet the Needs of Young People into the 21st Century', led directly to the development of new initiatives.

The foundation has also recently been working on a new welfare rights service for the area, following the closure of the CAB and other advice services.

The 10-year review provided the following analysis on the nature and size of grants over the period:

GRANTS BY TYPE

	Amount	*%*	*No.*
Capital	£1,339,000	15%	81
Revenue:			
for one year	£5,419,000	59%	5,655
for two years	£1,278,000	14%	63
for three or more years	£1,116,000	12%	39

NB Some grants were given for both capital and revenue

THE CRIPPLEGATE FOUNDATION – GRANTS BY SIZE, TEN YEAR PERIOD 1990–99

	Amount	*%*	*No.*
Over £50,000	£1,660,000	18%	21
Between £10,000 and £50,000	£4,101,000	45%	223
Between £1,000 and £10,000	£2,287,000	25%	294
Under £1,000	£1,104,000	12%	5,296

Grants approved in 1999

The foundation's four best-supported areas of work were social welfare, projects for young people, projects for schools, and arts, leisure and the environment. Together these categories accounted for three quarters of the funds approved in the year.

Social welfare (£257,000)

By far the largest grant awarded in the year was for £150,000 to Camden Community Transport, towards the cost of purchasing vehicles and for running costs to establish a 'Plusbus' service in south Islington over a three-year period. Two more organisations received more than £25,000: Quaker Social Action (£32,000, two grants for rent, service charges and moving costs for its New Life Electrics project) and the Peel Institute Company (£27,000 over two years for services for Somali, Bengali and 'frail' pensioners in the King's Cross area). There were 11 other grants for under £10,000.

Work with young people (£220,000)

The largest grants went to the Rose Bowl (£48,000 over two years, full-time youth worker's salary); Islington Boat Club (£40,000 to create moorings for narrowboats), and Somali Speakers Association (£30,000 over three years for youth work in Barnsbury and Clerkenwell). A further 14 grants were for amounts between £1,000 and £25,000.

Schools and work with schools (£175,000)

Primary schools can apply for up to £10,000 over two years, secondary and special schools for £20,000 over the same period. In 1999, 20 schools received awards ranging from £650 to £19,000. Also supported were the Grand Union Orchestra, Junior Choral Project, Theatre Adad and QUIT, for work involving schools in the area.

Arts, leisure and environment (£80,000)

Grants ranged from £300, to St Paul's Shrubbery Festival, to £30,000, to Islington Music Centre (salaries and running costs). Other recipients included Clerkenwell Visitor Centre (£5,000, running costs); Finsbury Neighbourhood Forum (£5,000 in four grants to community organisations for various environmental improvements), and Art in Sacred Places (£7,000 for a millennium art trail).

Other

The foundation's remaining grants, accounting for a quarter of the total expenditure, were categorised as follows:

Addictions	£65,000
Education and training	£58,000
Community groups and infrastructure	£50,000
Disabilities	£45,000
Work with older people	£25,000
Provision for the under-fives	£15,000
Health and mental health	£9,000

Large grants in some of the above categories included those to Islington Voluntary Action Council (£48,000, salaries and running costs over two years); Guildhall School of Music & Drama (£40,000 to support postgraduate student bursaries over two years); Angel Drug Project (£35,000 for the refurbishment of new premises); City and Hackney MIND (£30,000 towards a service for Asian women dependent on tranquillisers), and Cripplegate and St Luke's Combined Holiday Scheme (£17,500 for holidays for older and disabled people).

More than 300 grants totalling £87,000 were also given for the benefit of individuals living or working in the area of benefit.

In the first edition of this book, written 15 years ago, we were somewhat dismissive of this foundation, noting mainly a then rather high level of expenses (especially, and perhaps rather enviously, those for 'wines and other stores for catering'). Since then, Cripplegate has become in many respects a model wealthy local charity. It has taken a proactive lead in seeking out the most urgent needs of its area of benefit (and they are extensive, despite the area's trendy present image); it has enlarged its area of benefit to one more suited to the resources at its command; it reports fully and clearly on its work; and it has reduced its administrative costs as a proportion of its income to an appropriate level. And its excellent review of its work in the last decade even gives a historical explanation for an interest in alcohol, Islington having been for years the base for much of London's booze, as the terminus for supplies of clean water from the New River.

Exclusions

- national charities and organisations, or organisations outside the area of benefit, unless they are carrying out a piece of work in the area of benefit;
- schemes or activities which would be regarded as relieving either central government or local authorities of their statutory responsibilities;
- grants to replace cuts in funding made by the local authority or others;
- medical research or equipment;
- national fundraising appeals or appeals to provide an endowment;
- advancement of religion and religious groups, unless they offer non-religious services to the local community;
- animal welfare;
- retrospective grants;
- commercial or business activities;
- grants for concerts or other events held in the Church of St Giles-without-Cripplegate.

Applications

Application forms can be obtained from the correspondent. They are also available as a Microsoft Word document, which can be supplied on receipt of a formatted 3.5 inch floppy disk, or by e-mail. *However, the foundation will not accept completed application forms by e-mail.*

The foundation welcomes a preliminary approach by telephone from charities, organisations or individuals who are unsure how to complete their application form or if they are eligible for a grant. The best people to speak to are Kristina Glenn, Grants Officer, or David Green, the Clerk to the Governors. Before an application goes to the governors an applicant will normally be visited and should allow time for this when applying.

Applications for less than £12,000 are considered at grant committee meetings in February, June and October. Applications for £12,000 or more are considered by the full board in April, September and December. Application forms are required to be returned at least six weeks before the meetings.

The Cripps Foundation

Education, healthcare and churches in Northamptonshire, Cambridge University

£162,000 (1999/2000)

Beneficial area Northamptonshire, Cambridge University.

Mellors Basden and Co, 8th Floor, Aldwych House, Aldwych, London WC2B 4HN

Tel. 020 7242 2444

Correspondent The Secretary

Trustees *Edward J S Cripps, Chair; D J T Cochrane; R W H Cripps.*

Information available Annual report and accounts available from the foundation for an exorbitant £25.

Summary

The foundation mainly supports schools and churches in Northamptonshire and colleges of Cambridge University. Almost all the money is given in a few very large awards to organisations previously supported by the trustees. A minimal amount is reportedly available to unsolicited applications from organisations in Northamptonshire.

General

The foundation has a small capital base and nearly all of its income comes from donations from the Chartwell Group of Companies. Income from this source in 1999/2000 totalled £200,000.

The major grants made in that year were £51,000 to Bilton Grange Trust (a preparatory school in Warwickshire); £50,000 to the College of Teachers, and a recurrent grant of £50,000 for Peterborough Cathedral. Five further grants totalled £11,000.

The level of grantmaking fluctuates widely from year to year, depending on the amount received in donations. In 1998/99 the income was £1.2 million and grantmaking totalled £1,389,000.

In previous years major beneficiaries included the Northampton School for Boys (£5 million over three years up to 1999) and Magdalene College, Cambridge (£250,000 in 1998/99).

The trust has previously said:

> Support is generally concentrated on, and committed to major single projects which would not otherwise be undertaken. The foundation does not welcome applications generally because it has a long list of projects it would like to support already when funds are available, and as it concentrates on major projects it has few funds for minor purposes.

The late Sir Humphrey Cripps, the founder, was a governor of Northampton School for Boys (where he was schooled) and of Northampton School for Girls, a member of the trust for Peterborough Cathedral, and an honorary fellow of the following Cambridge Colleges: St John's, Selwyn, Queen's and Magdalene. Large grants in most years have gone to these organisations.

Exclusions

No grants are made to individual applicants or to organisations based outside the beneficial area.

Applications

Applications should be by letter or by direct approach to the trustees. The trustees have a number of projects to which the majority of their funds are committed (see above), but there is a relatively small amount open to unsolicited applications. Applications are filtered by assessing whether or not they strictly fit the areas of interest: Is it local? Is it a religious charity? Is it an educational charity? Suitable applications are then passed on to the council of management (the trustees) for consideration. Both applicants and recipients are visited by the foundation, particularly in the case of larger projects.

Itzchok Meyer Cymerman Trust Ltd

Jewish Orthodox education, other Jewish organisations

£907,000 (1998/99)

22 Overlea Road, London E5 9BG

Correspondent I M Cymerman

Trustees *Mrs H Bondi; I M Cymerman; M D Cymerman; Mrs R Cymerman; Mrs S Heitner.*

Information available Inadequate annual report and accounts. List of grants over £1,000, but lacking analysis or review.

General

The objective of the trust is 'to advance religion in accordance with Orthodox Jewish faith and general charity'. All funds are awarded to Jewish organisations, religious or otherwise. The list of beneficiaries changes very little, if at all, from year to year.

In 1998/99 the trust's assets totalled £1,990,000 but income was £775,000. There were 48 grants of over £1,000 each, and more for sums of less than £1,000; however, the latter amounted to less than 1% of total grant expenditure. The recipients included two schools, a ladies' guild, immigrant aid charities and homes for people with disabilities.

The funds were distributed roughly equally into three grant sizes. One third of the total was spent on a grant of £100,000 (to Vehodarto P'nei Zoken) and four further grants of £50,000. Another 12 awards in the range £20,000 to £49,999 accounted for £312,000 (34% of the total). The final third was disbursed in smaller grants.

Recipients included a Culture and Research Centre (£40,000); Eli Siach Handicapped Home (£30,000); Russian Immigrant Aid Fund (£25,000); House of Gur, Manchester (£6,000) and Yesodei Hatorah Ladies' Guild (£3,000).

Applications

In writing to the correspondent.

The D'Oyly Carte Charitable Trust

Arts, medical welfare, environment

£1,491,000 (1999/2000)

Beneficial area UK.

1 Savoy Hill, London WC2R 0BP

Tel. 020 7420 2600 **Fax** 020 7240 8561

Correspondent Mrs J K Thorne, Secretary to the Trustees

Trustees *J Leigh Pemberton, Chair; Sir John Batten; Sir Martyn Beckett; E J P Elliott; Dr R K Knight; Mrs F Radcliffe; Mrs J Sibley.*

Information available Application form and guidelines. Annual review and accounts.

Summary

Grants, typically one-off, start at around £500 and can sometimes be for £100,000 or more, and are made in the following areas:

- arts
- medical welfare
- environment

General

The trust was founded in 1972 by Dame Bridget D'Oyly Carte. Its distributable income increased significantly firstly on her death in 1985, when it inherited her shareholding in The Savoy Hotel plc, and again in 1998 following the hotel's sale. In 1999/2000 its assets stood at over £47 million, giving an income of £2.6 million.

The trust supports general charitable causes connected with the arts, medical welfare and the environment. Certain charities in which the founder took a special interest continue to be supported on a regular basis. The trustees have recently conducted a review of their policy and have determined that their priorities for support for the next three years will focus on:

- the promotion of access, education and excellence in the arts for young people;
- the provision of hospice care and hospice care at home, particularly for children and young people;
- support for children with autism and their carers to ensure access to appropriate education, care and support services;
- support for the deafblind and their carers;
- support for charities concerned with alleviating the suffering of those with chronic medical conditions who have difficulty finding support through traditional sources;
- respite care and care for carers;
- the preservation of the countryside and its woodlands;
- heritage conservation.

Most grants are one-off, although grants for up to three years are given occasionally, particularly in respect of bursary funding for educational establishments, mainly in the arts sector. In 1999/2000, 233 grants totalling £1,491,000 were paid out, compared with 207 grants totalling £632,000 in the previous year. In 1999/2000, the trust reported on its grants under the following three headings.

The arts

A total of 76 grants amounting to £635,300 and ranging from £500 upwards was made. The largest grant went to the National Youth Music Theatre which received £115,000, in particular to reduce the cost of participation for young people involved with NYMT's activities. Further support of £50,000 a year for two years was also agreed.

Other grants included: £75,000 to the British Library, half the funding required to purchase Sir Arthur Sullivan's autograph manuscript of *Ruddigore*; £50,000 to the Koestler Award Trust as part sponsorship of the annual Koestler Awards Scheme; £20,000 a year for three years to the Wordsworth Trust, towards the maintenance and preservation of Dove Cottage; £20,000 each to the Actors Charitable Trust (for Denville Hall) and the Royal Society of Musicians (the Henry Wood Fund), both causes which the founder supported during her lifetime.

Maintaining its wish to assist students seeking further education in the arts, scholarships and bursaries totalling £65,000 were again awarded to deserving students on the recommendation of the Arts Educational Schools, the City and Guilds of London Art School, the Royal Academy of Dramatic Art, the Royal Ballet School and the Royal Northern College of Music. This funding is to be continued for a further two years.

Smaller grants in this category included £15,000 a year for three years to The Crafts Council's Setting-Up Scheme and to the Royal Needlework Society's Apprentice Scheme, £10,000 each to Opera Brava and the Textile Conservation Centre, and £5,000 each to Chantry Singers, Huntingdon Hall, the Mendelssohn on Mull Festival and Shakespeare's Globe Trust.

Medical/welfare

A total of £707,200 was given in 129 grants. The main beneficiary was the Winged Fellowship Trust, which received £100,000. Breakthrough Deaf Hearing Integration continued to be supported, receiving £20,000 as the second instalment of a three-year grant towards the charity's Contact Information Training programme, and a special one-off grant of £28,000, to match National Lottery funding to develop the use of video conferencing.

Other grants included £30,000 to the Haven Trust; £20,000 each to Dementia Relief Trust's Admiral Nurse Service and Guy's and St Thomas's Hospital Kidney Patients' Association (towards the cost of Homechoice automated peritoneal dialysis machines); £11,000 to Evelina Children's Hospital Appeal and £10,500 to the Cystic Fibrosis Trust. Other grants ranged from £500 to £10,000.

The environment

In this category 28 grants totalled £148,000, the largest being a pledge of £35,000 to the Painshill Park Trust towards a new Visitors and Education Centre. St George's Church in the village of Kelmscott received £11,000 for urgent repairs, although the trust prefers to make grants towards the preservation of historic churches through umbrella organisations.

Grants of £10,000 each went to the Philip Henman Foundation (in respect of the recruitment of young people, mainly from east London, to be apprenticed as watermen and lightermen); St Clement Danes 40th Anniversary Appeal, and the Woodland Trust. Other grants included £7,500 to the National Trust for Montpesson House (Salisbury) restoration appeal; £6,000 to Thames Salmon Trust, to help with building of fish passes on the River Kennet, and £5,000 each to Fauna and Flora International, Historic Chapels Trust, Maidstone Trust for the Kent River Walk, Plantlife, and the Zoological Society of London.

Exclusions

The trust is unlikely to support the following:

- applications from individuals
- charities whose operational area is outside the UK
- large national charities which enjoy widespread support
- individual schools (other than special schools)
- medical research
- conferences or seminars
- expeditions and overseas travel

Applications

Potential applicants should write to the correspondent with an outline proposal. Applicants qualifying for consideration will then be required to complete an application form. Applications for specific projects should include clear details of the need the intended project is designed to meet, an outline budget and, where appropriate, a copy of the latest annual accounts should be provided. The trust also requires applicants to provide, in a covering letter (not exceeding one page), on how the work supported will continue after the trust's grant has been completed. The trustees meet twice a year in June and December and applications for consideration should be submitted one month in advance.

The Roald Dahl Foundation

Haematology, neurology, literacy

£419,000 (1998/99)

Beneficial area UK.

92 High Street, Great Missenden, Buckinghamshire HP16 0AN

Tel. 01494 890465 **Fax** 01494 890459

website www.roalddahl.org

Correspondent Linda Lazenby, Deputy Director

Information available Guidelines for applicants. Exceptionally clear, complete and well-written annual report and accounts.

Summary

About 80 grants to organisations are made a year, normally between £500 and £50,000, with an emphasis on helping young people in the following fields:

- Literacy: work to assist children and young people who may need extra help to achieve this essential basic skill.
- Neurology: help for children and young people up to the age of 25 (and their families) who suffer from epilepsy, head injury and degenerative neurological disorders such as Batten's disease and Tay-Sachs.
- Haematology: help for the same age group with blood disorders which are not cancer related – most commonly haemophilia, sickle cell and thalassaemia sufferers.

There is a small grants scheme to give individual assistance to children and young people (and their families) who fall within the medical categories. Almost 300 grants were awarded under this scheme in 1998/99.

General

This energetic foundation receives most of its income from the annual Readathon event (whose proceeds are shared with the Sargent Cancer Care for Children charity). However the charity is expanding its direct fundraising activity, centring this on the area around Great Missenden where the foundation is based. The investment in this is admirably and unusually reported in the annual reports and accounts.

The foundation says:

> Throughout his life, Roald Dahl gave of his time and money to help people in need. When he died his widow, Felicity Dahl, established the ... Foundation to continue this generous tradition. The Foundation's aim is to help people in three major areas:
>
> - literacy, because it was Roald's crusade;
> - neurology, because brain damage has so often struck the Dahl family, and
> - haematology, because leukaemia was the cause of Roald's death.

Information for applicants

In general, we aim to provide help to organisations to whom funds are not readily available. We prefer to help small or new organisations [rather than] long-established, large or national organisations.

Neurology and haematology

In these fields we are keen to help children and young people up to the age of 25 (and their families) who suffer from blood disorders which are not cancer related, from epilepsy and head injury. Specifically, grants may be made for:

- pump-prime funding of specialist paediatric nursing and other care, especially where there is an emphasis on community care, for a maximum of two years. We will require information about the source of permanent funding after the two year period.
- assistance to residential and day care centres for children and young people who come into the above medical categories. Such grants would normally be awarded on a project basis.
- small items of medical equipment that will allow the patient to be cared for in the home, with community care/hospital back-up;
- individual grants of £50 to £500 to the children in the above categories from families that are suffering financial hardship, for specified needs.

Literacy

Through its association with the Readathon, the national sponsored reading event, the foundation is already actively involved in promoting literacy throughout the UK. In the next few years we will be particularly interested in making grants for:

- after school clubs for children and their families who would like to improve their literacy skills;
- centres which offer or wish to initiate literacy programmes for young people (16–25) as part of their normal activities.
- computer/technological assistance for reading for the partially sighted, blind or head injured.

We do not currently consider applications concerning dyslexia. Before he died, Roald Dahl with one of our trustees, Quentin Blake, donated a large sum to the Dyslexia Institute through the auction of their book *The Vicar of Nibbleswicke*.

Grant size

The range is wide. At the moment, the individual grants vary from £50 to £500 and those to organisations from £500 to £25,000.

Grants in 1998/99

The number and value of grants to organisations was categorised as follows:

Neurology	25	£243,000
Haematology	5	£28,000
Literacy	53	£162,000

The largest grant was £53,000 for a Roald Dahl Foundation nurse at Ninewells Hospital in Dundee. By the end of the year the foundation had funded or agreed to fund 17 such specialist nursing posts since the inception of this programme, 8 of which are now funded by the NHS trust concerned.

Other major medical grants were to St Elizabeth's School (£40,000), the Epilepsy Association of Scotland (£25,000) and Rehab UK (£15,000).

Only two of the literacy grants were for five-figure sums, to Community Service Volunteers (£20,000) and the Foundation for Communication for the Disabled (£10,000). More typical were the grants to Calibre (£1,000), Readiscovery (£3,600) and Help for Carers (£4,000).

Exclusions

The foundation does not consider grant applications for:

- general appeals from large, well-established charities or national appeals for large building projects
- research in any field
- any organisations which do not have charitable status or exclusively charitable aims
- statutory bodies
- core funding
- outside the UK
- school or higher education fees

Applications

On the straightforward form provided, with a covering letter if necessary.

Applications are considered throughout the year. Decisions on smaller sums can take as little as a few weeks. Applications for grants of several thousand pounds may take several months to be considered.

Baron Davenport's Charity

Almshouses/hospices/ residential homes, children, in the West Midlands

£509,000 (to institutions, 1999)

Beneficial area Birmingham and those parts of the West Midlands that are within 60 miles of Birmingham Town Hall.

Portman House, 5/7 Temple Row West, Birmingham B2 5NY

Tel. 0121 236 8004 **Fax** 0121 233 2500

Correspondent J R Prichard, Secretary

Trustees *G R Willcox; A C Hordern; P A Gough; P Heath. There is also one ex-officio trustee, Mrs S A Wood, the Director of Finance of the City of Birmingham.*

Information available Report and accounts, now with grants list though still without the required narrative review.

Summary

The charity makes over 400 grants a year, most of them for modest amounts. In 1999 there were only four awards of £10,000 or more. Grants for more than £2,500 are usually for almshouses, residential homes or hospices.

General

The charity was endowed in 1930 by Mr Baron Davenport, mainly with £80,000 worth of shares in Davenport's Brewery in Birmingham. This was taken over in 1986 and the charity now has invested assets of over £30 million.

Of the income, 40% goes in grants for individuals, specifically for widows, spinsters, divorcees (of 50 years and over) and women deserted by their partners together with their children who are in financial need. Fatherless children are also included.

The remaining 60% of the income is distributed equally to

- almshouses, residential homes and hospices;
- organisations that assist children and young people, up to 25, who are disadvantaged or in need.

Almost all the more substantial grants are made under the first heading 'there being far fewer applicants within that category compared to the number of applications from children's charities/organisations whose share of the income is the same. Additionally their needs are greater as they frequently involve capital projects.' However the great majority of grants are for amounts of £1,000 or less.

With such a lengthy list of beneficiaries, some organisations are almost inevitably funded in consecutive years, but every grant must be separately applied for each year; there is no automatic renewal.

The largest beneficiaries in 1999 were as follows:

- St Mary's Hospice, Selly Park, Birmingham (£20,000)
- Acorns Children's Hospices, Selly Oak, Birmingham and Walsall (£15,000)
- Charity of Thomas Oken and Nicholas Eyffler (£10,000)
- Katherine House Hospice (£10,000)

Organisations receiving £2,500 (the lowest amount recorded in the grants list) included the Duke of Edinburgh Award Scheme, the Association of Brain Damaged Children and Mid Staffordshire SCOPE.

'As many visits as possible are made to organisations receiving grants ... During 1999 a total of 109 visits were made.' This is an impressive number.

This is one of the last of the large, old established trusts to make the welcome decision to release its list of beneficiaries. Let us hope that the experience is not as bad as it may have feared.

Exclusions

None, providing the applications come within the charity's objects and the applying organisation is based within the charity's benefit area, or the organisation's project lies within or helps young people who live in the benefit area.

Applications

In writing, accompanied by the latest accounts. Distributions take place twice a year at the end of May and November and applications should be received at the charity's office by 15th March or 15th September. All applications are acknowledged and those not within the trust's objects are advised.

The 10th Duke of Devonshire's Charitable Trust

General, especially in Derbyshire

£573,000 (1998/99)

Beneficial area UK, with a preference for Derbyshire.

Messrs Currey & Co, Solicitors, 21 Buckingham Gate, London SW1E 6LS

Tel. 020 7802 2700 **Fax** 020 7828 5049

Correspondent The Trustee Manager

Trustees *Marquess of Hartington; R G Beckett; N W Smith.*

Information available Full accounts, but without the required analysis or review of the charity's activities.

General

This trust had an income in 1998/99 of £285,000 from its investments, but a further £469,000 was received in new donations. The main activity is support of the Chatsworth House Trust, which received £360,000 (and £263,000 in the previous year). A further £213,000 was given in grants to other organisations. Only the 36 grants of £1,000 or more are individually listed but there were nearly 100 further grants for lesser amounts.The listed beneficiaries are divided roughly equally between those local to Chatsworth and those elsewhere in England. Very few had also been supported in the previous year. Five beneficiaries accounted for £121,000, or a fifth of the total:

- Pilsley School, Derbyshire (£50,000)
- NCH Action for Children (£26,000)
- YWCA Eastbourne Appeal (£25,000)
- NSPCC (£10,000)
- Cavendish Centre for Cancer Care (£10,000)

The recipients of the £1,000 awards were varied. They included N E Derbyshire Angling Club, Keighley Sea Cadets, DeafBlind UK, Help the Hospices, and Derby Archaeological Society.

Exclusions

No grants to individuals.

Applications

In writing to the correspondent.

The Diana, Princess of Wales Memorial Fund

Children and young people in the UK, overseas

£9,584,000 (1999)

Beneficial area UK, including UK organisations working overseas.

The County Hall, Westminster Bridge Road, London SE1 7PB

Tel. 020 7902 5500 **Fax** 020 7902 5511

e-mail memorial.fund@memfund.org.uk

website www.theworkcontinues.org

Correspondent Dr Andrew Purkis, Chief Executive

Trustees *Lady Sarah McCorquodale, President; Christopher Spence, Chair; Jenny Brindle; Earl Cairns; John Eversley; Michael Gibbins; Andrew Hind; Anthony Julius; Baroness Pitkeathley; Nalini Varma.*

Information available Grant application pack and grant criteria. Annual review. Annual report and accounts.

Summary

The impressive grantmaking by this fund is out of the normal run. In Britain a relatively small number of large awards – usually between £100,000 and £300,000 over three years – are made each year for work with children and young people within an annually chosen and quite tightly specified field. In 1999 there were 40 grants in the UK to organisations working with those 'who had suffered loss and bereavement'.

In 2000 the theme was 'The Transition to Adulthood and Independence'. That for 2001 had not been decided as this book went to press. In all cases support is only for work with children and young people between the ages of 12 and 25. Within this, and within the theme for the year, the fund prioritises the following areas:

- refugees and asylum seekers
- prisoners' families
- young people and mental health
- young people with learning disabilities
- advocacy

Grants are only for work 'of national significance', though it can be locally based.

The fund has been strikingly successful in its efforts to support minority ethnic groups, with 45% of the UK grants in 1999 going to black-led charities or to projects specially designed to meet minority ethnic requirements.

About one third of the fund's grants go to international work, particularly for those causes with which Princess Diana was associated during her lifetime, such as the campaign to ban landmines and to help people in those communities affected by conflict. Particular priorities are likely to change from year to year; for up to date information potential applicants should obtain the current copy of the fund's guidelines or should consult its website.

There is a system of 'Grant Rounds', two a year for UK grants and one a year for overseas grants. Applicants are notified of decisions about four months after the closing date for the round concerned. For the relevant application pack availability, closing and decision dates, see the website or ring the number above.

General

The fund's income comes mainly from three sources: trading subsidiaries licensing the sale of Diana-related products (£7.8 million in 1999), income from investments (£3.8 million), and donations and gifts (£4.6 million). This last included £1.6 million donated by Universal Music from the proceeds of the sales of 'Candle in the Wind', a gift made possible by the generosity of Sir Elton John. In recognition of this, the fund has committed £1.5 million to the work of the Elton John AIDS Foundation (qv) for work around the world. Another £162,000 was given in grants in Canada in recognition of Ontario's waiver of sales tax on the song.

A minor source of income came from 10% of the takings from visitors to Althorp, Princess Diana's childhood home, down from £305,000 in 1998 to £123,000 in 1999.

The trustees aim to donate an average of £7 million a year. The fund's net income of £14 million was well in excess of its expenditures in 1999, especially as there were further capital gains of £2.8 million. However, two of the main income streams may be expected to diminish as memory of the Princess fades. The income from the investments in the charity's general fund will remain but the trustees do not intend this to become a permanent endowment. The work of the charity will continue even if this means drawing on the capital. When this ends, then, no doubt, so will the work.

Grant-making policy

This book does not cover in detail overseas grant programmes (they will be described in the forthcoming *International Directory* published by the Directory of Social Change). The following information applies to grants in the UK.

There is a Grants, Advocacy and Strategic Development Committee with the following members:

Christopher Spence, Chair
John Eversley
Lady Pitkeathley
Nalini Varma

'The intention is to make a limited number of substantial grants rather than a large number of small ones and to concentrate on groups and causes that would otherwise find it difficult to receive recognition and support.' The guidelines reprinted below were due for revision shortly after this book went to press. The 1999 annual review described the fund's key grant-giving policies more generally:

- The Fund wants to support organisations working with the most disadvantaged people.
- Since Diana, Princess of Wales was based in the UK but international in her interests and influence, and since about one third of the Fund's income has come from overseas, about one third of the Fund's grants currently go to international work.
- Broad priority themes are:
  – displaced people
  – people at the margins
  – survivors of conflict and those requiring conflict mediation
  – dying and bereaved people.
- Each year the Trustees publicise specific priorities within these areas, on which to concentrate for the year (this enables the Fund to make a cumulative impact on particular needs and avoid the much larger numbers of unsuccessful applications which would result from looser guidelines).
- We particularly welcome applications from organisations which otherwise find it difficult to get recognition and support.
- The Fund supports awareness-raising and advocacy as well as practical work.
- The Fund prefers to make a limited number of generous grants which have a major impact, rather than a large number of small ones.
- All work supported in the UK, even if it is locally based, must have wider national significance, offering innovation and insights which can be applied elsewhere.
- The Fund emphasises the importance of learning and sharing the lessons from the projects it supports.
- The Fund will also help charities by helping to raise awareness of needs or by bringing representatives of disadvantaged people together with decision makers.
- The Fund will continue to give away an average of at least £7 million per year (more in the years 2000 and 2001) even if this means drawing down the capital of the Fund.

The following more detailed information is reproduced from the fund's criteria for the UK funding programme in 2000. The guidelines also include detailed categories that can be supported under the theme in force at the time, but these cannot be reproduced here.

General criteria

1. We will only fund work of potential national significance. This means work that:
- Takes a new approach to an issue
- Is good practice that can be applied in other areas of the UK
- Has particular strategic significance in the development of an area of work.

Organisations do not need to be national organisations and projects can be nationally significant in a rural or inner-city context. If the work addresses issues specific to one of the four UK countries there would need to be lessons or insights that could be applied elsewhere.

2. We are determined to ensure that funded work reaches *groups who are particularly disadvantaged as a result of discrimination within society*. All applicants will be expected to demonstrate how their work seeks to include these groups. Priority will be given to work with young people who are from ethnic minorities, have disabilities, are gay, lesbian or bisexual, and to work with young women. We recognise that organisations in rural areas have access to fewer resources and so we will give these organisations some priority.

3. All applicants will have to demonstrate how *user involvement* is built into their work. This means that the users (or potential users) of a service or a project must be involved in an appropriate way at all stages. The aim should be to give the young people more choice and control, both individually and collectively, and to ensure that the organisation working with them operates in a way that best meets their needs.

4. We have a commitment to ensuring that funded work is *evaluated and lessons learnt, and examples of good practice are made widely available*. Evaluation and sharing of good practice should be built into the budget of every application. We may be able to help you with evaluation and sharing of best practice, including finding sources of help and support.

5. We will accept applications for *action research, evaluation of work* (this does not need to be work previously grant-aided by the Fund) and the *sharing of good practice*. ...

Grants in 1999

The fund made 76 grants totalling over £9.5 million, 40 being for organisations working in the UK, which received an average grant of £163,000. These were divided as follows (with amounts for 1999):

- UK-wide work (£1,418,000)
- local, innovative work of national significance (£2,130,000)
- national work in one or more of the four countries of the UK (£814,000)
- pilot projects in one or more areas of the UK (£1,050,000)

Grants are well spread throughout the UK without the usual bias in favour of London and the south of England.

The fund's theme in 1999 was children and young people between the ages of 12 and 18 who had suffered loss and bereavement; this appears to have been adhered to strictly, as shown by the categories reported:

	Amount	*%*
Unaccompanied young refugees	£2,042,000	33%
Bereaved young people/ young people who have suffered loss and bereavement because of violence	£1,984,000	33%
Young people in care	£1,388,000	23%
Young people with a parent/prime carer in prison	£661,000	11%
Other	£26,000	<1%
Total	£6,101,000	100%

Examples of grants were as follows.

UK-wide projects

Childline/National Youth Advocacy Service – £299,000; After Adoption – £210,000; The British Refugee Council – £150,000; Roadpeace – £60,000; Prisoners Abroad – £35,000.

National projects

Ulster Quakers Service Committee – £243,000; Children's Rights Officers and Advocates – £212,000; Child Bereavement Trust – £159,000; Scottish Refugee Council and Welsh Refugee Council – £30,000 each.

Local projects of national significance

Acorns Children's Hospice, Birmingham – £212,000 for a special project to help siblings cope with the death of a brother or sister.

Tara Counselling and Personal Development Centre, Omagh – a five-year grant worth £118,000 for an art therapist to work with children and adolescents coming to terms with the effects of the Omagh bomb in August 1998.

Llamau Housing Society, South Wales – £235,000 over three years for its 'Learning for Life' programme, helping young homeless people.

Pilot projects

Albanian Youth Action – £287,000 to support a five-year programme of practical support and advice to unaccompanied Albanian-speaking young refugees (12 to 18 years old) from Kosovo.

Other

Other grants included £299,000 for the Save the Children Fund; £292,000 for the Federation of Prisoners' Families Support Groups, and £115,000 for the Scottish Council for Research in Education.

Diana, Princess of Wales Memorial Fund – Annual review 1999

Who gets a grant? How the fund decides

In developing its policies on who should receive grants, the Fund's emphasis is on openness and accessibility. Thorough consultation, especially within the charity sector, lies behind the Trustees' decisions on criteria for each new grants round. When we have decided on these guidelines we publish and circulate them very widely, taking pains to try to get through to smaller and less well off organisations as well as the bigger ones. We try hard to make our application process easy to understand, and have published specific information for people with learning disabilities so that they can participate in seeking the Fund's support.

We are very pleased that, as a result, we have been able to fund many less well-known, emerging organisations and those who otherwise find it difficult to get support, as well as some well-known charities mounting innovative new projects. The Trustees' determination to overcome the barriers which often deter ethnic minority groups has been fruitful: over 45% of our UK grants in 1999 have gone to black-led charities or to projects specially designed to meet minority ethnic requirements.

The Fund has now pledged £25 million in grants to 113 projects in the UK and 54 overseas. The initial phase of grant-giving, announced in the spring of 1998, was centred on all those organisations with which the Princess had a formal association (e.g. as President or Patron) during her lifetime. A full description of this programme was given in last year's Annual Review. By 1999, the Fund had settled into its long-term pattern of grant-giving and wider support for charitable causes.

The Fund's policies run consistently through all our grant-giving and support in the UK and overseas. For 1999, the Trustees concentrated on work in the UK with 12 to 18-year-olds struggling to cope with personal loss on top of the other problems of adolescence; for the international grants, the focus was on work with people whose lives were severely damaged by violent conflict. ...

The Fund also supports charities by making its meeting rooms in the heart of London available free of charge. In 1999, we welcomed a total of 49 different charities using our facilities on 114 occasions. We are in no doubt from their feedback that this is a special and highly valued resource, particularly for organisations which would otherwise find it difficult to afford such a venue. Guidelines on applying to use these facilities are available from Debra Cook at the Fund or from our website.

Exclusions

The trust will not fund:

- projects outside its funding priorities
- individuals
- services run by statutory or public authorities
- organisations that are principally fundraising bodies
- arts and sporting activities which give little benefit in terms of social inclusion
- academic research
- schools, colleges and hospitals
- repayment of loans
- promotion of religious beliefs
- rapid response to emergency situations
- retrospective funding
- debts
- capital expenditure for religious institutions or buildings
- party political organisations
- fees for professional fundraisers

While the trust will not fund activities which are the responsibility of any statutory agency, for example a government department, local council or health authority, and it will not fund projects that are direct replacements of statutory funding, it welcomes applications for collaborative projects and those involving both the voluntary and public sectors.

Applications

An excellent application pack is available from the fund, from which the following information is taken.

What we'll need from you:

- A completed application form and a photocopy of the completed form.
- A constitution or set of rules (this may be a memorandum of articles or a trust deed). It should include your organisation name, objectives, aims and how they are achieved, details of how the management committee or governing body is elected or appointed and how, if applicable, the organisation admits members. Your management committee must have formally adopted your constitution or set of rules.
- Confirmation of your organisation's bank account details.
- A set of your latest audited or certified and signed annual accounts.
- A copy of your equal opportunities policy and code of practice and/or implementation strategy.
- An annual report or published information from your parent organisation.

These should be sent to the Grants Committee (Applications) at the address above. In 2000, the deadlines for the receipt of completed application forms fell in March and August, with awards being announced in July and December. Unsuccessful applicants are informed in writing of the broad reason why they were unable to get a grant.

The Djanogly Foundation

Education, arts, Jewish charities, general

£1,309,000 (1998/99)

Beneficial area UK, with a special interest in Nottinghamshire, Israel.

28 Savile Row, London W1X 2DD

Correspondent The Secretary

Trustees *Sir Harry Djanogly; Michael S Djanogly.*

Information available Report and accounts, with grants lists but without the required analysis or review.

Summary

Large annual payments to academic institutions in Nottingham and recurrent awards to well known arts establishments in London account for most of the funds. Much of the remainder is for Jewish charities, also regularly supported. Small grants, usually for amounts up to £2,000, are widely spread and occasionally repeated.

General

In 1998/99 assets of over £17.5 million (down from £21 million two years previously) produced an income of £1,346,000, of which £1,309,000 was distributed in grants to 70 charities.

The following examples of grant recipients show the foundation's commitments in the three areas mentioned above. All of the recipients of six-figure sums had been supported in the previous year and most were receiving support for at least the third consecutive year.

- The Tate Gallery (£350,000)
- Royal National Theatre (£130,000)
- Victoria and Albert Museum (£25,000)

In all, 45% of the funds went to the following educational establishments in the Nottingham area:

- University of Nottingham (£165,000)
- Nottingham High School (£150,000)
- Nottingham Trent University (£145,000)
- Nottingham City Technology College (£120,000)
- Manor House School, Notts. (£12,500)

Jewish organisations supported included the Jerusalem Foundation (£97,000); Oxford Centre for Hebrew and Jewish Studies (£25,000); Jewish Care (£10,500), and Maidenhead Synagogue (£10,000). All receive regular donations.

A total of 43 grants were for £1,000 or less. A sample of recipients included: Animal Welfare Trust (£1,000); Army Benevolent Fund (£840); Balfour Diamond Jubilee Trust (£100, repeat); Ben Gurion University Foundation (£380); British School of Osteopathy (£250), and the Charities Aid Foundation (£67).

Applications

In writing to the correspondent.

The Drapers' Company Charities

General

£1,451,000 (1998/99)

Beneficial area UK, with a special interest in the City and adjacent parts of London.

Drapers' Hall, Throgmorton Street, London EC2N 2DQ

Tel. 020 7588 5001 **Fax** 020 7628 1988

Correspondent Debbie Thomas, Charities Administrator

Trustees *The Drapers' Company. Chair of the Charity Committee: Peter Bottomley MP.*

Information available Report and accounts with full grants lists.

Summary

The various charities of this City livery company give most of their money to schools, colleges and almshouses with which they have strong historical connections. The remaining 50% or so of the grants for organisations are said to be concentrated on an annually chosen 'theme', and on causes with links to the company and its members. Because of this policy, the charities will not generally consider unsolicited applications.

It is not yet clear how far these aspirations will be fulfilled in practice. The 1998/99 report said that the priority during the year had been to strengthen the company's traditional links with schools, Oxbridge colleges and other educational establishments – a purpose amply fulfilled – together with the continuation of the emphasis placed on grants to Northern Ireland. However there were just four grants for that region, amounting to 4% of the grant total, from the full list of over 100 awards.

The remaining grants cover a wide range of causes, partly because the 32 members of the Court of the company each have a personal allocation of £1,000 to give from the Fund's resources to give to the charity of their choice (the Master has £5,000).

Other small grants are decided by the members of the charity committee; potential applicants will need, therefore, to seek the support of the people concerned. These editors have been told that they cannot be usefully named here as they change annually, which must be a challenge to the continuity of effective grantmaking.

For 2000/01 the new annual theme will be 'the causes and effects of social exclusion among Inner City Youth in the London area with a particular emphasis on education' for which the charities are proactively seeking their own projects to support – though on available precedent, the amounts concerned may still be modest in proportion to the resources of the charities.

General

This entry covers those five of the charities administered by the company which give grants to organisations outside the company's immediate connections. They are, with the amounts given to organisations in 1998/99, as follows:

- The Drapers' Charitable Fund £902,000
- The Drapers' Consolidated Charity £403,000
- Henry Dixon's Foundation for Apprenticing £62,000
- Sir William Boreman's Foundation £44,000
- Charities General for the Poor £40,000

The guidelines that follow apply specifically to the first of these, but all the charities are administered together. The Charitable Fund was set up by the Drapers' Company in 1959. It manages 24 charities: 4 general charities; 5 almshouse charities; 12 education charities; and 2 poor relief charities. In the past, grants have varied from less than £100 to over £500,000 and there has been no typical amount. Beneficiaries have generally been national charities, and organisations where there has been a connection with the City or Mayor of London, with the Drapers' Company or its members, or with the drapery or textile trades.

Guidelines for applicants

- Over recent years, the Charities Committee has established tight criteria in line with the limited resources that we have available for charitable giving.
- We are now focusing our energies on a relatively few number of causes.
- In addition, the Charities Committee also selects a charitable theme every year for which we research certain projects for possible support. Moreover, our policy is to be proactive in identifying these causes.

The major charitable themes for the year (2000/01) should remain:-

(a) The causes and effects of social exclusion among Inner City Youth in the London area with a particular emphasis on education. We are researching our own projects for possible support.

(b) Causes with strong historic links with the Company, including appeals for the support of textiles.

(c) Northern Ireland. (Primarily projects in Moneymore and Draperstown.)

In the previous edition of this book we wrote that 'the charity's new practice of being wholly proactive, and not even considering unsolicited applications, is wholly acceptable ... provided that the alternative process is thorough and informed, as should be visible in future annual reports'. Unfortunately it is not visible.

The major theme (Northern Ireland) is a reference just to the grants to Project Moneymore (£25,000), Workspace Draperstown (£10,000), and to Lisson House and the National Trust, Northern Ireland (£4,000 each).

This £43,000 was far outweighed by the grants to connected schools (mostly fee paying) and colleges such as Bancrofts (£95,000) and Howells School, Denbigh (£72,000). The largest award (of £125,000 to Queen Mary and Westfield College) may also belong in this category.

Such grants reflect the history of the charity. However there was also a mass of smaller grants, totalling hundreds of thousands of pounds, that had no visible connection to the stated policies, let alone their 'major theme'. They cover a wide range, including the following: Hertford College, Oxford (£30,000), British School of Osteopathy (£10,000), the Kirov Opera (£3,500), Blundells School (£6,000), the Royal Naval Museum (£1,250) and St Anne's College, Oxford (£11,000).

The many smaller grants, of less than £1,000, were equally well spread. Recipients included the Multiple Sclerosis Society, Dorset Opera, Grantham Samaritans, the Gurkha Welfare Trust, Wadham College, Oxford, the Independent Schools Council, Venice in Peril and the Tyne and Wear Foundation.

The grant total from the Consolidated Charity was exceptionally large in this year because of an award of £300,000 to the Providence Row Housing Association for a 'Foyer' scheme in Bethnal Green, London, to be named after the company. There were 23 other grants, led by £30,000 to the Family Welfare Association. Four Oxford colleges received between £5,000 and £10,000 each. The universities of East Anglia and De Montfort got £1,000 and £800 respectively.

There was just one relevant grant from the Charities General, of £40,000 for Counsel and Care for the Elderly. The 10 Henry Dixon grants were mostly for colleges of music, art or drama, but led by £13,000 for Heriot Watt University.

The Boreman charity only covers parts of south east and east London, where its grants cover a wide range of educational causes.

Exclusions

The following will not generally be supported:

- unsolicited requests
- running costs
- statutorily funded organisations

Applications

'No new unsolicited requests for funding to be considered unless there is a prior connection with the Drapers' Company.'

The Vivien Duffield Foundation

See the entry for the Clore and Duffield foundations. As the two trusts are operated together and are seeking to amalgamate as the Clore Duffield Foundation, their entries have been combined in this book.

The Dulverton Trust

Youth and education, welfare, conservation, general

£3,137,000 (1999/2000)

Beneficial area Unrestricted. Mainly UK in practice, but major exceptions are possible. Limited support to parts of Africa. Few grants for work in London or Northern Ireland.

5 St James' Place, London SW1A 1NP

Tel. 020 7629 9121 **Fax** 020 7495 6201

e-mail trust@dulverton.org

Correspondent Major General Sir Robert Corbett, Trust Secretary

Kemp-Welch; Sir Ashley Ponsonby; Lord Taylor of Gryfe; J Watson; Dr Catherine Wills; C A H Wills.

Information available Good reports and accounts with analysed grants schedule; leaflet stating policy and practice.

Summary

Grants vary between £1,000 and £125,000 (average £10,000) and are concentrated on youth and education, conservation and general welfare. Other areas of priority are religion (principally through the Farmington Trust in Oxford), peace and security, and, to a lesser extent, industrial understanding.

Grants, often substantial, are made outside these specified areas of interest but probably only on the personal recommendation of a trustee. There is an extensive small grants programme for local causes, whose coverage is probably more general still.

About one in every seven applications leads to a grant. Over 100 grants of less than £1,500 are made. After an application has been submitted, reapplications are not considered until at least a further 18 months have elapsed.

Though most grants go to national projects, there is increasing openness to regional or local projects. Awards are made towards capital or revenue costs, and are normally one-off payments. Limited weight should be put on the tentatively expressed guidelines; the pattern of grants suggests that the published priorities are often overridden. It is possible that staff have the authority to reject applications outside the priority areas unless they have the support of a trustee (a common enough situation).

General

This charity, based on the Wills tobacco fortune, though it may also be both efficient and effective, is old fashioned, and even ornamental, in its chosen style of work. It has an impressive set of trustees, ranging from members of the founding family, some of them ennobled, to distinguished and elevated veterans. It is based in its own premises in one of the most valuable areas of real estate in the world, St James's, London.

Each application, restricted to two sheets of paper, is 'treated on its merits' without the trust indicating where it considers such merit to lie. Grants are one-off. Unusually, the trust states openly what is often a truth carefully concealed, that a project supported by a trustee can be funded even though it falls outside the trust's stated areas of priority. The present Lord Dulverton has an allocation of £25,000 for grantmaking around his home in the Cotswolds, an area known for its relative prosperity.

The trust also has characteristics that might be less expected. It seldom gives grants in the London area, thereby helping reduce the scandalous pro-London bias in trust grantmaking generally. It has regular quinquennial reviews of its activities (though the changes resulting from the most recent review seem largely to recognise existing developments). Finally, the trust spends enough on its administration, about 10% of its grant total, to have four full-time staff, and to be able to discuss personally with applicants most substantial proposals that go forward for serious consideration.

Grant-making guidelines

These are often expressed in tentative terms and do not correspond all that closely with the grants described in at least the 1999/2000 annual report. Some of the variations are noted in the text that follows.

The main work of the trust is conducted in three areas which the Trustees consider of particular relevance. These are Youth and Education, Conservation, and General Welfare [*in previous editions Religion had been added to this first list. Ed*]. Further areas of priority are causes in support of Christianity, followed by Industrial Understanding, Peace and Security, Preservation and other appeals decided by Trustees to be of special merit. Overseas assistance is generally restricted to a small number of old contacts and associations in Central and East Africa. Occasional grants are made in response to appeals from South Africa. [*In 1999/2000, however, a grant of £50,000 was made to CARE International for its work in Macedonia. Ed*].

The Trust is very seldom able to support appeals from the broad fields of medicine and health, including drug addiction and projects concerning the mentally and physically handicapped. Also generally excluded are projects concerning museums, churches, cathedrals and other historic buildings [*though in practice these may be funded. Ed.*].

The whole field of the arts is excluded together with projects for schools, colleges and universities [*but see below. Ed.*]. The Trust rarely operates within the Greater London Area or in Northern Ireland.

Cases of particular merit within excluded categories may be considered if the application is personally recommended by a Trustee. Visits are frequently made by officers of the Trust to evaluate proposals at first hand or to follow up progress.

The Trust prefers to support national projects but will make grants to regional and local organisations if appropriate. Whilst seeking to help the disadvantaged, Trustees also recognise the need to encourage those, perhaps less deprived but nonetheless deserving, and those caring for others.

Apart from a restricted list of annual policy grants, recurring grants are very seldom made. Subsequent applications will only be considered after an interval of at least 18 months.

Though the 1999/2000 grants lists do not give the purposes of the grants, some of the listings still contrast with the admittedly general statements above. For example, grants were made to two universities, Reading (£60,000) and Oxford (£125,000 for Dulverton Scholarships); cathedrals and churches, those in Hereford (£5,000) and St Mary's Uggeshall (£2,000); to schools and colleges, Chipping Campden School (£2,000) and Atlantic College (£10,000); in the area of health, to King Edward VII Hospital for Officers (25,000); and in the arts, to the National Gallery (£25,000) and London Sinfonietta Trust (£10,000).

The largest beneficiaries, as in previous years, included the University of Oxford Dulverton Scholarships (£125,000), Farmington Trust (£140,000), and the Ditchley Foundation (£100,000). All of these get ongoing support and provision has already been made for this to continue in future years. Overall, somewhere in the region of a quarter of funds went to organisations also supported in the previous year. Repeated annual grants made up about 15% of the trust's overall grant-making capacity in 1999/2000.

Annual report

The 1999/2000 annual report includes the following from its review of policy and practice:

The first Lord Dulverton was determined that the Trust should be wide ranging, flexible and enterprising in its grant making policy, and these principles are said to have been continued by its successors, adapted as necessary to suit changing circumstances [*though the trust is certainly wide-ranging, and may well be flexible, these editors see limited evidence of enterprise, when comparing these grants lists to those of other trusts described in this book. Ed.*].

The 1998 [five-yearly] review examined all areas of Trust policy and concluded that apart from some minor changes of emphasis, the areas covered by the Trust should remain largely unchanged. ... The Trustees decided that they would wish to continue to support national projects, although they would in future also make grants to regional and local organisations as appropriate. Whilst helping the disadvantaged, they also recognised the need for the Trust to attempt to encourage those, perhaps less deprived but nonetheless deserving, and those caring for others.

The main work of the Trust is aimed at three areas that are of particular relevance; these are Youth and Education, Conservation and General Welfare. Other areas of priority are Religion, in which the main emphasis is the promotion of development of religious education in schools, principally through the Farmington Trust in Oxford, followed by Peace and Security, Preservation and to a lesser extent, Industrial Understanding. Other causes considered by the trustees to have special merit may also be supported under the Miscellaneous category. Limited grants are made to historic contacts and associations in East Africa and occasional grants are made in response to appeals from South Africa [*but note the grant to CARE for work in Macedonia. Ed.*].

Annual Policy Grants represent a significant proportion of the Trust's work . The number of these grants is restricted, currently to a maximum of 20% of the Trust's grant-making capacity, and the Trustees review them annually, with one year's notice of cessation. [*These are not separately identified in the annual report but the trust has said that regular recipients include the Farmington Trust, the Royal United Services Institution, the Royal Society for Nature Conservation, the Duke of Edinburgh's Award, Fairbridge, Trident Trust, Book Aid and Age Concern. There also appears to have been repeated support for the Ditchley Foundation, the Dulverton Scholarships at Oxford University, and Atlantic and Rendcomb Colleges. Ed.*] There is also a small and specific list of recurring grants, but both these, and grants phased over a number of years, are kept to a minimum to allow other charitable projects their turn.

Minor Appeal Grants are made to an annual total of £125,000. Grants in this category cover a wide spectrum of charitable works throughout the United Kingdom.

... grants are not normally made in the following fields areas unless the project is personally recommended by a Trustee, and is considered to be of special merit.

- The broad fields of Medicine and Health, including drug addiction and work with the mentally and physically handicapped.
- Historic Building, Museum, Church and Cathedral projects [*but see above. Ed.*].
- The Arts, together with projects for Schools, Colleges and Universities [*but see above. Ed.*].
- Charitable projects based in the Greater London area, in Northern Ireland (except for a very small number of nominated charities) and Overseas (except Africa) [*but see above. Ed.*].
- For Expeditions or to Individuals.

THE DULVERTON TRUST – SUMMARY OF GRANTS

	1999/2000		*1998/1999*	
Youth and education	£1,103,000	35%	£1,057,000	36%
General welfare	£613,000	20%	£443,000	15%
Conservation	£204,000	7%	£277,000	9%
Religion	£235,000	8%	£227,000	8%
Africa	£108,000	3%	£101,000	3%
Minor appeals	£100,000	4%	£100,000	4%
Peace and security	£66,000	2%	£133,000	4%
Industrial understanding	£20,000	1%	£40,000	1%
Preservation	£115,000	4%	£125,000	4%
Annual subscriptions	£30,000	1%	£25,000	1%
Local appeals	£25,000	1%	£20,000	1%
Miscellaneous	£493,000	16%	£395,000	13%
Total	£3,137,000		£2,967,000	

Youth and education

Youth and Education continues to be the largest single category supported by the Trust, accounting for over one third of the grants by value. This reflects the priority placed by the trustees on assisting the development of young people, particularly those suffering from disadvantage. The Trust also seeks to reward excellence, as indicated for example by the grants for Arkwright Scholarships and to the National Association for Gifted Children. The largest grants went to the Dulverton Scholarships at Oxford University, increased from £100,000 to £125,000 this year, and to the Ditchley Foundation, in memory of the work of Sir David Wills. Although on the margins of Trust Guidelines, the problems of disability were recognised by the grants to Blind in Business, Queen Elizabeth's Foundation for Disabled People and the Michael Palin Trust for Stammering Children. Trustees decided to continue the grant to the Refugee Studies Programme at Oxford University for a further year.

General welfare

General Welfare is the next largest category, accounting for one fifth of Trust expenditure. As always, a very wide range of charitable activity falls under this heading. The largest grant went to CARE International for their urgent work in Macedonia. A number of grants were made to regional bodies which carry out sterling work – much of it voluntary – within their communities; examples include the Scottish Community Foundation, Liverpool Personal Service Society, St Louis Family Service and the Greater Bristol Foundation.

A proportion of grants went to the vulnerable at both ends of society, to children and to the elderly. Grants for the care of children were made to the newly-formed Association of Children's Hospices, Research Education and Aid for Children with Terminal Illness, ChildLine and Home Start UK. For the care of the elderly, grants included the Ex-Service Fellowship Centres, Abbeyfield Societies, Age Concern and Help the Aged.

Miscellaneous

This category embraces charities which Trustees considered to be worthy of support, despite being at the margins of the Trust's Guidelines. A number of diverse but excellent appeals were considered this year and the total awarded in this category has increased as a result. The largest grant went to the development of the Agriculture Faculty at Reading University. Ethox was commended for its invaluable work to develop the training of medical students in how to communicate with patients, and the Royal Hospital at Chelsea received a grant for its Millennium Project. The Walter Segal Self Build Project and the Retired Executive Action Clearing House were supported because of the assistance which they are able to provide to a range of other charities.

Religion

JC2000 received a substantial further grant to help mark the Christian element of the Millennium, but the main theme of grants in this category continued to be the development of religious education. The largest such grant went to the Farmington Trust, with smaller sums to Atlantic College, and for a study of Religious Education to be conducted under the auspices of the Portsmouth Roman Catholic Diocesan Trust.

Conservation

The largest grant in this category went to the World Wide Fund for Nature (UK). Support was given to the work of the Country Trust in providing opportunities for inner city children to visit the countryside and a variety of other environmental projects in England, Scotland and Wales also received assistance.

Minor appeals

The sum of £125,000 was set aside by Trustees to support small local appeals, within a maximum grant of £1,500 for each appeal. ... A total of 98 grants were awarded to organisations such as Scout Groups, Youth Clubs and Community Associations, with an average value of £1,275.

Preservation

The largest grant in this category was made to help provide visitor access for the last remaining World War Two destroyer, HMS Cavalier, which is now based in a fitting setting at the Historic Dockyard at Chatham. The grant to Old St Mary's Church, Clonmel, for restoration of the organ, was made in memory of the work of Colonel Sidney Watson.

Africa

A modest level of support continues to be provided for projects in the east and south of Africa. The largest grant was awarded to the University of Cape Town Trust, for the excellent work they are conducting for the advancement of multiracial education. The Kenya Wildlife Trust was awarded a three year grant.

Peace and security

The proportion of grants awarded in this category declined last year and the four awards made were annual Policy Grants, the largest of which was to the Royal United Services Institute.

Industrial understanding

Since the demise of the Jim Conway Foundation, there has been a dearth of worthy appeals which fall in this category. Only one grant was made, to the newly established Industrial Trust, to help arrange school visits to industries, past, present and future, in South Yorkshire.

Exclusions

(The following exclusions may not always be rigidly applied. Ed.)

The trust does not operate within the broad fields of medicine and health, including drug addiction and projects concerning the mentally and physically handicapped. Also generally excluded are projects concerning museums, churches, cathedrals and other historic buildings.

The whole field of the arts is excluded together with projects for schools, colleges and universities. The trust very seldom operates within the Greater London area, or in Northern Ireland except for specific nominated charities.

No grants to overseas charities, except for the limited activity on a reducing scale with old contacts and associations in Central and East Africa. Grants are not made to individuals or for expeditions.

Applications

Applications should be made in writing to the secretary. Trustee meetings are held four times a year – in January, May, July and October. There is no set format for applications, but it is helpful if they can include the background and a clear statement of the aims of the appeal, together with the funding target and any progress made in reaching it. Applications should, if possible, be restricted to a letter and maximum of two sheets of paper. Initial applications should always include a summary of the previous year's accounts.

The Dunhill Medical Trust

Medical research, elderly

£4,183,000 (1999/2000)

Beneficial area UK, with some special interest in West Sussex.

1 Fairholt Street, London SW7 1EQ

Tel. 020 7584 7411 **Fax** 020 7581 5463

e-mail dmt@dunhillmedical.demon.co.uk

Correspondent Claire Large, Assistant Director

Information available Annual report and accounts, including a full grants list for the previous financial year. Donation policy and terms and conditions (to be reviewed in autumn 2000).

Summary

Almost 100 grants were made in 1999/2000, mainly for a wide range of medical research projects, but these may not be a good guide to future grantmaking, which is intended to prioritise:

- research into and care of the elderly;
- the related issues of disability and rehabilitation.

Background

The trust is in the process of developing its structures and practices. It describes these changes as follows:

A number of developments and changes aimed at modernising the structure and administration of the Trust have taken place during the year 1999/2000, following a strategic review and discussions with the Charity Commissioners on how this might be most appropriately implemented. These have included:

- a separation of the roles of Senior Trustee and Administrator: during 1999, the Trustees accepted the resignation of Mrs Kay Glendinning as a Trustee and agreed that she would continue to provide a very valuable contribution through her wide knowledge and expertise as Director of the Trust;
- the appointment of an Assistant Director with 15 years' experience in public health and business management in the NHS, medical education and research;
- the streamlining of other support posts within the Trust;
- further development and computerisation of the grant administration system;
- improved systems for day-to-day financial administration and monitoring.

The modernisation process is ongoing and it is envisaged that there will be incremental changes in management and administration over the next few years in line with this.

Additionally during 1999/2000, following a periodic review of the Trust's financial strategy, the Trustees reorganised their portfolio of investments and their investment management arrangements. Management of the Charity's main investment portfolio is now divided between Bailey Gifford and Investec, with a separate bond portfolio being managed by a specialist manager, Colchester Global Investors Limited. This reorganisation has been part of a continuing process to ensure that the Charity obtains best value from its management and custodian services.

These changes start to address a number of issues on which the previous edition of this book, two years ago, was critical of the trust, but many of these changes had not become apparent by the end of the 1999/2000 financial year.

The previous senior trustee, Mrs Kay Glendinning, is now shown as the employed director of the trust. In 1999/2000 she was paid 'salary and benefits' of £107,000 as the trust's administrator and there were further 'trustees' pension contributions' of £35,000. These editors do not believe that trustees need to have paid anything approaching this sum for the effective administration of a charity of this kind, even if the person concerned is now an employee rather than a trustee. The trusts says that different arrangements came into place in July 2000 and will be described in due course in the 2000/01 report and accounts.

The pensions contribution for trustees is odd. If for the benefit of Mrs Glendinning, it will have been additional to the total of £107,000, although that figure included 'benefits' as well as salary.

If not, this money is being paid for other trustees, in a most unusual arrangement. It is striking that there were an average of six employees during the year, but that their pension contributions totalled just £4,000.

On the basis of the annual report for 1999/2000 it appears that the trust is continuing to use (to the extent of £12,000) a firm of solicitors, Vizard Oldham, of which one of the trustees, Ronald Perry, is a partner. These editors always regret the existence of such arrangements unless, in the words of the Charity Commission, there is no realistic alternative. If this trust does indeed represent such an exceptional case, the reasons for this should be spelt out in the annual report. There was a further regrettable arrangement under which a company, Delaware Investments, of which another trustee, T Sanderson, was a director, was paid the very large sum of £195,000 for investment management costs. Happily this arrangement has been brought to an end.

The accounts also note a profit of £19,000 on the disposal of a motor car. It is hard to imagine a charity's business requiring a vehicle capable of generating such a sum on its second-hand sale.

Three trustees and the director claimed the unusually large sum of £7,000 for travel, entertainment and sundry expenses.

The annual report notes that the changes described above have been made following discussions with the Charity Commission. It is to be hoped that these will continue; in particular, the apparently unnecessary remuneration of a trustee appears to conflict with the Commission's excellent new guidance published in the summer of 2000.

Grant-making policy

This is described as follows:

The Trust is committed to funding new and innovative projects which are less likely to receive funding from mainstream sources. It prefers to provide support to organisations directly, rather than through a third party, where possible. The Trustees have recently agreed that, in the light of the demographic changes towards an increasing elderly population, the future strategic direction of grant giving should have a major focus on

- research into and care of the elderly and
- the related issues of disability and rehabilitation.

Additionally, the geographical spread of grants is being examined in relation to ensuring an equitable approach to grant-giving.

During 1999/2000, however, the Trust has continued to support a fairly wide spectrum of medical research, and associated equipment and buildings, in addition to the priorities listed above. The intention is to shift the emphasis incrementally to achieve a 'critical mass' in the priority areas over time.

Over the last two years, the Trust has made a number of large scale commitments. These included the support of a 'Cinderella project' (£2.5m over 5 years), and the Trustees were proactive in seeking an appropriate recipient for this grant in the priority areas listed ... Another major development has been the Trustees' decision to endow two University Chairs to mark the 50th anniversary of the death of Herbert Dunhill, founder of the Trust. The tendering process resulted in the establishment at King's College of a Chair in Rehabilitation (a priority for the Trust), and at Oxford University a Chair in Imaging Science (to carry out translational research which will have a direct impact on clinical treatment of patients). Both are complementary in addressing different aspects of neurological disease.

The Trust has also continued and expanded its commitment to the Research Fellowship Programme, which now involves some 20 Fellows in a wide range of disciplines and institutions. The Trustees are now considering extending the programme to provide opportunities for other clinical professionals (such as nurses, pharmacists and therapists) to undertake a period of research, in addition to those who are in medical training programmes. This innovative development is still in its early stages, and fits well with the Government's emphasis on multidisciplinary research.

These large scale commitments have necessarily restricted the amount of available resources for other projects. It has thus underlined the importance of the Trustees' commitment to having a clear strategic direction in order to maximise the effectiveness of grants given. It is envisaged that a more proactive approach to grant-making will be taken in the future to ensure that grant-making reflects need rather than just demand, eg. where a pilot project is funded, by commissioning an evaluation to assess the effectiveness of the grant given.

Grant application process

The Trust receives a large number of applications (around 400 in 1999/2000), 60% of which met the criteria for consideration for funding [*70 grants were made, representing a success rate for eligible applications of 29%. Ed.*]. Every request receives a prompt and individual response. Many applicants request a copy of the donation policy as an initial step, and advice and information is often provided by phone.

Rather than proceed to formal application at a stage when many applications may not meet the criteria, the Trust suggests that potential applicants provide a brief outline of the proposed project on one side of A4 paper, together with details of the financial support requested and timescales. If the proposal meets the criteria for funding, the applicant is then usually visited by the Director or Assistant Director to elicit further information, after which a formal application may be invited.

Where appropriate, professional advice or peer review is sought, which may be provided by the very wide range of clinicians and academics known to the Trust, or by members of the Trust's Medical Advisory Board. The Trustees meet on a quarterly basis to consider proposals which reach this stage and applicants are informed as soon as practicable thereafter. The timescale between initial enquiry and decision is kept as short as is practically possible, commensurate with the need to ensure that all appropriate steps are taken to reach an informed decision. All applications are therefore normally processed within three months.

In the case of an application for a research grant, the Trust requires confirmation that the applicant has received ethical approval from the Local Research Ethics Committee (or Committees, where a multi-centre research project is proposed), before a donation can be granted.

Grantmaking in 1999/2000

The trust has given the following examples of its grants in 1999/2000:

- Connect (formerly City Dysphasic Group at City University), £2,500,000 over five years.

This has been adopted by the Trust as its 'Cinderella Project'. Connect provides therapy services, backed up by research and education, for people living with communication disabilities following a stroke.

- Institute of Obstetrics & Gynaecology Trust, Imperial College School of Medicine, London, £1,000,000.

A grant for one floor of the new Institute building, which will be dedicated to finding genes important in development and growth, particularly in relation to premature birth and genetic disorders.

- Northwick Park Institute of Medical Research, Middlesex, £600,000 over three years.

A grant to carry out a major research programme which will study the local multi-ethnic population with coronary heart disease, as well as multiple studies with cells and biopsy material.

- Department of Rheumatology, University of Newcastle upon Tyne, £300,000 over three years.

A grant for equipment and consumables needed to take forward a major research programme investigating the destruction of joints through arthritis and rheumatism.

- The ARK Facility, North Hampshire Hospital, Basingstoke, £100,000.

A grant towards a multidisciplinary postgraduate medical centre, which aims to improve surgical procedures and to provide educational facilities to bridge the gap between hospital sessions and healthcare within the community.

- Department of Vascular Surgery, St Richard's Hospital, Chichester, £108,603 over three years.

A grant for a multi-centre study of screening for abdominal aortic aneurysms and follow-up, which will evaluate the duration of any benefit resulting from screening, particularly the assessment of life years gained as a result of detection and treatment.

- CARE, Ide Hill, Sevenoaks, £75,000.

A grant towards purpose built housing for people with learning disabilities, to provide specialised facilities tailored to meet the individual needs of residents.

- The PACE Centre, Aylesbury, Bucks, £54,580 over two years.

A grant for a research occupational therapist to undertake an exploratory study which will describe the services provided at PACE for children with a range of disabilities.

- ExtraCare Charitable Trust, Coventry, £36,000 over three years.

A grant for a longitudinal evaluation of the innovative Berryhill Retirement Village, Stoke-on-Trent, being carried out by Keele University, which is examining the extent to which independent living in an age-segregated environment impacts on the health of older people.

Looking at this list, these editors are relieved that the trust is now seeking a fairer geographical distribution of its money.

Exclusions

The trustees will not normally approve the use of funds for:

- providing clinical services that, in their opinion, should or could be provided by the National Health Service
- individuals or organisations outside the UK
- charities representing specific professions or trade associations
- institutional overheads
- travel/conference fees

Applications

To the Assistant Director. Trustees meet in March, May, September and December.

The E B M Charitable Trust

Health, welfare, bloodstock

£933,000 (1998/99)

Beneficial area UK.

St Paul's House, Warwick Lane, London EC4P 4BN

Tel. 020 7248 4499

Correspondent Richard Moore

Trustees *Richard Moore; Michael Macfadyen; Harry Holgate; Cyril Fitzgerald.*

Information available Inadequate annual report and accounts.

Summary

There appear to be few limits to the size of grants, which can be for anything from £500 to £300,000, though most range from £10,000 to £50,000. Larger amounts tend to go to charities concerned with the welfare of horses or to regularly supported organisations, including maritime charities and those for children and disabled people.

The trust wrote in 1999 that 'The trustees' funds are fully committed and therefore unsolicited applications are not requested.' The trust is touchy; a draft of this entry, even without the information below about the remuneration of trustees, produced warnings of possible legal action.

General

As is the charity's practice, the 1998/99 trustees' report said simply that 'beneficiaries included charities involved in animal welfare and research, youth development and the relief of poverty'.

The trust's assets stood at £33.7 million, which generated a low income of just over £1 million. Grantmaking totalled £933,000.

In a practice always regretted by these editors, two of the trustees are partners in organisations paid by the charity in return for services supplied. Richard Moore is a partner at Moore Stephens, which was paid £43,500, and Michael Macfadyen is a consultant at Charles Russell, which received £9,500 in administration fees. Such payments, in the view of the Charity Commission, constitute remuneration and the Commission has recently emphasised its view that trustees should not be remunerated by the charity concerned if there is any realistic alternative.

Of the 29 grants, 14 were for organisations supported in the previous year. The largest two, for £100,000 each, went to Fairbridge (£4,000 in 1997/98) and Lord Mayor Treloar School. The remaining grants could be grouped into the following categories, including examples of other large awards:

Animal welfare: British Racing School (£50,000); Thoroughbred Breeders Association Equine Fertility Unit (£40,000); Racing Welfare Charities (£20,000); PDSA (£24,000); Cambridge University Veterinary School (£16,000).

Health/disability: The Children's Hospital Trust Fund (£97,500); Colon Cancer Concern (£63,000); Evelina Children's Hospital Appeal (£54,000); Chicken Shed Theatre (£37,000); Iris Fund (£30,000); National Star Centre for Disabled Youth (£20,000); Ex-Services Mental Welfare Society (£20,000).

Social welfare/other: Salvation Army (£50,000); Youth Sport Trust (£35,000); Worshipful Company of Shipwrights Charitable Fund (£30,000); Maritime Volunteer Service (£25,000).

Applications

In writing to the correspondent, but see above.

The Sir John Eastwood Foundation

Social welfare, education, health, in Nottinghamshire

£491,000 (1997/98)

Beneficial area UK, but mainly Nottinghamshire in practice.

Burns Lane, Warsop, Mansfield, Nottinghamshire NG20 0QG

Tel. 01623 842581

Correspondent Gordon Raymond, Chairman

Trustees *Gordon Raymond, Chair; Mrs C B Mudford; Mrs D M Cottingham; Mrs V A Hardingham; P M Spencer.*

Information available Accounts available for £15. Those for 1997/98 were the latest received by the Charity Commission in July 2000.

Summary

Grants, normally ranging from £500 to £2,500, are awarded on an ongoing basis almost exclusively to charities in Nottinghamshire. The foundation says that 'particular emphasis is given to charities which help the disabled, the elderly and children with special needs', though the beneficiaries are often wider in scope, with educational institutions receiving the largest grants in 1997/98.

General

The foundation says that

> priority is given to local charities benefiting Nottinghamshire although appeals are considered from organisations who operate further afield ... The charity supports a number of registered charities on a regular basis by making donations each year to those particular charities. The prime target of the trustees each year is to ensure the continuance of these regular donations. Once these have been ensured the trustees consider special projects applications and then other individual applications. These are reviewed and donations made as the trustees determine appropriate out of surplus income.

In practice, appeals from outside Nottinghamshire are unlikely to be unsuccessful, as the number of grant recipients based outside the county is minimal.

Income in 1997/98 totalled a high £689,000 from assets of £11.5 million. About 175 grants were made, amounting to £491,000. Almost all were in Nottinghamshire, with a concentration on the area around Warsop and Mansfield where the foundation is based. Five grants for more than £10,000, accounting for 38% of the total, went to the following beneficiaries:

- Portland College (£100,000)
- Yeoman Park School (£30,000)
- St John Council, Nottingham (£25,000)
- Sherwood Coalfield Regeneration Trust (£15,000)
- All Saints Church, Clipstone (£15,000)

Of the remaining recipients, only three local charities could be identified as being outside Nottinghamshire: East Hull Community Farm (£10,000); Lincoln Toy Library (£1,000) and the Papworth Trust (£250). The only international organisation supported was Sight Savers International (£1,000).

Other grants for £10,000 went to Newark and Notts. Agricultural Society and Colonel Frank Seely School.

Charities supported in the trust's home town included Warsop & District Mentally Handicapped Association (£5,000), Warsop Youth Club (£2,000), Rotary Club of Warsop (£1,000), and Warsop Mothers Union (£300).

Other beneficiaries included St Martha's Church PCC (£5,000); Shelter Nottingham (£2,000); Age Concern Nottingham (£1,000); 1st Mansfield Baden-Powell Scout Group (£1,000); Nottinghamshire Aid Convoys (£2,000); Barnby Moor Village Hall (£2,500); Oaklands Handicapped Centre (£5,500); Stanham Housing Association (£1,000); Nottinghamshire Royal Life Savings Society UK (£1,000); Mansfield Cassette Magazines Association (£500); Ashfield and Mansfield Youth (£1,500).

Exclusions

No grants to individuals.

Applications

In writing to the correspondent.

The Maud Elkington Charitable Trust

Social welfare, general, in Northamptonshire and Leicestershire

£428,000 (1998/99)

Beneficial area Northamptonshire and Leicestershire (especially Desborough and Kettering).

c/o Messrs Harvey Ingram Owston, 20 New Walk, Leicester LE1 6TX

Tel. 0116 254 5454 **Fax** 0116 255 4559

Correspondent The Clerks to the Trust

Information available Accounts with grants list showing only awards over £2,000. No narrative report on grant-making policy or practice.

Summary

The trust makes about 200 small grants a year in the counties of Northamptonshire and Leicestershire, about 80% being for less than £2,000. Typically, around 10 large grants of over £10,000 are made each year, with amounts of over £25,000 being exceptional.

General

Income in the year to April 1999 was £581,000, down from £613,000 in the previous year, and 210 organisations received grants worth a total of £428,000.

Grantmaking does not stray very far from Desborough and Kettering, except for donations to institutions such as universities, or for county-wide projects in Leicestershire and Northamptonshire, which often go to the local/regional branches of national charities. Once a charity is funded it is often supported again and again, perhaps indefinitely.

An unusual characteristic of the trust is that all three trustees are paid, with amounts varying from £2,600 to over £4,000. It is the opinion of these editors that it should be possible to find competent and knowledgeable trustees to undertake, free of charge, the agreeable task of giving away someone else's money, especially on this local scale.

The total administrative costs of the trust were unusually high, at about 16% of the value of grants. This is despite the fact that most grants are given to the same organisations year after year.

A total of 41 grants of more than £2,000 are listed in the 1998/99 trustees' report. Only 11 were for more than £5,000, while a further 169 grants of £2,000 or below were made.

The larger grants appear more likely to go to organisations new to the trust. The largest, of £34,000, was to the Heart of the National Forest Foundation (visitor centre). Others were to Desborough Community Transport (£20,000); Northampton & District MIND (£15,000), and the University of Leicester (Children's Asthma Centre) (£15,000).

The main characteristic of the list, however, is the familiarity of the names, which change little from year to year. Of the 41 organisations on the list, 30 had been funded in the two previous years.

Unusually, Leicester Children's Holiday Centre (Mablethorpe) received £100,000 in 1997, then small grants of £3,000 in the following two years.

Of other charities receiving substantial sums during the period 1996–99, Desborough Town Cricket Club got £25,000 in 1998/99, which added up to £86,000 over three years; Northamptonshire Social Services received £29,000 in the year, making £78,000 since 1996/97.

Other grants reflect the mainly healthcare and welfare charities supported:

Age Concern (£3,500); Barnardos (£3,000); British Red Cross (£13,000 in

Northamptonshire, £2,000 in Leicestershire); Leicester Grammar School Bursaries (£20,000); Kettering General Hospital NHS Trust (£13,000); Army Benevolent Fund (£2,500); PDSA (£2,000).

Exclusions

Individuals.

Applications

In writing to the correspondent. Trustees meet every eight or nine weeks.

The John Ellerman Foundation

Health, welfare, art and conservation, for national organisations

£4,350,000 (planned for 2000/01)

Beneficial area UK and overseas, other than Central and South America.

Aria House, 23 Craven Street, London WC2N 5NS

Tel. 020 7930 8566 **Fax** 020 7839 3654

e-mail postmaster@ellerman.prestel.co.uk

website www.ncvo-vol.org.uk/jef.html

Correspondent Eileen Terry, Appeals Manager

Trustees *Peter Pratt, Chair; Angela Boschi; Dr John Hemming; David Martin-Jenkins; Dennis Parry; Admiral Anthony Revell; Beverley Stott.*

Information available Guidelines for applicants. Excellent annual report with analysis of grantmaking and a full list of donations.

Summary

About 100 grants a year, nearly all between £10,000 and £100,000, to national organisations only (though they need not be big) for core, project or capital costs, over one, two or three year periods. There is a particular interest in innovation and in co-operation between charities (of which the foundation believes there to be too many).

'The trustees aim to make larger grants than have been made in the past.' This trust and its predecessors once made many small awards. However there are also no grants being made for more than £100,000.

Background

This charity incorporates the two former Moorgate trust funds, which once had separate entries in these books:

John Ellerman was born in 1910 into a home of considerable affluence but, early on in life, he showed great concern for other people, particularly those less fortunate than himself. Once he had inherited his wealth, derived principally from the shipping industry and other commercial activities, ... he created The Moorgate Trust Fund in 1970 and The New Moorgate Trust Fund in 1971 and transferred to these bodies some 79% of the shares in Ellerman Lines Ltd. ... He died in 1973 and thus did not live to see the continuing good that these two grant-making trusts would do.

In 1983, facing the need to diversify the investments of the Trust Funds and in order to obtain a greater return on these assets, the Trustees of the two Funds sold the shares in Ellerman Lines ... and ... in 1992, the Trustees amalgamated the two Trust Funds. At the same time, the name was changed to The John Ellerman Foundation ... thus honouring the man who made this gift to charity and his father who created the wealth from which the gift came.

The foundation has five staff, led by its director, Chris Hanvey.

Guidelines for applicants

The charity, which welcomes preliminary telephone enquiries from potential applicants, has published the following guidelines:

The Foundation aims to support a broad cross-section of charities doing work of national significance, in the following categories [*with planned expenditure in 2000/01 in brackets. Ed.*]

- *Medical and Disability* [£1,957,000], including preventive medicine, treatment, relief of suffering, care and support, physical and learning disability, mental illness.
- *Community Development and Social Welfare* [£1,305,000], including children, youth work, substance abuse, housing and homelessness, disadvantaged people and communities.
- *The Arts* [£653,000], including archaeology, historic buildings, museums.
- *Conservation* [£435,000], including the environment.
- The Foundation continues to fund some overseas work, principally in southern Africa. Only charities with a UK office will be considered. The Foundation cannot make donations to the continents of America south of the United States of America.

Recognising that the running of charities has become a highly complex operation in a rapidly-changing world, the Foundation is working towards making fewer but larger grants, and towards developing partnerships with charities. Trustees have a preference for working with headquarters organisations and umbrella bodies rather than local groups. While recognising the value of small amounts of funding to local organisations, the Foundation's view is that smaller trusts, often having local knowledge, are better placed to provide this. *For this reason, applications from local charities will not be considered.*

The Foundation, as one of the larger grant-making trusts, is able to make larger grants, which it is hoped will enable charities to make a difference to the people they serve. The minimum grant is, therefore, £10,000, and it is intended that the average grant will be much higher. The Foundation has at present a particular interest in supporting

- innovatory work
- co-operation between two or more charities.

How to apply

In common with other Foundations, many more applications are received than can possibly be funded. In 1999/2000, only 13% of all appeals within our guidelines were successful. Trustees recognise that preparing good applications places heavy demands on the time and resources of charities and diverts energies from their ultimate purpose. Accordingly, potential applicants are asked to write initially with a brief description of the charity and its current need for funding.

This letter should be no more than one or two pages of A4 and there is no need to send annual reports or background material at this stage. Trustees will decide from this letter whether they want to invite a formal application; if so, an application form will be sent. Whatever the decision, all letters will receive a reply.

Trustees are aware that core funding is becoming increasingly difficult to obtain and they are open to receiving applications for this purpose. At the same time, they expect that charities, which have received core funding, will be able to account for its expenditure and identify what it has enabled them to do. Requests for a contribution to large capital appeals are not encouraged.

The Appeals Manager and staff are happy to discuss potential applications by telephone.

Grant-making policy

The foundation is now making less than 100 new grants a year, normally for amounts between £10,000 and £100,000. By value, almost half the foundation's expenditure is in grants between £10,100 and £25,000. About 35% of grants are for payments extending over two to three years. About 20% are for capital expenditures. The amounts allocated for each of its chosen categories for 2000/2001 are shown in the box below.

These totals presumably include a proportion for allocation to overseas activities, which received £374,000 in 1999/2000, about 8% of the total value of grants.

The Trustees have a special interest in two areas for funding. Applications are particularly encouraged from charities carrying out innovative work and from two or more charities working together. In recognising the day-to-day funding needs of charities, the Foundation also welcomes applications for core costs.

There is further information about the foundation's interests in the material reprinted below from its annual report.

The foundation is operating a new and interesting two stage application procedure. An initial one or two page letter (though scarcely any applicants manage to cheer the trust by keeping just to a single page) is first checked to see if it falls within the guidelines. In 1999/2000 53% of applications failed this test. The letters are then sifted by a committee of a single trustee and one member of staff. Of these applications, 72% were rejected, the remaining 28% being asked to complete a detailed application form. The completed forms are examined by another committee, where around another quarter are rejected.

At this stage surviving applicants have about a 50% chance of receiving funding. Another 3% are found, on inspection of their full application, to be outside the guidelines and 4% are rejected at the trustees' meeting, leaving a final success rate of 6% (13% of all relevant applications).

This is a very low success rate, probably accounted for by the fact that this foundation, and its predecessors, once made many more grants and therefore may still be seen by such organisations as a possible source of funding.

The 1999/2000 annual report appears to list grant payments rather than new awards, to a total of £4,239,000, but without indicating whether the payment is part of a multi-year award.

As a result it is neither possible to tell either if an entry represents a new award or what was the value of the award.

The report does offer eight examples of complete major grants, 'chosen to reflect the variety of work reported'. Rather oddly, they are all instances of grants that are spread over two years. They include:

- Crisis: £80,000 for work with single homeless people with mental health problems.
- Habitat (GB): £30,000 for funding the Director's post, and matching a grant from the Department of the Environment.
- National Autistic Society: £40,000 over two years to support the work of the charity's development team.
- Project Fullemploy: £60,000 towards the charity's capacity building programme. The programme's Director contrasts this with 'short-term project funds'.
- RAFT (Restoration of Appearance and Function Trust): £50,000 to support the charity's group leader in cell biology.

Medical and disability (91 payments totalling £1.8 million)

The foundation decided in September 2000 that it would no longer fund medical research.

As in previous years the largest payment, of £100,000, was to Help the Hospices, but this is exceptional as that charity passes the money on, in turn, to individual hospice charities.

Payments of £50,000 were made to the following: Institute of Obstetrics (building costs); Cystic Fibrosis Research Trust (towards running costs of its support services); Children's Trust (for building costs); Guy's Medical School (for the study of bowel disease); Natural History Museum (biomedical research centre); the Prostate Cancer Charity (for genetic research projects) and the Thrombosis Research Institute (for the Ellerman Computational Biology Unit).

Community development and social welfare (71 payments totalling 1.2 million)

The grants are widely spread. Out of 71 payments (not new awards) in 1999/2000, 14 were for umbrella organisations such as the National Council for One Parent Families or the Housing Services Agency. As yet, only a few grants were for collaborative working between individual charities, such as that made jointly to After Adoption and Parents for Children or to enable the Blessed Trinity Housing Association to work with the Passage Day Centre.

Payments of £50,000 included those to the Association of Community Trusts and Foundations (for its London unit), the National Homeless Alliance (for core costs) and the Depaul Trust (for salaries). The largest payment for capital expenditure, also of £50,000, was to the Passage.

Many grants take the form of short term contributions to core costs, such as £7,000 for the running costs of the Riding for the Disabled Association. In a vivid phrase, Peter Pratt, the new chairman of the foundation, says that offering such grants 'helps to ensure that the central activities for which a charity was established are not too dazzled by the bright lights of project funding'. However the position now adopted does not seem to answer the problem other than by offering postponement. There is an argument for long term support of core costs, where the continued existence of the organisation is important to achieving the funders objectives; or for shorter term investment specifically directed at helping a charity achieve sustainability. This foundation has already moved far in a constructive direction, but it does not yet appear to these editors to have reached a safe haven in this respect.

Arts grants (28 payments totalling £452,000)

Unusually for a trust working in this field, most grants are for core or running costs for national arts organisations, mainly in the fields of orchestral or vocal music, but including grants for art galleries, museums, literature and ancient buildings.

The major beneficiaries were the Shakespeare Globe Trust and English National Opera (£50,000 each), and Suffolk Cathedral (£25,000). The National Youth Orchestra and the National Youth Dance Company each received £10,000, as did the Association of British Choir Directors.

THE JOHN ELLERMAN FOUNDATION

The percentages and amounts allocated for each of its chosen categories for 2000/2001

Medical and disability	45%	£1,957,000
Community development and social welfare	30%	£1,305,000
The arts	15%	£653,000
Conservation	10%	£435,000
Total		£4,350,000

The John Ellerman Foundation – Annual report 1999/2000

Chairman's introduction

... Few areas of the Foundation's funding are remarked upon more frequently than the Trustees' continuing commitment to core funding. The argument that infrastructure costs are more difficult to cover than, say, project funding, finds a resonance with almost all organisations that approach us. In this context it is, therefore, gratifying to find that a 1999 report (Who Pays for Core Costs?) commissioned by the Association of Chief Executives of National Voluntary Organisations and funded by the Joseph Rowntree Foundation, strongly supports the stance taken by the Foundation.

Supporting core costs brings challenges all of its own. It means that a substantial percentage of the income can be already tied up at the start of a new financial year and evaluating exactly where money has gone can be difficult. However, it helps to ensure that the central activities for which a charity was established are not too dazzled by the bright lights of project funding.

The Trustee Board is shortly to undertake a skills audit to fill future vacancies and, in this respect, we were pleased to welcome Mrs Beverley Stott as a new Trustee. A knowledge of overseas work, the needs of young people and the workings of the voluntary sector help to supplement other areas of expertise represented by Board members ...

Grantmaking

Currently, there are over 187,000 registered charities in the UK. However, some trusts would argue that the Charity Commission's review of the Register could profitably have been extended to an inclusive debate about the nature of voluntary activity and the ability of the sector to sustain an ever-growing number of charities. While changes to Payroll Giving, new exemptions for small scale trading activity and the abolition of the lower limit for Gift Aid payments all, undoubtedly, represent helpful Treasury developments for operational charities, the reality remains that more and more charities are fishing in a pond which is not growing exponentially. In this context the role of Foundations can prove significant.

Last year, The John Ellerman Foundation received a total of 1,400 applications for its funds. It is salutary to note that the success rate, for all applications, remained at 6%, although this increases to 13% when eligible applications only are considered – a rise of 2% on last year's figures.

That more than half the applications were outside our existing guidelines has to raise important issues both for the Foundation and for those who seek funding. Part of this can possibly be explained by a shift in policy, which moved the Foundation's emphasis to national and regional charities and away from more local initiatives. It was felt that a more effective contribution could be made by concentrating on larger organisations. Nevertheless, the question of 'How can we do what we do better and more effectively?' has to be uppermost for all the staff. To this end we have re-issued the guidelines and strengthened the web-site. We also use whatever public occasions present themselves to talk about the Foundation's funding criteria.

In this context, the Foundation also introduced a two-stage application process, which has been in existence long enough to permit some proper evaluation. Initially, applicants are encouraged to write in, on one or two sides of A4, outlining exactly what it is they wish to have funded. For promising applicants there is then a simple form to complete which goes to the full Trustee Board. The aim is not to set up a series of increasingly difficult hoops through which hapless operational charities are expected to jump, but to avoid needless effort for those applicants who have little chance of success. Trustees are only too aware that requests can take many hours and much effort to complete. They can represent a considerable investment in resources for charities where such resources are in scarce supply. Telephone advice, visits and personal contact all help to ensure that all applicants have the best chance possible and the maximum opportunity to make their case for funding. Evidence indicates that charities have welcomed this phased approach as it allows a dialogue from initial ideas to, hopefully, the successful award of a grant ...

Funding across ... a broad span has both advantages and drawbacks. ... the policy of paying for core costs, in particular, is welcomed. As organisations like the National Lottery Charities Board continue to debate whether or not they will pay some element towards the day to day running costs of operational charities, there seems to be growing recognition that organisations will become unsustainable if more and more projects are supported by inadequate infrastructures ...

Lastly, the Foundation continues to be both outward looking and to contribute to the wider debates within the voluntary sector. This seems essential, not simply to keep in touch with good practice but to influence the way in which charities are developing. Over the last twelve months staff of the Foundation have been involved in chairing a major report by the Association of Chief Executives of Voluntary Organisations into core costs; contributing to the work of the Charity Sub-Committee of the Institute of Chartered Accountants in England & Wales; and chairing the Association of Charitable Foundation's Steering Group on Information Technology.

Conservation grants (20 payments totalling £345,000)

There were two payments of £50,000, for the Wildscreen@Bristol display centre and to the Wildfowl and Wetlands Trust for its centre in Barnes, London. £25,000 was given for the captive breeding programme of lions and tigers by the Scottish Zoological Society and, going overseas, £20,000 for the Niassa Reserve in Mozambique. Support for policy work and campaigning was shown by the grants for Forum for the Future (£20,000) and the Soil Association (£10,000 for its sustainable timber programme).

Overseas grants (23 payments totalling £374,000)

Grants appear to be made under the medical and welfare headings. There were no visible arts grants and the only overseas conservation grants were classified under the Conservation heading in the annual report.

Of the 13 geographically identifiable grants, 12 were in Africa – four in South Africa with which there is an historical Ellerman Lines connection. Four were for Uganda or neighbouring west Kenya. A grant outside the normal categories was for Book Aid International (£10,000).

The largest payments were to the Commonwealth Society for the Deaf (£40,000 for its HARK mobile clinic in the western Cape) and to MERLIN (£30,000 for running its Africa desk). There was support for generalist charities such as Population Concern (£10,000), though this may have been for work in Southern Africa. Only one payment was definitely for another continent; the £10,000 to the Gordon Layton Trust towards a new eye hospital in Pakistan.

Exclusions

Grants are made only to registered charities, and are not made for the following purposes:

- medical research
- for or on behalf of individuals
- individual hospices
- local branches of national organisations
- 'Friends of' groups
- education or educational establishments
- religious causes
- conferences and seminars
- sports and leisure facilities
- purchase of vehicles (except for those used for aid transport)
- the direct replacement of public funding
- deficit funding
- domestic animal welfare

Circulars will not receive a reply. The foundation cannot make donations to the continents of America south of the USA.

Applications

See Guidelines, above.

In the first instance, send a letter of not more than one or two pages of A4 without enclosures. From this, trustees will decide whether they want to invite a formal application. If so an application form and further details will be sent. All letters will receive a reply.

'We are happy to discuss potential applications by telephone; please ask for the appeals manager' (Eileen Terry).

The trustees meet regularly throughout the year and there are no deadlines.

Entindale Ltd

Orthodox Jewish charities

£708,000 (1998/99)

14 Mayfield Gardens, London
NW4 2QA

Correspondent Mrs B L Bridgeman, Trustee

Information available Inadequate annual report and accounts.

General

The trust aims 'to advance religion in accordance with the orthodox Jewish faith'. Over 100 grants are made a year, most for £1,000 or less, down to as little as £13 (to Norwood Ravenswood, one of the smallest donations recorded in this book).

Its assets are held almost entirely in the form of investment properties and a substantial part of its income is still in the form of continuing donations. In 1998/99 four grants of over £30,000 went to:

- British Friends of Beis Meir (£77,000)
- Menorah Grammar School (£66,000)
- YH Training and Enterprise (£41,000)
- Kahol Chassidim Bobov (£34,000)

Although some of these had been supported previously, this does not appear to be in the form of regular ongoing support.

The Equitable Charitable Trust

Education of disabled/ disadvantaged children

£2,453,000 (1999)

Beneficial area UK.

5 Chancery Lane, Clifford's Inn, London EC4A 1BU

Tel. 020 7242 1212

Correspondent Brian McGeough, Managing Trustee

Information available Full reports and accounts.

Summary

Grants, sometimes for six-figure sums, are made for both capital and revenue projects to schools and other educational organisations catering for the educational needs of disadvantaged children.

Background

The trust was established as part of a commercial school fees pre-payment scheme. The annual surplus was applied for charitable purposes. Schemes of this nature are no longer allowed but existing commitments can still be met. The effect of this is that the income is now diminishing year by year and will end when the education of the last pupils already in the scheme is complete.

However, the trust has already begun accumulating a part of its income into a permanent endowment, so that the trust will continue to operate after its present source of funds comes to an end. By the end of 1998 this new capital fund stood at £3.8 million.

Grantmaking

The trust is managed by Brian McGeough, one of its trustees, who was formerly the treasurer of Smith's Charity.

The trustees will continue to concentrate on the educational needs of disadvantaged children by making grants for specific projects to schools and other organisations catering for such needs. They will also fund interesting and innovative educational projects of all kinds wherever they can find them, especially if they are capable of being introduced into a large number of schools to supply needs not adequately met at present.

They will continue to make grants available for the purchase of computer equipment for use by disabled young people in connection with their education. These will continue to be the only grants made to individuals.

In 1999 about 75 new awards were made, few of them for less than £10,000. There was no grant comparable to the £400,000 committed in the previous year to the British Museum for the Education Centre in its Great Court development. However, £171,000 over three years was given to Total Learning Challenge's work in north east schools with children who have emotional or behavioural disturbances, while £91,000 over three years went to the Who Cares? Trust. £60,000 over three years was given to Working Support, for work in east London.

In the previous year, grants had included those to Cerebral Palsy Care (£25,000), Rathbone C.I. (£105,000 over three years for projects in Wigan), Side by Side (£30,000 for accommodation for work with children with special needs in London) and YMCA Building Bridges (£20,000 for work in Bristol).

The work of the trust is unevenly distributed across the country. Of 67 grants in 1998 for work in identifiable localities, 60 were in England, 3 in Northern Ireland and 2 each in Wales and Scotland. Within England, if the country is divided into two halves of equal population, 41 grants were for work in the southern half and 19 in the northern half.

Exclusions

No grants to individuals except for the purpose of purchasing computer equipment necessary for the education of disabled students.

Applications

In writing to the correspondent. The charity does not use application forms but offers the following guidelines to applicants for grants:

1. Applications should be no longer than four A4 sides (plus budget and accounts) and should incorporate a short (half page) summary.

2. Applications should:

a) State clearly who the applicant is, what it does and whom it seeks to help.
b) Give the applicant's status (e.g. registered charity).
c) Describe the project for which a grant is sought clearly and succinctly; explain the need for it; say what practical results it is expected to produce; state the number of people who will benefit from it; show how it will be cost effective and say what stage the project has so far reached.

d) Enclose a detailed budget for the project together with a copy of the applicant's most recent audited accounts. (If those accounts show a significant surplus or deficit of income, please explain how this has arisen.)
e) Name the applicant's trustees/patrons and describe the people who will actually be in charge of the project giving details of their qualifications for the job.
f) Describe the applicant's track record and, where possible, give the names and addresses of two independent referees to whom the Equitable Charitable Trust may apply for a recommendation if it wishes to do so.
g) State what funds have already been raised for the project and name any other sources of funding to whom the applicant has applied.
h) Explain where the ongoing funding (if required) will be obtained when the charity's grant has been used.
i) State what plans have been made to monitor the project and wherever possible to evaluate it and, where appropriate, to make its results known to others.
j) Ask, where possible, for a specific amount.

3. Please keep the application as simple as possible and avoid the use of technical terms and jargon. The trustees are in regular contact with each other and deal with applications as and when received.

The Eranda Foundation

Research into education and medicine, the arts, social welfare

£1,467,000 (1998/99)

Beneficial area UK.

New Court, St Swithin's Lane, London EC4P 4DU

Tel. 020 7280 5000

Correspondent Rebecca Mellotte, Secretary

Trustees *Sir Evelyn de Rothschild; Lady de Rothschild; Leopold de Rothschild; Sir Graham Hearne; Mrs Renée Robeson.*

Information available Accounts with a brief report. A grants list was not seen by these editors.

General

The report says that:

'The ongoing policy of the Foundation is to promote original research and the continuation of existing research into medicine and education, fostering of the arts and promotion of social welfare.'

In 1998/99, unrealised gains on investments helped to increase the foundation's asset base by 50%, to £62.5 million. Income was £1,545,000 and grants totalled £1,467,000, categorised as follows (with grant totals for the two most recent years for which information is available):

	1998/99	*1997/98*
The arts	£528,000	£465,000
Health, welfare and medical research	£477,000	£319,000
Education	£462,000	£672,000
Miscellaneous	–	£5,000

Though a grants list is shown to the Charity Commissioners, the foundation prefers not to make it publicly available, as it wishes to remain anonymous to its beneficiaries. However, the SORP requires public disclosure of grants and an inclination to anonymity is not enough to justify the failure to meet this requirement.

Applications

In writing to the correspondent.

The Eveson Charitable Trust

Health, welfare in the West Midlands area

£2,416,000 (1999/2000)

Beneficial area Herefordshire, Worcestershire and the West Midlands, including Birmingham and Coventry.

45 Park Road, Gloucester GL1 1LP

Tel. 01452 501352 **Fax** 01452 302195

Correspondent Alex D Gay, Administrator

Trustees *Bruce Maughfling, Chair; Rt Revd John Oliver, Bishop of Hereford; Peter Temple-Morris MP; J Martin Davies; David Pearson .*

Information available Full report and accounts and guidance notes for applicants.

Summary

In 1999/2000 the trust made no less than 310 grants. Though occasional grants can be for more than £50,000 for both capital and running costs, most grants are for amounts of less than £10,000.

General

Although the trust has assets of almost £80 million these only generated the low income of £2.5 million in 1999/2000. As the trustees are not restricted in their expenditure to investment income alone, they are free to base their work on the 'real return' on their endowment. On this basis they should be able to achieve 5% of net assets year on year, or about £4 million a year at 2000 prices, which would allow a substantially higher level of grantmaking even after taking administrative costs into account.

Grantmaking is restricted by the trust deed (which is the will of Mrs Violet Eveson) to support of the following causes:

- physically handicapped people (including those who are blind or deaf)
- mentally handicapped people
- hospitals and hospices
- children in need, whether disadvantaged or physically or mentally handicapped
- elderly people
- those who are homeless
- medical research in any of these categories.

Grants are currently restricted to the geographical areas outlined above, as a policy decision of the trustees. The trust does not instigate programmes of its own, but responds to the applications which it receives (and the submission of which it actively encourages).

The number and value of grants in 1999/2000 were categorised as follows (with the previous year's totals in brackets):

Accommodation	41	£342,000	(£288,000)
Healthcare	39	£687,000	(£760,000)
Social care and development	134	£1,386,000	(£1,670,000)

Annual report

The annual report notes the coverage of these headings, to which these editors have added examples of the larger grants:

Accommodation

Includes grants to organisations providing non-health related accommodation and respite/holiday accommodation.

The major awards were to YMCA Worcester (£50,000 for the capital costs of a foyer project); Droitwich Women's Refuge (£46,000 for salaries over three years); Birmingham Women's Aid (£25,000 for the salary of a worker over three years); Wellington Charities, Herefordshire (£20,000 for refurbishing almshouses); Worcester Women's Aid (£20,000 for staff costs).

Healthcare

Includes grants to organisations that focus on the prevention or treatment of specific diseases, the prevention or treatment of diseases generally and/or health problems, the rehabilitation of disabled individuals, residential nursing homes for the frail, elderly, severely disabled and those offering terminal care.

This heading covers medical research and accounted for three of the largest grants: £75,000 to Birmingham University towards a research nurse for a study into pancreatic cancer; £78,000 to the Islet Research Laboratory at Worcester Royal Infirmary, for research into diabetes; and £50,000 for the Institute for Cancer Studies, also at Birmingham University.

Other major grants went to the Cystic Fibrosis Unit at Birmingham's Heartlands Hospital (£50,000); St Michael's Hospice (near Hereford) Development Trust (£60,000); and Acorn Children's Hospice, Walsall (£50,000).

Social care and development

Includes organisations providing human and social services to a community or target population, including services for children, young people, physically and mentally disabled, elderly people and homeless people.

The grants under this heading were more numerous but also smaller, with 86 grants of £2,000 or less. The largest grants went to Sandwell Community Caring Trust (£31,000 for refurbishment of a day care facility); Victoria School, Birmingham (£25,000 for a garden for sensorily deprived children); Hereford and Worcester Advisory Service on Alcohol and Haywood High School, Hereford (£25,000 each); and Breakthrough Deaf Hearing Integration (£27,000).

Exclusions

Grants are not made to individuals, even if such a request is submitted by a charitable institution.

Applications

The trustees meet quarterly, usually at the end of March and at the beginning of July, October and January.

Applications can only be considered if they are on the trust's standard, but very simple, Application for Support form which can be obtained from the administrator at the offices of the trust in Gloucester. The form must be completed and returned (together with a copy of the latest accounts and annual report of the organisation) to the trust's offices at least six weeks before the meeting of trustees at which the application is to be considered, in order to give time for necessary assessment procedures, including many visits to applicants.

Before providing support to statutory bodies (such as hospitals and schools for people with learning difficulties), the trustees require written confirmation that no statutory funds are available to meet the need for which funds are being requested. In the case of larger grants to hospitals, the trustees ask the district health authority to confirm that no statutory funding is available.

Where applications are submitted that fall clearly outside the grant-giving parameters of the trust, the applicant is advised that the application cannot be considered and reasons are given.

All applications that are going to be considered by the trustees are acknowledged in writing. Applicants are advised of the reference number of their application and of the quarterly meeting at which their application is going to be considered. The decisions are advised to applicants in writing soon after these meetings.

The Esmée Fairbairn Charitable Trust

Social welfare, arts and heritage, education, environment

£19,865,000 (1999)

Beneficial area UK.

7 Cowley Street, London SW1P 3NB

Tel. 020 7227 5400 **Fax** 020 7227 5401

e-mail enquiry@efct.org.uk

website www.efct.org.uk

Correspondent Margaret Hyde, Director

Trustees *John S Fairbairn, Chair; Jeremy Hardie; Sir Antony Acland; Ashley G Down; Mrs Penelope Hughes-Hallet; Martin Lane-Fox; Baroness Linklater; Lady Milford; Lord Rees-Mogg; William Sieghart.*

Information available Detailed guidelines for applicants (revised guidelines available during the first quarter of 2001). Excellent annual report and accounts.

Summary

The trust gives grants under the four programmes named above, for which excellent guidelines are available. Unfortunately these were due to be revised shortly after publication of this book, so those interested should contact the trust for the most up to date information. Grants can be of all sizes, but average about £25,000. There is an admirably simple application scheme for small grants of amounts up to £5,000.

The trust is developing rapidly, as its income has greatly increased. It has taken on new staff and is increasingly concentrating on revenue projects, with capital projects accorded a low priority. The success rates for applications is about 25% – for those that pass an initial screening for conformity with trust policies, and for basic assessability, it is about 45%.

Each programme has a separate section in this entry, in which will be found the relevant guidelines for applicants, and excerpts from the general description of the programme printed in the 1999 annual report. These follow the parts of the guidelines that apply to all programmes and which give an excellent account of the grantmaking as a whole. The entry ends with some general information on the work of the charity in 1999.

The trust has also begun to operate its own initiatives, starting with 'Heads You Win' in 1999, a scheme to develop the leadership and management skills of primary school headteachers, while another interesting project being developed concerns attitudes to prison and alternative punishment. These are welcome examples of proactive initiative by this increasingly energetic trust.

Background

The trust was founded by Ian Fairbairn, a pioneer of the unit trust industry through the M&G company, in memory of his wife Esmée who was killed by a flying bomb during the Second World War.

In 1999, the company having been taken over by Prudential, the trust's shareholding in M&G had been realised and the proceeds were invested in a diversified endowment. This is producing a much higher income for the trust, over £30 million in 1999 (against £15 million in 1998), which has enabled the trust to set a level of grantmaking of £26 million a year, after allowing up to a sensible seven per cent for administration.

To match its increased resources, the trust has entered a period of development in both policy and organisation. Though the overall areas of grantmaking remain unchanged, there are now unlikely to be more of the major capital grants such as the £500,000 given a few years ago to the Royal Opera House; there is to be a concentration overall on revenue rather than capital grants; there appears to be an energetic effort to spread grantmaking across the country, with an emphasis on areas of disadvantage; and the previous interest in the promotion of free market economics has been watered down to a fairly mainstream preference for the use of market forces, where appropriate, to deliver social benefits.

Backing this, the staff of the trust is being greatly expanded, to a total of 26, an appropriate number for a large trust such as this, with wide interests. Ongoing administrative costs in 1999 were a moderate six per cent of the value of grants.

The trust also makes extensive and welcome use of expert advisers. They, and permanent grantmaking staff, are listed towards the end of this entry.

Grant-making policy and practice

Grantmaking is being reorganised, with a separate trustee group for each of the four programmes. The main board will concentrate on trust strategy and on the largest grants.

This is a welcome development, setting up a structure in which trustees and staff will work together in specific areas of expertise. Though doubtless this already happens in an informal way in numerous trusts, its formal establishment here is likely to become a model for others.

Another welcome development is the appointment of a policy and research officer (Jane Rintoul). Trusts whose knowledge of the sectors they fund comes mainly from the applications they receive, and from the warmly glowing reports of those that they fund, often end up with a distorted view of what is actually going on.

The appointment of a communications officer (Liz Rose) may help to achieve a pattern of applications more closely matched to the needs to be met than is found in the postbag of trusts generally (the first edition of this book, 15 years ago, quoted an outspoken trustee as saying 'the problem is, all the best applications seem to come from Surrey' – we hope he exaggerated, but the underlying problem remains real).

The trust's grant fund is currently £24 million and almost 4,000 applications are received each year. There is no typical grant size: grants vary from a few hundred to a few hundred thousand pounds. There is no set pattern for making grants up to a specific percentage of the cost of a project and grants of up to 100% are made (though the sharing of costs, say with another foundation, is viewed positively).

Grants can be awarded singly or phased over a longer period and may be made towards revenue, capital or project expenditure [*though three years appeared to be the maximum grant duration in 1999. Ed.*]. The trust is concentrating increasingly on revenue projects, with capital projects being accorded low priority.

Once an application has been considered the trust does not usually accept another application from the same organisation within 12 months from the date of the decision.

About 24% of applications were successful, though not necessarily for the full amount requested. Over 2,000 were ruled out by staff as being outside the stated policies or too weak for detailed consideration. The success rate for the remainder was 45%.

Small grants scheme

The trust operates a small grants scheme covering grants of up to £5,000. Preference is given to projects that might be substantially enabled to happen with the trust's funding, rather than to projects where a grant would form part of a larger funding scheme. Local district and smaller national organisations are particularly encouraged to apply. (For details of how to apply under this scheme, see under 'Applications' at the end of this entry.)

The trust's guiding principles

- The purpose must be *charitable* and normally the trust will only consider applications from registered charities.
- The trust's area of interest is *UK-wide*. The trustees aim to give particular attention to less advantaged areas.
- In general the trust favours projects which will contribute to the preservation and development of a *free and stable society*.
- There is a preference for projects which are *innovative*, *developmental*, designed to make a *practical impact* on a particular problem and reflect the principles of *market forces*. Especially in the case of local projects preference is given to those which demonstrate *active local participation* and support *self-help*.
- The trust welcomes applications from *black and minority ethnic groups*.
- The trust will be alert to the needs of *disabled people* in all appropriate funding decisions.
- The trust looks favourably on projects undertaken in *partnership*, for example with another charitable trust.
- The trust attaches importance to the *assessment and dissemination* of the results of work it has funded, so that others might benefit.

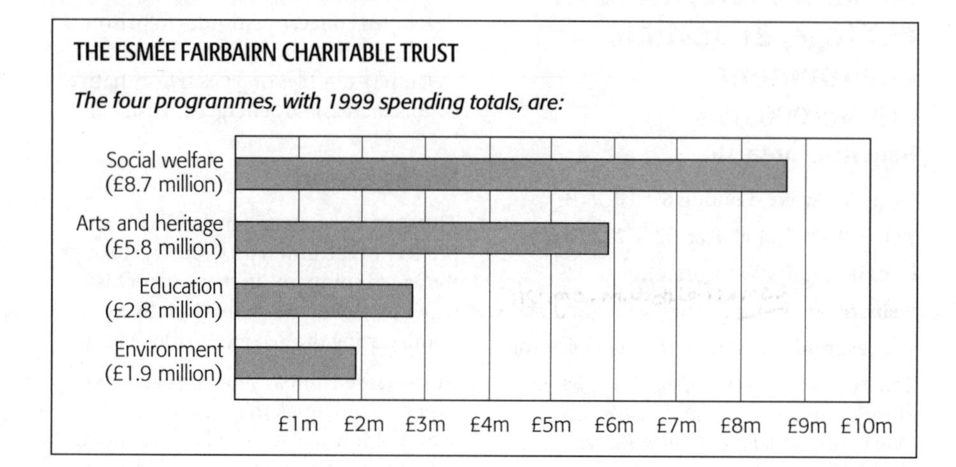

Social development (£8,722,000, 1999)

Sector group

Chairman: Baroness Linklater

Trustees: Sir Antony Acland, Jeremy Hardie, William Sieghart

Programme Director: Nicola Pollock

Grants Manager: Sharon Shea

Grants Manager: not appointed at time of writing

Sector Grant Team Assistant: Frances Thompson

Adviser: Baroness Stern

[From an article in *Trust Monitor* magazine, autumn 2000]

The power to do more good

The Esmée Fairbairn Charitable Trust is now one of the largest trusts in the country. *Trust Monitor* talked with its director, *Margaret Hyde*

During the first quarter of 2001 all fundraisers should be alert for announcements of [the trust's] new funding guidelines.
Whilst the trust has decided not to restrict the types of grant it is prepared to make it 'will concentrate increasingly on revenue projects, with capital projects being accorded low priority' (chairman's report 1999). Margaret Hyde pointed out the trust has shifted over the past few years to making larger grants, many for a three-year period, and that repeat grants are made 'on occasion'. Many of its grants are for 'core' costs. The trustees wish to be as 'flexible as possible'. In addition they have decided to maintain smaller grants below £10,000 because 'they can make a real difference to so many organisations' despite the fact that they are costly to administer.

New proactive initiatives

The trust has a stated interest in 'moving practice forward and influencing policy development' and now has the 'capacity for a more imaginative range of initiatives'. A key feature promises to be its more proactive approach towards selected issues. An interesting trust-generated project currently being developed concerns attitudes to prison and alternative punishment. Bids will be invited by the trust during 2001. This is not an entirely new direction. The trust co-operated several years earlier with the Royal Society of Arts on a major Early Learning programme. Along with other strategic policy and practice developments in early learning funded by the trust, this had a direct effect on the Department for Education and Employment's major initiative, Sure Start. In 1999 it started its 'Heads You Win' project, a programme for the professional development of primary headteachers, for which it set aside over £3/4 million. It solicited proposals from state primary schools and local education authorities which resulted in 12 grants spread throughout England and Wales covering a wide variety of approaches to leadership. The results will be carefully evaluated before a report is launched into the public domain at a major conference in 2001.

Maximising the impact of its grants

Whilst these initiatives are few and absorb, as yet, only a small part of the trust's annual funding, they illustrate an important part of the trust's wish to maximise the impact of its grants. In the future we may expect a trust with a more publicly known face. It intends actively to 'market or promote' valuable work, preferring these terms to 'dissemination of good practice'. The trust's website (www.efct.org.uk) has been launched and will be used creatively 'to bring the good work of those we fund to wider attention' – part of the work of the new Communications and Information Officer, who is also drawing up communications strategy for the trustees. Whilst it is premature to guess its thrust, we may expect a concerted effort to 'put over a friendly face' within the regions with help from its regional advisers, new specialist staff, local surgeries, CVSs and key intermediary bodies. In doing so it will aim to extend its support more effectively to its targeted interests such as disadvantaged areas and the black and minority ethnic communities.

Devolved grantmaking structure

The trust has radical plans to introduce a devolved grantmaking structure. These promise to give the trust new energy and commitment. Small trustee groups have been formed to deal with each of the four sectors of grantmaking interest, and they have been meeting since spring 2000 to discuss their future policies and priorities. It is intended that these groups will have the power to decide grants up to £100,000. Each group will have its own annual budget and meet quarterly. Decisions for grants of £100,000 or more will be passed upwards to be considered at the full board's quarterly meetings. These measures will draw more intensively and effectively on the trustees' particular interests and experience with support also from the advisers and the new programme directors appointed to each of its four sectors. Their work should become far more active and focused, with greatly increased direct contact with applicants through visits, presentations at meetings and so on.

Another hugely significant change is the proposal that decisions on grants of up to £10,000 be delegated to its new specialist staff teams. This is a rare, bold departure for a trust. These measures to streamline and speed up its smaller grants release the sector groups and the trustee board to take a wider and more in depth view of issues which concern them. The shape of grantmaking meetings to come will contrast (16 sector groups meetings plus four full board meetings a year) with the system running to date whereby some 250 applications are decided at the four board meetings. The trust is awaiting the decision of the Charity Commission on the revision of its trust deed before this structure can come into effect.

Specialist teams, looking for wider connections

Margaret Hyde firmly stressed that the trust aims to avoid the 'silo approach' and that the sector groups are not expected to be 'too narrowly specialist' but will be 'looking for points of connection' between areas. The new programme directors have been appointed because of their track record in their sector and their capability to take a 'wide view of the world'. The trust's work will also be supported by three new 'generalist' officers – a policy and research officer, a communications and information officer and an evaluation and audit officer.

The trust made a positive decision to maintain a centralised staff structure, increasing its London staff to 26, rather than devolving to a regional way of working as at least one other trust has done. Margaret Hyde firmly believes 'We are London-based and need to build on a strong direct sense of ourselves' and that it is 'hugely important we ourselves maintain a direct grip on our work and what we are using the money for'. Added to this the staff will have a far greater capability to get out and meet applicants in the regions as well as drawing upon regional advice.

Margaret Hyde holds the view that grantmaking is a 3-D activity – an art rather than a science – and in an earlier article for *Trust Monitor* wrote, 'the less definable skill of intuition, laced with a healthy dose of experience, is a critical component in any judgement'. It will be immensely interesting to see how the trust develops its personality in the next few years and handles its large new resources, both financial and human. Certainly the structures are being set in place for it to perform with style and vigour.

Guidelines

The current guidelines (to be replaced in early 2001) read as follows:

The trust prefers prevention to palliatives. It wishes to foster self-help and the participation of those intended to benefit; enable less advantaged people to be independent, gain useful skills and overcome handicaps; and encourage volunteer involvement. The trust supports practical initiatives embodying some or all of these characteristics in the following priority fields:

- Permanent physical and sensory disabilities;
- Mental health and learning disabilities;
- Young people, especially those who are under-achieving or living in difficult circumstances;
- Parenting and family support;
- Carers, ie people caring for the sick, elderly or disabled people at home;
- Homelessness;
- Ageing, ie social aspects of elderly people living in the community;
- Crime prevention and the rehabilitation of offenders and ex-offenders;
- Substance abuse;
- Regeneration and other schemes which support and develop community resourcefulness, particularly in less advantaged areas.

Grants in 1999

New grants over £10,000	£7,408,000
New grants £10,000 and under	£1,314,000
Percentage of new grants	44%
Number of new grants	466
Average grant size	£19,000

The annual report notes that

in its Social Welfare spending the Trust aims to foster self-help, participation and independence, through a wide range of practical activities. Be it services to families, young people, homeless people or regeneration of whole communities, preventive strategies are favoured over palliatives.

Grants were headed by those to:

- National Schizophrenia Fellowship: £157,000 over three years for an educational project for young people.
- Pilotlight: £153,000 over three years for salaries.
- Shaftesbury Homes: £150,000 over three years for activity workers.
- British Juvenile and Family Courts Society: £105,000 over three years for the director's salary.
- RICA: £102,000 over three years for salaries.
- The Bourne Trust: £100,000 over three years for a new First Night in Custody welfare project at HMP Holloway, London.

There were nearly 200 grants for amounts under £10,000. A typical section of the list of beneficiaries reads as follows:

East Midlands Shape	£1,000
The Edinburgh Mela	£1,000
Eglwys Gymunedol Noddfa	£5,000
ESCAPE Family Support	£4,000
Exmoor Community Centre Trust	£9,000

Arts and heritage (£5,794,000, 1999)

Sector group

Chairman: Lord Rees-Mogg

Trustees: Penelope Hughes-Hallett, Felicity Milford

Programme Director: Shreela Ghosh

Grants Manager: not appointed at time of writing

Sector Grant Team Assistant: not appointed at time of writing

Adviser: Hilary Bartlett

Guidelines

The current guidelines (to be replaced in early 2001) read as follows:

The trust wishes to help extend the artistic and business development of the performing and creative arts.

The trust is more likely to support organisations or projects less able to raise substantial funds from other sources. The trust's priorities are:

- The professional development of performers and other artists who have completed their formal training and are in the earlier stages of their careers. No grants are made to individuals;
- Initiatives which improve the management, artistic or business performance of arts organisations, or their financial independence;
- The public presentation or performance of contemporary work;
- Arts provision amongst groups or places less well-served;
- Audience development;
- Arts education work involving local communities, particularly those less well served.

Grants in 1999

New grants over £10,000	£4,862,000
New grants £10,000 and under	£933,000
Percentage of new grants	29%
Number of new grants	306
Average grant size	£19,000

The annual report notes that

the Trust's grantmaking in the Arts and Heritage field has been responsive in character, guided by its stated policy priorities which concentrate on helping to extend the artistic and business development of the arts. In 1999 the Trust approved 306 new grants totalling £5.79 million.

The trust gives higher priority to revenue grants than to capital, a policy which will be formalised in new guidelines to be published early in 2001. While capital grants tend at the moment to arise more frequently in Arts and Heritage than in other sectors, there will be fewer in future.

Grants were headed by those to:

- London Guildhall University: £221,000 over three years for archivist posts to help move the Fawcett Library.
- National Museums and Galleries on Merseyside: £150,000 capital grant.
- National Youth Orchestra: £150,000 over three years, for residential courses.
- Dulwich Picture Gallery: £150,000 to the building appeal.
- Monteverdi Choir and Orchestra: £100,000 towards the Bach Cantata Pilgrimage.
- Women's Playhouse Trust: £100,000 to help convert Wapping Hydraulic Pumping Station into a cultural centre.

There were 140 grants for £10,000 or less, though there were few arts grants for less than £5,000 under the small grants scheme. A typical part of the list of beneficiaries reads as follows:

Lontano Trust	£4,500
Lyric Theatre, Hammersmith	£5,000
Made in Wales Stage Company	£3,000
Magpie Dance	£5,000
Manchester Youth Theatre	£2,250
Momentary Fusion	£5,000

Education (£2,662,000, 1999)

Sector group

Chairman: Sir Antony Acland

Trustees: Penelope Hughes-Hallett, John Fairbairn

Programme Director: Hilary Hodgson

Grants Manager: Bernie Morgan

Sector Grant Team Assistant:* Rachel Faulkes

Advisers: Sir Christopher Ball, Professor Hugh Lawlor

**shared position*

Guidelines

The current guidelines (to be replaced in early 2001) read as follows:

The trust is interested in supporting projects which will contribute to the development of a better educated society. Projects falling in the following fields are given priority:

- early learning, covering the years 0–7;

- further education of 16–19 year olds, particularly the academically less able;
- the professional development and further training of teachers;
- adult education, especially where this combats earlier under-achievement or creates second chances.

(No grants are made to individuals).

Grants in 1999

New grants over £10,000	£2,456,000
New grants £10,000 and under	£205,000
Percentage of new grants	13%
Number of new grants	89
Average grant size	£30,000

The annual report notes that

the Trust aims to support projects that will contribute towards the development of a better educated society. It is particularly concerned with laying the foundations for learning. Its grantmaking also aims to address the further education of 16 to 19-year-olds, adult education and the professional development of teachers.

Grants were headed by those to:

- Liverpool Hope University College: £140,000 for capital and salary costs.
- Return to Learn Support Group: £122,000 for salaries in Durham.
- The Place To Be: £102,000 over three years, for salaries.
- Who Cares? Trust: £97,000 over three years for a salary.

Environment (£1,948,000, 1999)

Sector group

Chairman: Lady Felicity Milford

Trustees: Ashley Down, Martin Lane Fox

Programme Director: Tim Keenan

Grants Manager: not appointed at time of writing

Sector Grant Team Assistant:* Rachel Faulkes

Adviser: Hugh Raven

**shared position*

Guidelines

The current guidelines (to be replaced in early 2001) read as follows:

The trust wishes to promote sustainable development principally through practical projects, research where this is geared to advancing practical solutions, and education. Its priorities are as follows:

- The preservation of countryside and wildlife, appropriately linked to public access;
- The reconciliation of the needs of the environment and the economy, ie projects which sustain the former and promote solutions to any adverse environmental effects associated with economic development;
- The development of alternative technologies that help attain these objectives.

Grants in 1999

New grants over £10,000	£1,843,000
New grants £10,000 and under	£104,000
Percentage of new grants	10%
Number of new grants	51
Average grant size	£38,000

The annual report notes that

the promotion of sustainable development is the key aim of the Trust's Environment funding. Priorities include promoting solutions to any adverse environmental effects associated with economic development, and preservation of the countryside and wildlife.

Grants were headed by those to:

- Green Alliance Trust: £225,000 over three years for core costs.
- Institute for European Environmental Policy: £218,000 over three years for work on fisheries policy.
- Wildfowl and Wetlands Trust: £100,000 for the Barn Elms Centre in London.
- Manchester Environmental Resource Centre: £90,000 for capital costs.

The geographical distribution of grants

Unlike most trusts that measure the regional distribution of their grants at all, Fairbairn has now started to do this according to their value per head of population, the only rational basis on which to do so. The results 'threw up some surprises' even to the trust itself (see the box below).

The annual report does not say whether the figure below for London includes those national charities based in London, or just projects where the work will be carried out in the city (obviously the more satisfactory approach).

Staff, consultants and advisers

Staff

Margaret Hyde, Director

Kathryn Sykes, Deputy Director

Judith Dunworth, Trust Secretary

Tim Keenan, Grants Manager

Bernadette Morgan, Grants Manager

Sharon Shea, Grants Manager

Faith Poyser, Grant Team Assistant

Frances Thompson, Applications Assistant

Charlotte Roundell, Applications Assistant

Advisers

Education: Sir Christopher Ball, Prof. Hugh Lawlor

Music: Hilary Bartlett

Environment: Hugh Raven

Social development: Baroness Stern

Scotland: Alison Rigg Campbell

THE ESMÉE FAIRBAIRN CHARITABLE TRUST

New grants by region 1999

	Total	*No.*	*Average*	*Per person*
England	£13,128,000	647	£20,000	28p
Scotland	£1,966,000	112	£18,000	40p
Wales	£930,000	58	£16,033	33p
Northern Ireland	£275,000	22	£12,522	18p
UK as a whole	£3,637,000	83	£44,000	–
International	£15,000	4	£3,750	–
Total	£19,951,000	926	£22,000	–
Regional summary				
Greater London boroughs	£3,408,000	148	£23,000	50p
North West England	£1,793,000	76	£24,000	27p
South East England	£1,354,000	76	£18,000	13p
South West England	£1,295,000	88	£15,000	28p
Midlands	£1,127,000	67	£17,000	13p
North East England	£809,000	50	£16,000	26p
Yorkshire	£807,000	54	£15,000	19p
South Wales	£459,000	29	£16,000	22p
East Anglia	£403,000	29	£14,000	20p
North Wales	£295,000	25	£12,000	38p

Northern Ireland: Bill Osborne
Northern England: Esther Salamon
N W England and N Wales: Elwyn Owens
S W England and S Wales: Celia Atherton

Consultants

Caroline Cuthbert, Janet Morgan, Patricia Thomas

Readers of earlier editions of this book may remember references to Janet Morgan, who was for many years with the Sainsbury Family Trusts, specialising in mental health, and Patricia Thomas, who was deputy director of the Nuffield Foundation.

Exclusions

Grants are made to registered charities only. Retrospective grants are not made. The trust is unlikely to support the following:

- charities whose operational area is outside the UK;
- large national charities which enjoy wide support;
- branches of national charities;
- individuals;
- overseas travel;
- medical (including research) or healthcare;
- expeditions;
- conferences or seminars;
- general appeals;
- sports;
- commercial publications;
- individual parish churches;
- animal welfare;
- sectarian religions;
- the direct replacement of statutory funding.

Applications

All applicants should first obtain the trust's guidelines (send an sae).

Applications for grants up to £5,000 should be made on the trust's application form. Copies are available from the trust.

Applications for grants over £5,000 should be in the form of a letter with supporting information. The following information is required:

1. A brief description of your organisation, its work, management and staffing structure, and current budget.
2. Description of the purpose of the project for which funds are required, the amount sought from the trust, who will manage the project, the project start/finish dates and the results expected.
3. A budget for the project, details of funds already raised and other sources being approached.
4. How your organisation intends to monitor and evaluate the project.
5. Your plans for sharing information about the project and what you learn from it with others in the field.
6. The most recent annual report and audited accounts.
7. Your organisation's charitable status, mentioning the charity's registration number.
8. The contact name, address and telephone number.
9. In addition, please quote the code for the current guidelines [*EFCT/G4 2000 for the guidelines used for this entry in the autumn of 2000, but note that new guidelines were expected later in that year. Ed.*].

Both kinds of application can be made at any time of the year. The process of dealing with an application, from receipt to communicating the trust's decision, can take between two and six months.

Once the application has been considered the trust does not usually accept another application from the same organisation within 12 months from the date of the decision.

The Fishmongers' Company's Charitable Trust

Relief of hardship and disability, education

£515,000 (to organisations, 1999)

Beneficial area UK, with a special interest in the City of London and adjacent boroughs.

Fishmongers' Hall, London Bridge, London EC4R 9EL

Tel. 020 7626 3531 **Fax** 020 7929 1389

Correspondent K Waters, Clerk

Information available Annual accounts, without the listing, analysis and explanation of grants that is required by the SORP, and with a two-line narrative report, rather than the required review of the charitable activities of the trust. This is surprising as among the trustees are people with ample experience of these requirements.

Summary

Some or all of the £500,000 or so spent on 'the relief of poverty and suffering' is given in grants, usually from £500 to £5,000, to charities that are either national or operating in the parts of London close to the City. Little further information is available, but anecdote suggests that the support of a member of the Wardens or Court of the Company may be an advantage in getting such a grant.

General

The trust had assets worth nearly £2 million in 1999. Income, mostly from donations from the Fishmongers' Company, amounted to £1,174,000.

Some of the trust's funds are committed to the upkeep of its own almshouses and ongoing educational bursaries and scholarships. The trust describes its funding policy as follows:

> In general, the company's charitable funds will be used for the relief of hardship and disability, education, the environment, heritage and fishery related charities. Applications will normally only be accepted from national bodies.
>
> Charities in the City of London and adjacent boroughs will also be eligible to apply. Preference will be given to charities seeking to raise funds for a specific project or for research rather than for administration or general purposes.
>
> In the case of requests for help for cathedrals, abbeys, churches and other old buildings, priority will be given to St Paul's Cathedral and Westminster Abbey.

It has previously been reported that only about one third of the total grants is given to ad hoc applications and that running costs are not funded, although start-up costs may be.

Of a reported £920,000 given in charitable donations and grants to organisations in 1999, £515,000 was given in grants to organisations for 'the relief of poverty and suffering'; £321,000 was given in educational grants and scholarships (£225,000 was designated for Gresham's School Scholarship and Discretionary Fund) and £83,000 went to the company's almshouses (£50,000 being for the Almshouse Repair Fund, to be spent on almshouses in Bray and Harrietsham).

Grants to charities unconnected to the trust usually range from £500 to £2,000, but can be up to £10,000.

Exclusions

No grants are made to individual branches of national charities or to regional or local charities, other than those in the City of London and adjacent boroughs. No grants are awarded to individuals except for education. Educational grants are not awarded to applicants who are over 19 years old.

Applications

In writing to the clerk. Meetings take place three times a year, in March, July and November, and applications should be received a month in advance. Grants are made on a one-off basis. No applications are considered within three years of a previous grant application being successful. Unsuccessful applications are not acknowledged.

The Donald Forrester Trust

Disability, general

£709,000 (1998/99)

231 Linen Hall, 156–170 Regent Street, London W1R 5TA

Tel. 020 7434 4021

Correspondent Brenda Ward

Trustees *Wendy Forrester, Chair; Anthony Smee; Michael Jones.*

Information available Annual report and accounts on file at the Charity Commission.

General

Established by the late settlor Gwen Forrester in 1986, the trust's grantmaking is concentrated on helping sick and disabled people, particularly older people and children. A smaller number of beneficiaries work in other areas, such as animal welfare, heritage and conservation, the arts and overseas aid. Over 100 grants a year, all in the range £1,000 to £10,000, are awarded mainly to well-known national charities.

The trust's assets of more than £10 million in 1998/99 were held mainly as investments in Film and Equipment Ltd. Income, at £746,000, came mostly from dividends and Gift Aid from the same source. The trust made 140 grants totalling £709,000. The majority of these were for £5,000 (101 awards, totalling £505,000), 17 were for £10,000, 1 for £3,000, 10 for £2,000 and 11 for £1,000.

Perhaps because of the limited number of charities eligible for support, nearly all the beneficiaries had received grants in previous years.

Typical recipients of £10,000 in the main area of support were as follows: British Heart Foundation; Alzheimer's Research Trust; Save the Children Fund; Guide Dogs for the Blind; Stroke Association; National Deaf Children's Society; Leonard Cheshire Foundation; St Kentigern's Hospice Project.

Other beneficiaries included the following (£5,000 each): National Gallery; Humane Slaughter Association; PDSA; National Trust; Woodland Heritage; Intermediate Technology; International Care and Relief.

Applications

'Regrettably, applications for aid cannot be considered as this would place an intolerable strain on administrative resources ...' The trustees meet in February and September.

The Hugh Fraser Foundation

General, mainly in Scotland

£1,640,000 (1998/99)

Beneficial area UK, especially western or deprived areas of Scotland.

Turcan Connell, Saltire Court, 20 Castle Terrace, Edinburgh EH1 2EF

Tel. 0131 228 8111 **Fax** 0131 228 8118

e-mail lkb@turcanconnell.com

Correspondent Heather Thompson

Trustees *Dr Kenneth Chrystie, Chair; Ann Fraser; Patricia Fraser; Blair Smith.*

Information available Annual report and accounts available for £10 a copy.

Summary

Most grants are for less than £5,000, though six-figure grants can be made. In 1998/99 the recipients of 275 grants worth £1.1 million, two thirds of the grant expenditure, were not disclosed.

General

The foundation was established by Lord Fraser of Allander and endowed by him with shares in House of Fraser and Scottish and Universal Investments (SUITS), the two companies based in the west of Scotland that he directed. The trust says:

> The trustees' policy is to pay special regard to applications from the West of Scotland and applications from those parts of Scotland where the local economy makes it more difficult to raise funds for charitable purposes. Applications from other parts of Britain and Northern Ireland are considered.
>
> The trustees consider that grants to large highly publicised national appeals are not likely to be as effective a use of funds as grants to smaller and more focused charitable appeals.
>
> The trustees also consider that better use of funds can be made by making grants to charitable bodies to assist them with their work, than by making a large number of grants to individuals.
>
> The trustees are prepared to enter into commitments over a period of time by making grants in successive years, often to assist in new initiatives which can maintain their own momentum once they have been established for a few years.
>
> The foundation makes donations to charities working in many different sectors, principally hospitals, schools and universities, arts organisations and organisations working with the handicapped, the underprivileged and the aged. The trustees are nevertheless prepared to consider applications from charities working in other fields.

From assets amounting to £30 million the foundation generated the high income of £2.5 million. Management and administration costs were low at less than two per cent of the income. The grants total for 1998/99 was £1.64 million in 284 awards.

Only the nine organisations which received grants of two per cent or more of the gross income were listed, the minimum required by Scottish law. These represented 33% of the grants total and were: The Lighthouse Project Glasgow 1999 (£235,000); Scottish Science Trust (£100,000); Columba 1400 (£40,000); Quarriers; Walter & Joan Gray Home (£30,000 each); Scottish Motor Neurone Association; The Murray Foundation; The Princess Royal Trust for Carers; and the Prince & Princess of Wales Hospice (£25,000 each).

The remaining 275 grants, all for less than £25,000, averaged £4,000. In the previous year there was just one large grant, of £100,000, to Erskine 2000.

Exclusions

Grants are not awarded to individuals. Major highly publicised appeals are rarely supported.

Applications

In writing to the correspondent. The trustees meet on a quarterly basis to consider applications.

The Gannochy Trust

General, in Scotland, especially Perthshire

£3,140,000 (1998/99)

Beneficial area Scotland, with a preference for Perth and its environs.

Kincarrathie House Drive, Pitcullen Crescent, Perth PH2 7HX

Tel. 01738 620653

Correspondent Mrs Jean Gandhi, Secretary

Trustees *Russell Leather, Chair; Mark Webster; James McCowan; Neil McCorkindale; Dr James Kynaston.*

Information available Annual report and accounts. The largest grants are disclosed and described, but this leaves nearly £2 million of grants a year to undisclosed beneficiaries.

Summary

More than 200 grants are made each year, of which over 100 will be for amounts of less than £5,000 to charities working for various causes. Typically a small group of large grants will account for half the value of donations.

General

In 1998/99 the trust's assets totalled over £130 million and its income was a low £4.5 million, at least in part because some of the endowment is in the form of inalienable property offering a low return. Administration costs were low, at three per cent of gross income, and staff salaries were all less than £40,000 each.

BREAKDOWN OF GRANTMAKING IN 1998/99
(compared with percentages for 1996/97, in brackets)

	1998/99	*1996/97*
Social welfare	27%	(22%)
Recreation	23%	(17%)
Education	19%	(23%)
Arts	11%	(9%)
Health	10%	(25%)
Environment	10%	(4%)

For some years the trust has noted that 'the interests of youth were amply served in all headings'.

The 1998/99 report, as in previous years, contains the following:

Prime objects for which donations are made to charitable organisations are the needs of youth and recreation, but the trustees are not restricted to these objects. The benefit of all donations must be confined to Scotland. There is an obligation to show a preference for Perth and its environs.

Donations are confined to organisations recognised by the Inland Revenue as charitable [*not as onerous a requirement as that for registration with the Charity Commission in England and Wales. Ed.*]. It is the practice of the trustees to scrutinise accounts before making donations.

The annual report for 1998/99 lists the following grants:

University of Edinburgh: £500,000 for its Science and Engineering Library

Phoenix Trust: £150,000 towards the restoration of Stanley Mills.

Perth and Kinross Recreational Facilities: £150,000, to a regular beneficiary, mainly for community halls.

Kincarrathie Trust: £107,000 to this connected charity for the elderly.

Quarriers Homes: £100,000 for residential facilities for disabled and disturbed children at Glasgow and Inverclyde.

Pitlochry Festival Theatre: £100,000 for extension and refurbishment.

Perth and Kinross Heritage Trust: £100,000 for the general purposes of that trust, a regular beneficiary.

In the previous year the major grants were uncharacteristically dominated by support for projects in Dundee. They included awards to Dundee Science Centre (£500,000), Dundee University for its cancer centre at Ninewells Hospital (£500,000), and Macmillan Cancer Relief for its Roxburgh House palliative day care centre (£300,000). Grants of £250,000 each were also made to Donaldson's College in Edinburgh and the Royal Hospital for Sick Children in Glasgow.

Exclusions

No grants to individuals. Donations are confined to organisations recognised by the Inland Revenue as charitable.

Applications

In writing to the correspondent, confined to two pages of A4, including:

- a general statement on the objects of the applicant's charity
- the specific nature of the application
- the estimated cost and how this is arrived at
- the contribution of the applicant's charity towards the cost
- the contributions of others, actual and promised
- estimated shortfall
- details of previous appeals to the trust – whether accepted or rejected
- a copy of the latest audited accounts.

Time rarely permits visits either to the trust office or to the charity concerned.

The Gatsby Charitable Foundation

General

£17,997,000 (1998/99)

See the entry for the Sainsbury Charitable Trusts

Tel. 020 7410 0330 **Fax** 020 7410 0332

website www.gatsby.org.uk

Correspondent Michael Pattison, Director

Trustees *Christopher Stone; Miss Judith Portrait; Andrew Cahn.*

Information available Excellent annual report and accounts.

Summary

This huge foundation is one of the Sainsbury Family Charitable Trusts, which share a joint administration. It makes awards over a number of years to chosen organisations in order to advance policy and practice within its selected areas, usually by means of research which is practically oriented. In doing so Gatsby is proactive and rather than responding to individual applications from the charitable sector it decides according to its own strategies which organisations it may or may not support. 'Trustees generally do not make grants in response to unsolicited appeals.'

Specific areas of support come under the following general headings (more detail may be found in the excerpts from the 1999 annual report below):

- technical education
- plant science
- cognitive neuroscience
- mental health

- disadvantaged children
- social renewal
- developing countries (Africa)
- the arts
- economic and social research

There are big annual fluctuations in the size of its new awards each year to different categories of work because of the large multi-year funding commitments decided by the foundation.

In a relatively minor programme, Gatsby makes a number of grants, about 25 in 1999, to local causes for disadvantaged children, some for amounts as low as £75 but others for amounts up to £2,000. Unusually both for the trust itself, and for the Sainsbury trusts as a whole, these grants are made in response to the applications received.

General

The Gatsby Charitable Foundation is one of the largest grant-making trusts in the UK, with an income of over £20 million a year. It allocates large sums to long-term programmes and so the figure for yearly grant approvals fluctuates considerably.

The foundation was set up in 1967 by David Sainsbury, created life peer and Lord Sainsbury of Turville in 1997. He resigned as chairman of Sainsbury plc in 1998 and has become a Labour minister with the Department of Trade and Industry. Lord Sainsbury himself has never been a trustee of Gatsby. He is still contributing massively to the endowment of the trust, with a further £13 million in 1997/98 and £0.5 million in 1998/99.

The trustees are Christopher Stone, a longstanding financial adviser to David Sainsbury, Andrew T Cahn, a recent (1996) appointee, who is a senior civil servant, and Judith Portrait, whose many roles include acting as Lord Sainsbury's solicitor, being a trustee of a number of the other Sainsbury family trusts, giving legal advice to this charity through Portrait Solicitors and now being the treasurer (effectively the chief executive) of the completely separate and very large Henry Smith charities. Though these trustees cannot properly have regard to anything other than the interests of the trust's beneficiaries, these interests might well include a close attention to the settlor's wishes, if this could encourage further endowments in the future.

Gatsby has one area of charitable giving that is less policy-oriented, relating to disadvantaged children. Here grants were made to some 30 local groups throughout the country.

The staff of the foundation in 1999 included:

Michael Pattison, Director (as of all the trusts in the Sainsbury group)

Dr Yvonne Pinto, Executive

Matthew Williams, Executive

Victoria Hornby, Executive

Mr Williams is concerned, no doubt among other things, with support for disadvantaged children. Victoria Hornby concentrates on social exclusion and overseas activities.

Three principal advisers are named:

Professor John Gray
Professor Horace Barlow
Dr John Sellars

Annual report 1999

This excellent report could serve as a model for other very large foundations. The rest of this entry repeats or summarises large parts of the document (where appropriate the values of actual grants have been added by the editor in brackets within the text). From it, readers will get a clear picture of the generally proactive way of working of not only this, but of most of the other Sainsbury Family Trusts.

Introduction

... The Trustees make grants for charitable activity which they hope will make life better for people, especially those who are disadvantaged. Over more than 30 years of grant-making, the Trustees have chosen to concentrate their support in a limited number of fields of activity. These fields are adapted over time with the help of outside experts and through interaction with the organisations whose work has been helped by the Foundation.

The Trustees support beneficiary organisations who wish to try different approaches to problems and opportunities. A grant-making trust is much less constrained than public authorities or corporate donors in choosing to support potential novel approaches. The Trustees are aware of both the privileges and responsibilities of their position.

Within each category, the Trustees usually concentrate on a few subjects at a time. They develop and implement grants programmes over a number of years. In most cases they start small and sometimes build up their support for particular programmes on the basis of learning by doing, in preference to commissioning external reports from which to derive specific strategies. In some cases they have created new charities in response to needs which are not met by existing institutions. The aim is to be original, to be pro-active, to be willing to work in unfashionable sectors, and to persist with particular programmes over a long period. The Trustees' support is for the objectives of a programme as defined by the organisation carrying it out. Sometimes particular grants achieve nothing more than demonstrating that the selected approach is not practicable. At other times grants produce useful outcomes which were not part of the objectives defined at the outset.

In all their funding, the Trustees support beneficiary organisations to work for the public benefit. By helping to develop new services and new discoveries, the Trustees seek to widen the choice available to the public, to individuals and to policy makers. They do not and could not seek to impose solutions on others but they do believe the work they support can point the way for productive change in society both in Britain and in developing countries.

The Trustees are supported by staff who work on projects across the Sainsbury Family Charitable Trusts. These staff assist in

How Gatsby operates

The previous edition of this book printed a brief informal account of the foundation's work by Christopher Stone, one of the trustees, and it is repeated here:

Gatsby is administered by a small office in London and the trustees meet every six weeks to consider progress reports on existing projects and new project proposals.

I hope that an observer looking at Gatsby would see that:

- there is a close and productive relationship between trustees, who set general policy and approve grants, and the executive staff, who advise the trustees and ensure that the programmes are effectively implemented;
- the aim of Gatsby's programmes is to bring about practical and measurable improvements in each area of activity, with clearly stated objectives whenever possible;
- Gatsby tends to begin its activities on a relatively small scale but is willing to persevere for long periods, gradually increasing the size of grants as the trustees become more confident in their understanding of the subject;
- Gatsby tries to be specific and consistent, yet flexible, in its approach and is willing to take risks;
- Gatsby nearly always works within the 'system' to bring about improvements, rather than trying to create new institutional structures;
- in each programme Gatsby works through and with people of integrity who are well respected within their communities and who share Gatsby's objectives.

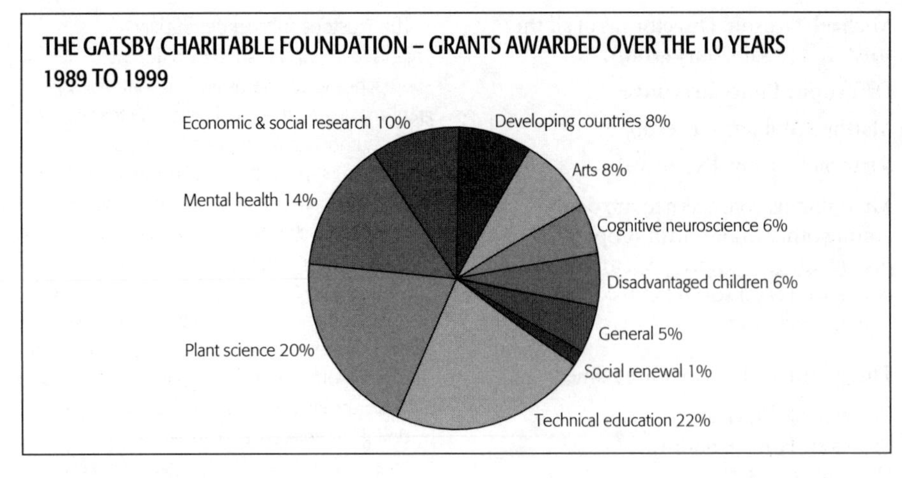

developing and implementing projects and advising the Trustees on their progress.

Technical education (total 1999 payments, £5.2 million)

'To support improvement in educational opportunity in the UK for a workforce which can better apply technology for wealth creation; and to encourage effective technology transfer from universities and other research centres to productive industry.'

The Trustees' programmes which seek to achieve this are:

- to encourage technology transfer between universities and industry;
- to encourage the most able technologists to enter manufacturing industry both at professional and at technician level;
- to encourage good teaching and good materials in schools in maths, science and technology as an essential prerequisite to the health of the manufacturing base;
- to encourage appropriate IT development which will enhance maths, science and technology in schools;
- to ensure that the courses and the awards are respected and valued by industry, parents and students.

The Trustees are encouraging developments in university/industry links. They wish to foster technology transfer in both product and production systems. They are supporting manufacturing education through the Advanced Course in Design, Manufacture and Management and a course for Leaders in Manufacturing at Cambridge University. The Trustees are also assisting Cambridge University's Institute for Manufacturing to work with industry, particularly small and medium-sized enterprises, and to develop collaboration between the university and instrumentation companies. This will form part of the industry network support which is being funded by the Trustees to provide a mechanism for technology transfer. The trustees are assisting with other technology transfer schemes between several universities and their industrial partner companies, which develop a range of models from which to demonstrate successful practice.

The foundation's main programmes under this heading are implemented through two separate charities it has set up, and which may attract other funding. They are the Gatsby Technical Education Project (GTEP) and SAPS (Science and Plants in School). Other major and ongoing beneficiaries are the Royal Academy of Engineering (with a further £1.8 million of funding in 1999) and SETNET.

However, there were also another 18 new awards. The largest of them, for £632,000, was in the form of partnership funding for Middlesbrough Education Action Zone (EAZ). Typically for large Sainsbury awards, this was not the result of an 'application'. Rather, six bids were evaluated in the foundation's search for an alternative model for technical education in an EAZ to that already being funded in York.

More modest awards included £106,000 over three years towards the salary of a deputy director for Women's Education in Building and £15,000 for Perse Girls School Appeal.

Plant science (total 1999 payments, £2.9 million)

'To develop basic research in fundamental processes of plant growth and development and molecular plant pathology and to encourage young researchers in this field in the UK.'

The main vehicle for the foundation's interest continues to be The Sainsbury Laboratory at the John Innes Centre in Norwich, which received another £13 million in funding for a further five years of research. There were only four other grant decisions, all to universities, including £389,000 for Dr Jim Haseloff's work at Cambridge University.

The annual report names no less than nine advisers under this heading, led by Professor John Gray.

Cognitive neuroscience (total 1999 payments, £796,000)

'To support world-class research in UK centres of excellence.'

The Trustees' emphasis in this relatively new category is on interdisciplinary developments which bring together theory and experiment with fundamental techniques and measurements, rather than problem areas or specific illnesses. They are conscious of the need to avoid providing funds when these should be available from the Research Councils. Therefore:

- Gatsby expects to support projects for which government funding of basic facilities is already in place, allowing Gatsby grants to be applied for specific and definable projects outside this normal funding;
- Gatsby will contribute in ways which are qualitatively different from Research Council funding and allow interdisciplinary and speculative projects.

A major commitment has been made to establish a unit at University College, London, to develop computational modelling under the direction of Professor Geoffrey Hinton. There were just four other awards to universities, plus a transfer of £60,000 to the foundation's advisory group to enable it to fund individual research programmes in this field.

Mental health (total 1999 payments, £5.2 million)

'To improve the quality of life for people with long-term problems by improved delivery of services.'

The programme is directed towards improving the quality of life for people with severe and enduring learning disabilities. 'There is still a stigma attached to mental health problems. A small number of well-publicised tragedies highlight gaps in provision which are damaging to people who are ill and potentially damaging to the wider community.'

The principal activity is via a core grant to the separate Sainsbury Centre for Mental Health (SCMH). A further £5 million was committed to support the next three years' work of the Centre. There were only three other beneficiary organisations in the year: SANE (£59,000), Talent to Work (£120,000) and the Revolving Doors Agency (£29,000).

There is a small programme, fitted in under this heading, for the support of palliative care. Under this, £120,000 was given in three grants to hospices, led by £70,000 for St Christopher's in London. In this field the foundation is advised by the Elizabeth Clark Foundation (see under the entry for the Sainsbury Family Trusts).

Disadvantaged children (total 1999 payments, £4.4 million)

'To explore new approaches to early diagnoses of barriers to personal development and to support the development of services to overcome these barriers.'

Two important initiatives were undertaken in this field in 1999. First, £1,400,000 over three years was committed to the National Children's Bureau for a new initiative to give children in care a better experience of education. For this editor, this initiative exemplifies the strengths of the Sainsbury foundations and a weakness of many others. He has seen repeated trust grants for organisations dealing with 'leaving care' but all the evidence has long suggested that this is often a time of crisis simply because the children concerned just do not have the education needed for proper employment and a decent life. But 'application driven' funding is not easily obtainable for work addressing such underlying issues.

Secondly, there has been a review of policy and provision covering 9 to 13 year olds, with a view to exploring whether to support new programmes in this age range.

The Trustees' key aim in this area is to fund projects which develop and deliver better services to young people with mental and physical disabilities and/or other social difficulties. The Trustees are concerned that people who may face multiple disadvantages should have access to opportunities to help themselves.

Within this key aim the Trustees have identified two areas of particular concern:

- communications skills for disabled/ disadvantaged children and young people;
- means of overcoming social disadvantage, particularly interventions to improve the mental health and well-being of children and young people.

The Trustees continued their core funding to the ACE Centre Advisory Trust [£690,000], which researches and develops communication aids for severely disabled children. Further support was given to the Children's Residential Care Unit at the National Children's Bureau project on good practice in residential childcare, which began in 1993 [£463,000 over two years]. This was for further dissemination of examples of good practice.

The Trustees made a further grant for the Royal College of Psychiatrists [£400,000] to establish a new centre researching and promoting good practice in child and adolescent mental health.

There were 14 other grants of over £50,000, including the following:

- AFASIC (Association for All Speech Impaired Children): £60,000 over two years towards extending the support for a national development officer.
- Aids for Communication in Education (ACE) Centre; £690,000 over three years towards core costs;
- Brighton and Hove Carers' Centre; £66,000 over three years towards the recruitment of someone to develop materials in personal social education.
- East London Schools Fund: £185,000 over two years towards extending funding on a two-year rolling basis towards core posts and office expenses, and over two years towards the salary of the Home–School Support Worker.
- Foyer Federation: £150,000 over three years towards establishing a challenge fund to promote better partnerships between foyers and social service departments.
- Improving the Self Esteem and Confidence of all Children and Adolescents: £65,000 over three years for professional training and pupil training.
- Research in Practice: £171,000 over three years towards the creation of a website for child protection social workers to give access to a database containing evaluated evidence and a children's service register.
- Sign (The Anastasia Society): £200,000 over two years towards a new specialist residential centre for deaf children with mental health problems.
- The Place To Be: £111,000 over three years towards the salary of the Head of Research and Development and the Senior Educational Psychologist.

Gatsby also supported numerous local causes for disadvantaged children, some for amounts as low as £75 but occasionally for amounts up to £35,000. Unusually for this group of trusts, a significant proportion of these were the result of conventional applications.

The beneficiaries included:

- Educational Theatre Services, Birmingham
- Electronic Aids for the Blind, Chislehurst, Kent
- Friends of the Community Playbus, Walsall
- Glenfrome Primary School, Bristol
- I-CAN, London
- Kids Family Centre
- Little Angels Project, London
- Mortlake Church of England Educational Foundation
- Musicworks Music Resource Centre, London

Social renewal (total 1999 payments, £255,000)

'To support new approaches to problems which can create social exclusion.'

The Trustees continued their current commitment to a programme created by the National Tenants Resource Centre (NTSC) and the London School of Economics (LSE) which supports the growth and development of local resident self-help groups. The project involves a linked training and grants programme which enables groups to participate in tailor-made courses and subsequently apply for small grants to undertake a specific project or activity. This initiative is proving to be a useful model for public bodies concerned with sustainable local regeneration.

Other projects supported were:

- Community Links: £180,000 over three years towards establishing its First Steps training programme outside London.
- St Christopher's Fellowship: £75,000 over three years towards the revenue costs of establishing training and employment services for homeless people at the Lime Grove Project.

Developing countries (total 1999 payments, £1.7 million)

'To promote environmentally sustainable development and poverty alleviation through selected programmes aimed at supporting basic agriculture and other enterprise in selected African countries.'

The Trustees have supported a range of projects in the Third World for over 20 years in the spheres of economic research and via direct programmes to help people in poverty. In the late 1980s the Trustees decided that, in order to maximise the value of their support, which in relative terms can only ever be a tiny contribution, they would concentrate their resources in Africa, in countries with reasonable stability and to support small-scale wealth creation in agriculture and manufacturing, and primary health care of women and small children. The Trustees also decided to work through local people to develop sustainable projects and ensure any effort was genuinely responsive to local needs.

Sub-Saharan Africa

In order to do this effectively, the Trustees supported the establishment of local trusts, directed by local Trustees, which now exist in Kenya, Tanzania, Uganda and Cameroon. ... [Support] is focused on two prime areas:

- Support to very small scale enterprise ...;
- Support for agricultural research geared to the identification of improved crop varieties ...

South Africa

Gatsby has instituted a major programme in the western Cape (£644,000 to give a three-year funding horizon) to enhance the maths, science and technical education of black South Africans, at all levels. The foundation is also supporting legal and community action (£67,000) to recover land lost to black South Africans during the apartheid era. Eight further grants were made, mostly for highly specific agricultural development projects.

The major financial commitment under this heading is in fact in the form of support for the John Innes Centre, based in Norwich (£563,000), to research the banana streak virus and for the study of cowpea.

Readers interested in overseas development are encouraged to obtain the full Gatsby report for 1999, which has further analysis of these interesting programmes, based on over 20 years' work on the ground. Gatsby is advised on its work in Africa by Laurence Cockroft.

The arts (total 1999 payments, £601,000)

'To support ... institutions with which Gatsby's founding family has long connections.'

The Trustees' grants under this category are focused on two major beneficiaries, the Sainsbury arts programmes at the University of East Anglia, and the Royal Shakespeare Company. Beyond these, small grants are made pro-actively for specific theatre and musical projects.

The Trustees do not consider unsolicited applications.

Five other organisations were supported, including the Royal Academy of Dramatic Art (£100,000), Sinfonia 21, London (£20,000), and the admirable and, in this book, ubiquitous Chicken Shed Theatre (£2,000).

Economic and social research (total 1999 payments, £1.1 million)

'To support institutions and individuals' studies which can help us to understand and improve our society.'

Eight new awards were made in 1999, led by £1 million over five years for a chair in the research and application of technology to management at the London Business School. Other beneficiaries included Kent TEC (£235,000 for a loan scheme to enhance Individual Learning Accounts) and the Social Market Foundation (£156,000 towards core costs).

General (total 1999 payments, £408,000)

The major grants were as follows:

- Caribbean Heritage Centre: £75,000 towards the proposed centre at Greenwich.
- University of Wales: £228,000 over three years towards the healthcare evaluation and assessment of education in patients with Chronic Fatigue Syndrome – a major interest of the Linbury Trust, another member of this group of trusts.
- St Paul's Girls' School, London: £32,500.
- Breast Cancer Care, London: £25,000.

There were nine further grants for amounts of £15,000 or less to Cancer Research Campaign, Clare Strange Trust, Co-operation Ireland, National Primary Trust, Roman Catholic Diocese of Brentwood: Refugee Project, Tree Aid (Bristol) and Waterford Kamhlaba, United World College of South Africa, Swaziland

Applications

See the guidance for applicants in the entry for the Sainsbury Family Charitable Trusts. A single application will be considered for support by all the trusts in the group. However, the trustees generally do not make grants in response to unsolicited applications.

The Robert Gavron Charitable Trust

Arts, policy research, disability, education

£614,000 (1998/99)

Beneficial area UK.

44 Eagle Street, London WC1R 4FS

Tel. 020 7400 4300

Correspondent Mrs Dilys Ogilvie-Ward, Secretary

Trustees *Lord Gavron; Lady Gavron; Jessica Gavron; Sarah Gavron; Charles Corman.*

Information available Full report and accounts.

Summary

Typically, half of the funds are given in a few large grants to institutions with which one of the trustees has personal connections. Small one-off grants, usually for less than £2,000, are given to nearly 100 charities a year.

General

The trust provides 'support for charities of which the trustees have special or personal knowledge; small charities for disabled children and adults; and promotion of the arts/arts access for young/underprivileged people'.

Over the ten years from 1990 to 1999 over £2.3 million was given in grants. More than £1 million (43%) went to three institutions, at all of which Lord Gavron is, or has been, a trustee. The Royal Opera House received a quarter of the money. The Institute for Public Policy Research, of which he is also treasurer, got 10% of the total. The next largest over the period was to the Open College of the Arts, which was a major beneficiary until 1997.

In 1998/99 half the funds went in large grants to five organisations, all except the last having been generously supported for a number of years. They were as follows:

- Royal Opera House (£201,000);
- Institute for Public Policy Research (£52,500);
- London School of Economics (£20,000);
- One World Action (£20,000);
- The Runnymede Trust – of which Lady Gavron is a trustee (£20,000).

Other long-term beneficiaries include Adventure Unlimited and the Ashten Trust, which received £10,000 and £12,000 respectively. A few others repeatedly supported get very small annual grants which appear to be more like subscriptions.

The following large grants to new beneficiaries accounted for a fifth of the year's total:

- London Business School Anniversary Trust (£100,000);
- RFH Breast Cancer Trust (£20,000);
- Human Rights Centre Appeal (£10,000);
- Brighton Society for the Blind (£10,000).

More than £150,000 was spent in other grants of between £100 and £12,000. Recipients were diverse, with grants going to organisations including Friends of the Earth, Jewish Care, Macmillan Cancer Relief, Prison Reform Trust, Sussex Autistic Society, Whitechapel Art Gallery and Wiltshire Wildlife Trust.

Exclusions

The trust does not give donations to individuals or to large national charities.

Applications

In writing only to Mrs Ogilvie-Ward. Please enclose an sae and latest accounts. However, the trust has said that it is fully committed to its existing areas of interest and the trustees would have difficulty in considering further appeals. There are no regular dates for trustees' meetings, but they take place about eight times a year.

J Paul Getty Jr Charitable Trust

Social welfare, conservation

£1,527,000 (1999)

Beneficial area UK (but see below).

1 Park Square West, London NW1 4LJ

Tel. 020 7486 1859

e-mail BOBTPGT@aol.com

Correspondent Ms Bridget O'Brien Twohig, Administrator

Information available Excellent guidelines for applicants and exceptionally full annual report and accounts

Summary

'The trust aims to fund projects to do with poverty and misery in general, and unpopular causes in particular, within the UK.' Over 100 new grants are made each year, mostly for revenue costs over three years (except for a number of smaller awards of hundreds rather than thousands of pounds) and generally to small local groups. Grants are typically for amounts between £5,000 and £30,000 (over three years), though occasionally they may be for as much as £60,000.

Few projects are supported in London.

There are also small programmes of generally small grants in the heritage and conservation fields.

Unfortunately, this trust receives very many more applications than it can support, compared with many others, less approachable, that are also described in this book. Applicants are usually visited by the trust before a grant is made.

General

The J Paul Getty Jr Charitable Trust is, and has been for a number of years, a model of excellence in its field.

This entry need do no more than repeat the excellent information available from the charity in its guidelines and in its 1999 annual report. Would that this were possible more often! The annual reports, in particular, deal with some of the current practical issues of grantmaking more clearly than can be found anywhere else.

The J Paul Getty Jr Charitable Trust started distributing funds in 1986. It was funded entirely by Sir Paul Getty, who lives in London. He continues to make major personal gifts to the arts and other causes in England (£50 million to the National Gallery, £3 million to Lord's Cricket Ground, £17 million to the British Film Institute, £1 million towards the Canova Three Graces, £1 million towards the Churchill Papers). These are personal gifts and have no connection with this trust. Nor has this trust any connection with the Getty Foundation in the USA, to which J. Paul Getty Senior left his money, and which finances the J. Paul Getty Museum in California. These two trusts, one very large and one small by comparison, are often confused by people who apply to us. This Trust, which now has capital of about £50 million, made grants totalling £1.5 million in 1999.

Guidelines

Beneficial areas

The trust aims to fund projects to do with poverty and misery in general, and unpopular causes in particular, within the U.K. The emphasis is on self-help, building esteem, enabling people to reach their potential. The trustees favour small community and local projects which make good use of volunteers. Both revenue and capital grants are made, but please read the [Exclusions] section below carefully, as it is possible that the particular aspect of your application rather than the general purpose of your organisation may be excluded.

Priority is likely to be given to projects in the less prosperous parts of the country, particularly in the North of England, and to those which cover more than one beneficial area ...

Grants are usually in the £5–10,000 range, capital and revenue, and those made for salaries or running costs are for a maximum of 3 years [*i.e. a total of £15,000–£30,000 for revenue grants. Ed.*]. Some small grants of up to £1,000 are also made.

Social welfare

Mental Health in a wide sense. This includes projects for:

- mentally ill adults;
- mentally handicapped adults;
- drug, alcohol and other addictions, and related problems;
- support groups for people under stress, e.g. battered wives, victims of abuse, families in difficulties, etc;
- counselling, especially young people;
- mediation.

Offenders, both in and out of prison, men and women, young offenders, sexual offenders.

Communities which are clearly disadvantaged trying to improve their lot, particularly projects to do with helping young people in the long-term.

Homelessness, particularly projects which help prevent people becoming homeless or resettle them.

Job Creation projects or ones aimed at making long-term constructive use of enforced leisure time, particularly ones set up by unemployed people.

Ethnic Minorities involved in above areas, including refugees, particularly projects aimed at integration.

Arts

Only the following will be considered:-

- therapeutic use of the arts for the long-term benefit of the groups under Social Welfare;
- projects which enable people in these groups to feel welcome in arts venues, and which enable them to make long-term constructive use of their leisure.

Conservation

Conservation in the broadest sense, with emphasis on ensuring that fine buildings, landscapes and collections remain or become available to the general public or scholars. Training in conservation skills. Not general building repair work.

Environment

Mainly gardens. Historic landscape. Wilderness.

Trustees' report 1999

General comments

Good news for applicants, as the number of applications dropped by 10% or so in 1999 and the chances of being funded therefore improved slightly. About 35% of applications were again outside our published criteria, a figure which holds steady year on year regardless of anything we do. Most are from applicants who have not read the guidelines, and wrongly assume that the trust is an arts funder or confuse us with the American Getty Foundation, while in fact the main area of interest is social welfare.

Income fell slightly in the year, but the number of grants paid and the total distribution remained close to the previous year. We have improved the take-up of grants by reducing the time-limit from 12 to 6 months, a plan mooted in the 1998 report. This was an extension of a successful stratagem put into action the previous year to reduce the time taken by applicants to respond to correspondence, requests for further information and grant offers, a problem known to other trusts but which surprises us all nonetheless. Every letter from the trust now gives a 7–10 day time limit for a reply, which has proved almost 100% effective.

J PAUL GETTY JR CHARITABLE TRUST

Summary of activity	*1999*	*1998*
Number of new applicants	1,764	1,942
Number of new applicants supported	128	140
Value of new grants authorised	£1,526,870	£1,741,800
Average size of grants (ex. small grants)	£9,111	£9,543
New applicant grants for more than one year	48	50
Total distribution	£1,463,120	£1,433,550

We continue to seek small, local organisations run by lively people, with a good understanding of the problems in their area, and practical ideas for tackling them. Our aim is to fund causes with little public appeal, such as mental illness, addictions and homelessness, and within this remit we are prepared to pay for items we are told are hard to raise funds for, such as running costs and salaries. Over a half of the major grants in 1999 were for these purposes, and for 2 or 3 years. Nearly all projects are visited by the Administrator before a proposal is put to the trustees, and we like to be kept in touch with good and bad news during the period of a grant. A few recipients run into trouble each year, and we like to be able to help when this happens.

While funding innovation has its own particular interest, and it is rewarding to see a new idea come to fruition, we do not like to see voluntary organisations going to the trouble of repackaging or adding to what they are doing just for the sake of it, in order to attract our attention. We recognise that many established projects doing much needed work find it harder to raise funds as time goes by. Nor are we particularly keen to be pulled in as the required element of private funding in order for a voluntary organisation (or partnership) to access statutory funds for a government initiative. Some needy people will inevitably not meet the criteria for help from such schemes, and we see our role as funding the projects which fill the gaps, and the people who fall into them.

Overall impressions in the year are that drug use is wider and younger; low standards of literacy and numeracy hamper employability more than lack of IT skills; the high cost of decent housing for single people is often beyond the wages of an unskilled job and can only be paid for by Housing Benefit; and the cost of transport in rural areas as petrol and bus fares rise makes getting to college or work extremely difficult for many. The projects we fund may not be able to change the big picture, but there remains a great deal they can do on a local scale: with the right help at the right time, people do come off drugs, others find jobs they can do or a family finds a new start with some hope for a better future.

Comments on geographical spread

There is no target distribution set for any area and all applications are shortlisted on merit. Priority has usually been given to the North of the country, and the Yorkshire towns and cities (Leeds, Sheffield, Bradford and the coastal towns) still receive a large proportion of the funding. Newcastle and Merseyside are now seen as less in need of funding than some of the market towns and rural areas in the rest of the country.

This is particularly true of Cornwall and Devon, where jobs are few now that fishing, farming and mining are all but finished, wages are low, transport costs high and funding harder to come by. The South Coast towns (Penzance, Portsmouth, Southampton, Brighton and Bournemouth) all attract young people, and drugs are easily available. Every year there is less difference between urban and rural areas in the types and scale of problems found.

Comments on categories

[*The value of each grant has been added. Ed.*]

There is also no target distribution for any of the categories funded, but the Youth category continues to receive the lion's share. Three quarters of the projects funded were for workers' salaries over three years. It now goes without saying that any project helping young people in need is dealing with drug and alcohol problems, and all the challenges they bring. Few of the young people are in paid work, though some are being encouraged and supported to undertake training of some kind, or voluntary work, but their standard of literacy and numeracy in many cases makes the acquisition of qualifications and a job very difficult.

The Meridian Trust Association in Portsmouth [£45,000 over three years] takes on young drop-outs as apprentices in boat building work which they enjoy and can do well, but the day release college course has proved beyond them, and we are contributing to a tutor to work on their basic skills.

The 'youth cafe' idea as an informal place to meet friends, keep off the streets and out of trouble, and get advice continues to spread, and this year we contributed to new ones setting up in *Wetherby, Ledbury* [£30,000 over three years] and *Ross-on-Wye* [£18,000 over three years]. *Streets Ahead* [£15,000 over three years] is a popular alternative type of club for very disaffected young people on an estate on the outskirts of Worcester.

Impact Community Development [£30,000 over three years] is an estate-based project in Bradford which has helped young people to take over a small block of derelict flats from the council and do them up for themselves. *The Amber Foundation* in Wiltshire [£40,000 over three years] takes in young people in danger of wrecking their lives with drugs and crime to give them another chance to find a more positive life plan.

The young people invariably have problems with where to live, so many of the projects could also be listed under the Homelessness category. *DIGS* in Whitehaven, Cumbria, [£15,000 over three years] helps young people into private accommodation by providing rent deposits, while the *Ferry Project* in Wisbech [£39,000 over three years] provides a shared home and support for those who have been in trouble.

Powys Challenge Trust [£36,000 over three years] provides volunteer adult mentors for young offenders in mid-Wales which is proving effective. *SARO* in Eastbourne [£20,000]

J PAUL GETTY JR CHARITABLE TRUST

	1999		*1998*	
Categories of new grants authorised	*No.*	*Total*	*No.*	*Total*
AIDS/HIV	–	–	1	£10,000
Community groups	15	£188,500	11	£124,500
Mental health	9	£109,000	15	£218,800
Family	6	£63,500	5	£85,000
Youth	25	£532,750	22	£322,250
Offenders	6	£98,400	7	£81,000
Drugs & alcohol	4	£80,000	9	£109,000
Homeless	11	£168,300	15	£341,000
Ethnic minorities	5	£81,200	6	£85,000
Women	6	£14,000	6	£149,000
Physically handicapped	–	–	6	£12,550
Heritage	25	£94,000	24	£133,750
Environment (gardens)	10	£91,500	6	£66,000
Miscellaneous	6	£5,720	7	£3,950
Total	128	£1,526,870	140	£1,741,800

provides a full-time day programme of activities and support for people making their third and fourth attempts to come off drugs.

Projects in the *Ethnic Minorities* category are usually chosen because they help refugees, an increasingly unpopular group of people. *West End Refugee Service* in Newcastle [£15,000 over three years] was set up by local church people in response to the first in-flow of refugees to the North where few arrangements for them had been made. *Positive Action in Housing* [£30,000 over three years] is not particularly aimed at refugees, but is fighting an uphill battle to ensure that the housing needs of ethnic minorities in Glasgow are not totally ignored.

In the *Community* category, *Firth Park Advice Centre* on the outskirts of Sheffield [£51,000 over three years] has been funded because of the quality of its work and its decision not to accept the restrictions which would accompany a legal aid board franchise. *Easington CVS* in Co. Durham [£9,000 over three years] is providing a very full service to small local voluntary groups, helping with fund-raising and doing their accounts.

We continue to support *Families* to cope with difficult times, this year funding sleeping-in staff for the *Women's Refuge* in Yeovil, and *Friends United Network* (FUN) [£30,000 over three years], which provides 'big friends' for lonely children in one-parent families, to set up in Brighton.

The dividing line between the *Mental Health* category and others is also becoming less clearly defined, as many projects in the Homelessness, Youth and Addiction categories are dealing with people suffering from a high level of distress and disturbance arising from terrible experiences. *Dove Designs* in Liverpool [£30,000 over two years] is a furniture factory which runs successfully on a majority workforce of people who cannot take the stress of a full-time job. *The Mental Health Action Group* in Sheffield [£10,000] is an unusual drop-in set up and run for several years entirely by sufferers, and *Clare Priory*, Suffolk [£10,000], and the *Monastery* at Hyning, just outside Lancaster, [£15,000] both provide a safe and peaceful haven, a kind listening ear but no counselling for those in need of a retreat.

The grants made in the *Heritage* category were mostly for the conservation of particularly fine old items in small churches (not for church or cathedral repairs), such as the monuments in the 14th century *St Cuthbert's Church* in Widworthy Barton in Devon [£500]. *The Georgian Group* also received a grant towards a caseworker's salary to advise on planning applications.

Landscaped gardens funded under the *Environment* category include *Downton Moot* in Wiltshire [£7,500 over three years] and *Painshill Park* in Surrey [£10,000]. The grant made to *The Centre for Alternative Technology* in Wales pays for another Information Worker to advise people on 'green' building techniques.

Exclusions

The trustees do not generally consider applications for the following:

- elderly
- children
- education
- research
- animals
- music or drama (except therapeutically)
- conferences and seminars
- medical care (including hospices) or health
- medical equipment
- churches and cathedrals
- holidays and expeditions
- sports or leisure facilities (including cricket pitches)

Residential projects or large building projects are unlikely to be considered. The trustees do not support national appeals or grant-giving trusts such as community trusts. Headquarters of national organisations and umbrella organisations are unlikely to be considered, as are applications from abroad.

No applications from individuals are considered. Past recipients are not encouraged to apply.

The project must be a registered charity or be under the auspices of one.

Applications

A letter no more than two pages long is all that is necessary at first, giving an outline of the project, a detailed costing, the existing sources of finance of the organisation, and what other applications, including those to statutory sources and the Lottery, have been made. Please also say if you have applied to or received a grant previously from this trust. Please do not send videos, tapes or bulky reports. They will not be returned. Annual accounts will be asked for if your application is going to be taken further. Send your letter to the administrator.

The project will also have to be visited before an application can be considered by the trustees. This may mean a delay, as it is only possible to visit a small part of the country between each quarterly trustees' meeting. Three months is the least time it can take to award a grant. Some small grants of up to £1,000 can be made without a visit, but only for specific purposes.

Applications can be made to the administrator at any time, and all letters of appeal will be answered – but please remember only two pages in the first instance.

The G C Gibson Charitable Trust

Churches, health, welfare, general

£562,000 (1998/99)

Beneficial area UK, with interests in East Anglia, Wales and Scotland.

Deloitte & Touche, Blenheim House, Fitzalan Court, Newport Road, Cardiff CF2 1TS

Tel. 029 2048 1111

Correspondent Karen Griffin

Information available Inadequate report and accounts, lacking the required analysis and review of grantmaking.

Summary

Grants, numbering about 150 a year, are made to a broad selection of charitable causes, often in East Anglia, South Wales or Scotland. They are typically for between £1,000 and £5,000 and are usually repeated.

General

The organisations supported work within a range of charitable fields, but as the trust does not categorise them it is difficult to discern trustees' preferences. Some of the better funded charitable fields are perhaps: churches, medical research, hospices/nursing homes, military welfare and youth/education.

The trust's grantmaking has previously been reported as follows:

Although grants are made for one year at a time, once a charity has been awarded a grant the trustees are likely to continue to make grants to that charity provided they are happy with the way the money is being spent. They are very happy that such grants should go towards core running costs. Some organisations have received regular grants from the trust for as long as 20 years. Occasionally grants are made on an explicitly one-off basis, usually for a capital project.

Grants for statutory bodies such as museums and hospitals will be considered, but these will usually be for a capital project, for example a hospital scanner appeal, or research costs. Co-funding arrangements will also be considered. The trustees have awarded several grants in conjunction with Lottery funding.

Particularly in the case of lesser-known charities, the trustees tend to look favourably on applications from charities that are recommended by someone they know.

Beneficiaries are frequently well-established national charities – about 10% have 'royal' or 'national' in their titles. The great majority of grants by number and value are for £1,000, £2,000 or £3,000. The previously reported maximum grant of £10,000 was exceeded in 1998/99 by a grant of £20,000 to the Cancer Research Campaign.

A sample of other beneficiaries included: Abbeyfield Breadalbane Society (£3,000); Cardiff YMCA (£3,000); Christian Children's Fund of Great Britain (£3,000); King Edward VII Hospital for Officers (£5,000); Riding for the Disabled (£3,000); St Mary's Trust, Old Harlow (£1,000), and Walford Parish Church Council (£3,000).

Exclusions

Only registered charities will be supported.

Applications

In writing to the correspondent in October/November each year. Trustees meet in December/January. Successful applicants will receive their cheques during January.

Organisations that have already received a grant should reapply describing how the previous year's grant was spent and setting out how a further grant would be used. In general, less detailed information is required from national charities with a known track record than from small local charities that are not known to the trustees.

'Due to the volume of applications, it is not possible to acknowledge each application, nor is it possible to inform unsuccessful applicants.'

The Glass-House Trust

Parenting, child development and family welfare, art, general

£818,000 (approved, 1998/99)

Beneficial area Unrestricted, but UK in practice.

See the entry for the Sainsbury Charitable Trusts

Tel. 020 7410 0330 **Fax** 020 7410 0332

Correspondent Michael Pattison, Director

Information available Weak annual report and accounts, with full grants listing.

Summary

This is one of the Sainsbury Family Charitable Trusts, which share a joint administration. Like the others, it is primarily proactive, aiming to choose its own grantees, and it discourages unsolicited applications.

The trust's major ongoing interest appears to be in family welfare and child development but it also funds major projects in other fields. In 1998/99 large amounts were given to a contemporary art project, The Pier Trust.

With only 29 grants being made in the most recent year, this is probably one of the most proactive trusts described in this book.

General

Alexander Sainsbury is the settlor of this trust, one of the few in the Sainsbury group whose endowment (£12.6 million in April 1999) is not recorded as being held largely in the form of shares in J Sainsbury Plc. However, the value of its investments had nevertheless fallen by over £3 million during the year.

The staff of the trust include Michael Pattison, director of all the Sainsbury Family Charitable Trusts, and Hester Marriott, executive.

The only information about general grant-making policies is the standardised remark that 'the trustees prefer to support innovative schemes that can be successfully replicated or become self-sustaining'.

The grants approved in 1998/99 were categorised by number and value as follows:

Parenting, family welfare & child development	16	£383,000
Art/architecture	3	£270,000
Social housing/urban environment	6	£113,000
General	4	£52,000
Total	29	£818,000

The 'parenting' awards were led by £217,000 in two grants to help the London Institute of Education's Social Science Research Institute with the running and research costs of A Space. There was support for the core costs of three national organisations, the Children's Play Council (£20,000), the Parenting Education and Support Forum (£30,000) and Parents at Work (£15,000).

In a typical pattern for a Sainsbury trust, there was also support for a small number of practical projects, led in this case by £46,000 in two grants for the African Caribbean Family Mediation Service for its home–school mediation work in London.

In a major arts award, £210,000 over two years was given to the Pier Trust for salary costs and 'to support innovative projects and educational events in the contemporary art field'.

The major housing grant was to the Tenants Participation Advisory Service (£41,000). Environmental groups supported included the Hackney Building Exploratory (£10,000) and the Arid Lands Initiative Urban Oasis Programme for an environmental regeneration programme in Salford.

Exclusions

Grants are not normally made to individuals.

Applications

See the guidance for applicants in the entry for the Sainsbury Family Charitable Trusts. A single application will be considered for support by all the trusts in the group.

However, 'proposals are generally invited by the Trustees or initiated at their request'.

The Glencore Foundation for Education & Welfare

Jewish charities, health

£1,225,000 (1999)

Beneficial area International, but mainly Israel.

c/o Glencore UK Ltd, 49 Wigmore Street, London W1H OLU

Tel. 020 7935 4455 **Fax** 020 7487 5431

Correspondent J Boxer, Secretary

Trustees *Danny Dreyfuss; M Paisner; L Weiss; J Boxer.*

Information available Annual report and accounts (in US dollars).

General

The foundation's review of activities in its 1999 annual report says:

> The Glencore Foundation for Education and Welfare was established in 1994, for general charitable purposes, but the principal area of activity has been within the fields of education and welfare with particular reference to Israel.
>
> The Charity's annual income derives entirely from Glencore UK Ltd. The choice of projects supported has been based on detailed study of the charitable needs and all such projects are monitored in order to ensure that the funds so applied are properly used for the chosen charitable objectives. The emphasis on education and welfare is likely to remain the principal policy of the trustees during the coming year.

Income was just over $1.9 million that year ($3.5 million in 1998) and nearly $1.8 million was spent on grants, down from $2.7 million the year before.

A full grants list for 1999 was not yet available as this book went to press, so the following examples are of grants made in 1998.

A total of 135 grants were awarded, most for $20,000 or more, predominantly to Jewish organisations working in Israel, with educational projects apparently having priority over welfare. Smaller amounts went to international aid organisations (UNICEF, $14,000 for work in Brazil and North Korea; Médecins Sans Frontières, $11,200 for HIV/AIDS projects), and a handful of UK health/disability charities.

The largest grants were all in the field of education, to the following recipients: Sad Schweiz ($118,000); Lezion Berina ($72,000), and Tauro Wedaas ($62,000), all of whom receive ongoing support from the trust. Relatively few non-Jewish UK charities were supported but they included Guide Dogs for the Blind, Help the Aged, Leukaemia Research, National Asthma Campaign and the Royal Marsden Hospital, which all received grants of between $1,000 and $5,000.

Applications

In writing to the correspondent.

The Gloucestershire Environmental Trust Company

Environmental improvements

£750,000 (income, 1998)

Beneficial area Gloucestershire only.

Moorend Cottage, Watery Lane, Upton St Leonards, Gloucestershire GL4 8DW

Tel. 01452 615110 **Fax** 01452 613817

Correspondent Lynne Garner

Trustees *Jonathon Porritt, Chair; David Ball; David Burton; Paul Holliday; Gordon McGlone; Jack Newell.*

Information available Report and accounts.

Summary

The trust can make grants for:

- the physical and natural environment;
- education and research on better waste management;
- open spaces, important buildings or public amenities near landfill sites.

General

This trust:

- is a body which exists to make grants for schemes that will benefit the environment and people of Gloucestershire;
- receives its income through a scheme set up by Cory Environmental under the landfill tax regulations;
- requires that schemes gaining its support shall satisfy one or more of its objects as described below;
- requires that schemes shall have gained approval from ENTRUST (see entry for Landfill Tax Credit Scheme and ENTRUST, page 174).

Preferential consideration may be given to projects which are close to the Hempsted, Stoke Orchard or Elmstone Hardwicke landfill operations.

The objects of the trust are:

> 1. The conservation, protection and improvement of the physical and natural environment within Gloucestershire.
> 2. The advancement of public education and research in encouraging more sustainable waste management practices and lessening environmental impacts, including recycling.
> 3. The provision of open spaces in the vicinity of landfill sites for the recreation ... of the public.
> 4. The restoration, preservation and repair of buildings of historical importance or architectural value, which are in the vicinity of landfill sites.
> 5. The maintenance and repair of public amenities in the vicinity of landfill sites. ...

The trust notes the following possible examples of fundable activities: repair or restoration of places of worship; canal restoration; purchase and development of nature reserves or public parks; research into sustainable waste management, etc.

Full or part funding is available. A maximum grant (or amount granted in one year for a single organisation) has been set at £50,000. It is envisaged that a wide range of bodies, not all of them necessarily registered charities, could receive grants. They include churches, community groups, wildlife trusts, village hall committees, historic buildings trusts, and waste management research establishments.

Beneficiaries to 1999/2000 included: Gloucestershire Wildlife Trust (£50,000 towards the purchase and restoration of Salmondsbury Meadows); National Waterways Museum, Gloucester (£98,000); Sandford Lido (£23,000 for heat retention covers); The Natural Step (£96,000 over two years for an advice programme for companies); Woodchester Mansion (£55,000); the Farming and Advisory Group (£29,000); and Seven Springs Play Centre, near Cheltenham (£5,000 for a climbing frame).

Applications

On forms available from the correspondent.

The Goldsmiths' Company's Charities

General, London charities, the precious metals craft

£1,736,000 (1998/99)

Beneficial area UK, with a special interest in London charities.

Goldsmiths' Hall, Foster Lane, London EC2V 6BN

Tel. 020 7606 7010 **Fax** 020 7606 1511

Correspondent R D Buchanan-Dunlop, Clerk

Trustees *The Goldsmiths' Company. Charity Committee: Lord Cunliffe, Chair; Sir Edward Ford; S A Shepherd; Miss J A Lowe; Dr M P Godfrey; Revd P D Watherston; W H Montgomery.*

Education Committee: Lord Tombs, Chair; Prof. D N Dilks; Prof. K J Gregory; Prof. R L Himsworth; Prof. Sir Robert Honeycombe; Sir Robert Balchin; Mrs B B Moriarty; R W Threlfall; Dr J R Wilson.

Information available Excellent report and accounts with full and well-presented grants list and narrative exploration of grants and grantmaking. The report also contains brief guidelines for applicants and a copy of the application form.

Summary

About 300 grants are made a year to support a broad array of causes, but to London-based or national charities only. Most grants are between £1,000 and £2,000, with a maximum of around £50,000. Half of the beneficiaries in any one year receive grants repeated over three years. Donations are mainly for revenue costs.

The excerpts from the annual report reprinted below show a welcome willingness to support charities working on new and emerging social issues.

Most of the educational work is either with institutions connected with the company or in support of interesting proactive programmes, ranging from the Primary School Literacy Project to support for Science for Society courses for A-level teachers.

General

This entry covers three of the charities of the Goldsmiths' livery company in London, namely: John Perryn's Charity; the General Charity; and Goldsmiths' Charitable Donation Fund. These share a single annual report and set of accounts.

In 1998/99 the charities had net assets of £60 million, generating a rather low income of £2.3 million. After taking capital gains into account, the value of the funds increased by no less than £6 million, after a £2 million increase in the previous year.

The grants are widely spread, but recent years have seen a specific interest in rural concerns with large grants for the excellent Wiltshire Community Foundation. However, it is agreeable to see that for its next set of grants in this field the trust is moving from one of the more prosperous parts of the country to one of the less so – Cornwall.

Grants in 1998/99 were categorised as follows:

Support for the precious metals crafts	£620,000
General welfare	£295,000
Education	£524,000
Medical welfare and the disabled	£105,000
Youth	£118,000
Arts	£46,000
Church	£19,000
Heritage and conservation	£60,000

Grant-making policies are described as follows:

Grants are made to London-based and/or national charities only; where charities are members or branches of an association, appeals are accepted from the governing body or head office only.

Applications from any organisation, whether successful or not, are not considered more frequently than once every three years.

General charitable support

The largest area of grantmaking is towards general charitable needs, ranging from the disadvantaged in society and general welfare to the churches and the arts.

Support for the goldsmiths' craft

Support is given to higher and further educational establishments, to students and apprentices, to promote excellence in design and craftsmanship, and to help young people develop their potential to secure jobs in the precious metals and jewellery industry. Exhibitions are also mounted to further the public's knowledge and enjoyment of silverware and jewellery.

Education

In addition to support for its craft, the company sponsors a number of general educational initiatives. These are directed mainly towards primary and secondary education. Grants are made to individuals only where they have a connection with the company or as part of one of the company's schemes; grants are not normally made to students whose claims fall outside the terms of those schemes.

The following section contains excerpts from the annual report, concentrating on the grant programmes of widest interest.

Annual report 1998/99

This report covers the three ... main charities: John Perryn's Charity (the only one to retain the name of its original benefactor), the General Charity and the Goldsmiths Charitable Donation Fund, which the Charity Commissioners have agreed may be treated as an entity for the purpose of the annual report and accounts. ... the purposes of the three charities are closely allied and in terms of the Company's overall grant-making policies are treated equally.

The Goldsmiths' Company's grant-making policies fall into three main areas:

a) General charitable work, i.e. the normal range of charitable giving from welfare to culture and heritage, but excepting education which is dealt with separately in the two discrete areas below, and the following specific areas: medical research, animal welfare, memorials to individuals and overseas projects;

b) Education in the broader sense, and

c) Education in support of the Goldsmiths' Company's craft of silversmithing and the making of precious metal jewellery.

Overview

The thrust of the Goldsmiths' Company's Charities' grant-making has remained unchanged over the past year.

General charitable work

... as in previous years over half the grants are part of recurring two or three year grants, and this policy has provided a large measure of stability to the pattern of grant-making in this area. Nevertheless, as the grant-making is very largely reactive rather than pro-active, the fact that the total number of grants is 300 and the average size of grant, excluding those above £5,000, is £1,638, which mirrors the previous year's figures closely, is more chance than grand design.

The one area which has been specifically pro-active is grant-making to rural foundations. This year saw the second tranche of £25,000 towards the Wiltshire Community Foundation's anti-poverty and social exclusion grant round. It was also the Company's final grant to this Foundation, making a total of £150,000 over four years.

WCF has been a model of efficiency and energy in making use of these grants and it is hoped that the latter have also been a catalyst in helping the Foundation to build up its endowment funds. As mentioned in the previous report, the Company has now turned its attention to Cornwall.

No community foundation has been created there yet but the newly established Cornwall Independent Trust is ably filling the gap. A grant of £50,000 was made to the Trust this year, with the promise of a further grant next year, and it is encouraging that other foundations, notably the Baring Foundation, are now also turning their attention to this county which has some of the worst social and economic deprivation in the United Kingdom.

General welfare

This sector covers a wide area from housing and community work to addiction and domestic violence. Grant-making amounted to nearly £300,000, a slight increase from the previous year, but the grants to the Cornwall Independent Trust and WCF mentioned above accounted for £75,000 of the total. Amongst the specific areas to be helped was the burgeoning problem of refugees and asylum seekers. It is becoming increasingly difficult to assess these appeals fairly and to determine at what stage a refugee group becomes an established ethnic minority community. In addition to others, recurring grants continued to be made to Asylum Aid and the Refugee Council, and an additional grant of £5,000 was made to the Refugee Council, specifically for Kosovan refugees.

Homelessness remains an apparently intractable problem despite the many excellent charities in this area; nine grants were made for homelessness and housing projects including the second tranche of £20,000 to the Housing Associations Charitable Trust ...

Assistance to prisoners, prisoners' families and ex-offenders has continued to be another prominent area for grant-making. ...

Medical welfare and disabled

The blind, the deaf, and those who are otherwise disabled or have learning difficulties have all received grants, as have a number of self-help associations for specific diseases.

Youth

The overall amount of grant-making in this area has remained steady. While grants to outward-bound type charities and for holiday schemes still feature, it is counselling and work with runaways and young people at risk which seem to predominate. These features of dysfunctional family life echo an increasingly worrying national trend.

Heritage and the Church

Although these subjects are shown as separate sectors in the list of grants, there is an overlap between the two because much of the assistance given to churches is for heritage conservation and the distinction between a grant to a church for specific heritage purposes and one for broader reasons can be blurred. The third tranche of a three-year grant was given to the Historic Churches Preservation Trust, and also to the Historic Chapels Trust and to the Council for the Care of Churches ...

Arts

The main thrust of grant-making to the Arts has been for music. As in previous years the major grant was £17,625 to the City Music Society for a series of six evening concerts. Otherwise outreach programmes for school children and youth have featured strongly, the latter including grants to the National Youth Orchestra, the National Youth Wind Orchestra and the National Youth Jazz Association.

Education

As mentioned earlier, a grant of £320,000 to Goldsmiths College for an extension to the students union building accounted for over half the £524,130 total of grants for education. The other major grants in this sector all stem from continuing pro-active projects. £25,000 to the BMA Educational Trust for bursaries to students studying medicine as a second degree continues to help a much needed source of doctors for which the government provides no funding. The Primary School Literacy Project is progressing well with a further tranche of £18,000 to the four primary schools involved.

The Science for Society courses for teachers of A-level science continue to run successfully and were all oversubscribed ...

Support of the craft

This sector has been dominated by grants to London Guildhall University ...

Exclusions

Medical research; memorials to individuals; overseas projects; animal welfare.

Applications

Applications for all of the charities applying for general charitable support should be made on an application form and should be accompanied by the following information:

- an outline of the current work and experience of the applicant organisation including details of staffing, organisational structure and use of volunteers;
- the organisation's most recent annual report, if one is published;
- a detailed budget for the proposed activity;
- the organisation's most recent audited accounts (or financial report required by the Charities Act);
- the methods by which the success of the project will be evaluated;
- the income/expenditure projection for the organisation for the current year;
- other grant-making organisations appealed to for the same project and with what result;
- preference for a single or annual grant for up to three years.

Trustees meet monthly except during August and September.

The Gosling Foundation

Naval charities, general

£848,000 (1998/99)

Beneficial area UK.

21 Bryanston Street, London W1A 4NH

Tel. 020 7499 7050

Correspondent A Yusof, Secretary

Trustees *Sir Donald Gosling; Ronald Hobson.*

Information available Accounts on file at the Charity Commission. The grants list for 1998/99 is absent.

Summary

Most of the 150 or so grants a year range from £100 to £5,000 and benefit a range of causes, with charities for children and disabled people featuring prominently. However, the largest proportion of the foundation's money (between about two thirds and three quarters depending on the year) is reserved for naval charities. These beneficiaries typically receive £10,000 or more each, with £383,000 in 1996/97 being the largest grant so far. Around half of the grant recipients, in all fields of work, get repeat funding.

General

As in the previous edition of this book, a grants list was unavailable for the year under review, so this entry must rely on grant information from the 1997/98 accounts, when a much lower amount (£533,000) was donated.

Out of 21 grants of over £5,000 each, 10 were for 'maritime' charities, some of which appeared to receive regular support. The largest award, for £55,000, went to HM yacht *Britannia*, which had also been funded in 1995/96. Others included the Royal Navy Submarine Museum (£25,000); Coastal Forces Heritage Trust (£25,000); King George's Fund for Sailors (£21,000); HMS

Marlborough Welfare Fund (£10,000), and Malta Maritime Museum (£10,000).

Other large, apparently one-off, grants went to national or London charities for children, or sick and disabled people, as follows: MENCAP (£25,000); Variety Club of Great Britain (£12,000); Greater London Fund for the Blind (£10,000); MIND in Barnet (£10,000), and Macmillan Nurses (£10,000).

About 120 grants ranged from £100 to £5,000, mostly around £1,000. Children's and armed forces charities, as well as those working locally in London, were prominent among the beneficiaries. Cursory examination suggests that over half had been supported before. Recipients included the Chelsea and Westminster Hospital Arts Project (£2,000); London Federation of Boys' Clubs (£1,500); Missions to Seamen (£1,500); Saints and Sinners Club of Scotland (£1,500); The Shepherd's Market Association (£1,250); Royal Horticultural Society (£1,000); Save the Children (£1,000); 1846 (Southall) Squadron Air Training Corps (£1,000), and Action on Addiction (£1,000).

Applications

To the correspondent in writing.

The Grand Charity of Freemasons

Health, hospices and welfare

£3,029,000 (in non-masonic donations, 1998/99)

Beneficial area England and Wales.

60 Great Queen Street, London WC2B 5AZ

Tel. 020 7395 9293 **Fax** 020 7395 9296

e-mail the.secretary@the-grand-charity.org

Correspondent Dudley Wensley, Secretary

Trustees *The council, consisting of a president and 24 council members, listed in the annual reports.*

Information available Application form with guidelines. Detailed annual report and accounts. Biannual newsletters available from the charity.

Summary

In addition to the charity's commitment to the masonic community, grants of almost every size, from £500 to £500,000, and for both capital and revenue, are made to registered charities that operate throughout England and Wales, or in London, but not to other local charities. Grants are given principally in support of general welfare, especially of the young and the old. Areas of support are broadly based and cover social care, health and medical research, education and employment training.

General

The Freemasons' Grand Charity is the central charity of all Freemasons in England and Wales. It was formally registered in 1981 and carries on a tradition of charitable support for both Freemasons and the wider community that has existed since 1727.

The Grand Charity provides grants for three purposes:

- The relief of 'poor and distressed Freemasons' and their dependants
- The support of other Masonic charities
- The support of all other charities

This work is funded entirely through contributions from individual Masons and their families.

Meeting the needs

A number of major grants were made during 1999. These included £400,000 to Help the Aged to launch several new HandyVan schemes, £500,000 to the Crocus Trust (renamed Beating Bowel Cancer) to support screening and diagnostic facilities in Centres around the country, £446,000 to fund three social worker posts for five years for Sargent Cancer Care for Children and £405,000 to help Crisis expand its SmartMove programme. A number of smaller grants were also made to charities around the country including support for the Alzheimer's Research Trust, Research Into Ageing, Refuge and the Implanted Devices Group at University College London.

The Grand Charity also made grants to hospices of £500,000, and £190,000 was provided to the British Red Cross and Masonic Districts overseas, to help alleviate the suffering of those affected by major disasters.

In addition, the Grand Charity spent more than £2 million to help Freemasons and their dependants who were in need, with a further £811,000 given to other Masonic causes.

The charity held assets in a general fund worth £26.7 million in 1999, with investment income of £865,000 down from £987,000 the year before, so most revenue is from continuing donations from freemasons.

Guidelines

Geographic coverage

Grants are made to registered charities in England and Wales. Applicant charities must operate nationally, throughout England and Wales, and be registered with the Charity Commission. Local charities (i.e. ones that serve an individual city or region) are not eligible for funding by The Grand Charity. These charities, if seeking Masonic support, should apply instead to the Provincial Grand Lodge of the region in which they operate. Masonic provinces equate roughly to the old counties and their offices are listed in telephone directories, usually under 'Freemasons' or 'Masons'. The exception to this rule is that charities that serve only London are eligible for support from the Grand Charity because there is no equivalent of a Masonic Province's charitable fund to meet local needs in the capital.

Size of grant

The Grand Charity gives grants ranging from £500 to £500,000. Most grants, for general charitable purposes, will be up to £5,000. Any grant greater than this amount must be for a designated purpose. In total, The Grand Charity makes grants to other charities of approximately £2 million a year.

Policy areas supported

The Grand Charity gives grants principally in support of general welfare in the widest sense, especially of the young and the old. Its areas of support are broadly based and cover social care, health and medical research, education and economic development.

For grants greater than £5,000, The Grand Charity will only provide funding for a specific project. These should be thoughtfully planned, with specific measurable objectives, a clear timetable for delivery, offering good value for money and addressing an issue of major community/social need.

Projects should also offer The Grand Charity the opportunity for its support to be viewed as a genuine contribution to the well being of the wider community and to be recognised and acknowledged publicly.

Grants are also given to hospices as part of a nation-wide project. These range from £700 to £3,000 each, to a total of £500,000 per year. Hospice grant applications should be made on a separate form which is available from either the appropriate Provincial Grand Lodge or The Grand Charity office.

Other grants in 1998/99

Apart from the major awards listed above, a further £630,000 was committed to four other charities, as follows: Refuge (£300,000); Research into Ageing (£150,000 over three years for three research projects); Implanted Devices Group (£150,000); Shaw Trust (£30,000).

The following beneficiaries received grants as part of commitments made in previous years: Prince's Youth Business Trust (£75,000); Parkinson's Disease Society, Brain Research Centre (£31,000 out of £60,000); Centrepoint (£26,000 out of £53,000); Alzheimer's Research Trust (£24,000 out of £103,000).

Three one-off grants were made to the Mines Advisory Group (£55,000), the Mobility Trust and Bridget's Trust (£25,000 each).

Grants to hospices (£500,000)

In 1998/99, 187 hospices received grants, compared with 178 the year before, with the average amount rising from about £1,400 to more than £2,600. The national charity Help the Hospices received the largest amount of £10,000, but most individual hospices got between £1,000 and £3,000. Only 10 received £5,000 or more, 4 of them in London.

Minor grants (£329,000)

A total of 243 grants for under £10,000 (typically from £1,000 to £2,000) were made to a wide range of beneficiaries. Many went to medical research organisations and charities providing support for disadvantaged people, particularly homeless people, people with disabilities, women, children and older people. Superficial analysis of the list of beneficiaries reveals that somewhere between a half and three quarters got repeat grants.

Of these grants, £255,000 was given to charities working nationally. Of the first 20 charities listed, 12 had received similar grants in the previous year. The largest, for £3,200, went to the National Deaf Children's Society. Other recipients included the Crimestoppers Trust, National Association for Gifted Children, Friends of the Earth, Jewish AIDS Trust and the Prison Reform Trust.

A further £74,000 went to 56 London charities in grants from £500 to £3,000. They included Eaves Housing for Women (temporary and long-term accommodation for single homeless women, £500); North Southwark Bereavement Care Association (£1,000) and Parents for Children (places children with difficulties in new families, £2,000).

Emergency grants (£190,000)

The amount given for emergency grants in 1999 was double the 1998 figure (£95,000). Of this, 84% was disbursed through the Red Cross, with which the charity has a long-standing relationship. The largest of four grants was for £100,000 to help refugees in Kosovo; the others were for work in India, Colombia and Turkey. Two grants of £15,000 each were made via the district grand lodges, to help refugees in Sierra Leone and Gambia, and hurricane victims in the Bahamas and Turks & Caicos Islands.

Exclusions

Local charities, except those serving London, are not eligible for funding. Grants are not normally given to:

- individuals (other than for the relief of 'poor and distressed Freemasons' and their poor and distressed dependants)
- organisations not registered with the Charity Commission
- activities that are primarily the responsibility of central or local government or some other responsible body
- organisations or projects outside of England and Wales
- animal welfare
- the arts
- the environment
- charities with sectarian (religious) or political objectives

Applications

Application forms are available from The Grand Charity office. They must be completed in full, either typed or written in block capitals, and accompanied by a copy of the latest annual report and audited accounts; these must be less than 18 months old.

Hospice grant applications are made on a separate form, available from either the appropriate provincial grand lodge or The Grand Charity office.

Applications may be submitted to the office of The Grand Charity at any time throughout the year.

For additional information, please contact Laura Chapman or Lucinda Stevenson on 020 7395 9296.

The Great Britain Sasakawa Foundation

Links between Great Britain and Japan

£653,000 (1999)

Beneficial area UK, Japan.

43 North Audley Street, London W1Y 1WH

Tel. 020 7355 2229 **Fax** 020 7355 2230

e-mail gbsf@gbsf.org.uk

website www.gbsf.org.uk

Correspondent Michael Barrett, Chief Executive

Trustees *Council: Prof. Peter Mathias, Chair; The Hon Yoshio Sakurauchi; Lord Butterfield; Michael French; Baroness Brigstocke; Jeremy Brown; Baroness Park; Earl of St Andrews; Kazuo Chiba; Prof. Harumi Kimura; Yohei Sasakawa; Akira Iriyama; Prof. Shoichi Watanabe.*

Information available A leaflet about the foundation, its aims and eligibility of applicants is available. Annual report with full list of grants.

Summary

Around 150 grants are awarded each year for initiatives which 'improve relations between the UK and Japan by furthering a better understanding between the peoples of both nations'. Fields supported include 'cultural, linguistic, sociological, educational, academic research, environmental, sport and youth exchange'. Grants are normally for amounts between £500 and £5,000, rarely for more than £10,000. Roughly three quarters of the beneficiaries are based in the UK and few receive recurrent awards.

General

The foundation was established following a meeting in 1983 when the late Ryoichi Sasakawa, a shipbuilding tycoon, and the late Robert Maxwell met a number of senior British politicians to discuss Anglo-Japanese relations. The foundation was inaugurated two years later with a gift of £9.5 million from the Japan Shipbuilding Industry Foundation (now called The Nippon Foundation). It has offices in both Tokyo and London.

In 1999 the foundation's assets were worth more than £24 million. The low income of £656,000 was disbursed in grants with the management costs of £163,000 paid out of capital growth. These editors would expect an endowment of this size to generate an expendable return of 5% (£1.2 million in this case) while still maintaining the value of the capital.

Guidelines

The foundation aims to advance the education of the citizens of Great Britain and Japan in many fields to develop mutual appreciation and understanding of the institutions, people and history, language and culture of the two nations, to promote research and to publish the useful results of such research.

The foundation has supported a wide range of projects including:

- visits between Japan and Great Britain by public servants, leading figures, writers and academics, students, teachers, journalists, artists, and former prisoners of war, their captors and others;
- work in the visual or performing arts, translation and publication of books serving foundation aims, and the teaching of the Japanese language in the United Kingdom;
- research in the fields of education, the arts, history, medicine and sociology and environmental studies.

In addition the foundation may conduct seminars, meetings and lectures and undertake other activities to encourage understanding between the peoples of Japan and the United Kingdom.

The foundation makes grants under nine headings, the first three having accounted for nearly two thirds of total expenditure up to 1998:

- cultural
- Anglo-Japanese relations
- youth exchange
- linguistics
- science, industry and technology
- medical and medical research
- Japanese studies
- sport
- religion, conservation, ecological and environmental

Out of £653,000 awarded during 1999, about half (£322,000) was donated in 126 small grants for up to £5,000. Only five out of the total 153 grants were for more than £15,000, to the following recipients:

- Youth Exchange Centre (£40,000, annual grant);
- Japan–UK Exchange Programme on Community Care with Citizens' Participation (£26,000, third and final year);
- UK–Japan NPO Exchange Programme in City Planning (£23,000);
- Hokkaido Tokai University (£16,000);
- Oxford and Cambridge University Judo Club (£15,000).

Other UK-based beneficiaries included: World Haiku Festival, Oxford (£10,000); University of Birmingham, Japan Centre (£7,000); Northern Ireland Karate – Do Wado Kai (£3,000); Arran Japanese Translation Services (£2,000) and The Ugly Men (Band, £500).

Exclusions

Grants are not made to individuals applying on their own behalf. The foundation can, however, consider proposals from organisations which support the activities of individuals, provided they are citizens of the UK or Japan.

No grants can be made for the construction, conservation or maintenance of land and buildings.

The foundation will not support activities involving politics, legislation or election to public office.

Grants are not normally made for medical research.

Applications

The awards committee meets twice a year, in mid May and mid November. Applicants should request an application form either from the London headquarters or from the Tokyo liaison office. Applications should contain the following information as appropriate:

- A summary of the proposed project and its aims;
- Total cost of the project and the amount of the desired grant, together with a note of other expected sources of funds. Estimated period for research projects, visits or study.
- A description of the applicant's organisation and, where relevant, brief career details of the main participants in any project, and where appropriate the ages of those individuals who may be the recipients.

Applicants are expected to make a careful calculation of all costs of a project before seeking a grant. Where a grant is approved no application for an increase will be accepted after approval except in very special circumstances.

The foundation will not consider making a further grant to an applicant until at least two years after a successful application. Organisations applying should be registered charities, recognised educational institutions, local or regional authorities, churches, media companies, publishers or such other bodies as the foundation may approve.

School applicants are requested to first file an application with Connect Youth, The British Council, 10 Spring Gardens, London SW1A 2BN (which is part of the British Council), whose Japanese Exchange Programme, to which the foundation grants external finance, is aimed at encouraging the exchanges (both ways) for schools in Great Britain and Japan.

All applicants are notified shortly after each awards committee meeting of the decisions of the trustees.

Greater Bristol Foundation

General, in Bristol

£481,000 (1999/2000)

Beneficial area Greater Bristol.

Royal Oak House, Royal Oak Avenue, Bristol BS1 4GB

Tel. 0117 989 7700 **Fax** 0117 989 7701

e-mail info@gbf.org.uk

website www.gbf.org.uk

Correspondent Helen Moss, Director

Trustees *Trevor Smallwood, Chair; Jennifer Bryant-Pearson; John Burke; Gillian Camm; George Ferguson; Alfred Morris; John Pontin; The Rt Revd Barry Rogerson; Tim Stevenson; Simon Storvik; Jay Tidmarsh; Heather Wheelhouse.*

Information available 'Grantmaking Policy and Guidelines' leaflet. Excellent annual review.

Summary

This community foundation was established in 1988 and had built up an endowment worth nearly £6 million by 2000. In addition to its own grant programme, described below, it makes grants on behalf of its donors and 'special advised grants' from a number of funds that have their own criteria and deadlines.

General

The foundation makes three types of grant from its own funds:

- Express grants – providing a quick response to requests for small amounts of money. Applications for grants up to £1,000 can be made at any time, and are dealt with within four weeks.

- Catalyst grants – linking funding on offer via the foundation with particular areas of need. These grants are generally between £1,000 and £5,000, occasionally more.
- Impact grants – longer-term, larger grants aiming to make a significant difference on a particular issue. Grants are for a maximum of £50,000 over three years, with no more than £25,000 available in any one year.

Grants made under these programmes amounted to £164,000 in 1999/2000. Further details can be found in the foundation's latest 'Grantmaking Policy and Guidelines' leaflet or on its website. The guidelines published in January 2000 describe the criteria as follows.

Criteria

In the Foundation's own grants programme we fund organisations that:

- meet the needs in the greater Bristol area
- reach those people that are most disadvantaged and isolated. People may be isolated due to poverty, disability, age or culture
- enable people to take opportunities that would otherwise not be available to them
- support people's involvement in improving their local community
- reflect the concerns and priorities of people living and working in our area of benefit.

We are particularly keen to support local organisations that are making a difference in disadvantaged areas. We are happy to help groups to draw up an application or arrange for assistance if another format or language is required.

Grants in 1999/2000

Examples are taken from the foundation's 2000 annual review.

Impact grants

Four projects totalling £47,000, including: The Southmead Project – £15,000 (second of three annual payments totalling £60,000) to develop a relapse prevention programme alongside a skill-based training project for people recovering from drug and alcohol addiction.

Catalyst grants

There were 15 grants totalling £62,000. Recipients included: Progress – £5,400 to run financial management training courses for local voluntary organisations; St Stephen's Community Work Project – £1,600 for involving local people in the development of an area of land as a community space in the Southmead area of Bristol.

Express grants

There were 74 grants totalling £55,000, including: Space Trust – £1,000 towards a bursary scheme that helps children of homeless families continue their education in their original schools; Stockwood Volunteers Group – £500, basic running costs for a local organisation providing practical help and assistance for older and isolated people in the area.

Donor advised grants

In all, 298 grants totalling £212,000 were made at the request of donors to a range of projects often outside the criteria of the foundation's own grant-making programmes. Recipients included: Aspire Community Enterprise, Bristol Cancer Help Centre, Bristol Samaritans, Bristol Schools' Orchestra, St Peter's Hospice and the University of Bristol.

Special advised grants

A total of 71 grants amounting to £105,000 were made from specific funds, including: Churngold Environmental Fund, to support environmental and educational projects; URBAN Key Fund, for inner city groups involved in local regeneration; High Sheriff's Fund, to support young people's community safety projects.

Exclusions

The foundation's own grants programme does not fund:

- general appeals
- statutory organisations or direct replacement of statutory funding
- promotion of religious causes
- overseas travel
- medical research, equipment or treatment
- sports without an identifiable charitable element
- arts projects with limited community benefit
- animal charities
- individuals

Vehicles, conferences and exhibitions will be given low priority.

Applications

Please contact the foundation to discuss the funding that you need. It will be looking for the following information in your application:

- that you are a registered charity or have a constitution that shows you have charitable purposes;
- that your project has up-to-date financial information;
- that you have plans for the long-term sustainability of your organisation;
- that you can show what the benefit of your work is for the wider community;
- that the users of any service you provide are involved in the design, planning and delivery of the services;
- a commitment to equal opportunities.

The foundation may contact you by telephone or arrange a visit if it needs more information.

If you need further information or assistance please contact Alice Meason or Ronnie Brown at the address above.

The Constance Green Foundation

Medicine, health, social welfare, general

£417,000 (1999/2000)

Beneficial area England, with a preference for Yorkshire.

c/o ASL Management Services, Bel Royal House, Hilgrove Street, St Helier, Jersey JE2 4SL

Correspondent M Collinson, Trustee

Information available Report and accounts.

Summary

The foundation makes over 50 grants a year, mainly in the fields of social welfare and medicine, and generally ranging from £1,000 to £10,000, though there a few larger awards. All kinds of organisations, national and local, are supported, but more than half the money in 1999/2000 appeared to be to support work in West Yorkshire.

The foundation is unusual in the extent to which its administration is carried out by people or institutions connected with the trustees. However, new arrangements were announced as this book went to press.

General

'Of the total grants given, over 90% were made to assist special projects ... rather than to provide core funding.'

Grants in 1999/2000 were classified as follows (the figures refer to the value of grants):

- Medical and social care, including terminal care, for children and young people – 34%
- The disabled, both physically and mentally – 25%
- The homeless – 16%
- Children and young people, including the disadvantaged – 12%
- Medical, including facilities and equipment – 10%
- The aged – 1%

Nearly £40,000 was also given to charities operating overseas.

During 1999/2000 the trustees agreed to give £250,000 to the Martin House Hospice in Wetherby, payable in 2000/01. This may reduce the amount available for other causes.

No doubt because of the wide spread of its grants, the foundation received over 1,000 applications.

The total administrative expenses of the charity, at £55,000, were high in comparison to most trusts described in this book, being 13% of the direct charitable expenditure, or £860 for every grant made.

As in previous editions of this book, these editors regret the extent to which the affairs of the charity are carried on by people and institutions connected with the trustees. The trust notes that this was the policy of the founder of the trust, that it is specifically authorised by the trust deed, and it therefore disagrees that the practice, in this case, is undesirable.

The recent Charity Commission guidance on this subject (Leaflet CC11, published September 2000) specifically states that such payments need to be backed by more than just legal power for them to be made: 'Even where there is express authority which enables a trustee to be paid a conflict [of interest] will still exist.' The guidance then lists the considerations to be taken into account if trustees nevertheless wish to consider such payments, noting that even before addressing these points it is important that the trustees have first carefully explored whether there are any other realistic alternatives. These editors believe that there almost always will be realistic alternatives for the supply of administrative services.

In this case N Hall is the managing director of the charity's stockbrokers, Cater Allen, who were paid £38,000 for various services during the year. A G Collinson is a partner in Evershed's, the charity's solicitors.

The trustees also had substantial reimbursement of expenses, totalling £8,153 or an average of over £2,000 each.

The three major grants in 1999/2000 were to Barnardos (£85,000), St Martin in the Fields (£50,000, for the church, not the orchestra), and Jersey Scout Association.

Awards of £10,000 each went to Brainwave; Harrogate Community Transport; Médecins Sans Frontières; the Wheelchair Sports Foundation; Cookridge Cancer Centre; Sense, in Leeds; the NSPCC; Lifetime Network International; Power (International Limb Project); Calderdale Community Foundation, and MENCAP.

Exclusions

Sponsorship of individuals is not supported.

Applications

At any time in writing to the correspondent (no special form of application required). Applications should included clear details of the need the intended project is designed to meet, plus an outline budget. Applications are not generally acknowledged unless an sae is provided.

Greggs Trust

Social welfare in the north east of England

£425,000 (1998)

Beneficial area Northumberland, Tyne and Wear, County Durham, Teesside.

Fernwood House, Clayton Road, Jesmond, Newcastle upon Tyne NE2 1TL

Tel. 0191 281 1444 **Fax** 0191 281 1444

e-mail jenniw@greggs.co.uk

Correspondent Jenni Wagstaff, Trust Officer

Information available Annual reports and accounts. Policy guidelines, and guide for applicants available.

Summary

The trust makes a large number of grants a year, both capital and revenue, for social welfare in the north east of England. There are four grants programmes:

- Major grants – typically one-off donations of between £1,000 and £5,000, or project or revenue funding of £5,000 or £10,000 a year, over two or three years.
- Small grants – normally for £500 or less, but occasionally up to £1,000.
- Hardship grants for individuals.
- Divisional Charity Committee grants.

General

The trust describes its policy as follows:

Main focus

It has been agreed that the alleviation of poverty and social deprivation should be the main objective of the Trust and that priority will be given to projects with this objective. Projects in the fields of the arts, the environment, conservation, education and health will be considered so long as they have a social welfare focus and/or are located in areas of deprivation.

Area of benefit

The intention of the Trustees is that the Trust should be of benefit principally in those areas in which Greggs businesses operate. The central fund of the Trust, as opposed to funds allocated by the Trust through the Charity Committees established in the Divisions of Greggs plc or in any other part of the business, is to be applied principally within the north east of England, i.e. in the counties of Northumberland, Tyne and Wear, County Durham and Teesside.

Local projects and grants to individuals in need

The Trustees will give priority to grants for local, or in certain cases regional, organisations and projects. They will also continue to allocate a proportion of the funds available for distribution, through a number of approved agencies, in grants to individuals experiencing hardship.

Examples of current interests

Major grants made during 1998 reflect the policy review undertaken in 1996 as well as an increase in the income of the Trust. As intended, the Trustees have approved a number of grants between £5,000 and £10,000, while still awarding a few grants between £1,000 and £5,000. Some projects are being supported for more than one year; but in order to retain the scope for annual distribution, the Trustees will set a limit on such commitments. There is a strong preference for community-based and locally-managed activity, and for estate and neighbourhood-based projects. Recent grants have included support for work with homeless people, older people, young people, children and women, fathers, including the unemployed, and for people with disabilities and ethnic and multi-cultural groups.

Applications from small community-led organisations and self-help groups are more likely to be successful than from larger and well-staffed organisations and those that have greater fundraising capacity. Exceptions may be made where innovative work is being developed by established agencies or where such agencies are providing services to smaller or local groups. Applicant organisations should be able to show that they are working in partnership with relevant statutory and voluntary agencies and that they are aware of, and are applying to, other available sources of funds.

Income for distribution and allocation of funds

The income of the Trust is derived from the profits of Greggs plc and from the donations of major shareholders. Income has recently amounted to approximately £500,000 p.a. and is likely to remain at this level if not to increase. Funds for 2000 will be allocated as follows, (approximate figures only):

- £200,000 in large grants, approved at twice yearly meetings of the Trustees;
- £75,000 in small grants mostly of £500 or less approved on a monthly basis;
- £60,000 for 'hardship' grants distributed on a continuous basis;
- £120,000 for the Charity Committees in Greggs Divisions (for distribution to local charitable causes) which includes funds to match what is contributed by employees through the Give As You Earn scheme and for the Challenge Grant award.

Grants in 1998 and 1999

The trust's report for 1999 was not yet available in September 2000, but a list was provided of major grants approved in that year. Grants from other programmes described here were taken from the 1998 report.

Special grants for the Community Foundation (serving Tyne and Wear and Northumberland)

£5,000 p.a. for five years towards the foundation's endowment fund, approved in 1995. £30,000 p.a. for three years (commenced in 1997) towards a funding partnership, the South East Northumberland Project, which is managed by the foundation. It is intended to benefit 'hard to reach' unemployed young people by improving their opportunities for further education, training and employment.

Major grants

During 1999, 18 major grants were approved, led by £12,000 a year for two years to North Tyneside District Disability Forum in North Shields for its Young People's Disabled Project. Other beneficiaries included:

Willows Community Centre, Stockton-on-Tees: £20,000 over two years for the extension of the Community Training and Employment Skills Audit project. It links skill shortages and the needs of local businesses and industry with training needs and existing skills within the community.

The Relationships Foundation, Citylife North East Project: £5,000 for development work. Citylife aims to encourage local companies, individuals and other bodies to make zero-interest loans, guaranteed returnable after five years. Capital and interest will be invested into creating jobs for the unemployed.

Community Campus 87, Middlesbrough: £5,000 towards the refurbishment of a property which will be renovated by young people who can gain a recognised qualification – the organisation provides affordable, self-contained and shared accommodation for single people between the ages of 16 and 25 in housing need.

Berwick Family Centre: £15,000 over three years towards running costs – the project aims to improve the well-being of children and their parents by providing services which include after-school homework groups, parent and toddler groups, a children's drama group, a family matters group, arts and crafts, positive parenting and holiday playschemes.

Small grants

More than 170 small grants amounting to £74,000 were paid in 1998.

The recipients of grants for £1,000 included Abuse Counselling & Training Centre, Ashington (towards running costs); Durham Wildlife Trust (for a centre in Sunderland providing environmental programmes); Newcastle Council for Voluntary Service (for training bursaries and 'Community Communications Fund'), and South Shields Activity Centre for the Unwaged (towards the upgrade of its music studio).

Details of hardship grants for individuals are available from the trust.

Divisional Charity Committee grants

Approximately 230 grants amounting to £113,000, including 27 payments of £1,000 or more. Examples of larger grants from some of the committees included:

- Greggs of Rutherglen (Scotland): £8,000 to Children First;
- Greggs of Treforest (South Wales): £4,500 to Children in Need;
- Greggs of Yorkshire: £4,000 to the Relationships Foundation (Citylife Unemployment Project in Sheffield).

Exclusions

Grants will not be made to:

- individuals, other than for hardship grants;
- national appeals and, other than in exceptional circumstance, appeals of national organisations for work at regional or local level;
- activities which are primarily the responsibility of statutory agencies or which are likely to get funding from such agencies on a contractual basis;
- appeals of charities set up to support statutory agencies; fundraising organisations; general fundraising appeals; fundraising events and sponsorship;
- hospitals, Health Service trusts, medically related appeals and medical equipment;
- school appeals other than for projects at LEA schools in areas of greater social need, such as after-school clubs and activities promoting parental and community involvement;
- advancement of religion or religious buildings (community aspects of church-based or religious projects may be considered if projects show outreach into the community or particularly to disadvantaged or at-risk groups);
- restoration and conservation of historic buildings and the purchase or conservation of furnishings, paintings, other artefacts or historic equipment;
- purchase, conversion and restoration of buildings other than community-based projects serving areas of greater social need and/or particularly disadvantaged or at-risk groups;
- capital appeals or running costs of fee-charging residential homes, nurseries and other such care facilities;
- appeals from organisations associated with the armed services;
- minibuses and vehicles, other than community transport schemes which serve a combination of groups in a wide geographical area;
- foreign travel and expeditions – including holidays and outings, other than in exceptional circumstances for children, young people or adults from areas of greater social need, or other disadvantaged groups;
- sports buildings, equipment and sporting activities other than where disadvantaged groups are involved and the activity is ongoing rather than one-off;
- academic and medical research; conferences, seminars, exhibitions, publications and events other than

where they are closely related to the trust's main areas of interest;
- festivals, performances and other arts and entertainment activity, unless of specific educational value and involving groups from areas disadvantaged by low income, disability or other factors;
- appeals for projects or from organisations working abroad;
- animal welfare;
- loans, repayment of loans or retrospective funding.

Applications

In writing to the correspondent.

Applicants for major grants are asked to set out their application briefly in a letter, giving full address, phone/fax number and a contact name, the purpose of the application, the amount requested, and details of other applications for the same purposes. More information about the project may be provided in supporting documents.

The following should be included:

- Latest audited accounts or financial report required by the Charity Commission and, if a period of three months or more has passed since the end of the year of the accounts/report, a certified statement of income and expenditure for the period.
- Latest annual report or, if not available, summary of current work.
- The applicant organisation's equal opportunities policy and practice.
- Details of constitutional status; charity registration number if applicable; organisational structure; composition of management; arrangements for the project for which application has been made.
- If support for a salaried post or posts is requested, the job description for the post(s).
- Details of the organisation's policy and provision for training of management body, staff and volunteers.
- Details of how it is intended to evaluate the work for which the grant is requested.

The trustees meet twice a year to assess major grants applications, usually in May and November. Applications should be sent no later than mid-March or mid September.

The trust aims to respond to applications for small grants within approximately two months and to acknowledge applications for major grants in the same period. Applicants will be informed if their applications have not been selected for further consideration.

The M & R Gross Charities

Jewish causes

£534,000 (1998/99)

Messrs Cohen Arnold and Co. Accountants, 13–17 New Burlington Place, London W1X 2JP

Trustees *Milton Gross; Mrs Rifka Gross; Sarah Padwa; Michael Saberski.*

Information available Accounts on file at the Charity Commission.

General

This trust makes grants to educational and religious organisations within the orthodox Jewish community. In 1998/99 it had assets of £12.3 million and an income of £2.4 million, over £1 million in Gift Aid donations and covenants. Grants totalled £534,000, down from £826,000 in 1997/98.

In all, 13 Jewish institutions were supported, mainly schools, colleges and synagogues. Over half the award total was spent on a grant of £295,000 to United Talmudical Associates. Large amounts also went to Kollel Shomrei Hachomos (£75,000) and the Square Foundation (£60,000).

Six small grants were in the range of £750 to £5,000.

Applications

In writing to the organisation.

The Gulbenkian Foundation

Education, arts, welfare

£2,092,000 (1999)

Beneficial area UK and the Republic of Ireland.

98 Portland Place, London W1B 1ET

Tel. 020 7636 5313 **Fax** 020 7908 7580

Correspondent Paula Ridley, Director

Trustees *The foundation's board of administration in Lisbon. UK resident trustee: Mikhael Essayan.*

Information available Fine annual reports with full details of the foundation's thinking, policies and grants. A free leaflet, 'Advice to Applicants for Grants', is also available. As the foundation is not a charity registered in Britain there are no files at the Charity Commission.

Summary

Though one of the best known foundations in Britain, Gulbenkian is not one of the largest, and very few of its grants are for more than £10,000. Its fame rests more in its careful investigation of areas of possible intervention, and its early, if modest, support for new initiatives. Typically, a published report on a particular subject will lead to a corresponding funding programme, to get things moving in the way recommended (and perhaps in the hope that heavier funding guns may then come in behind).

Current examples of the process range from participatory music to children and violence.

The foundation presently operates specific grant-making programmes in four fields, as follows (with the 1999 grant totals). Note that Republic of Ireland grants are now handled within the other programmes.

Social welfare	£689,000
Education	£532,000
Arts	£517,000
Anglo-Portuguese cultural relations	£204,000
(Republic of Ireland	£151,000)

General

This entry starts, after a brief introductory section, with the foundation's excellent 'Advice to Applicants' leaflet, and then reprints sections of the 1999 annual report – these documents have a long history of clear and trenchant comment on the work of the foundation and on the problems that it addresses, as well as describing many of its specific grants.

Background

Calouste Sarkis Gulbenkian was an Armenian born in 1869. He became a British citizen, conducted much of his work in Britain, and finally settled in Portugal. The Calouste Gulbenkian Foundation was established in 1956, a year after his death.

The headquarters of the Foundation are in Lisbon and consist of the administration, which deals with grant-giving throughout the world, together with a museum housing the founder's art collections, a research library, a centre for scientific research, concert halls, indoor and open-air theatres, exhibition galleries and conference halls, a centre for modern art, a children's pavilion, an orchestra, a choir and a ballet company. The Foundation also maintains a Portuguese Cultural Centre in Paris, and a grant-giving branch in London for the United Kingdom and the Republic of Ireland.

The last activity mentioned is the subject of this entry. The UK branch (referred to here, for convenience, simply as the Gulbenkian Foundation), does not have its own endowment, but is funded directly from Lisbon. The foundation is substantially and expertly staffed, and, as well as making grants, organises its own projects and publications.

Advice to applicants (January 2000)

The work of the Foundation's UK branch is divided into programmes in Arts, Education and Social Welfare. There is also a separate programme for Anglo-Portuguese Cultural Relations. A few special grants dealt with by the Director respond to or initiate particularly interesting and worthwhile new projects that do not fall into one of the priority areas. This enables us to explore potential areas for involvement in the future.

We regret that the number of applications in relation to the limited funds available is so large that many good proposals, even though they fit our priorities, unfortunately still have to be refused.

Preference is given to original developments, not yet part of the regular running costs of an organisation; and to projects which are either strategic, such as practical initiatives directed to helping tackle the causes of problems; or seminal, because they seem likely to influence policy and practice elsewhere, and are of more than local significance. Good applications from places outside London are particularly welcome.

The Foundation gives grants only for proposals of a charitable kind, usually from organisations, which should normally be registered charities or otherwise tax-exempt.

Applicants should bear in mind the size of grant the UK Branch of the Foundation is normally able to make. As a guide, in 1999 the majority of grants were for an average of £5,000. At present there is a notional limit of £10,000 to any one grant.

Arts

Assistant Director, Siân Ede

The Arts Programme deals with the arts for adults and young people out of formal education settings.

Mainly for non-professional practitioners:

1. Participatory music

[This programme ended in 2000.]

For professional and non-professional practitioners:

2. The spoken word

[New programme.]

For professional practitioners:

3. The arts and science

This programme is designed to encourage professional artists and arts groups to produce practical projects which demonstrate a creative engagement with new thinking and practice in science and technology. The Foundation will also support a small number of initiatives to encourage science institutions to establish arts policies. This programme is linked to a new publication, Strange and Charmed: Science and the Contemporary Visual Arts, although applications are welcome from across the art forms.

For professional practitioners:

4. International experiment

The Foundation recognises the value of early research and development activities in the creation of new artworks and for the past five years has run a programme offering support to groups of professional artists to undertake short periods of try-out and experiment. Increasingly this programme will now focus on encouraging British groups to invite international arts practitioners to participate in British or Irish based research and development activities. These should take place well before the normal rehearsal or preparation stage and may lead to eventual productions in Britain or Ireland. Consideration will also be given to applications for advanced creative training activities involving international practitioners.

Support is for self-generated practical activity and not for academic research, visits, conferences or discussion.

Please note that ideas for potential applications to the Arts Programme should be broached at least three months in advance of a projected starting date for the project applied for.

Education

Assistant Director, Simon Richey

1. Educational innovations and developments

The emotional well-being of children and young people

Applications are invited from agencies that work with children and young people or from pre-school groups, schools and youth services to support projects specifically established for the purpose of:

(i) promoting the emotional well-being both of pre-school children and children in primary schools who are causing concern.

(ii) promoting the emotional literacy of young people of secondary school age either in schools, after school clubs or in youth service settings.

All applications should show how the projects will be monitored and evaluated. Where appropriate, additional funds may be offered to enable successful applicants to buy in external support and advice for this purpose.

Applications should also indicate a commitment to disseminating the lessons and benefits of the project. Please note that applications from arts projects are not eligible.

Education for parenthood

Support is offered for projects in schools or youth service settings designed to help young people of secondary school age consider what it means to be a parent.

2. Arts for young people

Access to cultural venues

This priority is linked to the Foundation's report *Crossing the Line: Extending Young People's Access to Cultural Venues*.

Applications are invited from cultural venues (theatres, galleries, etc.) for support towards new incentives that help teenagers become familiar with and enjoy cultural venues local to them. There must be clear evidence in the application that the project has been developed in close collaboration with local schools, colleges, youth services or groups of young people (whichever applies). Applications should also indicate how the project will be monitored and evaluated.

Pupil referral units and in-school learning support units

Help with the costs of residencies by companies or artists, and with the costs of evaluating and disseminating the initiatives in question; priority will be given to especially original or enterprising developments.

Social welfare

Deputy Director, Paul Curno

Tackling the causes and consequences of multiple deprivation

The Programme aims to enhance the ability of individuals, families and communities in deprived urban and rural areas to reduce poverty, to alleviate multiple social problems and to promote social inclusion. To that end, support will be given to seminal UK-wide national or regional programmes which are likely to lead to the development of new policies or practice, and which:

(i) Promote community-focused approaches to reducing family poverty.

(ii) Assist the development, effectiveness and financial self-sufficiency of community based organisations which enable residents to organise in response to their needs.

(iii) Develop out-of-school services and facilities which redress the educational and social disadvantages of children in deprived neighbourhoods in an innovative way.

(iv) Assist disadvantaged groups and community agencies to utilise lessons from their experience to inform the development of public policy at local, regional or national level. This is likely to be achieved by undertaking:

A. Research which contributes to knowledge about how public policy and services affect those experiencing social exclusion, and which identifies new policy options.

B. Evaluation of their own work, usually with the aid of an external consultant or facilitator, drawing out key lessons for policy-makers.

Anglo-Portuguese cultural relations

Assistant Director, Miguel Santos

This programme aims to help projects that promote contemporary Portuguese culture in the UK and Ireland. 'Cultural relations' are taken to include social welfare, as well as activities in the arts, crafts and education. The programme includes:

(i) activities in the UK and the Republic of Ireland concerned with Portugal – its language, culture, people – past and present (performances, exhibitions and festivals may be considered);

(ii) cultural and educational interaction between British or Irish and Portuguese people;

(iii) the educational, cultural and social needs of the Portuguese immigrant communities (but not individual Portuguese immigrants or visitors) in the UK or the Republic of Ireland.

But grants are *not* normally given for projects focused upon:

- sporting activities, tourism, holidays
- full-time teaching or research posts or visiting fellowships
- the maintenance, salary or supervision costs of researchers
- attendance at conferences or similar gatherings
- fees or expenses of individual students pursuing courses of education and training, or doing research
- UK cultural or other work in Portugal.

Annual report 1999

The annual reports of the foundation are exceptional in the detail with which they show how the value of grantmaking can be enhanced by the active involvement of the trust's personnel. This is not just in supporting the work of applicants but also in using this work to advance policy and practice more widely, and to develop constructive new directions for grantmaking in the future. Excerpts from the reports are therefore reprinted extensively in these volumes. We have left in the text the references to individual grants, although they are not separately listed here, to show the connections between the general issues discussed and the actual grants made.

The arts programme

The Foundation's three arts programmes are very different and assessing them side by side often presents a stimulating challenge. *Participatory Music* projects – using music-making to improve and gladden people's lives – are always wonderfully worthwhile and it is not difficult to gauge their value, whether it be providing tuition in singing for groups of women in inner-city housing estates or isolated rural villages (grants 12 and 3), funding a Musician in Residence at a hostel for homeless people (grant 14) or supporting specialist music teaching for disabled children in rural Scotland (grant 9).

These projects, and many like them, could run and run. Indeed the *Participatory Music* programme has run for four years and will continue, although we are less and less likely to support projects that are 'outreach' from the mainstream activities of professional music organisations, because education and community work have become central to the requirements of the statutory funders. The new Lottery-funded National Foundation for Youth Music is taking on some of the good professionally run participatory projects which we have supported in the past and at present we are active partners in this. Small-scale work, however, still cannot anticipate regular funding and it is to be hoped that statutory funders, including those involved in new Lottery schemes, will recognise that basic regular tuition is essential if we are to remain a musical nation, and that trust and foundation support cannot continue for ever.

We unashamedly turn down applications for support towards prestigious awards for 'brilliant performers', preferring instead to support people who hardly know where to begin. They may indeed possess talent, but how would anyone know? ...

The second programme, *Time to Experiment*, which makes available support for professional artists to experiment and develop ideas at a very early stage, has attracted less support in this fourth year of its implementation: certainly those within our Art and Science programme have taken a higher priority because they also experiment, but with fascinating contemporary subject matter and new expressive forms...

THE GULBENKIAN FOUNDATION
Geographical distribution of 1999 grants

	No.		*Value*	
National	112	(49%)	£1,228,386	(59%)
London/Dublin	34	(15%)	£230,415	(11%)
Other regions	82	(36%)	£633,561	(30%)
Grant total			£2,092,362	

The education programme

Much of the Education Programme's work is devoted to what might broadly be described as the emotional well-being of children and young people, which, in the context of schools, forms part of the provision for pupils' personal and social development, both implicitly and explicitly.

Some 18 months ago the Programme began developing a curriculum framework which would provide opportunities for pupils' personal and social development – the PASSPORT Framework – in an attempt to bring to this area of the curriculum the coherence and continuity it formerly lacked. This initiative has subsequently influenced and shaped the Government's own frameworks for Personal, Social and Health Education (PSHE) and Citizenship, which were published last autumn as part of the revised National Curriculum ...

For a number of years now the Education Programme has pressed for the inclusion of parenthood education as a component of the PSHE and Citizenship curriculum and supported projects that further this aim. It is gratifying to note, therefore, that the Government has recently commissioned the drafting of guidance for schools on this subject to be published later in 2000. The Education Programme will meanwhile maintain its support for parenthood education since assistance for schools to develop imaginative initiatives in this area, prompted by the Government's guidance, is likely to prove especially timely.

Many children begin their schooling with a variety of emotional difficulties which, if left unchecked, can worsen. Furthermore, a report published during the year by the Mental Health Foundation confirmed that the rates of recorded mental health problems among children and adolescents are rising. That same report also laid stress on the importance of early intervention.

This year the Education Programme is introducing priorities to assist a range of such interventions by pre-school groups, primary schools and professional agencies that work with children and young people. An additional priority aims to help the generality of pupils at secondary level develop their emotional and social learning. This latter priority is designed to encourage schools and those agencies that work with them to exploit the opportunities afforded by the new PSHE and Citizenship frameworks and develop imaginative and enterprising initiatives in this field. This new set of priorities will therefore promote the emotional well-being of children and young people from pre-school right through to secondary school ...

A proportion of the Education Programme's work is devoted to supporting the arts in schools. Central to the health of the arts in schools is the quality of teacher training in arts disciplines, since poorly trained teachers are unlikely ever to communicate the necessary skills or knowledge to their pupils, still less to enthuse them...

The social welfare programme

The Social Welfare Programme adopted a new set of priorities at the beginning of 1999 to address the causes and consequences of multiple deprivation. The intention is to support work which assists individuals, families and community groups in urban and rural deprived areas to alleviate poverty and to promote social inclusion ...

Over the past year three lines of action have emerged ... for future development. In the first place, it has become clear that many organisations intend to take advantage of what they perceive to be a willingness on the part of Government departments and agencies to stimulate creative ideas in response to social exclusion, and they have therefore committed themselves to developing new models and/or strategies to meet local needs. For example, with the Foundation's help, the Association of Community Trusts and Foundations (ACTAF) commissioned Julia Unwin to explore the contribution of community foundations in tackling multiple deprivation through local knowledge and grant-making (grant 130). Community Links was funded to set up the first Social Enterprise Zone in Britain, in Newham, East London, where, drawing on the experience of Business Enterprise Zones, statutory authorities work with local residents and voluntary agencies to change policies and administrative practices to the benefit of the economic and social regeneration of the area (grant 135). The Association of Chief Executives of National Voluntary Organisations (ACENVO) is producing guidelines for national voluntary organisations concerned with social deprivation on the implications for their work of devolution and regionalisation (grant 129). Other examples are Community Matters (National Federation of Community Organisations) which is taking a detailed look at the role and model of the more than 3,000 community associations in the UK in the promotion of local democracy for the next century (grant 137); and Citylife, which is exploring the potential of a new social investment programme in which city residents can invest directly in creating jobs and services in their local communities (grant 160).

A second area for our support which emerged during the year was that of improving the effectiveness of local organisations and groups through the development of new structures and technical skills. For example, the fast-growing Development Trusts Association is establishing a new training and development programme for improving the quality of the services and management and leadership skills of its members (grant 141); the London Regeneration Network is promoting new approaches to the replication of good practice among voluntary and community sector organisations working with excluded groups in London (grant 145); and the Northern Ireland Council for Voluntary Action (NICVA) appointed a Community Journalist to assist community organisations to develop writing skills, produce informative and well-designed newsletters, and establish good links with the media in Northern Ireland (grant 148).

Third, and finally, funding has been provided to organisations contributing new thinking to the development of policies and services dealing with intractable problems. Examples include the New Policy Institute which is assessing current policies and services in health and welfare for ethnic minority and disabled young adults (aged between 16 and 25), a study which will result in recommendations for action by Government (grant 147). The Revolving Doors Agency is establishing an innovative advice and training initiative for local organisations working with people who offend and who also have mental health, drug or alcohol difficulties, or are homeless. Based on successful pilot programme, it involves an intensive team approach to the needs of each individual (grant 168). The needs of children whose parents suffer from mental health problems are being looked at in a new programme run by the Family Welfare Association, which aims to encourage greater collaboration between childcare and mental health services (grant 142). 'Mentoring' has become a popular response to many difficult issues, yet it means different things to different people. Demos is therefore drawing on national and international experience to propose a national mentoring strategy for the voluntary sector and Government (grant 140). Community Links in East London will undertake a national study next year through which local activists running projects dealing with family poverty and social exclusion will analyse their experience as a prelude to generating new activities and policies (grant 136).

Over the coming year the Foundation will continue to develop its funding programme in these three areas while consulting, learning and seeking out new areas for strategic work ...

The Republic of Ireland programme

... Besides responding to those imaginative applications which do come our way, the Foundation is sometimes able to discuss new ideas and set up negotiations on behalf of organisations with other Irish funders. As an example, the Education Programme has initiated the post of Education Officer at the Abbey Theatre in Dublin, negotiating with the Department of Education and Science and the Irish Arts Council to establish education at the heart of the theatre's activities. The Foundation was also instrumental in setting up meetings between senior staff at the London Arts Board and Irish arts administrators and artists and will now be involved in a new London–Dublin arts strategy ...

In supporting this new initiative, the Foundation was concerned not only to help the many groups in Ireland working to tackle the causes and consequences of poverty, but also to gain valuable knowledge and experience in preparation for the establishment of similar programmes in the UK.

Exclusions

The foundation gives grants only for proposals of a charitable kind, usually from organisations, which should normally be registered charities or otherwise tax-exempt. It does not give grants for:

- the education, training fees, maintenance or medical costs of individual applicants;
- the purchase, construction, repair or furnishing of buildings;
- performances, exhibitions or festivals;
- conferences or seminars;
- university or similar research;
- science;
- medicine or related therapies;
- holidays of any sort;
- religious activities;
- establishing funds for scholarships or loans;
- projects concerning drug-abuse or alcoholism;
- animal welfare;
- sports;
- equipment, including vehicles or musical instruments;
- stage, film or television production costs;
- commercial publications;
- basic services or core costs (as opposed to imaginative new projects);
- overseas travel, conference attendance or exchanges;
- housing.

We never make loans or retrospective grants, nor help to pay off deficits or loans, nor can we remedy the withdrawal or reduction of statutory funding. We do not give grants in response to any large capital, endowment or widely distributed appeal.

Applications

Applicants should read the relevant parts of the current 'Advice for Applicants' at the time concerned.

Please apply in writing to the UK branch at the address shown above, *not* by telephone nor in person. There is no standard application form, nor any specified format or length (though succinctness is welcome). Certain information, however, should be included:

- The exact purpose for which the proposed grant is sought and what difference a grant would make, were one to be awarded.
- The amount required, with details of how the budget has been arrived at.
- Information about other sources of income, if any: those that are firm commitments as well as those being explored.
- Information about the aims and functions of your organisation and about its legal status.

(If your organisation is a registered charity, it is essential to send the registration number; if it has an official tax exemption number or letter, send the reference. The foundation sometimes makes a grant available to an organisation which does not yet have charitable status through an organisation which does, when there is a suitable association between them. If you are uncertain, consult the foundation.)

Also include:

- Your last annual report and any available audited accounts.
- Your plans for monitoring and evaluating the work.

You should remember that preliminary work on a grant application may involve consultations and discussions, modification or development, and often an on-site visit, all of which takes time. Fully prepared proposals are considered at trustee meetings held in February, April, July and November, though the papers have to be finalised six weeks before each meeting. Approximately the same amount is distributed in grants at each meeting.

The Gur Trust

Jewish causes

£591,000 (1998/99)

16 Grangecourt Road, London N16 5EG

Tel. 020 8800 4140

Correspondent J Schreiber, Trustee

Trustees *J Schreiber; M Mandel; S Morgenstern.*

Information available Very thin accounts on file at the Charity Commission.

General

The trust's aims are to support 'the advancement of the Jewish religion in general and in particular the worldwide organisation of the Grand Rabbi of Gur. The Gur Talmudical College in London continues to be supplied.'

It has limited assets, with nearly all the income coming from donations (£597,000 in 1998/99). Grants totalled £591,000, but no further information was available.

Applications

In writing to the correspondent.

H C D Memorial Fund

See below

£807,000 (1998/99)

Reeds Farm, Sayers Common, Hassocks, West Sussex BN6 9JQ

Tel. 01273 832173 **Fax** 01273 832146

e-mail debenham@btclick.com

Correspondent Jeremy Debenham, Secretary

Trustees *Nicholas Debenham, Chair; Jeremy Debenham; Catherine Debenham; Bill Flinn; Dr Millie Sherman.*

Information available Accounts with a brief report and informative grants list.

Summary

In its own words, this is 'a tight-knit family charity, largely dependent on annual voluntary donations from its contributors', which 'makes grants to charities of all sizes, but prefers medium and small. About half in UK/Ireland, and half overseas.'

Type of grant:

- normally £5,000 to £50,000, typically £10,000 to £20,000
- capital and revenue
- usually one-off; can be up to three years; exceptionally can be longer.

At the time of writing the charity was in the process of establishing policy guidelines with clear priority areas.

General

The 1998/99 report, showing little difference from those in previous years, said that support had been given during the year to organisations involved in:

- third world development;
- food, medicine and material aid and support for volunteer workers in Africa, India, Mexico and Honduras;
- help for the homeless and the disabled and other social, medical and educational work in the UK and Irish Republic; and
- a hospital in Mexico.

The trust prefers to make grants through the personal contacts of its 16 donors, who are all members of the same family.

In 1998/99, the trust had an income of £397,000, mostly from donations. Administrative costs were negligible.

The trust has provided substantial support for a home in Barcombe, for people with disabilities, through the Agape Trust, which received an exceptional £368,000 in 1998/99 (46% of the total).

A commitment to Sussex Emmaus, benefiting homeless people in Brighton, continued with a £40,000 grant. London Emmaus also received a large grant, for £100,000, to help homeless people in Stockwell, while the Lodge Hill Trust got £50,000 for a youth centre.

Other beneficiaries included Schools Outreach (£19,000 for pastoral care support); Soil Association (£15,000 for the GMO campaign); Toynbee Training (£10,000 for vocational training); Womankind (£5,000, Bristol women's counselling), and the National Trust (£2,000, Snowdon Appeal).

A further 10 grants totalling £153,000 were made for work overseas, the recipients including the following: Concern America (£30,000 for 'PISTA/ volunteers' in Mexico and £20,000 for flood relief in Honduras); Hope and Homes for Children, Ukraine (£40,000); Intermediate Technology (£25,000 for agricultural development in Africa); Oxfam (£15,000 for flood relief in Bangladesh), and Angels International, Belarus (£8,000 for children's hospital equipment).

Exclusions

Individuals and animal charities.

Applications

In writing to the correspondent, although please note that the trust has a preference for seeking out its own projects and only rarely responds to general appeals.

'Unsolicited applications are acknowledged, but very rarely accepted. The majority of projects have been found through first- or second-hand contacts of a contributor.'

Hact (The Housing Associations Charitable Trust)

Housing and related social need

£796,000 (1999)

Beneficial area UK.

78 Quaker Street, London E1 6SW

Tel. 020 7247 7800 **Fax** 020 7247 2212

e-mail hact@hact.org.uk

website www.hact.org.uk

Correspondent Dawn Jackson, Head of Programmes

Trustees *June McKerrow, Chair; Peter Stevenson; Matthew Bennett; Rosalind Brooke; Nicholas Gage; Trevor Hendy; Peter Molyneux; Philip Richardson; Bert Rima; Paul Tennant; Janis Wong.*

Information available Very full information, including detailed guidelines and advice sheets for applicants, annual report and accounts, available from the trust.

Summary

Hact makes grants and loans to:

- voluntary organisations and community groups (including groups in the process of formation) with housing related aims; and
- housing associations;

and focuses its support on organisations with limited financial resources.

Applications must fit in with one of the trust's priority areas, which are:

- housing for older people;
- housing for people with support needs;
- housing for black, minority ethnic and refugee communities.

The trust's latest guidelines note that about 300 applications are dealt with each year, and around 150 receive financial support. These grants accounted for roughly three quarters of the trust's charitable expenditure in 1999. The trust's other programmes include the provision of support and advice for small and emerging organisations, in particular fundraising advice for refugee community organisations, and the promotion of housing issues through research and policy development.

The trust aims to raise and distribute £1 million a year in grants.

General

The following is reproduced from the trust's leaflet 'How to Apply for Funding from hact':

About hact

- Hact aims to develop solutions promoting people's well-being and enabling people to live in their homes and communities with dignity and independence.
- Hact raises and distributes funds to explore, develop and test solutions to issues affecting groups that are marginalised from mainstream housing and related provision.

About hact grants

Hact provides grants to voluntary organisations and community groups (including those in the process of formation) engaged in housing or related work in England, Wales and Northern Ireland. [*Also in Scotland. Ed.*]

Hact makes grants of between £500 and £20,000 (either as a one-off or over a two/three year period) for revenue, salary, consultancy or research costs. Capital costs or expenditure for which statutory funding is available are not eligible.

Hact funds projects that promote imaginative service delivery, policy development or capacity building and that place a strong emphasis on user involvement and social inclusion.

Hact prioritises applications from organisations and groups with limited financial resources.

Funding programmes and priorities

Two themes underpin our development and grantmaking programmes:

- *Independent Living* – promoting the well-being and quality of life of individuals and their ability to live independently.
- *Community* – promoting mutual support, interdependence and enhancing the health and well-being of communities.

Hact's priorities under these two themes are:

- housing for older people
- housing for people with support needs
- housing for black, minority ethnic and refugee communities.

Housing for older people

Hact is interested in projects that improve the housing prospects and options for all older people, though it particularly welcomes applications that address the specific needs of BME elders, older people threatened with or experiencing homelessness or who are suffering from dementia or other mental health conditions.

The following examples are not exhaustive but give an idea of the types of projects hact funds under this priority.

- feasibility studies or needs assessment surveys to produce information which will help projects to receive statutory or other charitable funding, e.g. for older people from particular minority ethnic communities or for older people with dementia
- new initiatives which enable older people to remain safe and secure in their own homes
- the development of specialist housing advice services which inform older people of their housing rights/benefits etc.
- extra provision in housing schemes to enable the extension of services to older people in the wider community.

There were 42 grants in total, starting at £1,000, and led by the following:

- Arlington Care – £37,000 towards the salary costs of a policy and practice officer working with older homeless people in Greater London.
- Care & Repair, Bristol – £34,000 to fund a housing resettlement service for older homeowners in Bristol over two years.

Grants of £30,000 each went to:

- Age Concern Tower Hamlets, to contribute to a new Bengali elders' advice service in London;
- Alcohol Recovery Project, to support a black elders' outreach programme based in Brixton, London, for people with alcohol problems;
- Rugby House Project, for housing and support work for older people from minority ethnic communities with alcohol problems in London.

Housing for black, minority ethnic and refugee communities

Hact's aim is to enhance housing provision and choice for BME and refugee communities by funding new services and by investing in the infrastructure of BME or refugee-led organisations and groups. We are particularly interested in projects that address the support issues arising from the country-wide dispersal of newly arrived asylum seekers.

The following examples are not exhaustive but give an idea of the types of projects hact funds under this priority.

- start up costs addressing clearly identified community needs
- conference travel bursaries and committee training costs in order to improve the level of service provided to their communities
- consultancies for business plans and organisational development
- supporting the development of organisations through early staff costs, e.g. grant to employ a member of staff to set up a new service
- support for newly arrived asylum seekers and refugees
- feasibility studies or needs assessment surveys making the case for statutory or longer term funding

- working on settlement issues with newly dispersed asylum seekers and the Nass local authority consortia.

Examples of grants included:

- SIRI – £15,000 to develop supported housing and outreach services for African-Caribbean people with mental health problems in Brent, London.
- Aashyana – £13,000 to fund a trainee Asian housing officer.
- The Welsh Refugee Council – £12,000 towards the salary of a housing development officer.
- Croydon People's Housing Association – £12,000 towards the salary of a community policy officer.

A further 22 grants ranged from £2,000 to £10,000.

Housing for people with support needs
Hact prioritises projects that test new models of service delivery for people needing support to live independently, that identify previously unmet support needs, that address discrimination in provision. … Again, hact particularly welcomes applications under this funding priority from organisations working with BME and refugee communities.

Hact is currently focusing its funds for supported housing on three areas so applications can only be accepted if they specifically relate to one of the following:

- the development of supported housing services in rural areas
- the active involvement of users in the development and management of supported housing services
- preparing for 'Supporting People'.

The following examples are not exhaustive but give an idea of the types of projects hact funds under this priority.

- projects that investigate new housing or support options for people insecurely housed or homeless in rural areas
- the development of housing advice services for people with support needs in rural areas
- projects that build the capacity and capability of organisations to participate fully in preparing for 'Supporting People' in their areas
- assisting local agencies to liaise effectively with local authorities and other voluntary groups in preparation for supporting people (we are very keen to look at partnership proposals)
- the development of user participation in management and advocacy schemes
- projects that explore imaginative ways of engaging and sustaining user involvement and participation.

Of 21 grants, 5 were for work in Wales, 2 for Scotland and 1 for Northern Ireland.

Four beneficiaries received £15,000 each, including the following: Craven Rural Housing Action, to assist disadvantaged young homeless people in the rural communities of Bentham and Settle; and HYPE, to develop supported housing services for young people in Ceredigion, Wales.

Others included:

- PUSH – £14,000 to develop supported housing for people with learning difficulties in rural areas of Perth and Kinross.
- Advance – £12,500 for action research to develop appropriate supported housing services for people with low dependency special needs in Rutland.

Exclusions

- projects which are eligible for statutory funding, including furniture and building costs of housing schemes
- ongoing revenue funding, including items which would normally be included in an organisation's annual budget
- individuals
- well-resourced organisations

Applications

The trust says that it is committed to making the process of applying for funding as straightforward as possible.

The application process is as follows:

- Hact sends you an application pack.
- You read the grant guidelines and decide whether your project fits.
- Complete and return the form.
- At any point during the above you can phone or e-mail the grants team for advice or clarification.

The decision-making process is as follows:

- Hact receives and acknowledges your application.
- It is assessed by a member of the grants and programme team.
- Hact aims to make a decision according to the following timetable:
  – grants up to £5,000: six weeks;
  – all other grants: two months.

NB: this timescale is dependent upon hact receiving all of the information it needs to make a decision.

Please remember that every application must be linked to one of the priority areas listed.

Potential applicants are invited to contact the programme team for further help and guidance:

- Head of Programmes – Dawn Jackson
- Programme Manager – Gulshun Rehman
- Programme Officer – Luchi Fernandez

The grant-making committee meets in February, April, June, September, October and December.

The Hadley Trust

Social welfare

£925,000 (1998/99)

Beneficial area Unrestricted, but see below.

Grandon, Hadley Green Road, Barnet, Herts EN5 5PR

Correspondent P Hulme, Trustee

General

The trust was formed in 1997. Its objects allow it to 'assist in creating opportunities for people who are disadvantaged as a result of environmental, educational or economic circumstances or physical or other handicap to improve their situation, either by direct financial assistance, involvement in project and support work, or research into the causes of and means to alleviate hardship'.

The trust received an initial endowment of £36 million which generated an income of £2 million. In 1998/99, 61 grants were made totalling £925,000. No further information was available on the grants. The trust stated in its report that it has successfully identified and established relationships with a number of registered charities which have objectives consistent with its own.

Applications

In writing to the correspondent.

The Paul Hamlyn Foundation

Arts, education, overseas, publishing

£2,209,000 (1999/2000)

Beneficial area UK and overseas (mainly India).

18 Queen Anne's Gate, London SW1H 9AA

Tel. 020 7227 3500 **Fax** 020 7222 0601

e-mail information@phf.org.uk

website www.phf.org.uk

Correspondent Patricia Lankester, Director

Information available 'Annual report and accounts' (but containing only a summary of the accounts). Good guidelines for applicants.

Summary

The foundation makes one-off grants, very seldom for more than £25,000 and in most cases for £5,000 or less, in four main fields (with the proportion of the grant total in 1999/2000):

- the arts (53%)
- education (21%)
- publishing (8%)
- overseas – India (10%)

The overall success rate for applications was 31% in 1999/2000, but for eligible applications – only 55% of those received – it was 56%.

General

The foundation describes its work as follows:

The Paul Hamlyn Foundation was established in 1987 and endowed with a personal gift of £50 million from the founder. The Foundation has four priority areas of funding – the arts, education, publishing and overseas projects, which are mainly concentrated in India. In all these areas Trustees' emphasis is on helping to increase the opportunities available to people. Arts grants to both national and local organisations all focus on participation and audience development. In Education there has been support for a variety of community projects which aim to ensure that teenagers at risk stay involved in school and, in Publishing, a range of individual grants enable people to benefit from innovative training schemes.

Most of the grants in India are to projects which can, and do, improve the quality of life for the disabled and for the very disadvantaged.

The Foundation's Guidance Notes [reprinted below] set out its priorities and general criteria for the assessment of applications and are also available [on the website as well as by post]. These define the main focus of the Foundation's operations, but Trustees are also committed to the spirit of flexibility and innovation which has always characterised the Foundation and enabled it to take risks with 'making a difference'.

The management and administration of the charity cost £596,000 (or 27% of the value of grants). There was a further £100,000 in support costs. These figures appear higher than those for other comparable trusts described in this book. The various grant schemes supported or administered do not appear sufficient to explain these cost levels, especially given the further £100,000 in support costs. The foundation had an average staff of seven and salary and staff costs of £345,000 – an average of £49,000 per person employed. The foundation pays one of its staff, presumably the director, one of the higher salaries – over £70,000 – recorded in the accounts of the trusts described in this book.

Staff with whom applicants are most likely to be in contact, apart from the director, are:

- Jane Attenborough, Arts Manager
- Susan Blishen, Publishing Projects Manager
- Faye Williams, Administrator

The foundation also has the following advisers:

- Sir Claus Moser (Arts)
- Sue Thomson (Publishing)
- Roger Graef (Penal Affairs)
- Ajit Chaudhuri (India)

THE PAUL HAMLYN FOUNDATION

Grants to organisations in 1999/2000, other than those for training schemes, were categorised as follows:

	No.	*Value*
Arts	65	£744,000
Education	22	£417,000
Publishing, books and reading	3	£35,000
Overseas	16	£163,000
Other	8	£139,000
Small grants (up to £3,000)	159	£297,000

The last named is based in India, where applications for support in that country are initially assessed.

Grants are normally one-off rather than recurrent, and very few are for more than £25,000.

In 1999/2000 the trust received 1,583 applications and made 483 grants, a success rate overall of 31%. However, this varied greatly according to the amount requested. For small grants (up to £3,000) there were 241 eligible applications and 159 awards, a success rate of 66%. The remaining 1,342 applications generated 114 larger awards, a rate of only eight per cent (though these figures may not take full account of applications for training grants or individual programmes).

The foundation also has its own programmes, of which the best known are the Paul Hamlyn Weeks at the Royal Opera House and the National Theatre in London.

More than half of all UK grants, and a higher proportion of the large grants, are for national organisations or for work in London or the south of England. The following table shows the main geographical areas served in 1999/2000, in terms of the number of grants and percentages of the total awarded:

London	208	43%
South East	53	11%
Scotland	42	9%
South West	40	8%
Eastern (E Anglia)	35	7%

In its annual report for 1999/2000 the foundation characterises its grants in its four fields of interest as follows:

The arts

The Foundation particularly supports projects which increase awareness of the arts, or which extend new opportunities to large numbers of people. It is also concerned to support talented individuals practising in a specific area, and to help ensure the centrality of arts in education.

Education

The Foundation's concern is to improve access to education and to enable greater participation at all levels. It gives support to practical innovation and projects which work to combat educational disadvantage. It has a strong interest in arts education and in after-school activities.

Publishing, books and reading

The Foundation's focus is on innovative schemes, which improve access to books and reading skills. Its support for publishing and bookselling is aimed at making training and education available to those who would not otherwise be offered these opportunities.

Overseas (India)

The Foundation's funding is concentrated on direct support for local projects in India. The priority areas are support for the disabled, for the children of the very disadvantaged and for the development of local NGOs.

Guidance notes for applicants

These guidance notes indicate the areas to which the Foundation currently gives priority and should help you to decide whether to make an application for funding. It is unlikely that support will be given to projects which fall outside these areas and you should certainly consult the Foundation before applying for such a grant. The Foundation does however take its own initiatives which may lie outside its declared priorities and open up new areas for the future. ...

The best thing is ... to make an exploratory telephone call or to write a letter describing your work before making a formal application to the Foundation. We are always happy to discuss your ideas at an early stage. There is no standard application form, but there is an indication of what we need to know [under 'Applications' below] ... If you call the Foundation you will be referred to the relevant member of staff.

The Foundation only considers supporting posts as part of a project in its priority areas. Funding from the Foundation is normally for one year only.

The arts

Increasing awareness of the arts

The Foundation has a long history of supporting projects which encourage new people to visit theatres, galleries, museums and other venues throughout the UK. Such projects have usually included a programme of outreach work, combined with discounted tickets, so that they will genuinely attract people for whom the arts is a new experience.

At this point the Foundation is particularly interested in:

- Supporting projects in parts of the country where there has not been much audience development work so far.
- Unusual projects of a high quality, which may show a new approach to broadening their audiences.

Arts in education

The priorities are:

- Out of school arts activities for children in places currently not well served.
- Partnerships between schools and other organisations which aim to promote the arts for pupils.
- Schemes which give primary and secondary teachers access to best practice in the performing and creative arts, thereby enhancing their pupils' own learning experiences.

Awards for artists

A Foundation Award for individual artists was launched in 1993. The award is currently for the visual arts, with a strong emphasis on experiment, innovation and cross arts collaboration. Five awards will be made each year to nominated artists.

Student bursaries

The Foundation provides bursaries to selected institutions for students on a small number of courses which are outstanding in their field. No other student bursaries are given.

Education

The Foundation is interested in small, experimental schemes which address problems of truancy, drop-out or exclusion from compulsory education or which seek to combat disaffection and alienation in young people. Priority will be given to projects which address problems arising from differences of language and culture between home and school. The Foundation looks to support innovation and experiment designed to help overcome barriers to learning in disadvantaged areas.

Schools

Priority will be given to schemes which schools or other organisations have originated themselves and which are likely to serve as pilots for others with similar problems and aspirations. The Foundation is particularly interested in schemes which address:

- General levels of attainment.
- Problems of motivating pupils who may not achieve any formal qualification by the school leaving age.

Lifelong learning

- Schemes which encourage pupils to stay on at school and to enter further and higher education.
- Schemes to promote access for mature entrants.
- Projects which offer learning opportunities to wider groups in innovative ways.

Publishing

Priority areas

The Foundation's support for publishing and bookselling focuses on:

Training and education

- Raising training standards in the UK and making skills training available to those working in the industry who do not have access to the training that some large companies offer.
- Providing publishing training support for the voluntary sector.
- Offering bursaries to selected institutions for students undertaking postgraduate courses in publishing.

Broadening access to and awareness of books and publishing

- Schemes to encourage wider access to books and reading for disadvantaged groups.
- Schemes to promote access to publishing as a career for ethnic minorities and other disadvantaged groups.

Small grants programme

The Foundation makes a number of small awards up to a maximum of £3,000 to support local schemes and initiatives, normally within its main areas of interest. Applications should be for specific projects rather than revenue or deficit funding and the grant requested should represent a substantial part of the funding required. These are considered on a monthly basis.

Overseas

The Trustees have decided to limit the Foundation's funding for the developing world to direct support for local projects in India. These focus on the following areas:

- Development schemes.
- Programmes to strengthen NGOs generally through training, information exchange and networking.
- Schemes which benefit disadvantaged children. Projects are initially considered by the Foundation's adviser in India.

Grants in 1999/2000

Arts

The 65 grants to organisations were headed by a wholly untypical £185,000 to the Royal Opera House, London for the costs of Paul Hamlyn Week 2000. Otherwise, there were six grants of £20,000, or a little more, to the Association of British Orchestras (for educational work), the London Philharmonic Orchestra (for improving access), for the Koestler Award Scheme, to the London Institute (for its Young At Art programme) to London Musici and for the education programme at Oxford's Museum of Modern Art.

Education

Another 'programme' grant headed the list, of £108,000 to the University of the First Age for teacher fellowships. There were two other large grants, to the Howard League for Penal Reform (£53,000 for the education of juveniles in prison) and to Refresh (£50,000 for a carers NVQ training course). In addition, £25,000 went to the Architecture Foundation to encourage black teenagers to consider training for the profession, and £20,000 to Adventure Unlimited.

Publishing

Most of the money under this heading went to schemes for the training of individuals, such as the £25,000 for training grants for small booksellers.

A further £15,000 was given to the Who Cares? Trust for its Right to Read campaign and £12,000 to the Federation of Children's Book Groups.

Overseas

The largest grant (£35,000) was for the Jaipur Foot programme, an initiative long supported by this foundation, for the supply of low cost artificial limbs. Also, £21,000 was given to Delhi Council for Child Welfare for its orthopaedic hospital and £15,000 to Mobile Creches for the care of the children of migrant workers at construction sites.

Other

The foundation made eight grants outside its main areas of support, led by £38,000 for the Runnymede Trust's Commission on the Future of Multi-Ethnic Britain. As well as that, £30,000 was given to the Daycare Trust for policy development and £25,000 to the Institute for Public Policy Research.

Small grants

These were made across all programmes.

Exclusions

The foundation is flexible but will only exceptionally consider applications which fall outside its declared areas of interest and priority. It will not give grants for:

- general appeals or endowments;
- capital projects at specialist schools;
- buying, maintaining or refurbishing property;
- support for individuals, except where the foundation has established a special scheme;
- general support for individual organisations (schools, theatre companies, productions, etc);
- education projects concerned with particular issues such as the environment or health.

The foundation will not normally consider applications which are looking for matching funding for National Lottery projects, nor does it support large national charities.

Applications

If you want to make an application:

- Talk to us first and ask to be sent a copy of our project details form if you wish to make an application.
- Applications by fax or e-mail will not be considered.
- Write not more than five single sides of A4 (unbound), with a further page for the budget. Supporting information may be supplied in appendices, but the main statement should be self-contained and provide the essential information required by the Trustees. This should include:
  - what sort of organisation you are
  - what is the general aim of the project and its specific objectives
  - how it is to be done and by whom
  - what problems you anticipate in doing it
  - whom it is intended to benefit and how many
  - when it will start and how long it will take
  - how much money you need and for what purposes (salaries, rent, administration and so forth)
  - how other interested parties will be informed of the outcome
  - how you will know whether or not it has succeeded
  - which other funders you have approached and with what success
  - if you will need funding beyond the period of the grant, where it is to come from.

Please enclose with your application a copy of your most recent accounts and details of the management and staffing structure, including trustees.

Applications will be acknowledged when received, but it may take some time to assess them. This may involve correspondence and meetings between staff and applicants and will involve consultation with the Trustees, advisers and independent referees.

Applications for sums of £3,000 or less are handled by a Committee which meets monthly. Grants will be made for one year only. Applications in consecutive years from the same organisation will not normally be considered. Applications received by the first Friday of each month, except August, will be dealt with in the same month, otherwise the following month.

Applications for sums from £3,000 to £25,000 are dealt with by a second Committee which meets every second month. These meetings will usually take place in February, April, June, September and November. Applications should reach the Foundation in the first week of the preceding month.

Applications for larger sums will be considered at the quarterly meetings of the Trustees, which generally take place in January, April, June and October. The closing date for applications is six weeks before each meeting. The exact dates are available from the Administrator at the Foundation.

Applications for grants in excess of £100,000 should also be submitted six weeks before each meeting. They will be considered in two stages: Trustees will decide whether or not they are prepared to consider an application at a first meeting, and if so will consider the application proper at the next stage.

The Hampton Fuel Allotment Charity

General, in Twickenham and Richmond

£757,000 (to institutions, 1998/99)

Beneficial area Hampton, the former borough of Twickenham, and the borough of Richmond.

15 Hurst Mount, High Street, Hampton, Middlesex TW12 2SA

Tel. 020 8941 7866 **Fax** 020 8979 5555

Correspondent Michael Ryder, Clerk

Trustees *John Webb, Chair; A Wood; Mrs M Cunningham; R Ellis; M Gill; J Gossage; Mrs M Martin; Dr R Millis; P Simon; Revd D Winterburn; Mrs M Woodriff.*

Information available Application form with guidance notes (also available on disk and in large print). Ten-year review (1989–99). Report and accounts with full grants list and narrative.

Summary

The charity makes donations to mainly social welfare and healthcare organisations in the London boroughs of Richmond upon Thames and Twickenham. In keeping with its original objective, every year over 1,000 grants are also given to individuals for fuel. Organisations usually receive grants, often repeated, of between £1,000 and £5,000.

General

As its name suggests, the charity was created (following the 1811 Enclosure Act) with a grant of land to produce a supply of fuel for the poor of the ancient parish of Hampton, which remains the priority area for grants. With the sale of the original 10 acres of land to Sainsbury's for over £21 million in 1988, it became, in the charity's own words, 'probably the wealthiest parish charity in the country'. This endowment was valued at £40 million by 1999, providing an income of nearly £2 million.

Policies

The trustees' current guidelines are as follows:

a. To meet a proportion of the fuel bills of individuals in need;

b. To provide essential equipment for individuals in need or distress;

c. To support organisations which deliver services for those in need in the area of benefit;
d. To allocate the charity's income within the broad headings of:
   1. General medical support which will benefit those in the area of benefit;
   2. Organisations assisting those suffering from disability;
   3. Organisations which support social or medical welfare needs;
   4. Organisations engaged in social welfare including the elderly, youth, recreation and leisure;
   5. Organisations providing housing for those in need;
   6. Organisations providing additional educational support;
   7. Organisations engaged in community activities.

The charity has donated large capital grants in recent years in order to provide facilities to local community groups. Two such projects were funding for the construction of The White House Community Association, and the Hampton & Hampton Hill Voluntary Care Group, which got help for the creation of the Greenwood Centre.

The 1999 chairman's report gives further examples of such support:

This year we have seen two buildings opened at Rectory School in Hampton and St Stephen's Church, East Twickenham, at opposite ends of our primary area of benefit. Both were the subject of considerable discussion and scrutiny before the grants of £550,000 and £300,000 were approved in 1996 and 1997 respectively. Our experience of other large projects suggests many people will benefit from these new community facilities. The charity wants to continue supporting projects like these but, as I have said in previous reports, while the calls upon the charity's funds rise, the vagaries of the stock market investment climate and the impact of recent adverse tax changes mean income may not rise to match demand. It is, therefore, unlikely we will be funding large projects at the levels we have done in the past. Our principal focus will remain people and the community the charity exists to serve. If our income does not rise then we must look at ways its effectiveness can be increased and that will take creative thinking.

All trustees have extensive local knowledge. The local authority nominates three and the three parish churches one each, while four others are co-opted for their specialist knowledge and the vicar of St Mary's is ex officio a trustee.

As an unsurprising result of this, the trustees awarded grants amounting to £247,840 (1998: £360,103) to 19 (1998: 27) organisations to which one or more trustees were related parties.

Many grants go to local branches of well-known charities like Age Concern, Marie Curie Cancer Care and Relate. Most support, however, appears to be concentrated on local community groups.

Grants in 1998/99

During the year 157 eligible grant applications were received and 118, worth £757,000, were approved by the trustees. One quarter were for no more than £1,000 each, and 70% of the grants were for £5,000 or less. However, nearly £250,000 was donated in six large grants, with the first three beneficiaries having been funded the year before:

£60,000 to Richmond Citizens Advice Bureau; £50,000 to Princess Alice Hospice, Esher; £25,000 to Richmond Music Trust (towards fee reduction for disadvantaged young people); £40,000 to the Mission in Hounslow Trust (to provide accommodation for young homeless people); £39,000 to the Hounslow Heath Estate Community Association (towards a children's play area and all-weather pitch), and £30,000 to Macmillan Cancer Relief.

In addition, Richmond upon Thames Churches Housing Trust received an interest-free loan worth £150,000 in 1998.

The following list shows some other typical grants:

Royal Star and Garter Home (£20,000, towards the cost of a new coach/ambulance); Ethnic Minorities Advocacy Group (£10,000); Bengal Youth Group (£1,000, rent of premises); Royal Hospital for Neuro-disability (£8,000 for specialist equipment); Marling Court Residential Home (£1,500, for a new piano).

Exclusions

The charity is unlikely to support:

- grants to individuals for private and post-compulsory education
- adaptations or building alterations for individuals
- holidays, except in cases of severe medical need
- decoration, carpeting or central heating
- anything which is the responsibility of a statutory body
- national general charitable appeals
- animal welfare
- religious groups, unless offering a non-religious service to the community
- commercial and business activities
- endowment appeals
- political projects
- retrospective capital grants

The trustees are also reluctant to support ongoing revenue costs of organisations unless they can show clearly that within the area of benefit a substantial number of people are being charitably assisted. They also expect organisations to show that other support will be forthcoming and that the organisation will become self-reliant over an identified period of years.

Applications

On receipt of your application form the clerk to the trustees will review it and may wish to ask further questions before submitting it to the trustees for consideration. All eligible applications will be put before the trustees.

The general grants panel meets every two months and considers all project grants. For grants over £20,000, it makes a recommendation to a meeting of all the trustees. There is a meeting of the full trustees every three months. The clerk to the trustees will be pleased to inform organisations about the dates of meetings when their applications are to be considered. Organisations are advised to lodge their applications well in advance of meeting dates.

In the case of major capital or other large projects it may be that, on occasions, a small group of trustees is asked to discuss the scheme with your organisation and its advisers. This may also involve a site visit or an independent evaluation by an assessor appointed by the trustees.

Trustees may attach conditions to any grant and may request that they be kept regularly informed as to the progress and effectiveness of a project. In certain cases, where conditions have been attached to the grant, written confirmation of acceptance of these by the organisation will be required prior to the grant being paid.

A version of the application form is available in electronic form. Copies can be obtained by supplying a clean 3.5 inch diskette 1.44 MB. The version will be Windows 95, Microsoft Word 97. All applications must be submitted in printed form.

The Philip and Pauline Harris Charitable Trust

General

£313,000 (1998/99, but see below)

Philip Harris House, 1A Spur Road, Orpington, Kent BR6 0QR

Tel. 01689 875135

Correspondent Donald Bompas, Managing Executive

Trustees *Malcolm Barton; Lord Harris of Peckham; Sir Hugh Sykes.*

Information available Report and accounts.

General

The previous edition of this book reported that the trust was being wound down. While that is true, substantial grants were still being made: £394,000 in 1997/98 and £313,000 in 1998/99.

However, the accounts for the latter year show that of the remaining assets of £620,000, £590,000 has been designated for ongoing projects. 'All investments have been disposed of. The trust has little other income and will not continue substantial grantmaking unless further donations are received.'

The trust is unlikely to appear in future editions of this book.

Peter Harrison Foundation

Sport for disabled or disadvantaged people, welfare of children and young people

£1,500,000 (estimated)

Beneficial area Unrestricted, but with a special interest in south east England.

42–48 London Road, Reigate, Surrey RG2 9QQ

Tel. 01737 228000 **Fax** 01737 228001

e-mail enquiries@peterharrison foundation.org

website www.peterharrison foundation.org

Correspondent Sophie Kilmister, Director

Trustees *Peter Harrison, Chair; Joy Harrison; Julia Harrison-Lee; Peter Lee.*

Information available Information supplied by the foundation.

Summary

This new trust was established in 1999 with a gift of £30 million from Mr Harrison. Applications are invited under three programmes:

Opportunities through Sport: support for sporting activities or projects to provide opportunities for disabled or disadvantaged people.

The Special Needs and Care Programme for Children and Young People: only in the south east of England, excluding London.

Small Grants Programme: only in the south east of England, excluding London.

Preference is given under all these programmes to areas where there is a high level of deprivation.

Guidelines for applicants

The foundation has provided the following very useful information.

The Peter Harrison Foundation was founded by Mr Peter Robert Harrison in April 1999. Mr Harrison is the Chairman and Chief Executive of Chernikeeff Networks Ltd, a company he founded in August 1978, and over 22 years developed into the largest privately held computer networking and 'internet' integration company in the United Kingdom.

In 1999 and 2000 Mr Harrison sold his shares in Chernikeeff and in October 2000 he and his family gifted £30 million from the proceeds realised from the sale as a capital endowment to the Foundation. The net annual income of the Foundation, estimated at £1.5 million, dependent on investment returns, may be made available for distribution each year ...

As a keen and active sportsman throughout his life Peter Harrison believes that education and sport – either as a team member or individually – provide the key stepping-stones to self-development, creation of choice, confidence building and self-reliance. He now wishes to share in his success by making these stepping-stones more readily available to those who may be disabled or disadvantaged and may not otherwise have the opportunity to develop their full potential. The creation of the Peter Harrison Foundation provides the vehicle through which this can be achieved.

Our programmes

The Trustees' general policy will be to support those charitable activities capable of demonstrating an existing high level of committed voluntary members with strong self help activities together with well planned and thought out projects under the following categories:

- Opportunities Through Sport Programme
- Special Needs and Care Programme for Children and Young People
- Opportunities Through Education Programme (applications not invited)
- Small Grants Programme
- Trustees Discretionary Programme (applications not invited)

If you feel your organisation is planning or running a project that falls within the programmes detailed below to which we invite applicants please contact the Foundation at the address [above], or visit our website for an application pack.

You may call the Foundation to discuss your project if you have any questions about the guidelines or filling in the application form. The application form and guidelines are available, on request, in large print and on audiotape.

Note:
(1) We do not invite applications in respect of the Opportunities Through Education Programme or the Trustees Discretionary Programme, where grants will be distributed according to the policy determined by the Trustees on a continuing basis.
(2) We will only be able to fund organisations that are registered charities or friendly or provident societies.
(3) We also have areas that we *do not* fund. Please see section headed [Exclusions below].

Opportunities through Sport Programme

One of the Foundation's aims is to support sporting activities or projects which provide opportunities for disabled people or those who are disadvantaged to fulfil their potential and for other personal and life skills to be developed. In particular we are interested in the following types of charitable projects:-

(i) Projects which provide a focus for skills development and confidence building through the medium of sport;

(ii) Projects that have a strong training and/or educational theme within the sporting activity;

(iii) Projects that deal with the provision of sporting equipment and recreational equipment to disabled or disadvantaged people;

(iv) Projects with a high degree of community involvement;

(v) Projects that are run directly by the people who will benefit from the project;

(vi) Projects that help to engage children or young people who may be at risk from crime, truancy or addiction;

This programme will fund national as well as local projects.

Grants will normally be mainly for capital projects and will be one-off. We will consider revenue funding if it is key to an established project's continuing success or survival or it is a brand new project that your organisation would like to start.

Before making a grant we will need to know how you plan to obtain future revenue funding to meet the continuing running costs of your organisation.

If you are seeking a grant of £500–£5,000 and you are based in the South East of England you may wish to apply through the Small Grants Programme under which we can process applications more quickly.

Special Needs and Care Programme for Children and Young People

Grants under this programme are only for organisations in the South East of England. For a definition of the South East please see [Applications below].

Grants will be considered in the following areas:

(i) Projects that work with, or otherwise benefit disabled, chronically or terminally sick children and provide support for the parents and carers of such children; and

(ii) Projects that help to engage children or young people who may be at risk from crime, truancy or addiction;

(iii) Projects organised for or by young people (aged 14–24) – in particular projects that are aimed at:

Young disabled people that help to foster independent living through information exchange, education and the provision of equipment;

Young people at risk from homelessness; Homeless young people who are wanting to make a fresh start.

Preference is given to projects benefiting areas where there is a high level of need and areas of particular significance and interest to the Trustees.

If you are seeking a grant of £500–£5,000 you may wish to apply through the Small Grants Programme under which we can process applications more quickly.

Small Grants Programme

Grants under this programme are only for organisations in the South East of England. Grants will be made within the following areas:

- Projects that fit within the Opportunities Through Sport Programme as detailed above;
- Projects that fit within the Special Needs and Care Programme for Children and Young People.

Grants will be for amounts from £500 to £5,000. Your organisation or group must be a registered charity or friendly or provident society and should be a small or medium sized local organisation.

The Foundation will not normally consider funding organisations that are seeking match funding for national lottery grants. The Foundation will fund capital and some revenue costs but will not contribute towards salaries. The Foundation will not support projects within the Excluded Areas [below].

Opportunities through Education Programme

The Foundation is interested in supporting education initiatives in the South East of England.

Support will be given to projects benefiting areas where there is a high level of need and areas of particular significance and interest to the Trustees.

In particular the Foundation may support government initiatives in education where charitable funding is instrumental in the release of match funded government money.

Specifically, the Trustees will be funding a number of bursary places to provide educational opportunities for able children from the Reigate and Redhill area to enable them to attend Reigate Grammar School.

The Trustees *do not invite* applications to the Opportunities Through Education Programme but details of the projects that are to be funded under this Programme can be found on the Foundation's website.

Trustees Discretionary Programme

As the Peter Harrison Foundation has only recently been established, a proportion of the funds will be available to support projects that are of particular interest to the Trustees. Applications are not invited for this programme. It is anticipated that this will lead to the development of further headline programmes as the Foundation begins to measure the outcome of its support.

General

1. If your application has been refused then we cannot accept a further application from your organisation for 12 months for the same project.
2. If your application is successful then we cannot accept a further application from your organisation for 2 years.

Exclusions

- animal welfare
- preservation of buildings and churches
- the funding of vehicles
- retrospective funding
- individuals
- holidays in the UK or abroad and expeditions
- overseas projects
- projects that are solely for the promotion of religion
- general appeals
- projects that replace statutory funding

Applications

If yours is a registered charity or friendly or provident society, and if your project is within the criteria for the Opportunities Through Sport Programme, The Special Needs and Care Programme for Children and Young People or the Small Grants Programme, then:

1. Use the application form obtainable from the foundation.

2. You can only apply to one of the programmes.

3. Local branches of national charities may apply only if they have the endorsement of their national head office or they are a local branch with a separate legal constitution.

4. All applications should be sent to the director of the Peter Harrison Foundation at the address shown at the top of the application form and *not* addressed to the individual trustees.

5. For the Special Needs and Care Programme for Children and Young People and the Small Grants Programme the South East is defined as:

- Surrey
- West Sussex
- East Sussex
- Oxfordshire
- Buckinghamshire
- Kent
- Berkshire
- Isle of Wight

6. No applications will be accepted by fax or e-mail.

7. Please call the foundation if you have any queries on the application or if you want to talk through your application before you send it.

8. All applications will be acknowledged.

9. If your application is not eligible the foundation will notify you as soon as possible.

10. For larger grants under the Opportunities Through Sport Programme and the Special Needs and Care Programme for Children and Young People, the foundation may consider your application in stages. If, after considering your initial application the trustees are keen to support your project, they may contact you for additional information for consideration at the next trustees' meeting.

The trustees have regular meetings throughout the year. However, it may be several weeks or months from the date that your application is received before the trustees are able to consider it. Please bear with them.

The Maurice Hatter Foundation

Education, health, Jewish, general

£1,300,000 (1998/99)

BDO Stoy Hayward, 8 Baker Street, London W1M 1DA

Tel. 020 7486 5888

Correspondent J S Newman, Trustee

Trustees *Sir Maurice Hatter; H I Connick; Jeremy Newman; Richard Hatter.*

Information available Full accounts on file at the Charity Commission.

General

In 1998/99 the trust had assets of £7.9 million and an income of £1.5 million, including £1 million in Gift Aid donations. Grants totalled £1.3 million. Many of the beneficiaries have been regular recipients.

The trust supports particular projects related to education and health. The largest grant was £1 million to the Department of Education's Summer Literary Scheme. World ORT Union's Samara Appeal received £58,000 for new technology courses – overall, the trust has pledged to give the appeal US$500,000. Special Trust for UCH – Hatter Institute was given £33,000.

Other larger grants included £31,000 to the Lubavitch Foundation, £20,000 to British Friends of Haifa University, £15,000 to Jewish Care, £11,000 to British ORT and £10,000 to Hebrew University.

Smaller grants included £5,000 to Leuka 2000; £2,000 to Hope Charity; £1,800 to Community Security Trust; £1,000 each to the Association of Baltic Jews and the Ear Foundation, and £760 to Norwood Ravenswood.

Applications

Unsolicited applications will not be considered.

The Charles Hayward Foundation

Welfare and health, medical research, overseas

£2,009,000 (1998/99)

Hayward House, 45 Harrington Gardens, London SW7 4JU

Tel. 020 7370 7063/7067

Correspondent Mark Schnebli

Trustees *I F Donald, Chair; Mrs A M Chamberlain; Sir Jack Hayward; Sir Graham Hearne; Mrs S J Heath; Dr J C Houston; B D Insch; J N van Leuven; A D Owen; Miss A T Rogers; Ms J Streather.*

Information available Good guidelines for applicants. Annual report and accounts with full grants list and some analysis of grantmaking.

Summary

This is a new charity formed from the merger of the previous Hayward Foundation and the Charles Hayward Trust. Grants, generally ranging from £1,000 to £50,000, are made mainly for capital expenditures in the fields noted above. The foundation's guidelines indicate three priority areas:

- elderly
- under fives
- medical research

The foundation also makes grants under a wider range of headings in the general fields of welfare and health, and there is some support for art, preservation and the environment.

General

The foundation's guidelines give an excellent account of the proposed work of the charity, as follows.

History

Sir Charles Hayward was born in 1893 in Wolverhampton, Staffordshire. In 1911, he started his own business making wooden patterns for the developing engineering trade. His early involvement in the motor industry proved to be a springboard for his later success culminating in the formation of Firth Cleveland Ltd. He was Chairman from its inception in 1953 until 1973 when he retired.

Sir Charles used his personal fortune to establish and endow two charitable trusts, the Hayward Foundation and the Charles Hayward Trust. The two charities were combined on 1 January 2000, to become the Charles Hayward Foundation.

The Charles Hayward Foundation runs a number of grant making programmes, which include one for larger national and regional charities, a community grants programme and an overseas fundiing programme.

Activities to which funds may be allocated

The trustees' policy is to support organisations in undertaking projects which are:

- Preventative or provide early intervention.
- Developmental or innovative.
- Promote or continue good practice.
- Add value to existing services.

Grants can be made towards the capital cost of buildings, extensions, adaptations, equipment, and furnishings.

Project funding is occasionally granted for start-up or development activities where these are not yet part of the on-going revenue requirement of the project.

Organisations eligible to apply

U.K. based registered national and regional charities, smaller local charities, churches and religious organisations, partnerships, community organisations, and mutual welfare societies which are responsible for their own management, finances and fund-raising.

Size of grant

Typically £1,000 to £50,000. From time to time, trustees may make larger grants or take considered risks in funding projects of an exceptional nature which show outstanding potential.

Funding areas within our policy

Areas of need have been categorised by trustees as 'Priority', 'Standard' and ' Minor'.

Priority areas

Elderly

Residential homes providing extra or extended care, nursing homes, day centres, visiting schemes and respite facilities. Day centres for the elderly, advocacy and befriending schemes, care and repair organisations, supported housing schemes. Research into the medical and social needs of the elderly.

Under fives

Parenting initiatives, intervention services for young children, support services for young families.

Medical research

Buildings, equipment and research costs for areas of medicine dealing with unusual diseases, and subjects of a peripheral or unpopular nature. Research into the causes and treatment of disorders that start in infancy.

THE CHARLES HAYWARD TRUST

The geographical spread of grants for 1998/99 was categorised as follows:

	No.	*Value*	*%*
North England	26	£124,000	26%
Midlands	22	£96,000	20%
London	21	£87,000	18%
South West	16	£55,000	11%
South East	10	£36,000	8%
East Anglia	7	£28,000	6%
Scotland	7	£28,000	6%
Wales	6	£21,000	4%
Northern Ireland	1	£5,000	1%

Standard areas

Community facilities
Community centres and village halls, church community projects, community organising, mediation schemes, advice bureaux, addressing need in rural areas, facilities for social and physical recreation for children and young people.

Youth at risk
Crime prevention schemes, youth work and mentoring programmes, diversionary schemes; advice and support for care leavers and other young people.

Special needs
Concentrating on the under fives and the elderly, support and treatment for specific medical conditions, learning disabilities and mental health problems, where these services are not a statutory duty.

Hospices
Day-care, domicilary care, and training.

Overseas projects
Sustainable development projects in the areas of health and hygiene, youth at risk, elderly and disabled in need, education, water resources.

Art, preservation and the environment
Priority will be given to the restoration of land and buildings for posterity, cultural heritage, and projects that provide a link with other areas of trustees' policy.

Mental health
Work, educational, social and rehabilitation facilities for those with mental health difficulties. Early prevention of substance abuse.

Minor areas

Criminal justice
Rehabilitation of offenders, prison reform, welfare of prisoners and their families; victim support and alternatives to custody.

Social research
Outcome studies of specific interventions, action research of new interventions and longitudinal studies.

Homelessness
Integrated schemes to help the homeless primarily outside of the capital and initiatives to prevent homelessness. Women's refuges.

Other charitable objects
The trustees may wish to consider projects outside their main areas of interest when such projects develop novel interventions into society's ills or address causes which are rare or unpopular. You are advised to telephone the Foundation offices to discuss any projects in this category, before submitting an application.

Geographical emphasis

Grants are made to projects within the United Kingdom. The policy of the trustees is to place emphasis on distributing their funds more widely outside of London and the south-east.

The Charles Hayward Foundation also has an overseas grants programme. Separate guidelines are available from the Foundation offices.

The value of overseas grants was historically small, but the production of new guidelines suggest that this may be a growing activity for the foundation. The new funding areas are as follows:

- Health: clean water, basic health education, provision of basic medical facilities, HIV/AIDS prevention, etc.
- Youth at risk: orphans, street children, children with HIV/AIDS-infected parents, child mental health.
- Education: capital grants for the building of schools, training of teachers, provision of books, equipment etc.
- Special needs: care and rehabilitation of people with learning disabilities, physical disabilities, and those with mental health problems.
- Elderly: relief of the elderly in need.

Finally, the Charles Hayward Foundation does not seek publicity concerning its grants.

Grants in 1999

The new merged foundation's larger grants are likely to reflect the grantmaking of the former Hayward Foundation, which was normally in the range £10,000 to £50,000. Smaller grants, typically for capital funding to more locally based charities, were formerly the preserve of the Charles Hayward Trust. Grants were more often for between £500 and £10,000.

Combined grantmaking for the Hayward Foundation (during 1999) and the Charles Hayward Trust (1998/99) was categorised as shown in the box below.

Examples of grants

The following are the largest grants in each category from each of the two formerly separate trusts in the most recent years reported.

Community and youth

Citizenship Foundation, London: £50,000, to develop a 'morals and citizenship' programme. YMCA West Bromwich & District: £15,000, for refurbishment of a hostel.

Special needs

Foundation for People with Learning Disabilities, London: £50,000, for research and projects on growing older with learning disabilities.

THE HAYWARD FOUNDATION AND THE CHARLES HAYWARD TRUST – GRANTMAKING

	Hayward Foundation		*C Hayward Trust*		*Combined*	
	Amount	*No.*	*Amount*	*No.*	*Amount*	*%*
Community and youth	£590,000	31	£139,000	24	£729,000	36
Special needs	£440,000	24	£102,000	24	£542,000	27
Elderly	£135,000	8	£83,000	14	£218,000	11
Medical/med. research	£209,000	6	–	–	£209,000	10
General welfare	£55,000	3	£68,000	13	£123,000	6
Art, education, preservation and environment	£62,500	3	£4,000	1	£66,500	3
Hospices	–	–	£61,500	6	£61,500	3
Overseas	£37,000	3	–	–	£37,000	2
Small grants/miscellaneous	£6,500	9	£16,500	35	£23,000	1
Total	£1,535,000	87	£474,000	117	£2,009,000	

Multiple Sclerosis Therapy Ltd, Berkshire: £10,000, towards building a new therapy centre.

Elderly

Guideposts Trust: £25,000, for a teaching nursing home for the elderly.

Abbeyfield Seascale & District Society: £15,000, for a new Abbeyfield day care centre in Gosforth.

Medical/medical research

Imperial College of Science, Technology and Medicine, London: £50,000, for a readership in medical imaging.

RAFT: £50,000, 'Hand Surgery Project – Dupuytren's Contracture'.

General welfare

Newport Cottage Hospital Care Centre, Salop: £25,000, for fitting out respite and day care facilities.

Emmaus in Greater Manchester: £7,500, capital costs.

Art, education, preservation and environment

Falkland Islands Memorial Chapel, Reading: £40,000, for a memorial garden.

Lea Road United Reformed Church, Wolverhampton: £4,000, for rewiring of the organ.

Hospices

Marie Curie Cancer Care Foundation: £17,000, pressure sore relief strategy.

Overseas

John Grooms Association for the Disabled: £20,000, rehabilitation co-ordinator, Bangladesh.

Exclusions

Grants are not made

- to individuals;
- for ongoing revenue expenditure;
- to pay off loans;
- for fundraising activities, transport, travel, holidays, bursaries, general repairs, computers, video or sound equipment, church restoration, academic chairs or endowment funds.

Grants are not made in replacement of government or Lottery funding, or towards activities primarily the responsibility of central or local government or some other responsible body.

Grants are not made to other grant-making organisations.

In an effort to ensure that funds are only distributed on the basis of need, organisations that restrict their benefit to one section of society are not supported. Animal welfare organisations and sports clubs are excluded.

Organisations that have large reserves or endowment funds and well established funding streams are given a lower priority.

Applications

Your application should be made in writing to Mark Schnebli, the administrator. It is generally best to start by sending a short résumé of the project, together with a set of your latest audited accounts. The foundation can then advise you whether more information is required. Your initial application should not exceed three sides of A4 paper, excluding enclosures.

All applications will receive an acknowledgement. However, as there is often a waiting list, and trustees meet only four times a year to consider applications, you may have a wait of several months before you receive a decision.

Please note that there are always many more applications than the foundation is able to fund out of its limited resources. On average, 1 in 20 applications is approved by the trustees. You are advised to read these guidelines very carefully, as inappropriate applications waste time.

Information required

Name and location of organisation – The official name of the organisation and its location.

Contact details – Give the name and position of the person submitting the application, contact telephone number and address.

Description of organisation – Provide a description of your present work and the priorities you are addressing. Quantify the scale of your operation: how many people do you help and how?

Description of proposed project – Describe the project you are undertaking, detailing the number of people and groups who will benefit and how. Specify how life will be improved for the target group.

Project cost – Give a breakdown of the costs for the full project. Capital and revenue costs should be kept separate. For a capital project, include only information on the capital costs.

Funds raised and pledged – Give a breakdown of the funds raised to date towards your target, separating capital and revenue, where applicable. Include the amount of any of your own funds or reserves going into the project, and any money you intend to borrow.

Outstanding shortfall – Specify the amount of money you still need for capital and revenue separately.

Timetable – State the timetable for the project; when it will start and be finished.

Enclosures and other information required

Please enclose with your application:

- One recent set of full audited accounts. Include accounts for connected organisations.

If applicable and relevant to the size of your project, please also provide further information, as follows:

- A summary of how you are going to evaluate the success of the project, and how you will report this back to the foundation.
- An annual report.
- References, recommendations or letters of support.
- Explanation of how you will fund the ongoing costs of your project.
- Floor plans, drawings, or pictures (no larger than A3).
- A list of any other funders who are actively considering making significant contributions.
- A prospectus or business plan for the project.
- Progress of any planning or statutory requirements required for your project to proceed.

Applications are accepted at any stage and are prioritised according to project timetable and suitability. Applicants are advised to write as soon as they have accurate details of their project.

You may wish to discuss your project before writing to the foundation. Mark Schnebli or David Brown can be contacted on 020 7370 7063 or 020 7370 7067.

The Hayward Foundation

See the entry for the Charles Hayward Foundation, with which this charity has now merged.

The Charles Hayward Trust

See the entry for the Charles Hayward Foundation, with which this charity has now merged.

The Headley Trust

Arts, environment, health, education, development

£6,014,000 (approved, 1999)

See the entry for the Sainsbury Charitable Trusts

Tel. 020 7410 0330 **Fax** 020 7410 0332

Correspondent Michael Pattison, Director

Information available Excellent annual report showing both grant approvals and payments.

Summary

This is one of the Sainsbury Family Charitable Trusts which share a joint administration. Like the others, it is primarily proactive, aiming to choose its own grantees, and it discourages unsolicited applications. The extent to which readers should be deterred by this is discussed in the separate entry, under the Sainsbury name, for the group as a whole (see page 272).

The trust has a particular interest in the arts and in artistic and architectural heritage and has made big grants, especially to help match Lottery funding, to museums, galleries, libraries and theatres. There are ongoing programmes for the repair of old churches and cathedrals. The trust also supports a range of social welfare issues. Its support for activities in developing countries is focused on sub-Saharan anglophone countries and on central and eastern Europe.

There is a small Aids for Disabled Fund (£30,000 in 1999).

General

The settlor of this trust is Sir Timothy Sainsbury. His co-trustees include his wife, eldest son and legal adviser. He appears still to be adding to the already huge endowment – assets worth a further £9 million were received during the year. Sir Timothy and his wife are also trustees of the sister Jerusalem Trust (which supports only Christian causes, and has its own entry in this book).

Staff include Michael Pattison (director, as of all the Sainsbury family charities) and Hester Marriott, executive.

In a phrase that is almost a ritual for many of the Sainsbury charities, 'the Trustees prefer to support innovative schemes that can be successfully replicated or become self-sustaining'. In this case there is an addition: 'The Trustees also support a number of arts and environmental developments of national or regional significance.'

The domination in the grant lists of the south of England generally, and of London in particular, is striking, even when allowing for the high proportion of national arts institutions based in that city. The figures for grants for such facilities or activities as are easily geographically identifiable under the arts/ environment and education/health/ welfare headings were as shown in the first box opposite (the parish church heading is omitted as this rotates by diocese).

There are excellent introductions to the list of new grants in the annual reports, under each of the charity's headings, explaining the policies and practices concerned. The number of new awards in 1999, and their total and average values, were categorised as shown in the second box opposite.

Arts and environment (home): 111 awards worth £3,796,000

The Trustees support a wide range of conservation projects, as well as arts projects with an educational element. The Trustees have also made substantial grants towards partnership funding for major National Lottery Grants, particularly for museums, galleries, libraries and theatres.

There were eight grants of six figures or more, as follows:

Victoria and Albert Museum, London: £1,550,000, mainly for the new Spiral Gallery.

Somerset House, London: £500,000, towards its restoration.

£100,000 each was given to the Royal Ballet School, London, for a new building; Southwark Cathedral, for its Millennium project; The Wildfowl and Wetlands Trust, for its new centre in Barnes, London; Sadler's Wells Theatre, London, for redevelopment; The Thomas Coram Foundation, London, for redevelopment; The Royal Institute of British Architects, to help relocate its Special Collections.

The other grants included £10,000 for the restoration of the De La Warr Pavilion in Bexhill, East Sussex, an example where a number of Sainsbury trusts have worked together.

Though most of the grants were for capital expenditures, there were also grants for salaries including, interestingly, £30,000 for the Bowes Museum Trust to develop its fundraising (a form of investment made from time to time by members of this group of trusts, and one that, in these editors' views, is too little supported by funders generally).

The beneficiaries of the 10 smaller grants, of less than £5,000, ranged from Ballet Rambert to the Isle of Wight International Oboe Competition.

There are two separate budgets for churches. The first is a 'cathedrals' budget (also applied to large churches), worth £150,000 in 1999.

Substantial grants are available for restoration or repair work to the fabric of cathedrals, parish church cathedrals and large churches of exceptional architectural merit. Trustees do not normally provide funding for modern amenities, organ repair or restoration, or choral scholarships. In 1999 this budget was divided between Holy Trinity, Hull, Norwich Cathedral, Selby Abbey and St Dunstan's and All Saints (sic).

There is also a programme for parish churches, with grants averaging between £1,000 and £2,000 and made on the advice of an expert adviser:

Funding for fabric repair and restoration is considered for medieval parish churches (or pre-16th century churches of exceptional architectural merit) in rural, sparsely populated, less prosperous villages, through a process of review diocese by diocese. Urban churches are not eligible, and funding is available for fabric only (including windows) rather than refurbishment or construction of church halls or other modern amenities.

Arts and environment (overseas): 11 grants worth £294,000

Trustees support art conservation projects of outstanding artistic or architectural importance; particularly the restoration of buildings, statuary or paintings, primarily in the countries of Central and Eastern Europe. Grants are channelled through established reputable conservation organisations in the countries concerned.

The major awards in 1999 were for the restoration of Uhrovec Castle in Slovakia

THE HEADLEY TRUST – NO. AND VALUE OF GRANTS BY GEOGRAPHICAL AREA

	Arts and environment		*Education and welfare*	
South of England	20	£3,076,000	17	£302,000
of which, London	*13*	*£2,922,000*	*13*	*£249,000*
North of England	2	£45,000	3	£32,000
Scotland	1	£25,000	1	£28,000
Wales	1	£53,000	1	£40,000
Northern Ireland*	0	–	1	£50,000

** This grant for work in Northern Ireland was the first to catch this editor's native and offended eye, after reading the grants lists of a number of Sainsbury trusts.*

THE HEADLEY TRUST

New awards in 1999	*No.*	*Total*	*Average value*
Arts and environment (home)	111	£3,796,000	£34,000
Arts and environment (overseas)	11	£294,000	£27,000
Medical	5	£184,000	£37,000
Developing countries	13	£425,000	£33,000
Education	19	£465,000	£24,000
Health and social welfare	111	£851,000	£8,000
Total	270	£6,014,000	£22,000

(£66,000), for wall paintings in a church in Iasi (£52,000) and for the Ieud conservation training programme (£45,000), both in Romania, a country with which the Sainsbury charities seem to have a collective relationship.

Other grants were for the Beautiful Bulgaria 1999 Project (£40,000), and to the Archaeological Museum in Gdansk, Poland, and the Peggy Guggenheim Museum in Venice (£30,000 each).

Medical: 5 grants worth £184,000

Trustees are particularly interested in research into ageing and osteoporosis.

The major grants were to Dementia North (£90,000 'to support the organisation in its early stages of development') and to Sinfonia 21 (£52,000 for its Alzheimer's project).

Developing countries: 13 grants worth £425,000

Priority is given to projects in sub-Saharan anglophone Africa, and Central and Eastern Europe and the former Soviet Union. Focus areas include

- water projects (e.g. which give disadvantaged communities access to safe water, preserve ecologically or culturally important wetland areas, improve sanitary conditions or promote better use of water);
- forestry projects (e.g. which preserve areas of natural woodland or encourage environmentally or socially sustainable methods of forestry);
- education and literacy projects (e.g. which improve quality of education and literacy standards for underprivileged people through supply of material, construction, training support etc.)
- health projects (particularly those which support blind or partially sighted people).

Trustees look for projects where income generation is an integral element.

The major awards in 1999 were as follows:

- Action Aid: £71,000 for an AIDS project in Malawi.
- Health Unlimited: £45,000 for the development of best practice in primary healthcare.
- The Mid-Africa Ministry: £39,000 for healthcare for disabled people in Uganda.
- The British Council, Ethiopia: £37,000 for learning resources for healthcare professionals.

A further grant under another heading was the £21,000 for a new mental health resource centre in Bucharest, Romania.

Education: 19 awards worth £465,000

The Trustees' main focus is the provision of bursary support, particularly for artistic or technical skills training. They have also helped to encourage high standards of literacy in children and young people.

The awards, mostly for amounts between £20,000 and £60,000, went to a varied range of organisations, from AES Tring Park School Trust (for 6th Form bursaries); African and Afro-Caribbean People's Advisory Group (to support excluded students in South London); Manchester Metropolitan University (for MA students of textiles); to Welsh National Opera's education and outreach programme.

Smaller grants included those to Working for a Charity [*which occasionally employs this editor as a trainer*] and the Lizard Outreach Trust for a boat-building project for young people.

Health and social welfare: 111 grants worth £851,000

Trustees contribute to a broad range of health and social welfare projects, particularly charities supporting carers of an ill or disabled relative, and those that support elderly people of limited means.

This programme appears to lack the focus of most funding by Sainsbury charities, with no clear theme being apparent from the grants lists. Areas of work supported include employment for people with mental health problems, hospice care, a children's centre in Northern Ireland, a night shelter in London, sailing for people with disabilities, holiday dialysis, and art and carpentry.

In view of the general nature of this programme, including 27 grants of less than £5,000, often to local groups, and in view of the disproportionate funding for London described above, potential applicants should not be discouraged from submitting their own proposals as clearly information about good work is not reaching trustees from all parts of the country. Chances of success may be small, but that is not unusual.

The largest grants were as follows:

- Housing Services Agency: £75,000 for a resettlement programme for homeless people.
- DARE (Disability and Rehabilitation Education Foundation): £60,000 for salary costs.
- Spirit of Enterprise: £50,000 for a revolving loan scheme for disabled business people.
- Share Community Ltd: £48,000 for premises.

Aids for Disabled Fund

There is a further small programme for small grants to charities and other organisations to enable them to provide aids for disabled individuals. This is applied for a range of aids and equipment, including, but not limited to, the following:

- specially adapted computer systems for the partially blind;
- voice-activated computers for people with spinal injuries;
- stairlifts and wheelchairs for people with restricted mobility.

Grants totalling £29,713 were made from this fund in 1999.

Applications

For information on the small Aids for Disabled Fund, ring the trust on 020 7410 0330.

Otherwise, see the guidance for applicants in the entry for the Sainsbury Family Charitable Trusts. A single application will be considered for support by all the trusts in the group.

However, for this as for many of the trusts, 'proposals are generally invited by the Trustees or initiated at their request. Unsolicited applications are discouraged and are unlikely to be successful, even if they fall within an area in which the Trustees are interested.'

For general guidance see the entry for the Sainsbury Family Trusts.

The Hedley Foundation

Youth, health, welfare

£996,000 (1999/2000)

Beneficial area UK.

9 Dowgate Hill, London EC4R 2SU

Tel. 020 7489 8076 **Fax** 020 7489 8997

Correspondent P T Dunkerley, Secretary

Trustees *P Byam-Cook, President; Christopher Parish, Chair; J Rodwell; Sir Christopher Airy; P Holcroft; G Broke; P Chamberlin.*

Information available 'Criteria for Grants' leaflet. Accounts and brief report. Full and informative grants lists.

Summary

Over 250 grants a year, the majority being for between £1,000 and £5,000. Most are for capital costs such as building refurbishment or to purchase equipment, but larger amounts (particularly when for £10,000 or more) are more likely to be for revenue or project funding, occasionally over a period of three to five years. Beneficiaries are typically local health and welfare charities for young or disabled people. The grants list shows a wide, and welcome, geographical spread across the UK.

General

The foundation describes its current funding priorities as:

- Young people: their education, training, health and welfare (currently about half the foundation's budget).
- Churches and local community centres: construction, adaptation or improvement for community use.
- Disabled people: provision of specialist equipment and assistance with access.
- Seriously ill people: the construction or extension of hospices and the setting up of specialist nursing schemes.
- Hospitals: the provision of specialist medical equipment and the support of medical research.

Grants are for specific projects only, mostly one-off but a limited number of recurring grants for three to five years. The average grant is £5,000. National and very large appeals are not considered.

Assets, held mainly as land and investments, were £24.2 million in 1999/2000. Grant giving amounted to £996,000 in 268 grants compared with £983,000 in 274 grants in 1998/99.

Grants in 1998/99

The grants list for 1999/2000 was not yet available as this guide went to press. In the previous year, the largest grants went to the Outward Bound Trust (£30,000, project costs) and Fairbridge (£20,000, 'voluntary sector coalition').

Nine grants of £10,000 each went to Cornwall Children's Hospital (for a new unit); Cumbria Association of Youth Clubs (annual donation); GAP Activity Projects (2nd of 3 annual donations); Help the Hospices (repeat); Pangbourne College (for the Chapel of Remembrance); Raleigh International (3rd and final donation); Royal Hospital for Neuro-disability (nurse call system); United World Colleges (2nd of 3 annual donations) and the YMCA (building redevelopment).

The following sample of grant recipients gives a fair representation of the foundation's grantmaking: Oak Trees County Primary School, £2,500 (drop-in centre); Odiham Cottage Hospital Redevelopment Trust (OCHRE), £5,000; Old Moat Youth Outreach Project, £5,000 (equipment); Orchid Cancer Appeal, £2,000 (research); Powys Challenge Trust, £6,000 (3rd and final annual donation); Prince's Trust Volunteers, £6,500 (team funding), and Progressive Supranuclear Palsy Association, £2,000 (workshop costs).

Exclusions

Grants are made only to registered charities. No grants to:

- overseas charities
- individuals, under any circumstances
- national and very large appeals

Applications

The trustees meet about every six weeks, so applications receive prompt attention. They should be accompanied by the latest available accounts, and a note of the present state of the appeal and its future prospects; in the case of buildings, it should also outline plans and details of planning status. For community schemes it would be helpful to have a brief description of the community, its history, present make-up and aspirations, what is going for and against it and so on to put flesh on the application.

Trustees individually have visited many charities to which the foundation might make or has made grants.

Help a London Child

Children in London

£844,000 (1999/2000)

Beneficial area Greater London and a few surrounding areas.

Capital Radio, 30 Leicester Square, London WC2H 7LA

Tel. 020 7766 6203 **Fax** 020 7766 6195

e-mail halc@capitalradio.com

website capitalfm.com

Correspondent Adam Findlay, Administrator

Trustees *David Mansfield, Chair; David Briggs; Richard Eyre; Martina King; Alan Schaffer.*

Information available Excellent application form with guidelines including tips for success and an example of how to fill in the 'costings' box. Annual review with full grants list and examples of projects funded. Annual report and accounts.

Summary

This is an annual charity appeal run by a London commercial radio station. It makes a large number of small grants each autumn to London children's charities.

General

Launched in 1975, this appeal, in the words of its annual review, 'has set the benchmark for community broadcast activity'. It 'aims to help disadvantaged children living within the 95.8 Capital FM transmission area. The charity is keen to support a wide range of activities and projects including playschemes, holidays and outings in the UK, equipment, music, arts and drama.' In defining children, it includes all those of 18 years and under.

Income in 1999/2000 was £970,000. In all, 388 grants were distributed, worth £844,000, up from 335 and £645,000 in the previous year. The guidelines state that there is no upper or lower limit on the size of the awards, but applicants are told to 'be realistic'. Correspondingly, the average grant was £2,000 and only very rarely was a grant of more than £5,000 awarded. Over 66% of applicants received a grant, but for about a third the amount awarded was less than that requested.

The charity describes its grantmaking as follows:

Every year, a panel of independent assessors is assembled to consider each application individually. The individuals on the panel work professionally in the voluntary sector or business, and give their time free of charge.

HALC will consider applications from any group. If you are not a registered charity, you can still apply, but you must have your application endorsed by a registered group willing to accept the grant on your behalf.

- The HALC panel look most favourably on projects that directly benefit children. Successful projects should illustrate how the money will go directly to the children involved rather than on administration.
- All projects funded by HALC should be completed within 12 months of receiving the grant.
- Grants to facilitate completion of a large capital project will be considered.
- Grants are awarded for salaries for a maximum of one year, and where applicable evidence of future funding for the post must be given.

Applicants are also advised to show how the project would maintain funding in future years if a repeat application were not successful.

Because the presentation of the grants list has been changed it is hard to tell the proportion of successful applicants who had also been supported in the previous year – a very small sample of just the larger grants suggested it might be between a quarter and a half. Successful applicants are, however, encouraged to reapply. Organisations can be funded repeatedly for three years or more as long as they can show new aspects of the project and, particularly, how the previous grant has enabled the project to develop. After this, the guidelines say that 'projects applying for a fourth year in a row will be given less priority than other applicants'.

Grants in 1999/2000

The beneficiaries were divided into eight broad areas:

- Community groups – £202,000 (24%): Local groups including tenants' associations and community centres, with specific child based activities.
- Health – £179,000 (21%): London and pan-London special needs and disability projects, including carers, groups, children's hospices and family support.
- Youth – £124,000 (15%): Clubs and centres focused on children over five years old, including Scouts and Guides and adventure playgrounds.
- Cultural – £101,000 (12%): Projects addressing the needs of local or pan-local ethnic, cultural and religious communities.
- Playgroups – £95,000 (11%): Groups offering primary play facilities to disadvantaged children under the age of five.
- Social/leisure – £76,000 (9%): Music, arts, drama and sport for young people.
- Refuge/homeless – £51,000 (6%): Organisations dealing with all aspects of youth homelessness, including domestic violence.
- Education – £16,000 (2%): Groups addressing non-statutory educational needs, including special needs and voluntary reading help.

Only 20 beneficiaries received more than £5,000 in 1999/2000 (seven of whom had also been supported in the previous year). They were led by grants to Children's Country Holidays Fund (£13,000); Toyhouse Libraries Association of Tower Hamlets (£12,000); Association for Research into Stammering (£11,000); National Missing Persons helpline (£9,000); Community Links, Newham (£8,000); Voice for the Child in Care (£8,000); Newham Toy Library (£6,000).

The following more detailed examples of grants in the previous year come from the annual review:

Pimento Project Education Scheme

Pimento provides educational help for children between the ages of 5 to 13 years. Help a London Child provided a grant to fund the Play Scheme which operates in an area of very high unemployment and is used by children from West Indian and other ethnic minority backgrounds. The scheme complements the supplementary school that is run during term time, targeting children who are underachieving in state schools and who are referred to Pimento by the Family Service Unit, mainstream schools and other agencies due to stressful family circumstances.

The Emery Theatre

The Emery Theatre's aim is to provide theatre in education programmes. These give local school children an opportunity to visit the theatre and join in a forum to discuss and evaluate the issues within the plays with the cast and director. In the first year HALC funded a special drugs awareness project which incorporated the development of a play called 'So Where's Charlie?'. The following year further funding was granted by HALC for a three week tour of the play around seven theatres in seven different areas of London.

Reflections

Reflections is a project which provides a unique multi-sensory experience for disabled children, creating an environment that is both stimulating and relaxing. The project opened in February 1994 and provides a leisure experience for profoundly disabled children as well as much needed support to parents and carers.

Exclusions

Help a London Child will not fund:

- individual children or families;
- retrospective funding;
- statutory funding – funding for schools or health projects that would otherwise be covered by designated statutory funding from the local authority;
- salary posts for more than 12 months;
- deficit funding or repayment of loans;
- medical research;
- purchase of a minibus;
- trips abroad;
- distribution to other organisations.

If seeking presents and food for Christmas, please contact 95.8 Capital FM's other charity, Share a Capital Christmas, in October.

Applications

Grants are awarded once a year only, normally in November. Application forms (including guidelines) are available from January to May and require an A4 sae. Completed forms must be sent or delivered by hand to the address above. Photocopies or faxes cannot be accepted. The closing date is typically around the end of May. Applicants will get an acknowledgement in June along with a reference number.

The allocations panel meets during the summer to consider all applications. While additional information may be provided in support of applications, the panel is only given copies of the application form. Applicants will be informed of the panel's decision, in writing, by November. The HALC office can be contacted on 020 7766 6203/6490 and applicants should quote their reference number.

The guidelines add:

Should you have any questions about filling in the form, please contact the HALC office on 020 7766 6203. Alternatively, you could contact the London Voluntary Service Council, who provide general information about applying for funding (020 7700 8113), or your local CVS office.

Help the Aged

Day centres, lunch clubs, hospices, general, for older people

£1,301,000

Beneficial area UK.

St James's Walk, Clerkenwell Green, London EC1R 0BE

Tel. 020 7253 0253 **Fax** 020 7251 0747

e-mail info@helptheaged.org.uk

website www.helptheaged.org.uk

Correspondent Brenda Doku, Regional Distributions Manager

Trustees *Jack Mather, Chair; Phillip Ashfield; Henry Bowrey; Peter Bowring; Priscilla Campbell Allen; Jo Connell; Brian Fox; Vera Harley; Anne Harris; William Hastings; Rosemary Kelly; Trevor Larman; William Menzies-Wilson; Chai Patel; Kevin Williams; Christopher Woodbridge; Angus Young.*

Information available Report and accounts. Annual review. Application form for grants.

Summary

The charity makes a large number of small grants to organisations helping older people and their carers. The average grant is about £5,000, though awards can be for as much as £50,000 or as little as £100.

General

For edition after edition of this book, Help the Aged denied to the editors of this book that it made any grants whatsoever, despite its audited accounts showing millions of pounds of grant expenditure. The charity now agrees that it 'has many years' experience of supporting community and voluntary organisations through its grant-aid programme'.

However, the long-running grant programmes it refers to, and which are described below, do not include the money raised by other charities with Help the Aged's assistance through its excellent fundraising advice service. This used to appear both as income, and then as grant expenditure, in Help the Aged's accounts (as well as in the accounts of the other organisations concerned), and was therefore described in previous editions of this book. This accounting practice has happily ended, which explains the apparent reduction in the level of grantmaking by the charity. The actual fundraising advice activity continues, though it is poorly reported in the charity's annual reports and reviews.

The charity has supplied the following information about its long-running, much valued and recently reorganised small grants programme:

In response to devolution, from September 2000, the grants programme and fundraising will form part of a new Regional Development unit to strengthen Help the Aged's presence throughout the UK. This multi-functional unit will support community groups by offering cash grants as well as fundraising, organisational and policy advice and development.

The Regional Development Team will, among other things:

- Create a 'one-door' entry for organisations seeking assistance from Help the Aged for their funding and development programmes thus creating a fast track approach for the community at large.
- Identify funding themes in any one year as well as continuing a small grants programme.
- Continue to assist approved locally based charitable organisations raise funds for their capital programmes.
- Develop strategic policy/planning links with national, regional, local voluntary and statutory groups in line with the aims of the Charity.

The number and total value of grants to community groups are listed as follows:

Year	*No.*	*Amount*
1999/2000	356	£1.3 million
1998/1999	261	£1.1 million
1997/1998	309	£1.0 million
1996/1997	271	£1.1 million

Main grants programme

This supports the work carried out by community and voluntary groups for the benefit of older people and their carers. Grants are made to a wide variety of projects, for example respite care, hospices, day centres and lunch clubs.

Senior mobility campaign

This scheme helps voluntary groups provide transport for older people, for example meals on wheels, mobile day centres and care and repair vans. Assistance includes grant aid, fundraising, a bulk buying scheme and a turnkey service whereby Help the Aged handles all the financial and legal paperwork involved in purchasing a vehicle.

The social exclusion programme

- Homeless older people
- Older people isolated in rural communities
- Ethnic minority elders
- Fuel poverty – home insulation scheme

Speaking up for our age

This is a three year programme providing development support for existing old people's forums and for the formation of new groups.

'Start Up' grants for new groups

These are designed to help new local groups with the initial costs associated with their first year of operation. Allowable items can include Stationery, Postage, Phone calls, Meeting Room Hire, Conferences, Travel, Publicity Material, Training and Sessional Staff for Specific Tasks, etc.: Maximum for Local Groups – £500.

For groups covering a larger area, for example a County, Region, Unitary Authority or Widely Dispersed Rural Area the grant may be increased to cover higher costs including those associated with assisting the formation of other new groups within their territory: Maximum for Larger Groups – £1,000.

'Development' grants for established groups

These grants are designed to help existing groups develop their range of activities and their effectiveness. In addition to the items listed above, groups can apply for the Cost of Schemes to Increase Membership, Advertising, further Training and Facilitator Fees, Additional Conferences, Publishing a Regular Newsletter, Permanent Office Equipment, Office Rental Costs, and further Sessional Staff.

Seed funding for a New Development Worker role may also be considered, but only when funding is in partnership with others, and is sustainable in the future.

Maximum for Development Grant – £4,000.

Grants in 1999/2000

Analysis of the 38 grants awarded in August/September 2000 showed an average value of just over £5,000, with 11 grants of between £10,000 and £20,000.

The largest grants in the financial year 1999/2000 were as follows: £48,000 each for Care & Repair Cymru, Wales, for new initiatives and a Best Value scheme, and to Nottingham Help the Homeless Association for a salary. Grants between £30,000 and £40,000 went to Thames Reach, London, for a salary, and to Support for Over Sixties, Norfolk, for a pilot project.

Other grants of over £20,000 were to Talbot Association, Glasgow; Holborn Community Association, London; Birmingham and District African-Caribbean Association; Cyrenians Cymru, Swansea; Huddersfield Deanery Project; and Dales-Care Centre, North Yorkshire.

A previous edition of this book noted a concentration of grants in Yorkshire, especially West Yorkshire. These areas receive more than a quarter of all the grants, because of a number of co-funding schemes there with local authorities. However, the grants concerned are usually small, and the proportion of the value, as opposed to the number of grants, is much less.

Exclusions

- retrospective deficits
- private organisations or companies
- statutory agencies
- loans
- shortfalls due to under bidding for service agreement
- major capital appeals
- residential/nursing/sheltered homes
- registered social landlords
- fabric appeals for public buildings including churches

Applications

In the first instance contact the Regional Distributions Department on 020 7253 0253 or by fax on 020 7251 0692.

The distributions committee meets approximately every other month.

Alan Edward Higgs Charity

Child welfare, in the Coventry area

£492,000 (1998/99)

Beneficial area Within 25 miles of the centre of Coventry only.

5 Queen Victoria Road, Coventry CV1 3JL

Tel. 024 7622 1311

Correspondent A J Wall, Clerk

Information available Inadequate report and accounts, without a grants list, on file at the Charity Commission.

General

Grants are made to benefit 'wholly or mainly the inhabitants of the area within 25 miles of the centre of Coventry ... in the promotion of child welfare, and particularly the welfare of underprivileged children'. At least half the grants in a typical year are repeated from the year before.

The charity says:

> It is the aim of the trustees to reach as wide a selection of the community as possible within the geographical limitations. They are happy to receive applications for grants from local bodies or associations and from national organisations which can show that any grant from the charity would be used to benefit persons resident within the geographical area. ... the increasing range and diversity of donations continue to be welcomed.

In 1998/99 the charity had an income of £1.3 million from total funds of £20.8 million and made grants totalling £492,000 to 87 organisations (£493,000 to 109 organisations in 1997/98). The average amount donated increased to £5,665, from £4,526 in the previous year.

The analysis of grantmaking was restricted to the statement: 'The largest donations amounting to £50,386 were given to various activities organised by the University of Warwick.' No further information was available.

Exclusions

Applications from individuals are not normally entertained.

Applications

In writing to the clerk to the trustees, along with:

- a copy of the latest audited accounts;
- charity number (if registered);
- a detailed description of the local activities for the benefit of which the grant would be applied; and
- the specific purpose for which the grant is sought.

The Hilden Charitable Fund

Minorities, overseas, penal, homelessness, general

£441,000 (1998/99)

Beneficial area UK, especially London, overseas.

34 North End Road, London W14 0SH

Tel. 020 7603 1525 **Fax** 020 7603 1525

e-mail hildencharity@hotmail.com

Correspondent Rodney Hedley, Secretary

Information available Guidelines. 'Summary of funding request' form. Report and accounts with full grants list and considerable narrative analysis of grants.

Summary

About 100 grants are made every year, mostly in the range of £2,000 to £6,000, with a maximum of £15,000. Roughly four fifths are new awards. Organisations working for ethnic minorities in the UK, and for projects in developing countries, receive the most support, normally accounting for half of the expenditure. Community groups and charities supporting causes such as the homeless and the rehabilitation of offenders are also funded.

General

With assets of more than £12 million, grant expenditure slightly outweighed income (£427,000) during the year 1998/99.

Guidelines for applicants

The trustees' main interests are:

- homelessness (particularly amongst the young);
- minorities and race relations;
- penal affairs;
- overseas countries.

Grants are rarely given to well established national charities or to individuals. Fund policy is directed largely at supporting work at a community level within the categories of interest stated above.

Priorities given to different types of work within the main categories may change from time to time, as dictated by circumstances. It should not be assumed, therefore, that an application, even though it may generally qualify, will necessarily be considered. Grants, capital or revenue, rarely exceed £5,000 and are not often made for salaries.

For projects overseas

The types of applications sought by trustees:

1. In supporting overseas development trustees wish to hear from projects which focus on community development, education and health.
2. Funds are available for capital and revenue funding. The funding programme is designed to help small and medium size initiatives.
3. Trustees will consider applications from countries within the developing world. At present applications from Ghana, Ethiopia, Tanzania, South Africa and Bangladesh are particularly welcome.
4. In supporting community development, education and health initiatives, trustees will particularly welcome projects which address the needs and potential of girls and women.
5. Where possible trustees would like to fund a number of projects in one geographical area. In funding projects, trustees will be interested in projects which develop the capacity of local people.
6. Trustees will be pleased to hear from UK NGOs and hope that UK NGOs will encourage their local partners, if appropriate, to apply directly to Hilden for grant aid.

The trustees are keen on matching funding, and feel that being aware of who else is funding a project is very important. Some 60 to 70% of projects are given funds for specifics (for example, volunteer costs are viewed favourably), with the other 30% being given on a more flexible basis.

Grantmaking in 1998/99

In the year 1998/99 the Hilden Office received 1,027 enquiries about grant aid, and 464 developed into full applications. (In 1997/98 there were 1,086 enquiries leading to 413 completed applications.) Of the applications considered, 111 grants were made, a 24% success rate for applicants.

Only 19 out of 111 beneficiaries got more than £5,000, with two organisations receiving the largest amount of £15,000. Of these recipients, 17 had been funded the year before.

The average grant was £5,000, but ranged from £3,000 in Scotland to more than £6,000 for third world projects.

Annual report 1999

[Amounts for particular grants are given in brackets.]

Minorities

Under this heading the needs of asylum seekers and refugees were met through grants to provide advice and support services, and a range of education and training classes: the Al-Hasaniya Moroccan Women's Project, West London [£3,500]; Asylum Welcome, Oxford [£5,000]; the Somali Advisory Bureau, Westminster [£4,000, repeat]; the Latin American Elderly Project, North London [£3,000]; Refugee Action, Kingston upon Thames [£5,000, repeat] and the South London Refugee Association [£5,500].

Hilden supported agencies serving the refugee population in Greater London: Asylum Aid [£7,500]; Detention Advice Service [£7,500, repeat]; the Joint Council for the Welfare of Immigrants [the Immigrants Aid Trust, £15,000] and the Refugee Support Centre [£5,000]. Grants were made for a number of black and minority self-help initiatives: the Bangladesh Centre, Birmingham [£5,000]; Islington Asian Women's Group [£1,200]; Salford Link Project [£1,000]; West Indian Ex-Servicemen's Association, London [£6,000, repeat]; Turkish Women's Group, Waltham Forest; and Family Friends, Brixton [£5,000, repeat]. The Pegasus Opera Company was grant aided to provide classes in Lambeth schools [£5,000]. Grants were made to programmes of work targeted at ethnic minorities: Brent Family Services Unit for a developmental play project [£5,000]; Community Matters [£3,000] and the National Coalition for Black Volunteering for training workshops [£3,000].

THE HILDEN CHARITABLE TRUST – GRANTMAKING IN 1998/99

Priority area	*No.*	*Amount*	*% of total*	*(1997/98)*
Minorities	31	£146,000	33%	(£152,000)
Third world	15	£94,000	21%	(£66,000)
Homelessness	15	£67,000	15%	(£82,000)
Penal	14	£57,000	13%	(£56,000)
Scottish Community Foundation	1	£26,000	6%	(£26,000)
Scotland	8	£24,000	5%	(–)
Playschemes	23	£10,000	2%	(£11,000)
Special	4	£17,000	4%	(£18,000)
Total	111	£441,000	100%	(£412,000)

Third world

Grants were made for a variety of development projects. In South Africa Hilden supported a rehabilitation scheme for young offenders run by NICRO, the South African charity for the care and resettlement of offenders [£6,000]; funding was given for a range of capacity training courses for voluntary agencies and NGOs provided by Interfund [£15,000]; and carpentry courses in a township outside Cape Town were funded through the Zenzele charity [£6,500]. Housing programmes were funded in India with grant aid to Ashram International [£5,000]. Help for credit and savings schemes were supported in Tanzania [Traidcraft Exchange, £5,000]; Uganda [UWESCO, £5,000] and Belize [The Fairtraid Foundation, £5,000]. Tools for Self-Reliance [£6,000, repeat] and the Tanzania Development Fund [£6,000] were supported to develop projects in Tanzania. The Ethiopian Gemini Trust was grant aided to set up a creative arts academy for street children in Addis Ababa [£1,000]. An orphanage and medical centre run by the Jesuits' Mission in Nepal, St Xavier's, was funded [£5,000]. The Cusichaca Trust was funded to pursue a major development programme in the Pampachir area of Peru [£5,000]. Trustees made grants to Oxfam [£10,000] and Action Aid [£10,000] to help the rebuilding of communities following destruction caused by the flooding in Bangladesh in 1998.

Homelessness

Grants were made to projects for the provision of services in hostels and day centres: Centrepoint, Boston [£3,500, repeat]; Homeless in Blackpool [£5,000]; New Connexion, Camborn [£4,000]; St Edmund's Society, Norwich [£5,000]; St Cuthbert's Centre and Elizabeth House, London [£2,000 and £5,000 respectively]; Lifeshare, Manchester [£5,000, repeat]; Petrus Community, Rochdale [£5,000]; and SPEAR, in Richmond upon Thames [£2,000, repeat].

Other initiatives supported under this heading were for: a recycling furniture scheme, North Staffordshire Furniture Mine [£4,500]; support for two employment schemes for homeless people, Breakout Lowestoft [£5,000] and Home and Dry Scarborough [£7,000]; and for a tenancy support service, Network Whitby [£5,000, repeat]. In Wales Hilden funded an emergency 'crash pad' accommodation project for young people at Mountain Ash YMCA [£5,000].

Penal affairs

Grants were made for rehabilitative regimes in prisons: RAPT, to provide drug addiction treatment programmes in prisons [£5,000]; the National Association of Toy Libraries for play facilities at the mother and baby unit at Styal Prison, Manchester [£3,000]; the London Community Cricket Association, for running coaching qualification courses for inmates at

Wandsworth Prison [£6,000]; and the New Assembly of Churches, for pre-release courses at Feltham Young Offender Institution [£5,000].

Families of prisoners were supported: Shropshire Help and Advice for Relatives and Friends of Prisoners [2 grants, £500 each]; and HALOW, London [£5,000, repeat].

Training schemes for ex-offenders were supported: CAST in London [£5,000], the Norfolk Association for the Care and Resettlement of Offenders [£5,000] and Consultancy Counselling and Training, in Ipswich [£5,000].

Programmes of treatment and therapy for sex offenders were funded through the Stepping Stones Trust and the Respond charity. A programme was funded to help rehabilitate ex-offenders with a history of violence against women, this was provided by the Hampton Trust, Hampshire [£4,000].

Playschemes

In 1998/99 the fund allocated £10,000 to support 23 summer play schemes. Applications from organisations working with refugee and immigrant communities were given priority. Most of the projects supported were based in Greater London.

Special

Complementing the main funding programme a grant was made to Kaleidoscope, in Kingston upon Thames, for combating drug dependency [£12,000, repeat]. A grant was made to the Guild of Psychotherapists for its clinic for people on low income in South London. A counselling project for people with colitis and Crohn's disease was supported in London [National Association for Colitis and Crohn's Disease, £2,000].

Grant aid in Scotland

Grants were made to Scottish voluntary agencies from Hilden's main funding programme. The Mendelssohn on Mull Trust and the Isle of Arran Museum Trust received grants [£1,000 and £3,000 respectively]. The Brunswick Centre, Glasgow and the Oasis Night Shelter, Aberdeen were two urban initiatives supported [both £3,000]. Grants were made to the African-Caribbean Advisory Service, Glasgow (YMCA) and the Minority Ethnic Learning Disability Initiative, Edinburgh [£4,000].

A grant of £26,250 was given to the Scottish Community Foundation to support a grants programme for community groups and small voluntary organisations. In the year 35 grants were made, an average of £715. Of these seven ethnic minority projects were supported; four penal affairs groups and two gay organisations.

Guidelines and application forms are available from: Scottish Community Foundation, Third Floor, 27 Palmerston Place, Edinburgh EH12 5AP. Tel: 0131 225 9804

[It has been reported that applications for grants of more than £1,000 should still be sent to the London office.]

Exclusions

No grants to individuals.

Applications

All applicants are required to complete a very brief summary form outlining their request before they are considered. Otherwise all applications will be regarded as enquiries. Potential applicants should contact the office for guidelines and forms.

Applications should include:

- most recent financially inspected accounts;
- most recent annual report;
- projected income and expenditure for the current financial year;
- explanation of how your reserves stand;
- particular features of your costs, e.g. high transport costs in rural areas;
- details of other funders approached;
- any significant achievements and/or problems or difficulties;
- how you approach equal opportunities;
- any 'matching grant' arrangements.

Please be clear in your application about when the proposed work is to commence, and give the relevant timetable.

For projects overseas applicants should provide:

- Evidence of commitment among local people and communities to the proposed work programme.
- A coherent plan of how the work is going to be carried out with relevant budgets. Budgets should be presented in the context of the overall budget of the applicant NGO.
- A plan of how the work is going to be maintained and developed in the future by involving relevant agencies and attracting money and resources.
- An explanation of why the local project seeks the help of a UK aid agency.
- Details of local costs (e.g. salaries of state-employed teachers and medical personnel; cost of vehicles, petrol, etc.), and notes of any problems over exchange rates or inflation.
- An account of the political, economic, religious and cultural situation in the country/area.
- A comment on the extent to which the project can rely on government and local state funding in the country concerned.
- Details of monitoring and evaluation.

Trustees meet approximately every three months.

Historic Churches Preservation Trust

Historic churches

£1,754,000 (in grants and loans, 1998/99)

Beneficial area England and Wales.

Fulham Palace, London SW6 6EA

Tel. 020 7736 3054 **Fax** 020 7736 3880

Correspondent Michael Tippen, Secretary

Information available Guidelines for applicants. Annual report and accounts with full grants list and review of the year's activities. Quarterly Review magazine.

Summary

A total of nearly 400 grants and loans are made each year towards the upkeep of fine Christian churches in England and Wales. They start at a few hundred pounds and normally peak at £7,500, though a new initiative for the year 2000 saw the introduction of a programme of grants for £20,000 or more. Loans of up to £10,000 are also given, usually in combination with a grant.

General

The trust was set up in 1953 after a report commissioned by the Church of England found that the nation's churches were in a state of decline. As these problems were not confined to the established Church, the trust was conceived as a non-denominational charity to help finance church repairs in England and Wales.

The trust also administers the smaller Incorporated Church Building Society (ICBS, established 1818). Both the trust and the society make interest-free loans and grants. The trust's money comes solely from voluntary donations, some of which have been used to create a capital base from which investment income can be generated. The trust runs a number of fundraising initiatives involving the general public, private companies and other grant-making trusts. It currently has a membership of 2,000 'friends'.

Churches must be over 100 years old, Christian and located in England (including the Isle of Man and Channel Islands) or Wales. Money is only donated or loaned towards fabric repairs on conservation standard churches where the parish church council has insufficient funds.

In the 15 months to 31 December 1999, the trust's income totalled £1,314,000 (ICBS's income was £80,000). Financial support to 391 churches was approved during the period; £1,490,000 in grants and £264,000 in loans.

In July 1998, the normal maximum grant was raised from £6,000 to £7,500 and 58 churches received this amount in the same period. However, in the 1999 annual report the chairman of the grants committee reported a desire to devote an extra £1 million in the year 2000 to grantgiving, all of it in large grants of £20,000 or more for cases of the greatest need. The main criteria were:

- Financial need: the cost of the work in relation to the resources of the people.
- Importance and priority of the work: the danger to the building if it is not done.
- Value to the heritage: the architectural or historical importance of the building.
- Local or regional importance: where the church or chapel stands out as a 'beacon'.

After 2000 we shall continue to offer some large grants every year, but the budget will depend on our ability to attract new supporters. As things stand, we shall have to scale down the budget for our new, larger grants to £250,000 next year, but if people respond generously to our lead, we shall be able to do much more.

Some funds are entrusted to the HCPT to be disbursed for specific purposes. The largest of these, dating from 1998/99, was a gift of £150,000 from the Rowlands Trust for churches in the south and west Midlands. Two churches got £10,000 each from this source.

Interest-free loans are repayable in four equal annual instalments starting one year after the date on the loan cheque.

Exclusions

The HCPT and ICBS will not fund new amenities; re-ordering; church clocks; heating and lighting; stained glass; furniture and fittings; organ repair; murals; monuments; decoration (except after repairs); rewiring; churchyards and walls; work that has already been started or completed.

Applications

A written approach should be made in the first instance to seek a preliminary assessment. The case is then referred to a diocesan advisory committee. With its recommendation secured, an application form is sent, to which full specifications etc. must be attached. Trustees meet nine times a year to assess grants.

The Jane Hodge Foundation

Medicine, education, religion, mainly in Wales

£1,069,000 (1998/99)

Beneficial area Unrestricted, but with a preference for Wales.

Ty-Gwyn, Lisvane Road, Cardiff CF14 0SG

Tel. 029 2076 6521

Correspondent Margaret Cason, Secretary

Information available Good annual report and accounts, but without a list of grants.

Summary

Over 300 grants a year, for anything from £100 to £100,000 or more, though most are under £5,000. As the foundation declined to provide a grants list, it is hard to tell the true extent of the grantmaking, though the larger projects described in the annual report, partly reprinted below, were mostly based in the Cardiff area. Support is also given to mainly religious charities working in developing countries.

In 2000 the foundation said it was receiving about 300 applications a month, so the likelihood of receiving a grant must be fairly slim. A large portion of the available funds goes on ongoing local commitments, such as funding chairs at the University of Wales and major building projects. In 1999 the foundation had future grant commitments worth over £5 million, including £3 million agreed towards the building of a new cathedral in the city.

General

In 1998/99 the foundation's assets stood at £26.7 million and income was £1,394,000. Grants were distributed under the following headings:

	1998/99	*1997/98*
Medical	£351,000	£401,000
Educational	£256,000	£109,000
Religious	£223,000	£236,000
Other	£240,000	£210,000
Total	£1,069,000	£956,000

Extracts from the annual report for 1998/99:

Wallich Clifford Community (Home for the Homeless) – £250,000 is still reserved for this and other projects to help the homeless, including Cardiff University Social Services in their provision of accommodation for those people released into the community from long term institutional care.

Hospice – The Little Company of Mary – The Foundation gave their support to the annual 'Light up a Life' appeal with a donation of £35,000 for 1998/99, and have also agreed to support their 1999/2000 Christmas 'Light up a Life' Appeal in the sum of £50,000.

University of Wales College of Cardiff – The Trustees have agreed to support the new Institute of Applied Macroeconomics at the Cardiff Business School by way of a payment of £100,000 per annum for the next five years. …

University of Wales College of Cardiff, New Chairs – As last year, £25,000 was paid as part of the £125,000 reserved for the establishment of two new Chairs at the Cardiff Business School, the Sir Julian Hodge Chair in Marketing and Strategy, and the Sir Julian Hodge Chair in Marketing and International Business.

Archdiocese of Cardiff, St Mary's Church Cardiff – In December 1998, £15,000 was paid as part of a Pound for Pound fundraising drive to raise money for the renovation of the church.

New Cathedral – The Foundation's commitment of £3,000,000 for a new Cathedral in Cardiff still stands.

Applications from developing countries – As in previous years, sympathetic consideration has been given to various charities based in developing countries, and include payments to One World Action, Salesian Sisters of St John Bosco in India, Missionary Sisters of the Holy Rosary, Society of Catholic Missionaries, and Father Tim Greenway (India).

British Heart Foundation – As agreed, £10,000 was paid during the year to support a fundraising concert.

MRI Scanner Appeal, East Glamorgan NHS Trust – As agreed, £100,000 was paid to match Pound for Pound the funds raised to purchase a Magnetic Resonance Scanner for the new hospital.

Salvation Army – The trustees have agreed to help with rebuilding and refurbishment costs by way of a Pound for Pound Appeal. ...

Jersey Animals' Shelter – A Pound for Pound scheme has been agreed to a maximum of £25,000 to help raise much needed funds for this organisation.

Poor Sisters of Nazareth – £18,000 was contributed during the year to pay for a new refrigerated van for the convent to enable them to meet the requirements of health and safety regulations.

Exclusions

The foundation makes grants to registered or exempt charities only. No grants to individuals.

Applications

In writing to the correspondent. The foundation says that every application is acknowledged, despite the volume of requests.

The Horne Foundation

Education, arts, youth, in or near Northampton

£1,200,000 (1998/99)

Beneficial area Mainly Northamptonshire.

Suite 33, Burlington House, 369 Wellington Road, Northampton NN1 4EU

Tel. 01604 629478

Correspondent R M Harwood, Secretary

Information available Accounts, but without the required list of grants or narrative report, were on file at the Charity Commission.

Summary

The trust makes long-term grants towards educational facilities, primarily in the Northamptonshire area.

General

In 1998/99 the trust had assets of £8.8 million and an income of £420,000. Grants totalled £1.2 million. No grants list was provided, just a breakdown of types of grants as follows (1997/98 figures in brackets):

- Major building projects, £1 million (£514,000)
- Local support, £87,000 (£109,000)
- Local youth/arts projects, £26,000 (£22,000)
- Student bursaries, £26,000 (£48,000)
- National appeals, £20,000 (£30,000)

Such a listing, without explanation, is not enough to enable the reader to form a true and fair view of what the charity is doing. In the past, the charity has offered further information which enabled the following to be written in a previous edition of Volume 2 of this guide:

The foundation gives about 30 grants a year, some of them recurrent, for capital or project work. Grants normally range from a few hundred pounds to £10,000, but the foundation has said that its funding priorities are 'predominantly large grants towards building projects (education, welfare) in which the foundation is the major contributor. The foundation does not respond to appeals from other charities or individuals'.

The foundation has a 'preference for local charities in the Northampton area, with occasional grants to national and international organisations dealing with the foundation's areas of interest'.

At that time (1994/95) the foundation cited the following sample grants: NBC Sixfields Athletics Club (£100,000 for new club house and track), Young People's Hostel in Kettering (£75,000), Young Mothers Education (£11,000), Central Opera Trust (£10,000), and Moulton Football Club (£5,000).

Exclusions

The foundation 'does not respond to appeals from charities providing local services in communities located outside Northamptonshire'. It prefers organisations without religious affiliation.

Applications

In writing to the correspondent at any time.

The Hospital Saving Association Charitable Trust

Healthcare, medical research

£643,000 (1998/99)

Beneficial area UK.

Hambleden House, Waterloo Court, Andover, Hampshire SP10 1LQ

Tel. 01264 353211 **Fax** 01264 333650

website www.hsa.co.uk

Correspondent Phillip Howard

Information available Annual report and accounts.

Summary

The trust makes a large number of small grants to medical/healthcare charities, individuals, hospitals and hospices throughout the UK. Its first priority is towards members of the Hospital Saving Association, so there is a focus on supporting organisations that are likely to benefit HSA contributors.

General

The HSA Charitable Trust was established in 1972 by the Hospital Saving Association, a non-profit healthcare assurance organisation. The trustees are also on the board of directors of the HSA, which covenants a large donation each year. This amounted to over £800,000 in 1998/99. Donations of £643,000 were made during the year.

The trust appeared to allocate roughly a quarter of the funds to each of the following areas:

- non-public funds of hospitals (674 grants, £146,000)
- scholarship awards to nurses, midwives and professional therapists (120 grants, £148,000)
- individual contributors to the HSA in exceptional financial hardship (169 grants)
- charitable institutions and hospices (156 grants)

The latter two areas received a combined total of £349,000, but the figure is not broken down in the annual report. The largest share of the funds probably went to charitable organisations, most of which received grants of £1,000 to £2,000. Superficial inspection of the report suggests that repeat funding seldom occurs, with about 10% of the recipients having been funded two years previously.

In its own words:

> Although the trust is committed to providing financial help to a wide range of deserving causes, it is particularly concerned to support those charities and charitable organisations that are likely to benefit a substantial number of HSA contributors. The principle for distribution of funds is that all charities with medical research, after care and welfare aims and ambitions are considered.
>
> We tend to be more sympathetic towards smaller and lesser known organisations – particularly those that might benefit HSA members. In addition, we do make substantial donations to the larger charities from time to time.
>
> The objectives of the trust are :
>
> - to provide monetary grants to members of The Hospital Saving Association (HSA) suffering exceptional financial hardship as a result of ill health but who are not entitled to normal benefits under the association's rules.
> - financially to support persons and institutions to enhance their ability to care for HSA members and their family when ill.
> - to provide and award scholarships and prizes for nurses, health visitors and others engaged in or undergoing a course of education, training, or preparation for the treatment or prevention of illness.

Only four institutions received five-figure sums in 1998/99: The Council of the Midwife Teachers Training College (£30,000); Bath Institute for Rheumatic Diseases (£10,000); Exeter Leukaemia Fund (£10,000) and NHS Trust – The Rocky Appeal (£10,000).

A selection from a list of the 50 largest grants reveals the mix of local and national organisations supported:

Cornwall Children's Hospital Appeal (£5,000); Lymphoma Association (£2,000); National Gulf Veterans & Families Association (£2,000); Northwick Park Institute for Medical Research (£5,000); Osteoporosis 2000 (£3,000); The Sick Children's Trust (£2,000); The Welsh Initiative for Conductive Education (£2,000).

Applications

In writing to the correspondent, including a copy of the most recent audited accounts. Trustees meet four times a year.

The Reta Lila Howard Foundation

Children

£760,000 (1998/99)

Beneficial area UK and Republic of Ireland.

Jamestown Investments Ltd, 4 Felstead Gardens, Ferry Street, London E14 3BS

Tel. 020 7537 1118

Correspondent The Company Secretary

Trustees *Gretchen Bauta; Alannah Weston; Geordie Dalglish; Mark Mitchell; Tamara Rebanks; Galvin Weston; Melissa Baron.*

Information available Accounts are on file at the Charity Commission, but without the required list of grants.

General

The founder of this trust had an interest in children's charities and the trust's grant-making focus is 'to support a few innovative projects that benefit children up to the age of 16 within the British Isles'. Funds are directed to selected projects, 'to support the education of young people or to ameliorate their physical and emotional environment'. Donations are given over a finite period, with the aim that the project can be self-supporting when funding has ended.

During the foundation's first period of existence, from incorporation in October 1994 to April 1996, it received a donation of £10 million from the Garfield Weston Foundation. Of this, £9 million was invested and £1 million was placed in the bank. In 1998/99, the investment income was £533,000, from assets then worth £14.9 million.

The amount donated has increased more than tenfold over a short period, from £72,000 awarded to seven organisations in 1996/97, £369,000 to 18 organisations in the following year and then 38 grants totalling £760,000 in 1998/99. The trust does not provide a grants list with its accounts. It has said that it wishes to remain anonymous to its beneficiaries, an aspiration difficult to square with the accountability requirements of a public charity receiving the appropriate tax reliefs.

Exclusions

Grants are not given to individuals, organisations which are not registered charities, or towards operating expenses, budget deficits, (sole) capital projects, annual charitable appeals, general endowment funds, fundraising drives or events, conferences, or student aid.

Applications

The trust states that it does not accept unsolicited applications, since the trustees seek out and support projects they are interested in.

The Albert Hunt Trust

Welfare

£451,000 (1997/98)

Beneficial area UK.

Messrs Coutts & Co., Trustee Department, 440 Strand, London WC2R 0QS

Tel. 020 7753 1000

Correspondent R J Collis, Trust Manager

Trustees *Miss M K Coyle; Mrs McGuire; Coutts & Co.*

Information available Accounts on file at the Charity Commission.

Summary

Donations of £8,000 each are made to around 50 national health and welfare charities, many of them on an annual basis. First-time beneficiaries receive grants of £2,000 each.

General

A legacy gift of nearly £8 million helped increase the trust's capital base from £3.2 million in 1996 to £12.4 million in 1997. By 1998 its assets stood at £17.9 million.

Consequently, grantmaking increased from £156,000 in 1996/97 to £451,000 in 1997/98, leading to this trust's 'promotion' from Volume 2 of this guide. The impact on the trust's policy was to raise the amount given to each of its normal beneficiaries from £3,000 to £8,000.

The newly increased endowment should raise the annual grant total to more than £750,000 a year. Such a large sum may call for a more energetic approach to grantmaking.

Typical regular beneficiaries include the British Home and Hospital for

Incurables, Shelter, Leukaemia Research Fund, Help the Aged, YMCA, CAFOD, Catholic Children's Society, The Simon Community and Sons of Divine Providence.

There were 21 new grants in 1997/98, almost all of them for £2,000 (the single exception being a £3,000 grant to the National Association of Almshouses).

The new additions to the list of beneficiaries included Action for Blind People; Covent Garden Research Trust; Wales Council for the Deaf; Sue Ryder Foundation; Institute of Orthopaedics; Harefield Hospital Fund; Foundation for Communication for the Disabled, and The Cot Death Society.

Applications

The correspondent states that no unsolicited correspondence will be acknowledged, unless a donation receives favourable consideration. Trustees meet in June and December. Applications should be received the previous month.

The Huntingdon Foundation

Jewish causes

£974,000 (1998/99)

Beneficial area Jewish communities in the UK.

Foframe House, 35–37 Brent Street, London NW4 2EF

Tel. 020 8202 2282

Correspondent Mrs S Perl, Secretary

Trustees *Benjamin Perl, Chair; Mrs S Perl; Mrs R Perl; S Perl (USA).*

Information available Annual report and accounts on file at the Charity Commission.

General

This trust concentrates its resources on the provision of Jewish schools. In 1998/99 it had assets of £7.5 million and an income of nearly £1.8 million. This included over £1 million in new donations and gifts received. Grants totalled £974,000, with three quarters of that amount (£739,000) going to the following five beneficiaries:

Beis Yaacov (Beth Jacob) Primary School (£385,000); Harrow Jewish Day School (£200,000); Mosdos Nadvorna (£60,000); Pardes House Day School (£54,000), and Massoret Institute Teachers Training (£40,000). The Pardes House and Harrow schools had originally been established with help from the trust.

A further 15 grants ranged from £1,000 to £15,500, while more than 200 grants were for lesser amounts, many for under £100, all to Jewish beneficiaries.

Applications

Grants appear to be given in March, June, September and December.

The Isle of Anglesey Charitable Trust

General, in Anglesey

£516,000 (1998/99)

Beneficial area The Isle of Anglesey only.

Isle of Anglesey County Council, County Offices, Llangefni LL77 7TW

Tel. 01248 752603 **Fax** 01248 752696

Correspondent David Elis-Williams, Treasurer

Trustees *The County Council. Chairman of the Trust: George Alun Williams.*

Information available Eligibility criteria for applicants. Report and accounts listing grants of £1,000 or more.

Summary

Grantmaking is divided, at present more or less equally, between the local county council and community and voluntary organisations in Anglesey, for which applications are considered once a year. Most grants are under £1,000, but a few organisations get large grants of £20,000 or more.

General

The trust was formed in 1990 by the then Isle of Anglesey Borough Council 'to administer investments purchased from monies received from Shell (UK) Limited when the company ceased operating an oil terminal on Anglesey'. This compensation money from the company was part of the agreement in the original 1972 private Act of Parliament which had enabled the terminal to be set up in the first place.

The objectives of the trust are 'to provide amenities and facilities for the general public benefit of persons resident in ... the Isle of Anglesey'.

There has been controversy locally about the maintenance of the necessary distinction between the affairs of the charity and those of the council. The 1998/99 report says that:

> The trustee wishes to note certain recent events:
>
> - In April 1998, the District Auditor reported that equipment and goods had been taken from the trust's lands at Rhosgoch without authority. These matters have been further investigated by the officers of the trust, and the County Council, in cooperation with the police.
> - In July 1998, an allegation was made that another potential buyer was interested in buying the trust's land, other than the purchaser who paid for the option on the land, and that relevant information was not disclosed to the trust. These matters have been investigated by the Charity Commission. [The Commission] stated that the Council was entitled to be told of all approaches ... It was also stated that no action was required by the Commission [which] now considers the matter closed. The police have announced there will be no criminal investigation ...
> - The police are investigating an application for a grant from the trust.

The trust receives a large number of ineligible applications and so wishes to emphasise that grants are made only for projects based in Anglesey.

In all, 102 grants totalling £516,000 were made to 75 organisations. More than half of the total went to the Isle of Anglesey County Council, including grants to 23 schools. Donations to Citizens Advice Bureaus, village halls and community and sports facilities accounted for a further 28% of the funds. There were three grants of £20,000 or more to local organisations, which together with the annual award to the county council made up around three quarters of the total expenditure. The recipients were: Holyhead CAB (£74,000); Rhosneigr Recreation Association (£30,000), and Llanfairpwll Football (£20,000). A further 34 grants were for amounts of £1,000 or more, going up to £8,000.

Exclusions

Individuals; projects based outside Anglesey.

Applications

In writing to the correspondent, following advertisements in the local press. The trust considers applications once a year.

Isle of Dogs Community Foundation

Social regeneration on the Isle of Dogs, London

£695,000 (1999/2000)

Beneficial area The Isle of Dogs (i.e. the wards of Blackwall and Millwall) in the London borough of Tower Hamlets.

Jack Dash House, 2 Lawn House Close, London E14 9YQ

Tel. 020 7345 4444 **Fax** 020 7538 4671

e-mail info@idcf.org

website www.idcf.org

Correspondent Tracey Betts, Project Co-ordinator

Information available Application form with guidelines. Annual report and accounts.

Summary

This foundation aims to revive the community living in the shadow of London's Canary Wharf development. After securing Single Regeneration Budget (SRB) funding worth over £3 million, and large donations from major financial companies in the area, its asset base and grant-making capacity have rapidly expanded. Grantmaking focuses on three key areas:

- community development
- education and youth
- training and employment

General

The foundation's expansion is reflected in the level of its grantmaking, which had reached over £1.2 million in 1998/99, a more than ten-fold increase from £103,000 in 1996/97. In 1999/2000 its total funds amounted to nearly £9 million, over £3 million of which was being held for a ' Museum in Docklands' project.

The foundation's annual report for that year described its grants thus:

The foundation offers three types of grants:

- Small grants of up to £400: Intended for small items of equipment, social outings, events and other items of one-off expenditure.
- Standard grants of between £400 and £5,000: For general purposes, capital items, or running costs.
- Strategic Priority grants – larger grants of around £15,000: Provided for strategic initiatives in the area …

In 1999/2000, grant payments totalled £695,000, including £203,000 awarded under the SRB programme. The foundation initiated a first round of £1.5 million in grants to eight community projects, from a combination of SRB funding, local company donations and the foundation's own funds. Some of these were described in the annual report, as follows:

Youth Employment Project [£248,000] – Led by Christ Church Vicarage, this project is critical to the effective training of young people. It provides a job 'brokerage' facility giving access to existing and emerging local employment opportunities for the under 25s, and is targeted through schools and youth facilities. …

Self Employment Opportunities – Led by the East London Small Business Centre, a grant of £135,750 was awarded to this project which helps new business start-ups to settle on the Island. It also assists voluntary organisations to build their capacity and deliver a professional and profitable service, and offers support to businesses seeking funding. …

The Robin Hood Millennium Green Trust – A grant of £70,000 was awarded to this project, led by SPLASH [South Poplar and Limehouse Action for Secure Housing], towards the cost of landscaping a vacant site in the centre of the Robin Hood Gardens Estate in Blackwall, and then furnishing the resulting 'Millennium Green' with play equipment. …

The foundation also made 115 standard and small grants, averaging £1,500. Two of the standard grants were for more than £5,000: £15,000 was provided for the staffing of the Island Advice Centre and £10,000 for the running costs of Cryptics Youth Club. Others included £5,000 to Trees for London for a 'schools greening project'; £2,400 to the Isle of Dogs Bangladeshi Association, for a co-ordinator's salary, and £1,200 for safety equipment and alterations at the Docklands Sailing Centre.

Applications

Groups working in the Blackwall and Millwall wards who wish to apply for small or standard grants can discuss their application by ringing 020 7345 4444 and then completing a form. The form is assessed and presented to the grants committee at a monthly meeting where a grant recommendation is made.

The board of trustees considers and approves the grants committee's recommendations, after which applicants are notified of the outcome. The process is normally completed within three months.

The J J Charitable Trust

Environment, in UK and overseas, literacy

£722,000 (approved 1998/99)

See the entry for the Sainsbury Charitable Trusts

Tel. 020 7410 0330 **Fax** 020 7410 0332

Correspondent Michael Pattison, Director

Information available Good annual report and accounts, with full grants listing.

Summary

This is one of the Sainsbury Family Charitable Trusts which share a joint administration. Like the others, it is primarily proactive, aiming to choose its own grantees, and it discourages unsolicited applications.

The trust gives its major support to environmental work, both in the UK and overseas. In addition the trust shows a particular interest in dyslexia and other problems affecting literacy, particularly among young people at risk.

Only a small number of grants are made. Few of them are for less than £5,000 and occasional grants can be for more than £100,000.

General

The settlor of this trust is Julian Sainsbury and he is still building up the endowment, with gifts of over £2 million in both 1998/99 and in the preceding year. At April 1999 it had assets of £14 million and a relatively low expendable income, for a trust in this group, of £513,000.

The staff of the trust include Michael Pattison, director of all the trusts in the group, and Jane Shepherd, executive.

THE J J CHARITABLE TRUST

Grants approved in 1998/99 were classified as follows:

	No.	Value
Literacy support	10	£271,000
Environment – UK	19	£344,000
Environment – overseas	4	£84,000
General	4	£23,000
Total	37	£722,000

The annual report gives useful comment about each of the main areas of grantmaking.

Literacy support: 10 awards worth £271,000

Grants are made to improve the effectiveness of literacy teaching in the primary and secondary education sectors for children with general or specific learning difficulties, including Dyslexia, and to do the same through the agencies working with ex-offenders or those at risk of offending.

Where appropriate, grants take account of new government initiatives, such as the Literacy Hour (National Literacy Strategy), and on-going developments within the prison education system. Consideration is given to projects that pilot new (well-founded) ideas for teaching and supporting people with specific learning difficulties or that provide demonstrations that are likely to be of wider interest. Given budget constraints within the education and criminal justice sectors, all such projects seek to deliver cost-effective solutions.

The main awards were as follows: British Dyslexia Association (BDA): £40,000 over three years, for general support.

Dyslexia Institute: £30,000 to help develop the distance learning course in order to make training more accessible to teachers.

Helen Arkell Dyslexia Centre (HADC): £107,000 over three years, towards a new initiative by HADC and Sutton Education Authority to provide a borough-wide approach to addressing dyslexia, combining screening, intervention and teacher training.

HM Prison Highpoint Dyslexia Project: £25,000, towards one-to-one volunteer support for inmates showing signs of dyslexia at HMP Highpoint and to carry out initial research at the women's prison.

London Connection: £39,000, towards a joint initiative to research the incidence and support needs of homeless people who have dyslexia.

Environment – UK: 19 awards worth £343,654

Grants are made for environmental education, particularly supporting projects displaying practical ways of involving children and young adults. Trustees rarely support new educational materials in isolation, but are more interested in helping pupils and teachers to develop a theme over time (such as organic growing), perhaps combining IT resources for data gathering and communication, with exchange visits and sharing of information and ideas between schools. Trustees are particularly interested in projects that enable children and young people to develop a sense of ownership of the project over time, and that provide direct support to teachers to deliver exciting and high quality education in the classroom.

The Trustees are also interested in the potential for sustainable transport, energy efficiency and renewable energy in the wider society. In some cases Trustees will consider funding research, but only where there is a clear practical application. Proposals are more likely to be considered when they are testing an idea, model or strategy in practice, such as the work being carried out by the Pedestrians Association.

The Trust has supported a small number of projects related to woodlands policy and tree planting.

The major awards were to the Children's Play Council (£68,000, second year, for engaging children in issues of sustainable transport), the Woodland Trust (£60,000 for work at Aveley Park) and Henry Doubleday Research Association (£47,000 to support the Schools Organic Initiative).

A very specific grant was the £15,000 for Renue to instal solar panels and an outdoor educational space at Singlegate First School in London.

Environment – overseas: 4 awards worth £84,413

The Trustees continue to support community based agriculture projects which aim to help people to help themselves in an environmentally sustainable way. The Trustees have also started to look at a small number of projects in Central and Eastern Europe.

Grants were awarded as follows: Prietenil Pamantului (Earth Friends), Romania: £30,000 over three years for their renewable energy and energy efficiency centre in Galati; Rainforest Foundation: £13,750 for work in western Thailand; Tree Aid: £10,000 for the Community Shade Trees Project in Burkina Faso; University of Wales: £31,000 over five years towards the Upland Rice Project in Nepal.

General: 4 awards worth £23,000

The main grant was to MERLIN (Medical Emergency Relief International) for £9,000 towards medical emergency work in Honduras.

Applications

See the guidance for applicants in the entry for the Sainsbury Family Charitable Trusts. A single application will be considered for support by all the trusts in the group. However, for this as for many of the trusts, 'proposals are generally invited by the Trustees or initiated at their request. Unsolicited applications are discouraged and are unlikely to be successful, even if they fall within an area in which the Trustees are interested.'

John James Bristol Foundation

Education, health, general in Bristol

£1,458,000 (1998/99)

Beneficial area UK, mainly Bristol.

7 Clyde Road, Redland, Bristol BS6 6RG

Tel. 0117 923 9444 **Fax** 0117 923 9470

Correspondent Julia Norton, Administrator

Information available Report and accounts with grants policy and list are on file at the Charity Commission or available from the foundation for the fee of £15.

Summary

In a typical year around a third of the funds is used for a couple of substantial donations, for amounts ranging from £250,000 to £750,000. Roughly another third of the money goes to local schools. After this, about 200 grants, most for under £1,000 and few for more than £5,000, are made to a varied group of local beneficiaries.

The charity now incorporates the Dawn James Charitable Foundation.

General

In 1998 the assets of the Dawn James (No. 2) Charitable Foundation were transferred to the John James Bristol Foundation as an expendable endowment. The newly merged foundation had an income of £1,782,000 in 1998/99, from assets of £44.7 million.

Grantmaking totalled nearly £1.5 million, almost a third of this being for local schools.

Two big grants made up £900,000 of the £1,022,000 spent on general donations. They were £500,000 for Bowel Cancer Research at the University of Bristol, and £400,000 for @Bristol, the city's big (and excellent) educational and leisure centre.

A further 26 grants were for £1,000 or more, led by £12,000 to Portway School Charitable Trust; £10,000 to Dementia Care Trust, and £6,000 each to Victim Support and the Pensioners Welfare Fund.

Other recipients included the Merchant Navy Association (£5,000); Salvation Army (£4,000); Tommy's Campaign (£2,500); Bristol Polio Fellowship (£2,000); Bristol Amateur Operatic Society (£1,500), and the Dolphin Society (£1,000).

A total of £36,000 was donated in 171 grants for less than £1,000.

Grants were distributed to schools as follows:

- Bristol Independent Schools Scholarship Fund (£280,000) – 10 grants, for either £20,000 or £30,000.
- Bristol Schools Special Prizes (£64,000) – 31 grants for £2,000, 2 for £1,000.
- Bristol Comprehensive Schools Enrichment Fund (£92,000) – grants ranging from £3,500 to £28,000 to nine schools.

Applications

In writing to the correspondent.

The Dawn James Charitable Foundation

This foundation was effectively merged with the John James Bristol Foundation (see preceding entry) on 30 September 1998, when all of its capital fund was transferred to the John James Bristol Foundation as an expendable endowment.

The Jerusalem Trust

Promotion of Christianity

£3,151,000 (1999)

See the entry for the Sainsbury Charitable Trusts

Tel. 020 7410 0330 **Fax** 020 7410 0332

Correspondent Michael Pattison, Director

Information available Annual report and accounts with full grants listing.

Summary

This is one of the Sainsbury Family Charitable Trusts which share a joint administration. Like the others, it is primarily proactive, aiming to choose its own grantees, and it discourages unsolicited applications. The extent to which readers should be deterred by this is discussed in the separate entry, under the Sainsbury name, for the group as a whole.

The trust supports a wide range of Christian evangelical and charitable activities at home and abroad. Unusually, these include Christian media activities and Christian art. Something over 100 grants are made each year, averaging over £20,000.

General

The activities of this trust are limited by its legal objects to the support of Christian activities or organisations, rather than by the policy choices of the trustees. Still being endowed by Sir Timothy Sainsbury, the trust supports a wide range of evangelical organisations, across a broad though usually moderate spectrum of Christian activity. Many organisations supported are generalist, such as Bibles for Children (£8,000) or Christians in Sport (£62,000), or have Anglican connections, such as the Diocese of Lichfield (£80,000 towards a Millennium presentation at Alton Towers), but there were also grants for the Luis Palau mission (£40,000 and £10,000), the Evangelization Society (£56,000) and the Kenya Methodist University (£56,000 for a youth officer).

The regular income of the trust in 1999 was £3.2 million, but additional donations were received of £9 million for the endowment and £530,000 in unrestricted funds. The major donation appears to have been in the form of further shares in the Sainsbury company. The decline in value of that company meant that total assets scarcely rose despite the gift; but income will increase, provided the profitability of the shops, rather than their share price, is maintained.

The staff of the trust include Michael Pattison, director and Miss J Lunn, executive.

There is no general information on the trust's grantmaking, but there are useful introductions in its annual list of new grants under each of its headings. These are unchanged from the previous edition of this book.

The number of new awards in 1999, and their total and their average values, were categorised as follows:

	No.	*Total*	*Average*
Christian evangelism/ relief work overseas	27	£674,000	£25,000
Christian media	11	£404,000	£37,000
Christian education	21	£722,000	£4,000
Christian art	4	£11,000	£2,500
Christian evangelism, social responsibility (UK)	54	£1,260,000	£23,000

Christian evangelism and relief work overseas: 27 grants worth £674,000

Trustees are particularly interested in proposals for indigenous training and support and production of appropriate literature and resource materials for Christians in Central and Eastern Europe, the former Soviet Union and Anglophone Africa.

Grants of £100,000 or more were given to the Tear Fund and World Vision (UK), both supported by this trust for at least three years, and the Ghana Institute for Bible Translation. The range of the rest of the grants was wide, from buying an aircraft for the Mission Aviation Fellowship in Mongolia (£30,000), to translating the New Testament into two non-slavic languages found in the Caucasus (£60,000 to the Institute for Bible Translation), to funding an inter-regional seminar by the Christian Police Association of Kenya (£20,000).

There were seven smaller grants, of less than £5,000 each.

Christian media: 11 awards worth £404,000

Trustees are particularly interested in supporting training and networking projects for Christians working professionally in all areas of the media and for those considering media careers.

By far the largest grant in 1999, of £295,000, was to Jerusalem Productions. In addition, £50,000 was given to the National Theatre for a cycle of Mystery Plays and £38,000 to Riding Lights Trust for a performance space in York.

Christian education: 21 awards worth £722,000

Trustees are particularly interested in the development of Christian school curriculum resource materials for RE and other subjects, support and training for Christian teachers of all subjects and lay training.

The major grants in 1999 were awarded to CARE for Education for a video and supporting materials (£175,000) and JC2000 for its millennium project (£155,000). The Centre for Youth Ministry and the Grubb Institute each received grants of £68,000, both for salaries, and £40,000 was given to the University of Exeter for its Biblos project.

Christian art: 4 payments worth £10,500

Trustees mainly focus on a small number of pro-active commission of works of art for places of worship. There were no such new grants this year.

It seems a pity that no sufficiently attractive propositions appeared in this interesting and generally neglected field.

Christian evangelism, social responsibility (UK): 54 awards totalling £1,260,000

Trustees are particularly interested in Christian projects which develop new ways of working with children and young people and projects which promote Christian marriage and family life. They are also interested in church planting and evangelistic projects which undertake Christian work with prisoners, ex-prisoners and their families.

Grants of £50,000 each were given to the Prison Fellowship Trust and to the National Gallery (for its Seeing Salvation exhibition). Typically, these are both institutions that have been previously supported by others of the Sainsbury family charities. Other major awards were to the Regeneration Trust (£30,000), Emmanuel Evangelical Trust (£38,000 for work with the Chinese community in London) and Christian Community Action (£48,000).

There were 17 smaller awards, of less than £5,000. Recipients included Christian Drama Resource, the Zion Trust and Barn Church, Kew.

Exclusions

Trustees do not normally make grants towards building or repair work for churches. Grants are not normally made to individuals.

Applications

See the guidance for applicants in the entry for the Sainsbury Family Charitable Trusts. A single application will be considered for support by all the trusts in the group. However 'proposals are generally invited by the Trustees or initiated at their request. Unsolicited applications are unlikely to be successful, even if they fall within an area in which the Trustees are interested.'

The Jerwood Charitable Foundation and the Jerwood Foundation

Education, arts, medicine, conservation

Over £5,000,000 (planned for 2000)

Beneficial area UK, but with a limited special interest in UK organisations operating in Nepal.

22 Fitzroy Square, London W1P 5HJ

Tel. 020 7388 6287 **Fax** 020 7388 6289

website www.jerwood.org.uk

Correspondent Roanne Dods, Director

Information available Guidelines for applicants. One annual report for both bodies, with summarised financial information and separately available financial statements for the charitable foundation. (As the Jerwood Foundation is not a British registered charity, it has no UK obligation to supply accounts.)

Summary

The Jerwood Charitable Foundation, as a new charity established in 1999, supports revenue projects while the associated Jerwood Foundation, established in 1977, by which it is funded, and which is not a UK charity, continues also to fund capital projects in its own name. The combined level of grantmaking is expected to rise to over £5 million in 2000.

Guidelines for grants and sponsorship (as at autumn 2000)

The Jerwood Charitable Foundation is a United Kingdom charity registered in 1999. It is supported financially and with other resources by the Jerwood Foundation, a private foundation established in 1977 by the late John Jerwood.

The Jerwood Charitable Foundation is now responsible for revenue awards, donations and sponsorship in the United Kingdom which were previously undertaken by the Jerwood Foundation itself.

It is dedicated to funding and sponsorship of the visual and performing arts, and education in the widest sense. It will continue to allocate a proportion of funding to conservation, environment, medicine, science and engineering.

The charity shares with the Jerwood Foundation a dedication to imaginative and responsible funding and sponsorship in areas of human endeavour and excellence which foster and enrich the fabric of society.

Funding policy

In every case the Foundation seeks to secure tangible and visible results from its grants and sponsorships. Influence and effect beyond the immediate recipient of a grant is encouraged. The Jerwood Charitable Foundation aims to be active in identifying and creating new projects for sponsorship.

We aim to monitor chosen projects closely and sympathetically, and are keen to seek recognition of the Foundation's support.

Our strategy is to support outstanding national institutions while at the same time being prepared to provide seed-corn finance and financial support at the early stages of an initiative when other grant-making bodies might not be able or willing to act. The Foundation may wish to be sole sponsor (subject to financial considerations) or to provide partnership funding.

In particular the Jerwood Charitable Foundation seeks to develop support and reward for young people who have demonstrated achievement and excellence, and who will benefit from a final lift to launch their careers. This special role is intended to open the way for young achievers and give them the opportunity to flourish.

The Jerwood Charitable Foundation has the benefit of association with capital projects of the Jerwood Foundation. These include the

Jerwood Space, the Jerwood Theatres at the Royal Court Theatre, the Jerwood Gallery at the Natural History Museum and the Jerwood Sculpture Park at Witley Court, Worcestershire. The support for these initiatives by the Jerwood Foundation will be a factor when considering any applications.

Although the Foundation normally funds projects based within the United Kingdom, it will also consider a small number of applications from UK organisations operating overseas, especially within Nepal.

The Jerwood Charitable Foundation will not merely be a passive recipient of requests for grants but will also identify areas to support and develop projects with potential beneficiaries.

We regret that inevitably there will be applications which will have to be refused, even if they fit within our funding priorities, as a result of the large number of applications we receive.

Current areas of special interest

The Jerwood Foundation has certain primary fields of interest, although these are constantly being reviewed and developed. All applicants should carefully read the exclusions [below] before preparing an application.

The arts

The Foundation is a major sponsor of all areas of the performing and visual arts. We are particularly interested in projects which involve rewards for excellence and the encouragement and recognition of outstanding talent and high standards, or which enable an organisation to become viable and self-financing.

We rarely sponsor single performances or arts events, such as festivals, nor do we make grants towards the running or core costs of established arts organisations. We do not fund individuals.

The Foundation is active in support of conservation of the artistic and architectural heritage. However, we do not make grants towards building restoration projects.

Education

The Charitable Foundation aims to support projects which are educational in the widest sense. Currently, preference is given to initiatives benefiting young people who have completed school and university or other similar further education and are continuing their vocational and educational development.

We regret that we are unable to make grants to cover course fees or maintenance for individuals. We do not contribute to fundraising appeals by individuals. We do not contribute to fundraising appeals by individual schools or colleges, nor except in very rare instances will the Foundation fund bursaries for a school or other institution.

Other fields

The Jerwood Charitable Foundation retains a small allocation for projects and award schemes within the fields of science, engineering, environment and conservation. The Jerwood Charitable Foundation will continue its support of the Jerwood Salters Award for Chemistry and will be supporting new initiatives such as the Jerwood Business and Conservation Initiative in association with the Wildlife and Conservation Research Unit at Oxford University.

Jerwood prizes and awards

The Jerwood Charitable Foundation will continue to fund and monitor established awards such as the Jerwood Painting Prize, Jerwood Applied Arts Awards with the Crafts Council, the Jerwood Choreography Awards with the Arts Council of England and Dance Umbrella, the New Playwrights Season at the Royal Court Theatre and the Jerwood Design Award for Natural History Interpretation on the Internet with the Natural History Museum. The charity will also develop new schemes which will reflect the Foundation's objective to support talent and excellence in our areas of interest.

Types of grants

The Foundation makes revenue donations on a 'one off' basis. There is a strong element of challenge funding, whereby the Foundation will make a grant provided the recipient or other interested party, such as central Government or Local Authority can match the remaining shortfall. The Foundation will rarely commit to funding over a fixed number of years, yet will be prepared in many cases to maintain support if consistency will secure better results, and the partnership is successful and producing good results.

Applications are made and assessed throughout the year. They are normally assessed initially by the Jerwood Charitable Foundation's staff, with the help of expert advisers where appropriate. Final decisions are made by the Board of Trustees; every effort will be made to achieve speedy decisions.

Applications will be acknowledged. Decisions can normally be expected within six weeks and will be notified immediately. In view of the number of appeals we receive, detailed reasons for the rejection of an application are not generally given.

Grants will vary between the lower range of up to £10,000 (often plus or minus £5,000) and more substantial grants in excess of £10,000 and up to £50,000. There should be no expectation of grant level as all applications will be assessed on merit and need.

How to apply

[See under 'Applications' below.]

Annual report 1999

This document exemplifies the unusual style and tone adopted by these foundations, lacking the conventional mannered restraint of most of the large funding bodies described in this book. It is the declared policy (rather than just the secret hope) that the foundations should get public recognition for their work and for the Jerwood name. The tone is promotional and the report reads more like a manifesto than the usual attempt at a measured and self-deprecatory assessment. The photograph of the present chairman, Alan Grieve, appears three times in a 12-page document.

To the present editor this is refreshing. Charitable trusts make much of their independence but very few would dream of making use of this to act in any way contrary to the supposed 'good taste' of the day.

The following section reproduces portions of this report, though most of the repeated comments about the excellence of the activities have been omitted in order to save space.

Chairman's statement

In the first part of 1999 the Jerwood Charitable Foundation obtained charitable status and became active from 1 April 1999. Its principal role is to develop Jerwood revenue grants, awards and sponsorships. It also represents and supports the Jerwood Foundation in relation to major capital grants. …

I shared with the Trustees great pleasure in the appointment of Roanne Dods as Director … Having practised as a lawyer in Edinburgh for some five years, she then had a career in dance – as a dancer and administrator – and joined us from Laban Centre London. …

Capital grants

The projects announced in late 1998 have now all been completed and, in my view, with great success. These were:

- The Jerwood Library at Trinity Hall, Cambridge …
- Jerwood Sculpture Park at Witley Court …
- Jerwood Gallery at the Natural History Museum, London …
- The Royal Court, London, with the Jerwood Theatre Downstairs and the Jerwood Theatre Upstairs …

Future capital projects

The Jerwood Hall takes its place within the St Luke's Project in the City of London, being developed by the London Symphony Orchestra. …

The Sea Cadets Association. The Foundation has just announced a grant of £1 million to be made to the Sea Cadets Association to enable the purchase of a new offshore power training vessel, which will be known as the training ship, John Jerwood. … Although the Foundation does not normally support young people of school age, we took this unique opportunity to step in and provide a facility which can stand alongside the sail training ship, Royalist, which is already in commission with the Sea Cadets Association.

Jerwood Centre for the Treatment and Prevention of Dance Injuries, developed in association with the Hippodrome, the Birmingham Royal Ballet and DanceXchange. …

Oakham School, Rutland – The Jerwood Sphere. The Trustees have produced a highly original and innovative proposal to establish a new Centre of Education which will carry forward the concept of taking young people out of the traditional compartments of the school curriculum, enabling them to experience different approaches to creativity and learning, and to make connections with the work place. …

In addition to these projects, which are in hand, we will continue to allocate funds and develop capital projects in the fields in which the Foundation has its mission. I am hopeful that within the near future we will be able to identify a building close to the Jerwood Space [in Southwark, London] where we can create a rehearsal and performance space for jazz ... It will be modelled on the Jerwood Space, and integrated within its management systems and established practices.

Some major projects in 2000

Young Theatre Director Scheme: Funding towards a bursary scheme for young directors which will select one talented individual to gain training and experience … in the Jerwood Theatre Downstairs at the Royal Court.

The Pumphouse at the Aldeburgh Festival …

Mendelssohn on Mull: Masterclasses and performances by talented violin players on Mull.

Tools for Schools: Recycling and refurbishing of computers donated by industry to be given to schools around the country.

Jerwood New Playwrights: Current British writing at the refurbished Jerwood Theatres at the Royal Court.

Jerwood Salters' Environment Award: An award for innovative young academic chemists achieving a more sustainable, cleaner and healthier environment, as well as creating competitive advantage through their work. …

Jerwood Fund

As I stated in earlier reports, the Fund is managed on a total return basis, and we treat capital and revenue expenditure together in our decisions and funding strategy. Taking the last three years, the average grants and funding from the Jerwood Fund and the Jerwood Charitable Foundation are at a level of approximately £3.5 million per year.

Although we have a small team, it is most effective, and I believe we bring credibility and expert knowledge in our fields where we always seek excellence and quality. We value personal relationships, straightforwardness and efficiency in our dealings with others, at the same time being keen to enhance and add value to projects wherever we can. …

I am well aware that all good organisations, large and small, need to plan, budget and secure their place in 2000 and beyond, but I am adamant that our flexibility and willingness to take some risks must remain as one of our identifying features. Public bodies are inevitably ring fenced, and so it is for private foundations such as Jerwood to innovate and do what has not been, and may not be, done by others. ...

It is for us to keep bureaucracy at bay, eschew committees, and persuade others to join us as partners in the ventures we undertake.

I feel a continuous sense of privilege and good fortune to be able to fulfil my role. I can give an assurance that our energies are unrequited to take us through 2000 and beyond, which will see the completion of ten years since the death of John Jerwood in 1991, and to establish the Jerwood Foundation as a major contributor in many fields of human endeavour and excellence. …

Director's report

Since becoming a UK registered charity, we now receive over five times the applications the Jerwood Foundation received in the past, with numbers of applications increasing all the time. The wealth of energy, talent and ideas from all fields which come through our door at Fitzroy Square cannot fail to stimulate the imagination of the most cynical. What makes it possible to steer through the numerous applications we receive every day is a clear focus, a light foot and a personal touch. We continue to seek out innovative and exciting projects and develop partnerships with national institutions whose reputation for excellence matches our own, and we do our best to respond quickly and responsibly. …

Alongside the Visual and Performing Arts, Education in its broadest sense is one of our primary areas of interest and one that we are keen to develop further. Many of our projects reflect this including Prussia Cove, English National Opera, Masterclasses with Thomas Hampson, Mendelssohn on Mull, Tools for Schools, Arvon Foundation, and so on. This coming year we plan to identify other significant projects in this area.

... after difficult deliberation, the Trustees have decided that we will no longer be supporting applications within the area of social welfare. The enormity of concentration and knowledge required for us to achieve the impact we like to encourage with our funding, makes it prohibitive and our input inadequate. …

Partnerships have always been fundamental to the way we work and are valuable to us. A partnership implies a relationship. Being independent and exacting we expect a lot of those with whom we associate. It is the engaging qualities that characterise the Jerwood Foundation and that make being part of the Foundation so challenging and enjoyable. It is particularly gratifying that some of the Jerwood traits which have been handed down from parent to offspring, so to speak, include a healthy candour, a regard for detail, a sense of style and a dose of mischief. We aim to seek out and attract others who complement these qualities.

Finally and importantly, the Jerwood Charitable Foundation owes an enormous debt of gratitude to the vision and encouragement of its Chairman, Alan Grieve.

Grants in 1999

The material above gives a good picture of most of the work of the charity. As there is no information about the value of individual grants or, in most cases, about the cost of particular programmes, it is not possible to produce the usual type of information under this heading. There are, however, a couple of grants or programmes described, of a kind not so far mentioned, in which the charity was active.

First, there was a one-off 'environmental' donation towards the work of the Hebridean Whale and Dolphin Trust. (As there was also support for music-making on Mull, there may be a special interest in this area.) The foundation has also established a high level Jerwood Business and Conservation Initiative.

Secondly, there were three payments for health and welfare work in Nepal.

There were only 19 projects with specific and readily identifiable locations. Of these, 13 were in London or the south of England, 2 were in the English midlands or north, and 4 were in Scotland.

Exclusions

The Jerwood Charitable Foundation will not consider applications on behalf of:

- individuals
- building or capital costs (including purchase of equipment)
- projects in the fields of religion or sport
- animal rights or welfare
- general fundraising appeals which are likely to have wide public appeal
- appeals to establish endowment funds for other charities
- appeals for matching funding for National Lottery applications
- grants for the running and core costs of voluntary bodies
- projects which are of mainly local appeal or identified with a locality
- medical research without current clinical applications and benefits
- social welfare, particularly where it may be considered a government or local authority responsibility
- retrospective awards

The trustees may, where there are very exceptional circumstances, decide to waive the exclusion.

Applications

Applications should be by letter, outlining the aims and objectives of the organisation and the specific project for which assistance is sought. With the application the foundation needs:

- A detailed budget for the project, identifying administrative, management and central costs.
- Details of funding already in place for the project, including any other trusts or sources which are being or have been approached for funds. If funding is not in place, the trust requires details of how the applicant plans to secure the remaining funding.
- Details of the management and staffing structure, including trustees.
- The most recent annual report and audited accounts of the organisation, together with current management accounts if relevant to the project.

The foundation may wish to enter into discussions and/or correspondence with the applicant which may result in modification and/or development of the project or scheme. Any such discussion will in no way commit the Jerwood Charitable Foundation to funding that application.

As the foundation receives a large number of applications, it regrets that it is not possible to have preliminary meetings to discuss possible support before a written application is made. Please read the section (above) on funding exclusions before submitting an application.

The application should be addressed to Roanne Dods, the Director, at the address above.

J G Joffe Charitable Trust

Development policy, projects in developing countries

£497,000 (1998/99)

Beneficial area Mainly the third world.

Liddington Manor, The Street, Liddington, Swindon SN4 0HD

Tel. 01793 790203 **Fax** 01793 791144

Correspondent Lord Joffe

Trustees *Mrs V L Joffe; Lord Joffe.*

Information available Basic report and accounts with grants list, but without information about the purposes of the grants.

Summary

Grants, seldom for more than £50,000 or less than £5,000, are made every year to a few dozen organisations that concentrate their activities in developing countries, dealing with such issues as debt relief, human rights and development.

General

Lord Joffe, the settlor of the trust, was the co-founder of what has become the Allied Dunbar insurance company. He is now chairman of Oxfam.

In 1998/99 the trust held assets of nearly £11 million which generated income of £331,000, but the trust realised sufficient of its capital gains to be able to meet its target of about £500,000 a year in grants.

'The trustees have an ongoing relationship with a number of charities and their decisions on which to support at any one time are based on their assessment of the quality of leadership and the impact that the initiatives which they support are likely to have.' The trustees go on to say that they do not consider 'applications' when making grants. Given their close involvement in charitable activities, this statement may, perhaps, be taken more seriously than some similar assertions elsewhere in this book.

The trust made 32 grants worth nearly £500,000 in total in 1998/99.

More than half of this amount went to four organisations, as follows:

- Institute of Community Studies (£85,000)
- 3WI Education Trust (£66,000)
- New Economics Foundation (£50,000)
- Jubilee 2000 Coalition Charitable Trust (£50,000)

The remaining grants ranged from £2,000, to the Sri Lanka Peace Foundation, to £25,000, to Amnesty International and Ashoka (UK) Trust. Other beneficiaries included the European Palestine Israel Centre, the Medical Foundation for the Care of Victims of Torture, Money Management Council, Mozambique Schools Fund, Tools for Self-Reliance, and War on Want.

Applications

No applications will be considered or acknowledged.

The Elton John AIDS Foundation

HIV/AIDS welfare and research

£1,574,000 (1999/2000)

1 Blythe Road, London W14 0HG

Tel. 020 7603 9996 **Fax** 020 7348 4848

e-mail admin@ejafuk.com

website www.eltonjohn.com

Correspondent Robert Key, Director

Trustees *Sir Elton John, Chair; Robert Key; John Scott; David Furnish; Lynette Jackson; Neil Tennant; Frank Presland; Colin Bell; Tim Cohen; Anne Aslett; Marguerite Littman; Johnny Bergius; James Locke.*

Information available Funding criteria and application procedure. Accounts and reports.

Summary

Grants for both capital and revenue, for up to three years, are made to organisations providing services for people affected by HIV/AIDS and AIDS prevention education programmes. The normal range of awards is from £5,000 to £50,000, with the grants in 1999/2000 divided between 62% made internationally and 38% in the UK.

Background

The Foundation was established in 1993 by Elton John, who serves as its Chairman. The Elton John AIDS Foundation is an international grant-making charity whose main objectives are to improve the quality of life of people living with HIV/AIDS, financing projects that help to alleviate physical, emotional and financial suffering caused by HIV/AIDS. The Foundation continues to fund prevention, education projects and direct care initiatives that help stop the spread of the HIV virus and is a major contributor to the UK Hardship Fund administered by THT [Terence Higgins Trust] and Crusaid. …

General

Income from donations in 1999/2000 amounted to more than £2.4 million, half of which was a £1.2 million donation from the Diana, Princess of Wales Memorial Fund (following a gift of £1.1 million in 1998/99). That fund benefits from Elton John's donation of royalties from his song 'Candle in the Wind'.

For the foundation's international guidelines, readers should see the DSC's *International Directory* (available summer 2001) or contact Ann Aslett or James Locke on 020 8846 9944.

The foundation's UK funding criteria for 2000/01 read, in part, as follows.

Guiding principles

- We will support organisations that contribute to local community life at the grassroots level.
- We will promote capacity building, and strategic and collaborative working within the voluntary sector.
- We will work in ways that are open and transparent.
- We will develop the skills, knowledge, experience and expertise of the Directors and staff to the optimum benefit of the Foundation.

The Foundation has two distinct UK grant-making funds:

1. Rapid Response Fund
2. General Fund

United Kingdom Rapid Response Fund (grants of up to a maximum of £5,000)

The Foundation would like to improve the efficacy of and support to its grant-making process by initiating a Rapid Response fund. The Rapid Response Fund provides a quick response mechanism for local HIV/AIDS initiatives. Rapid funds are intended for use by non-governmental organisations (NGOs) and community based/self-help groups to design and implement HIV/AIDS prevention and care activities in low prevalence rural areas of the United Kingdom.

The mechanism is designed to be flexible and user-friendly, to stimulate creative and innovative ideas, and to maximise support and opportunities for groups not experienced in obtaining funding. These activities will also build on the Foundation's commitment to encourage, and strengthen, the capacity of community/self-help groups by providing them with opportunities to design, manage and evaluate activities.

The areas of interest include:

- Prevention/education: initiatives that provide the appropriate information, safe sex messages.
- Access to Treatment Information in rural areas.
- Direct care: activities generally undertaken in conjunction with prevention work including counselling and the provision of complementary therapies.
- Capacity building: helping community/self-help groups develop their capacity and the tools needed to run effective AIDS projects and to become sustainable after withdrawal of support, thus strengthening the HIV/AIDS sector. Grants could include the purchase of consultancy services, payment of room costs for self- help groups, [or] the purchase of office equipment.
- Sexual health strategies: Gay men's health prevention [sic]; immigrant and incarcerated populations (Prisons and Detention Centres): working to incorporate information, access to treatment and counselling, support groups and workshops with these 'high risk' populations.

United Kingdom General Fund

Who is eligible to apply?

Any registered charity that is running programme(s) specifically to benefit those infected or affected by HIV/AIDS.

Criteria for funding

The Foundation will consider applications designed to alleviate physical and emotional suffering caused by HIV/AIDS and which meet a recognised, demonstrable need. Clear aims and objectives; practical indicators for work-in-progress, and relevant monitoring and evaluation of the results should all be integral to any project proposal. All funding will be awarded on a yearly basis i.e. 1 April 2000 to 31 March 2001.

(Please note that the most frequent reason for the Director not being able to fund an organisation is when the level of demand exceeds the funds available.)

For what will not be funded, see 'Exclusions' below.

Grants in 1999/2000

In all, 62 grants were made, totalling £1,574,000. Of this amount, 21% (£323,000) was given to the Elton John Foundation in the United States.

Six out of the top ten beneficiaries had received similar grants in the previous year, including Body Positive Soho (£75,000); Population Services International (£55,000); Terence Higgins Trust (£50,000); Actionaid (£50,000) and Crusaid (£40,000).

The largest new donations were for the International Aids Vaccine Initiative (£150,000); Care (£60,000); Family Health International (£58,000), and Landmark (£50,000).

Of the remaining grants, 36 ranged from £10,000 to £32,000, and 16 were for lesser amounts. Of these beneficiaries, 11 had been funded in the previous year.

Exclusions

- research programmes
- individual grants
- repatriation costs
- conferences or educational courses
- drug treatment costs
- capital costs
- retrospective funding

The Rapid Response Fund will not fund, in addition to the above:

- salaries for permanent staff

Applications

Potential applicants should obtain a copy of the appropriate guidelines, either for the UK or International.

Organisations applying to the foundation for funds must provide full information about their work, including their objectives and evaluation plan. Those applying to the UK Rapid Response Fund should include a copy of the latest annual report or accounts as well as a 'Certificate of Charity Registration'.

Applicants to the General Fund should enclose the following supporting information:

- constitution or memorandum and articles of association
- budget relating to the application
- the latest audited accounts
- financial management and accounting procedure
- latest annual report

The Jones 1986 Charitable Trust

General, especially in Nottinghamshire

£1,037,000 (1998/99)

Beneficial area UK, mostly Nottinghamshire.

Berryman Shacklock, St Peter's House, Bridge Street, Mansfield, Nottinghamshire NG18 1AL

Tel. 01623 626141

Correspondent Messrs Berryman Shacklock

Information available Report and accounts with full grants list but with no further analysis of grants and grantmaking.

Summary

Grants, often for £15,000 or more, are given mainly to organisations in the Nottingham area, usually for charities assisting disabled people, or for medical research into disabilities. The trust also gives a few grants to a variety of social welfare organisations and animal welfare charities. Nottingham Health Authority, via Nottingham University, receives substantial annual funding, accounting for nearly a quarter of the total expenditure in 1998/99.

General

The Charity was established in 1986 with very wide charitable purposes but it is the trustees' intention to make grants primarily to organisations in the Nottingham area.

Most of the trust's income, which was just over £1 million in 1998/99, comes from five family settlements. Management and administration costs were very low, at £6,000, or just half a percentage of grant expenditure.

Grants in 1998/99

Grant expenditure was up 25%, from £826,000 the year before. Of the 47 grants listed in the annual report, 21 were for amounts over £15,000, while 17 were for £5,000 or less. An analysis of grants by category is set out below:

Category	*1999*	*1998*
Animal welfare	£50,000	£50,000
Education	£50,000	–
Medical research	£297,000	£303,000
Purposes beneficial to the community	£73,000	£94,000
Relief of poverty	£28,000	£26,000
Relief of sickness or disability: aged	£8,000	£5,000
Relief of sickness or disability: generally	£349,000	£193,000
Relief of sickness or disability: young	£79,000	£61,000
Welfare of the aged	£47,000	£47,000
Welfare of the young	£56,000	£47,000

By far the largest grant, as usual, was for £237,000 to Nottingham University, for medical research on behalf of Nottingham Health Authority.

Of the further £500,000 disbursed for other medical research purposes or for the 'relief of sickness or disability', grants of £50,000 each were made to the Royal Nottinghamshire Society for the Blind and the Royal School for the Deaf, with £32,000 going to Nottinghamshire Leukaemia Appeal.

Other substantial grants went to Nottinghamshire Wildlife Trust (£57,000); Nottingham High School (£50,000); Cope Children's Trust (£40,000); St John's Waterwings (£37,500), and the NSPCC (£35,000).

There were perhaps only half a dozen new grants in the year. Two significant recipients that did not appear in the 1996/97 list were Nottingham Regional Society for Autistic Children & Adults (£26,000) and Nottinghamshire Council for Voluntary Services (£25,000).

Examples of apparently non-Nottinghamshire beneficiaries include Riding for the Disabled, Highland Group (£30,000); Isle of Man Home of Rest for Old Horses (£5,000), and Chernobyl Children's Lifeline (£1,000).

Exclusions

No grants to individuals.

Applications

The trustees identify their own target charities and do not wish to receive applications.

The Jordan Charitable Foundation

General, especially in Herefordshire

£462,000 (1999)

Beneficial area Unrestricted, with apparent interests in Herefordshire, the Scottish highlands, and the USA.

Rawlinson and Hunter, Eagle House, 110 Jermyn Street, London SW1Y 6RH

Tel. 020 7451 9000

Correspondent R A Stockwell, Trustee

Trustees *Sir R A B Miller; Sir G Russell; R A O Stockwell; Snowport Ltd; Parkdove Ltd.*

Information available Accounts are on file at the Charity Commission.

Summary

The main areas of funding, where the foundation can make very large donations, are Herefordshire, and to a lesser extent the Scottish highlands and the USA. In 1999 about £200,000 was also given to a broad range of national charities, with grants, often recurrent, for amounts between £1,000 and £10,000.

There appear to be specific interests in the animal kingdom (fish included), and in heritage conservation.

General

In 1999 the foundation had assets of nearly £39 million, which produced an income of £1,144,000. The major activity reported was the provision of facilities at a new county hospital to be built in Hereford. Following a £100,000 grant in 1998 towards a new stroke unit, the trustees agreed in 1999 that they would fund the installation of an MRI scanner at the hospital, likely to cost over £1.2 million.

In 1998, £150,000 was donated to the Boston Public Library Foundation. The foundation also entered into a five-year commitment worth $20,000 annually to fund the Francis A Countway Library of Medicine at Harvard Medical School.

Grants in 1999

The foundation paid out 63 grants totalling £462,000, all but 14 being to charities also supported in the previous year. The largest, for £123,000, was a new award to the Parish Church Council of Brockhampton, Gloucestershire.

New grants also went to the local branches of mental health charities, to Herefordshire MIND (£25,000) and Herefordshire Headway (£7,000), while the County Air Ambulance Trust received a repeat grant of £10,000.

Other beneficiaries with local connections, each receiving £5,000, included Hereford Sea Cadets Corps (repeat), Hereford Cathedral Perpetual Trust (third and final year), Dyson Perrins Museum Trust (for Museum of Worcester porcelain) and Victoria and Albert Museum (Hereford Screen).

In Scotland, the major beneficiary was the Highland Hospice (£28,000; £20,500 in 1998), while other grants were made to Kildonan and Kilbrace Amenities Association (£5,000, repeat) and the Children's Hospice Association (£1,000).

The national organisations supported were mainly health/welfare or conservation charities.

Grants for £10,000 were made to the Royal National College of the Blind (third of five) and Riding for the Disabled.

The beneficiaries in the following sample received grants of £5,000, unless otherwise stated, and all had been supported in the previous year:

Atlantic Salmon Trust, Breast Cancer Care, British Lung Foundation (£2,000), Canine Partners for Independence, Council for the Protection of Rural England (£2,000), Fairbridge, Game Conservancy Trust, Help the Aged,

Imperial Cancer Research Fund, National Art Collections Fund, PDSA, Stroke Association, Water Aid, Wildfowl and Wetlands Trust (£2,000), WWF-UK.

New national beneficiaries (£5,000 each) included Action for Dysphasic Adults, ASPIRE, Society for the Welfare of Horses and Ponies, and the Special Air Services (SAS) Association.

Applications

In writing to the correspondent.

The Ian Karten Charitable Trust

Computer technology centres for disabled people, postgraduate education

£2,300,000 (1999/2000)

Beneficial area Great Britain and Israel, with some local interest in Surrey and London.

The Mill House, Newark Lane, Ripley, Surrey GU23 6DP

Tel. 01483 225020 **Fax** 01483 222420

Correspondent Ian Karten

Information available Report and accounts.

Summary

This trust, managed by its founder and donor, has two main activities. The first is the establishment within existing charities of centres for computer-aided training, education and communication (CTEC centres) to improve the quality of life, employability and independence of people with severe disabilities or with mental health difficulties. The second main area is the provision of postgraduate scholarships, a field not covered by this book. The small remainder is set aside for more general donations, particularly to medical and Jewish charities. There is also a smaller separate budget for modest donations to other charities.

General

The trust was founded in 1980 with an endowment from Ian Karten, and its income comes from that original endowment, supplemented by further gifts and loans from the donor, including over £1 million in 1999/2000. Assets stood at nearly £8 million.

Expansion of the network of CTEC centres has become the major focus of the trust's activities. At the end of the first three years of this programme 15 such centres were under way, an average of five centres a year. In the following year, 1999/2000, there was an almost four-fold increase in this rate to 19, bringing the total to 34 centres under way, 24 operational and 10 under construction. The trust describes this enterprising programme as follows.

> The trust identifies suitable charities and offers them generous funding for the establishment of a CTEC centre including the total cost of high performance computers, peripheral equipment, networking, assistive devices, software programmes and furniture, and in some cases a contribution to related costs. In return the trust requires undertakings from the charity concerning the professional management of the centre, that the charity will continue to operate it for at least four more years, and that it will participate with the trust and other CTEC centres in an on-going exchange of information, so as to benefit from each other's expertise and to spread best practice. The trust also expects to fund research into novel ways to use adaptive computer technology to assist disabled people, and to make the results of this research available to all CTEC centres.

Donations for CTEC centres in 1999/2000 averaged about £100,000, depending mainly on the size of the centre. With the fall in the cost of computing equipment, the figure is expected to be significantly lower in 2000/01.

The year 1999/2000 was the last for which the trust awarded grants directly to students. The trust has now established and funded scholarships at a number of universities, conservatoires and the like which will administer the scholarships themselves.

Of the donations to disability or medical charities, the largest in 1998/99 were to SeeAbility – Tadley House (£15,000) and the Disability Aid Fund, which had also been funded previously (£4,000). Other donations were to Remembering for the Future 2000 (£5,000) and World Jewish Relief (£2,000).

The trust makes further small grants, generally of £100 to £200, to almost 300 charities – mostly national ones, but some in Surrey and London.

Exclusions

No grants to individuals.

Applications

Those interested in the CTEC programme should contact Mr Karten. Students should approach their university. Applications for other grants should be accompanied by recent accounts and other material about the charity's activity.

The Kay Kendall Leukaemia Fund

Research into leukaemia

£2,085,000 (approved, 1998/99)

See entry for the Sainsbury Family Charitable Trusts

Tel. 020 7410 0330

Correspondent Michael Pattison, Director

Information available Good annual report and accounts.

Summary

This fund is one of the Sainsbury Family Charitable Trusts which share a joint administration. It only supports research into leukaemia and approves just a handful of new projects in most years.

General

The fund has an income of about £2 million a year. Grants are allocated on the advice of its scientific advisers: Professor John Goldman, Chairman; Professor Mel Greaves, and Professor Tony Green.

The fund outlines its policy and guidelines for awarding grants in its annual report. They may be obtained in full from the fund. It is prepared to consider proposals from both UK and non-UK based organisations, but those from the latter must involve some degree of collaboration with UK colleagues. Capital requests and large single items of equipment are considered. Research grants are normally awarded for five years, with initial support for three years and support for the final period subject to a progress review.

The guidelines for awarding grants were published as follows in the 1998/99 annual report:

> 1. Grants will be awarded for research on aspects of leukaemia and for relevant studies on related haematological malignancies.

2. Grants will also be awarded for the support of programmes associated with the care of patients with leukaemia subject to the conditions laid out below.

3. Requests for capital grants for leukaemia research laboratories or for clinical facilities for leukaemia will be considered either alone or in conjunction with proposals for the support of research and/or patient management.

4. Requests for single large items of equipment will be considered.

5. Preference will be given to proposals which are close to application to the care of leukaemia patients or to the prevention of leukaemia and related diseases.

6. Requests for support for basic science programmes may be considered but are likely to be funded only in exceptional cases. Project grant proposals or other small requests are not normally eligible.

7. Clinical trials will not be supported.

8. Grants are usually awarded to give additional support to programmes already underway, the aim being to further strengthen activities which are already of high quality. It follows that the KKLF will accept proposals from groups which already have support from other agencies.

9. The trustees will consider proposals from both UK and non-UK based organisations. Proposals from the latter must involve some degree of collaboration with UK colleagues.

10. Circular appeals for general support are not accepted.

11. Research grants are normally awarded for programmes of five years' duration. Support may be awarded for 3 years in the first instance with the final 2 years being dependent upon a review of progress over the first 3 years.

12. Programme grants may be renewed once for a period of up to five years. The maximum period of funding will be ten years. It is intended that the KKLF funding should not be the 'core' funding of any research group. Applicants should state clearly how their proposal relates to their core funding.

13. It is hoped that recipients of KKLF grants will try to ensure that support from other agencies is not withdrawn as a consequence of funding having been given by the KKLF.

14. Support for the costs of clinical care may be requested but this is normally permitted for a fixed term only (two to five years). A written assurance that the recurring costs will be taken over at the end of the period by the appropriate Health Authority or NHS Trust will be a condition of awarding the grant.

Grants approved in 1998/99

Anthony Nolan Bone Marrow Trust	£50,000
Guy's and St Thomas's United Medical and Dental Hospital	£10,000
Institute of Cancer Research, London	£766,000
Guy's, King's and St Thomas's School of Medicine, King's College	£40,000
Imperial College School of Medicine, Hammersmith Hospital	£423,000
Leukaemia Research Fund	£106,000
Royal Bournemonth Hospital	£26,000
University College, London	£201,000
University of Birmingham	£463,000

Applications

See above, and the guidance for applicants in the entry for the Sainsbury Family Charitable Trusts.

The Kennedy Charitable Foundation

Roman Catholic ministries, general, especially in the west of Ireland

£952,000 (1998/99)

Beneficial area Unrestricted, but mainly Ireland with a preference for County Mayo and County Sligo.

Brown St. Nominees Ltd, Deloitte and Touche Private Clients, PO Box 500, 201 Deansgate, Manchester M60 2AT

Tel. 0161 455 8380 **Fax** 0161 829 3803

Correspondent M Baines

Trustees *Patrick J Kennedy; Kathleen Kennedy; John G Kennedy; Brown Street Nominees Ltd.*

Information available Accounts on file at the Charity Commission.

General

Grants are made almost exclusively to support organisations connected with the Roman Catholic faith, mainly in Ireland, and unsolicited applications are not accepted.

The trust was established in 1995 and the following year received Kennedy Construction Group Ltd £1 ordinary shares valued at £544,000 from P J Kennedy Charitable Trust.

The income in 1998/99 totalled £707,000, most of which was as Gift Aid donations. Management and administration costs were a minimal £10,882, and £952,000 was paid out in grants. In 1998 the trust made a three-year loan of £1 million to the Catholic University of Mayo Ltd to establish a Catholic University or Institute in the vicinity of Ballina, County Mayo.

In all, 97 grants were awarded, with the six largest beneficiaries accounting for £545,000 (57% of the total), as follows (1997/98 figures in brackets):

Newman Institute, County Mayo	£200,000	(–)
Clifton College	£150,000	(£7,000)
Sligo County Enterprise Fund	£60,000	(£40,000)
The Restoration Ministries	£50,000	(£50,000)
Loreto Convent	£45,000	(£1,000)
Knock Shrine	£40,000	(£2,000)

Most other grants ranged from £1,000 to £10,000, and were chiefly to Catholic organisations, though a few were made to other types of charities, with examples including the Rainbow Trust (£10,000); The Boys' and Girls' Welfare Society (£4,000); Romania Challenge Appeal (£3,000); The Samaritans (£2,000); Fund for Epilepsy (£1,000); Irish Heart Foundation (£1,000); RNLI (£500); Share a Dream Foundation (£250).

Applications

In writing to the correspondent.

King George's Fund for Sailors

The welfare of seafarers

£3,193,000 (1999)

Beneficial area UK and Commonwealth.

8 Hatherley Street, London SW1P 2YY

Tel. 020 7932 0000 **Fax** 020 7932 0095

Correspondent Captain Martin Appleton, Director-General

Trustees *The General Council. Admiral Sir Brian Brown, Chairman; Captain A D Braithwaite, Deputy Chairman.*

Information available Excellent annual report and accounts; good leaflet showing grant recipients.

Summary

Grants, often recurrent, for a wide but little changing range of charities for the benefit of seafarers. Grants range from a few hundred pounds to several hundred thousand. The fundraising costs of the charity remain extremely high.

General

The fund was set up in 1917 as a central fundraising organisation to support other institutions working for the benefit of seafarers and their dependants. It has a large fundraising operation, with a network of area committees, but most of its income comes from the interest and dividends on its investments.

Grantmaking in 1999

While about nine out of ten organisations appear regularly in the grants lists from year to year, amounts can vary substantially, and the fund makes special awards to help with major capital or development programmes, in addition to its more regular subventions.

Grants in 1999 were categorised as follows (with 1998 awards in brackets):

Hospitals, rest homes, rehabilitation centres, homes for the aged, etc: £873,000 in 35 grants (£620,000). The largest grant, £309,000 (£32,000), was for Pembroke House at the Royal Naval Benevolent Trust. Other major beneficiaries were the Ex-Services Mental Welfare Society, £110,000 (£15,000), and the NUMAST Welfare Funds Park Estate in Wallasey, £70,000 (£66,000).

Children's homes, training ships, schools, scholarships and bursaries: £555,000 in 18 grants ranging from £200 to £275,000. The outstanding grant was given to the RN and RM Children's Trust, for seafarers' dependants, £275,000 (£355,000), followed by the Royal Merchant Navy School Foundation, £70,000 (£70,000), and the Sea Cadet Corps, £59,000 (£59,000).

Funds supporting needy seafarers or their dependants: £1,493,000 in 34 grants. The major beneficiary was the Shipwrecked Fishermen and Mariners Society, £524,000 in three grants (£532,000), followed by the Royal Navy Benevolent Trust, £338,000 (£330,000).

Missions, clubs, societies and associations: £286,000 in 10 grants. The largest grants were given to the Royal National Mission to Deep Sea Fishermen, £136,000 (£120,000), and to the Seamen's Mission, London: Queen Victoria Seamen's Rest, £65,000 (£62,000).

Fundraising costs

Once again we must comment with dismay on the extraordinarily high fundraising costs of this charity: 'Voluntary income raised in 1999 totalled £678,000. ... Fundraising expenditure in 1999 totalled £692,000.' The admirably explicit annual report could have reasonably added that there was a further £358,000 income from legacies, doubtless the result of earlier fundraising investments. Even when this income is included, 68p in every pound donated was taken up by fundraising costs.

Though the problem has been recognised in the annual reports of the charity for a number of years, and steps have been taken to reduce costs, these have been unsuccessful.

Fortunately most of the charity's income is not from its fundraising – an actual contribution of £330,000 – but from its endowment. This generated £1.8 million income in 1999, with a further £5.9 million in capital gains.

These editors have expressed alarm at the level of fundraising costs ever since the 1989 edition of this book, and in the last edition they called for the straightforward closure of all fundraising activities. The situation has now been prolonged for a further two years and the trustees' failure to take decisive action, over such a long period, is hard to defend.

Exclusions

The fund does not make any grants direct to individuals but rather helps other organisations which do this. However, the fund may be able to advise in particular cases about a suitable organisation to approach. Full details of such organisations are to be found in the companion volume from the Directory of Social Change, *A Guide to Grants for Individuals in Need.*

Applications

Applications from organisations should be addressed to the Director, Finance and Grants. Trustees meet in July and November.

The King's Fund (King Edward's Hospital Fund for London)

Health and healthcare in London

£2,070,000 (1999)

Beneficial area London.

11–13 Cavendish Square, London W1M 0AN

Tel. 020 7307 2495 **Fax** 020 7307 2801

e-mail grants@kehf.org.uk

website www.kingsfund.org.uk

Correspondent Susan Elizabeth, Grants Director

Trustees *The management committee under the authority of the president and general council, including Sir Graham Hart, Chairman.*

Information available Annual report and accounts with full grants list and narrative analysis; clear and detailed guidelines for applicants (reprinted below).

Summary

The fund makes about 120 grants a year ranging from £300 to £80,000. Both voluntary and statutory sector organisations are supported under three programmes:

1. 'Programme' grants, with beneficiaries chosen by the fund, after open advertisement, on a proactive basis.
2. 'Development' grants, awarded on the basis of applications received.
3. 'Stimulus' (small) grants, up to a maximum of £5,000.

The priority themes for the development and stimulus grants are:

- encouraging equal access to healthcare;
- strengthening the voice of the user;
- improving patients' experiences: easing the transition across service boundaries;
- linking the arts and health.

There is also an 'open' category for 'projects that deal with new or unexpected health needs as they arise'.

Although the funding priorities change over time, they are all aimed at improving public healthcare, with a general emphasis on innovative and potentially influential projects.

General

The fund was established by King Edward VII (who was Prince of Wales at the time) to support the improvement of healthcare in London. Today it fulfils this mission with a range of activities, among which grantmaking (accounting for about one sixth of its charitable expenditure) is relatively minor. However, in the last few years, under its new director Julia Neuberger, the fund has narrowed its spread of interests and is emphasising more strongly the need for a specific London connection in all its work. This entry covers just the grants programmes.

The fund produces detailed and informative guidelines for applicants for its two reactive grant programmes and those for 1998–2000 are reproduced below (where relevant, we have added further information about 1999 grants in brackets). These are not expected to change drastically after 2000, but emphases will alter and there may be new priorities added, so potential applicants should ensure that they see the most up to date set of guidelines. These can be found on the fund's website.

Grants are made to a wide variety of organisations in the health sector, both statutory and voluntary. In all cases grant applications must show how the work will affect either the provision or the commissioning of health services in London.

Programme grants (£500,000 in 1999)

Each year the grants committee makes a substantial investment in a grant programme which addresses a particular theme identified by the fund. In addition to grant monies, we will usually provide educational development support throughout the programme, and commission an independent evaluation of the work. Programme themes are advertised each year, inviting bids to join the programme. Unsolicited applications will not be considered.

The new programme in 1999, costed at £1 million over a number of years, was for Health Advocacy for Ethnic Minority Communities.

Development grants (38 grants totalling £1,292,000 in 1999)

Most of these grants are given for work in priority areas identified below in the following grant guidelines, after some general guidance for applicants:

What we look for when we judge an application:

- Will it improve London's health care? Applications must show that their project will improve either the health of Londoners or the development of London's health services.
- Is it promoting fairness in health care? We are keen to support vulnerable or disadvantaged groups that need our help, including minority ethnic communities.
- Will it involve health service users? Applications must show that they have the interests of health service users at heart. They must be able to describe how they will involve or consult people who will benefit from the work.
- Will it be clear whether it works? Applications must show plans to monitor the results of the work against their aims and objectives, and demonstrate how the work will be evaluated.
- Will others be able to learn from this work? Applications must show how learning from the project will be shared.
- Does it support equal opportunities? We are committed to equal opportunities for everyone. We expect organisations to show the same commitment in their employment practices and in how they run their services.

Within these criteria preference will generally be given to projects which:

- demonstrate a new approach, or a new way of thinking;
- seem likely to influence policy and practice elsewhere;
- are of more than local significance.

How to apply for a development grant

Please read all the following notes carefully. We have written them to help you with your application, and to make sure you have included all the information we need. …

It is important that you ask for what you need. Do not assume that an under-budgeted application is more likely to be successful. However, the largest development grant awarded in the past three years was £80,000. If you are applying for a large and expensive project, you will probably need to find partner funders, and give details of who you have approached or intend to approach for this. …

We are willing to give grants to both voluntary and statutory organisations.

Statutory organisations applying for a grant must show that the work cannot take place without our support. They must also explain why they cannot get money from statutory sources or, if they can, show that it would not be enough to pay for the work. In some cases, statutory organisations can improve their chances of success if they can show that they are working in partnership with a voluntary organisation.

In general, very new or small voluntary organisations (such as those with no paid staff and income under £10,000) are unlikely to be awarded development grants. These organisations may want to apply for a stimulus grant. … From our point of view, this is a good way for us to begin to get to know new organisations.

We do not support clinical research. We will look at research projects that are in our priority areas as long as they can show how the results of the research will be shared with other organisations, and can be used to improve health services. In general we are keen to support projects that will:

- evaluate new approaches to, and new types of, health care;
- share their research findings to bring about change;
- use the results of research to develop new health services.

We will only consider small research projects, or small contributions to large research projects. We are unlikely to give more than £25,000. We will not pay for overhead costs of academic institutions or for the purchase of computer hardware. We will not consider applications unless they include a clear plan for how the work will be used to influence health service provision.

Projects that encourage equal access to healthcare (15 grants, £375,000)

London has a very mixed population and a high concentration of vulnerable or disadvantaged people who need health care. London has more elderly people, more one-parent families, more refugees and more homeless people than any other part of the country. There are also large minority ethnic communities who do not get the health care they should. Health services find it difficult to overcome barriers caused by cultural and language differences, and to identify new ways to help people who have special needs.

We look for applications that:

- will make it possible for minority ethnic communities to express what their health needs are, and set up new services to meet those needs. Within this priority the committee has a specific interest in the health needs of refugee communities, particularly those that have been settled in the UK for less than ten years. We will give preference to applications from organisations which:
  – are user run;
  – can show how they have assessed the need for a health project;
  – can demonstrate that they have established contact with mainstream health services.
- address the health needs of homeless people, including refugees and asylum seekers.
- will work to open up existing health service to patients from a range of disadvantaged groups, including minority ethnic communities, homeless people and people with disabilities.

(Examples of 1999 beneficiaries include: Naz Project, £57,000; Afiya, £52,000; PACE, £52,000; An Viet Foundation, £32,000; Women in Secure Hospitals, £30,000.)

Projects that will strengthen the voice of the user (3 grants, £134,000)

The fund believes that the people who use London's health services must be involved in decisions about the future of those services. It is important that:

- users and patients are consulted and listened to;

- groups who are experienced or disadvantaged in relation to the statutory health service are included in consultations in an effective way;
- genuine agreement is built up between the different groups of patients, the health and local authorities who manage the resources, and the GPs, hospital and social work staff who provide service costs.

We look for applications that:
- will help service users to express their priorities and to take part in local planning services. We are looking for examples of good practice, which can be used by others for a guide. For this reason, we prefer applications with a strong emphasis on assessing how effective they have been;
- will strengthen the voluntary health sector by:
  - setting up new organisations that will offer information, self-help or advocacy support to users of health services, usually where no similar organisation exists; or
  - helping existing voluntary organisations to express users' views more effectively.

(Westminster Mental Health Advocacy Project, £56,000; University of Newcastle/CREUE, £50,000; National Centre for Social Research, £28,000.)

Projects that link the arts and health (5 grants, £118,000)

In recent years there has been a growing interest in the 'holistic' approach to health. While the traditional approach to health looks at the individual and their illness, the holistic approach looks at the whole person and at their relationships with their family, the community and the environment. Within the holistic approach, there is growing evidence that the arts can improve health, both in individuals and in the wider community.

We have limited sums available for applications that want to show the impact of arts on better health. We look for applications that:
- will explore, or show, how art and design can create positive surroundings for effective health care;
- will use the creative arts to improve the health of individuals or communities.

(National Network for the Arts in Health, £40,000; Community Groundwork, £38,000; Rosetta Life, £35,000.)

Improving the patient's experience: easing the transition across service boundaries (9 grants, £395,000)

People with long-term illness or disability do not fit neatly into health and social care categories. To maintain a good quality of life they are likely to need support from different parts of the health care system (GPs, hospitals, community services); from local authority services such as housing, day care and domiciliary services; and from voluntary sector organisations providing advice, support or direct services. However, despite the hard work and good intentions of many people in many agencies, 'the system' often fails to function as well as the parts. Efforts to create flexible and individually appropriate 'packages of care' have been dogged by a range of organisational problems:
- the different funding regimes of health care and social services
- funding patterns lagging behind the changing patterns of hospital use and growing emphasis on community-based services
- difficulties of establishing effective methods of inter-agency collaboration
- entrenched professional divisions or rivalries
- the complexity of managing chronic illness or disability

Our concern is to develop responsive, flexible services which allow people with long-term illness or disability to move through the social and health care systems with the minimum of difficulty and to receive the services which ensure the best possible quality of life.

Our emphasis is on supporting processes of change, rather than one-off projects. We believe this has the most likelihood of achieving lasting improvement in existing services. Support from the fund will be offered in the form of the grant, plus consultancy help to support the process of change. The exact nature of this support will be agreed with applicants, following discussion.

We invite bids for funds to support the process of achieving change across traditional service, or sector, boundaries. Examples might include pilot studies of new ways of working between existing services, joint appointments across services or the creation of new, integrated services. Applications need to show:
- a commitment to practical improvements in the delivery, or commissioning of services, for people with a long-term disability or illness
- a clear statement of the difficulties to be overcome
- an appreciation of the role which organisational development support could have in achieving change
- evidence of a senior level commitment from a partnership, or consortium of agencies or professional groupings
- involvement of service users in the process of change
- willingness to share learning from the process with other agencies or professional groups

(Citizen Advocacy Information and Training, £76,000; The Befriending Network, £70,000; Under One Roof, £65,000; The North Middlesex Hospital, £50,000.)

Open category (7 grants, £272,000)

We are always aware that we must be ready to support projects that will deal with new or unexpected health needs as they arise. We will look at applications that do not come under one of the above headings, but they must meet our general conditions for grants and all the following conditions:
- the project must be work new to the UK;
- the application must be able to show that it will have practical results for either the provision or the commissioning of health services;
- the application must prove that the work cannot take place without our support.

(Open Door, £77,000; The Place To Be, £50,000; CompMed Bulletin, £40,000.)

Stimulus grants (51 awards amounting to £135,000 in 1999)

These are small grants, given to support the setting-up of new health projects targeting disadvantaged groups, or to encourage the exploration and sharing of new ideas in the health field, via publications, conferences and networking. The biggest grant under this scheme is £5,000, but most grants are for much less than the maximum.

The Stimulus Grants Programme is particularly for
- small and new voluntary organisations and community organisations for specific small scale health projects within our priority themes
- sponsorship of events/publications and other activities which aim to promote debate, spread ideas and share good practice within our priority themes.

(Beneficiaries in 1999 included the following: African Culture Promotions, £1,000; Age Concern, Enfield, £1,250; Bedford Hill Gallery, £2,000; Children's Express, £3,750; Hounslow and Spelthorne NHS Trust, £800; 'Mind the gap', £4,000; Streatham Grove Surgery, £2,000; The Who Cares? Trust, £3,000.)

Exclusions

- Medical or clinical research
- General appeals
- Long-term funding (maximum length of funding is three years)
- Capital projects (buildings and equipment, including medical equipment)
- Holidays and outings
- Individuals
- Local projects based outside London
- Projects where the work has already started
- Projects that are seeking ongoing funding after a statutory grant has run out
- Vehicles

Applications

Applications need to be received at least three months before the meeting at which they will be considered. The fund's guidelines read as follows:

We give here a general guide to help you with your application. If your application does not cover all these points properly, we will have to contact you for more information. This will delay the decision on your application.

Please make your application clear and to the point. Try not to use jargon because the committee members may not be experts in your field. All applications must meet our general conditions, and your work must fall within one of our priorities.

Put your case using no more than six sides of A4 paper. Please also send a budget, a work plan and a job description for any job you are asking us to fund.

We cannot accept faxed or e-mailed applications.

Please give a brief description of your organisation, including:

- its aims, legal status, charity number (if you have one), size and history;
- how it funds its work;
- whether you have applied to us before.

The background to the problem you want to tackle

- Why is your project needed?
- What are the causes of the problem?
- Are you building on earlier work, done by your organisation or by others?
- How will you avoid overlap with other organisations?

The project

- What are the aims of the project?
- What are your objectives and targets (i.e. how will you achieve your aims)?
- How will the work be supervised and managed?
- What is your organisation's track record in this field, and why are you the right organisation to undertake this project?

The cost

- How much are you asking for from the King's Fund?
- What is it for? (is it for a salary, a publication, an event?)

The timescales

You must tell us when you want the project to start, and how long it will run. (Remember to apply at least four months before you plan to start the project.)

Monitoring and evaluation

We believe monitoring the project and evaluating its success are extremely important, and you should tell us what plans you have for monitoring and evaluation. The following summary may help you:

Monitoring means collecting information to see what progress you are making. It may include:

- keeping a record of the facts and figures about your work;
- asking users what they think of your work;
- getting progress reports from the people managing, or working in, the project;
- organising meetings of the project team to discuss the work, and any problems, successes or new developments, and:
- checking that you are getting, and giving, value for money.

Evaluation means using the information you have collected from your monitoring to see what you can learn from the work so far. For instance:

- Have your methods been successful in doing what you set out to do?
- How does your approach compare to other ways of tackling the problem? What have you learnt about how to develop this kind of work, in relation to your staff, your clients, or other organisations?
- Have you learnt anything that might help future projects?

Sharing the lessons you learn

We believe that if you learn important lessons in the course of your work, it is very important that you share this information with other people working in the same field. You should include in your application your plans for sharing what you learn from the work. This is especially important if you are applying for a grant for a research project.

Job description

If you are asking us to fund the salary for a post, you should include a full job description, which shows salary scale and details of who will oversee the post.

Work plan

It is helpful for us to see an outline work plan for at least the first year of the project, showing what you hope to achieve by certain points in time. This need not be more than one side of A4.

Your budget and accounts

Please read this section carefully. Your budget should be on a separate page at the end of the application. It must include:

- the full cost of the project;
- the exact amount you are asking for;
- details of how you arrive at that figure.

We will also need to know:

- What other income you will have from this work, if any. Please tell us about firm commitments of money as well as those that you are exploring. If you are not asking for the full cost of the project, please tell us how you intend to raise the rest.
- How you expect to pay for the future work once the grant is finished.
- What money you are likely to raise from any work that will be paid for by the grant. This is particularly important if you are asking for a grant towards a publication or event.
- If you are applying from a statutory organisation, we need to know what statutory sources of funds you have applied to, and what the results were.
- If you are applying for a salary, you can also include recruitment costs, and inflation costs, if you are asking for a salary of more that one year.
- You can also include suitable overheads in your calculations. In general, the maximum amount we will consider for overheads is 25% of any salary. This figure would include all employer's contributions, management costs and running costs (i.e. heat, light, telephone and rent). This figure would not have to include direct project costs (the additional funds needed to run the project, such as producing literature and running events). In all cases you must show how you have worked out all the costs shown in the budget.

We cannot consider your application unless you send it with a copy of your most recent audited accounts. If your organisation has a gross income under £100,000, then we will accept an independent examination of the accounts, but this examination must be undertaken by a qualified accountant who is a member of one of the five main recognised supervisory bodies in the UK. However, we reserve the right to request audited accounts in certain circumstances. Please contact the grants department if you need to discuss this further. If no accounts are available because your organisation has been formed recently please explain this in your application letter, and send a budget for the organisation.

Extra literature

Please do not send any extra literature, such as brochures or press articles, unless we ask for them. If you think there is something important in the literature tell us about it in your application.

Checklist

Before you send in your application, please make sure that you have included:

- your written application, with a covering letter on your organisation's headed paper. Please make sure that this letter is signed, and gives the grant applicants contact details, and a direct dial telephone number if one is available;
- a budget;
- a work plan;
- a job description, if you are asking us to fund a post;

- your organisation's most recent accounts and annual report.

How we will deal with your application

If the kind of work that you want to do is not what we normally make grants for, we will write to you as soon as possible to tell you that we cannot help – usually within four weeks. If we do normally make grants for the kind of work that you want to do, our staff will look into your application more closely. This may involve meeting with you, and asking for confidential external advice. This helps the grants committee to learn more about your work, but it does not guarantee that a grant will be made. Applications for the development grants programme are considered five times a year, in February, May, July, September and November, but they need to be submitted at least three months before the meeting concerned, and at least four months before the project starts. Usually you can apply only once a year, but you can apply more than once if your applications are for different projects. Applications for the stimulus grants programme are considered at the end of each month with the exception of August and December. Applications need to be received at least six weeks before the meeting concerned. Both sets of guidelines give detailed advice on the presentation of applications, which should be read carefully before an application is submitted.

The Mary Kinross Charitable Trust

Mental health, penal affairs, youth

£516,000 (allocated for 2000/01)

Beneficial area UK.

36 Grove Avenue, Moseley, Birmingham B13 9RY

Correspondent Fiona Adams, Trustee

Information available Excellent reports and accounts with full grants list and narrative exploring large grants.

Summary

Between 10 and 20 new grants a year, normally multi-year awards for revenue costs worth between £5,000 and £25,000 annually, to projects within the areas of interest outlined above. Small one-off donations are very occasionally made in response to a particular need. The trust is not open to applications.

THE MARY KINROSS CHARITABLE TRUST – GRANTS PAID

	1999/2000		*1998/99*	
	No.	*Amount*	*No.*	*Amount*
Mental health	5	£61,500	8	£1,113,000
Medical research	3	£26,000	2	£6,000
Penal affairs	4	£18,000	7	£37,000
Youth	8	£104,000	6	£102,000
Miscellaneous	9	£76,500	8	£110,000
Total	29	£286,000	31	£1,368,000

General

The trust says:

From the start the aim has been to use the majority of the Trust income to support a few carefully researched projects, rather than make small grants in response to applications.

At least one trustee takes responsibility for ensuring the Trust's close involvement with organisations to which major grants are made.

In recent years trustees have concentrated grants in the fields in which they have some knowledge and professional experience – mental health, penal affairs and youth. Because of the involvement of trustees, most grants are made in the areas in which they live, which are London/south east or Birmingham/west midlands.

For organisations which we support we will pay core office costs which can enable staff to apply to other sources of funding.

In 1999/2000 the trust had assets totalling £25.7 million, generating an income of £508,000. Grants worth £286,000 were made during the year, down from almost £1.4 million in 1998/99, when a single grant of £1,035,000 created an endowment fund for the Brain Research Trust.

Grants paid under each of the trust's headings in those two years were as shown in the box above.

At least half of these grants would have been part of ongoing commitments to organisations well known to the trustees. £516,000 had already been committed to 15 organisations for 2000/01, and a further £150,000 for 2001/02. The major recipients for grants in those years were to be as follows:

	2000/01	*2001/02*
Institute of Cognitive Neuroscience	£160,000	–
FARE (Family Action in Easterhouse and Rogerfield) development fund	£125,000	–
Centre for Vascular Biology & Medicine, UCL	£55,000	£55,000
Moseley Community Development Trust	£50,000	£50,000

The larger grants paid in 1999/2000 were described in the report as follows:

Mental health

Penrose Housing Association (£22,500): This grant is towards the cost of furnishing flats, so enabling mentally disordered ex-offenders to move into supervised accommodation.

Women in Secure Hospitals (WISH) (£15,000): This was the final instalment of a three year grant to pay half the costs involved in employing the Project Director.

Medical research

St Mark's Hospital (£20,000): This donation contributed further to the prototype colonoscopy teaching simulation work being carried out … under the direction of Dr Christopher Williams with the aim of benefiting hospitals throughout the UK.

St Bartholomew's and the Royal London School of Medicine (£5,000): Continuation of a grant to fund elective bursaries offered to final year medical students interested in immunology, including HIV/AIDS.

Penal affairs

SOVA – Society of Voluntary Associates (£10,000): This grant is a continuation of the Trust's contribution to SOVA's Basic Skills Teaching Project in Feltham Young Offenders Institution and Remand Centre.

Restorative Justice Consortium (£5,000 for each of three years): … This is a forum for national organisations with a common interest in promoting the restorative justice approach to the criminal justice system, by balancing the concerns of the victim with the need to reintegrate the offender into society.

Youth

Youthwise (Warstock and Billesley Detached Youthwork Project) (£25,000): This grant represents an ongoing commitment for the payment of salaries of youth workers who contact and assist 'at risk' young people in an outer-ring housing estate area of Birmingham. It was increased this year, with a further commitment next year, to pay for an extra salary.

Brunswick Park Primary School (£20,000) and Royal Free and University College Medical School (£18,000): The literacy project being carried out in this south London primary school has continued for a third year and will be extended until February 2001 to allow for the completion of the evaluation by two psychologists from the Royal Free and University College Medical School. The final results will be published and a conference is being planned to disseminate them as widely as possible.

Miscellaneous

Balsall Heath Church Centre (£30,000): This grant is for the purchase of a new ambulance bus used by a day centre in Birmingham to transport elderly people.

The Bendrigg Trust (£22,000): The Bendrigg Trust is a project initiated and established by the Trustees of the Mary Kinross Trust. This grant will enable completion of the building project, and retention of a member of staff whose post was threatened by changes in funding from the Cumbria Probation Service, thus ensuring the continuation of work with young offenders at Bendrigg – one of the original aims of the Founder.

Charities in receipt of smaller grants included the Who Cares? Trust (£3,000); Refugee Council (£2,000; £3,000 in 1998/99); Women's Nationwide Cancer Control Campaign (£1,000), and Dartmoor Friends of the Home Farm Trust (£1,000, ongoing commitment). Five grants were for under £1,000.

It is surprising, and regrettable, that so few trusts follow this model of informed trustees seeking out a small number of opportunities for substantial investments.

Exclusions

No grants to individuals.

Applications

'Neither written applications nor telephone calls are welcome. There is no application form or timetable and procedure for assessing applications.' Trustees meet quarterly.

The Graham Kirkham Foundation

General

£455,000 (1998/99)

Beneficial area UK and Ireland.

Bentley Moor Lane, Adwick-le-Street, Doncaster DN6 7BD

Correspondent Sir Graham Kirkham, Trustee

Trustees *Sir Graham Kirkham; Lady P Kirkham.*

Information available Annual report and accounts on file at the Charity Commission.

Summary

The foundation makes 10 to 15 grants a year, typically large one-off donations for £20,000 or more, with £450,000 the largest single amount to date. Preference has been given to animal welfare, arts and healthcare organisations.

General

As there is no endowment, grantmaking is sustained largely by donations from the settlor (£500,000 in 1997/98, £250,000 in 1998/99) and consequently the amount donated fluctuates from year to year: £361,000 in 1996/97, £845,000 in 1997/98 and £455,000 in 1998/99.

The main objectives of the charity, set out in the 1999 trustees' report, are as follows:

- the promotion or development of the study and/or appreciation of literature, art, music or science
- the advancement of education of persons at any age and the advancement of physical education of young people at school or university
- the relief of poverty and hardship by providing financial assistance and accommodation for affected persons and their dependants and relatives
- the relief of illness and disease by providing treatment, financial assistance and accommodation. The company also supports research into treatment and prevention of illness
- the relief of the suffering of birds and animals through the support of rescue homes, hospitals, sanctuaries and other similar organisations
- the relief of poverty and hardship and the promotion of well being of persons connected to the Armed Services
- the provision of support and protection to those dependent upon or in danger of becoming dependent on drugs
- to provide in the interests of social welfare facilities for public recreation
- to protect and preserve buildings of architectural interest or sites of historical interest or natural beauty

As the foundation apparently aims to provide a limited number of charities with large awards, not all of these areas can be assisted in a single year. In 1997/98 the foundation finally began to provide a list of grant recipients with its accounts, though there was still no explanation of grants. In that year £845,000 was donated in 14 grants, with £700,000 (83% of the total) going to the following two beneficiaries:

- War On Cancer (£450,000)
- River and Rowing Museum (£250,000)

A substantial grant of £54,000 was also donated to the Animal Health Trust, which is apparently the only organisation which has received large annual donations for a number of years.

Other beneficiaries included Wessex Children's Hospice Appeal (£10,000); The Rocking Horse Appeal (£10,000); Dementia Relief Trust (£3,000); Victoria Art Gallery (£3,000), and Riding for the Disabled (£2,000).

In 1998/99 10 grants totalling £455,000 were made to the following beneficiaries:

- National Gallery of Ireland (£217,000)
- Animal Health Trust/Lord's Taverners (£100,000)
- The President's Award GAISCE (£50,000, repeat)
- Leeds Girls' School Bursary Appeal (£25,000)
- Burlington Magazine Publications Ltd (£20,000)
- North London Hospice (£20,000)
- Lord Mayor's Appeal of Leukaemia 2000 (£10,000)
- Calderdale Community Foundation (£5,000)
- Adam Share Educational Grant (£5,000)
- Friends of War Memorials (£2,600; £2,000 in 1997/98)

It is agreeable to find such an idiosyncratic grants list. Though many trusts talk of their freedom to be different, very few are.

Applications

In writing to the correspondent.

Ernest Kleinwort Charitable Trust

General

£1,860,000 (1999/2000)

Beneficial area UK and overseas, with a special interest in Sussex.

PO Box 191, 10 Fenchurch Street, London EC3M 3LB

Tel. 020 7956 6600 **Fax** 020 7956 6059

Correspondent The Secretary

Trustees *Kleinwort Benson Trustees Ltd; Madeleine, Lady Kleinwort; the Earl of Limerick; Sir Richard Kleinwort; Miss M R Kleinwort; R M Ewing; Sir Christopher Lever; S M Robertson.*

Information available Full accounts on file at the Charity Commission, but without the required narrative report or analysis and explanation of grants.

Summary

More than 200 grants are made each year, widely spread and typically for amounts ranging from hundreds of pounds up to about £10,000. However, half the money is disbursed in larger grants, of £25,000 or more and often on a recurring basis, to about 20 national and international organisations. Grantmaking on a local scale is confined to Sussex, where the trust provides regular support in the form of small subscriptions to 120 charities. Grants overseas are for conservation and planned parenthood.

A high proportion of grants are to regularly supported charities, and the chances of success for new applicants may be smaller than the sheer number of grants might have otherwise suggested.

General

In 1999/2000 the trust had assets of £59 million, which produced a rather low income of £1.6 million. These editors would expect an endowment of this size to be able to sustain grantmaking of about five per cent of its net worth, or £2.4 million a year. Grants made in the year totalled £1,860,000. The trustees' report said:

> During the year under review the Trustees made a total of 284 donations, principally in the fields of wildlife and environmental conservation, disabled, medical research, elderly welfare, and youth welfare, and preference was given to charities in Sussex.

A significant amount of this was donated to charities working in developing countries, particularly for conservation and welfare, including family planning. Most of the fields mentioned were covered by the six largest grants over £50,000, which amounted to 21% of the grant total. The recipients in 1999/2000 and in the previous year were:

The River Trust (£85,000, and £100,000); Stowe School (£67,000); The Tusk Trust (£75,000 and £54,000); Marie Stopes International (£70,000 and £30,000); St Catherine's Hospice (£59,000 and £55,000); Wildfowl and Wetlands Trust (£58,000 in each year) and Chichester Cathedral (£50,000 and £58,000).

A further 31% (£581,000) was spent on 18 grants in the range £25,000 to £50,000, while just under 50% of the total consisted of grants for lesser amounts, down to £200.

The recipients fell into the following categories (with examples given from 1998/99):

Wildlife and environmental conservation: Conservation International (£50,000); Dian Fossey Gorilla Fund (£25,000); Royal Botanical Gardens, Kew (£25,000); Galapagos Conservation Trust (£20,000); Jersey Wildlife Preservation Trust (£10,000); Wild Camel Protection Fund (£7,000).

Aid for developing countries: Population Concern; Intermediate Technology (£30,000 each); Merlin (£10,000); Jamaica Family Planning Association (£8,000).

Medical research and care: Ronald Raven Cancer Appeal (£30,000); International Spinal Research Trust (£25,000); Leukaemia Research Fund (£13,000); Friends of Moorfields Eye Hospital (£5,000).

Welfare: Agape Trust (£50,000); Crisis (£30,000); Lodge Hill Trust (£30,000); 21st Century Learning Initiative (£25,000); Samaritans (£16,000); John Grooms Association for Disabled People (£15,000).

Grantmaking in Sussex was led by £50,000 for Chichester Cathedral Millennium Endowment Appeal. Larger grants made in the area tended to be for county-wide organisations such as Sussex Association of Clubs for Young People (£12,000); Age Concern, West Sussex (£11,500) and East Sussex Association for the Disabled (£7,500). Other grants included £3,000 each for East Grinstead Town Museum and Findon Wattle House, and £450 each for Eastbourne Area Parents Action Group and Hastings Unemployed and Claimants Advice Centre.

Exclusions

Local charities outside Sussex are normally excluded.

Applications

To the correspondent. International grants are for conservation and planned parenthood. Trustees meet in March and October.

The Sir James Knott Trust

General, in the north east of England

£1,312,000 (1999/2000)

Beneficial area Tyne and Wear, Durham and Northumberland.

16–18 Hood Street, Newcastle upon Tyne NE1 6JQ

Tel. 0191 230 4016

Correspondent John Sharland, Secretary

Trustees *Viscount Ridley; Mark Cornwall-Jones; Prof. Oliver James; Charles Baker-Cresswell.*

Information available Annual report and accounts available for £8 a copy.

Summary

Over £1 million a year is donated to a wide range of charities in the north east region (a minimal amount goes to other areas). Over half of the 300 or so grants are one-off donations, mostly for under £5,000. Perhaps three quarters of the funds, however, maintain ongoing support to long-standing beneficiaries, occasionally with grants for £25,000 or more. The trust does not make multi-year commitments, but where long-term support has been provisionally agreed, it reassesses existing grants on an annual basis and renews them where appropriate. Nearly half of the applications received have resulted in grants in recent years.

General

In 1998/99 the trust's assets of £36 million produced an income of £1,335,000 and grantmaking totalled £1,123,000. In its annual report for that year, the trust's policy, unchanged since the previous edition of this book, was described thus:

> Grants are normally only made to registered charities, in response to applications from within the North East of England and from national

charities either operating within, or where the work may be expected to be of benefit to, the North East of England. Grants will not normally be made outside of this area.

Grants will commonly be in response to appeals to support universities, general education, training, medical care and research, historic buildings and the environment, music and the arts; as well as the welfare of the young, the elderly, seamen's and services charities, the disabled and the disadvantaged. Grants are made out of income and not normally out of capital.

We do not issue specific guidelines for applicants but discuss the requirements of potential applicants with them as and when necessary. Rather than issue strict guidelines/ pro formas on what we want, we find it helpful to listen to what the applicant thinks is important first: we then ask supplementary questions as necessary. ...

The Trust has continued to support action to encourage the co-ordination/co-operation among North East Grantmaking Trusts, both by informal gatherings of Chairmen, action through the North East Trust Secretaries Group and co-operation with the Association of Charitable Foundations. ...

THE SIR JAMES KNOTT TRUST – GRANTMAKING IN 1999/2000

Summary by category (Categorisation is a crude approximation, with numerous overlaps among categories)

	Amount	*%*	*No.*
Community welfare	£498,000	38%	129
Youth/children	£181,000	14%	62
Education/expeditions	£147,000	11%	17
Heritage/museums	£105,000	8%	19
Handicapped	£96,000	7%	37
Elderly	£82,000	6%	6
Conservation/horticultural	£57,000	4%	8
Service charities	£45,000	4%	21
Medical	£36,000	3%	9
Maritime charities	£29,000	2%	11
Arts	£21,000	2%	8
Housing/homeless	£15,000	1%	6

Summary by area

	Amount	*%*	*No.*
Northumberland	£397,000	30%	75
Tyne and Wear	£396,000	30%	123
Durham	£298,000	23%	77
NE general	£147,000	11%	41
Other	£73,000	6%	16
Total	£1,312,000	100%	332

The tables in the box (right), showing a breakdown of grantmaking in 1999/2000, were provided by the trust. In that year 734 applications were processed and 332 grants were made (727 applications and 307 grants in 1998/99). The trust made 214 donations over £1,000 and 118 for amounts up to £1,000. Some of the donations would have been repeated from the year before, following a reassessment of the previous year's grant.

Grants in 1998/99

The 1998/99 annual report, seen at the Charity Commission, was still without commentary on the purposes of its grants.

The trust told us that 'Since all the beneficiaries are registered charities, the trustees do not feel that a narrative explanation of the grants made is appropriate or necessary. Grants are awarded to registered charities in support of and for the furtherance of their charitable aims.'

In all, 190 grants over £1,000 totalled £1,034,000 and 117 for lesser amounts amounted to £89,000.

The largest was a repeat donation of £100,000 to Durham University. Further donations went to the Community Council of Northumberland (£50,000; £10,000 in 1997/98) and Citizens Advice Bureaux Northern Region (£25,000, repeat) while Tyneside Foyer received a new grant of £25,000.

Roughly a quarter of the total expenditure was accounted for by 28 grants ranging from £10,000 to £20,000. As above, some of these beneficiaries had the previous year's grant renewed.

These grants were led by a repeat donation of £20,000 for Northern Counties School for the Deaf. Recipients of grants for £15,000 included Prince's Youth Business Trust (NE); Northumberland Association of Clubs for Young People; Cancer Relief Macmillan Fund, Tyneside; Newcastle Diocesan Board of Finance: Church Repair and Building Fund; and Moredun Research Institute, Scotland. Those receiving £10,000 included SENSE; Northern Pinetree Trust; Northern Sinfonia Trust, and the Calvert Trust (Kielder).

A sample of recipients of grants in the range £1,000 to £6,000, half receiving repeats, reads as follows: Royal Regiment of Fusiliers, Northumberland; Seaham Comprehensive School, Co. Durham; Shipwrecked Mariners' Society; Who Cares? Trust; Ryedale Folk Museum, North Yorkshire; South Tyneside Multi-Cultural Project; Sustrans; VSO.

Grants under £1,000 were not listed, but included North East Sea Cadet Units (£750 each), schools, local projects and youth clubs.

The trust deed's exclusion of Roman Catholic beneficiaries is interpreted in the most liberal sense allowable by the present trustees: 'Roman catholic charitable work can and has been funded where beneficiaries are multi- or non-denominational.' Nevertheless the continued existence of the clause should not be accepted by the trustees, who should ask the Charity Commission for permission to remove it. If the Commission will not, then at least the responsibility for such an illiberal measure will have been transferred.

Exclusions

The trust deed excludes Roman Catholics. No applications are considered from individuals or from non-registered charities. Grants are only made to charities from within the north east of England, and from national charities either operating within, or where work may be expected to be of benefit to the north east of England.

Applications

In writing to the correspondent. 'Please be brief. Do not, for example, explain at great length why it is that a blind, starving, bankrupt, one-legged man from Jupiter, needs help.' Despite the plea for brevity, the trust requests that applicants should address the following questions, although 'not all the questions necessarily apply to you, but they give an idea of the kind of questions that the trustees may ask when your application is being considered':

- Who are you? How are you organised/ managed?
- What is your aim? What co-ordination do you have with other organisations with similar aims?
- What do you do and how does it benefit the community? How many people 'in need' actually use or take advantage of your facilities?
- How have you been funded in the past, how will you be funded in the future? Enclose summary of last year's balance sheet.
- How much do you need, what for and when? Have you thought about depreciation/running costs/ replacement? If your project is not funded in full, what do you propose to do with the money you have raised?
- What is the overall cost, what is the deficit and how are you planning to cover the deficit? Is it an open-ended commitment, or when will you become self-supporting?
- If you will never be self-supporting, what is your long-term fundraising strategy? Have you even thought about it?
- Who else have you asked for money, and how have they responded? What are you doing yourselves to raise money?
- Have you applied to the National Lottery? When will you get the result? If you have not applied, are you eligible and when will you apply?
- What is your registered charity number, or which registered charity is prepared to administer funds on your behalf? How can you be contacted by telephone?

Trustees normally meet in February, June and October. Applications need to be submitted up to two months in advance.

The Kreitman Foundation

Jewish charities, the arts, general

£791,000 (1998/99)

Beneficial area UK and Israel.

Citroen Wells (Chartered Accountants), 1 Devonshire Street, London W1N 2DR

Correspondent Eric Charles, Trustee

Trustees *Hyman Kreitman; Mrs Irene Kreitman; Eric Charles.*

Information available Full accounts on file at the Charity Commission.

General

The 1998/99 accounts state the trust supports 'education, culture, the environment, health and welfare'.

In 1998/99 the trust had assets of £31 million, generating an income of £1.1 million. It made over 50 grants, totalling £791,000.

The largest grants were £452,000 to the Tate Gallery Foundation, £164,000 to the Royal National Theatre and £103,000 to Ben-Gurion University Foundation. Other grants were for amounts up to £19,000 (Friends of Hebrew University of Jerusalem). Examples are as follows: arts organisations such as the Royal Academy Theatre (£5,000), British Friends of the Arts Museums of Israel (£4,700), British Museum Development Trust (£1,500) and Friends of the Jerusalem Rubin Academy of Music and Dance (£1,000). Medical groups included Jewish Association for the Mentally Ill (£1,600) and Jewish Care (£1,300). Religious establishments included St Andrew's Church, Thursford (£2,000) and West London Synagogue (£1,300). Other purposes included Wizo Charitable Foundation (£7,500), Community Security Trust (£5,000) and Wiener Library Endowment Trust (£1,000).

Of the recipients, 10 had also received awards in the previous year, when the largest grant of £2 million went to Ben-Gurion University Foundation.

Exclusions

No grants to individuals.

Applications

Grants are only given to charities of which the trustees have a personal knowledge. The trust is unable to respond to applications.

The J W Laing Biblical Scholarship Trust

Christian evangelism

£1,051,000 (1998/99)

PO Box 133, Bath BA1 2YU

Tel. 01225 427236 **Fax** 01225 427278

e-mail jwlaingtrust@stewards.co.uk

Correspondent B J Chapman, Secretary

Trustees *The Stewards' Company; Dr W E Naismith, Chair.*

Information available Full accounts, but without the required narrative annual report reviewing the work of the charity.

General

The trust was established in 1947 and is administered by the Stewards' Company, as is the J W Laing Trust (see separate entry). In 1998/99 the trust had assets of £24 million, which generated an income of £1.1 million, but there were further capital gains of nearly £5 million. Donations totalled only £1.1 million, which was distributed to 25 organisations dealing mainly with Christian teaching. As is usual for the trust, most beneficiaries had also been supported in previous years.

The largest grant was, again as usual, to The Universities and Colleges Christian Fellowship (£585,000). IFES received £120,000, up from £90,000 in the previous year. The remainder of the grants ranged from £53,000 (to London Bible College) to £3,000 (for Capernwray Bible School).

Exclusions

No grants to individuals.

Applications

In writing to the correspondent.

Maurice and Hilda Laing Charitable Trust

(formerly the Hilda Laing Charitable Trust)

Promotion of Christianity, relief of need, in the UK and overseas

£2,745,000 (1999, but see below)

Box 1, 133 Page Street, Mill Hill, London NW7 2ER

Tel. 020 8238 8890

Correspondent Miss Elizabeth Harley

Trustees *Sir Maurice Laing; Lady Hilda Laing; Peter Harper; Robert Harley; Thomas Parr.*

Information available Excellent annual reports.

Summary

This trust is funded primarily by transfers from the associated Maurice Laing Foundation. It is mainly concerned with the relief of poverty in the UK, largely through Christian organisations, and relief of poverty overseas, with a particular emphasis on work with children, as well as with evangelism.

See the entry on the Laing Family Foundations for the work of the group as a whole.

General

This is the trust in the Laing family group that concentrates, though not exclusively, on Christian activity and on the work of Christian-based welfare charities. In 1999 an exceptional grant of £1,750,000 was made for the Faith Zone in the Millennium Dome, with contributions from all the other trusts in the group.

Otherwise, over 100 grants are made annually, ranging from a few hundred pounds to many hundreds of thousands. They are probably (to judge by the precedent of other trusts in the group) of a wide range of types, from one-off awards, through multi-year projects to ongoing annual support.

Grant-making policy is set out as follows:

The Trust has identified three main areas of giving:

Advancement of the Christian religion

Priorities are

- evangelistic activities intended to spread the gospel message, both in the UK and overseas.
- Religious Education, from primary school to postgraduate level.
- projects designed to promote Christian ethics/family life especially among young people.

Relief of poverty in the UK

Support for projects in this category is usually confined to those with a Christian basis to avoid overlap with the Maurice Laing Foundation, ie. to projects where Christian faith is being manifested through practical action to help those in need. Preference will be given to projects of a practical nature rather than to research projects. Priorities include projects run by churches or Christian organisations to help

- disadvantaged children
- the homeless
- elderly/disabled particularly in inner city areas.

Relief of poverty overseas

Many beneficiaries will have a Christian foundation but this requirement is not exclusive in this category. Any overseas project aimed at relieving poverty is eligible but particular priorities are:

- work with children in need
- projects addressing the issue of population control through work to improve the basic education of women and the quality of reproductive and primary health care and education.

The 1999 grants were classified as follows:

	Grants	*Value*
Religion, advancement of	25	£534,000
Religion, social action	11	£151,000
Health and medicine	4	£95,000
Overseas aid	9	£82,000
Child and youth	1	£5,000

Grant-making policy and practice is well reviewed and illustrated in the annual reports. That for 1999 follows.

Annual report 1999

As indicated by the Trustees in the report which accompanied last year's financial statements, the Trustees formally resolved during the course of the year in question to rename the charity (formerly the Hilda Laing Charitable Trust) the Maurice & Hilda Laing Charitable Trust. The new name took effect from 1st July 1999.

The Maurice & Hilda Laing Charitable Trust continues to derive its income from the Maurice Laing Foundation, although donations of £50,000 were also received from the J W Laing Trust and Laing's Charitable Trust as part of a combined grant of £2 million from the Laing Family Trusts to the Faith Zone in the Millennium Dome. In view of this commitment the Trustees of the Maurice Laing Foundation, who have undertaken to distribute half of the Foundation's annual distributable income to the Maurice & Hilda Laing Charitable Trust, made an additional £650,000 available for this purpose.

The Trustees' support for the Faith Zone was founded upon their desire to ensure that the Christian significance of the year 2000 received due prominence in the country's Millennium celebrations. The following statement was made on behalf of all the Laing Family Trusts for inclusion within the Faith Zone:

'We are celebrating the birth of Our Saviour Jesus Christ 2000 years ago. His life, death and resurrection changed the course of the whole world and influence for good the lives of countless individuals worldwide today. The Laing Family Trusts, as Christian foundations, wished to see that this was fully reflected in the nation's Millennium celebrations. We are therefore pleased to have been able to ensure that Christianity is represented, alongside other faiths, in the Dome.'

Although the Millennium has been a particular focus for the Trust's activities over the course of the past year, there has been no significant change in the priorities of the Trustees, which remain the advancement of the Christian religion, relief of poverty in the UK, largely through Christian organisations, and relief of poverty overseas, with a particular emphasis on work with children. The following list of grants of £25,000 and above reflects these priorities:

Lambeth Fund – £250,000, the last of four promised grants to enable the Archbishop of Canterbury to pursue evangelistic initiatives in support of his mission to strengthen and expand the Church of England. The Trustees have subsequently extended their support for a further period of two years.

Bible Society – £50,000, the second of three grants to the Open Book Project, a programme of activities intended to explore the relevance of the Bible in today's culture.

John Grooms Association for the Disabled – £50,000 to the charity's Capital Appeal to support the construction of new residential and wheelchair accessible homes.

Care Trust – £31,000 towards the development of a drugs education resource for use in primary schools.

SAT-7 (Christian Television for the Middle East) – £30,000 to fund the appointment of local Middle Eastern staff and the development of a UK support base.

Dorothy Kerin Trust – £25,000, a further grant towards the cost of running Burrswood Healing Centre.

Premier Radio – £25,000, the last of three grants to support the development of London Christian Radio.

Solent Christian Trust – £25,000 towards the development of an interactive multi-media CD ROM addressing the issues raised by young people exploring the Christian faith.

All grants of £5,000 and above are listed in the financial statements. In addition a further 59 gifts, ranging in size from £50 to £4,000, were made from funds deposited with the Charities Aid Foundation. In all a total of £2,744,500 was distributed to charitable causes.

Exclusions

No grants to groups or individuals for the purpose of education, travel, attendance at conferences or participation in overseas exchange programmes.

Applications

The trust is administered alongside the Beatrice Laing Trust, the Maurice Laing and the Kirby Laing Foundations. None of the trusts issue application forms and an application to one is seen as an application to all. In general the trusts rarely make grants towards the running costs of local organisations, which they feel have to be raised from within the local community.

An application for a grant towards a specific capital project should be in the form of a short letter giving details of the project, its total cost, the amount raised and some indication of how it is to be financed.

A copy of the organisation's latest annual report and accounts, together with a stamped addressed envelope, should be enclosed. Unless an sae is enclosed applicants are asked to accept non-response as a negative reply.

Trustees meet quarterly to consider applications for larger grants (above £10,000). Applications for smaller amounts are considered on an ongoing basis.

The Laing Family Foundations

General

£10,366,000 (1999)

Box 1, 133 Page Street, Mill Hill, London NW7 2ER

Tel. 020 8238 8890

Correspondent Miss Elizabeth Harley

Trustees *See entries for individual trusts.*

Information available Excellent information available on the individual trusts.

General

There are four trusts with the Laing name which are administered from a common office in north London and for which an application to one is seen as an application to all. However, they have different funding patterns and each has its own entry in this book. They are:

- The Maurice and Hilda Laing Charitable Trust (formerly the Hilda Laing Charitable Trust)
- The Kirby Laing Foundation
- The Maurice Laing Foundation
- The Beatrice Laing Trust

Despite the request for a single application, the trusts are, however, separate institutions with distinct, though overlapping, patterns of giving. There is an evangelical Christian background to the group, but the grants lists are catholic overall, covering most fields of charity, at home and overseas. Support for medical research, of the scientific sort, is limited, and there is no general support for the arts (though one trust has a limited interest in this field).

Over 1,000 grants a year are made, many of them very small but some of them not at all. There is some support for local charities through the Beatrice Laing Trust, but collectively the group concentrates on national organisations, though many of these may be very small. By and large, the size of grants is not closely connected to the size of the applicant organisation. Oxfam seems as likely to receive £1,000 as a local ferry project in Bangladesh to get £17,000.

Most of the large awards are for national rather than local organisations, big or small. The grants are often for projects that are for general benefit, but of the eight in England in 1999 that appeared to be for locally based work, seven were in the south east.

Some of the trusts have quite specialised interests, among their wider concerns. The most prominent are

- advancement of Christianity: the Maurice and Hilda Laing Charitable Trust
- smaller local grants for welfare and disability: the Beatrice Laing Trust

The arts are only funded by the Kirby Laing Foundation, and then on a limited scale. There is usually a scattering of nautically connected charities in the lists of the Maurice Laing Foundation.

Some if not all of the trustees are highly involved in the grant-making process, and it is likely that they take a personal interest in many of the larger projects supported.

The trusts do not normally act collectively, but an exception was made in 1999 when they decided to contribute £2 million to the Faith Zone in the Millennium Dome.

The general application requirements are set out below. These will suffice for all except specialist applications.

Exclusions

No grants to groups or individuals for the purpose of education, travel, attendance at conferences or participation in overseas exchange programmes.

Applications

None of the trusts issue application forms and an application to one is seen as an application to all. In general the trusts rarely make grants towards the running costs of local organisations, which they feel have to be raised from within the local community. An application for a grant towards a specific capital project should be in the form of a short letter giving details of the project, its total cost, the amount raised and some indication of how it is to be financed.

A copy of the organisation's latest annual report and accounts, together with an sae, should be enclosed. Unless an sae is enclosed applicants are asked to accept non-response as a negative reply. Applications for small amounts are considered on an ongoing basis.

Philanthropy and the Laing family

In all there are nine foundations with the Laing name and a further one, Rufford, established by a member of the family. Only the four we have called 'The Laing Family Foundations' are collectively administered, but they all derive from the fortune initially created by Sir John Laing, a Cumbrian stonemason who moved to London, setting himself up in Mill Hill, where the company and a number of the trusts are still located. Sir John died, aged 99, in 1978.

Sir John's original foundations, both with their own entries in this book, were the J W Laing Trust and the Laing Biblical Scholarship Trust. Laing's Charitable Trust is the company's trust. Sir John's sons Kirby and Maurice Laing established or play a leading role in the four 'Laing Family Foundations'.

Then there are four more trusts, also separately administered, and with grandsons of the family as trustees. The biggest of these, also with an entry in this book, is the Rufford Foundation (John Hedley Laing). The Martin, Christopher and David Laing foundations are, as yet, too small to feature in Volume 1 of this book, giving amounts of between £50,000 and £200,000.

The total annual donations of all the trusts deriving from the Laing family business are about £18 million a year. They form part of a tradition of philanthropy in the British construction industry also represented in this book by the names of the Bilton, Sunley, Wates and Wimpey companies (the last being the origin of the funds of the Tudor Trust).

The Kirby Laing Foundation

Health, welfare, Christian religion, general

£2,890,000 (1999)

Box 1, 133 Page Street, Mill Hill, London NW7 2ER

Tel. 020 8238 8890

Correspondent Miss Elizabeth Harley

Information available Report and accounts showing all grants of £5,000 and over and with brief narrative report on the year's grantmaking.

Summary

Along with other Laing family trusts, this is a general grantmaker, with a Christian orientation and awarding almost all kinds of grants.

General

The grants are widely spread, the large ones in particular probably representing close personal interests of the trustees. Their wide range is well represented by those described in the trust's excellent annual report, and reprinted below.

Grants may be of almost any size and kind, one-off, ongoing or spread over a number of years. They include a grant of £25,000 to Drive for Youth 'towards the reduction of their overdraft', another towards donor development and one for a building for a telescope.

The individual recipients of the numerous small grants are not disclosed but 'a considerable proportion of these grants represented annual donations to the core funding of national organisations working in a variety of fields'. The report goes on to say that the foundation does not normally make ongoing commitments to the running costs of local branches of national organisations or of small local charities, 'and this remains a major reason for rejection of applications'.

Alone in the group, the grants of this foundation show substantial grants to arts organisations (a field in which Sir Kirby Laing has been personally involved), with recipients including Dulwich Picture Gallery (£10,000), the Royal Society of Portrait Painters (£7,000) and Sir John Soane's Museum (£5,000). The foundation is keen to point out that there is no general programme of grants for the arts.

The range of the medium-sized grants is remarkable. Recipients from 1999 include Barnardos (£10,000), the Royal School of Needlework (£5,000), the Juvenile Diabetes Foundation (£5,000), Leaf for Life Projects (£5,000), the Bible Society (£6,000), and the Engineering Education Scheme in Wales (£6,000).

Grants in 1999 and 1998

Grants of £25,000 or more are named and described in the text of the annual report. Excerpts from the 1999 report are reprinted below. Grants overall are categorised in the box below.

Annual report 1999

Giving by the Foundation to charitable causes more than doubled, leading to a deficit on the income account of some £1,065,391. ... The increase was largely accounted for by an exceptional grant of £1.25 million to Cheltenham and Gloucester College of Higher Education for the purpose of endowing a Chair in New Testament Theology. ... This is the College's first endowed Chair and it is the Trustees' hope that it will form the foundation of the College's new Centre for International Biblical Studies.

Two other six figure grants were made. The Trustees were concerned to ensure that, in recognition of the Christian significance of the Millennium, Christianity was represented within the Millennium Dome. £250,000, part of a combined grant of £2 million from the Laing Family Trusts, was therefore made available to the New Millennium Experience Company to help finance the Faith Zone. A grant of £150,000 was made to King Edward VII Hospital for Officers' Centenary Appeal.

A further nine organisations benefited from grants of £25,000 and above:

Abbeyfield Development Trust – £50,000 towards the establishment of pilot Integrated Care Communities.

Brendoncare Foundation – £25,000 towards capital development programme.

Demand (Design & Manufacture for Disability) – £25,000, 2nd tranche of grant towards relocation and development of new workshop.

Drive for Youth – £25,000 towards the reduction of their overdraft.

John Grooms Association for Disabled People – £50,000. Capital Appeal.

Oriel College, Oxford – £50,000 for student accommodation.

Restoration of Appearance and Function Trust – £25,000, last of five grants towards Burns Scarring Research Project.

SAT-7 – £30,000 towards donor development and recruitment of local staff.

University of London Observatory – £50,000 towards new telescope building.

There has been no significant change in the Trustees' priorities over the year, with an interest in health and medical issues and in support for Christian organisations still clearly evident.

In addition to the 95 grants listed ... a further 116 grants were made from funds deposited with the Charities Aid Foundation. These ranged in size from £50 to £4,000. Once again a considerable proportion of these grants represented annual donations to the core funding of national organisations working in a variety of different fields. Unfortunately the Trustees do not feel that they are in a position to make similar ongoing commitments to the running costs of local branches of national organisations or of small local charities and this remains a major reason for the rejection of applications to the Foundation.

The cost of administration in relation to income was further reduced from 5.8% to 5.5%.

Exclusions

No grants to individuals; no travel grants; no educational grants. The foundation rarely gives to the running costs of local organisations.

Applications

One application only is needed to apply to this or the Maurice Laing Foundation or the Beatrice or Maurice and Hilda Laing

THE KIRBY LAING FOUNDATION – GRANTS IN 1999 AND 1998

	1999		*1998*	
	Grants	*Value*	*Grants*	*Value*
Child/youth (inc. education/training)	15	£1,464,000	14	£275,000
Religion	24	£440,000*	25	£303,000
Health and medicine	25	£249,000	16	£203,000
Social welfare	10	£269,000	4	£23,000
Overseas aid	9	£75,000	9	£164,000
Cultural and environmental	12	£89,000	11	£94,000
Small grants (<£5,000)	116	£230,000	115	£245,000

* This figure includes an exceptional grant of £250,000 for the Faith Zone in the Millennium Dome.

trusts. Multiple applications will still only elicit a single reply. These trusts make strenuous efforts to keep their overhead costs to a minimum. As they also make a very large number of grants each year, in proportion to their income, the staff must rely almost entirely on the written applications submitted in selecting appeals to go forward to the trustees.

Each application should contain all the information needed to allow such a decision to be reached, in as short and straightforward a way as possible. Specifically, each application should say:

- what the money is for
- how much is needed
- how much has already been found
- where the rest is to come from

Unless there is reasonable assurance on the last point the grant is unlikely to be recommended. The trusts ask applicants, in the interest of reducing costs, to accept a non-response as a negative reply; if more is sought, a reply-paid envelope must be sent with the application.

Decisions are made on an ongoing basis.

The Maurice Laing Foundation

Environment, medicine (often complementary), overseas, general

£1,162,000 (to unconnected organisations in 1999)

Box 1, 133 Page Street, Mill Hill, London NW7 2ER

Tel. 020 8238 8890

Correspondent Miss Elizabeth Harley

Information available Report and accounts with grants list showing all grants of £5,000 and above. A short review explains the larger grants.

Summary

This foundation has become a major funder of a small number of environmental initiatives, with very large grants, for example, for Conservation International and the World Humanity Action Trust. More grants, though not so large, are made to medical institutions, with a particular focus on a small number of university departments carrying out scientific research into the efficacy of complementary therapies. There is limited support for welfare organisations and an extensive programme of small-scale support for the core costs of a range, perhaps little changing, of national organisations.

However, the pattern may change, as the record shows, and trustees may decide at any time to make a major intervention on the largest scale in any of their fields of interest.

This entry is best read alongside those for the others in the group of Laing Family Foundations (*qv*), since an application to one is taken as an application to all.

General

This trust, as reported below, has decided to donate half its income each year to the associated Maurice and Hilda Laing Charitable Trust, itself a grant-making body with its own entry in this book. In addition, in 1999 a further £650,000 was transferred to that trust as this foundation's contribution to the joint Laing trusts' support for the Faith Zone in the Millennium Dome. To minimise double counting, the grant total listed above does not include these transfers, and so the reduced level of grantmaking recorded in this book compared with previous editions is apparent rather than real.

The foundation makes about 200 grants a year. They may be one-off, spread over a period of years, or ongoing. They can be very large, up to several hundred thousand pounds. Many of the small grants, of less than £5,000 each, represent annual donations to the core funding of national organisations working in a variety of fields. There are, however, very few grants to local branches of national organisations, or to local charities whose work is similar to that carried out elsewhere by other organisations.

The trust emphasises its interest in complementary medicine, an unusual concern in this book. Though all the trusts in the group seem to share an underlying Christian ethos, this is expressed by this foundation solely through the grants made with its money by the Maurice and Hilda Laing Charitable Trust.

The trust, along with the others in this group, is lightly staffed and has very low administrative costs.

Grants in 1999 and 1998

Grants of £25,000 or more are named and described in the text of the excellent annual report, with excerpts from the 1999 report reprinted below. Grants overall are categorised in the box below.

Annual report 1999

The Trustees are disappointed that the loss of ACT credit and its implications for charities was not addressed in the Government's review of charity taxation. The long term effect remains to be seen as compensation for the loss is further reduced over the next four years. Nevertheless, the fears expressed in last year's report that it would not be possible to maintain the Foundation's financial performance have so far proved to be unfounded. Despite the fact that the loss of ACT credit began to bite from April 1999 (a quarter of the way through the Foundation's financial year) the Foundation's investment income increased by some 12.8%.

Expenditure exceeded income for the second year in succession. ... Administration costs accounted for 2% of total expenditure.

Of the total of £3,911,616 disbursed to charitable organisations during the year in question, £2.25 million was transferred to the Maurice & Hilda Laing Charitable Trust (formerly the Hilda Laing Charitable Trust). As stated in the past, it is the Trustees' intention to donate 50% of total income to the Trust each year for distribution to causes complementary to those supported by the Maurice Laing Foundation. To this end quarterly payments of £350,000 were made to MHLCT 'on account' for 1999 together with a special payment of £200,000 based on MLF's final income in 1998. In addition an exceptional payment of £650,000 was made to the Trust as the Maurice Laing Foundation's contribution towards the combined grant of £2 million from the Laing Family Trusts to the Faith Zone of the Millennium Dome.

THE MAURICE LAING FOUNDATION – GRANTS IN 1999 AND 1998

	1999		*1998*	
	Grants	*Value*	*Grants*	*Value*
Cultural and environmental	13	£790,000	12	£804,000
Health and medicine	25	£366,000	23	£320,000
Child and youth	13	£121,000	14	£141,000
Overseas aid	6	£57,000	9	£418,000
Social welfare	4	£70,000	7	£56,000
Small grants (<£5,000)	136	£260,000	136	£245,000

This exceptional support for the Faith Zone apart, there has been no significant change in the priorities of the Trustees. The Trustees continue to encourage scientific research into the efficacy of complementary health remedies and to make significant sums available to environmental and conservation organisations. Projects falling into the fields of youth development, social welfare and overseas aid also continue to be of interest to the Trustees. In the latter category the Trustees have been delighted to follow the progress of Impact's Riverboat Hospital, to which a grant of £255,000 was made in the previous year, in its first year of operation. The Foundation's Administrator attended the launching ceremony in Mawa in April and the Trustees believe that the boat is now making a significant contribution to health care in Bangladesh.

The Trustees' wide range of interests is reflected in the gifts of £25,000 and above made during the past year:

Abbeyfield Development Trust – £50,000 towards the establishment of integrated care communities for elderly people

College of Health – £25,000 towards the cost of running the National Waiting List Helpline

Commonwealth Society for the Deaf – £50,000 to cover the purchase of a landrover for the HARK (Hearing Assessment and Research Centre) project in South Africa

Conservation International – £100,000 as core funding for the newly established UK arm of the charity

Dove Healing Trust – £89,000, on-going support for the Complementary Medicine Research Unit at the University of Southampton

FRAME (Fund for the Replacement of Animals in Medical Experiments) – £50,000 to endow a series of annual lectures

Marine Stewardship Council – £46,000 towards the salary of the Fisheries Officer RYA

Sailability – £25,000, the first of four grants towards the organisation's Regional Development Programme

World Humanity Action Trust – £380,000, a continuation of the Foundation's funding for WHAT's two year programme looking at issues of governance in relation to the global environment

World Wide Fund for Nature – £140,000, the last of two grants towards the 'Forests for Life' campaign, although support for WWF's forestry work has since been renewed.

All grants of £5,000 and above are listed by category in ... the accounts. In addition a further 136 gifts, ranging in size from £100 to £4,000, were made from funds deposited with the Charities Aid Foundation.

Exclusions

No grants to groups or individuals for education or travel purposes, including attendance at conferences and overseas exchange programmes. Support is rarely given to the running costs of local organisations.

Applications

One application only is needed to apply to this or the Kirby Laing Foundation, the Beatrice Laing Trust or the Maurice and Hilda Laing Charitable Trust. Multiple applications will only receive a single reply. The trusts ask applicants, in the interest of reducing costs, to accept a non-response as a negative reply; if more is sought, a reply-paid envelope must be sent with the application.

Each application should contain all the information needed to allow a decision to be reached, in as short and straightforward a way as possible. Specifically, it should cover:

- what the money is for;
- how much is needed;
- how much has already been found;
- where the rest is to come from (unless there is reasonable assurance on this point the grant is unlikely to be recommended).

A copy of the charity's latest annual accounts should also be enclosed. Applications for smaller amounts are considered on an ongoing basis; larger grants are considered quarterly; the exact dates of meetings vary from year to year.

The Beatrice Laing Trust

Health, welfare, in the UK and overseas

£789,000 (1998/99)

Box 1, 133 Page Street, Mill Hill, London NW7 2ER

Tel. 020 8238 8890

Correspondent Miss Elizabeth Harley

Information available Report and accounts with full grants list and brief review of the year's grants.

Summary

This is the member of the Laing family group of trusts that concentrates particularly on small grants for the relief of poverty and distress. Most of the more than 400 grants are for amounts between £500 and £1,500. As with the other trusts in the group, many are in the form of regular annual payments to national charities, large and small, but in this case a number of local causes are also supported, both in the UK and overseas.

Grants in 1999

	Grants	*Value*
Child and youth	46	£372,000
Health and medicine	158	£285,000
Social welfare	10	£269,000
Overseas aid	31	£100,000
Religion	9	£15,000

Grants of £25,000 or more are named and described in the text of the excellent annual report. They can be found under that heading further down this entry. The following sample listing gives a flavour of the causes supported through the smaller grants that represent the core of the work of this trust:

Family Holiday Association	£1,250
Shepherd's Bush Families Project	£1,000
National Playbus Association	£1,000
Selby Peter Pan Nursery	£1,000
Raleigh International	£500
Whitley Bay Boys' Club	£500
Drugcare St Albans	£750
British Deaf Association	£1,250
Merthyr Tydfil Association for the Blind	£2,000
British Red Cross	£1,000

To check the geographical distribution, the editors took their usual division of England into two halves of equal population, and examined all the grants that were locally identifiable. The results were as follows:

South of England	45 grants
North of England	24 grants

This probably reflects quite closely the pattern of applications received, though these editors have argued for years that 'national' trusts should actively seek to remedy this widely found north–south disparity, if necessary by setting appropriate budgets and seeking local partners to promote applications.

The support for Scotland is generous. The figures for Wales and Northern Ireland are too low for any conclusions to be drawn.

Scotland	13 grants
Wales	3 grants
N. Ireland	3 grants

Annual report 1999

Charitable giving increased by 5.3%. A total of 408 grants were made, ranging in size from £150 to £21,250. The following organisations received grants of £10,000 or above:

ApT Design and Development: £10,000, as a further contribution towards the 'Aid to Artisans' project in Ghana Cottage Homes: £10,000 towards refurbishment costs

Echoes of Service: £28,000 in support of Echoes' evangelical missionary work (in four tranches)

Mariners: £17,400 to provide engines for a barge to create a ferry link between the island of Chinde and Mozambique

Mulberry Bush School: £10,000 towards the Redevelopment Appeal

National Autistic Society: £10,000 towards building work at Helen Allison School in Kent

Royal London Society for the Blind: £10,000 towards the Workbridge programme

Shelter: £10,000 towards Shelterline

Sobriety Project: £21,250 to be allocated towards the development of a new project in Rotherham

The Passage: £20,000 towards the refurbishment of a building to be used as a permanent night shelter

Toxoplasmosis Trust: £10,000 towards computer equipment facilitating the production of information leaflets

United Nations Association International Service: £11,000 in completion of a commitment to the Urban Sanitation Project in Mali

YMCA Croydon: £10,000 towards the refurbishment of Lansdowne Road Hostel

The diversity of these grants, offering support to the homeless, the elderly, the socially excluded and those with disabilities within the UK as well as aid to developing countries, reflects the Trustees' desire to support a wide range of charities working for the relief of poverty in its broadest sense. These grants totalled £177,650, representing 22.5% of charitable expenditure, a more significant percentage than in previous years. Provided that income continues to increase, the Trustees expect to maintain the proportion of larger grants made at this higher level.

At the same time the Trustees recognise that it is often their smaller grants, amounting to no more than a few hundred pounds, which are of the greatest value in enabling small local organisations to make a significant difference to those in need within their local communities. While the Trustees do not feel that they are in a position to make an on-going commitment to the running costs of such organisations, which they feel must be raised locally in order to ensure long-term sustainability, they continue to make a number of small to moderate sized grants to organisations which might otherwise find difficulty in attracting funds from the larger grant-making trusts. This policy is once again reflected in the list of donations for the year in question, the remainder of the grants made representing annual donations to the core funding of national organisations.

The cost of administration in relation to income fell to 4.7%.

Exclusions

No grants to individuals; no travel grants; no educational grants.

Applications

One application only is needed to apply to this or the Maurice, Hilda or Kirby Laing trusts. Multiple applications will still only elicit a single reply; even then applicants are asked to accept non-response as a negative reply on behalf of all three trusts, unless an sae is enclosed. Applications are considered monthly.

These trusts make strenuous efforts to keep their overhead costs to a minimum. As they also make a very large number of grants each year, in proportion to their income the staff must rely almost entirely on the written applications submitted in selecting appeals to go forward to the trustees. Each application should contain all the information needed to allow such a decision to be reached, in as short and straightforward a way as possible. Specifically, each application should say:

- what the money is for
- how much is needed
- how much has already been found
- where the rest is to come from

Unless there is reasonable assurance on the last point the grant is unlikely to be recommended.

These editors would add that, in the light of the very large number of grants being made by a small staff, the plea above for simple, straightforward applications is even more appropriate than for other funders.

The J W Laing Trust

Christian evangelism, general

£4,405,000 (1998/99)

PO Box 133, Bath BA1 2YU

Tel. 01225 427236 **Fax** 01225 427278

e-mail jwlaingtrust@stewards.co.uk

Correspondent B Chapman, Secretary

Trustees *The Stewards' Company; Dr W E Naismith, Chair.*

Information available Full accounts, but without the required narrative annual report reviewing the work of the charity.

General

This trust is administered alongside the J W Laing Biblical Scholarship Trust (see separate entry) by the Stewards' Company Ltd. The trust benefits Christian work in the UK and overseas, with particular reference to the Christian Brethren Assemblies. A portion of the gifts made is nominated by the Beatrice Laing Trust, to which substantial transfers are made by this trust (and which also has a separate entry).

Assets for 1998/99 amounted to £110 million, generating an income of about £4.4 million, and the same amount was given out in grants in three broad categories; overseas, £2.2 million; home, £1.9 million; and transfers to the Beatrice Laing Trust, £0.2 million.

The annual report has a list of 66 grants of £10,000 or over. However, it is likely that most grants are for lesser amounts. Grants are classified as follows:

Overseas (£2,236,000)

Three major grants appear to be identifiable, all of them to beneficiaries also supported, though usually with different amounts, in the previous year: Echoes of Service (£938,000); Interlink (£116,000), and the Beatrice Laing Trust (£85,000). Otherwise general headings are given in the lists. They include:

- Church buildings £195,000
- Scriptures and literature £183,000
- Educational and orphanages £128,000
- Education of missionaries' children £79,000
- National evangelists £54,000
- Missionaries' vehicles £46,000

Home (£1,948,000)

Main headings included:

- Scriptures and literature £457,000
- Church buildings £407,000
- Evangelistic associations £258,000
- Youth and children £148,000
- Teachers and evangelists £46,000

There was also a transfer under this heading of £499,000 to the Beatrice Laing Trust.

Charitable organisations and objects (£220,000)

In previous years we have reported extensive grantmaking under this heading. In 1998/99 there was just one transfer, of £220,000 to the Beatrice Laing Trust, which has taken on some of these responsibilities.

Other

Major beneficiaries not identified above included the Scripture Gift Mission (£350,000), Medical Missionary News (£79,000), Gospel Literature Outreach (£35,000) and Mountsandel Christian Fellowship, Coleraine (£40,000).

Applications

The trust states that it does not accept applications from those outside its own particular circles.

Laing's Charitable Trust

General

£797,000 (to organisations, 1999)

Beneficial area UK.

133 Page Street, Mill Hill, London NW7 2ER

Tel. 020 8959 3636

Correspondent Michael Hamilton, Secretary

Trustees *R A Wood; Sir Martin Laing; D C Madden; C Laing.*

Information available Minimal annual report and accounts, without the required narrative review of grantmaking.

Summary

Nearly 1,000 grants are made a year, most of them for amounts of less than £1,000. About half of the funds are disbursed in larger grants, from £1,000 up to £50,000, mostly to regularly supported beneficiaries, typically youth or community development organisations.

General

Accounts for 1999 showed an income of £1.9 million, generated from assets totalling £46.5 million. A total of £797,000 was distributed to organisations and £876,000 to approximately 1,000 individuals (Laing's past and present employees and/or their dependants).

The top 50 donations to institutions, listed with the accounts, totalled £585,000. Of these, 17 ranged from £10,000 to £50,000 and these accounted for 54% of the grant total. Nearly all of the recipients of grants of this size had been supported in the previous year, many in the preceding three years or more.

From those grants whose purpose could be identified, the following categorisations could be made.

Youth/child welfare

Drive for Youth – £50,000; Young Enterprise – £30,000; Prince's Trust – £25,000; Raleigh International – £20,000; Weston Spirit – £10,000; Children's Society – £7,000; Divert Trust – £5,000; NSPCC (Anglesey) – £3,000.

Community/homelessness

National Homeless Alliance – £40,000; London Enterprise Agency – £37,000; Business in the Community – £30,000; Empty Homes Agency – £20,000; Community Development Fund – £15,000; National Tenants' Resource Centre – £5,000.

Health/disability

Marie Curie Cancer Care – £30,000; Great Ormond Street Hospital – £24,000; Midland Sports Centre for the Disabled – £7,000.

Welfare

Who Cares? Trust – £25,000; Wintercomfort – £5,000; Sisters of Charity of St Vincent de Paul – £4,000.

Education

Include – £20,000; Springboard Trust – £5,000; United World College of the Atlantic – £18,000; South Wales Baptist College – £5,000; Institute of Economic Affairs – £5,000; University of Oxford – £5,000.

Environment

World Wide Fund for Nature (UK) – £10,000; Hertfordshire Groundwork – £8,000; Global Action Plan – £5,000; Forum for the Future – £6,000; Edinburgh Green Belt Trust – £5,000.

Arts/heritage

Royal Opera House – £23,000; National Museum of Wales – £5,000.

Exclusions

No grants to individuals (other than to Laing employees and/or their dependants).

Applications

In writing to the correspondent. No particular application form is required. Receipt of applications is not acknowledged unless successful – or unless a reply paid envelope is sent with the application. The trust does not encourage exploratory telephone calls on 'how best to approach the trust'.

Lambeth Endowed Charities

Education, general social needs in Lambeth, London

£725,000 (to institutions, 1999)

Beneficial area London borough of Lambeth.

127 Kennington Road, London SE11 6SF

Tel. 020 7735 1925 **Fax** 020 7735 7048

Correspondent Robert Dewar, Director and Clerk

Trustees *Fifteen co-optative trustees and governors, and two representative trustees and two representative governors appointed by Lambeth Borough Council. Dr Jean Weddell (Chair, Hayle's Charity); Gerald Bowden (Chair, Walcot Charities).*

Information available Exemplary report and accounts and information leaflet.

Summary

Lambeth Endowed Charities is an umbrella title for three charities, administered from the same offices, benefiting people living in the London borough of Lambeth. Over 100 organisations a year are supported with grants usually for amounts up to £5,000.

The charities produce a single information leaflet which gives more details of funding available for individuals. The parts relevant to organisations are reprinted below.

General

The grantmaking of the charities covers the following areas (with the totals donated to organisations by each in 1999 supplied by the trust):

Walcot Educational Foundation (£531,000) – grants for broadly 'educational' purposes, including employment, recreation, social and physical training, as well as vocational training and academic studies. The beneficiaries must be people under 30 years old living in the borough of Lambeth.

Hayle's Charity (£159,000) and the Walcot Non-Educational Charity (£35,000) – grants to encourage community activities, and to meet other social and health-related needs of Lambeth residents.

More detailed information from the relevant sections of the charities' information leaflet is reprinted here and under 'Exclusions' and 'Applications' below.

Who can apply?

Applications are considered from a wide range of organisations as well as from students and individuals with urgent needs, provided the application meets their main objectives. Typical applicants include schools, children and youth projects, community centres, pensioners' projects, counselling and advice centres, disability projects, medical and health projects, and employment and training schemes.

Projects and organisations

One-off grants

Applications for specific requirements – social or educational – are considered at grant meetings. Normally, only one grant will be made in the course of a year.

The Small Grants Programme: grants for youth and community groups

At the beginning of each year, the Trustees set aside funds for the following recurring requirements, which may be applied for at any time. These grants may be made in addition to 'one-off' grants for a specific requirement. Again, normally only one such grant per project can be made in the course of the year.

Parties/Cultural Festivities – Grants can be made to groups organising parties for children, older and disabled people.

Playschemes – Grants can be made to Easter and Summer Playschemes.

Group Holidays/Outings – Grants can be made to support coach outings, day trips and holidays for people with disabilities and long-term illness, older people and families in need.

Equipment, Facilities and Urgent Needs – There are a limited number of small grants available for projects and organisations under this category.

Grants in 1998

The full accounts for 1999 were not yet available as this book went to press. In 1998, grants for community, educational, social and health projects from the combined charities totalled £451,000. Over 100 grants of £1,000 or more were listed in the annual review. The major beneficiaries were Hurley Clinic – Schools Link (£20,000 for an education link worker's salary) and Family Friends (£20,000 for a Home School Mediation project).

Other beneficiaries, in receipt of grants of between £1,000 and £5,000, included Thrift Urban Housing (for volunteer training/recruitment costs); Lambeth Voluntary Action Council (running costs); Child & Sound (music event for disabled children); Alcohol Counsel & Prevention (helpline running costs); Woodcraft Folk (building refurbishment); All Change (arts project for people with learning difficulties); Clapham Under 5s (computer equipment), and Brixton Music & Drama Society (drama workshop and production).

The Walcot Educational Foundation donated £125,000 to voluntary-aided schools and £74,000 to other schools, most grants being for £5,000 or less.

Exclusions

Beneficiaries must be residents of the London borough of Lambeth.

- National charities – The Lambeth Endowed Charities do not normally make grants in response to general appeals from national charities, especially where similar needs are being met by local projects. However, consideration may be given if a national charity can show how its work relates specifically to Lambeth residents.
- Revenue funding – Normally, the trustees will not consider revenue funding. However, occasionally they are prepared to make a large grant which will be paid in instalments over a two or three year period. Priority will be given to small local projects. Applicants for such funding will need to show how any balance of funds required can be raised and that alternative sources of funding can be found in the future.
- Statutory sources – No grants may be made where funds from statutory sources can be obtained.
- Debts – No grants may be made to meet the costs of debts already incurred.

Applications

All applications must be made on an application form, available on request from the office. The trustees meet quarterly, usually in early March, June, October and December, and applications must be received at least six weeks before the date of the relevant meeting. Please ring the office to check deadlines for applications.

Once your application has been received you will be contacted by the director or the fieldworker, who will usually arrange to visit your project to discuss your application in more detail.

Successful applicants will be asked to give a report about how a grant has been used within 12 months of receiving it.

The John and Rosemary Lancaster Charitable Foundation

Christian causes

£2,061,000 (1998/99)

Beneficial area Unrestricted, with a local interest in Clitheroe.

c/o Text House, 152 Edisford Road, Clitheroe, Lancashire BB7 2LA

Tel. 01200 444404

Correspondent Mrs R Lancaster, Chair

Trustees *J E Lancaster; R Lancaster; S J Lancaster; J R Broadhurst.*

Information available Full accounts are on file at the Charity Commission.

General

Set up to promote the spreading of the Christian message, the trust says that 'the prime objective of the trustees is to continue supporting their existing charitable activities. Funds available for additional new projects are minimal.'

In 1997/98, its first year of operation, the trust received a donation of shares in Ultraframe plc, a company of which one of the trustees is a director. The shares were valued at £96,000, and following the company's floatation on the stock exchange in October 1997 they were sold with a net gain to the trust of £8.3 million.

In 1998/99 there was a further donation of shares in Ultraframe plc (worth £5.1 million) and the foundation's assets increased from £7.5 million to £13.9 million over the year. Grants totalled £2,061,000.

Some 90% of the funding over the two-year period has gone to Mission Aviation Fellowship (£1,888,000 in 1998/99) and 'NGM' (£1 million in 1997/98; £50,000 in 1998/99). Other grants in 1998/99 were for the following: Message to Schools (£46,000; £17,000 in 1997/98); Love and Joy (£27,000); Trinity Skill Share

(£26,000); Adopt A Child (£11,000), and NET (£5,500). A further £6,300 was donated in grants of under £1,000 each.

A substantial grant of £80,000 to Clitheroe Community Church in 1997/98 suggested an interest in benefiting the trust's local area.

Applications

The trust says:

We do not consider applications made to us from organisations or people unconnected with us. All our donations are instigated because of personal associations. Unsolicited mail is, sadly, a waste of the organisation's resources.

Landfill Tax Credit Scheme and ENTRUST

Environmental improvement

£183,000,000 (between 1997 and August 1999)

Beneficial area UK.

6th Floor, Acre House, 2 Town Square, Sale, Cheshire M33 7WZ

Tel. 0161 972 0044 **Fax** 0161 972 0055

website www.entrust.org.uk

Summary

Grants for environmental improvement, funded from the proceeds of the landfill tax, are available from a range of sources. For those interested, it is necessary to read the full entry below.

General

The landfill tax is a source of funds for environmental organisations that cuts across all the usual funding classifications. It is public expenditure, it comes from companies and some of it is allocated by grant-making charities. This entry covers the sources of landfill tax funding as a whole, and is similar to that in *A Guide to Funding from Government Departments and Agencies,* also published by the Directory of Social Change.

In 1996 the first green tax, the landfill tax, was introduced on waste disposal going to landfill sites in the UK in order to give an incentive to industry to reduce waste and its associated problems.

HM Customs & Excise collects the tax at variable rates depending on the type of waste. Landfill operators may divert up to 20% of their tax liability to environmental projects. They are reimbursed for 90% of the amount contributed. (They are expected to cover the remaining 10% themselves, although in many cases another organisation may do so for them.)

ENTRUST is not a supplier of funds, but is the official regulatory body of potential beneficiaries. Groups registered with ENTRUST are then eligible to receive grants directly from a participating company. But registration and project approval from ENTRUST in no way assure funding from a landfill operator.

The scheme leaves funding decisions entirely to landfill operating companies. Participating companies can hand over the money to the variety of intermediary funding bodies that have been set up by, or are working for, some companies (see below for examples); or they can give money directly to applicant organisations. But either the intermediary or the direct recipient, or sometimes both, must first be enrolled and registered with ENTRUST. Since enrolment with ENTRUST costs £100, small groups may well seek funding, at least in the first instance, only from those already registered intermediary bodies who do not make this a requirement for their applicants.

Organisations applying for funding must be non-profit-distributing bodies. They have to meet criteria for approved work under this scheme which includes:

- land reclamation for economic, social or environmental use
- pollution reduction
- research into sustainable waste management
- education on waste issues
- provision of public amenity facilities in the vicinity of a landfill site
- reclamation and creation of wildlife habitats
- restoration of buildings of architectural and heritage interest in the vicinity of a landfill site
- provision of financial, administration and other services to environmental bodies.

'Vicinity' is interpreted as about a 10-mile radius from the landfill site. The following listing is not exhaustive. There is no central listing or description of the organisations involved, and environmental organisations will often want to make their own local enquiries in the waste management industry. Some starting points are given under 'Applications' below.

The Royal Society for Nature Conservation

The RSNC administers two major national award schemes. The boards of each consist of three members from the company concerned and three from RSNC. Applications can be made by any organisations registered with ENTRUST. These funds are not directed only at local wildlife trusts as some people have assumed.

Biffaward for Biffa Waste Services
Funding: £6.4 million (1999)

Hanson Environment Fund
Funding: £3.7 million (1999)

In 1999 the fund introduced a community grants scheme of £250,000 a year to assist small environmental projects with awards of between £500 and £2,000.

Contact: Andrea White
Royal Society for Nature Conservation, The Kiln, Waterside, Mather Road, Newark NG24 1WT
Tel: 01636 670000; Fax: 01636 670001;
E-mail: grants@rsnc.kix.co.uk;
Website: www.rsnc.org

RMC Environment Fund (administered by the Environment Council)

Funding: about £1.6 million per year
Contact: Sasha Grigg, Landfill Tax Fund Coordinator
The Environment Council, 212 High Holborn, London WC1V 7VW
Tel: 020 7632 0127; Fax: 020 7242 1180;
E-mail: rmcenvironmentfund@envcouncil.org.uk;
Website: www.greenchannel.com/tec

WREN

Funding: £9 million per year
Waste Recycling Group, with operations in Cambridgeshire, Cheshire, Derbyshire, Lincolnshire, Nottinghamshire, Norfolk, Suffolk and Yorkshire, has set up WREN – Waste Recycling Environmental Ltd – registered as an environmental body which administers its funds via the advice of a series of county committees.
Contact: The Administration Team
Wren House, Manor Farm, Bridgham, Norwich NR16 2RX
Tel: 01953 717165;
Website: www.wren.org.uk

Enventure Limited

Enventure acts as professional fund manager for companies contributing to the tax credit scheme. 'Enventure was approved as one of the first enrolled

environmental bodies in the country and accounts for a significant proportion of the total Landfill Tax Money being spent on the environment.'
Contact: Maggie Bignall, Chris Jones
Bank House, Wharfebank Business Centre, Ilkley Road, Otley, West Yorkshire LS21 31P
Tel: 01943 850089; Fax: 01943 462075;
Website: www.enventure.demon.co.uk

Essex Environmental Trust

Funding: about £1 million (1999)
This trust was set up as a county council initiative and gets funding from six landfill operators in the county.
Contact: Keith Derry, Trust Secretary
Mackmurdo House, 79 Springfield Road, Chelmsford CM2 6JG
Tel: 01245 265555; Fax: 01245 495427

South West England Environmental Trust (SWEET)

The trust is set up as a limited company. Its title is misleading as it apparently assists projects throughout the UK. It provides services for landfill operators and for environmental bodies seeking funds.
Contact: Sally Campbell or Paul Verniquet
Bridge House, 48–52 Baldwin Street, Bristol BS1 1QD
Tel: 0117 929 7151; Fax: 0117 904 6001;
E-mail: sweet@lyonsdavidson.co.uk

Onyx Environmental Trust (UK-wide, Onyx Environmental Group)

Funding: £2.5–£3 million a year
Five regional panels with local representation meet regularly to recommend projects for approval.
Contact: Douglas Davis Ruthdene, Station Road, Four Ashes, Wolverhampton WV10 7DG
Tel: 01902 794600; Fax: 01902 794646

S.I.T.A. Environmental Trust (UK-wide, S.I.T.A).

Funding: about £5 million a year
The company has over 40 operational sites – in the East Midlands, Shropshire, Dorset, Surrey, Newcastle and Scotland.
Contact: John Brownsell
Willoughby House, 2 Broad Street, Stamford, Lincolnshire PE9 1PB
Tel: 01780 753821; Fax: 01780 751556

Cleanaway

The company has three main sites in the South East and one in Birmingham. Four trusts have been set up in the South East, particularly in Essex, where its operations are concentrated.

Cleanaway Pitsea Marshes Trust and Cleanaway Havering Riverside Trust
2 Chiltern Close, Goffs Oak, Waltham Cross, Hertfordshire EN7 5SP
Tel: 01707 874558
Contact: Eric Dear

Cleanaway Mardyke Trust
c/o Cleaning and Greening Department, Thurrock Council, Civic Offices, New Road, Grays Thurrock, Essex RM17 6SL
Tel: 01375 652296
Contact: The Secretary

Cleanaway Canvey Marshes Trust
c/o Castle Point Borough Council, Kiln Road Offices, Thundersley, Benfleet, Essex SS7 1TF
Tel: 01268 882470
Contact: Chris Moran

Cory Environmental

Cory has set up a series of trusts in its main areas of operation. In addition it contributes directly to the Resource Recovery Forum, Thames 21, Trees for London, Wastebusters Ltd and Business Eco Logic Ltd.

Cory Environmental Trust in Carrick District
Funding: about £80,000 a year

and

Cory Environmental Trust in Kerrier
Funding: about £10,000 a year

both at 32 Henver Gardens, Reawla, Gwinear, Hayle, Cornwall TR27 5LM
Tel: 01736 850984; Fax: 01736 850163
Contact: Shirley Collings

Cory Environmental Trust in East Northamptonshire
Funding: about £50,000 a year
c/o Environmental Health Department, East Northamptonshire House, Cedar Drive, Thrapston, Northamptonshire NN14 4LZ
Tel: 01832 742052; Fax: 01832 73483

Gloucestershire Environmental Trust Company (see separate entry)
Funding: about £750,000 a year
Contact: Lynne Garner, Secretary
Moorend Cottage, Watery Lane, Upton St Leonards, Gloucestershire GL4 8DW
Tel: 01452 615000; Fax: 01452 613817

Essex Environment Trust
Funding: about £650,000 a year
Mackmurdo House, 79 Springfield Road, Chelmsford, Essex CM2 6JG
Tel: 01245 265555; Fax: 01245 495427

Cory Environmental Trust in Colchester
Funding: about £120,000 a year
c/o Colchester Borough Council, PO Box 331, Town Hall, Colchester CO1 1GL
Tel: 01206 282918; Fax: 01206 282916
Contact: Sue Warrener

Cory Environmental Trust in Rochford
Funding: about £90,000 a year
c/o 53 Westbury, Rochford, Essex SS4 1UL
Tel: 01702 541413; Fax: 01702 543654

Cory Environmental Trust in Southend-on-Sea
Funding: about £80,000 a year
589 London Road, Westcliff-on-Sea, Essex SSO 9PQ
Tel: 01702 340334; Fax: 01702 338282
Contact: Les Barker

Cory Environmental Trust in Thurrock
Funding: about £1 million a year
Civic Offices, New Road, Grays Thurrock, Essex RM17 6SL
Tel: 01375 652485; Fax: 01375 652784
Contact: Geoff Howell, Secretary

Western Riverside Environmental Fund
Funding: about £250,000 a year
c/o Groundwork, 1 Kennington Road, London SE1 7QP
Tel: 020 7922 1230; Fax: 020 7922 1219

UK Waste Management Limited

Funding: about £3 million a year
Eight sites in England, Scotland and Northern Ireland. This company manages its landfill tax account in-house. Its funds are split between national programmes and local projects. In addition it has established regionally based environmental bodies which distribute money generated locally on local projects.
Contact: Barbara Broadhead/Claire Olver, Public Relations, Head Office, Rixton Old Hall, Manchester Road, Rixton, Warrington, Cheshire WA3 6EW
Tel: 0161 775 1011; Fax: 0161 775 7291

Applications

To find out about landfill operators in your area, ring:

- The Environment Agency general enquiry line: 0645 333111. The local offices of the agency maintain a public register of waste disposal and treatment sites and operators. The agency has 26 areas and a greater number of offices.
- Landfill Tax Register, available from Customs & Excise Landfill Tax Help desk: 0645 128484
- ENTRUST Regional Offices:
  Northern Office: 0141 561 0390
  Central Region: 0161 973 1177
  Wales and the West: 029 2086 9492
  Southern Area: 020 8950 2152

The Allen Lane Foundation

Disadvantaged minorities, unpopular causes

£505,000 (1999/2000)

Beneficial area UK, with a separate programme for the Republic of Ireland.

Suite 4, Parr House, Broadway, Bracknell RG12 1AG

Tel. 01344 311866 **Fax** 01344 319119

e-mail heatherswailes@allenlane.demon.co.uk

website www.allenlane.demon.co.uk

Correspondent Heather Swailes, Executive Secretary

Information available Excellent annual report with full grants list and detailed analysis of grantmaking and grants; accounts; guidelines.

Summary

Beneficiaries are normally small or medium sized organisations supporting disadvantaged people – particularly those on the margins of society. Grants generally range from about £250 to £10,000 for one-off grants, and from £1,000 a year to £5,000 a year (up to three years) for revenue grants. About a third of grants are repeated over two or three years.

The foundation is a leader in identifying and supporting small organisations that are developing new ways of working in some of the most difficult fields of social welfare.

General

In 1999/2000 the foundation, endowed by the late Sir Allen Lane, founder of Penguin Books, had a sharply increased income of £681,000 (up from £456,000 in the previous year).

The foundation's Guidance for Applicants gives the following excellent account of its work:

Where do grants go?

The Foundation makes grants for work all over the United Kingdom but not overseas. Trustees give priority to work outside London and this means that grants are hardly ever made for work in Greater London. The Foundation tries to target about 80% of its funds on national, regional or county-wide work and about 20% on local projects. Apart from a small programme in the Republic of Ireland the Foundation does not make any grants overseas.

What kind of work does the foundation fund?

Trustees are interested in imaginative or innovative projects, and the size of its grants (which are modest) makes start-up funding of smaller projects particularly appropriate. Grants are made for project costs, or core costs.

The broad areas of work which are priorities for Trustees include:

- the provision of advice, information and advocacy
- community development
- employment and training
- mediation, conflict resolution and alternatives to violence
- research and education aimed at changing public attitudes or policy
- social welfare

Who does the foundation wish to benefit from the work it funds?

The Trustees make grants to organisations whose work the Trustees believe to be unpopular. Priority groups for the Foundation include

- refugees and asylum-seekers,
- people from black and ethnic minority communities,
- those experiencing mental health problems,
- those experiencing violence or abuse,
- offenders and ex-offenders and travellers amongst others.

What size?

Grants generally range from about £250 to £10,000. Grants to local projects are normally less than £2,500. Grants are usually single payments but may sometimes be for up to three consecutive years. Grants for more than one year are often tapered.

The Trustees wish to make grants which will make a significant impact and, as the grants are relatively small, priority is given to organisations of a modest size. The Foundation only very rarely makes grants to national organisations with an income of more than £500,000 per annum or to local organisations with an income of more than about £150,000.

Grants may be made for project costs, or revenue costs.

The Trustees are able to fund only a small proportion of the applications that do fall within their priorities. Applications far exceed the funds available – currently by a ratio of nine to one. We are sorry if we are unable to help you.

In order to give as many applicants [as possible] a chance of funding, we do not accept applications from the same organisation more frequently than once a year.

Funding in the Republic of Ireland

The Foundation has a small funding programme in Ireland which focuses on penal reform and work with offenders and ex-offenders. Trustees expect to spend approximately £40,000 per annum in this programme. Applications should be made in the same way as applications for the UK programme, except that the budget should be presented in punts.

Annual report 1999/2000

The foundation produces fine, comprehensive annual reports that might well serve as models for other trusts described in this book. They are easily accessible on the foundation's excellent website, so only a few sections are repeated here.

Getting the message across

Like most grant-makers, the Allen Lane Foundation is keen to receive good applications which meet its criteria. To that end considerable time and effort is spent trying to ensure that clear information reaches applicants about the Foundation's priorities. In addition to an information leaflet (just over 1,300 copies posted to enquirers this year) there is now information on the Foundation's website (www.allenlane.demon.co.uk) which at the end of the year had received just over 2,800 visits. Some requests for information are received and responded to by e-mail.

But all is not electronic! The Executive Secretary visits groups around the country to meet potential applicants face to face and talk about the Foundation's current priorities ...

The following table suggests that a continued emphasis on good communication is reducing the number of inappropriate applications. The Foundation is very grateful to applicants who take care to target their requests appropriately.

	99/00	*98/99*	*97/98*	*96/97*
Enquiries	1301	909	732	492
Applications	1069	1201	1414	1540
New grants committed	124	125	119	159
Refusals	943	1073	1295	1381

New grants

The number of new grants committed each year has remained very similar in the last three years, but the total value this year was £505,098 – a significant increase on last year (£483,000) ... The following table shows a slight increase in two year grants, compared to one-off and three year commitments. Trustees recognise the tension between providing longer-term funding, particularly core funding, while keeping enough funds free to respond to new applications.

	Grants			
	One-off	*Two year*	*Three year*	*Total*
1998/1999	86	26	13	125
1999/2000	74	39	11	124

New applicants or repeat grants?

Last year, for the first time, we looked at the proportion of grants which went to organisations which had already had at least one grant from the Foundation in the past, and how much went to 'first-timers'. We wanted to see whether there was a tendency to support organisations we already knew. The figures are not very different from last year. This year 19% of grants (by number) went to organisations which had previously had some funding from the Foundation. However, this was a rather larger proportion when looked at by value – 27% of the total value of grants committed. Last year the figures were 16% by number and 22% by value ...

Categories of work

Generally, the Foundation is reactive – responding to the applications which arrive in its office. The following table shows figures for 1999/2000 and (1998/99)

Mediation, conflict resolution, non-violence	24%	(14%)
Advice, information and advocacy	21%	(20%)
Policy orientated research and public education	18%	(34%)
Social welfare	16%	(7%)
Employment and training	12%	(12%)
Community development	9%	(8%)

Beneficiaries in 1999/2000 (1998/99)

The pattern of beneficiaries has not significantly changed this year. The Foundation does not generally regard women as a target beneficiary group per se, but they are most often those who are experiencing violence or abuse and it is often within that category that grants have been made.

One difference from last year is that no grants were made for work with travellers, compared to 3% (by value) last year and 6% in the year to April 1998. Again this reflects the reactive nature of the Foundation – only two applications were received for work with travellers last year, neither of which were appropriate. This may also be an example of a phenomenon which grant-makers experience quite commonly – where one criterion is excluded by another. In this case, the fact that the Foundation does not make grants in London excludes a significant number of traveller groups.

Everyone/open to all	33%	(27%)
Offenders/ex-offenders	18%	(14%)
People with mental health problems	16%	(13%)
Women	8%	(9%)
Black and ethnic minority	8%	(19%)
Other specific group (eg. children)	8%	(3%)
Refugees/asylum seekers	6%	(6%)
Lesbian and gay	3%	(2%)

The Foundation continues to receive (and reject) many applications relating to work targeted at specific beneficiary groups which are not among its priorities – for example, children and young people, people with disabilities, elderly people etc. Although the largest single group of work related to 'everyone', that is to say they were generalist services, it is fair to say that where work is focused on a single beneficiary group the Foundation is unlikely to fund those which are not among its priorities.

The policy of not funding in London, because of the greater resources available there, has made it easier to distribute funds to more rural areas, and to areas farther from the capital.

Refusals

The table below shows the reasons why 943 applications were refused. The analysis is rather depressing.

Outside stated policies	29%
Not one of the stated priorities	29%
Not exceptional	21%
For London	8%
'Final'	8%
For an individual	6%

The Foundation's guidelines give an explicit list of subject areas or kinds of funding which are outside its current policy. It also states clearly that we do not make grants to individuals nor (other than in exceptional circumstances) in London. (The category 'Final' in the chart refers to repeated applications outside the Foundation's policy to which a response is no longer made.) Together these account for 43% of all refusals.

The Foundation can perhaps take some of the responsibility for those applying from London and those whose applications were 'not a priority'. The Guidance leaflet says the Foundation will only fund in London in exceptional circumstances – many applicants will feel or hope that their project will be regarded as exceptional.

The applications turned down as 'not a priority' fall into a grey area: because of the pressure on choice, the Foundation rarely makes grants outside its explicit priorities – but there are many areas of work which, while not on the priority list, are also not on the exclusion list, and perhaps it is understandable that applicants hope it may be worth a try.

Grants in 1999/2000

The annual report, as well as listing all the grants made, with the purposes of each, also includes under each heading two recipients' brief descriptions of their work. The following section includes examples of these, as well as part of the full listing of grants under the first heading, in order to give a flavour of the lists as a whole.

Advice, information and advocacy

Family Rights Group (£5,000 per annum for two years towards the cost of a nationwide advice and advocacy helpline).

'Family Rights Group supports families who are involved with social services, and works with families and professionals to improve services for families from all sections of the community. It works in England and Wales and was set up in 1974.

'Becoming involved with social services can be a terrifying experience for any family, and too often families find their voice is unheard, they cannot access the services they need, and they feel powerless and frightened by what social services may do. Over one thousand families a year call our advice service and, in confidence, speak to a qualified solicitor or social worker who is able to advise them on their rights and on the best way to get the services they want.

'We advise families who are subject to a child protection investigation, whose children are in care, whose children may be adopted, or who are having difficulties getting the help they need. Advice sheets, available in a number of languages, give families more detailed information on the law, their rights, and on what social services can and cannot do. Families tell us how important it is to talk to someone who is independent and who understands the system.'

Speakeasy Advice Centre: £6,000 over three years (£3,000, £2,000 and £1,000) towards the core costs of providing free legal advice in Roath, Cardiff.

Fife Advocacy Project: £3,000 per annum for two years towards the costs of volunteer co-ordination.

Community development

Women Acting in Today's Society (£3,000 per annum for three years towards the core costs of the organisation which facilitates the involvement of women in their communities in the West Midlands).

Employment and training

Fine Cell Work (£10,000 over three years [£5,000, £3,000 and £2,000] for core costs of prison craft work project).

'Fine Cell Work is a new national charity working in prisons, and was founded in 1997 by Lady Anne Tree. Our aim is to give prison inmates a craft skill they can practice in the long hours when they are locked in their cells, and from which they can earn money ...

'Fine Cell Work, as its name implies, teaches mainly male prisoners to a professional standard of tapestry, quilting and embroidery. Their work is sold to top London shops such as Colefax & Fowler and Jane Churchill, as well as by auction and commission.'...

Mediation, conflict resolution and alternatives to violence

LEAP Confronting Conflict (£5,000 per annum for three years towards the core costs).

'LEAP Confronting Conflict is a national voluntary youth organisation with a twelve year history of exploring the causes and consequences of conflict in young people's lives. ...

'LEAP works through engaging young people (14–25 years) and those who work with them in accessible, practical and relevant training and volunteering programmes ...

'The Foundation's support is contributing to our action research projects e.g. Gang Conflicts and Territorialism; our training programmes e.g. the Quarrel Shop; our networking opportunities e.g. the Young Mediators' Network, and our publications, courses and conferences.'...

Policy-orientated research, public education and awareness-raising

Slower Speeds Initiative (£10,000 for educating the public and decision-makers about the need for slower speeds on the roads).

'The Slower Speeds Initiative is a coalition of nine national community and transport organisations comprising the Children's Play Council, Cyclists' Touring Club, Environmental Transport Association, Pedestrians' Association, Pedestrians' Policy Group, Road Danger Reduction Forum, RoadPeace, Sustrans and Transport 2000.'...

Social welfare

Mind Cymru (£10,000 to develop a Wales-wide network of survivors of childhood abuse).

'Mind Cymru is part of Mind, the National Association for Mental Health ... the leading mental health charity in England and Wales.

'We plan to develop a Wales-wide survivor organisation that will aspire to meet the needs of adults who experience distress and mental health problems as a result of abusive childhoods. This is in response to the needs of service users who identified such a network as a top priority in a survey Mind Cymru carried out in 1997...'

Irish programme

Katharine Howard Foundation (IR£20,000 over two years for a research project).

'The Katharine Howard Foundation is a grant-making trust with many similar areas of interest to the Allen Lane Foundation. This project aims to produce a comprehensive picture of the origins and process of male marginalisation in Ireland. It will look at young men who typically have no participation in family life, community life, education or employment. Some will be fathers and some not. Increasing numbers, living in both urban and rural areas, are becoming socially excluded. Many are turning to drink, drugs and suicide.'

Exclusions

The foundation does not generally make grants to:

- academic research;
- addiction, alcohol or drug abuse;
- animal welfare or rights;
- arts or cultural or language projects or festivals;
- holidays or playschemes, sports or recreation;
- housing and homelessness;
- individuals;
- large general appeals from charities which enjoy widespread public support;
- medical care, hospices or medical research;
- museums or galleries;
- overseas travel;
- private and/or mainstream education;
- promotion of sectarian religion;
- publications;
- purchase of property, building or refurbishment;
- restoration or conservation of historic buildings or sites;
- vehicle purchase;
- work which the trustees believe is rightly the responsibility of the state;
- work outside the UK (except the Republic of Ireland);
- work which will already have taken place before a grant is agreed;
- endowments or contributions to other grantmaking bodies.

The foundation will not normally make grants to organisations which receive funding (directly or indirectly) from commercial sources where conflicts of interest are likely to arise.

Applications

In writing to the correspondent (not the trustees). Grants are normally made only to or through registered charities. There is no application form. An application should be no more than 4 sides of A4 (but the budget may be an extra page) and should be accompanied by the last annual report and accounts. It should answer the following questions:

- What are the aims of your organisation as a whole?
- How do you try to achieve these aims?
- What do you want our grant to help you do and how will you do it?
- How much will it cost? (Please submit a budget showing how the total figure is calculated)
- Are you asking the foundation to meet the whole cost? – What other sources of funding are you approaching?
- How will you know if your work has been successful?
- How will the work, and the way it is done, promote equal opportunities? If you do not think equal opportunities are relevant, please state why.

If further information is needed this will be requested by the secretary and a visit may be arranged when the application can be discussed in more detail.

In order to give as many applicants a chance of funding as possible the foundation does not accept applications from the same organisation more frequently than once a year.

Applicants should plan well ahead to allow sufficient time for applications to be assessed. If the foundation is unable to help it will try to give a decision within a few weeks, but grants are allocated at meetings of the trustees which are held three times a year so it may be as long as four months before a decision is made.

The Lankelly Foundation

Social welfare, disability

£4,912,000 (1999/2000)

Beneficial area UK, except London.

2 The Court, High Street, Harwell, Oxfordshire OX11 0EY

Tel. 01235 820044

Correspondent Peter Kilgarriff, Director

Trustees *Shirley Turner, Chair; Leo Fraser-Mackenzie; W J Mackenzie; Georgina Linton; Lady Merlyn-Rees; S Raybould; Nick Tatman.*

Information available Comprehensive report and accounts. Information leaflet.
www. lankelly-foundation.org.uk

Summary

This trust, which has expanded greatly since it was described in the previous edition of this book, makes substantial grants mainly to social welfare and disability charities outside London.

Its grantmaking is flexible and grants can, for example, include support for core costs or to make up shortfalls, and they can be renewed to run over a number of years beyond the usual three year initial maximum. Many grants are for £15,000, and there are few for less than this. There are not many grants for more than £50,000.

The foundation is known for the close personal contact it maintains with many of the charities that it supports. Applicants whose proposals are to be considered by the trustees are normally visited in advance of this. Not surprisingly, the foundation's support is much sought after, and success rates for applications are low. However they vary substantially for the different areas of its work, as will be seen in the sector by sector descriptions below. This is mainly because in some fields there are many fewer applications.

The foundation's priorities are to support:

- neighbourhood communities and families striving to create an environment in which they can flourish;
- people whose mental and physical disabilities require special resources;
- groups who are marginalised because of poverty, unemployment or crime, including domestic violence.

Background

The Lankelly Foundation was established in 1968. In 1998, following the (anonymous) settlor's death, it received a further legacy of over £70 million, which brought the value of the endowment to almost £110 million by March 2000. This has already led to a sharp increase in the value of the foundation's grants, up from the £3 million reported in the previous edition of this book to the £4.9 million noted above.

The trustees 'continue to help in wide areas of social need and, deliberately, they remain reactive, responding to needs identified by those directly involved in the provision of services. Nevertheless, the foundation's detailed and personal response involves considerable dialogue and visits by members of the staff.'

The administration of the foundation is linked to that of the much smaller Chase Charity (described in Volume 2 of this book), whose grants are also typically small. Nevertheless, the Lankelly Foundation and the Chase Charity remain two distinct trusts to which separate application has to be made.

The trustees have diversified their investments after their increased endowment, which came largely in the form of the foundation's settlor's bequest of a single holding in Slough Estates plc.

With the increased resources have come a third assistant director, Susan Ash, to join Ailsa Holland and Brian Whittaker. There is now a total of seven staff.

Information for applicants

The charity publishes the following information:

These guidelines have been drawn up following a full policy review in November 1998 and will be reviewed again towards the end of the year 2001.

Where we work

We are based in Oxfordshire but we work throughout the United Kingdom with the exception of the Greater London area. In Northern Ireland, however, we limit our grant-making to work which addresses the needs of elderly people. Otherwise we aim to treat different geographical areas fairly and welcome applications from groups who feel isolated by their location. The Trustees recognise the special problems which London faces but, because the Capital has greater access to charitable funds, they have confirmed their previous decision to concentrate on other areas of the United Kingdom until they next review their grant-making policies. Charities based in London but organising projects elsewhere will still be eligible to apply unless this application concerns London based staff [but see 'Exclusions' below].

What we support

For the next three years [*to autumn 2001. Ed.*] our broad priorities are:

- the support of neighbourhood communities and families who are striving to create an environment in which they can flourish
- the support of people whose mental and physical disabilities require special resources [but see 'Exclusions' below]
- the support of groups who are marginalised because of poverty, unemployment or crime, including domestic violence.

These broad areas will include elderly people, homelessness, alcohol and drugs, penal affairs, ethnic minorities, community arts and young people.

We shall be expecting to support community initiatives to meet local needs. We shall look for user involvement as well as the proper use and support of volunteers and you will have to produce evidence of sound management and a culture which fosters equal opportunities. A charity offering residential care should be working towards being inclusive rather than creating an exclusive environment which limits choice and opportunity. We intend to concentrate upon smaller charities, many of whom will have only a local or a regional remit. The Trustees will consider applications from large national charities but support will be rare and limited.

We want our grants to be effective, to achieve something which would otherwise not happen, or to sustain something which otherwise might fail, but we do not make grants to replace funds that have been withdrawn from other sources, or consider applications to replace time-expired grants from the National Lottery Charities Board. Grants are rarely less than £5,000 and are always made for specific purposes but they may cover capital or revenue needs. We will consider revenue support to a maximum of five years, although three year support will be more common. We shall monitor the effectiveness of all grants but those made over a number of years will involve more detailed evaluation and further visits from staff.

The Trustees have decided to make funds available to the [associated] Chase Charity to be disbursed in the fields of heritage and the arts. For further details please request a copy of the Chase Charity guidelines.

How we work

We receive many more applications than we can help, over 2,000 per annum of which approximately 160 will receive support from the Trustees. This inevitably means that we have to disappoint good schemes which meet our criteria. All letters receive a written answer and we attempt to reply to all correspondence within one month.

The Trustees meet quarterly in January, April, July and October. Applications may be submitted at any time but you should be aware that agendas are planned well ahead and you should expect a period of 6–9 months between an initial application and formal consideration by the Trustees.

The length of this process depends to some extent upon the size of the appeal but [also] upon your readiness to keep us informed. If we think we may be able to help, we will talk to you to clarify issues, give time for your plans to mature and for other funders to give an initial response.

In the period leading up to formal consideration at one of the quarterly Trustees' meetings one of the staff will arrange to visit you to discuss your application in more detail.

[*For how to apply, see under 'Applications' below. Ed.*]

Grant-making policy

This is summarised by the chair in the 1999/2000 annual report as follows:

Our main aim, in our new position as a more generous funder, is to continue quietly to support small-scale face-to-face initiatives, involving local people and users of the service. It is particularly satisfying that we can now consider recurring grants, up to 5 years, and assist with core costs, because security for a reasonable period is what so many valuable small enterprises need. This is more strenuous for all our staff, with increased emphasis upon monitoring and evaluation, but we are assured of the value of the Lankelly/Chase way, with generally no forms to fill and a very personal contact. Our grant categories, described in the Director's Report, may look diverse and haphazard and indeed to some extent they are, because they have developed in the context of our Settlement's 'general charitable purposes' according to the interests and experience of both Trustees and Staff. An example is the category called Penal Affairs in which our Director is playing a more proactive role in the efforts to support non-governmental organisations aiming at rehabilitation in prisons and in after-care.

During the year 2000–2001 we shall be starting to think of alternative ways of organising Trustees' involvement, leading up to our next quinquennial review in the autumn of 2001.

This was amplified by the director, Peter Kilgarriff:

1998 saw a dramatic increase in the Lankelly Foundation's assets which presented a welcome challenge to both Trustees and Staff. This year we have been putting some of our plans into effect and this report outlines the result.

Whilst wanting to continue to respond to wide areas of need we had a number of important aims:

- To find a balance between making more grants and supporting work over a longer time frame when warranted
- To consider supporting the core costs of organisations rather than simply concentrate upon project funding
- To improve our monitoring and evaluation of grants, especially those made over a number of years
- To preserve the link between investigation and presentation; ie: there is always someone who has seen the work and met the people concerned at the meeting where grants decisions are made
- To continue to give priority to disadvantaged neighbourhoods or groupings who find it difficult to attract support; to target the smaller rather than the larger, the local rather than the national and the poorer rather than the richer.

The Foundation made 152 grants, 36% more than the year before, and disbursed a total of £4,911,870, more than half as much again than in the previous year. The following ... give[s] a broad picture of who sought our help and where our money went.

Applicants

Overall we received significantly less applications than in previous years (down by 15% on last year) in a trend which other grant-making trusts are experiencing. This may be a result of the ubiquitous Lottery funds which are making a determined effort to target needs of all sizes or it may also be due to our own policies having a clearer focus.

The Foundation is becoming known for its particular interest in certain areas and the fact that we do not generally fund in London is now more widely understood (although applications from the Capital remain stubbornly high). Whatever the reason, applications outnumber grants by ten to one and although we hope to improve on this 'hit rate' we take heart from the fact that it has fallen since last year when only one in every sixteen applicants received a grant.

Geographical distribution

We also monitor where applications come from and how many grants were made in particular geographical areas as a result. We aim for a fair geographical spread and by visiting, talking to groups and using local networks we set out to attract applications from those areas which are under-represented. The results of this work are unpredictable but it is good to see an increase in the number of grants to Wales and the West and East Midlands. On the other hand the drop in the number of grants we were able to make in the North was not planned and we are working to address this.

The annual report gives regional totals. When recalculated on a per head basis they show a remarkably even distribution across the country, London excluded.

We welcome applications from minority ethnic groups and, although we do not record these grants separately, they are represented in the various grant categories. During the year we made grants to 8 such organisations totalling £281,600.

During the year, the Trustees decided to continue their grant-making in Northern Ireland. This had been suspended whilst the effects of the 'Peace and Reconciliation' funds became clearer. After assessing the situation they decided to target future grants on work with older people and those with disabilities for there appears to be a consensus that these two large groups have not benefited as much as others from the extra funds from Europe. They made six grants totalling £194,020.

Grants

Almost 40% of all grants made last year went to support an organisation over a number of years, helping to pay for staff and other running costs which may or may not be attributable to a particular project. The majority remain one-off grants, either for capital needs (eg: buildings or equipment) or to cover a revenue short-fall in the short term. This increase in the number and length of our grants has led to an increase in monitoring work both inside and outside the office. As with all the stages in the grant-making process, this is an area which we are assessing and it is clear that follow-up visits in a second or subsequent third year of our grant benefit both the organisation we are supporting and ourselves. They provide an opportunity for both parties to assess each other and their own practices or policies.

Our grant categories describe the principal purpose of the grants agreed.

These editors have added the number and value of grants, and the success rate of applications, for each heading. Note that the latter are based on small numbers of grants and can therefore be expected to vary substantially from year to year. The value of individual grants has also been added, or examples of grants under each heading.

Disability and special needs (35 new grants worth £992,000. Success rate 8%)

This has been a priority area for the Trustees for a very long time and last year 35 agencies and groups received a total of £992,320, over a fifth of the annual grant budget. As can be seen, grants were made to a wide range of agencies although the list does not reflect the detailed discussion which accompanied many grant decisions. Invariably this centred on the approach an organisation takes to people with disabilities; how they are involved and included in decision-making; the quality of independence and choice offered by a scheme; how it represents itself to the wider public and how well it is integrated into its local community.

The largest grant was to the Breakthrough Trust in Birmingham (£90,000 over three years) for an innovative training scheme. MIND in Oxford received £30,000 over three years for a salary, but more typical grants were those of £15,000 each for Caithness Mental Health Support Group in Scotland, for an animal husbandry tutor at the Bridle Gate Project in Leek, Staffs, and to enable Shopmobility in Merthyr Tydfil to buy wheelchairs.

Children and young people (19 new grants worth £736,000. Success rate 6%)

This is a major area of funding which received almost 15% of our total giving; 19 major grants were agreed totalling £735,550. Our policy of sustaining work over a number of years is very evident here but the list also includes some significant capital grants especially when there is an historic interest (eg: Alton Castle in North Staffordshire, £50,000 capital grant). Unusually, this list contains significant grants to Barnardo's and the NSPCC (£90,000 over three years in each case). These were not made as contributions to large national appeals but to support particular pieces of work with the most vulnerable young people. The Trustees recognise the important role these widely respected organisations have to play in focusing society's sometimes unwilling attention on unpopular issues.

This category also includes a separate programme of small grants to summer play and holiday schemes throughout the country. 131 such grants were made last year totalling £40,550.

Penal affairs (17 new grants worth £657,000. Success rate 61%)

This is another area in which our grantmaking has increased significantly in the last year with a total of £656,750 going to 17 different agencies. These work both within and without prisons, working towards a more effective resettlement by improving employment chances (eg: The Foundation Training Company in HMP Norwich (£100,000 over three years) and Comeback in the Kent prisons – £15,000 to meet a shortfall) or supporting family contact (eg: HALOW, Birmingham – £15,000 and SHARP in Shropshire – £9,000).

Mental ill health and substance abuse are often elements in a repeating cycle which includes homelessness, offending behaviour and arrest and the Trustees were pleased to see The Revolving Doors Agency extend their work into prisons (£96,000 over three years). They, in turn, agreed to extend their funding for the High Wycombe scheme for a further three years.

Homelessness (11 new grants worth £478,000. Success rate 14%)

The Trustees made 11 grants in this field, five of which provide revenue support over a period of years. In total they amount to £478,400 and they focus on single homeless people; on schemes which offer support to those in hostels or tenancies of their own and on services for people who are actually homeless for it is our view that outreach work remains important.

£75,000 over three years was given to GIPSIL in Leeds for a support worker, and £69,000, also over three years, to IMPACT Community Developments in Bradford. Smaller awards included grants of £15,000 each to the Ferry Project in Wisbech, Cambs, and to Julian House in Bath.

Community welfare (11 new grants worth £414,000. Success rate 3%)

Under this heading we gather together those grants which support services which cannot properly be described as local or neighbourhood services. They might often have an impact upon local communities (eg: CVS York – £15,000) but they might have a national, regional or city-wide remit. Here again, however, the Trustees concentrate on agencies which tackle social need and deprivation (eg: ATD – £13,000 – or St. Faith's Trust in Norwich – £45,000 to buy a building) but not to the exclusion of other needs. For example, we are keen to work with community foundations where we can. Our three year support of the Scottish Community Foundation (£75,000) enabled that organisation to restructure so that it would be better placed to plan and manage its future growth.

Also included in this category is the Trustees' grant of up to £10,000 in support of Southampton 2000, the biennial conference of the Association of Charitable Foundations. In all we made eleven grants in this category totalling £413,600.

Neighbourhood work (21 new grants worth £411,000. Success rate 30%)

This category brings together agencies which provide services to a local community or neighbourhood. They may be based in a church building – a number of our grants reflect religious organisations' growing concern to make sure that their buildings meet local social needs (eg: The Hill Top Wesley Community Association in West Bromwich – £9,000) – or they may be estate-based (eg: Meadow Well Community Resource Centre in Newcastle – £60,000 over three years). Either way, the Trustees look for local community involvement in the planning and management of resources as well as evidence of practical responses to local needs. This is an important part of our work and the Trustees made 21 grants totalling £410,600.

Elderly people (15 new grants worth £397,000. Success rate 15%)

The themes which underpin our work with people with disabilities surface again in our grant decisions for agencies working with older people: independence, choice, community centred services and continuing care. Last year we made grants to 15 mainly local charities totalling £396,900.

The largest grants were to Pravasi Mandal in Wellingborough (£40,000 to finish a day centre) and to Lydbrook Community Care in the Forest of Dean (£48,000 to relocate).

Heritage and conservation (7 new grants worth £264,000. Success rate 9%)

This is another long-standing area of interest and the Trustees made seven grants totalling £264,000 in addition to those made in this area through the Chase Charity. However, the Foundation Trustees keenly evaluate the social use and purpose behind restoration or conservation schemes. The Mansfield Traquair Trust in Edinburgh (£40,000) were able to show that their plans for restoring the remarkable murals in Mansfield Place Church were based on the future community use of the building and the National Museums and Galleries on Merseyside (£100,000) was again able to attract a large grant because they could demonstrate their wide appeal to the people of Liverpool and beyond.

Domestic violence (10 new grants worth £205,000. Success rate 24%)

Our involvement in this field has more than doubled since last year. As we ourselves are learning more about the complexity and the widespread nature of the problem, rapid social changes, particularly in family and relationship structures, are also highlighting it. Our grants are mainly targeted at improving refuge accommodation but outreach support is also very important. In all we made 8 grants, one to every four applicants, totalling £204,500.

The largest grant, of £58,000, was to Women's Aid, Dumfries for an outreach worker.

Alcohol and drugs (4 new grants worth £94,000. Success rate 11%)

This remains an important area of work but because it overlaps with other priority areas both the number of specific applications we receive and the number of grants made are comparatively low; four organisations received a total of £94,250. However, these grants do highlight the importance we attach to supporting local agencies either at their inception or when they are going through a difficult patch.

£49,000 was given to Alcohol and Drug Abstinence Service (ADAS) in Stockport to employ a counsellor.

Exclusions

In general terms the foundation does not contribute to large, widely circulated appeals. More particularly, it does not make grants in support of:

- the advancement of religion
- conferences or seminars
- travel, expeditions or holidays
- festivals or theatre productions
- research and feasibility studies
- endowment funds
- individual needs
- publications
- schools for people with special needs
- formal education, including institutes of further and higher education
- NHS hospital trusts and appeals from associated charities concerned with medical projects
- animal welfare
- sport
- individual youth clubs
- publications, films or video
- medical research
- other grant-making bodies
- under fives

Applications

Your initial letter should describe what you do and why you are seeking the foundation's help. There are no application forms, except for the programme of small grants for summer playschemes. The trustees meet in January, April, July and October.

Your letter should contain brief information about the origins and current company/charitable status of your organisation. It should be accompanied by your most recent annual report and accounts.

It should also answer the following questions:

- How much do you need to raise?
- How soon do you need to raise it?
- What support have you already attracted?
- Who else have you asked to help?

A separate application needs to be made to the Chase Charity, which shares the same administration.

The Law Society Charity

Law and justice, worldwide

£1,200,000 (1999/2000)

113 Chancery Lane, London WC2A 1PL

Tel. 020 7320 5899

Correspondent K M Jones

Trustees *G W Staple, Chair; Ms Howells; J N W Dodds; K P Byass; F A Smith; S Gadhia.*

Information available Accounts on file at the Charity Commission.

General

In 1999/2000 the trust's income was £2.2 million, most of which was received under a deed of covenant from The Law Society and The Law Society Services Limited. Grants totalled £1.2 million and £1 million was transferred to the trust's capital account.

The trust makes grants in support of charitable activities which are in the furtherance of law and justice. This includes:

- charitable educational purposes for lawyers and would-be lawyers;
- legal research;
- promotion of an increased understanding of the law;
- charities concerned with the provision of: advice; counselling; mediation services connected with the law; welfare directly/indirectly of solicitors, trainee solicitors and other legal and Law Society staff and their families.

The largest grant in 1999/2000, of £810,000, was given to The Law Society for educational purposes. Other larger grants were £73,000 to SolCare; £70,000 to The Solicitors Benevolent Association; £45,000 each to The Citizenship Foundation and The Solicitors Pro Bono Group; £28,000 to Galleries of Justice, and £15,000 to Capital Cases Charitable Trust.

The remaining grants were for £10,000 or less, including a number to human rights organisations, such as: Fair Trials Abroad (£10,000), Amnesty International (£4,800), Prisoner Advisory Service (£3,500), Asylum Aid (£2,000) and Justice (£960).

Most grants appear to be one-off.

Applications

In writing to the correspondent. Applications are considered at quarterly trustees' meetings, usually held in April, July, September and December.

The Leathersellers' Company Charitable Fund

General

£1,072,000 (to institutions, 1998/99)

Beneficial area London.

15 St Helen's Place, London EC3A 6DQ

Tel. 020 7330 1444

Correspondent Capt. J Cooke, Clerk

Trustees *'The Warden and Society of the Mistery and Art of the Leathersellers of the City of London.'*

Information available Annual report and accounts on file at the Charity Commission.

Summary

Most funds are disbursed in ongoing annual donations or recurrent grants, normally for between £10,000 and £50,000, to a largely fixed list of beneficiaries. However out of 170 or so grants a year, typically half are one- off payments under £5,000.

General

The 1998/99 annual report says:

> The policy of the trustees is to provide support to registered charities associated with the Leathersellers' Company, the leather and hide trades, education in leather technology and for the welfare of poor and sick former workers in the industry and their dependants. Thereafter financial support is provided to registered charities associated with the City of London and its environs.

The trustees have further written that it is their policy to give at least £1 million a year. Grants are made in the areas set out below. Three types of grants are given:

- single grants;
- guaranteed annual grants – a fixed annual sum paid for a set period (usually four years);
- recurrent annual grants – fixed or variable annual payments made for an undefined period or variable annual sums paid for a fixed period.

In 1998/99, 172 of the reported 198 grants were disbursed by type as follows:

	Amount	*No.*
Single	£164,000	81
Guaranteed annual	£602,000	78
Recurrent	£298,000	8
Grants-in-kind	£10,000	5

Grants to institutions were classified into the following categories:

Education and sciences	£343,000	(32%)
Relief of those in need and welfare	£211,000	(20%)
Disabled	£87,000	(8%)
Children and youth	£210,000	(19%)
Medicine and health	£106,000	(10%)
Arts	£76,000	(7%)
Advancement of religion	£25,000	(2%)
Environment	£15,000	(1%)
Other	£8,000	(1%)

Income for 1998/99 amounting to £1.38 million was generated from assets of £31.5 million. Grantgiving totalled £1.08 million, disbursed in 198 grants: 152 to institutions and 46 to individuals.

The accounts listed 56 grants of £5,000 or more, totalling £967,000. As in most recent years, the largest was for £105,000 to the Leathersellers' University Exhibition. Major new beneficiaries were the Tate Modern gallery in London (£50,000) and the Refugee Council (£45,000).

Large grants to charities supported the year before, mostly regular beneficiaries, were as follows:

Colfe's Educational Foundation (£64,000); Prendergast School (£50,000); British School of Leather Technology, Nene College (£46,000); Centrepoint Soho (£41,000); Rainbow Trust (£40,000); Woodland CentreTrust (£35,000); London Connection (£30,000); ChildLine (£25,000); Leather Conservation Centre (£20,000); Whizz Kidz (£20,000); Opportunities for People with Disabilities (£20,000).

Many grants for lesser amounts also went to previously supported beneficiaries: Fitzwilliam College, Cambridge (£16,000); St Catherine's College, Oxford (£16,000); Whitechapel Mission (£10,000); Rockingham Forest Trust (£6,000); Historic Churches Preservation Trust (£5,000).

Single grants average £2,000 and most of the recipients are not shown in the grant list. Higher amounts to recipients not appearing in the previous year's list were mostly healthcare charities assisting children or disabled people, including: Cardiac Risk in the Young (£8,000); Voice for the Child in Care (£8,000); AFASIC (£5,000); Starlight Foundation (£5,000); Tommy's Appeal (£5,000).

Applications

To the correspondent in writing. 'It should, however, be noted that before an award is made, the charity is thoroughly investigated and visited which, of necessity, limits the number of appeals capable of being processed in any one year.'

The William Leech Charity

Health and welfare in the north east of England, overseas aid

£491,000 (1998/99)

Beneficial area Northumberland, Tyne and Wear, Durham and overseas.

4 St James Street, Newcastle upon Tyne NE1 4NG

Tel. 0191 232 7940

Correspondent Mrs Kathleen M Smith, Secretary

Information available Annual report and accounts, which include guidelines for applicants, are on file at the Charity Commission and may sometimes be sent on request.

Summary

The charity's mission is 'to encourage local and community spirited people to create and sustain interest in voluntary charitable work'. Supported organisations are usually in Northumberland, Tyne and Wear, and Durham. Work in Teesside and other adjacent areas is said to be no longer supported.

Awards are usually one-off grants for amounts up to £1,000 – 133 out of a total of 175 grants in 1998/99. The usual maximum grant is for £5,000.

The charity also makes crisis loans (often to churches) and 'challenge grants' which match other funding £1 for £1.

Roughly one third of the income is used to support research projects at the University of Newcastle, while a separate designated fund 'awards grants to charities with a local connection assisting projects in underdeveloped areas in the world with special emphasis on the third world'.

General

The charity was established by property developer Sir William Leech in 1972 with an initial gift of property worth £550,000. By 1998/99 its assets were worth over £13.5 million. Income generated that year amounted to £578,000, of which £491,000 was paid out in 175 grants.

In the original guidelines, Sir William wrote:

I would avoid clubs, etc who receive substantial grants or donations from local councils or the Government. I do not regard them as charities because they are subsidised.

It is not my intention to subsidise social services even if grants by the Government or Council have been reduced. It is my intention to do what the social services do not support or do.

I would fully support independent boys' and girls' clubs, YMCA, YWCA, Scouts, Guides (Boys Brigade) and Christian youth clubs and Christian teaching colleges.

Guidelines

Extracts from the amended guidelines agreed by the trustees in August 1999 read as follows:

Geographical area

... Grants are normally made to organisations for work in the counties of Northumberland, Tyne and Wear and Durham. Grants for other areas are sometimes made if there is a substantial connection with the Settlor or a local organisation [*but see above. Ed.*].

Preferred categories

1. Organisations in which a high proportion [at least two thirds] of the work is undertaken by voluntary unpaid workers. [See 'Volunteer Support Programme' below.]
2. Organisations with a close connection to the Settlor, or with districts in which William Leech (Builders) Ltd built houses during the time when the Settlor was active in business.
3. Organisations with an active Christian involvement.
4. Organisations working in deprived areas for the benefit of local people, especially those which encourage people to help themselves. (In response to the occasional need for 'qualified and necessarily paid work' an inner city grants programme has been developed to 'favour three or four charities and give them larger annual donations towards running costs and salaries.')
5. Organisations doing practical new work and putting new ideas into action.

Low priority categories

[See 'Exclusions' below.]

Crisis loans

Where an organisation (often but not exclusively churches) is faced with an unexpected crisis a loan may be made in place of a grant. This is usually in order to allow them to get on with the building work, avoiding inflation costs. Loans are normally repayable over 5 years by annual instalments. Maximum loan £10,000. There are standard conditions.

Challenge grants

Where an organisation is raising funds by individual personal effort, the Trustees are often willing to match £1 for £1. There are standard conditions.

Amount of grants

a. Large number of £250 to £1,000 grants plus pump-priming £50 to £100 grants. In the belief that a small amount can give considerable encouragement to the type of organisation we wish to support.
b. Larger grants of up to £5,000 for new projects. In appropriate cases we will promise future support for up to three years to allow a project to get off the ground.
c. About one third of our income after the University allocation will be set aside for occasional large grants of £50,000 to £150,000 to major local appeals. In this case it will normally be a condition of support that

part of a project will be specifically named in honour of the Settlor.

Volunteer Support Programme

Volunteer Support Programme is an additional grants programme to assist volunteers in registered charities where at least two-thirds of the charitable work (excluding admin and fundraising) is done by volunteers. Likely grants will be in the region of £250 to £500.

Lady Leech Fund guidelines

This fund has an income of around £40,000 per annum, which is to be distributed to developing third world projects which have, if possible, a strong connection with our area (Northumberland, Tyne & Wear and Durham). Grants will probably be up to about £5,000, and would be payable to a registered charity (not individual). In suitable cases grants could be extended up to three years. The ideal arrangement would be for someone whose home is in our area, but is actually working with the project overseas. An annual written report would be expected.

University of Newcastle upon Tyne

... A substantial part of the income (at present one third) is granted ... For readerships or research lectureships ... For research in medicine and related sciences, including medical engineering ... However the following methods of assisting research would be considered:

a. Posts funded for shorter terms
b. Posts at less senior level, even possible student 'apprentice' researchers
c. If any existing post has difficulty due to lack of 'back up' we would consider a grant on a short-term basis. However we focus on people; so we remain less keen on funding machines or buildings.

Before his death the Settlor wished it to be known that he was firm in his belief that mental attitudes can affect physical health and recovery from illness, and that it would be appreciated if some of the research could be targeted in this direction.

Trustees' report 1998/99

Grants are made at the discretion of the Trustees, with an emphasis on those who are voluntarily helping others, but the guidelines do not favour giving charitable support to individuals, students, the Arts, holidays and expeditions, or minibuses except in very special circumstances. Registered charities write to the Charity and appeals are considered at bi-monthly meetings and either a grant is given or fixed term interest free loans are offered to successful applicants.

Although each request is given due consideration, it remains the policy of this trust to maintain its support of the original beneficiaries as defined in our guidelines before making grants to organisations traditionally supported by Local Authorities. On average over one hundred and twenty appeals are considered at each meeting.

The Volunteer Support programme has continued to be successful for small voluntary groups whilst applications to the Lady Leech Fund have been few to date although it is expected that as details about this Fund are more widely circulated, appeals will increase.

As in recent years, one third of our income is allocated to the University of Newcastle upon Tyne Medical School for Research lectureships. [*£213,000, or 37% of income, was awarded for this purpose in 1998/99. Ed.*]

During the year the Trustees awarded 175 separate grants (190 in 1998) ranging in value from £50 up to over £100,000. ... The Relate Family Foundation received £40,000 towards their North East £1 m appeal. This was to help recruit and train more volunteers and develop parenting programmes in schools in the North East.

The Alzheimer's Research Trust received £13,000 towards the setting up of a research network unit in Newcastle enabling the unit to pay a full part in Alzheimer's Research Trust proposed future research programme to understand and seek a cure for this awful affliction. A grant of £10,000 was made to the People's Kitchen to help meet the running and property costs of their building providing essential needs and support to homeless people in Tyneside. The Trustees are particularly keen to help this charity, as it has remained a charity where people are voluntarily helping others. Since it is allied closely with the intention of Sir William Leech the Trustees have continued to offer support. A grant of £10,000 was given to the St Paul's School Community Project towards the development of the project in expanding the role of the Children's worker.

The majority of grants are in the up to £1,000 category. This year grants have tended to support the elderly, young people and disabled people. Approximately £32,000 comprising 10 grants have been awarded from the Lady Leech Fund. Emergency disaster help was given to Bangladesh and Honduras. Other grants have helped children and communities in Ghana, Romania and Malawi.

During the year the Charity provided 4 (1998: 8) new interest free loans to the value of £45,000 (1998: £51,000) mostly repayable over a period of 5 years.

Grants in 1998/99

Donations summary (excluding the grant to the University of Newcastle):

Size	*No.*	*Amount*
Up to £1,000	133	£60,500
£1,001–£5,000	20	£48,000
£5,001–£10,000	15	£75,500
£10,001–£25,000	5	£54,000
£25,001–£100,000	1	£40,000
Total	174	£278,000

Not mentioned in the report was St John's College, Durham, which has apparently been awarded a multi-year grant of £11,000 a year.

Organisations working overseas supported from the Lady Leech Fund included Water Aid (£5,000), VSO (£3,000) and Action Health (£3,000), while Christian Aid got £5,000 from the main fund.

Some of the more typical recipients were as follows: Big Issue North East (£300); Darlington Association on Disability (£250); East Durham Play Network (£750); Oxclose Church (£1,000); Prudhoe Street Mission (£300); RNIB (£1,000); Seahouses Hostel (£5,000); Tyneside Macmillan Appeal (£3,500); Victim Support Middlesbrough (£150).

Exclusions

The following will not generally receive grants. The chairman and secretary are instructed to reject them without reference to the trustees unless there are special circumstances:

- Community centres and similar (exceptionally, those in remote country areas may be supported).
- Running expenses of youth clubs (as opposed to capital projects).
- Running expenses of churches. This includes normal repairs. But churches engaged in social work, or using their buildings largely for 'outside' purposes, may be supported.
- Sport.
- The arts.
- Applications from individuals.
- Organisations which have been supported in the last 12 months. It would be exceptional to support an organisation in two successive years, unless we had promised such support in advance.
- Holidays, travel, outings.
- Minibuses (unless over 10,000 miles a year is expected).
- Schools.
- Housing associations.

Applications

A full written application is required. Appeals are considered at bi-monthly meetings. Investigation of applications:

- Low priority: none.
- Proposed grant up to £1,000 or loan up to £10,000: written application only.
- Proposed grant of £1,001 to £10,000: one or more trustees must enquire further.

- Proposed grant of over £10,000: full papers must be circulated to the trustees to be discussed and approved.

For 'Volunteer Support Programme' grants, an application should consist of a one page letter identifying the following as a minimum:

- The organisation's name and charity number.
- The name and address of correspondent.
- The project's aims, progress, funds raised to date and how much is still required, and for what.
- Numbers of paid workers, annual salary costs and total administration overheads, plus numbers of unpaid volunteers.

This information should be sent to the trust secretary at the address above.

The Leeds Hospital Fund Charitable Trust

Hospitals in Yorkshire, charities in Leeds

£751,000 (1999)

Beneficial area Yorkshire.

Riverside House, 7 Canal Wharf, Leeds LS11 5WA

Tel. 0113 245 0813 **Fax** 0113 234 0815

Correspondent Angela Romaine, Secretary

Trustees *Mrs P J Dobson, Chair; C Asquith; C S Bell; T Hardy; R T Strudwick.*

Information available Report and accounts.

Summary

Most donations, by both number and value, are awarded to hospitals, hospices and convalescent homes. Main grants are typically for about £13,000 but unusual grants have gone as high as £150,000, and an annual £275,000 is paid to the connected Convalescent Homes Charity. Only rarely are grants made to organisations without a medical connection – in a broad sense.

General

The Leeds Fund was formed in 1887 as a non-profit healthcare insurance scheme, one of many of its kind, known generically as the Hospital Saturday Funds. In 1948 a new post-NHS scheme was introduced offering financial help to contributors and a convalescent service to help in recuperation. As the fund is non-profit making, it uses its surplus investment income to make grants to health/welfare organisations in the Leeds area, through the charitable trust described in this entry.

In 1999 the trust received £934,000 in covenanted income from the company fund. Donations totalled £751,000 and were distributed as follows:

Hospitals	11 grants	£286,000
Hospices	9 grants	£109,000
Other	31 grants	£59,000
Christmas gifts	5 grants	£22,000
The Convalescent Homes Charity	–	£275,000

In the hospitals category most grants were for equipment or furnishing costs and for amounts between £13,000 and £21,000. The exception was a major grant of £145,000 to St James' Hospital for a range of medical equipment needs.

Nine hospices, most of them regular beneficiaries, received £11,000 each towards their running costs, except St Gemma's and Wheatfields (£16,000 each).

The 'Other donations' and 'Christmas gifts' programmes make much smaller awards (for capital or revenue costs) and the recipients vary from year to year. The beneficiaries are a varied group and not confined to specifically healthcare charities, though most of them are. Grants were led in 1999 by £7,500 for the running costs of Leeds Children's Holiday Camp and £5,000 for equipment for the Cookridge Cancer Centre Appeal. Other beneficiaries included the Red Cross (£5,000 to hire a vehicle for a year), the Home Farm Trust (£1,500 towards running costs) and the Friends of Dolphin Manor (£300 to sponsor a concert). A small grant was to the York and Humberside Association for Music in Special Education (£260 for parachutes). This sounded like a surprisingly small sum for a perilous purpose, until this editor was himself educated in the use of such 'parachutes' in primary schools.

These editors always note when trustees are paid for services supplied to their charity, regarding this as undesirable in principle. Few such instances can be as small, or as unexpected, as the £135 paid by this charity to R T Strudwick 'for his professional services as toastmaster at the Trust's annual presentation ceremony'.

Exclusions

Individuals.

Applications

The trustees meet in February, May, July and November to consider applications.

The Kennedy Leigh Charitable Trust

Jewish charities, medical research, general

£1,142,000 (1998/99)

Beneficial area UK and Israel.

Suite 402, 258 Belsize Road, London NW6 4BT

Tel. 020 7316 1854 **Fax** 020 7316 1891

e-mail naomi@klct.freeserve.co.uk

Correspondent Naomi Shoffman, Administrator

Trustees *Michael Sorkin, Chair; Adelaide Kennedy Leigh; Lesley Berman; Leila Foux; Michele Foux; Geoffrey Goldkorn; Gerald Leigh; Angela Sorkin; Carole Berman Sujo.*

Information available Report and accounts with outline of grant-making policy, but with a grants list covering just four awards and less than half the grant expenditure. This is stated to be with the consent of the Charity Commission.

Summary

The activities of this public institution are not clear, and they should be. It has been said to support medical research in the UK and racial understanding in Israel, as well as giving regular support to a range of smaller organisations in the UK. However, this may be incorrect or no longer the case. The trust does not solicit applications, and states that its funds are fully committed.

General

The assertion that the non-disclosure of grants was with the consent of the Charity Commission has been queried. The Commission says that it was told of the trustees' view that disclosure would be harmful 'and did not challenge it', which could be taken as consent. However, the Commission added, in a most welcome new development in its practice, 'the Commission will now be contacting the trustees to discuss the question of the future disclosure of grants in the light of the more stringent disclosure provisions of the revised Charities SORP' (though in these editors' view, the new requirements are no more stringent than in the original SORP).

Three quarters of the available funds in a given year are for the benefit of organisations in Israel, with the remainder to be disbursed in the UK or elsewhere. Apart from large scale support for Cambridge University (for unknown purposes), for Jewish Care and for two named organisations in Israel, the trust did not disclose the beneficiaries, size, number or nature of its grants in 1998/99, the most recent year for which any information is available.

The trust has been reported elsewhere to be interested primarily in medical research in Britain and racial understanding in Israel (which might account for a desire to withhold details of beneficiaries in that field), and also to fund a range of small organisations on a regular basis, many local branches of national welfare charities receiving amounts from £1,000 to £10,000. However, none of this has been confirmed. Income amounted to £1,139,000 in 1998/99, from net assets worth nearly £18 million. Most of the assets are in the form of freehold property. A prudent diversification may be expected.

The 1998/99 report gives the names of four organisations which received donations during the year, but does not disclose the purposes to which the funds were to be put.

Continuing support was given to the University of Cambridge and St Mark's Research Foundation, with grants of £100,000 and £80,000 respectively, as in previous years. The trustees say that they:

> ... also made a major commitment to Jewish Care to be paid over a period of one year of which £250,000 was paid in the year under review. Since the year end the trustees have been pursuing a number of projects of which they have committed to two as follows:
>
> - The Shahaf Organisation, Kibbutz Naan. The trustees agreed to fund the relocation of a centre for the treatment of eating disorders to new premises.
> - Alyn Orthopaedic Hospital, Jerusalem. The trustees agreed to fund a sleep laboratory.

During 1998/99 the trustees formulated their guidelines in a mission statement of such generality as to be of limited interest:

> The trust will support projects and causes which will improve and enrich the lives of all parts of society, not least those of the young, the needy, the disadvantaged and the underprivileged. In meeting its objectives the trust expects to become involved in a wide range of activities. The trust is able to provide several forms of support and will consider the funding of capital projects, set-up costs and bridging running costs. The trust is non-political and non-religious in nature.
>
> The trust's objects state that three quarters of the available funds in a given year is for the benefit of organisations in Israel, with the remainder to be disbursed in the UK or elsewhere.

Exclusions

Private individuals.

Applications

'None considered. Funds fully committed.'

The Leverhulme Trade Charities Trust

Charities benefiting commercial travellers, grocers or chemists

£443,000 (to organisations, 1998/99)

Beneficial area UK.

1 Pemberton Row, London EC4A 3BG

Tel. 020 7822 6915

Correspondent A Clinch, Secretary

Information available Report and accounts available.

Summary

Grants are made only to:

- trade benevolent institutions supporting people working in the occupations set out above; and
- schools or universities providing education for them or their children.

General

The Leverhulme Trade Charities Trust derives from the will of the First Viscount Leverhulme, who died in 1925. He left a proportion of his shares in Lever Brothers Ltd upon trust and specified the income beneficiaries to included certain trade charities. In 1983, the Leverhulme Trade Charities Trust itself was established, with its own shareholding in Unilever, and with grantmaking to be restricted to charities connected with commercial travellers, grocers or chemists, their wives, widows or children. The trust has no full-time employees, but the day to day administration is carried out by the director of finance of the Leverhulme Trust (see separate entry).

In 1998/99 the trust's assets stood at £25.6 million and income was £808,000. There were 12 grants totalling £479,000, almost all to long-standing beneficiaries.

Two thirds of the funds went to the following three recipients:

- Commercial Travellers' Benevolent Institution (£160,000)
- Royal Pinner School Foundation (£80,000)
- The Girls' Public Day School Trust (£78,000)

Others included UCTA Samaritan Fund (£40,000) and the Royal Pharmaceutical Society (£25,000 for the Benevolent Fund and £15,000 for research fellowships). Another £36,000 was disbursed in student bursaries. An exceptional one-off grant of £20,000 was made to the National Eczema Society, a beneficiary apparently outside of the funding margins, but the trust said that a grant of this kind would not be made again.

The trust has gained unsolicited praise for its helpfulness to potential applicant organisations.

Exclusions

No grants to individuals.

Applications

By letter to the correspondent. All correspondence is acknowledged. The trustees meet in February and applications need to be received by the preceding October.

The Leverhulme Trust

Research

£14,827,000 (1999)

Beneficial area UK and developing countries

1 Pemberton Row, London EC4A 3BG

Tel. 020 7822 6938 **Fax** 020 7822 5084

e-mail policies@leverhulme.org.uk

website www.leverhulme.org.uk

Correspondent Professor Barry Supple, Director

Trustees *Sir Kenneth Durham, Chair; Viscount Leverhulme; N W A Fitzgerald; Sir Michael Angus; Sir Michael Perry.*

Information available Detailed annual booklet on policies and procedures, and an annual report, available from the trust. Full information on the website above.

General

Although this impressive trust makes over £12 million of grants to institutions, this is all for research projects conducted by individuals or by small groups of scientists or scholars, a type of grantmaking not covered by this book.

Those interested should read the very full material available on the trust's website.

Applications

The trust has detailed and specific requirements and procedures which applicants must meet, both as to timing and to content. All applicants should first ask for the trust's current 'Policies and Procedures' brochure before attempting to submit an application. The website may also be consulted.

Lord Leverhulme's Charitable Trust

Education, welfare, arts, general

£450,000 (1996/97)

Beneficial area UK, especially Cheshire and Merseyside.

PricewaterhouseCoopers, 1 Embankment Place, London WC2N 6NN

Tel. 020 7583 5000

Correspondent The Trustees

Trustees *A Heber-Percy; A Hannay.*

Information available In July 2000 the most recent audited reports and accounts received by the Charity Commission were those for 1994/95. A faxed draft copy of the accounts to April 1997 was in the Commission's file in June 2000, and the accompanying grants list was used for this entry.

Summary

More than 100 grants were made in 1996/97, mostly to organisations previously supported, starting at a few pounds and occasionally for £50,000 or more. First-time beneficiaries were unlikely to receive more than about £20,000.

General

There are two restricted funds within the trust. One generates £30,000 a year, which is paid to the Merseyside County Council for the trustees of the Lady Lever Art Gallery. The second is Lord Leverhulme's Youth Enterprise Scheme; the income from this sponsors young people in the Wirral and Cheshire areas who receive support from the Prince's Youth Business Trust (£27,750 was given in 1996/97, in nine grants of between £2,000 and £5,000 to enterprises managed by young people).

In 1996/97 grants totalled £450,000. Three were for more than £20,000, all of which appeared to be part of ongoing commitments: to Hammond School (£61,000); the Royal College of Surgeons (£50,000) and the Animal Health Trust (£31,000). Together with the next three largest beneficiaries, they accounted for 45% of the total grantmaking. These three were: King George VI & Queen Elizabeth Foundation of St Catherine; Bolton School, and the Cancer Gene Fund. Each received £20,000, the latter two being new recipients.

More than half of the 100 or so other grants were for less than £1,000, and many were under £100, with local branches of national welfare charities, community organisations, youth and arts beneficiaries all represented. Some payments as low as £5 appeared more like annual subscriptions, to, for example, the Newsvendors' Benevolent Institution and Chester Music Society.

Commitments to Cheshire and Merseyside were still strongly evident, accounting for perhaps three quarters of the beneficiaries. A specific interest in the village of Thornton Hough on the Wirral was also apparent, with £6,000 going to Thornton Hough Village Trust, and the Royal British Legion, All Saints Church and playgroup in the village receiving grants ranging from £500 to £1,500.

Perhaps as many as four out of five of the recipients of even the smallest grants had previously been supported. A sample is as follows: Abbeyfield Society, Widnes (£5,000); Adventure for Life (£2,000); Age Concern, Bootle (£250); Artists' General Benevolent Fund (£25); Ascot Charity Race Day (£1,000).

Exclusions

Non-charitable organisations.

Applications

By letter addressed to the trustees setting out details of the appeal, including brochures.

The Levy Foundation

(formerly the Joseph Levy Charitable Foundation)

Young people, elderly, health, medical research, Jewish charities

£1,014,000 (1998/99)

Beneficial area UK and Israel.

6 Camden High Street, London NW1 0JH

Tel. 020 7874 7200 **Fax** 020 7874 7206

e-mail administration@levyfoundation.org.uk

Correspondent Sue Nyfield, Grants Manager

Trustees *Mrs N F Levy; Mrs Jane Jason; Peter Levy; Silas Krendel; Neil Benson.*

Information available Full accounts and grants list, with a brief report.

Summary

About three quarters of the grants by number are small, often repeated, donations for between £100 and £5,000. However, perhaps as much as 90% of the funds are used for a number of substantial long-term commitments, from £10,000 to £250,000 a year, mainly to organisations involved with medical care and research or youth welfare, and for Jewish causes.

General

Formerly the Joseph Levy Charitable Foundation, two related trusts were merged with the foundation during 1999 and the name was changed to the Levy Foundation. Consequently, the foundation's asset base more than doubled, from £10.8 million in 1996/97 to over £22 million in 1998/99, largely due to transfers of over £4 million from the Lawrence Levy Charitable Trust and £0.5 million from the Joseph Levy 1961 Discretionary Settlement. The income of £973,000 was bolstered by a £779,000 recognised gain in stocks and shares.

The amount spent on management and administration, other than portfolio management and accounting costs, was £169,000, including a salary and pensions package for the executive director worth £73,000. This represented one sixth of the grant total, or nearly £2,000 per grant. This issue is currently being addressed by the foundation.

Direct charitable expenditure totalled £1,014,000, disbursed in grants to 87 beneficiaries.

60% of the funds went to the following organisations, which the foundation says it will continue to support in the future:

	1998/99	1997/98
Dementia Relief Trust	£257,000	£255,000
London Youth	£145,000	£145,000
Cystic Fibrosis Trust	£82,000	£95,000
B'nei Arazim	£50,000	£5,000
English Blind Golf Association	£40,000	£30,000
Tavistock Clinic Foundation	£35,000	£35,000

Ongoing support was given to a range of Jewish organisations, which accounted for perhaps a fifth of the grant total. Recipients included the Ashkelon Foundation (£25,000); Institute for Jewish Policy Research (£28,500); Joint Jewish Charitable Trust (£21,000); Norwood Ravenswood (£13,000); Jewish Council for Racial Equality (£11,000); Community Security Trust (£10,000); Jewish Association for the Mentally Ill (£5,000) and many others, down to small awards such as £550 to Jewish Care and £500 to the Centre for Jewish Christian Relations.

Other grants for £10,000 or more included those to Youth at Risk (£25,000); Cystic Fibrosis Holiday Fund for Children (£25,000); University of Bristol – Blood Cord Project (£20,000); YouthNet UK (£20,000); Cancer Bacup (£20,000); Motivation (£15,000); Children in Crisis (£13,000); Imperial College of Science, Technology and Medicine (£10,500), and the International Myeloma Foundation (£10,000). Nearly all had received the same amount in the previous year.

Exclusions

No grants to individuals, under any circumstances.

Applications

In writing to the Grants Manager at any time.

Lewis Family Charitable Trust

Medical research, health, education, Jewish charities

£399,000 (1998/99)

Chelsea House, West Gate, London W5 1DR

Tel. 020 8991 4500

Correspondent David Lewis

Trustees *David Lewis; Bernard Lewis.*

Information available Inadequate annual report and accounts, listing 27 grants over £1,000, but without the required analysis or review.

Summary

Large grants, normally in the range £15,000 to £50,000, tend to go to organisations regularly supported by the trust, mostly for medical research. Small grants, ranging from under £1,000 to £3,000, are made in the areas mentioned above and seldom repeated.

General

Grants are made, in particular, to charities involved in the promotion of medical research. In addition, Jewish charities have in the past accounted for a large part of the trust's grant expenditure, but the proportion appears to be reducing.

In 1998/99 net assets were £3,304,000, but a £500,000 donation saw the trust's income rise to £679,000, up from £206,000 the year before.

Out of 12 organisations receiving grants of over £10,000 (accounting for over three quarters of the total), 10 had been supported in the previous year. Most were medical research organisations receiving repeat awards, many with a long-standing relationship with the trust, including:

- King's College Hospital, £58,500 (£25,500 in 1997/98)
- Birth Defects Foundation, £57,000 (£59,000)
- Association for the Advancement of Cancer Therapy, £42,000 (£25,000)
- University of Nottingham, £19,000 (£25,000)
- Queen Mary and Westfield College Hospital, £19,000 (also funded in 1996/97)
- Imperial Cancer Research, £17,000 (£55,000)

In addition, the British Council received £40,000 for the Lewis Fellowship Fund, while the largest grant to a Jewish organisation was for £21,000 to UJIA/ Joint Jewish Charitable Trust, both long-term beneficiaries.

The only apparently new beneficiary receiving a large grant was the Bedford Square Charitable Trust (£30,000).

A further 15 recipients got grants ranging from £1,000 to £3,000. Only Norwood Ravenswood and CACDP had been supported in the previous year, receiving £2,000 and £1,750 respectively.

Others included Chernobyl Children's Lifeline (£3,000); the Multiple Sclerosis Society (£2,000); West London Synagogue (£1,000); Teenage Cancer Trust (£1,000), and the Council for Christians and Jews (£1,000).

Another £15,000 was spent on grants under £1,000.

Exclusions

No grants to individuals.

Applications

To the correspondent in writing. Grants are normally made only once a year. The trust states: 'grants are not made on the basis of applications received'.

The Linbury Trust

General

£7,068,000 (1998/99)

See entry for the Sainsbury Family Charitable Trusts

Tel. 020 7410 0330

Correspondent Michael Pattison, Director

Trustees *Lord Sainsbury of Preston Candover; Lady Sainsbury; Miss Judith Portrait.*

Information available Good annual report and accounts, with full grants listing.

Summary

One of the Sainsbury Family Charitable Trusts which share a joint administration, this trust was established by Lord Sainsbury of Preston Candover.

Much of the trust's support has been for major capital projects in the arts and education. It has funded the Oxford University Business School and given generous support to many of the major national arts institutions, such as the National Gallery and the Royal Opera House, as well as other museums and galleries. It also supports colleges of arts education and has a particular interest in dance and dance education. The trust has pioneered research funding of Chronic Fatigue Syndrome. It is also concerned with some social welfare issues such as drug abuse, homelessness and the problems of young people at risk.

Though unsolicited applications are 'only successful occasionally ... all applications in the listed fields are considered on their merits'. In the 'built environment' field, it is again stated that 'trustees consider appeals on their merits, particularly historic buildings and major art institutions', so the usual Sainsbury strictures discouraging unsolicited applications do not apply.

General

The trust has an income of about £8 million and payments in 1998/99 totalled £7 million (new approvals, though, were just £3.3 million). Its staff include Michael Pattison, director of each of the trusts in the group, and David Brown and Dr Patricia Morison, administrators.

The annual reports are unusual for this group of trusts in that they describe policies and give the totals for grants approved under various headings, but for individual grants list payments, often in respect of major grant decisions taken in previous years, rather than new grant approvals. So for example, under the 'Education' heading, nearly £1.5 million in new capital grants is noted for 1998/99, but the largest individual payment recorded for the year was of £75,000. There were clearly one or more very large capital awards, but the recipients will not be known until the money begins to be drawn down.

New grant approvals in 1998/99 were classified as shown in the box below.

Annual report 1998/99

This section of the entry reprints the report's description of the trust's grantmaking under each heading, and also some of the major grant payments (not grant approvals) made in that year.

Trustees give priority to charities in which they have a particular interest and personal knowledge or experience. For the areas where they do not have such interest, knowledge or experience they seek expert advice from those who are highly qualified to give such advice. Because of the Trustees' proactive approach, unsolicited applications are only successful occasionally, although all applications in the listed fields are considered on their merits. Applicants are always required to provide a detailed budget for their proposal and up to date audited accounts with a copy of the most recently published annual report.

The net unrestricted income of the Trust for the year after charging the cost of consultancy and administration amounted to £8.03 million, which added to the sum of £11.58 million brought forward from 1997/98, gave a total of £19.61 million available for future distribution.

Payments made during the year totalled £7.04 million.

The Trustees approved 107 grants amounting to £3.36 million. The balance of grants approved but not yet paid is £13.61 million. Of the grants awarded during the current year £1.24 million is due within one year and the remainder for payment over the next five years.

Arts and art education

The Linbury Trust has been an influential and consistent supporter of national excellence in the visual and performing arts over the past 30 years, with substantial donations to the National Gallery, The Royal Academy of Arts, Dulwich Picture Gallery, the Royal National Theatre, the Royal Ballet, Sadler's Wells and Rambert School of Dance. In keeping with this support for the visual and performing arts, in 1998 the Trustees were pleased to be able to release £4.5 million from an earlier commitment to the new Royal Opera House. This grant is part of an ongoing commitment to the Development Appeal for The Royal Opera House.

Trustees have continued to support art and ballet schools in a number of ways, including a Teaching Fellowship in Life Drawing at Wimbledon School of Art, student bursaries at City and Guilds of London Art School, the Junior Summer School at the Royal Ballet School and bursaries at Rambert School of Dance, within Brunel University, for young South African students. ...

Major grants paid included the following:

- Royal Opera House: £4,500,000 towards the Development Appeal.
- Philharmonia/Kirov Ballet: £24,000.
- Royal National Theatre: £125,000 for a new fly tower (total grant £250,000).
- Wimbledon School of Art: £26,008 for a tutor in Life Drawing (total grant £50,000).
- South African Rambert Dance Scheme: £21,345 for students from South Africa.
- Royal Ballet School: £25,000 for the Junior Summer School (total grant £100,000).
- Buildings Book Trust: £10,000 to help continue revision of the Pevsner Buildings of England series (total grant £30,000).
- Sadler's Wells Theatre: £100,000 for a new dance studio (total grant £200,000).
- The Hermitage Museum, St Petersburg: £12,000 towards the museum's development programme.
- Oscar Wilde Monument: £25,000 towards the sculpture by Maggi Hambling in Adelaide Street, London.

Chronic Fatigue Syndrome research

Trustees continued to fund research into CFS during Linbury's tenth year in this field. Over this period, more than £4 million has been invested in a broad portfolio of research carried out in hospitals and university departments throughout the UK. This represents the most sustained body of research into this debilitating and poorly understood condition in the United Kingdom. The Trustees are advised by the following panel:

Professor A M McGregor, Chair: Professor of Medicine at Guy's, King's and St Thomas' Medical School, London

Professor L Borysiewicz: Professor of Medicine at University of Wales College of Medicine, Cardiff.

Professor T K J Craig: Professor of Community Psychiatry at Guy's, King's, St Thomas' Medical School, London

Professor R S J Frackowiak: Professor of Neurology, Institute of Neuroscience, London.

THE LINBURY TRUST – NEW GRANT APPROVALS IN 1998/99

	Revenue	*Capital*	*Total*
Arts and art education	£251,000	£350,000	£601,000
Chronic Fatigue Syndrome research	£435,000	–	£435,000
Drug abuse	£56,000	–	£56,000
Education (especially dyslexia)	£82,000	£1,460,000	£1,542,000
Environment and heritage	£69,000	£100,000	£169,000
Medical	£14,000	–	£14,000
Social welfare	£213,000	£20,000	£233,000
Third world education/welfare	£310,000	–	£310,000
Total	£1,430,000	£1,930,000	£3,360,000

Trustees are pleased to note that the Chief Medical Officer's Working Group on CFS/ME, under the chairmanship of Professor Allen Hutchinson of University of Sheffield, has begun its work. The CMO's recognition of the seriousness and prevalence of this illness represents an important breakthrough and has brought encouragement to thousands of CFS sufferers. Following Linbury's lead, NHS Research and Development, Wellcome Trust and the Medical Research Council have all expressed a willingness to consider applications for research grants in the field.

A total of 15 payments were made under this heading, the largest being to the Regional Virus Laboratory at Ruchill Hospital (£112,000) and for Professor Garralda at Imperial College, London (£45,000).

Drug abuse

Trustees have maintained the dual strategy of helping major providers of therapy and care whilst at the same time supporting innovative ideas in the field, through which young offenders can be dealt with more speedily and in a non-custodial way.

The eight grants paid were as follows:

- Addaction: £20,000 for two projects in London.
- Tacade: £10,000 for the dissemination of a 'Parent Power Package'.
- Turning Point: £30,000 for young people's projects in Sheffield and Leeds.
- Re-Solv: £10,000 for an information officer (total grant £20,000).
- Phoenix House: £10,000 to a pilot vocational training project in South Shields (total grant £30,000).
- Standing Conference on Drug Abuse: £15,000 towards the salary of the Head of Education and Prevention (total grant £30,000).
- Cascade: £13,000 to replicate a drug education programme in Rugby.

Education

Trustees continue to support charities that help children with literacy problems, particularly dyslexia. A priority for Trustees is to enable teachers to be trained in the diagnosis of dyslexia and in how to help children with such needs, especially those who are not identified early enough.

Trustees occasionally make capital grants to Schools and Colleges and in 1998/99 Bute House and Sparsholt College were helped. Innovative projects, like the Everyman's Millennium, the Voices Foundation and Education Extra, appeal to the Trustees as they are original, creative and good value for money. General appeals on behalf of schools or individuals or for help with fees are not normally supported.

Major grant payments included the following:

- Bute House, London: £10,000 for a new hall appeal.
- Sparsholt College, Hampshire: £75,000 for a new building (total grant £350,000).
- Everyman's Millennium Library: £50,000 for collections of 250 titles to all UK secondary schools.
- Helen Arkell Dyslexia Centre, Surrey: £12,000 for teacher bursaries (total grant £36,000).
- Constable Education Trust: £50,000 towards the establishment of a secondary school for dyslexics in London.
- Changemakers: £30,000 to develop the scheme in more schools.

Social welfare

Trustees have continued to help charities supporting disadvantaged people who are in care or homeless and above all they have sought out organisations that give young people an opportunity to change their lives. Trustees seek to help young people to have a second, or even a third chance, whether through a close mentoring project or through one to one literacy support.

Trustees also support initiatives that improve the quality of life of older people and through which they are helped to continue living in their own home. Whilst this is not a major category or priority, trustees will always consider innovative ideas in this field.

Major grant payments included the following:

- Include: £20,000 to develop a project for excluded pupils in the north east of England.
- Staying Put for the Elderly: £15,000 for improvement work for older people in their own homes, over two years.
- Centrepoint, Soho: £50,000 to help enhance the educational component of the service.
- Youth at Risk: £50,000 to divert young people from crime, over three years.
- National Institute of Conductive Education: £110,000 capital grant for a new building.
- Fairbridge: £100,000 for a centre for young people at risk, over two years.
- Alive and Kicking, Glasgow: £15,000 to refurbish an older people's drop-in service.

Third world education and social welfare

Trustees have continued to concentrate their help on a small number of specific activities overseas. Linbury is funding undergraduate bursaries for a fifth year at the University of Cape Town. The Trust is now also supporting 10 PhD students at UCT who will spend two of their years at UCT and one year at either Bristol, Oxford or Sheffield Universities in the UK. The rationale behind this programme is to attract and keep some of the ablest African students within the teaching faculties at a time when the Universities have to compete for talent with industry and commerce.

Major grant payments included the following:

- Antigua Board of Education: £50,000 to help repair the island's schools after Hurricane Georges.
- Butrint Foundation: £80,000 for an Albanian archaeological project.
- Merlin: £25,000 for the Afghanistan earthquake appeal.
- Nelson Mandela Children's Fund: £75,000 for a children's project in South Africa, over three years.
- University of Cape Town Trust: £179,898 for undergraduate and postgraduate student bursaries.

Environment and heritage

In the built environment Trustees consider appeals on their merits, particularly historic buildings and major art institutions. This year The College of Arms, The Tower of London and Burton Opera House were supported.

In the natural environment Trustees continue to support The Woodland Trust millennium initiative.

Major grant payments included the following:

- Burton Opera House: £50,000 for additional facilities.
- College of Arms: £20,000 for the refurbishment of a building.

Medical

Linbury's main activity in the medical field is in CFS Research (see above). From time to time Trustees make small grants for other specific activity in this field, particularly for causes that appear neglected by other charities.

Applications

See the guidance for applicants in the entry for the Sainsbury Family Charitable Trusts. A single application will be considered for support by all the trusts in the group.

However, 'because of the Trustees' proactive approach, unsolicited applications are only successful occasionally, although all applications in the listed fields are considered on their merits'.

Enid Linder Foundation

Health, welfare

£477,000 (1998/99)

35 Tranquil Vale, Blackheath, London SE3 0BD

Tel. 020 8297 9884

Correspondent Brian Billingham, Secretary

Trustees *Jack Ladeveze; Audrey Ladeveze; M Butler; G Huntly; J Stubbings.*

Information available Report and accounts on file at the Charity Commission.

Summary

Around 100 grants a year, most in the range £1,000 to £5,000 and peaking at £35,000. There are no more than 10 new grants each year, with most money going to a mixed group of regularly supported beneficiaries, mainly in the field of health, particularly that of children and disabled people. Local (normally London and the south), national and international charities are supported.

General

In 1998/99 the trust had an income of £568,000, part from investment income on its assets of £8 million, and part from a subsidiary property investment company, Industrial Partners Ltd. Grant giving of £477,000 was recorded, plus a further £97,500 of direct charitable expenditure on 'teaching hospitals and universities'.

The accounts listed 98 grants, plus a further £16,000 as 'donations to beneficiaries'. This sum may be for small grants, but the main list already includes grants as low as £100.

Eight grants for £10,000 or more amounted to £142,000, or 30% of the total. Only two were for organisations not supported in the previous year: Kent Association for the Blind (£25,000) and Newcastle Paediatric Therapy (£10,000).

The other major beneficiaries, all receiving repeat grants for the same amount as in the preceding year, were the Royal College of Surgeons (£35,000); Médecins sans Frontières (£25,000); Victoria and Albert Museum (£15,000); 'Cancer Research' (£12,000); Stroke Fund (£10,000), and Intermediate Technology (£10,000).

Others included Leukaemia Research (£6,000); Mildmay Mission (£2,000); NSPCC (£3,000); PDSA (£4,000); Riding for the Disabled, Knightsbridge (£2,000); Southwark Community Education (£1,500); Torbay and South Devon Hospital (£2,500); UNICEF (£2,500); Whizz Kidz (£2,000); Youth Sports Trust (£3,000).

Some new beneficiaries, not in the list of those supported in the previous year, were Glasgow Dental Hospital (£3,000); Jennifer Trust for Spinal Muscular Atrophy (£2,000); Motivation (£2,000), and Forest Philharmonic (£3,000).

Applications

In writing to the correspondent.

The George John Livanos Charitable Trust

Health, maritime charities, general

£877,000 (1999)

Beneficial area UK.

c/o Jeffrey Green Russell, Apollo House, 56 New Bond Street, London W1Y 0SX

Tel. 020 7499 7020

Correspondent Philip Harris, Secretary

Trustees *Mrs S D Livanos; P N Harris; A S Holmes; P D Powell.*

Information available Sets of accounts available from the trust for £10.

Summary

The trust disburses around two thirds of its funds in a small number of one-off capital grants, occasionally for more than £100,000, though more than half its grants are for under £10,000. Grants are regularly made in support of maritime causes, while others are made mainly to a range of medical charities for older people or children. Grants of over £10,000 are more likely to be recurrent.

General

In 1999 the trust had assets of £5.5 million, generating £392,000 in income. Administration costs were high, at £103,000 or 12% of grants expenditure, much of which was spent on accounting and consultancy fees. In all, £877,000 was paid in 44 grants, 14 going to organisations supported in the previous year.

Of the total, 66% was disbursed in seven large capital donations. Four of the recipients had maritime connections: Maritime Volunteer Service (£125,000); University of Hull Maritime History Trust (£55,000); Sail Training Association (£50,000) and the Royal Standard of Peter the Great Maritime Education Trust (£36,000). The other recipients were St Mary's Hospital, Paddington (£165,000); Abbeyfield (£100,000) and Fight for Sight (£50,000).

Most of the other large grants went to beneficiaries that had been supported in the previous year, including Crimestoppers (£30,000); Martlets Hospice and Alzheimer's Reports (£25,000 each); and Barnardos, Children's Liver Disease Foundation and University College London (£20,000 each).

Of the 31 remaining grants, 25 were in the £500 to £5,000 bracket, mostly to new recipients, including the High Blood Pressure Foundation, Pain Association of Scotland, Downs Syndrome Association, Swansea YMCA, Kent Kids, Thrift Urban Housing, Rockingham Forest Trust and the 3H Club.

Applications

The trust requests that no unsolicited applications be sent.

Lloyds TSB Foundation for England and Wales

Social and community needs, education and training

£17,311,000 (1999)

Beneficial area England and Wales. (See separate entry for the Lloyds TSB Foundations for Scotland and Northern Ireland.)

PO Box 140, St Mary's Court, 20 St Mary at Hill, London EC3R 8NA

Tel. 020 7204 5276 **Fax** 020 7204 5275

e-mail guidelines@lloydstsbfoundations.org.uk

website www.lloydstsbfoundations.org.uk

Correspondent Kathleen Duncan, Director General

Trustees *Joanna Foster, Chair; Prof. Murray Stewart, South West; Revd Rachel Benson, North East and Yorkshire; Virginia Burton, South East; Jacqueline Carr, London; Dr Christine Kenrick, West Midlands; Dr Pauleen Lane, North West; Paddy Linaker; John Penny; Howard Phillips, East of England & East Midlands; Linda Quinn, Wales; Colin Webb.*

Information available Guidelines for applicants. Excellent annual report and accounts. Strategy document. Good website.

Summary

This foundation has become one of the most important national sources of grants, which are generally modest in size and usually for local organisations. About half of all applications have been successful in obtaining grants, though not always for the full amount asked.

Potential applicants are encouraged to discuss their plans with the foundation's staff before submitting their applications, and this, too, tends to increase the chances of success.

The foundation works in two fields (the third field possible under its objects, medical research, is not being funded at present):

- social and community needs;
- education and training for disabled and disadvantaged people of all ages.

Applications for over £5,000 are more likely to be successful if they fall within one of the foundation's three areas of special interest:

- family support
- challenging stigma and discrimination
- promoting effectiveness in the voluntary sector

Most of the money is allocated to 10 regional budgets on the basis of population, weighted for deprivation. A proportion is for appeals which benefit people across England and Wales as a whole.

Grants may be made under one of two programmes:

Community programme

Regional

'As a general guide, the Trustees make donations up to £5,000 to applications which fall outside the Areas of Special Interest, and up to £10,000 to those which do fall within these areas.' Multi-year grants may occasionally total as much as £30,000.

National

For projects covering England and Wales as a whole, or where there is potential for dissemination on a national basis. Donations are generally in the region of £10,000 to £30,000, though they can go up to about £100,000, and they are often for two or three year funding.

Collaborative programme

Donations to support collaborative activities between charities at local, regional or national levels. 'Applications are particularly welcomed for the sharing of good practice.' This is a new programme.

General

The Lloyds TSB Foundations own 1.4% of the Lloyds TSB Group's share capital and receive 1% of the Lloyds TSB Group's pre-tax profits averaged over three years.

The foundations are legally independent of the group and their policies are determined by independent boards of trustees.

However, there are still close links with the bank group. In particular, all requests for charitable donations made to companies within the group are handled by the appropriate Lloyds TSB foundation. This gives the mistaken impression that the funding for these foundations is an act of philanthropy by the bank group, which it is not. The foundation's original shareholding in the TSB was a necessary recognition of the existing element of public ownership of that bank at the time of its floatation. When TSB merged with Lloyds, the new company had to accept in turn the public obligations that had been established.

The Foundation for England and Wales is the largest of the four foundations, receiving 72% of the income. This has grown rapidly following the merger of the banks but may now be reaching a point of greater stability.

The foundation is energetic. It has appointed a range of regionally based trustees, after open advertisement; it has set regional budgets based on need as well as on disadvantage; and it has worked hard at developing a range of thought-through policies. It is open and accessible, welcoming informal contact from applicants in advance of formal applications, and it is playing a vigorous part in the promotion of the wider interests of the voluntary sector. Especially at regional and local level, it is setting standards of grantmaking that are a welcome example for many of the less focused trusts described in this book.

Grant-making policy

Grants are made for capital, project and core costs. In the case of the latter, future sustainability is always an issue when making grant decisions. Increasingly, multi-year grants are being 'tapered', with less being given in the second or third years. However, at present, the foundation is unlikely to fund investment by an applicant in developing its own voluntary income.

There is little or no repeat funding as 'successful applicants will be expected to leave two years before applying for further support. Unsuccessful applicants should leave at least one year before reapplying.'

There is a new programme of support for 'collaborative working'. This is explained below, but nevertheless it remains for the moment a little unclear to this editor. It is said to be concerned primarily with collaboration between charities rather than between charities and other agencies. The annual report talks of the burden for staff 'of working up applications involving several partners'. However, the annual report quoted below also talks of promoting collaboration between grant-making bodies (which might or might not concern only charitable funders) and 'between charities and public agencies'.

One focus is on sharing and disseminating good practice, another on supporting representative bodies such as the currently fashionable regional forums. However, the regional report for London also talks of the need to 'overcome duplication of service provison'. This is a need typically prominent in the minds of funders and of local authorities hoping to rationalise the sector, but in this editor's experience is much less obvious to most local organisations and their beneficiaries. At this level the sector's diversity and the enormous differences between the styles and ethos of different organisations offering what, on paper, seem to be overlapping services, are more often regarded as strengths rather than weaknesses.

Guidelines for applicants

The foundation publishes detailed guidelines for its applicants, though their presentation is not as clear as it might be. They are reprinted in the accompanying box (paper, large print and audio versions are available from the foundation; ring 020 7204 5276).

Annual report 1999

The covenanted income to the Foundation was £19.2 million which compares with

Lloyds TSB Foundation for England and Wales – Excerpts from the Strategic Plan 2000

Guiding principles

A number of fundamental guiding principles underpin the work of the Foundation and the way in which it works to fulfil its mission.

- We will pursue an independent, philanthropic and generalist approach to grant-making.
- We will maintain a local presence in each of the regions of England and Wales.
- We will support organisations which contribute to local community life at the grassroots level.
- We will promote capacity building, and strategic and collaborative working within the voluntary sector.
- We will strive to demonstrate best practice, including equality of opportunity, in the ways in which we work.
- We will work in ways that are open, transparent and unbureaucratic.
- We will develop the skills, knowledge, experience and expertise of Trustees and staff to the optimum benefit of the Foundation.

Objectives

The objectives of the Foundation over the next 3–4 years are:

1. To establish two distinct programmes of grant-making, a Community Programme and Collaborative Programme. ...
2. To make an informed choice of a limited number of Special Interests in order to focus our grant-making into areas in which the Foundation can have a real and measurable impact. ...
3. To establish and maintain best practice in grant-making policies and processes.
4. To establish a monitoring and evaluation regime which enables the Foundation to measure its own organisational performance and the effectiveness of our main grant programmes.
5. To secure the knowledge, skills and talents required to support effective grant-making through continuous development of our staff and Trustees, and bringing in external expertise where appropriate.

Community programme

The Foundation is proud of its focus on funding at the grassroots. We wish to make this focus explicit by structuring our core grant-making activity into a Community Programme. This will incorporate the existing work of the Foundation, and will now have two component parts.

- The Community Programme (small grants) will respond to applications for one-off small donations for charitable activities at local community level. Up to 10% of the funding will be directed to areas of Special Interest.
- The Community Programme (medium grants) will provide one-off grants and longer-term funding to organisations at local, regional or national level. Both a reactive and active approach will be taken. Approximately half of the funding will be directed to areas of Special Interest ...

Collaborative programme

The Trustees believe they are well-placed to facilitate new ways of working in the sector and to promote the exchange of ideas, knowledge and good practice. The Foundation will support collaboration between operational charities, grant-making bodies and public agencies. The aim is to make a real and lasting impact.

At national level 30% of the budget will be allocated to Collaborative Donations or Activities, and we would envisage donations in the region of £100,000 for the first year of a multiple donation. Collaborative projects will form a key part of the Foundation's work at national level.

At Regional level an equal sum for each Region (£100,000 per Region in 2000) will be set aside to be used both as large donations and to be available to fund consultations or other events to promote the exchange of ideas, knowledge and good practice within and beyond the voluntary sector. We envisage 3–5 Collaborative Donations or Activities per year, of around £20,000, either within areas of Special Interest or with a focus on capacity building.

Each Region will identify its own strategic objectives, prepare a strategy to achieve those objectives and will have flexibility to implement a programme appropriate to the circumstances and needs of the Region.

Up to 80% of the Collaborative Programme will be spent on the Foundation's Special Interests and, more broadly, the development of the voluntary sector itself. This collaborative work will enable the Foundation to remain informed about the needs and priorities of the regions, and will help to identify and inform the review of the Foundation's Special Interests ...

Special interests

The objective is to make an informed choice of a limited number of Special Interests in order to focus our grant-making into areas in which the Foundation can have a real and measurable impact.

This can be achieved in two ways: not only by making a large number of small grants through the Community Programme, but also by targeting a significant proportion of our larger grants, through both the Community and Collaborative Programmes, on areas of priority social need.

The number of Special Interests and the scale of funding allocated to them will depend upon the overall funds available to the Foundation, and on the priorities set by Trustees for specific areas of social need. The approach, however, is:

a. To have a rolling programme of areas of Special Interest
b. To have 3–5 Special Interests at any one time
c. To keep Special Interests in the programme for 3–5 years
d. To review the programme each year
e. To have a clear timeframe and budget for each Special Interest at the outset

Approximately 45% of the Foundation's total regional and national spend will be allocated to Special Interests. The first three ... identified are:

- Family support
- Challenging disadvantage and discrimination
- Promoting effectiveness in the voluntary sector.

£15.3 million in 1998. £16.5 million was paid to 3,283 charities during the year. This compares with 3,061 donations paid in 1998, totalling £12.7 million. In conjunction with the other Lloyds TSB Foundations, an additional £227,240 was paid to UK-wide projects, and £766,000 was committed through the Staff Matched Giving Scheme. …

Strategic review

One of the key features of the Strategic Plan [*see box on page 193. Ed.*] is the formation of the Collaborative Programme. The Trustees believe they are well-placed to facilitate new ways of working in the sector, and to promote the exchange of ideas, knowledge and good practice, including collaboration between grant-making bodies, and between charities and public agencies.

The Trustees have selected three areas of social need which will remain areas of special interest for a minimum of three years: Family Support, Challenging Disadvantage and Discrimination, and Promoting Effectiveness in the Voluntary Sector. The Collaborative Programme will concentrate on these three areas.

As part of the strategic review it was decided that the Foundation's expertise lies in the areas of social and community needs and education and training, and that this is where the Foundation can make the most effective use of the funds available. It was therefore agreed that no further funds would be made available for the third of the Foundation's three objects, medical research. On an exceptional basis, the

Lloyds TSB Foundation for England and Wales – Guidelines for applicants 2001

The Foundation primarily allocates its funds to support local communities, helping people to improve their quality of life.

The majority of the Foundation's income is allocated to ten regional budgets, which mirror the government's Standard Statistical Regions. These budgets are determined on the basis of population, weighted for deprivation. A proportion of the Foundation's funds is also allocated to appeals which benefit people across the whole of England and Wales.

Grant-making programmes

The Trustees have two grant-making programmes: the Community Programme and the Collaborative Programme.

Community programme

Regional

Applications for local or regional donations are considered by the Foundation's ten Co-ordinators, normally by telephone or visit once the completed application form has been received. Applications are then assessed by the Trustees.

Applications of up to £3,000. All applications will be considered on merit, donations are normally one-off payments, and there is no particular emphasis given to those which fall within the Foundation's areas of Special Interest.

Applications for more than £3,000. Most donations are one-off payments, although commitments over two or more years are also considered. The Trustees aim to spread funding evenly between the three areas of Special Interest and projects falling within the Foundation's wider remit.

As a general guide, the Trustees make donations up to £5,000 to applications outside the areas of Special Interest, and up to £10,000 to those within these areas.

The Trustees are pleased to receive applications for either projects or running costs. The Trustees do not usually support building costs but will consider appropriate and specific aspects of a building project (for example, accessible facilities).

National

A proportion of the Foundation's income is available for projects that will benefit the whole of England and Wales, and an additional amount is set aside for pilot projects where there is potential for dissemination on a national basis. Donations made within these national programmes are generally in the region of £10,000–£30,000, and two or three year funding is often appropriate.

The Trustees aim to donate approximately half the funding to the Foundation's areas of Special Interest.

Collaborative programme

The Trustees are keen to support collaborative work within the sector and have set aside funds specifically for this purpose. Applications will be sought on a pro-active basis.

What are the foundation's guidelines?

The Trustees' policy is to support underfunded charities which enable people, especially disadvantaged or disabled people, to play a fuller role in the community.

The Foundation has two main areas to which it allocates funds:

1. Social and community needs

The Foundation supports a wide range of activities. The following examples are only a guide:

Advice services

Addictions (particularly substance misuse), Bereavement, Counselling, Emergency and Rescue Services, Helplines, Homelessness (particularly helping homeless people back into mainstream society), Housing, Parenting.

Community relations

Crime Prevention (particularly activities involving young people), Mediation, Promotion of Volunteering, Rehabilitation of Offenders, Victim Support, Vulnerable Young People.

Community services

After School Clubs, Clubs for Older People, Community Centres, Family Centres, Playschemes, Youth Clubs.

Cultural enrichment

Improving participation in and access to the arts and national heritage for disadvantaged or disabled people.

Activities with an educational focus for all ages.

Projects which have a strong focus on benefit to people and the social environment.

Disabled people

Advocacy, Carers (particularly information and support services, and provision of respite care), Day Centres, Information and Advice, Sheltered Accommodation, Transport.

Promotion of health

Day Care, Information and Advice, Mental Health, Holistic Medicine, Home Nursing, Hospices, Independent Living for Older People.

The Trustees will, on an exceptional basis, also fund research projects in health-related areas.

2. Education and training

The objective is to enhance learning opportunities for disabled and disadvantaged people of all ages. The following examples are only a guide

- Lifelong learning.
- Literacy skills.
- Pre-school education.
- Promotion of life skills and independent living skills (particularly creating positive opportunities for disabled people).
- Skills training for disabled people, including pre-vocational training.
- Skills training for disadvantaged people, to enhance their potential to secure employment.

Areas of special interest 2000–2002

The Trustees regularly review changing social needs and identify specific areas they want to focus on within their overall objectives.

The following areas of Special Interest apply from 2000–2002.

1. Family support

The Trustees wish to support the development and strengthening of organisations, programmes and projects which sustain families and improve the quality of family life.

The Foundation places particular emphasis on work which aims to equip people with relationship, parenting and caring skills, and to provide the support needed to be effective parents and carers. There is a specific focus on:

- Enabling men to play a more active role in parenting and caring
- Developing and improving relationships between generations
- Helping young people, especially those in or leaving care, to develop relevant lifeskills
- Supporting families coping with challenging behaviour

2. Challenging disadvantage and discrimination

The Trustees wish to support activities which address disadvantage, discrimination or stigma.

The Foundation places particular emphasis on work which aims to raise awareness of these issues and to promote the involvement of all people within society. There is a specific focus on:

- Helping disadvantaged people to participate in decision-making processes which affect their lives
- Promoting understanding and encouraging solutions which address disadvantage, discrimination or stigma
- Challenging disadvantage, discrimination and stigma within the field of mental health

3. Promoting effectiveness in the voluntary sector

The Trustees wish to enhance the capacity of the voluntary sector to provide effective services.

The Foundation places particular emphasis on work which aims to improve management skills and to promote collaborative working and sharing of good practice. There is a specific focus on:

- Supporting the development of regional voluntary sector networks
- Encouraging communication and collaboration
- Supporting the training of Trustees, management, staff and volunteers
- Encouraging organisations to review and assess the effectiveness of their work

What areas fall outside the guidelines?

[See under 'Exclusions' in the main text.]

General advice to applicants

In 2000, the Foundation was able to meet the requests of approximately 70% of eligible applicants either in part or in full. The most common reasons for the Trustees not being able to make a donation include:

- the level of demand always exceeds the funds available
- requests being made for sums in excess of the ranges stated in the Guidelines
- application forms not being fully completed
- applications not falling within the guidelines

Applicants are strongly advised to seek advice from the Foundation before submitting an application for support, in particular if considering applying for multi-year funding. Details of the ten Co-ordinators, who are able to advise potential applicants for local or regional funding, and of the National Appeals team for national funding, are available from the Foundation's central office. Regional applicants are encouraged to send their completed application form to the appropriate regional office or the Wales national office.

Assessment

Applicants are required to submit their most recent report and accounts with their completed application form (unless a new group in the first year of operation).

As part of the assessment process, the Trustees ask for information about applicants' commitment to equal opportunities.

The Foundation has a monitoring and evaluation policy. Grant recipients may be requested to complete a feedback form and/or may be visited by a member of the Foundation's staff to discuss progress. [See under 'Applications' in the main text for details of the application procedure.]

Trustees may consider research in broader health-related fields, for example links between poor housing and ill health, or the effect of stress on carers, but clinical research will no longer be eligible for support. In recent years less than 1% of the Foundation's spending has been on medical research. …

Overseas pilot

Until the merger with Lloyds Bank, all the Foundations' income was derived from banking activities in the UK. With a significant minority of the Group's profits now being earned overseas, the Trustees thought it appropriate to explore making a very small proportion of the funds available for overseas donations. It was agreed that as a starting point it would be best to consider projects in areas in which there is a staff presence as this will provide a means to obtain feedback on the outcome of the donations from a source other than the charity itself or its operational partner overseas.

Representatives of ten charities working in Central and Latin America were invited to a meeting in August to inform the Foundation of social needs in Argentina, Brazil and Colombia and to give their views on where the priorities lie. This process has resulted in two donations being approved, to CAFOD and to TearFund, both for projects in North East Brazil. These donations have been made very much on a trial basis, and the Trustees will carry out a careful review before committing to any further funding overseas.

Director-general's report

1999 has seen additional important changes in the Foundation's evolution, with further growth in income and our aspiration to be at the forefront of best practice.

Some 6,800 applications were received, to which we have been able to respond with 3,283 donations (48%). This compares with 3,061 donations from 6,500 applications received in 1998 (being 47%). Whilst the volume of applications has levelled off, the number of eligible applications rose in 1999 as the number of ineligible requests fell once again (12% in 1999 compared with 16% in 1998). Encouraging applicants to discuss potential applications before completing the application form is both encouraging this trend, and also improving the quality of applications received.

Regionally, the Foundation made larger grants in 1999. The rise in the Foundation's income (25%) exceeded the rise in the number of donations (7.3%) and, as a result, the average regional donation increased to £4,067 from £3,325. Overall spending on regional donations increased from £9.8m to £12.5m.

Nationally, the Trustees chose to use the increased income in making more grants (203 compared with 155 in 1998) and consequently the average size of donation remained stable at just over £19,000.

54% of Foundation spending was given to support work in the eight areas of Special Interest. Of these, three areas received in excess of £1 million: Positive Opportunities for Disabled People (£1,769,443), Family Support (£1,542,364) and Homelessness (£1,181,612).

52% of the Foundation's donations were allocated to core funding (compared with 42% in 1998). …

Strategic plan

We are excited by the new Strategic Plan for 2000 … It is estimated that over the next three years some £30 million will be allocated to the three new areas of Special Interest – *Family Support*, *Challenging Disadvantage and Discrimination*, and *Promoting Effectiveness in the Voluntary Sector*. A major task for 2000 will be establishing a framework within which we will be able to measure what difference we have made in these areas. We look forward to continuing our relationship with Compass Partnership in this task.

The development of the new Collaborative Programme, as outlined [above], is another exciting activity. During 1999 a few donations of this nature were made as part of a pilot scheme. At national level these included a three-year commitment totalling £100,000 to Skill: National Bureau for Students with Disabilities for core funding. This donation provided financial stability during a period of constitutional change in the charity … Regional pilots included two-year support for the West Midlands Trustees' Forum in collaboration with Birmingham Voluntary Service Council, providing training opportunities for Trustees in the region. …

Areas of special interest

In 1999 the Foundation donated £8.7 million to projects within the eight areas of special interest [*note that these have now been replaced by three new areas of special interest. Ed.*].

- Advocacy (£657,000)
- Creating Positive Opportunities for Disabled People (£1.8 million)
- Crime Prevention (£848,000)
- Family Support (£1.5 million)
- Homelessness (£1.2 million)
- Independent Living for Older People (£963,000)
- Prevention of Substance Misuse (£840,000)
- The Needs of Carers (£909,000)

Staff matched giving scheme

2,462 members of staff claimed donations totalling £766,000, to match their own efforts raising £1.3 million for charities which fall within the Foundations' guidelines, making a combined benefit of over £2 million. …

The Scheme was extended in 1999 to enable staff to claim a donation in respect of voluntary time given to charities. This has been well received by staff and charities alike, with 251 members of staff claiming a total of £23,685 for the charities in which they are involved.

Training for voluntary sector managers

Managers from the voluntary sector have continued to attend, free of charge, appropriate in-house management training courses held at the Group's Management Centre in Solihull, through a scheme administered by the Foundation. This year 22 managers attended courses, including 'Managing the Pressures' and 'High Performance Teams' …

The places this year were offered to managers working, predominantly, in the field of disability. As before, delegates were nominated by the Regional Co-ordinators and the National Appeals Manager. …

Grants in 1999

East of England

The East of England consists of six counties – Bedfordshire, Cambridgeshire, Essex, Hertfordshire, Norfolk and Suffolk. ... During the year we made 245 donations, and the average donation increased to £3,887.

We are pleased to have achieved a more even balance of donations throughout the region, increasing our support to charities in Bedfordshire, but the East Anglian counties continued to receive the majority (75%) of our regional donations. …

The urgent requests from charities to meet their 'core funding' requirements meant we decided to support a high percentage of 'core funding' applications (68%). …

Our collaborative work has already started with work to set up a Refugee Support Forum in Suffolk, and a regional Conference exploring the need to improve family support services for fathers.

Examples of 1999 grants

Burwell Community Print Centre is based in rural Cambridgeshire, working to provide validated training for adults with learning disabilities. A donation of £7,500 is helping towards the salary costs of a Project Trainer.

Turnabout Trust is a newly formed charity providing advice and training to unemployed and disadvantaged people in south Essex. They aim to enhance the individual's opportunities to secure employment and to help each individual achieve their potential. The Lloyds TSB Foundation donated £5,000 towards core costs.

East Midlands

The East Midlands region supported 237 charities with grants totalling £936,852. The average size of grant increased to £3,953. …

Some parts of the region submit more applications for funding than others and the focus over the past 12 months has been to try and encourage a fair distribution of grants ... both demographically and geographically. Areas that we have concentrated on have included Lincolnshire, Northamptonshire and minority ethnic communities. We have worked with a variety of organisations to deliver training in submitting funding applications for small community groups.

Examples of 1999 grants
Trinity Arts – Gainsborough: £5,000 for each of two years towards the cost of setting up a theatre company for people with learning disabilities.

Aspire Trust – Long Eaton: £3,915 towards the cost of setting up an office and drop in centre for homeless people.

Hadhari Project – Derby: £2,500 towards the cost of furniture for Derby African Caribbean Mental Health Association.

Greater London

With the increase in the Foundation's income of 1999, the London region was able to meet more of the demands placed upon it, making 432 donations totalling some £1,883,263 (1998: 332 totalling £1,207,071). This enabled us to provide an average donation of £4,359. ...

In London we decided to focus on assisting small groups with fundraising skills, and address this through support for a programme of workshops and seminars run by the London Voluntary Service Council. This has enabled many under-funded voluntary groups to be more successful in conducting their fundraising strategies. ...

During 2000 we anticipate a higher level of collaboration between community groups to help overcome duplication of service provision.

Examples of 1999 grants
Age Concern – Islington: This organisation provides support for older people and was allocated £4,350 towards the cost of their Crime Prevention Workshops. Age Concern expect that the cultivation of intergenerational relationships will help to prevent potential offenders getting into trouble.

North London Family Mediation Service: This recently formed organisation affiliated to the National Family Mediation Service, was allocated £12,452 towards core costs. The project's beneficiaries are those families that are currently separating.

North east

Much emphasis was placed on making and consolidating contacts in the voluntary sector, including close links with umbrella bodies and with other funders. The Co-ordinator visited a high proportion of applicants prior to applications being submitted, and also organisations which received funding.

237 donations were made, totalling £884,077, at an average of £3,730. This compares with 208 donations totalling £727,967 in 1998. ...

Examples of 1999 grants
The Lazarus Centre in Sunderland received £9,988 to help them install a new kitchen. This centre will help those who are following a detoxification programme from either drugs or alcohol.

Byker Bridge Housing Association in Newcastle upon Tyne. We further supported their day services with a donation of £5,000. This organisation works with people who are suffering from or recovering from mental health problems.

The Mea Trust (£15,000). Based in Newcastle upon Tyne, The Mea Trust manages MEA House. The property is used by around 50 different charities and has in excess of 50,000 visitors per annum. The property was opened in 1974 and is in need of complete refurbishment. The project is estimated to cost £4m in total.

North west

During the past twelve months the North West Region broke new ground in that it donated over £2 million to 433 local charities (1998: £1,694,563 to 400 charities), at an average of £4,828 (1998: £4,236). ...

One of the pleasing aspects of our work last year was that the number of beneficiaries in each county in the region, Cumbria, Lancashire, Merseyside, Greater Manchester and Cheshire, was proportional to the population. ...

Examples of 1999 grants
Age Concern – Liverpool: The new Active Age Centre, which was opened in 1999, provides facilities such as information technology training, leisure and keep-fit activities, in addition to information and advice. The Foundation made a donation of £30,000 towards the salary of the Centre Co-ordinator over a period of three years.

Aisha Childcaring Group – Manchester: The Aisha Childcaring Group works in the multicultural districts of Hulme and Moss Side in Manchester providing childcare and support to families. The Foundation gave a grant of £1,000 towards a holiday for disadvantaged children and their parents/carers at the Ghyll Head Education Centre in the Lake District.

South east

1999 was a challenging year for the South East as the increase in demand exceeded the increase in our income. It was decided that rather than give a small grant to a high proportion of applicants, we would try and meet more fully the requests of a smaller proportion of applicants. During the year we made 312 donations totalling £950,495 at an average of £3,046 (compared with 325 donations totalling £829,517 in 1998, average £2,552). ...

Examples of 1999 grants
The McDermott Trust – Southampton: The Foundation donated £30,000 over three years towards the core costs of a Volunteer Co-ordinator. The McDermott Trust supports homeless individuals and families and those living in inadequate housing or on very low incomes. ... The Trustees were particularly impressed with their innovative food collection and redistribution programme. ...

Minorities Agricultural Rural Equestrian Skills (MARES) – Amersham: MARES provides unusual day therapy as well as skills based activities for people suffering from long-term mental health problems. It is particularly aimed at the black and minority ethnic community. The therapy and skills are all rural and equestrian based. ... The Foundation provided £2,500 towards core costs.

South west

As is now expected, demand for grants increased more than the increase in funding in 1999. 429 applications were received (378 in 1998) of which 313 were funded in full or in part, totalling £941,221, compared with 297 totalling £785,819 in 1998. The average grant was £3,007 compared with £2,646 in 1998. The spread of grants was reasonably even across the seven counties: Cornwall, Devon, Somerset, Dorset, Wiltshire, Gloucestershire and the former Avon. ...

Examples of 1999 grants
Cornwall Deaf Children's Society: The charity works on all aspects of problems which affect deaf children in Cornwall. The Foundation donated £5,000 towards the production of two video films. The first addresses the issues of Further Education from the student's perspective as well as the teacher's ... The second film addresses the problems and challenges encountered in employment, from the perspective of both employee and employer ...

Bristol Children's Playhouse: The charity works in one of the most deprived inner city areas in the United Kingdom. Their objective is to bring support to young families who may be isolated by social, economic, cultural or ethnic divisions. ... The Foundation has donated £7,397 over two years towards salary costs.

Wales

The Foundation is one of the largest independent grant-giving organisations within the Principality ... In 1999, 242 applicants received donations totalling £930,316, of which over 40% related to core funding. This compares with 224 donations totalling £731,968 in 1998. ...

On a strategic level, the Foundation has played a major role in creating a new organisation within the Principality – the Wales Funders' Forum. The Forum aims to bring together funders from the statutory, corporate and charitable sectors that have an interest in supporting the voluntary sector in Wales. The Co-ordinator is Chair of the Forum. We have also worked with the National Assembly in developing its Compact with the voluntary sector.

Examples of 1999 grants
Swansea YMCA: The Foundation donated £10,000 towards equipment and staff costs for the IT training project. Situated in the heart of the city and near the Sandfields area, these projects provide facilities for the local community and especially focus on the local ethnic population. Funding will support equipment and staff costs.

Conwy Voluntary Services – Community Transport Scheme: ... Our support will ensure additional clients will have access to the service. £6,400 was provided towards a new electric wheelchair, and new hardware and software to co-ordinate the service.

West Midlands

The increase in the Foundation's income allowed us to satisfy the demands of more of our applicants and has enabled us to increase the size of individual grants. During the year we made 350 donations totalling £1,435,797. (1998: 381 totalling £1,178,185.) ...

Examples of 1999 grants
Home Start, Shrewsbury: Home Start is a voluntary organisation offering support, friendship and practical help to families at home with children under 5. ... The Foundation has donated £24,000 over three years towards core costs of the organisation.

Arthritis Care, Lichfield: Arthritis Care provide help and information to arthritis sufferers of all ages. Outings and holidays in specially equipped hotels, owned and run by Arthritis Care, are organised for those members who are unable to plan and arrange for themselves. The Foundation donated £600 towards a holiday and towards an advisory service.

Yorkshire

The Yorkshire region has seen a significant increase in income over the last few years which has enabled us to assist more charities with larger individual grants. During the year we made 277 donations totalling £1,514,365 (1998: 296 totalling £1,096,321). ...

Examples of 1999 grants
North Frodingham Playgroup: This charity operates a pre-school playgroup in an isolated area of East Yorkshire. The Foundation provided £1,000 for secure accommodation to store children's toys.

The Sobriety Project: The Foundation donated £17,750 towards Sessional Workers at the new site in Rotherham. This charity has been specialising in using waterways to deliver innovative training to unemployed people since 1973. In 1994 they opened The Waterways Museum which in 1996 was judged by National Heritage to be the UK's Best Industrial and Social History Museum.

England & Wales and new initiatives

1999 was an excellent year for national grant giving in the Foundation with £3,927,891 being allocated to 203 charities, compared with £2,963,985 to 155 charities in 1998. A total of £3,025,947 was granted to 162 charities who work throughout England and Wales and £901,944 to 41 charities who were carrying out pilot or development work for national dissemination.

64% of donations were focused upon the eight areas of Special Interest [*note that these have now changed. Ed.*] and on average 35% of donations were towards salary costs highlighting the Trustees' recognition of the need for core funding of charities.

The extended area of Creating Positive Opportunities for Disabled People received particular focus in 1999, and new donations made in this area included a donation of £9,200 to Thrive, a charity who promote the use of gardening and horticulture for therapy, training and health. The donation was towards regional 'seeing is believing events' with the aim of networking existing gardening projects for people with physical and/or learning disabilities throughout England and Wales.

Another donation in this area of Special Interest was a three-year donation totalling £108,460 to the National Schizophrenia Fellowship towards an Interactive Educational Programme for young people aged between 16 and 25. This project focuses upon awareness of the first stages of schizophrenia using the internet as a communication medium as well as a CD Rom which will hopefully identify opportunities for 'early intervention' and support for individuals and carers.

The Trustees were able to make 48 new multiple year donations this year in addition to their commitments from 1997/1998. These new donations included a donation to Skill, the National Bureau for Students with Disabilities of £100,000 over three years towards core funding, and to the Alzheimer's Disease Society for a donation of £30,000 over three years towards the salary of the Head of Branch Support, a key management post within the organisation.

New pilot or developmental work that was funded in 1999 included a donation over two years of £99,278 to the British Red Cross towards a Young Carers' Respite Service pilot project across England and Wales looking at the respite needs of young people from inner cities, rural areas, black and minority ethnic groups and Wales. A donation of £22,000 to support development work was given to Telesafe, a new charity focusing upon life skills training and personal safety issues for people with learning disabilities.

The new year brings with it a new Strategic Plan, new areas of Special Interest and the creation of a new grant programme – the Collaborative Programme. The focus of collaborative grants for the national programme will be within the areas of Special Interest and the Trustees will be looking for opportunities to support innovative yet practical work that will not only have impact at a national level but also at regional, local and grass-roots level – in keeping with the underlying ethos of all Foundation grantmaking.

Examples of 1999 grants
National Youth Ballet: £10,000 towards an outreach programme in primary schools and the community.

National Association of Citizens Advice Bureaux: The Foundation donated £90,240 over two years towards eight regional CABnet 2000 consultants. The aim of the project is to create a national network of consultants to provide free specialist IT support to the managers and management committees of the 700 CABx in England and Wales as they introduce CABnet 2000 to transform the CAB advice service in England and Wales.

Crime Concern Trust: £75,000 over two years for developing a Quality Standard for Crime Reduction Partnerships.

Migraine Trust: £8,550 for a guide for young sufferers.

National Playbus Association: £80,000 over three years for salaries and administrative support.

Youth Access: £35,000 over two years for a training and development officer for Youth Advice Services.

Exclusions

The main areas of concern normally considered to be outside the foundation's guidelines are:

- Organisations which are not recognised charities.
- Activities which are primarily the responsibility of central or local government or some other responsible body.
- Activities which collect funds for subsequent redistribution to other charities or to individuals.
- Animal welfare.
- Corporate affiliation or membership of a charity.
- Endowment funds.
- Environment – conservation and protection of flora and fauna, geographic and scenic.
- Expeditions or overseas travel.
- Fabric appeals for places of worship.
- Fundraising events or activities.
- Hospitals and medical centres (except for projects which are clearly additional to statutory responsibilities).
- Individuals, including students.
- Loans or business finance.
- Overseas appeals.
- Promotion of religion.
- Schools, universities and colleges (except for projects specifically to benefit disabled students or which are clearly additional to statutory responsibilities).
- Sponsorship or marketing appeals.

If you are not sure if your proposed application is within foundation guidelines, then please contact a member of foundation staff for advice before completing the application form.

Applications

Application forms are available from the foundation's office or the regional co-ordinators (or can be downloaded from the foundation's website) and can be returned at any time by post to the relevant regional co-ordinator's office or the foundation's central office, together with a signed copy of your latest annual report and accounts.

E-mailed or faxed applications will not be accepted.

Information requested on the form includes:

- registered charity number or evidence of an organisation's tax-exempt status;
- brief description of the activities of the charity;
- details of the project for which a grant is sought;
- details of the overall cost of the project and a breakdown;
- what funds have already been raised towards the overall cost and how the remaining funds are being raised;
- an outline of plans for evaluation;
- trustees' report and full edited or independently examined accounts.

All applications are reviewed on a continual basis and the board of trustees meets quarterly to approve donations. Decision-making processes can therefore take up to three months but all applicants are informed of the outcome of their applications.

Successful applicants will be expected to leave two years before applying for further support. Unsuccessful applicants should leave at least one year before reapplying.

Potential applicants are encouraged to make contact initially with the appropriate regional co-ordinator (or with the head office for national projects), as follows:

North East: Peter Ellis, Lloyds TSB Foundation, PO Box 779, Newcastle upon Tyne NE99 1YJ Tel: 0191 261 8433

Yorkshire: Stephen Robinson, Lloyds TSB Bank plc, St Helens Square, York YO1 2QW Tel: 01904 628200

North West: David Kay, Lloyds TSB Bank plc, Time Square, Warrington WA1 2AJ Tel: 01925 444652

West Midlands: Karen Argyle, Lloyds TSB Bank plc, PO Box 427, 40 Gaolgate Street, Stafford ST16 2NS Tel: 01785 247488

East Midlands: Sue Denning, Lloyds TSB Bank plc, PO Box 510, 11 Low Pavement, Nottingham NG1 7D Tel: 0115 958 8745

East of England: Mark Ereira, Lloyds TSB Bank plc, 16 Abbeygate Street, Bury St Edmunds, Suffolk IP33 1UP Tel: 01284 750168

South West: Rodney Thorne, Lloyds TSB Bank plc, 18 High Street, Bridgwater TA6 3BJ Tel: 01278 444743

London: John Aldridge, Lloyds TSB Bank plc, 111 High Street, Ilford IG1 4NN Tel: 020 8478 7262

South East: John Paton, Lloyds TSB Bank plc, 4 West Street, Havant PO9 1PE Tel: 023 9248 0774

Wales: Mike Lewis, Lloyds TSB Foundation, Black Horse House, Phoenix Way, Swansea Enterprise Park SA7 9EQ Tel: 01792 314005

National Appeals Manager: Birgitta Drury (address as head office above) Tel: 020 7204 5559/5001

Lloyds TSB Foundation for Northern Ireland

Social and community needs, education and training, scientific and medical research

£1,600,000 (2000)

Beneficial area Northern Ireland.

The Gate Lodge, 73a Malone Road, Belfast BT9 6SB

Tel. 028 9038 2864 **Fax** 028 9038 2839

Correspondent Mervyn Bishop, Secretary

Trustees *Lady McCollum, Chair; Roy MacDougall; Brenda Callaghan; Ian Doherty; Breidge Gadd; Dawn Livingstone; Angela McShane; David Magill; David Patton; Anne Shaw; Dennis Wilson.*

Information available Guidelines for applicants. Poor annual report and accounts, without a grants list.

Summary

The smallest of the three Lloyds TSB Foundations described in this book (each one wholly independent of the others), this charity also supports local communities.

Most donations are one-off, with a small number of commitments made over two or more years. The trustees say that they prefer to make donations towards specific items rather than contributions to large appeals, though the trust will consider core funding for small local charities.

Applications which help to develop voluntary sector infrastructure are encouraged.

Donations are generally between £2,500 and £5,000, but there is no minimum amount set by the trustees. Applications for larger amounts will be considered where there is wider benefit.

This trust may have a higher success rate for applications than any other trust described in this book, with 514 applications resulting in 437 grants in 1999 (85% successful).

General

It is regrettable that this charity, while accepting tax reliefs from the population generally, does not say to which organisations it gives its, and their, money.

The trust has three main objectives, described in the guidelines as follows:

Social and community needs

A wide range of activities are supported and the following are meant as a guide only.

Community services: family centres, youth clubs, elderly people's clubs, after school clubs; playschemes, help groups, childcare provision.

Advice centres: homelessness, addictions, bereavement, parenting, helplines, counselling, housing, emergency and rescue services.

Disabled people: sheltered accommodation, day centres, transport, carers, information and advice, mental and physical disabilities.

Promotion of health: information and advice, mental health, hospices, day care, holistic medicine, home nursing, AIDS.

Civic responsibility: youth at risk, crime prevention, promotion of volunteering, victim support, rehabilitation of offenders, mediation.

Cultural enrichment: improving participation in and access to the arts and national heritage for disadvantaged and disabled people

Education and training

The objective is to enhance educational opportunities for disadvantaged and disabled people of all ages.

Projects which help socially excluded people develop their potential and secure employment.

Employment training (for disabled and disadvantaged people).

Promotion of life skills, independent living skills for disabled people.

Enhancing education for disabled young people, preschool education, literacy skills.

Scientific and medical research

The objective is to support underfunded fields of research which are particularly relevant to social conditions in Northern Ireland.

In 1999 the foundation made 437 grant allocations worth £1,305,000, averaging £3,000. Unfortunately no grants list was produced.

Exclusions

Areas of concern outside the guidelines:

- organisations which are not recognised as charities by the Inland Revenue
- animal welfare
- environment – geographic and scenic, conservation and protection of flora and fauna
- overseas appeals
- activities that are the primary responsibility of central or local government or some other responsible body
- schools, universities and colleges
- hospitals and medical centres
- sponsorship or marketing appeals
- fabric appeals for places of worship
- promotion of religion
- activities which collect funds for subsequent redistribution to other charities or individuals
- endowment funds
- fundraising events or activities
- corporate affiliation or membership of a charity
- loans or business finance
- expeditions or overseas travel

Applications

Application forms are available.

The information requested includes:

- registered charity number and evidence of tax-exempt status
- a brief description of the activities of the charity
- details of the project for which the grant is sought
- details of overall funding needed for the project, including a breakdown
- what funds have already been raised
- how the remaining funds will be raised
- trustees' report and full audited or independently examined accounts

Trustees meet quarterly to review applications.

Lloyds TSB Foundation for Scotland

Social and community needs, education and training, scientific, medical and social research

£4,808,000 (1999)

Beneficial area Scotland.

Henry Duncan House, 120 George Street, Edinburgh EH2 4LH

Tel. 0131 225 4555 **Fax** 0131 260 0381

Correspondent Andrew Muirhead, Chief Executive

Trustees *J George Mathieson, Chair; Archie Robb; Prof. Sir Michael Bond; Fiona Crighton; E Avril Denholm; Ms Rani Dhir; Colin Donald; Revd Ronald Ferguson; Alastair Findlay; Susan Moody; John Scott; C Anne Simpson.*

Information available Criteria, priorities and principles booklet. Excellent annual reviews and application packs. Full report and accounts, but the grants list is neither categorised nor presented in alphabetical sequence, or by size of grant.

Summary

This is Scotland's largest grant-making trust, with up to £5 million distributed in grants every year. Most are from £1,000 to £15,000. Higher amounts are given, but rarely for more than £50,000 in a single year and not for periods of more than three years. Grant categories are as follows (figures for % of grant value in 1999):

Social and community needs	71%
Education and training	23%
Scientific, medical and social research	6%

There is an unusual and interesting capacity-building programme, described below. The success rate for eligible applications for the general donations programme ran at 54% in 1999 (though not always for the full amount requested). A further 15% were outside the foundation's fairly general criteria.

The foundation is accessible, helpful and enterprising. Potential applicants (to this and to other trusts) may be particularly interested in the discussion below on the most frequent reasons why applications have to be rejected.

The foundation makes extensive efforts to reach and encourage its potential applicants. A surgery 'tour' in 2000 was visiting no less than 65 venues. Most applicants are visited by foundation staff before a grant decision is made.

The foundation also matches, pound for pound, the value of income and time raised for charities by staff of the Lloyds TSB Group (now including Scottish Widows).

Background

The Lloyds TSB Foundation for Scotland, formerly known as TSB Foundation for Scotland, was formed in 1986 as one of four independent charitable trusts established by the then TSB Group. Collectively the foundations receive 1% of the bank's pre-tax profits for distribution. The Foundation for Scotland receives 19.46% of this amount. In common with the Foundations for England and Wales, Northern Ireland and the Channel Islands, the Foundation for Scotland receives its income under a Deed of Covenant with the Banking Group. Since the merger between Lloyds Bank and the TSB Group in December 1995, income to the foundation has grown significantly ... The foundation was originally formed to support local community groups, and to this day is still very much a 'community foundation' with the majority of awards being made to grassroots charities.

More than £5 million was available for distribution in 1999 with sums exceeding £20 million likely to be granted in the three-year period commencing January 2000.

Grant-making policy

The foundation allocates its funds in support of the Scottish community, to enable people, primarily those in need, to be active members of society. Although the majority of awards are for local charities, the foundation does consider larger appeals where benefit is provided across Scotland. There is no minimum or maximum sum granted, with awards ranging from a few hundred pounds to tens of thousands of pounds.

Following a full review by working parties gathering input from the voluntary sector, 1999 saw the publication of 'Criteria, Priorities and Principles' for the next three years (to December 2002).

Criteria, priorities and principles 2000–2002

Principles

The undernoted principles will apply to all applications and priority support will be considered for projects demonstrating one or more of the following which:

- Encourage empowerment by consulting and involving users.
- Help and encourage independent living and development of life skills.
- Provide new and continuing opportunities for personal enrichment and quality of life, e.g. skills training across all age bands.
- Collect information through contacts or research to establish, consolidate and promote good practice and develop policy.
- Represent and promote the needs of people through advocacy, advice, information and support. In particular for people with mental health problems, physical and learning disabilities and the elderly.
- Demonstrate a collaborative approach by networking with other agencies/providers to avoid duplication of services.
- Demonstrate equality of opportunity.
- Promote anti-racism and discourage anti-social behaviour.
- Demonstrate good evaluation and monitoring procedures.
- Adopt preventive measures and stimulate early intervention programmes.
- Encourage the involvement of volunteers.
- Recognise cultural diversity and particular needs that may arise.

The trustees are keen to support innovative projects but recognise the value of established services which provide support for vulnerable people. Both approaches are seen as having equal value and will be considered for support on the merit of individual projects.

General criteria

The trustees of the foundation are focused on the needs of disadvantaged and marginalised people in Scottish communities and allocate funds to charities that provide support, which enables people to be active members of society and to improve their quality of life. Children, young people, ageing population and minority groups are among those which are of particular interest, and can be assisted through the three main objectives to which the foundation seeks to allocate funds, which are:

- Social and community needs;
- Education and training;
- Scientific, medical and social research.

General donation programme

Social and community needs

This is the foundation's largest area of spend with 313 charities gaining 71% of total funds awarded. During the year there was a growth in applications from charities focusing on health issues with submissions from community activities, crisis and advice centres, disabled people, civic responsibility and cultural enrichment maintaining the previous year's levels.

- Community Activities – Elderly People's Clubs, Family Centres, Youth Clubs, After School Clubs, Playgroups/Nurseries (within areas previously designated as Areas of Priority Treatment by The Scottish Office), Self-Help Groups.
- Crisis and Advice Services – Homelessness, Addictions, Family Guidance, Bereavement, Counselling, Befriending, Money Advice.
- Disabled People – Day Centres, Residential Accommodation, Carers, Advice and Support, Transport.
- Health Issues – Information and Advice, Mental Health, Home Nursing, Hospices, Day Care for the Elderly.
- Civic Responsibility – Crime Prevention, Offenders and their Families, At Risk/Hard to Reach Young People, Promotion of Good Citizenship.
- Cultural Enrichment – Access to the arts and national heritage specifically for disadvantaged and disabled people.

Education and training

Support has grown from 22% in 1998 to 23% in 1999, with 79 awards granted, of which 10 awards were towards employment training, 13 focused on training for the disabled, 33 to help promote life skills and 23 to enhance education.

- Motivation – Projects which assist individuals to obtain employment, with particular emphasis on guiding young people to develop their potential, improve literacy skills, build self-confidence and self-esteem.
- Employment – Training which will provide disadvantaged and disabled people with employment opportunities.
- Life Skills and Independent Living – Particular interest in young people, the elderly, and those mentally or physically disadvantaged.

Scientific, medical and social research

The trustees particularly welcome applications for projects related to under-funded fields of research which are 'less fashionable' and harder to find funding for. Whilst total research funding still represents a relatively small proportion of our giving at 6%, we anticipate that this level will grow in future years. In the year, we have embarked on a four year collaborating initiative with the Royal Society of Edinburgh, which will result in substantial sums being focused on research into enhancing the quality of life for people as they age.

Priorities

Every three years the trustees establish and confirm priorities from within our general criteria. Priority support will be considered for projects which include the following:

Children – Projects which:

- Provide a safe place where children can talk about their worries/concerns/emotional issues, e.g. children's counsellors or therapeutic services.
- Create a safe environment for children to have the opportunity to play together.
- Build self-esteem and self-confidence, which will enhance life chances and experiences for children, broaden their horizons through opportunities which they may not have, e.g. life skills projects/drama/art.
- Promote peer support and advocacy giving children a voice and encouraging empowerment.
- Support for children as young carers and their siblings, including siblings of special needs children.

Young People – Projects which:

- Value young people by listening to them and addressing their problems.
- Show evidence of young people's involvement by including them in decision making.
- Work with hard to reach young people who do not include themselves in organised youth work.
- Support Detached and Outreach work which reaches the most vulnerable young people in our society.
- Promote accreditation of young people by recognising their contribution through involvement as a volunteer or as a service user, thus building self-esteem.

Ageing Population – Projects which:

- Represent and promote the needs and wellbeing of older people through advocacy, advice, or support; encourage inclusion and reduce isolation.
- Support older people who provide direct services, i.e. work done by older people for older people.
- Support inter-generational projects or themes, which strengthen contact across generations and cultural divides.
- Help and encourage independence and independent living.

Parenting – Projects which:

- Promote parenting skills, which help with understanding and responding to children's social, emotional and developmental needs.
- Encourage male participation by promoting the importance of the role of fathers, and their active involvement in the lives of their children.
- Support opportunities which allow families to take part in ordinary family life, e.g. outings/ holidays (within the UK).

Rural Disadvantage – Projects which:

- Promote access to groups and communities through transport, befriending, buddies schemes and volunteering.
- Encourage social inclusion and improve services in rural communities.

Physical and Mental Disability – Projects which:

- Improve the quality of life for disabled people by promoting independence and raising awareness of disability.
- Assist people with learning difficulties, sensory impairments and users of mental health services.

Homelessness – Projects which:

- Establish support networks to assist homeless people back to mainstream society.

- Provide information, advice, and raise awareness of available services.
- Work with people living in supported/ temporary accommodation.

Substance Misuse – Projects which:

- Focus on early intervention, including education, and alternative activities aimed at building awareness and minimising harm.
- Provide support, advice and information to people whose lives are affected by the misuse of drugs, alcohol or volatile substances, e.g. solvents.

Minority Groups – Projects which:

- Represent and promote the needs of minority groups through advocacy, advice and awareness raising.
- Promote anti-racism and provide support for people who suffer from bullying and prejudice.

Infrastructure – to assist with:

- Operational efficiencies or improve access to funding for charitable organisations.
- Development of staff and volunteers, as well as the skills of user groups, for the good of their communities.
- Provision of training for Chief Executives and Management staff to ensure their professional/personal development is continued.
- Training of Management Committees to equip them with the knowledge of responsibilities required in the role of Trustee/Director.

The capacity building grant programme

Following a year-long pilot involving 40 Scottish charities, in October 1999 the foundation launched a grant-making process which provides funding for voluntary organisations to access a panel of independent consultants. The consultants are experienced in the voluntary sector and can assist in resolving many of today's issues affecting charities. The panel of consultants has skills in areas such as:

- financial management
- fundraising planning
- good governance
- information technology
- marketing
- strategic planning
- staff development

The foundation issues a separate note for applicants interested in this programme. Some of its contents are as follows:

[This is] a programme which will support growth and development activities and address short-term skills gaps within the voluntary sector in Scotland. ... we anticipate considerable interest in this programme and we are unlikely to be able to meet all requests.

... Essentially, we have constructed a panel of external specialists with a wide range of skills relevant to the management of voluntary organisations. A member of the panel will make arrangements to meet with you to review your needs and establish the level of input required ... and to discuss a plan of action and establish the associated costs. ... Assuming you are happy to proceed, your application, now costed, ... will go forward to our Trustees.

The foundation has budgeted a substantial £300,000 for this programme in 2001 and expects to make something over 50 grants. Experience suggests that the average grant will cover about 10 days' consultancy.

In summer 2000 enquiries about the programme were coming in at the rate of about 300 a year. Of these, about a third would get to the first stage of an initial application and costing, and a majority of these applications were successful.

As is usually found in programmes of this kind, many applicants start off by thinking that what they need is fundraising advice and help, but discussion often suggests that funding difficulties are due, at least in part, to lack of convincing strategies and plans, and that addressing these is the priority.

Fuller details about this new grant programme can be obtained from Geoff Weir, the Capacity Building Grant Co-ordinator, on 0131 225 4555.

Scientific, medical and social research

This accounted for six per cent of the value of the foundation's general grants, or something under £300,000. The beneficiaries could not be easily identified from the undifferentiated grants list, nor is there any information on the number of applications or grants, or on the way in which applications are assessed. In particular, it is not known whether the conventional process of peer review is applied.

Grant-making practice

The 1999 review provides the following exceptionally full and interesting information about the foundation's grantmaking.

Types of grant

The foundation will consider support for both capital (e.g. equipment, property) and revenue (salaries, rent, heat & light) costs.

If you are applying for funding to purchase a piece of equipment or a vehicle, we will expect competitive quotes to have been obtained as well as consideration given to the necessary operational training required and on-going maintenance costs.

When examining applications relating to salary costs we will be assessing your experience as an employer or your plans to acquire the necessary skills. We will look closely at the objectives supplied and the way in which they can be measured as well as how you will fund the salary cost at the end of our support period.

Although the majority of awards are made on a one-off basis, the trustees will consider commitments over two or three years, which are normally in respect of revenue funding. Each release of funds will be subject to the receipt of a progress report, objectives for the coming year, and recent audited accounts, and the completion of a satisfactory assessment review. We will be particularly interested in how the objectives for the previous year have been achieved. Please remember that we can only commit a limited amount of our funds into future years and that support is, of course, dependent on the foundation's income.

In some circumstances awards are granted subject to certain conditions being met, e.g. an order being placed for equipment, remaining funding for the project being raised, salary posts being filled, works commencing etc. Any conditions must be met within 2 years, otherwise funds which have not been claimed in this timescale will become available for re-allocation.

Multi-year awards

The trustees are acutely aware of the need for certainty in funding for voluntary organisations as they aim to deliver immensely valuable services often to those most disadvantaged and marginalised in society. In response to this we are increasingly awarding donations which span two or three-year periods, in 1999 we made 115 such awards, with current and future year implications of almost £3.7 million. More than 250 Scottish charities hold multi-year awards at year- end.

Application volumes and allocation of funds

In the year around 1,300 applications were considered and only 15% of these were rejected as being 'outwith criteria'. This is an immensely pleasing statistic, as just four years ago the level was around 50%.

Assessors considered more than 900 eligible applications, under our general programme of grantmaking. Distributions under this procedure at £4.7 million represent 98% of total funding distributed. We should not lose sight of the fact that following very careful consideration 335 eligible submissions did not attract support.

Finally, we welcomed a significant growth of 56% in applications under the 'Matched Giving' scheme. This is where we match the charitable fundraising efforts and voluntary time given by staff of Lloyds TSB Group in Scotland on a pound for pound basis.

Issues on rejection

The trustees regret that demands made on the foundation's funds always outstrip the funds available and this means that many good applications, whilst meeting criteria, cannot be supported. Owing to the high quality of applications in general, there is often a narrow margin between success and failure.

In assessing past applications, there were a few recurring features in those which were unsuccessful:-

- Limited completion of application form relying on a range of attachments. Attachments cannot be circulated to trustees.
- The trustees will only see your application form plus one other A4 sheet containing supporting information. The assessor responsible for your case will only see any other documents.
- Lack of clear plans for other fundraising.
- Insufficient detail on potential benefits a project would create.
- 'All or nothing' requests for large appeals. (The foundation would prefer to see a part-funding option.)
- Inadequate explanation about the financial position of an applicant, e.g. policy on reserves, reasons for changes in level of costs year on year, etc.
- No clear strategy on safety/security, particularly important where a group are working with children or vulnerable adults, or engaged in transport.

Multi-year funding:

- Lack of strategy for the period beyond which funding was being sought.
- Vague objectives.

It should be stressed that applications are generally of a very high quality, however applicants may find the above to be a helpful checklist.

In particular the foundation emphasises the following, to be remembered when completing the application form:

- Keep it simple – be concise and direct;
- Stress the difference our support will make – facts and figures are important;
- Always provide a detailed breakdown of costs;
- Tell us about other fundraising – we will be particularly interested to learn of local community fundraising as well as approaches to other charitable trusts;
- It is essential that objectives relating to revenue funding are 'SMART' – Specific, Measurable, Achievable, Realistic and Testing.

The foundation has six full time assessors and an ongoing grant-awarding process.

Examples of grants in 1999

About half of the grants were for £5,000 or less, and most of those were one-off. Multi-year awards are rarely for less than £3,000 a year. Only 37 out of 452 grants (eight per cent) were for more than £20,000.

There were five awards of £50,000 or more in 1999, to:

- Children 1st (£62,000 for the Parentline project, 3rd of 4 payments);
- Muslim Cultural Welfare Centre (£59,000 for disabled access and a training room/internet cafe);
- National Museums of Scotland (£50,000 for the Discovery bus project, 2nd of 4 payments);
- University of Glasgow Development Campaign (£50,000 for installation of a lift to make the medical school accessible to all);
- The Donaldson Trust (£50,000 for a pre-school suite, 3rd of 4 payments).

Further large grants went to:

- Royal Society of Edinburgh (£48,000 to fund research fellowships);
- Royal College of Surgeons (£35,000 to complete the research into the management of inflammatory bowel disease syndrome, 1st of 2 payments);
- Harmeny Education Trust Ltd (£30,000 for a new music and drama facility, 2nd of 3 payments);
- Scripture Union Scotland (£25,000 for new football pitches and games areas at the Lenrick Muir Centre);
- Alzheimer Scotland Action on Dementia (£23,000 for finance director's salary, 1st of 3 payments).

Other recipients included:

- Nolly Barge Project (£15,000 for weekday skipper's salary, 1st of 3 payments);
- Meningitis Research Foundation (£10,000 for Scotland information and advice officer's salary, 1st of 3 payments);
- Rape Crisis Centre, Glasgow (£10,000 for 50% of training worker's salary, 1st of 3 payments);
- Sue Ryder Foundation (£9,000 for purchase of a new minibus);
- Rossie Farm School (£7,000 for six new computer workstations);
- Counselling & Family Mediation – Western Isles (£6,000 for rent and rates);
- Birds of Paradise Theatre Company (£4,500 for radio drama workshops for schools with special needs children, and to schools in rural or deprived areas);
- Shetland Allotment Project (£3,000 for the co-ordinator's salary, 1st of 3 payments);
- Queensferry Youth Crime Prevention Panel (£2,000 to subsidise the places of 150 delegates to a conference at the Scottish Police College);
- Sighthill Community Education Centre (£2,000 for Easter and summer holiday activity programmes);
- 18th Inverness (Muirtown) Scout Group (£950 for purchase of wetsuits);
- Caithness Heritage Trust (£750 for video production costs);
- St Mary's Parish Church, Motherwell (£400 for purchase of fibre optic lights, lunar lamps and moving-sand pictures).

Exclusions

The trustees regret they cannot support all fields of voluntary and charitable activity. To focus funding on the foundation's priority areas, the following purposes are deemed to lie outwith criteria, and will not be considered:

- Organisations which are not recognised as a charity by the Inland Revenue.
- Individuals, including students.
- Animal welfare.
- Environment – e.g. geographic and scenic, conservation and protection of flora and fauna.
- Mainstream activities of schools, universities and colleges.
- Hospitals and medical centres.
- Activities which collect funds for subsequent redistribution to others.
- Sponsorship or marketing appeals.
- Endowment funds.
- Expeditions or overseas travel.
- Fabric appeals for places of worship, other than where such buildings provide accommodation to community groups.
- Historic restoration.

Applications

On application forms, complete with comprehensive guidance notes, available from the foundation.

These can be requested by telephone or e-mail, and are available on paper or disk (Microsoft Word Version 6.0).

Foundation staff are always willing to provide additional help. During the course of 2000 an internet site will be launched to ease access for applicant groups. The foundation says, 'If you need help – ask us!'

The trustees hold six board meetings each year, in February, April, June, August, October and December, usually during the first week of these months. Closing dates are 12 weeks prior to the board meeting date (precise dates for immediately forthcoming meetings can be obtained from the foundation.

To qualify for consideration, an application must be received in the foundation's office before 5pm on the closing date.

The Lolev Charitable Trust

See below

£846,000 (1998)

14A Gilda Crescent, London N16 6JP

Tel. 020 8806 3547

Correspondent A Tager, Trustee

Trustees *A Tager; E Tager; M Tager.*

Information available Accounts for 1998, without grants lists or narrative review, on file at the Charity Commission in July 2000.

General

The objects of the charity are the relief of the sick and needy and the support of Orthodox Jewish education. There is still no information about what this charity actually does with its money (including that part of it subscribed, through tax reliefs, by the public).

The Charity Commission is remiss in permitting this state of affairs to remain unexplained.

Applications

See above.

The Lord's Taverners

Minibuses and sports equipment for people with disabilities, cricket

£1,544,000 (1999)

Beneficial area UK.

10 Buckingham Place, London SW1E 6HX

Tel. 020 7821 2828 **Fax** 020 7821 2829

e-mail hq@lordstaverners.org

website www.lordstaverners.org

Correspondent Mark Williams, Chief Executive

Trustees *The Council of The Lord's Taverners comprising Roger Smith, Chairman, and 17 others.*

Information available Guidelines for applicants. Annual report and accounts.

Summary

The charity says that its aim is 'to give young people, particularly those with special needs, a sporting chance' by:

- providing incentives to play cricket and other team games in schools and clubs;
- creating recreational facilities in conjunction with the National Playing Fields Association;
- encouraging those with disabilities to participate in sporting activities;
- giving mobility with The Lord's Taverners minibuses.

There is a two-year waiting list for minibuses, which are given to schools, homes and organisations looking after young people under the age of 25 who have special needs and/or disabilities.

General

'Founded in 1950 at the Old Tavern at Lord's by a group of actors, the Charity has raised over £20 million in 49 years – from £15,000 in year one to £1.75 million in 1999.'

In its annual report, the charity says 'the administration costs of the Lord's Taverners have been calculated at 10p in the £. Costs directly attributable to fundraising add a further 12p in the £. Thus overheads for running the Club and Charity are contained at 22p in the £ (1998: 19p) as a proportion of our overall income.'

In 1999 the charity's income was £3,978,000. Three quarters of this amount (£2,959,000) was raised through fundraising events and the remainder came from donations, subscriptions and investments. The accounts showed the amount spent on fundraising as £1,766,000 (44% of income). Administration costs were a further £470,000 (£260,000 on salaries), or 12% of income.

Guidelines

The charity's guidelines are reprinted here and under 'Exclusions' and 'Applications' below:

Disbursement of grant aid

Grants are disbursed by The Foundation under three categories determined by The Trustees of The Lord's Taverners, its governing body. Disposable funds are usually allocated to these categories at laid down percentages as follows:-

Youth Cricket	50%
Lord's Taverners Minibuses	40%
Sport for Young People with Disability	10%

Youth cricket

The Lord's Taverners concentrate their resources available for cricket at the grass roots of the game targeting young people at clubs and schools. Grant aid is available for:

- Kwik Cricket;
- provision of cricket equipment bags – youth (under 16's) & junior (under 13's)
- grants towards the installation of non-turf pitches (maximum £1,000);
- grants towards the cost of a non-turf practice 'end' (maximum £500);
- grants towards the cost of netting (maximum £300); and
- support for schemes at local level.

Lord's Taverners minibuses

Specially adapted minibuses are donated to schools, homes and organisations which look after youngsters under the age of 25 who have special needs and/or disabilities. A contribution of £8,000 towards the cost of the vehicle is required from the recipient organisations. There is currently a two year waiting list. The cost of a fully accessible minibus fitted with a tail lift is approximately £29,500.

The Lord's Taverners will provide as *standard* either:

- a 12, 15 or 17 seat standard minibus; or
- a 14 seat accessible minibus with a semi-automatic under floor tail-lift which gives wheelchair facilities for a maximum of 4 wheelchairs.

The Lord's Taverners welcome sponsorship of minibuses which currently requires a donation of £12,000 in addition to the self-help donation from the recipient organisation. The sponsor will be invited to choose a project from our existing waiting list. The company name and logo may be placed on the rear of the minibus. The sponsor will be invited to the bus presentation.

Alternatively, a sponsor who has significantly supported an event for a number of years may have a minibus donated in their name in recognition of their contribution to the Charity. However, this will need to be supported by the Minibus Committee who will offer the sponsor a limited selection of projects from the current programme.

Sport for young people with disability

Funds for sports related equipment and facilities are granted to organisations to encourage youngsters (under the age of 25 years) with physical or mental disabilities to participate in sporting and recreational activities within a group environment.

Grant aid in 1999

	Amount	% of total
National Playing Fields Association	£25,000	2%
National Cricket Association	£230,000	15%

English Schools' Cricket Association	£100,000	7%
Direct cricket grants	£247,000	16%
Kwik Cricket	£20,000	1%
Total cricket	*£597,000*	*40%*
Minibuses	£752,000	49%
Sports for disabled people	£170,000	11%
Total	£1,544,000	100%

The annual report for 1999 notes that under 'Sport for young people with disability', 'from more than 1,000 applications received last year, the foundation awarded 44 grants totalling £170,428 (1998: £123,749) to such wide-ranging sports related projects as sailing and canoeing, equipment for gymnastic clubs, sports wheelchairs and specialised play equipment'.

Exclusions

Youth cricket: The following is not normally grant aided:

- building or renovation of pavilions
- sight screens
- bowling machines
- mowers/rollers
- overseas tours

Sport for young people with disability: The following will not normally be considered for a grant:

- capital costs
- medical costs
- running costs including salaries
- individuals
- holidays

Minibuses: Homes, schools and organisations are entitled to only one minibus per location, although applications are accepted for a replacement.

Applications

Youth cricket

Cricket grants are normally considered by the Foundation on the recommendation of the ECB (English Cricket Board) and the necessary application forms are available from local county cricket boards.

Minibuses

All organisations applying for a minibus are required to sign an Annex H VAT exemption form. If this is not possible then the organisation will be required to make an additional contribution to cover the cost of the VAT on the vehicle (approximately £5,000) in addition to the standard donation of £8,000.

It is also a condition of grant aid that the minibus has to be used for the stated purposes for a minimum period of five years. In the event of winding up or bankruptcy of the recipient organisation title of the minibus will automatically revert to The Lord's Taverners.

Sport for young people with disability

Applications will be reviewed on an individual basis by the local Lord's Taverners Regional Chairman whose recommendation is essential before final consideration is given by the Foundation Committee. In certain instances, estimates and quotations for the equipment will be requested.

The Foundation Committee meets quarterly to review applications for grant aid. All applications must be presented on the appropriate application forms and should be submitted to the Foundation Secretary no later than one month before the Foundation Committee Meeting.

Application forms are available from the Foundation Secretary.

John Lyon's Charity

Children and young people in north and west London

£2,082,000 (1999/2000)

Beneficial area The London boroughs of Barnet, Brent, Camden, Ealing, Kensington and Chelsea, Hammersmith and Fulham, Harrow and the Cities of London and Westminster.

45 Pont Street, London SW1X 0BX

Tel. 020 7589 1114 **Fax** 020 7589 0807

e-mail jlc@pglaw.co.uk

Correspondent David Robins, Grants Administrator

Trustees *The Keepers and Governors of the Possessions Revenues and Goods of the Free Grammar School of John Lyon. Grants committee: Prof. Michael Edwards, Chair; Mrs G M Baker; H V Reid; Prof. D M P Mingos; N W Stuart. Co-opted member: David Lindsay-Rea*

Information available The charity publishes an excellent annual report and guidelines for applicants.

Summary

The charity gives grants to organisations, generally in the range £5,000 to £20,000, 'to enhance the conditions of life and improve the life chances of children and young adults' in the areas of London specified above. The grants are awarded three times a year. There is no limit on the amount available, but grants rarely cover a period longer than three years.

General

John Lyon's Charity is a third branch of John Lyon's Foundation, a primarily educational charity. Its history began in the late 16th century when John Lyon donated a 48 acre farm as an endowment for the upkeep of two roads from London to Harrow. In 1991, the charity was given discretion to use the revenue from the endowment to benefit the inhabitants of certain London boroughs. Today the site of the original farm is better known as Maida Vale.

During 1999/2000, a £30 million unrealised surplus on the revaluation of properties and further unrealised gains on investments helped the charity's assets grow by 46% from £76 million to nearly £112 million over the year. Income amounted to £2.2 million, with management and administration expenses of £237,000 representing 11% of this.

Guidelines for applicants

We give grants:

- to help young people achieve their full potential
- to support education and training, particularly for young adults, and in conjunction with projects for the homeless, the unemployed and other disadvantaged groups
- to provide childcare, support for parents, and help where parental support is lacking
- to broaden cultural horizons, through activities such as dance, drama, music and the visual arts
- to enhance recreation and leisure, through sports and youth clubs, holiday and play schemes
- to promote the needs of children and young adults.

Certain types of scheme are supported, for example:

- Bursaries and allowances for education and training
- Schemes for the homeless linked to education and training
- Youth clubs and sports
- Counselling projects which are properly structured
- Pioneering childcare and parental support schemes

- Youth arts
- Partnership projects with the local authorities.

Support has not been limited to the disadvantaged. There has been an equal concern to encourage talent and 'enable the enabled'.

What we can fund

- Capital costs (eg. equipment, furniture, etc.) or revenue costs (eg. salaries, running costs).
- The maximum length of any grant is three years.
- There are no strict limits on the amount of a grant that may be rewarded.

Grants in 1999/2000

The charity apportioned its grants broadly in the following categories (with the amount donated in 1999/2000):

Education and training	£615,000	30%
Arts	£318,000	15%
Sport	£308,000	15%
Youth clubs and youth services	£283,000	13%
Childcare and parental support	£254,000	12%
Special needs/disability	£112,000	5%
Counselling	£109,000	5%
Promotion of youth issues/other	£46,000	2%
Housing and homelessness	£38,000	1%
Total	£2,082,000	100%

New grants were made to 71 organisations, some of which are described here:

The largest grants, of £70,000 each, were made under the 'sport' category, to North Kensington Amenity Trust for construction costs, and a capital grant to Westminster Boating Base. Grants of £50,000 were made to St Matthew's CE School Orchard Appeal (for building works); Harrow Club (salary costs over three years); Chelsea Centre (construction costs), and Barnet Educational Services (refurbishment costs at Colindale Primary School).

Other beneficiaries included the Gabbitas, Truman & Thring Educational Trust (£30,000 for masterclasses for gifted children); Shooting Star Trust (£30,000 for the Avenue Hospice Fund); Paddington Arts (£30,000, running costs over three years); Pimlico Toy Library (£20,000, revenue funding); Howard League for Penal Reform (£10,000, Citizenship and Crime Project); Camden Youth Service (£10,000, 'Youth Work Plus' mentoring scheme) and St Mary le Bow Church Homeless Project (£9,000 in total, revenue costs).

Bursary funding was provided to five organisations, including the Central School of Ballet (£11,000) and the Michael Palin Centre for Stammering Children (£10,000).

Small grants

A total of 44 grants of between £200 and £1,000 were awarded, to charities from Apple to Young Pavement Artists. Five of the beneficiaries had also received small grants in the previous year, including Ashburnham Adventure Playground and Ebury Bridge Youth Club, which had been funded in each of the two preceding years.

Exclusions

The charity cannot give grants:

- to individuals;
- for research, unless it is action research designed to lead directly to the advancement of practical activities in the community;
- for feasibility studies;
- for medical care and resources;
- in response to general charitable appeals, unless they can be shown to be of specific benefit to children and young people in one or more of the geographical areas listed;
- as direct replacements for the withdrawals of funds by statutory authorities for activities which are primarily the responsibility of central or local government;
- to umbrella organisations to distribute to projects which are already in receipt of funds from the charity;
- for the promotion of religion or politics;
- for telephone helplines.

Applications

You should put in a letter the following information:

- a summary of the main purpose of the project
- details of the overall amount requested
- over what timescale
- some indication of how funds from the charity would be allocated

If your first proposal is assessed positively, you will be sent an application form. This must be completed and returned by the deadline date in order for your project to be considered for funding.

The grants committee meets three times a year. The closing dates for the return of completed application forms in 2001–02 are:

- Friday 19 January 2001 for the meeting in March 2001
- Friday 20 April 2001 for the meeting in June 2001
- Friday 21 September 2001 for the meeting in December 2001
- Friday 18 January 2002 for the meeting in March 2002

The M K Charitable Trust

Jewish charities

£412,000 (1998/99)

Beneficial area UK, especially the north east of England.

c/o Cohen Arnold & Co, 13–17 New Burlington Place, Regent Street, London W1X 2JP

Tel. 020 7734 1362

Correspondent Cohen Arnold & Co

Information available Inadequate annual report and accounts on file at the Charity Commission.

General

This trust, formerly known as Mendel Kaufman, has never listed the recipients of any of its grants. However, the trust said, some years ago, that it 'supports Jewish organisations, with a preference for the North East of England, especially the Gateshead area'.

In 1998/99 the trust had assets of over £4 million. Income of £739,000 was generated mainly from property revenue (£461,000) and donations received (£65,000). A total of £412,000 was distributed in grants, slightly less than in 1997/98 (£452,000).

Applications

In writing to the correspondent.

The Mackintosh Foundation

Performing arts, general

£1,546,000 (1998/99)

Beneficial area UK, with an interest in western Scotland, and overseas.

1 Bedford Square, London WC1B 3RA

Tel. 020 7637 8866 **Fax** 020 7436 2683

Correspondent Sherry Dennehy, Appeals Secretary

Trustees *Sir Cameron Mackintosh, Chair; Martin McCallum; Nicholas Allott; D Michael Rose; Patricia Macnaughton; Alain Boublil.*

Information available Good annual report and accounts. Detailed and excellent information note available from the foundation, a large part of which is reprinted below.

Summary

Around 300 grants a year, up to 90% being for amounts under £10,000 and typically running from £1,000 to £5,000, for a wide range of causes. The few large grants, peaking at £150,000, are usually to support the theatre, while those for community projects tend be made in the west of Scotland.

General

The foundation was established to:

- promote and develop theatrical, musical and dramatic arts
- relieve suffering from and promote research into the causes and treatment of AIDS
- provide for medical research generally and the relief of sickness
- provide relief for the homeless and poverty stricken
- provide for the relief of refugees
- provide funds for any other objects which are exclusively charitable under English law

In 1996 the objects were extended to include the promotion of the conservation, protection and enhancement in the UK of nature and the amenities of the countryside, including areas of natural beauty and areas of buildings of special scientific, historic or architectural interest for the benefit of the public.

A useful 'General Information Hand-out' in January 2000, provided in response to enquiries about the foundation's aims, operation and funding, and since updated (in September 2000), is largely reprinted here:

To date the vast majority of the funding received by the Foundation has come from the personal patronage of Sir Cameron Mackintosh whose companies have so far provided the Foundation with sums aggregating to more than £17.12 million.

At the instigation of Sir Cameron part of the monies received by the Foundation from his companies (namely £3.5 million) has been allocated to the establishment of a capital endowment base for the Foundation which when last valued at the end of March 2000 was worth over £7.85 million.

During the 12 years since it was set up the Foundation has made over 2,600 separate grants (including repeats) totalling over £13m to over 1,000 different charities or charitable objects. It has endowed Oxford University at a cost of well over £1m with a fund known as 'The Cameron Mackintosh Fund for Contemporary Theatre' at Oxford University, part of which has been used to set up a Visiting Professorship of Contemporary Theatre at the University. It has also agreed to provide a fund of £1m over a period of ten years (now largely paid up) to The Royal National Theatre, for revivals of classical stage musical productions under the auspices of the RNT. It has provided financial support to a number of projects in the United States by US registered not-for-profit tax exempt bodies with exclusively charitable objects, including a major grant of US$1.5m over 5 years (now completed) to The Alliance of New American Musicals to foster, encourage and promote the creation and production of new dramatico-musical plays by American writers and artists. The Foundation has also set up a Drama School Bursary Award Scheme to provide financial assistance for needy and deserving students on UK accredited drama school courses. 29 students to date have received awards under the scheme since it was set up in 1992. The Foundation has also pledged £500,000 over 5 years in respect of selected applications by theatres under the Arts Councils' 'Arts 4 Everyone' scheme of National Lottery funding.

Other major projects include £250,000 to Prior Park College, £100,000 to Mallaig Health Centre, £70,000 to Jefferies Research Wing Trust for medical equipment, and over £1m through the separate 'Bui Doi Fund' for refugees and [those who might be called] the 'dust of life' in and from war-stricken and oppressed territories. [*However, this fund has now been discontinued. Ed.*] ...

The Foundation has to date tended not to be involved very much in 'hands-on' administration of any charitable projects but has concentrated on providing funds to others for that purpose. The main reason for this is that the Trustees of the Foundation are all very busily engaged in other activities with little time to become more directly involved in the way its funds are used although there are some instances in which help has been provided to needy individuals. Administration costs are kept to a minimum (in each of the years ending March 1991 to March 1999 amounting to less than 6.7% of income) since at present the Foundation has no office establishment of its own and has comparatively few overhead expenses other than the cost of the professional time of its solicitors (who deal with much of the administration as well as legal work), an appeals and bursaries secretary and, of course, its auditors/accountants.

Because of the Foundation's limited monitoring resources, it has tended to concentrate its funding on other registered charities who are supervised in the conduct of their affairs by the Charity Commissioners, but the Foundation not infrequently makes exceptions, particularly where overseas applicants and individuals are concerned.

Unusually, and very desirably, this foundation seeks further donations to support its work.

Trustees' report

The 1998/99 trustees' report, partly reprinted here, provided further details about grantmaking:

The Bui Doi Fund

For some years the Foundation has operated a separate fund known as the 'Bui Doi Fund' ('Bui Doi' meaning Dust of Life), for the support and relief of the poor, the deprived, the homeless and the sick in, and refugees from, Vietnam and other territories in S E Asia and related activities. The income of this fund has been derived from a share of the revenue from performances of the stage musical show 'Miss Saigon' in various parts of the world and to a very small extent from public donations. During the year the Foundation made grants of £115,427 from the 'Bui-Doi Fund', the largest of which were £15,000 to The Refugee Council and £10,000 to each of Song Saigon's Children's Charity and Ockenden Venture for specific projects within the fund's terms of reference.

The Bui-Doi Fund's source of income has been gradually declining and it is anticipated that the Bui-Doi Fund as a separate restricted fund of the Foundation is likely to be wound up by the end of 1999. Any future grants of a similar nature which the Trustees may wish to make, will be made from the general fund.

Arts 4 Everyone

On 21 November 1998, the Foundation pledged £500,000 over the next five years in conjunction with the Arts Council of England and the regional Arts Councils' new 'Arts 4 Everyone' scheme (the main scheme and not the 'Express' scheme for grants of £5,000 or less). Under arrangements made between the Foundation and the Arts Councils the latter was to refer suitable applicants for 'partnership funding' to the Foundation for consideration as to those which the Foundation … may decide to support. However with the knowledge and approval of the Arts Council of England the sum of £75,000 of the first year's allocation was diverted to certain theatres which were threatened with loss of funding both from the London Arts Board and from commercial sponsors, and a further £25,000 was reallocated to the London Arts Board's 'new production fund'. Of the said £100,000 only £25,000 (to King's Head Theatre) was paid during the year … it has been agreed that the remaining £400,000 will be allocated by the Council's Drama Department over a three-year period to provide additional funding to certain approved theatre companies, some of whom are already in receipt of A4E funding.

Other major donations during the year were: £100,000 to The Highland Council towards development and construction costs of a day care centre and sheltered housing complex in Mallaig, Invernesshire; £75,000 to The Knoydart Foundation towards its purchase of the Knoydart Estate in the Western Highlands of Scotland for the benefit of the local community; and £50,000 to each of the Almeida Theatre Company Limited and the Royal National Lifeboat Institution.

Grants in 1998/99

The foundation classifies its grants as follows (with the % of grant total in 1998/99):

Theatre and the performing arts	39%
• *theatre companies and buildings*	*20%*
• *promotion of new theatrical works and classical music repertoire*	*8%*
• *theatrical training and education*	*9%*
• *theatre related pastoral care*	*2%*
The homeless	12%
Children and education	10%
Medical	12%
Community projects	12%
The environment	6%
Bui Doi Fund	7%
Overseas	2%

Grants were distributed by size as follows:

Size range	*Number of grants 1998/99*	*1997/98*
£150,000–£199,999	1	–
£100,000–£149,999	1	–
£50,000–£99,999	4	1
£20,000–£49,999	7	11
£10,000–£19,999	22	25
£5,000–£9,999	45	44
£1,000–£4,999	142	125
Less than £1,000	70	118
Total	292	324

Substantial awards not mentioned in the trustees' report included those to Donmar Warehouse Projects (£26,000); the Theatre Investment Fund (£25,000), and Charity Projects Ltd (the operational name for Comic Relief, £25,000).

Recurrent grants to Forum for the Future (£21,000) and Centrepoint Soho (£20,000) constituted the largest donations for the benefit of the environment and homeless people.

Many of the larger medical grants were given to organisations involved with HIV/AIDS, including the Terrence Higgins Trust (£11,000); Crusaid (£10,000), and the National AIDS Trust (£10,000).

International charities benefiting from the general fund included Pestalozzi Overseas Children's Trust (£5,000); UNICEF (£2,000); Send-A-Cow (£1,000), and Save the Rhino International (£1,000).

As a grants list was not included with the 1997/98 accounts in the Charity Commission's file, it is hard to tell what proportion of grants is repeated. However, between a quarter and a half of the recipients of small grants had also been supported two years previously.

As the following samples show, well represented among the beneficiaries were charities for medical care (particularly HIV/AIDS), children and the arts.

Alone in London; Body Positive; Born Free Foundation; British Divers Marine Life Rescue; Cerebral Palsy Action; Islington Arts Factory; Marie Curie Cancer Care; Merseyside Council for Voluntary Service (£5,000 each).

Cystic Fibrosis Research Trust; Action for Kids; City Ballet of London Trust; Skye Environment Trust; Variety Club of Great Britain; Elton John AIDS Foundation; Haslemere Festival (£250 to £350 each).

Exclusions

Religious or political activities. Apart from the foundation's accredited drama course bursary award and some exceptions, applications from individuals are discouraged.

Applications

In writing to the appeals secretary at the address above. The trustees meet in May and November in plenary session, but a small grants committee meets weekly.

The MacRobert Trusts

General, mainly in Scotland

£678,000 (1998/99)

Beneficial area UK, mainly Scotland.

Cromar, Tarland, Aboyne, Aberdeenshire AB34 4UD

Tel. 013398 81444

Correspondent Major General John Barr, Administrator

Trustees *I Booth; Mrs C Cuthbert; D Heughan; J Mackie; W Morrison; Group Capt. D A Needham; Dr J Paterson-Brown; R Sherriff; A Summers; Cromar Nominees Ltd.*

Information available 'Guidelines for Applicants' leaflet and detailed reports and accounts (but see below).

Summary

There are five MacRobert Trusts, three of which give grants to organisations. They have a particular interest in ex-service charities, especially those connected with the RAF, but fund a wide variety of other causes, mostly in Scotland. Over 100 grants are made a year, which may be for as much as £50,000, sometimes on a recurring basis.

General

The trusts' 'Guidelines' read as follow:

The trusts are reactive so, with very few exceptions, only applications that are made to the trusts are considered by the trustees.

The trustees consider their policy and practice of grant giving every five years, most recently in 1997. However it did not lead to any substantial changes in the information available. The beneficial area is UK wide but preference is given to organisations in Scotland. Grants are made normally only to a recognised Scottish charity or a registered charity outside Scotland.

Currently the major categories under which the trustees consider support are:

- Science and technology
- Youth
- Services and sea
- Disabled and handicapped
- Ex-service hospitals and homes
- Education
- Community welfare

The minor categories are:

- Agriculture and horticulture
- Arts and music
- Medical care
- Tarland and Deeside

The trustees recognise the need to assist voluntary organisations which need funds to complement those already received from central government and local authority sources. However this is not to say that the trusts make a grant where statutory bodies fail to provide.

The trusts are prepared to make core/ revenue grants where appropriate, but favour projects.

The trustees recognise that, at present, experiment and innovation are much more difficult to fund and the trusts' role in funding them the more significant.

This view that experiment and innovation are 'much more difficult to fund' is surprising. The opposite view is more generally held.

In 1998/99 more than half the grants ranged from £500 to £5,000, but about a quarter were large grants of £10,000 or more. About 90% of grants went to organisations based in Scotland, or the Scottish arms of national organisations. Most recurring donations were to organisations benefiting the armed services, particularly ex-servicemen's hospitals.

The report lists the grant recipients but does not describe what each grant is for. They are categorised as follows:

	Paid	*No.*
Education*	£113,000	12
Ex-servicemen's hospitals	£105,000	7
Medical care	£90,000	8
Community welfare	£89,500	18
Youth	£89,000	18
Disabled & handicapped	£53,500	13
Armed services & merchant marine	£36,000	12
Science & technology	£25,000	2
Music & the arts	£22,000	6
Agriculture & horticulture	£16,000	6
Tarland & Deeside (local area)	£16,000	9
Unspecified	£8,000	2
Total	£678,000	113

(* Plus educational grants to schools on behalf of individuals: £16,000)

The largest grants in 1998/99 were to the University of Aberdeen (£50,000, repeat); Royal Air Forces Association, Sussexdown Convalescent Home (£25,000, repeat); and Marie Curie Cancer Care, Edinburgh (£25,000).

£20,000 each was give to REACT Richmond; Institute of Nano Technology; Boys' Brigade in Scotland, Larbert; Bournemouth War Memorial Homes; Scottish Veterans' Garden City Association.

Other grants included: Royal Air Force Benevolent Fund (£10,000, repeat); Royal Star and Garter Home (£10,000, repeat); Arkwright Scholarship Trust (£3,000, repeat); National Library of Scotland (£5,000); Musselburgh War Memorial Remembrance Fund (£500); King George's Fund for Sailors (£2,500, repeat); SENSE in Scotland (£5,000, repeat); East Renfrewshire Mental Health Project (£500); Victim Support Scotland (£3,500); Association for the Protection of Rural Scotland (£5,000); Scottish Chamber Orchestra (£5,000); Moray Youth Theatre (£3,000); Chest, Heart & Stroke Scotland (£5,000); Brain Research Trust (£15,000); Aberdeen International Youth Festival (£5,000, repeat); Belfast Central Mission (£3,000); The Royal Institution (£4,600); Tomnaverie Stone Circle Trust, Tarland (£4,000); St Thomas' Church, Aboyne (£600, repeat).

Exclusions

Grants are not normally provided for:

- religious organisations (but not including youth/community services provided by them, or projects of general benefit to the whole community, or local churches);
- organisations based outside the UK;
- individuals;
- endowment or memorial funds;
- general appeals or mail shots;
- political organisations;
- student bodies (as opposed to universities);
- fee-paying schools (apart from an educational grants scheme for children who are at, or need to attend, a Scottish independent secondary school and for which a grant application is made through the head teacher);
- expeditions;
- retrospective grants;
- departments within a university (unless the appeal gains the support of, and is channelled through, the principal).

Applications

There is no application form. Note that in addition to the requirements set out below and which are taken from the printed guidelines, the trust also asks that applications should be clearly and concisely set out on no more than two sides of A4 paper. They should include:

- the charity title and description of the organisation's activities;
- registered charity number or evidence of tax exempt status;
- list of the charity's key people;
- details of the project for which a grant is sought including costings, funds raised in relation to the target and funds promised (if any);
- the latest fully audited accounts and annual report;
- details of any application made, or intended, for funding from any National Lottery source.

The trustees look for clear, realistic and attainable aims.

Unsuccessful organisations should wait at least one year from the date of applying before re-applying. Successful organisations should wait at least two years from receipt of a donations before re-applying.

In most cases the application undergoes scrutiny which may include a visit from the administrator.

The trustees meet in March and October each year. Applications for the March meeting need to reach the trusts by late October, and for the October meeting by early June. Applicants are informed of the trustees' decision within one week of the meeting.

The Manifold Trust

Historic buildings, environmental conservation, general

£855,000 (1999)

Beneficial area UK.

Shottesbrooke House, Maidenhead SL6 3SW

Fax 01628 820159

Correspondent Miss C C Gilbertson

Information available Brief grant guidelines. Annual report and accounts.

Summary

The trust mainly supports charities involved in conservation, but also contributes to educational establishments, the arts and social welfare charities. Most funding is for the preservation of historic buildings, particularly churches, so its main commitments are to organisations that work in that area. Most grants are between £400 and £5,000, but can be considerably higher.

General

Founded in 1962, the trust had assets of over £12 million in 1999, and an income of more than £800,000, mostly from rents on a number of properties, but as the

THE MANIFOLD TRUST – GRANTMAKING

	1999 Amount	%	1998 Amount	%
Churches and other historic buildings	£480,000	56%	£475,000	60%
Arts and education, including museums	£285,000	33%	£174,000	22%
Environment	£50,000	6%	£71,000	9%
Social causes	£40,000	5%	£71,000	9%
Total	£855,000		£791,000	

accounts have stated: 'For many years the payments made by the trust have exceeded its income, the trustees believing that it is better to meet the present need of other charities than to reserve money for the future.'

The trust has close connections with the Landmark Trust, also founded by Sir John Smith. This charity rescues fine and interesting buildings and restores them for use as holiday homes. Fluctuations in grant-giving over the years have largely been associated with how much was given to the Landmark Trust – which got over £15 million in 1996. The yearly donations to that trust have been decreasing since then, to £500,000 in 1997, £121,000 in 1998 and £54,000 in 1999. Hence, the trust's overall level of grant-making had been falling dramatically, but had reached a sustainable level by 1999. Big interest-free loans have also been made in the past – £10 million to the Warrior Preservation Trust and £2 million to the Landmark Trust in 1997.

Other significant long-term beneficiaries are Magdalene College, Cambridge and New College, Oxford, which in 1999 got £20,000 and £16,500 respectively.

Each year, as many as 200 parish church councils receive small grants, seldom for more than £1,000, but the trust provides the following guidance notes:

Churches seeking money for structural repairs should not apply. The trust does indeed provide money for such churches, and is keen to do so, but it is not equipped to compare their relative merits. Accordingly it makes a block grant instead to the Historic Churches Preservation Trust [which has an entry in this book] and to the equivalent body in Scotland, the Scottish Churches Architectural Heritage Trust, 15 North Bank St, The Mound, Edinburgh EH1 2LP.

The trust is also very keen to help churches bring into use again bells which have not been rung for many years, and to augment old peals of less than six bells. Applications for grants for this purpose should be made, not to the Manifold Trust, but to Ian Oram Esq, The Cottage, School Hill, Warnham, Horsham RH12 3QN who acts for the Bells Restoration Funds Committee of the Central Council of Church Bellringers. He advises the trust on these matters.

Apart from payments to churches as described, the trust's annual report does not describe what grants are for, but summarises grantmaking as follows:

In 1999, 245 grants were made. Roughly half of these (113) were for less than £1,000, and a further 105 ranged from £1,000 to £5,000. However, just three large grants accounted for over a third of charitable expenditure. These were to the Historic Churches Preservation Trust (£158,000; £29,000 in 1998); Buckfastleigh Trust (£83,000), and the Landmark Trust (£54,000).

In addition to the regular beneficiaries already mentioned, organisations receiving a third consecutive award in 1999 included the Airfields Environment Trust (£10,000); Avoncroft Museum of Buildings (£7,500); Cornwall Historic Churches Trust (£2,000), and the British School of Rome (£2,000).

Other beneficiaries were St Michael's Abbey, Farnborough (£29,000; £21,000 in 1998); The Lambeth Fund (£25,000); Shottesbrooke Parochial Church Council (£18,000); Mikron Theatre Company (£10,000); Lake District Art Gallery & Museum Trust (£10,000); Wey and Arun Canal Trust (£2,000; £4,500 in 1998), and Agro Forestry Research Trust (£500).

The trust gives a small number of modest donations to charities working with children, and 'with which it has particular connections'. In 1999 it made grants of between £200 and £1,000 to NCH Action for Children, Tommy's Campaign, Orphan Aid, Children with Leukaemia and the NSPCC.

Exclusions

'The trust does not give grants to churches for "improvements"; nor, with regret, to individuals for any purpose.'

Applications

The trust has no full-time staff. Therefore, general enquiries, and applications for grants, should be made in writing only, by post or by fax, and not by telephone. The trust does not issue application forms; applicants should please:

1. Describe the cause or project.

2. State how much money it is hoped to raise, and

3. If the appeal is for a specific project, state also
a) how much it will cost;
b) how much of this cost will come from the applicant charity's existing funds;
c) how much has already been received or promised from other sources;
d) how much is therefore still being sought.

4. List sources of funds to which application has been or is intended to be made (for example local authorities, or quasi-governmental sources, such as the National Lottery).

5. If the project involves conservation of a building, send a photograph of it – a snapshot will do – and a note (or pamphlet) about its history.

6. Send a copy, if it is not too bulky, of the charity's latest income and expenditure account and balance sheet.

Applications are considered twice a month, and a reply is sent to most applicants (whether successful or not) who have written a letter rather than sent a circular.

The Jim Marshall Charitable Trust

General

£466,000 (1998)

Beneficial area UK.

c/o Marshall Amplification plc, Denbigh Road, Milton Keynes MK1 1DQ

Correspondent Julie Lancaster

Trustees *J Marshall; L Smith; K Saunders; B Charlton; S Marshall.*

Information available Inadequate annual report and accounts, lacking any information about grants. Those for 1998 were the most recent available at the Charity Commission in July 2000.

Summary

Under its deed the trust was set up to benefit five named charities and 'others'. In practice it is operated by Mr Marshall on a personal basis and its grants, most of which are probably for health and welfare charities, may be better regarded as his personal benefactions and not as part of any institutional programme.

General

The trust was founded in 1989 by its namesake, who is also the founder of Marshall Amplification plc. It has limited assets (£323,000 in 1998), with grantmaking sustained by annual donations from Mr Marshall. The charities 'expressly ... to benefit' according to the deeds are:

- Variety Club Children's Charity
- London Federation of Boys' Clubs
- Wavedon All Music Plan
- MacIntyre Homes
- Buckinghamshire Association of Boys' Clubs

Other charities will also be considered.

In 1998 income from donations was £480,000 and grants totalling £466,000 were given 'mainly to organisations for the benefit of children, young people, families and the sick and disabled'. A previously stated interest in the Milton Keynes area can no longer be confirmed, as no further information was available.

Exclusions

Probably no grants to individuals.

Applications

Unsolicited applications have not in the past been welcomed.

Mayfair Charities

Orthodox Judaism

£2,481,000 (1998/99)

Freshwater House, 158–162 Shaftesbury Avenue, London WC2H 8HR

Tel. 020 7836 1555

Correspondent C Morse, Secretary

Information available Annual report and accounts on file at the Charity Commission.

General

About 200 grants were made in 1998/99, nearly all to various Jewish educational institutions and synagogues, in the UK, USA and Israel.

In the annual report the trustees say that they have decided to 'support certain major projects ... which have received substantial financial grants from the Company. At the present time the Governors have entered into commitments for financial support of colleges and institutions which would absorb approximately £5 million over the next five years.'

Income for the year totalled £4.25 million, generated from assets of £56.5 million. Grantmaking totalled £2,481,000, down from £3,713,000 in 1997/98.

A third of grant expenditure went on a single grant of £833,000 to Beth Jacob Grammar School, a long-standing major beneficiary. A further £919,000 (37% of the total) was donated to the following four organisations:

Hibath Jerusalem Kolel (£324,000); Mosdos Bobov, Chesed Acc. (£244,000); Society of Friends of the Torah (£231,000), and Merkaz Lechinuch Torani (£120,000).

Most of the remaining grants were in the range £350 to £10,000; typically between £500 and £2,500. Where the locality could be identified, UK organisations in London, Manchester and Gateshead were among those supported.

Applications

In writing to the correspondent.

The Medlock Charitable Trust

Education, health, welfare, mainly in Bath and Boston

£1,121,000 (1998/99)

Beneficial area Normally UK, especially Bath and Boston.

St George's Lodge, 33 Oldfield Road, Bath BA2 3NE

Tel. 01225 428221 **Fax** 01225 428221

Correspondent David Medlock, Trustee

Information available Report and accounts with full grants list and a narrative review of grantmaking.

Summary

This trust is a major funder of educational establishments in two areas of the country, Bath and Boston, where the trustees have strong connections. Hospitals are the next major beneficiaries. The bulk of the funds is used to fund big capital or research projects, over periods of up to five years.

Nearly half of the grant total in 1998/99 was taken up by the final tranche of a £750,000 grant for the construction of a volunteer centre in Boston.

About 100 smaller grants, most of them between £500 and £5,000 (and about a quarter of them repeated), go mainly to local schools and healthcare charities. These grants are also centred in the two localities, but are occasionally made slightly further afield.

General

The trust describes its policy as follows:

> The trustees have identified the City of Bath and the Borough of Boston as the principal but not exclusive areas in which the charity is and will be proactive. These areas have been specifically chosen as the founder of the charity has strong connections with the City of Bath, the home of the charity, and has family connections of long standing with the Borough of Boston.
>
> To date the charity has supported and funded a number of projects in these areas by making substantial grants. These grants have been made to fund projects in the areas of education, medicine, research and social services all for the benefit of the local community. During the year, the trustees also receive many applications for assistance from many diverse areas in the United Kingdom. These are all considered sympathetically. ...

The 1998/99 review of the trust's activities is reprinted here, with specific amounts paid in the year added by these editors.

> This year saw the final build stages of the Voluntary Centre at Boston where the keys were finally handed over in October 1999 after a considerable gestation period. ... The extensive funds allocated to this project [£540,000] have restricted grants available for others.
>
> However, we have resourced the third year for research into aortic balloons for neurosurgery with the results yet to be presented [£50,000 to Southampton General Hospital]. The Chair at Bath University continues [£100,000] and our large commitment to Schools for design technology, IT and other miscellaneous projects all contribute to a considerable amount invested in all parts of the education spectrum.
>
> New projects include two grants of £25,000 this year and next for CLIC to fund six editions of a new magazine for the organisation and a grant of £50,000 p.a. for the next five years to the Royal United Hospital Appeal, subject to approval of where the money will be spent.

We are now reaching the stage where projects are dealt with over a period of years. This will restrict the availability of new grants. Some grants are only being released to applicants who are successful with other fundraising activities. This does restrict the flexibility but also extends the number of schemes which can be considered.

We have also considered projects where the Trust acquires property on behalf of other registered charities which are unable to meet the immediate commercial commitment. The property is then subsequently sold back to the charity when sufficient funds have been raised from elsewhere. This occurs where all possible advice has been taken and the risk involved is far outweighed by the gain to the recipient's charity. Several schemes have been considered but only the purchase of New King Street, Bath and subsequent sale to Bath Churches Housing Association has been completed.

The Trustees have received 515 applications and are still receiving requests from individuals whom we do not support. 108 grants have been made during the year.

The Trustees are currently receiving an increasing number of applications. We endeavour to send a reply in due course and the Trustees are still actively pursuing new opportunities as well as supporting our established links.

Grants in 1998/99

About two thirds of the grant recipients were based in Bath or Boston or the immediate area and grantmaking does not usually appear to extend much beyond the adjacent counties, such as Avon and Wiltshire or Lincolnshire and Cambridgeshire.

Schools were the most frequent beneficiary. For example, 10 primary schools in Boston received recurrent grants between £1,000 and £6,000, while a number of independent schools in Avon got grants of around £7,500 each. Other beneficiaries work in the field of health, including regional charities such as Wessex Cancer Trust and Wessex Cardiac Trust (£2,500 each).

The largest grants outside the main area of benefit were £15,000 for the Kimbolton 400 Appeal (Cambridgeshire) and £11,000 for La Retraite Swan, Salisbury.

The few national organisations supported included Barnardos (£5,000); British Trust for Conservation Volunteers (£2,000); SCOPE (£500), and Breakthrough Breast Cancer (£270).

An unusual overseas beneficiary was the Karnataka Parents' Association, Bangalore.

Exclusions

Individuals.

Applications

In writing to the correspondent.

The Mental Health Foundation

Mental health & learning disability research, community work

About £500,000 annually

Beneficial area UK.

20–21 Cornwall Terrace, London NW1 4QL

Tel. 020 7535 7400 **Fax** 020 7535 7474

e-mail mhf@mentalhealth.org.uk

website www.mentalhealth.org.uk

Correspondent Research & Support Officer (Grants)

Trustees *Christopher Martin, Chair; Lady Euston; Sue Fraser; Giles Ridley; Jack Barnes; Jennifer Bernard; Lord Dholakia; Prof. Rachel Jenkins; the Earl of Dalhousie; Dr Zenobia Nadirshaw; Michael Roberts; Lady Weston; Mike Wilson.*

Information available Report and accounts, without the required details of grants.

General

The foundation says it has no general grant programmes of the kind that this book seeks to cover. However, it does make grants to its research and development partners for its particular programmes. These are numerous, specialised and fast changing. Organisations working in the field of mental health are recommended to look at the Programmes section of the foundation's website.

Exclusions

- individual hardship, education and training
- travel
- attendance at conferences
- capital
- expenses such as vehicles or property
- general appeals
- general running costs

Applications

Please contact the foundation offices for current grant priorities, guidelines and closing dates. Scottish organisations should contact the Scotland office at 5th Floor, Merchants House, 30 George Square, Glasgow, G2 1EG (Tel: 0141 572 0125; Fax: 0141 572 0246).

The Mercers' Company Charities

Independent schools, almshouses, general

£2,278,000 (to organisations, 1998/99)

Beneficial area UK, in practice mainly London and the southern half of England.

Mercers' Hall, Ironmonger Lane, London EC2V 8HE

Tel. 020 7726 4991

website www.mercers.co.uk

Correspondent H W Truelove, Grants Manager

Trustees *The Mercers' Company.*

Information available Report and accounts containing limited grants list. 'Charitable Grants Report' lists all grants of £5,000 or more, but without proper explanation.

Summary

Grants normally range from £200 to £5,000 for first-time applicants. Large grants of up to £100,000 are reserved for institutions closely linked to the Mercers' Company.

General

The Mercers' Company is one of the ancient livery companies of the City of London. It acts as trustee of numerous charities, which together donate over £2 million a year to organisations, largely for work in England, but some for projects overseas. It also has a housing association and runs four almshouses. The grantmaking is organised centrally for all its charities and is treated as a single operation for this entry.

Grant-making trusts managed by the Mercers' Company distributed £2.8 million in the year to September 1999, more than £500,000 of which went to individuals. This activity is summarised in the box below.

Policy and procedures

Mercers' Charitable Foundation

Grants are made for the following purposes:

- social welfare (in particular prison welfare, ex-offenders, drug and alcohol addiction)
- youth
- education (higher and further education, primary and secondary education) – inner city areas (especially London) are favoured. Capital projects are not usually supported
- the arts (performing arts, fine art and design)
- heritage and the environment – grants are made to museums, libraries and art collections, and towards the conservation of works of art and archives, and the preservation of buildings and for the conservation of the countryside and its wildlife
- the advancement of the Christian religion – the emphasis is on pastoral work. Appeals for grants for fabric restoration are not normally entertained, an annual grant being made for this purpose to the Historic Churches Preservation Trust.

The greater part of the funds available is committed to schools, colleges and other institutions with an historical or other long-standing association with the Company. Grants rarely exceed £3,000, and in the cases of arts, heritage and religion, the normal range is £200 to £1,500.

Sir Richard Whittington's Charity

Grants are made to institutions to relieve hardship and distress. The emphasis is on medical welfare, homelessness, community & social welfare, and handicapped & disabled.

Grants are made to individuals only at the request of a social worker or health visitor. Grants are also made in relief of need to several agencies by way of block grants, but unsolicited applications are not entertained.

Grants to institutions are in the range of £500 to £5,000 and rarely exceed £5,000 in the case of unsolicited applications, the trustees' policy being to support capital projects which have been initiated by them.

Earl of Northampton's Charity

Grants are limited to institutions providing care for elderly or disabled people in homes or other institutions.

Grants in 1998/99

The Mercers' Company charitable grants report describes the activities of all the grant-making trusts it manages.

GRANTS TO ORGANISATIONS, 1998/99

	Paid	*No.*
Education	£793,000	128
General welfare	£484,000	110
Handicapped and disabled	£343,000	66
Medical	£160,000	33
Elderly	£138,000	15
Church and religion	£129,000	63
Heritage	£122,000	73
Arts	£56,000	18
Relief in need	£53,000	18
Total	£2,278,000	524

The company says:

We tend to support charitable organisations which are well known to us, and where our staff are best placed to evaluate the organisation and monitor the use of funds granted. This means that the bulk of our grants are made to charities in the London area. In the year 1998/99, 65% of grants were made to organisations in the London area. Large grants, of £10,000 and above, are usually made as a result of detailed research on the initiative of the Company, or to organisations with which we have a long-standing association, rather than in response to unsolicited approaches.

During 1998/99 1,150 completed applications for grants were received from charitable bodies, of which 747 (65%) received a grant. Most grants to institutions fall within the range £1,000 to £15,000; within this range the average grant was £2,700.

The grants report does not list the recipients of less than £5,000, but the charities state that their policy is to favour smaller locally based charities for awards of this size.

THE MERCERS' COMPANY CHARITIES

	1998/99		*1997/98*	
Source of funds	*Amount*	*%*	*Amount*	*%*
Mercers' Charitable Foundation	£1,692,000	60%	£1,700,000	53%
Whittington Charity	£568,000	20%	£875,000	27%
Earl of Northampton's Charity	£242,000	9%	£255,000	8%
Mercers' Educational Trust	£250,000	9%	£285,000	9%
Charter 600 Charity	£20,000	1%	£20,000	1%
Miscellaneous charities	£57,000	2%	£65,000	2%
Total	£2,829,000	100%	£3,200,000	100%

The largest grants, amounting to at least a third of the total, go to the schools, colleges and almshouses which are associated with the company. Such institutions often receive grants from two or more of the Mercers' Company's charities simultaneously. In 1998/99, five of the seven largest grants (for £50,000 or more) went to educational establishments. They were:

Gresham College Trust and the Gresham Professorships (£132,000); St Paul's School (£83,000, final instalment of a grant towards development costs); Thomas Telford School (£80,000, various grants); College of Richard Collyer, Horsham (£54,000, various grants), and Dauntsey's School, Devizes (£50,000, various grants).

These are independent fee-paying schools, with the exception of Thomas Telford School in Shropshire, jointly sponsored with Tarmac plc, which opened in 1991. In the company's own words:

The City Technology College initiative launched by Kenneth Baker, the Secretary of State for Education, in October 1986 enabled the Mercers' Company to extend its educational interests into the national system. The objectives were attractive – to deploy private sector management and investment in an all-ability secondary school, to give children from deprived urban areas fresh educational opportunities, and to provide a model for educational development. However, at a time of fundamental reform to the educational system these objectives were highly controversial, but the potential justified the effort.

Thomas Telford School was in the news in autumn 2000 as the only comprehensive in the country to achieve a 100% GCSE pass rate.

The other two grants of at least £50,000 were given to Elizabeth Fitzroy Homes (£100,000 towards the costs of building a replacement for the Greenways home in Birmingham) and the Mercers' Company Housing Association (£50,000). In 1997/98 the latter received £310,000 from the Whittington Charity, the last major tranche of a series of grants to assist with the funding of a sheltered housing scheme at Priory House in Clerkenwell, London.

Other recipients of £5,000 or more included:

Education

Lucy Cavendish College, Cambridge: £5,000, towards the costs of a fellowship in the Centre for Women in Senior Management; Culloden Primary School, Tower Hamlets: £5,000, including grants for Deaf Arts Week and ICT equipment; Newham Education Action Zone: £5,000, for the Saturday School Programme.

Elderly

Lady Mico's Almshouses, Stepney: £43,000, annual grant; 2Care: £5,000, for facilities for elderly people with care needs and mental health problems.

Arts

English National Opera: £20,000, for the 'Studio Nights' performances, and £5,000 for the Benevolent Fund; Tate Gallery of Modern Art: £20,000, towards the development costs of the education programme.

Handicapped and disabled

DEMAND – Design and Manufacture for Disability: £15,000, to make furniture for people with severe disabilities; Norfolk and Norwich Association for the Blind: £5,000, to provide accommodation and care to blind and partially sighted people.

Medical

Richard House Trust: £20,000, towards the cost of building, equipping and running a London children's hospice; Society for Mucopolysaccharide Diseases (MPS): £5,000, for the support of families having children with MPS.

Heritage and environment

Wildfowl and Wetlands Trust: £11,000, towards a bird watching hide at Arundel, and £5,000 for the development of educational projects; Landmark Trust, Chipping Camden: £5,000, for the restoration of a 17th century banqueting house.

Relief in need

Care and Comfort Romania: £7,000, towards building costs of a nursing home and children's nursery; Ex-Service Fellowship Centres: £5,000, for maintenance costs at a care home.

Church and religion

St Ethelburga's, London: £10,000, for a visitors' centre, lending library, new landscaping, cleaning and lighting; St Mary the Virgin, Fairford: £5,000, for the restoration of the stained glass windows.

General

Southwark Habitat for Humanity: £10,000, for a volunteer-based community self-build partnership helping those on low incomes to build and own their home; Book Aid International: £10,000, towards the development and implementation of the African publishing support programme; St Paul's Church, Bow: £5,000, towards restoration.

In addition to the grants listed above, £550,000 went to individuals: 378 pensions were awarded to elderly people in need, amounting to £300,000; and the Mercers' Company Educational Trust Fund gave £250,000 in grants to students and schoolchildren.

Exclusions

The company does not respond to circular (mail shot) appeals. Unsolicited general appeals are considered but not encouraged. Grants are only made to individuals in the form of educational support – see the Directory of Social Change's companion volume *The Educational Grants Directory.*

Applications

Initial applications should be in the form of a brief letter (about two sides of A4), giving details of the charity, its activities and the proposed project, with some ideas of costs, and sent to the grants manager. Qualifying applicants will then be sent an application form. The charitable trustees meet every month; the educational trustees every quarter.

The staff have indicated that applications are considered at trustees' meetings in January, April, July and October.

The Metropolitan Hospital–Sunday Fund

Sick and disabled people in London

£883,000 (1999)

Beneficial area Greater London, within the boundaries of the M25.

45 Westminster Bridge Road, London SE1 7JB

Tel. 020 7922 0200 **Fax** 020 7401 3641

e-mail mhsf@peabody.org.uk

website www.mhsf.org.uk

Correspondent Howard Doe, Secretary

Information available Guidelines for applicants on the website. Excellent annual report, accounts and annual review.

Summary

The fund awards capital grants to registered charities for hospitals, homes and other medical organisations outside the National Health Service. These grants aim to:

- help maintain, improve and stimulate the care they provide for sick and disabled people;
- provide facilities and support for carers.

It also provides 'Samaritan' grants for use by social workers in NHS hospitals and local authorities to assist individual patients.

The major project in recent years has been to finance the construction of the Sundial Centre, a day care facility for older people in Tower Hamlets, which was due to open in 2000. The centre is to be managed by the Peabody Trust, which has worked in partnership with the fund since 1995.

Background

The Metropolitan Hospital–Sunday Fund was established in 1873, when the Lord Mayor of London invited religious and hospital leaders to a meeting at Mansion House.

Appalled by the effect of inadequate housing and poor sanitation on impoverished Londoners, they decided that on one day each year ('Hospital Sunday'), places of worship would hold a collection to raise funds for the sick and needy. This practice has continued to this day in the form of our annual appeal.

General

Funds raised from the annual collection on Hospital Sunday (£15,000 in 1999) are used towards the cost of the Samaritan Grants Scheme, described below. Most income now comes from investments and interest on balances built up over the years, and totalled £511,000 in 1999. A further £437,000 was raised in donations for the Sundial Centre.

The amount spent on fundraising and publicity was a minimal £6,000, in relation to the return achieved. A total of £505,000 was spent on a capital grant to the Sundial Centre, while grants made under the fund's other programmes amounted to £378,000.

Guidelines

Grants are available to charities and organisations operating within the boundaries of the M25 or national organisations for projects which are within the London area. Following an internal review of the administration of the Fund, a new grant procedure will come into effect from 1st January 2000. Our grants will then fall into two categories:

Capital grants (formerly known as specific purpose grants)

For registered charities, hospitals, homes and other organisations providing care for sick and disabled people. These grants will be distributed on a three times per year cycle, and interested organisations may make an application at any time during the year.

Samaritan grants (formerly known as the Samaritan Fund and special reserve grants)

There are two types of Samaritan grants – block and individual. Block grants are available to social work teams to allocate to in-patients and out-patients of NHS and NHS Trust hospitals who have immediate personal needs that cannot be met from statutory sources.

Individual grants are provided through social workers who make a separate application when the amount required exceeds the delegation level of the social work team. Items funded by these awards include clothes, household equipment and convalescent or respite holidays.

Social workers holding a Samaritan Grant may apply for renewal of the grant at the end of their financial year. Additional funding may be obtained during the year, providing there is evidence of need.

The aim of the new system is to enable MHSF to provide a more efficient service to our clients and also to allow staff the time to be more proactive in developing the work of MHSF. New guidance notes and grant application forms will be issued in due course.

The 1999 annual report included the following:

During 1999, approaches were made to various religious denominations with a view to developing a new Ministers' Grant programme along the lines of the successful Samaritan Grant Scheme, which MHSF has operated with social workers for many years. This has attracted the interest of two denominations so far and plans are now well in hand for the pilot scheme to be launched during 2000.

Grants in 1999

The number of applications received for capital grants was 127, compared with 111 for 1998, of which 33 were from applicants seeking a grant for the first time or from those who had not applied for over five years. Grants totalling £92,000 were made to this group, while £239,000 was for applicants previously known to MHSF.

In total, 79 capital grants worth £330,000 were awarded in 1999 (averaging just over £4,000 each).

In all, 26 capital grants totalling £129,000 were made to independent hospitals and homes, the largest being for £16,000 to Mission Care, for various homes in London. Other typical grants included £5,000 to St Raphael's Hospice, North Cheam, for bedroom radiators; £4,000 to the House of St Barnabas, Soho (a hostel for homeless women), for a CCTV system; £5,000 to the Congregation of the Poor Sisters of Nazareth, to refurbish the reception at Nazareth House, and £3,000 to Mental Aid Projects, for lunches at Flitcroft Day Centre, Surbiton.

Another 53 capital grants to other charities and institutions amounted to £201,000. Grants for £10,000 were made to the Association of Wheelchair Children, for building alterations; the Grace Organisation, towards a minibus; and Queen Elizabeth Foundation for Disabled People, for driving assessments at its mobility centre. Other recipients included the British School of Osteopathy (£5,000 for the running costs of its Children's Clinic in Southwark); Bromley User Group (£9,000 for the cost of leaflets), and the Psychiatric Rehabilitation Society (£3,000 for arts and crafts materials at the Et Cetera Gallery).

In addition, £31,000 in Samaritan individual grants was given to social workers for their clients, and £16,500 was given in block grants to social work teams in hospitals, community mental health teams and local authorities.

Of the total Samaritan individual grants, 102 were for the purchase of essential clothing and household equipment (46 in 1998). Other grants were awarded for respite breaks and special items of equipment and services.

Exclusions

No grants to individuals, except through NHS hospital social workers. Organisation grants to registered charities only.

Applications

Application forms are available from the grants administrator at the address above and must be returned by the end of March (for new applications) or June (for existing applicants). Awards are made annually in December. There is no restriction on the number of successive years that the same charity may submit an application, or on the number of years that an applicant may be awarded a grant.

Hospital social workers may apply at any time for Samaritan grants.

The Monument Trust

Arts, health and welfare (especially AIDS), environment

£4,807,000 (1998/99)

Beneficial area Unrestricted, but UK in practice.

See entry for the Sainsbury Family Charitable Trusts

Tel. 020 7410 0330

Correspondent Michael Pattison, Director

Information available Annual report and accounts with a good listing of grants but minimal analysis of grant-making policy.

Summary

This is one of the Sainsbury Family Charitable Trusts which share a joint administration. Like the others, it is primarily proactive, aiming to choose its own grantees, and it discourages unsolicited applications.

It makes over 100 grants a year of all sizes in the fields given above.

General

This trust was endowed by Simon Sainsbury but he has never been a trustee. Its staff include Michael Pattison, the director of all the Sainsbury Family Charitable Trusts, Matthew Williams and Victoria Hornby, executives.

There is very little information about the trust's policies, beyond what can be deduced from the grants listings. The trust itself merely says that 'the Trustees prefer to support innovative schemes that can be successfully replicated or become self-sustaining. The Trustees also support a number of arts and environmental developments of national or regional significance.'

The associated Monument Historic Buildings Trust is not a grant-making body but an active restorer of buildings at risk. One project in Cambridge has been completed and a further project is being investigated.

Grants in 1998/99

Grant approvals (rather than the payments reported above) in 1998/99 were classified as follows:

	No.	Value
The arts	23	£1,196,000
Social development	31	£1,095,000
Health and community care	36	£434,000
AIDS	18	£404,000
The environment	17	£318,000
General	1	£75,000
Total	126	£3,522,000

Though some grants were of hundreds of thousands of pounds, and spread over periods of up to five years, there were also a modest number of quite small grants under most headings.

While most grants were to national institutions or not geographically identifiable, there were 43 grants for work in specific localities. After dividing England into two halves of equal population, 30 grants were for the south of England, eight each for the north of England and for Scotland, and one for Wales.

Of the south of England grants, 13 were for work in parts of London and six for work in Sussex. Two of the latter were to the 'Friends' of local hospitals, a kind of charity not usually supported, and two were to general Sussex heritage causes, again a type of charity not supported elsewhere, so there is probably a definite though limited local interest in this area.

The arts: 23 awards worth £1,196,300

The major new awards were to the Royal Academy, London (£283,000 over five years for conservation), Cambridge Foundation (£377,000 to encourage good design in commercial products) and the Wallace Collection in London (£140,000 to help match its Heritage Lottery Fund grant). £125,000 was given to the University of Westminster for its Culture as a Commodity study and £100,000 to the Textile Conservation Centre.

As with other trusts in the group, there was support (£18,000) for the new statue of Oscar Wilde in Adelaide Street, London – there seems to have been some sort of family whip-round for this excellent cause.

There were eight 'small' grants, averaging £3,000 each, to organisations including the Hunterian Art Gallery, Grosvenor Museum and the Royal Opera House.

Social development: 31 awards worth £1,094,601

The major awards were as follows:

NACRO: £289,000 over three years towards a pilot resettlement project for young offenders at Portland.

Community Service Volunteers (CSV): £182,000 in four grants for various programmes.

Centrepoint: £75,000 towards core costs.

Closing the Gap, London: £70,000 over two years to extend its supplementary literacy schemes.

Almost all the grants were to help meet core or project costs. That for Homestart (£25,000) was listed simply as a 'donation'.

The five small grants for an average of less than £2,000 included awards to national organisations such as the Howard League for Penal Reform, as well as the apparently purely local, such as Glasgow Brunswick Boys' Club.

Health and community care: 36 awards worth £439,973

Much the largest new award was of £165,000 to St Mungo's for its Make it Work initiative with older homeless people in London. £76,000 was given to SARO for community drug services in East Sussex and £40,000 to Release, for work outside London.

There was the unusually large number of 15 smaller grants, of less than £10,000, under this heading. Beneficiaries were a varied group, including the Book Trade Benevolent Society, the Anglo-Israel Society and the Diana Memorial Fund.

AIDS: 18 awards worth £403,597

The trust maintained its long-standing support for work in this field, with its main grants going to Body Positive, London (£115,000 in two grants), Crusaid (£70,000) and the Mildmay Mission Hospital (£50,000). £35,000 over two years was given to the Red Hot AIDS Trust towards its director's salary.

The environment: 17 awards worth £317,950

These grants appear to show a particular concentration on Sussex and surrounding areas. For instance £100,000 was given to Chichester Cathedral Trust, £75,000 to the Friends of Pallant House, a long-standing beneficiary of this trust, and smaller grants to Sussex Heritage Trust and Sussex Historic Churches Trust. The other large grant, of £65,000 over two years, was to Ancoats Buildings Preservation Trust in Manchester (where initial Monument funding has led to a project raising £5 million from the Heritage Lottery Fund).

There were 10 small grants, averaging less than £2,500.

Exclusions

Grants are not normally made to individuals.

Applications

See the guidance for applicants in the entry for the Sainsbury Family Charitable Trusts. A single application will be considered for support by all the trusts in the group.

However, for this as for many of the trusts, 'proposals are generally invited by the Trustees or initiated at their request. Unsolicited applications are discouraged and are unlikely to be successful, even if they fall within an area in which the Trustees are interested.'

The Henry Moore Foundation

Visual art, particularly sculpture

£856,000 (1998/99)

Beneficial area Europe, mainly UK.

Dane Tree House, Perry Green, Much Hadham, Herts SG10 6EE

Tel. 01279 843333 **Fax** 01279 843647

e-mail director@henry-moore-fdn.co.uk

website www.henry-moore-fdn.co.uk/hmf

Correspondent Timothy Llewellyn, Director

Trustees *Sir Rex Richards, Chair; Sir Alan Bowness; Marianne Brouwer; Anthony Brown; Prof. Andrew Causey; Joanna Drew; Sir Ewen Fergusson; Patrick Gaynor; Sir Ernest Hall; Margaret McLeod; Lord Rayne; David Sylvester; Greville Worthington; Henry Wrong.*

Information available Review magazine with a list of donations without figures. Separate guidelines for grant applicants.

Summary

The foundation gives grants, of an undisclosed size, for

- exhibitions
- academic research
- acquisitions

- conservation
- publishing

General

Based on the estate of the sculptor, the foundation concentrates on the support of sculpture, drawing and printmaking generally, and on the work of Henry Moore in particular. Grantmaking is a relatively minor activity of the foundation, which runs directly the Moore Gallery in Leeds and the associated Institute and Studio at Dean Clough, and has recently opened a new and much praised gallery, the Sheep Fields Barn at Perry Green. The foundation also organises numerous exhibitions and events.

However, as the 1998/99 annual report noted, the foundation has maintained its policy of giving financial support to a broad range of institutions and activities. It gives, for potential applicants, the following account of its work:

The functions of the foundation are achieved through specific projects initiated within the foundation both at Perry Green and in Leeds, particularly exhibitions and publications, and by giving grant aid to other suitable enterprises. Grants are usually restricted to support for undertakings in the following categories:

- Exhibitions (established galleries only).
- Conferences, workshops, symposiums.
- Fellowships and bursaries for artists and art historians at appropriate institutions.
- Research grants for post-graduate projects at appropriate institutions.
- Museum and gallery acquisitions of sculpture.
- Conservation work and research.
- Minor capital projects, primarily those designed to provide improved facilities for the exhibition of sculpture.

The foundation does not give grants to individual applicants and cannot fund on a regular basis revenue expenditure of galleries and other publicly supported institutions.

There were 83 grants in 1999 and the recipient organisations or activities are listed in the foundation's excellent review. Unfortunately, though, the value of the individual grants is not disclosed, nor is there any reference to the preferred range of values in the otherwise very clear 'Advice to Applicants' sheet. It is possible that most of the grant total is accounted for by just one or two very large awards, and that the rest are only very modest amounts; or grants may be well spread around the average of about £10,000.

Grants to organisations are classified under the following headings (with examples from each category).

Exhibitions

A total of 35 exhibitions were supported. Of these, 13 were in London, at venues ranging from the Tate Gallery to Camden Arts Centre. Four were outside the UK, in Dublin, Frankfurt, Stuttgart and Lausanne.

Conservation

Five recipients included the Victoria and Albert Museum, for restoration of sculptures, and Norton Priory in Runcorn for the re-siting of a medieval statue.

Conferences

There were three recipients, including Sussex University for a conference on Rodin.

Capital grants

Five recipients included Milton Keynes Gallery for equipment and the British Museum for its ethnographic galleries.

Research projects

Five recipients included two London art colleges for students' research projects.

Acquisitions

There were two grants, to the Contemporary Arts Society in London and the Ashmolean Museum in Oxford.

Public sculpture

Five recipients included Nottingham Playhouse for a work by Anish Kapoor and Birmingham's public art commissions agency, for work by Jochen Gerz.

Publications

Six publications were supported, including an issue of the Burlington Magazine and, for Glasgow School of Art, a handbook of sculpture in the city.

Exclusions

The foundation does not give grants to individual applicants and cannot fund on a regular basis the revenue expenditure of galleries and other publicly supported institutions.

Applications

In writing to the director. The guidelines state that all applicants should cover the following.

- the aims and functions of the organisation;
- the precise purpose for which a grant is sought;
- the amount required and details of how that figure is arrived at;
- details of efforts made to find other sources of income, whether any firm commitments have been received, and what others are hoped for;
- details of the budget for the scheme and how the scheme will be monitored.

Applications are usually considered at quarterly meetings of the donations sub-committee, which makes recommendations to the management committee of the trustees.

The Moores Family Charity Foundation

This foundation ceased to operate on 30 April 1999. Its assets were transferred to four other Moores trusts.

John Moores Foundation

Social welfare in Merseyside and Northern Ireland, emergency relief overseas

£867,000 (1998/99)

Beneficial area Merseyside (plus Skelmersdale, Ellesmere Port and Halton), Northern Ireland, South Africa.

7th Floor, Gostins Building, 32–36 Hanover Street, Liverpool L1 4LN

Tel. 0151 707 6077 **Fax** 0151 707 6066

Correspondent Tara Parveen, Grants Director

Trustees *Jane Moores; Barnaby Moores; Mary McAleese; Peter Bassey.*

Information available Policy leaflets providing guidance for applicants. Annual report and accounts with categorised grants list and short narrative analysis of grants.

Summary

Up to 75% of grants are for £5,000 or less, mostly for revenue costs, to charities based in the areas set out above, though 'each year the Trustees may also make grants to a small number of charitable organisations outside these areas where the trustees have a particular knowledge, interest or concern'. About a quarter of the grants are repeated and the foundation also makes a limited number of multi-year grants for up to a maximum of three years.

Something over one in five applications leads to a grant.

General

The foundation says:

During the last fifteen years the Trustees have confined their giving to five main categories

- Merseyside
- Northern Ireland
- South Africa
- World crisis
- One-off exceptional grants that interest trustees.

1. Merseyside is the first concern of trustees.
2. Northern Ireland would normally receive about 10%.
3. Post-apartheid South Africa has very great needs in literacy and health, particularly as they affect women and children. The Trustees remain committed to making a realistic contribution to these areas but only to projects known to or initiated by Trustees because of the difficulties of monitoring overseas projects.
4. World crisis tends to include man-made or natural disasters such as famine, flood or earthquake which by definition need large one-off grants to prevent loss of life. These donations are normally made to one of the big aid agencies such as British Red Cross.
5. Occasional grants (such as Cottage Homes or Trinity College, Dublin) are rare and unspecific.

Trustees do not respond to unsolicited applications requests in categories 3, 4 and 5.

More generally:

JMF aims to enable people who are marginalised, as a result of social, educational, physical, economic, cultural, geographical or other disadvantage, to improve their social conditions and quality of life. The Foundation seeks to do this by making grants to projects run by charitable community organisations whose aims fall within the Foundation's areas of interest … [*see below. Ed.*].

The Foundation is particularly interested in supporting those groups that find it more than usually difficult to raise money and are small or new rather than long-established.

Purposes for which grants are given

The Foundation makes grants for running costs, one-off project costs, equipment, and occasionally helps towards salaries and minor building refurbishment. It does not make grants for capital building projects.

Size of grants

The size of grant varies, but in general over 75% of grants are £5,000 or less and about a third are £1,000 or less. The Foundation's annual income is in the region of £750,000. Of this income, approximately 10% is set aside for grants to voluntary organisations in Northern Ireland.

Grantmaking

In 1998/99 the foundation's assets totalled over £13 million and its income was £965,000 (including £135,000 received from the Moores Family Charity Foundation). Some 75% of grant expenditure was disbursed within Merseyside and other selected areas nearby (outlined below), 9% went to organisations in Northern Ireland and the remainder was for work overseas.

More detailed information about work the foundation will consider funding can be found in the policy leaflet. This is summarised in the annual report, as follows.

Policy

The Foundation's Trustees made slight changes to policy during the year. The Trustees made the decision not to fund Citizens Advice Bureaux in the future and extended the criteria to include funding projects that offer complementary therapies. New policy leaflets were published for Merseyside and Northern Ireland.

Grantmaking is mainly directed towards new and/or small organisations in the area of Merseyside (including Skelmersdale, Ellesmere Port and Halton) and in Northern Ireland, who work with disadvantaged or marginalised people who find it more than usually difficult to raise money from other sources. Preference is given to organisations seeking funds for projects which fall within the foundation's target areas for giving which are:

- women, including girls;
- black and ethnic minority organisations;
- race, gender and disability awareness;
- advice and information to alleviate poverty;
- tranquilliser users;
- second chance learning;
- grassroots community groups;
- people with HIV/AIDS, their partners and families;

And, in Merseyside only:

- people with disabilities;
- carers;
- support and training for voluntary organisations;
- homeless people;
- unemployed people;
- childcare
- small grants to a wide range of charitable organisations which do not fall within the above target areas.

Grants in 1998/99

During the year 399 written applications were received (335 in 1997/98), of which 179 were from Merseyside, 120 from Northern Ireland and 100 from other areas.

A total of 93 grants were made (89 in 1997/98) totalling £866,809 (£558,447 in 1997/98). Of these, 14 were revenue grants of more than one year. …

75% of grants given were for £5,000 or less and a little over 15% for £1,000 or less. The largest grant was made to Cottage Homes. In the light of the windfall income they received from the sale of Littlewoods stores, and in view of the fact that this may have caused hardship to some employees, the Trustees decided that 10% of this windfall would be given as a grant to be administered by Cottage Homes. This charity works for the benefit of people employed in the retail trade, including people employed by Littlewoods, and may be able to assist employees in cases of hardship.

Trustees made 3 exceptional grants, 2 for overseas emergency relief (Central America and Sudan) and 1 to Cottage Homes. …

These exceptional grants accounted for nearly half of the total grant expenditure, with Cottage Homes receiving £300,000, while grants of £50,000 each went to Christian Aid, for emergency relief in Sudan, and the British Red Cross Emergency Appeal for Central America.

Two substantial grants went to charities for which one of the trustees, Jane Moores, also acts as a trustee. The largest was for £81,000 to Merseyside Information and Advice Project (£67,000 in 1997/98), followed by a repeat grant of £30,000 to the Women's Education Fund for Southern Africa. Another beneficiary in Africa was the Zamani Soweto Sisters, South Africa (£10,000; £17,000 in 1997/98). These latter two charities are included under the heading of 'women' in the table below:

Including the grant to Cottage Homes under 'social welfare', the grants were categorised as follows:

	No.	*Total*
Merseyside and other local areas	*63*	*£786,000*
Advice	7	£116,000
Women	10	£92,000
Community organisations	5	£48,000
Black and ethnic minority organisations/anti-racism	6	£27,000
Disabled	9	£27,000
Childcare	6	£23,000
Second chance learning/ training for community groups	2	£19,000
Carers	6	£18,000
Social welfare	8	£314,000
Youth	1	£1,000

Homeless	1	£500
Overseas emergency relief	2	£100,000
Northern Ireland	*30*	*£81,000*
Advice	11	£38,500
Women	6	£22,000
Social welfare	5	£9,000
Community organisations	4	£8,500
Second chance learning	1	£1,500
Black organisations	1	£1,000
HIV/AIDS	2	£500

There were a further four recipients of grants for more than £10,000, as follows (* also supported in the previous year):

Bronte Youth and Community Centre, Liverpool (£25,000); Liverpool 8 Law Centre (£22,000)*; Sheila Kay Fund (£15,000 under the heading of second chance learning/training for community groups)*; West Lancashire Women's Refuge, Skelmersdale (£12,000).

In Northern Ireland, grants for £5,000, the maximum, were made to seven organisations, including: Claudy Rural Development Agency; Creggan Pre-School Training Association, Derry*; The Committee on the Administration of Justice*, and the Women's Information Group, Belfast. The average donation was £2,700.

Exclusions

Unsolicited applications for projects which fall outside current policy will not be considered. The foundation does not give grants for:

- academic or medical research
- animal charities
- arts, heritage or local history projects
- new buildings
- churches for church-based or church-run activities. (although community groups running activities in church premises which come within the foundation's policy guidelines will be considered)
- conservation and the environment
- employment creation schemes
- festivals
- holidays, expeditions and outings
- individuals
- medicine or health
- national organisations
- parties and outings
- schools, universities or colleges
- sponsorship, including fundraising events
- sport
- statutory bodies
- vehicles
- victims – other than rape crisis and domestic violence projects

Applications

Applications should be in writing and accompanied by an application form, copies of which are obtainable from the grants director. Before submitting an application, please make sure that your project does not fall into one of the excluded areas (see 'Exclusions'). If you are unsure and you would like to discuss your application, telephone the grants director.

Applications are expected to contain the following information:

- A description of your organisation, its work and existing sources of funding.
- A description of the project for which you are applying for funds.
- Detailed costings of the project, including details of funds already raised or applied for, if any.
- Details of how the projects will benefit people within the foundation's target groups.

Applicants should also send if possible:

1. Latest accounts.
2. Latest annual report.
3. List of management committee members.
4. Equal opportunities policy.

Unsolicited applications which fall outside current policy will *not* be considered.

Most groups who apply for funding are visited, but the foundation may simply telephone for more information.

Trustees meet every six weeks, although organisations are advised to allow up to three months for a decision to be made.

The Peter Moores Foundation

The arts, particularly opera, social welfare

£4,007,000 (1998/99)

Beneficial area UK and Barbados.

Wallwork Nelson and Johnson, Derby House, Lytham Road, Fulwood, Lancashire PR2 4JF

Correspondent Peter Saunders

Information available Annual report and accounts, without the required list of grants, on file at the Charity Commission.

Summary

The main focus is on supporting the creative arts, particularly opera. Millions of pounds have been spent in recent years on the Compton Verney House opera project. However, more than 50 grants a year are made to a more varied group of beneficiaries, particularly for youth and HIV/AIDS. The foundation also has commitments to social and environmental projects in Barbados, mainly through continuing support for the Peter Moores Barbados Trust.

Because of the regrettable decision to withhold the names of grant recipients, in defiance of the Charity Commission's SORP, much of this entry describes grants made in 1997/98, the last year for which proper information was available.

Background

Peter Moores established the foundation, of which he remains a patron, in 1964 to support activities reflecting many of his personal interests. He received musical training after university and then worked in opera production at Glyndebourne and Vienna State Opera. He has sponsored many complete recordings in English of a wide range of operas, and been a trustee of the Tate Gallery and a governor of the BBC.

General

The foundation's objectives are to give preference to the following:

- the raising of the artistic taste of the public, whether in relation to music, drama, opera, painting, sculpture or otherwise in connection with the fine arts;
- the promotion of education in the fine arts;
- the promotion of academic education;
- the promotion of the Christian religion;
- the provision of facilities for recreation or other leisure-time occupation.

In 1998/99 just over £4 million was paid out in grants, £1,315,000 (33%) of which went to the Compton Verney House Trust. In addition, the Peter Moores Barbados Trust received £216,000 and the Donatella Moores Charitable Trust £21,500.

The accounts only showed amounts paid to the related parties outlined above, but the trustees' report included the following short commentary on more general grantmaking in the UK:

The Trustees were pleased to be able to support a venture by The British Museum to have the Museum's collection of Japanese Samurai sword blades repolished in Japan … A substantial grant was given to ChildLine in support of their CHIPS (ChildLine in Partnership with Schools) Project. This is a scheme intended to encourage young people to consult their fellow students about personal problems at School. Thirteen grants were given towards work done by organisations providing therapy to alleviate the condition of people infected by HIV or AIDS. The Trustees agreed that they would continue to set aside an annual sum for this purpose until such time as a cure is found for the disease.

In Barbados funding was agreed, for a further three years, for a chair in tropical horticulture at the University of the West Indies, which had received annual awards of around £45,000 in the preceding years.

In 1997/98 more information was available. In that year nearly £2.5 million went to Compton Verney House, bringing the total granted to £4,530,000. This was categorised as follows:

	No.	*Amount*
Fine art	7	£2,426,000
Music	84	£1,660,000
Barbados	4	£270,000
Health	30	£74,000
Youth	16	£49,000
Race relations	5	£16,000
Heritage	6	£7,000
Social	4	£4,000
Environment	2	£3,000
Donatella Moores Charitable Trust	1	£21,500

The recipients were further subdivided as follows, with examples of the larger grants included:

Music

- *Performance (£210,000):* Glyndebourne Productions (£60,000); Rossini Opera Festival (£50,000); Almeida Theatre (£50,000).
- *Recording (£1,335,000):* 'Cav & Pag' (£227,000); La Bohème (£203,000); Maria De Rudenz (£193,000).
- *Training (£115,000):* 43 individual awards amounted to £61,000.

Fine art

In addition to the grant to Compton Verney House Trust, six further grants were made, including £2,750 to the Tate Gallery Foundation and £1,500 to the British Museum.

Other

The largest grants in the trust's other categories were as follows:

Health: Denholm Elliott Project; Immune Development Trust; Kairos in Soho (£10,000 each).

Youth: Millfield School (£16,000); Christ Church, Oxford (£12,500); NSPCC (£6,000).

Race relations: CHALCS (£10,000); Royal Northern College of Music (£4,000).

Heritage: University of St Andrew's (£2,500); Woodland Trust (£1,500).

Social: Camphill Village Trust (£2,000).

Environment: Euro Council for Small Towns (£1,750); Middleton Botanic Gardens (£1,000).

Barbados: Peter Moores Barbados Trust (£211,000); University of the West Indies (£45,000).

Applications

In writing to the correspondent, but applicants should be aware that its 1999 report states that the foundation 'will normally support projects which come to the attention of its patron or trustees through their interests or special knowledge. General applications for sponsorship are not encouraged and are unlikely to succeed.'

The National Art Collections Fund (The Art Fund)

Acquisition of works of art by museums and galleries

£4,220,000 (1999)

Beneficial area UK.

Millais House, 7 Cromwell Place, London SW7 2JN

Tel. 020 7225 4800 **Fax** 020 7225 4848

e-mail info@nacf.org

website www.art-fund.org

Correspondent Mary Yule, Assistant Director and Head of Grants

Information available Fine and weighty annual review with accounts which gives a full illustrated record of all works assisted. Leaflet 'Information for Grant Applicants'.

Summary

Each year more than £3.5 million is paid in over 100 grants to museums and galleries all around the UK to subsidise the purchase of works of art. At least half of the money goes toward the acquisition of paintings, although the fund supports work of all kinds. There is no upper or lower limit to the level of grant assistance, but the range is normally £1,000 to £20,000. In 1999 there were a record 21 grants of more than £50,000, while one grant of £550,000 was the largest in the fund's history.

General

The National Arts Collections Fund (The Art Fund) is Britain's leading visual arts charity. Since its foundation in 1903, it has helped museums, galleries and historic houses all over the UK to acquire over 100,000 works of art of every kind. … .

[The Art Fund] is an independent charity which receives no government funding. Grants are financed by the subscriptions of our members, as well as donations, legacies and investment income. An increase in legacies in particular contributed to a growth of £1.75 million in income in 1999, to more than £6 million. Total assets stood at over £36 million.

Fundraising for the arts is an expensive business. One quarter of the fund's income (other than from investments) was spent on fundraising and administrative costs. Several trusts described elsewhere in this book regularly give significant donations to the fund. Supporters in 1999 included the Wolfson Foundation (£100,000), Garfield Weston Foundation (£30,000), John Ellerman Foundation (£20,000), 29th May 1961 Charitable Trust and Rayne Foundation (£10,000 each).

In 1999 the fund gave £4.2 million in grants to 86 museums and galleries across the country. Nearly half of this amount went to the top three beneficiaries: the Tate Gallery, London (£895,000 towards seven works); National Gallery of Scotland, Edinburgh (£800,000, four works), and the Ashmolean Museum, Oxford (£355,000, seven works). Four large awards starting at £200,000 accounted for nearly a third of the total value of grants paid.

Exclusions

Grants are restricted to establishments which are constantly open to the public.

Applications

To the correspondent. A basic information leaflet is available for applicants, and an application form.

Applicants are expected to have approached other sources of help, and, except in very special circumstances, museums are expected to make a contribution to the purchase from their own funds.

The trustees meet monthly, apart from January and August. Meeting dates are available from the Grants Office, and the deadline for applications is two weeks before the meeting.

The National Lottery (and Awards for All)

website www.awardsforall.org.uk

General

There is no such thing as a grant 'from the National Lottery'. The 'good cause' money is divided up between a number of different 'distributors' who actually make the grants (and who are absolutely independent of each other). The National Lottery Charities Board has a brief entry in this book. All the other Lottery distributors except NESTA also make grants to organisations. The only cross-distributor programme is the excellent Awards for All small grants scheme, described briefly below. Details of the grants programmes of the other distributors can be obtained as follows:

Arts Councils

www.artscouncil.org.uk

England 020 7973 6517

Scotland 0131 226 6051

Wales 029 2037 6500

Northern Ireland 028 9038 5200

Heritage Lottery Fund

020 7591 6000 www.hlf.org.uk

Millennium Commission

020 7880 2001 www.millennium.gov.uk

National Endowment for Science, Technology and the Arts (NESTA)

www.nesta.org.uk 020 7645 9500

New Opportunities Fund

www.nof.org.uk
(Head Office) 0845 000 0120

For grant application packs:

England 0845 000 0121

Wales 0845 000 0122

Scotland 0845 000 0123

Northern Ireland 0845 000 0124

Sports Councils

England 0345 649649
www.english.sports.gov.uk

Scotland 0131 317 7200
www.sportscotland.org.uk

Wales 029 2030 0500
www.sports-council-wales.com

Northern Ireland 028 9038 1222
www.sportni.org

Awards for All

– England (£50 million, 2000/01)

– Scotland (about £6 million, 2000/01)

Grants for amounts between £500 and £5,000 are made to community organisations, normally those with an income of under £15,000. They can be for community welfare, arts, sports or heritage activities.

There is a simple application form and there should be a decision within two or three months (still unnecessarily long, in these editors' opinion). The programme is administered on behalf of all the lottery distributors concerned by the National Lottery Charities Board; in England, from their regional offices.

In autumn 2000, the success rate for applications was just under 50% in England, and 63% in Scotland.

For the application pack, ring 0845 600 2040; or visit the website at www.awards forall.org.uk.

The National Lottery Charities Board

Those at greatest disadvantage in society

About £360,000,000 (estimated for 2001/02)

Beneficial area UK and UK charities working overseas.

St Vincent House, 16 Suffolk Street, London SW1Y 4NL

Tel. 020 7747 5300 **Fax** 020 7747 5214

minicom 020 7747 5347

e-mail enquiries@nlcb.org.uk

website www.nlcb.org.uk

Correspondent Timothy Hornsby, Chief Executive

Trustees *Board members: Diana Brittan, Chair; Dame Valerie Strachan, Deputy Chair; Richard Martineau, Chair, England Committee; Elisabeth Watkins, Chair, Wales Committee; Kay Hampton, Chair, Scotland Committee; Noel Stewart, Chair, Northern Ireland Committee; Tessa Baring; Rhiannan Bevan; Steven Burkeman; Jeff Carroll; Anne Clark; Douglas Graham; Prof. Jimmy Kearney; Maggie Lee; Barbara Lowndes; William Osborne; Ben Whitaker.*

Information available Full information available. For current application packs and information, ring 0845 791 9191. For other information contact the relevant national office, as listed at the end of this entry.

Summary

The NLCB had four funding streams at the end of 2000. They were as follows (with approximate values for 2000/01):

- Community Involvement and Poverty and Disadvantage: continuous open application (£308 million). These programmes were about to be merged, but this was not expected to mean any significant change.
- International: an annual cycle, with autumn application (£25 million).
- Research grant programme (£8 million in 2001/02).
- Small grants in Wales (£1.9 million) and Northern Ireland (£1.3 million): in England and Scotland these are distributed by Awards for All, described in the preceding entry.

Grants, except under the small grants scheme, are generally for any amount between the minimum £5,000 and a seldom exceeded £500,000 (or less in some regions), can be for capital or project funding, and for up to three years (five years, and sometimes larger sums, for International grants). Only a handful of grants have been for amounts between £500,000 and the highest yet awarded of £1.4 million. There is no requirement for matching funding. Few grants within the main programmes are for less than £25,000.

General

This is not an independent charity, but a government appointed body responsible for spending some of the proceeds of the public's gambling. However, as it is a member of the Association of Charitable Foundations, and behaves in many ways like a grant-making trust, it has been given a brief entry here. The money available for grantmaking is expected to decline sharply in 2001/02, by perhaps £100 million. This is partly because of the NLCB catching up with earlier underspends, and partly as the removal of some of its percentage of Lottery gains to the government's New Opportunities Fund programmes begins to bite.

Note that this is only one of a number of bodies making grants from the proceeds of the Lottery. For contact details for the Arts and Sports Councils, the Heritage Lottery Fund, the Millennium Commission and the New Opportunities Fund, see the preceding entry for the National Lottery. That entry also covers the excellent cross-distributor Awards for All small grants scheme which is administered by the NLCB.

The Charities Board (NLCB) chose, as its admirable mission, 'To help meet the needs of those at greatest disadvantage in society and to improve the quality of life in the community'. Two years ago the previous edition of this book said it had tackled this job 'with energy and enterprise, and in doing so has set new standards for many of the other trusts whose work is described in this book'.

This praise cannot be generally repeated. Excellent new work is being done by individual regional or national offices, such as the Brass for Barnsley initiative by the Yorkshire and Humberside region, or the very good 'feedback' arrangements in Scotland. At national level, however, the NLCB at present appears to be like a ship lying dead in the water. In the absence of forward movement, problems with its work, formerly accepted as inevitable but temporary imperfections, are becoming more pronounced the longer they stay unaddressed. The one big proposal for change that is on the table, the 'rebranding' of its programmes under a new name, risks backfiring in the absence of substantial new developments in grant-making practice. The expected introduction of a 'medium-grant' simplified application process is a welcome minor change, even if long called for and years overdue. The fact that even now it is only to be introduced on a pilot basis is regrettable. The awaited merging of the community involvement and the poverty programmes is of mainly internal interest; they have appeared as one since they were introduced.

The big issues are not being addressed or even, so far as can be told, discussed. In particular, the three-year project funding basis for most of the huge sums of money involved is becoming increasingly criticised on the grounds that it is distorting the work of the sector. It is not the kind of funding, critics say, that is needed to enable many charities to be at their most effective. Yet the issue has been strikingly absent from the various consultations carried out by the board.

In one respect there has been a step backward. Some Directory of Social Change publications, though happily not the previous edition of this book, praised the NLCB for publishing on its website the contents of its excellent grant assessment manual. This lasted only a short time before the heart of the manual and the part of by far the greatest interest to the voluntary sector – the guidance on how the board's criteria are scored – was deleted.

Grant-making practice

Grants are made following a formal, scored assessment against published criteria. This mainly involves judging how competent the organisation is to carry out effectively the work concerned, and how far this work meets NLCB policies – which are very properly weighted towards the 'empowerment' of disadvantaged communities through the maximum practicable user or beneficiary participation in the activities supported.

The application process is, in these editors' view, excellent and fair for larger 'project' grants, but inappropriate for those seeking lesser amounts. Because the process is so elaborate, few charities bother to make applications for amounts of less than £25,000, thereby further distorting the distribution of NLCB money which is already concentrated on one very narrow section of the voluntary sector.

Though there has been administrative devolution, this system allows for only slight local variation – up to 5% of the total points can be used to give priority to local needs.

Success rates are now running at about one in two applications.

There are development officers in all the board's offices, whose responsibility includes assisting potential applicants. Though this cannot always be done on an individual basis, all have information programmes locally.

All applications must be made on the appropriate application form. The telephone numbers from which these can be obtained are set out under 'Applications' below – or copies can be downloaded from the NLCB's website, as above (though they can only be filled in 'on screen' with difficulty).

National offices

UK office

St Vincent House, 16 Suffolk Street, London SW1Y 4NL
Tel: 020 7747 5300 Fax: 020 7747 5214

Head of UK and Corporate Planning: Gerald Oppenheim

Scotland office

Ground Floor, Norloch House, 36 King's Stables Road, Edinburgh EH1 2EJ
Tel: 0131 221 7100 Fax: 0131 221 7120

Director: Adrienne Kelbie

Office for Northern Ireland

2nd Floor, Hildon House, 30–34 Hill Street, Belfast BT1 2LB
Tel: 028 9055 1455 Fax: 028 9055 1444

Director: Ann McLaughlin

Wales office

2nd Floor, Ladywell House, Newtown, Powys SY16 1JB
Tel: 01686 621644 Fax: 01686 621534

Director: Roy Norris

England office

1st Floor, Reynard House, 37 Welford Road, Leicester LE2 7GA

Tel: 0116 258 7000 Fax: 0116 254 9780

Director: To be appointed

Applications

In all cases, applications can only be made on the appropriate application forms; ring 0845 791 9191 for a pack (or visit the website given above).

For Awards for All small grants, ring 0845 600 2040 – see also the preceding entry for the National Lottery.

The Network Foundation

Third world debt, environment, human rights, peace, arts

£556,000 (1998/99)

3 Churchgates, Church Lane, Berkhamsted, Hertfordshire HP4 2UB

Correspondent Vanessa Adams, Administrator

Trustees *A Bergbaum; John Broad; Oliver Gillie; J McClelland; Dr F Mulder; M Schloessingk.*

Information available Annual report and accounts on file at the Charity Commission.

Summary

This is the grant-making arm of the Network for Social Change, a group formed in the 1980s to support progressive causes. Grants, for up to £15,000, typically go to campaigning organisations addressing such issues as environmental sustainability and economic and social justice.

'Projects funded by the Network Foundation are all researched and sponsored by members; unsolicited applications are not considered.'

General

The foundation's income comes from donations by members of the associated company, the Network for Social Change Ltd, 'a community of wealthy individuals seeking to realise their visions in ways that enable others'. The accounts for 1998/99 showed an income of £625,000 and grant expenditure totalling £556,000.

The foundation's annual report describes its work thus:

The Network Foundation makes awards on the basis of proposals put forward by the members. We aim to fund hopeful, cutting-edge projects that will promote social change, in the UK and overseas. Members meet at conferences twice a year. ...

There is an annual funding cycle, in which grants to a maximum per project of £15,000 are made, falling into five categories:

- Arts for Change
- Education
- Health and Wholeness
- Human Rights and Peace
- Preservation

The focus is on projects which are likely to effect social change, whether by example, publicity, lobbying, or other legal and charitable means. The Network supports projects which redistribute wealth to those in need, promote alternative healthy living options, promote human rights, safeguard the earth's resources, and promote peace and nonviolence.

Smaller grants are also made four times each year, on the basis of members' earmarked contributions, also to projects sponsored by members.

Larger grants, usually spread over several years, can be made where a group of Network members join together to co-ordinate the most effective means of bringing about social change in one particular field. This year [1998/99], a Major Project on nuclear disarmament has been established, which provides funding to the Oxford Research Group over a two-year period.

Jubilee 2000, the highly successful debt cancellation campaign, was established following a significant initial contribution from Network [*£92,000 in 1997/98. Ed.*]. A further grant to Jubilee 2000 was made this year.

Information for potential members is provided by contacting the Network for Social Change at BM 2063, London WC1N 3XX.

Grants in 1998/99

With the accounts was a list of the 50 largest donations, from £1,000 upwards, which totalled just over £500,000.

The 10 largest, ranging from £13,000 to £15,000, went to the following beneficiaries: Antidote (The Schools Project); Greenwich & Lewisham Young People's Theatre (refugee project); Campaign against the Arms Trade (fundraising development co-ordinator); The Gaia Foundation (the 'kernel glenn' pilot project); The Ethiopian Gemini Trust (video project); Committee for Computer Science (CD ROM on human rights); Action for Conservation through Tourism (demo of community-led tourism); Medical Foundation for the Care of Victims of Torture (public affairs); Rebuilding Society Network ('RSN-Micro Phase 1 Set up'), and Newham Monitoring Project (development project).

A sample of the other grant recipients reads as follows:

The Kaloko Trust (£11,000 for a women's dairy project in Zambia); Creggan Health Information Programme (£10,000, women's skills development); Jajarkot Permaculture Programme (£9,000, core funds); The GalGael Trust (£7,500, Govan Longhouse & Boat Project); Credo Arts Community (£5,500, 'One Small Step for Mankind'); Devonport Action Against Poverty (£5,000, community participation and empowerment); Plaid Cymru Group of MPs (£5,000, research assistant's salary); Ecovillage Network UK (£4,500, development of network); Projects in Partnership (£4,000, development of social businesses); Big Brother Survival Kit (£3,000); Sarajevo Drum Orchestra (£3,000); The Happy Pear (£2,000), and The Green Party (£1,350, fund for 1999 European elections).

Applications

The Network chooses the projects it wishes to support and does not solicit applications.

Unsolicited applications cannot expect to receive a reply. Information for potential members is provided by contacting the Network for Social Change at BM 2063, London WC1N 3XX.

The Frances and Augustus Newman Foundation

Medical research and equipment

£537,000 (1999/2000)

c/o HLB Kidsons (Chartered Accountants), 33 Wine Street, Bristol BS1 2BQ

Tel. 0117 925 2255

Correspondent Elizabeth Yeo, Secretary

Trustees *Frances Moody Newman; Lord Rathcavan; Sir Rodney Sweetnam; John Williams.*

Information available Report and accounts with full grants list.

Summary

About 25 grants for medical research projects or equipment are made each year, typically for between £15,000 and £40,000, roughly a third payable over two or three years. At a meeting in June 2000, the trustees approved grants amounting to £342,000 to be paid in 2000/01.

General

The 2000 report tells us that 'The Trustees continued with their policy of supporting various projects in the main related to medical research.'

A regular beneficiary is the Royal College of Surgeons, with which the foundation has particular links. Two of the trustees are fellows of the college, and the foundation awards some research fellowships through this institution.

In 1999/2000 assets of the foundation amounted to £11.5 million, with an income of £549,000. A total of £537,000 was given out in donations ranging from £2,000 to £60,000, usually to well-established hospitals, research centres and national organisations. Half of these sums, including those for research fellowships, were for £20,000 or more. Grants were categorised as follows (with grant totals for the two most recent years):

	1999/2000	*1998/99*
UK ongoing research	£279,000	£253,000
UK 'one-off'	£234,000	£349,000
Overseas	£24,000	£24,000

Medical research and equipment – 'ongoing research'

In all, 11 grants were made, including £60,000 to the Royal College of Surgeons, for speciality training courses; £43,000 to Professor Monson, University of Hull, for research into colorectal cancer; £38,000 to Professor A Darzi, Imperial College School of Medicine, for a surgical skills research programme, and £10,000 to King Edward VII Hospital for Officers, towards its centenary appeal to develop Horace Evans House.

'One-off' grants

Eight grants were made, including £30,000 to the Royal College of Physicians, for 'The Stroke Project'; £19,000 to Mr G Peek at the University of Leicester, for work on the treatment for acute respiratory distress syndrome; £5,000 to Action Arthritis, funding for a proposed Clinical Chair of Trauma and Orthopaedic Surgery, and £2,000 to the Children's Hospital Trust Fund, for specially equipped cots for newborn babies. Four research fellows each received funding of £35,000 for one year.

Overseas

There was just one recurrent award, of £24,000 for the Paracare Association of Palm Beach.

Exclusions

With one exception, no applications are accepted from overseas.

Applications

Applications should include a detailed protocol and costing and be sent to the secretary. They may then be peer-reviewed.

The foundation awards some research fellowships through the Royal College of Surgeons of England which evaluates each application and to which applications by members and fellows of the college should be addressed.

The trustees meet in June and September each year and applications must be received at the latest by the end of April or July respectively.

NiKeNo Trust

Local in Sussex, medical research

£550,000 (1998)

Beneficial area UK, especially Sussex, and overseas.

PO Box 216, Wadhurst, East Sussex TN5 6LW

Tel. 020 7235 9560 **Fax** 020 7235 9580

Correspondent Elaine Owen, Secretary to the Trustees

Information available Full accounts on file at the Charity Commission.

General

The NiKeNo Trust mainly donates to charities in its local area (Sussex), or to charities involved with medical research into head injury or facial disfigurement. However, the trustees also make donations at their discretion and there are no formal guidelines.

In 1998 a wide range of organisations received support, including a number of charities concerned with children and some arts causes. In 1998 the assets stood at £4.7 million, generating an income of £235,000. Grants totalled £550,000, an increase of £480,000 from the previous year. In all, 22 causes were supported, 19 in the UK (totalling £108,000) and 3 overseas (totalling £441,000).

The largest grant was £380,000 to Kulturen. Other substantial grants were £31,000 to Formmuseets Vanner and £30,000 each to Changing Faces, DEBRA and Human Rights Watch. Grants of £10,000 each went to Children Nationwide, Frenchay Hospital and the Jack and Jill Appeal.

Other grants over £1,000 included £5,000 each to the Blond McIndoe Centre, the Cambodia Trust and Orbis, and £2,000 to Theatre Works.

Smaller grants of £1,000 or less went to Childhope, Order of St John, Pony Club, Rye Health & Care, St John Ambulance, Scope, the Wildside Trust and the Wishbone Trust.

Applications

In writing to the correspondent. Due to the volume of applications, the trust cannot reply to unsuccessful applicants.

The North British Hotel Trust

Welfare, health, mainly in Scotland

£450,000 (1999/2000)

Beneficial area UK, but mainly Scotland.

1 Queen Charlotte Lane, Edinburgh EH6 6BL

Tel. 0131 554 7173

Correspondent Clifford Leivesley, Clerk to the Council

Information available Perfunctory annual report, accounts, uncategorised grants list.

General

The trust makes over 50 grants a year, more than half for £1,000 or less.

Giving is concentrated in areas where the North British Trust Hotels company operates (a holding of shares in that company constitutes the charity's endowment). It is possible that the trust operates as the recipient of applications addressed to the company's hotels.

There are over 20 such hotels in Scotland, covering much of the country. There are also four hotels in England, with grants being made close to those in Scarborough, Harrogate and Barnby Moor in Yorkshire, and Eastbourne in East Sussex.

Most identifiable grants are for welfare purposes, especially those benefiting older or disabled people, or for health.

In both 1998/99 and in 1999/2000 there were a few major grants, as follows:

- Harmeny School, Balerno (£100,000)
- Scottish Veterans' Garden City Association (£80,000)

- Inverness Schizophrenia Research (£50,000)
- Columba 1400 (£100,000)

Other beneficiaries in 1999/2000 were Rukba Scotland (£5,000), Lorn Gaelic Partnership (£1,000), Scarborough Homeless (£3,000) and Strathpeffer Senior Citizens (£250).

The trust has funded 'homes from home' in both Edinburgh and Glasgow for CLIC (Cancer and Leukaemia in Childhood) in major programmes now nearing completion. It has also provisionally committed over £300,000 to a scanner for Argyll and Bute NHS Trust.

Applications

In writing to the correspondent.

The Northern Ireland Voluntary Trust

Community development, social welfare

£11,654,000 (including European funding, 1998/99)

Beneficial area Northern Ireland and the six border counties of the Republic of Ireland.

22 Mount Charles, Belfast BT7 1NZ

Tel. 028 9024 5927 **Fax** 028 9032 9839

e-mail info@nivt.org

website www.nivt.org

Correspondent Avila Kilmurray, Director

Trustees *Mary Black, Chair; Vivienne Anderson; Maureen Armstrong; Baroness May Blood; Mark Conway; Barney Devine; Sammy Douglas; Mari Fitzduff; Jim Flynn; Noreen Kearney; Mike Mills; Philip McDonagh; Angela Paisley; Ben Wilson.*

Information available 'Guidelines for Grant Seekers'; separate guidelines for specific schemes; detailed annual reports; Strategic Plan 2000–10.

Summary

NIVT is the major funder of community action in Northern Ireland, using both its own fundraised income and resources given it by other funders. The specific funding programmes are listed below.

No doubt driven by the unusual local pressures, NIVT is one of the few trusts in this book to have developed and published a detailed and clearly thought through strategy for work in this field. Unfortunately too long for inclusion in this book, it is available through the website above.

General

In financial terms, NIVT is primarily an independent distributor of statutory funds. Of the 1998/99 income of nearly £12 million, less than £1 million was from its own resources. Nevertheless its own donations of nearly £400,000 and its endowment of over £7 million represent a remarkable achievement for one of the new community foundations that are a welcome development in the trust world.

NIVT as a Community Foundation sees its role as a catalyst for social change, through influencing policy and funding activity on the ground – working at the margins with the most marginalised and most disadvantaged. We can not, nor should not become the 'mainstream' funder of community development activity and indeed if we were to do so would inhibit others from taking responsibility for what may be a statutory duty. Sustainability is key to the change process and we accept our shared responsibility alongside government, other funders and community based groups themselves in ensuring that impact is sustained in the longer-term. We therefore see our role as a funder operating where others do not and one which can promote innovation and take risks with groups and organisations that work at the sharp end tackling poverty, exclusion and discrimination.

NIVT grants are distributed throughout the province (and now in the adjoining border areas of the Irish Republic).

This entry first lists the various programmes that are funded by statutory, European or corporate sources, but gives no details as such activities are not covered by this book. Fuller information is given about the grant programmes carried out from the trust's own resources.

For a full set of guidelines for any of the programmes, contact NIVT administration officers at 028 9024 5927 or 028 7137 1547.

Externally funded programmes

- European Union Special Support Programme for Peace and Reconciliation (this Programme is closed to applications)
- European Structural Funds – Regional Community Support Programme (RCSP) and Belfast Community Support Programme (BCSP)
- The NIVT Core Funding Grant Scheme for Victims/Survivors Groups (funded by the Victims Liaison Unit)
- The NIVT Seeding/Development Funding Scheme for Victims/Survivors (funded by the Victims Liaison Unit)
- Telecommunity Fund (a partnership of BT Northern Ireland, British Telecom Union Committee and the Trust)

NIVT Fund

The Northern Ireland Voluntary Trust has its own capital base which has been invested during the last five years while the Peace Programme was being administered. The capital base has grown significantly during that time. The Trustees have recently decided to re-open the fund for applications from community groups.

Groups applying for funding are required to submit a written proposal to NIVT. There are no application forms. This is a rolling Programme with no closing date. Grants will not exceed more than £1,000. Decisions will be taken by the Trustees at their bi-monthly meetings.

NIVT Social Justice Initiatives Fund

This is a new 2 year funding initiative which has been established to encourage local community and self-help groups to become involved in peace-building through reflection, discussion and action on issues related to social justice, human rights and equality.

With an annual grants budget of £100,000, a limited number of grants will be made in the small grants and main grants categories.

Small grants: Less than £1,500
Main grants: Between £1,500 and £8,500

Community based voluntary or self-help groups can apply to the Fund. Priority will be given to groups in areas of high social and economic deprivation and/or have suffered levels of violence and deprivation as a result of the Troubles. Grants will be considered from groups working in Northern Ireland and/or in the six border counties of Donegal, Monaghan, Cavan, Leitrim, Louth and Sligo.

Priority in the first year of funding will be given to those projects which seek to encourage greater community participation and understanding of the issues relating to Human Rights, Social Justice and Equality.

Groups making application to this Programme are required to submit a written proposal to NIVT. There are no application forms. A Grant Advisory Committee will assist in the assessment of the funding applications. Closing dates for consideration of applications are ... 26 January 2001, 30 March 2001, 29 June 2001, 14 September 2001, 16 November 2001. For a copy of the grant guidelines and applications details, please contact NIVT Administration on 028 90 245927.

Exclusions

Individuals; ongoing running costs of organisations; major capital building programmes; travel; vehicles; holiday schemes; play groups; sports activities; housing associations; promotion of religion; paying off debts; retrospective grants; general appeals.

Neither will the trust fund projects where there is a statutory responsibility or respond to cutbacks in statutory funding.

Applications

Many of the grant programmes administered by NIVT do not have a set application form. Instead the trust asks applicants to write a letter of request. This letter should detail:

- The name and address of your group and the lead contact person.
- Background information about your group including
  – why you have set up
  – what your aims and objectives are
  – what activities you are currently involved in and
  – who your activities are for or with.
- A description of your proposed project including
  – where the idea for this project came from
  – what you hope to achieve through this project
  – why it is needed.
- How people who are often excluded from activities or programmes will be included.
- The costs of the project and how much is needed from NIVT. If there are other funders supporting the work as well please say who they are and what they are giving.
- How you will record and assess the progress of your project.

You should also attach:

- A copy of your group's constitution.
- Your latest annual report (if you have one).
- A copy of your most recent accounts or, for new groups, a current income and expenditure record.

The Northern Rock Foundation

Disadvantaged people in northern England and Scotland.

£9,200,000 (estimate for 2000)

Beneficial area Mainly the north east of England, but applications also considered from Scotland, Cumbria and the north west of England.

21 Lansdowne Terrace, Gosforth, Newcastle upon Tyne NE3 1HP

Tel. 0191 284 8412 **Fax** 0191 284 8413

e-mail generaloffice@nr-foundation.org.uk

website www.nr-foundation.org.uk

Correspondent Fiona Ellis, Director

Trustees *P R Harbottle, Chair; Lady Bonfield; R H Dickinson; L P Finn; Lord Howick; A E Kilburn; Lady Russell; Miss E E Slattery; J P Wainwright.*

Information available Guidelines and application forms. Excellent report and accounts.

Summary

This large and welcome new organisation is now in full action as a major grantmaker in the north east of England and in surrounding areas. It makes grants of all sizes, up to hundreds of thousands of pounds, for capital or for revenue purposes and for periods of up to four years. There are the following grant programmes, some of them recently introduced. There are unlikely to be substantial further changes for some time.

- Empowering people with disabilities – including work with carers, but only in the core area of Durham, Northumberland, Teesside and Tyne and Wear.
- Quality of life in the third age – including helping people remain in their own homes, maintain economic independence, stay active, stay safe and cope with change.
- Helping the very young (aged 0 to 7) – including work with first-time parents, the effects on children of parental problems, safety and health and child development.
- Grants for small organisations – between £1,000 and £10,000, usually for organisations with less than £25,000 a year.
- Urban and rural regeneration – generally at neighbourhood level.
- Creative communities: the arts in social regeneration – emphasising community artistic activity.
- Outside-in: to combat the effects of discrimination against gay men and lesbians.
- Community training awards – a limited programme, with projects generally instigated by the foundation.
- Exceptional grants – for important projects within the aim of helping those at disadvantage.
- Big projects fund (details for 2001 not yet available in autumn 2000) – for major regional projects whose benefits extend beyond helping those at disadvantage.
- Annual special programme (£1 million) – for the year 2000 this is an investment in a penal reform programme with the Inside Out Trust.

There is detailed information for applicants, reprinted below, covering all except the last four of these programmes, which are generally or entirely proactive, with the foundation seeking out its own projects to support.

The foundation is accessible and welcomes preliminary discussion of possible applications.

This entry, after a short introductory section, reprints the foundation's extensive 'Information for Applicants'. This is followed by much of the content of the text of the 1999 annual report, which reviews grantmaking in detail, programme by programme, and the entry gives examples of actual grants under each heading. This section may give a clearer view of the kinds of grants being made in practice.

Background

The aim of the foundation is to help those who are disadvantaged in society, mainly, but not exclusively, in the north east of England. No grants are made for work south of Yorkshire or the Manchester area, or in Wales or Northern Ireland, but work in Scotland is supported.

The foundation gets its income under a covenant from Northern Rock plc, which transfers five per cent of its pre-tax profits to the foundation each year. In 1999, this amounted to £10.8 million. The arrangement was made when Northern Rock converted from a mutually owned organisation to a limited company, and properly recognises the element of mutual community ownership that had been built up over the years.

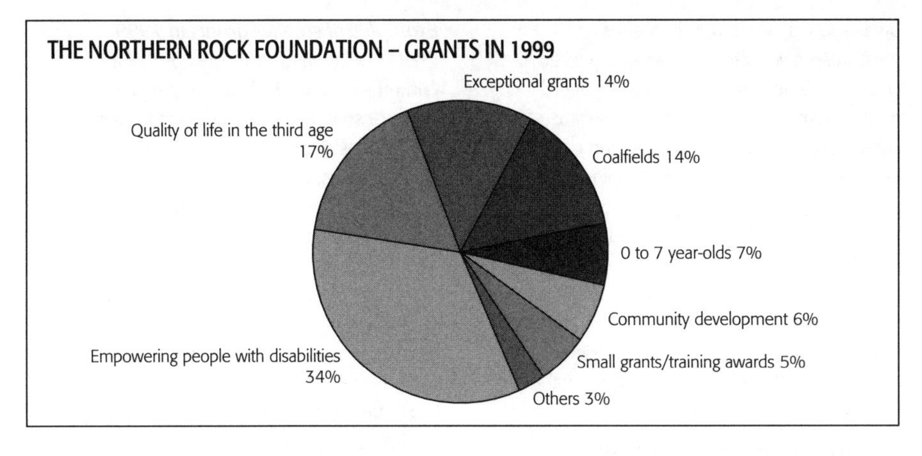

THE NORTHERN ROCK FOUNDATION – GRANTS IN 1999

Without this arrangement, it is unlikely that the privatisation could have gone ahead and references by the foundation to the company as its 'benefactor' and to the company's 'massive generosity' are, in these editors' view, inappropriate. The benefactors are rather the generations of mutual owners who created this valuable commercial organisation and transferred it to its present shareholding owners.

The company now sees the payment to the foundation as its voluntary contribution to the community, which is inappropriate. So also are the arrangements whereby a budget has been set aside from the foundation's income to be disbursed to charitable causes chosen by the chief executive of the company, and the practice of using the foundation's funds to match the charitable giving of the company's staff (unless this was freely decided as an optimal way of making effective distributions within the foundation's objectives).

The trustees incurred expenditure on grant assessments and administration of £145,010 and £346,155 respectively. This resulted in a cost/income ratio of 4.45%, which was well within the 5% budget ceiling set by the trustees.

In 1999, the trustees allocated £8,155,000 to beneficiaries for capital and/or revenue grants which were for a term of between one and four years (see the pie chart above).

Geographical spread of grants

This was listed as shown in the box below, although it is not altogether clear because of the appearance of three (or possibly four) regions as well as individual counties, but not unitary authorities. It would be more sensible to use the standard regions and local authorities, and to express the figures as the value of grants per head of population. However, the inclusion of success rates is unusual and welcome.

It looks as if something between 25% and 30% of the money is being allocated outside the north east region, to the north west or to Scotland. Although the success rate for Scottish applications was among the lowest, it was the same as that for Durham, at the heart of the funded area, so this may not show a greater reluctance to make grants in Scotland.

Though no exhaustive analysis has been made, the most southern grants noticed by these editors were in Manchester and east Cheshire on the west and Bradford and Sheffield on the east. Scottish grants went at least as far north as Angus.

Grant-making policy

The primary objective of the foundation is to help improve the conditions of those disadvantaged in society. It mainly supports causes in the north east of England, especially Northumberland, Tyne and Wear, Durham and Teesside.

Grants may be made for limited capital, core or project funding and for varying periods of time. Support from other funders 'helps establish confidence in your project'.

The foundation is unlikely to make

- An unbroken series of grants to the same organisation. You should leave a gap of at least six months from the date on which you submitted your final report.
- Numerous grants which incorporate an element of core costs to the same organisation.

Re-applications

- If your application is turned down you cannot reapply for the same purpose unless your rejection letter explicitly tells you that you can and under what circumstances.
- You should not normally have more than one grant from the Foundation at a time. Once your grant has expired i.e. it has been used for the term and purpose for which it was given, and you have reported as requested, you may apply again six months later.
- It may occasionally be possible to extend core or project funding for an organisation that has received a grant over several years. You should discuss this with your grants officer before your grant expires. Such extensions will be rare: you should start looking for new sources as soon as you receive a grant from the Foundation.

Grants are assessed by the staff of the foundation, who include Fiona Ellis, Director; Anne Burleigh, Assistant Director; Dave Anderson and Richard Walton, Grants Officers. The rest of the information for applicants is reprinted in the box on 'Information for Applicants', starting on page 229.

Annual report 1999

Review of the year

The Trustees had agreed to add new grant-making programmes for 1999, looking at the needs of 0–7 year olds and of those in active older age. We had also modified our small grants programme and reviewed the pilot scheme, Developing our Communities. Meantime the majority of our applications continued to be under our programme for disabled people and their carers at least partly because we were still best known in that area. One of our first big tasks for the year was to launch the new programmes and to make the diversity of our grantmaking interests better known ... It is unlikely ... that we will add new interests for a few more years.

Although we cannot meet every potential applicant in advance of an application, all staff are willing to answer preliminary enquiries by telephone and will be as helpful as possible.

THE NORTHERN ROCK FOUNDATION

	No. of grants	*Success rate*	*Amount*	*% of total*
Tyne & Wear	77	48%	£2,335,000	(29%)
Northumberland	32	56%	£1,112,000	(14%)
Durham	59	23%	£985,000	(12%)
North East region	19	35%	£782,000	(10%)
North West	29	39%	£701,000	(9%)
Cleveland/Teesside	28	30%	£531,000	(7%)
Scotland	24	23%	£516,000	(6%)
Yorkshire	23	33%	£482,000	(6%)
Cumbria	14	40%	£282,000	(4%)
Northern region	63	1%	£214,000	(3%)
Grand total	311	38%	£7,940,000	(100%)

While 1998 had contained three grants of £100,000 or more amounting to a total of £351,000, the Trustees decided that the time was right to make even more of these. In 1999 there were seven in all, totalling £1,325,000. Such grants are intended to make a strategic difference to projects and frequently involve large capital contributions. We intend to continue to offer such large contributions where they can make a tangible difference to the success of a project.

The Trustees are aware of the position a grant-maker of the Foundation's size inevitably occupies in its core area ... While still wishing to dig deeply to lasting effect rather than widely for transitory popularity, the Trustees have given considerable thought to requests which do not fall within our guidelines. They have taken three initiatives, two in 1999 and a third added in 2000.

First, they set aside an allocation for exceptional projects, which, although still within our overall objective of helping disadvantaged people, were unlikely to prosper under our other grant programmes. Grants under this heading are described [below].

Next, they have established a programme worth £1 million, the theme for which will change annually. This year the result is our Coalfields Programme described [below]. For the year 2000 we will be investing in a penal reform programme with the Inside Out Trust.

The third initiative is the Big Projects Fund, the only one of our programmes not restricted to help for disadvantaged people. This new programme, to be launched in 2000, will assist substantial and significant projects in Tyne and Wear which are of benefit to the whole North East.

Grant programmes

Empowering people with disabilities (112 grants totalling £2,784,000)

The aim of this programme is to improve the quality of life of disabled people and encourage their full and active participation in their local community. We ask applicants to demonstrate clearly the involvement of, and consultation with, disabled people and their carers ...

A number of our awards supported training and employment opportunities. The Scottish Society for Autistic Children used a grant to develop a horticultural project for young adults with autism. The project not only provided training, but also, through selling what was grown, offered a service to the general public.

Taking services out to disabled people is a challenge for many organisations in urban and rural areas. Benefits advice agencies are particularly good at this work. We have given grants to several of them to recruit and train staff and volunteers, all with local knowledge and expertise. Such organisations often have impressive track records for generating additional annual benefits for their clients ...

During the first year of the Foundation's operation we supported a number of carers' organisations. Some of the carers we encountered were children as young as eight years old. Others were people with special needs looking after older parents. Because carers can be of virtually any age and have at least as many differing needs as things in common, we decided to commission CENTRIS to research how best we could help. We asked them to find out what organisations and individual carers thought of what we had done so far and what they thought we should do in future. We await the results of the research and are confident that it will help us to wring the best value for carers from our grants.

Examples of large grants in 1999

Breakthrough Deaf-Hearing Integration, to set up a mobile information and advice service – 3 years, £80,000

Mary Seacole Halfway House, towards providing evening supervision to vulnerable young disabled people from ethnic minorities – 2 years, £72,000

Cleveland Arts, towards a project to train disabled people for future employment in the arts – 3 years, £71,000

Princess Royal Trust Borders Carers' Centre, towards establishing a young carers' project – 3 years, £70,000

Examples of smaller grants in 1999

King Ecgbert Integrated Resource Unit, towards an innovative supported employment project for young adults with autism in Sheffield – 1 year, £10,000

MOBEX North East, towards a project providing outdoor social and leisure activities for young disabled people – 2 years, £10,000

Quaker Opportunity Playgroup, towards the core running costs of a playgroup in Newcastle – 2 years, £10,000

Quality of life in the third age (41 grants totalling £1,363,000)

We define 'Quality of Life' initiatives as those which enable people to retain economic independence, stay active, feel safe and deal with change, and which support people wishing to remain in their own homes. Many of the projects we assist are conceived by older people themselves to improve their own lives and those of their friends and neighbours. These projects contribute to the overall objective of keeping people healthy, independent and active in mind and body.

Examples of large grants in 1999

Caring Hands, towards the running costs of an organisation that provides services to support the independence of older and disabled people – 3 years, £90,000

Crosslink (Cleveland), towards core funding and to enlarge an independent living service for older people in Middlesbrough – 2 years, £88,000

Sunderland Community Heating, Advice and Insulation Project, to support a handyperson and gardening project – 3 years, £78,000

Examples of smaller grants in 1999

Chat Shop, towards the core costs of a community café which acts as a venue for a range of services including a credit union and the Citizens' Advice Bureau in Newcastle's West End – 2 years, £10,000

Easington District Communicare, towards a transport scheme for elderly and disabled people in East Durham – 1 year, £10,000

Baildon Men's Veterans' Association, to pay for improvements to premises used by old soldiers in a village in West Yorkshire – 1 year, £3,000

Elmtree Park Community Association, to provide electric wheelchairs to increase mobility for elderly residents – 1 year, £2,000

Helping the very young (12 grants totalling £612,000)

Governments spend substantial amounts of money dealing with the effects of youth disaffection. So indeed do trusts – a high percentage of trust funding goes to youth projects for young people from about 12 years old until they become adults. For years it was the prevailing view that the under 7s could largely be left to grow up without help. Social services, youth services and so forth had enough on their hands dealing with delinquent teenagers. The attitude seemed to be that if the small ones became troublesome then they would receive attention. But lately there has been an acknowledgement that some of the causes of adolescent problems might lie in the early years and that they may be preventable. Our new programme for children up to 7 years old was launched just as the government was recognising and addressing such ideas with its Sure Start and Early Years plans. We are trying, as always, to complement what statutory funders do and to add, where possible, a quality dimension that public funding finds difficult.

Accepting the proposition that 'a baby born into a poor home is likely to die significantly younger than a baby born into a prosperous home' (Kellner, Institute for Public Policy Research, 1999), the Trustees have sought to make compensatory improvements in the lives of economically disadvantaged children. During 1999 we have made two grants which exemplify our thinking. The first is to build a new nursery in Scotswood so that babies and toddlers in this economically deprived part of Newcastle can be given every advantage that can be provided outside the home. We intend that they will enjoy good food, warmth and care, stimulation and approbation. The Scotswood Area Strategy has enthusiastically taken on the project and hopes also to help Scotswood parents to care for their children and for themselves ...

By geographic contrast, we have made a partnership with the rural pit village community of Hadston in Northumberland, where Coquet Early Years Excellence Centre is building a new Centre for the very young. While statutory funders, through their new schemes, will provide a basic service, we believe that children

The Northern Rock Foundation – Information for applicants

Empowering people with disabilities

The aim of this programme is to improve the quality of life for disabled people by promoting independence, raising disability awareness and thus enabling disabled people to play a full and active role in society.

This programme is only for applicants in our core area: Durham, Northumberland, Teesside and Tyne and Wear.

We particularly wish to assist people with learning disabilities and people with mental health problems. We may consider applications from organisations addressing the needs of people with other disabilities but we will give them a lower priority. We favour applications led by beneficiaries themselves. In all cases, we will look for evidence that applicants have actively consulted users and/or beneficiaries in the design and delivery of the work.

We are especially interested in the following types of project:

- Support for independent living initiatives
- Improving services in rural communities
- Improving the quality, delivery and usage of information
- Adult education, training and work experience
- Assistance into employment
- Personal development
- Removing barriers from social/leisure opportunities

There are some projects which we cannot help. For example, we do not fund access improvements to or adaptations of buildings; nor do we contribute to large capital projects.

Carers

We welcome applications from carers groups for programmes to assist carers of people with disabilities in maintaining their own health, skills and access to social and cultural opportunities. *This programme is only for applicants in our core area: Durham, Northumberland, Teesside and Tyne and Wear.*

Helping the very young

The Foundation welcomes imaginative proposals from organisations working on behalf of young people between the ages of 0 and 7 years to ensure that they have the best and fairest start in life. We particularly welcome proposals in the areas described below.

First-time parents

- Projects to help mothers-to-be to understand their own healthcare and diet needs and those of the new child
- Projects to help new parents learn how to care for their children

The effects on children of parental problems

- Initiatives to help separated parents keep in contact with young children, including those separated by, for example, imprisonment
- Help for children in coming to terms with separation from parents
- Initiatives to help children of women seeking refuge from domestic violence to maintain their educational and social development
- Help for children of refugee families
- Help for children living in households with substance abusers
- Initiatives to help children come to terms with bereavement

The safe and healthy child

- Initiatives to promote the health and safety of the very young
- Initiatives to combat physical and sexual abuse
- Initiatives to help children who have been abused

The developing child

- Projects giving children access to a full creative and cultural life
- Projects promoting the physical development of the young child through sport or active play
- Projects to encourage children in making decisions about their own lives, to support them in making their needs, wishes and aspirations heard and understood

We do not support projects that can achieve their objectives using local or central government resources. We will prefer projects that take an ambitious and imaginative view of the capabilities and needs of the very young.

This programme is not intended to address the particular needs of disabled children or children with special needs. Applicants seeking help in this area should refer to our programme for disabled people.

Quality of life in the third age

The Foundation welcomes proposals from organisations seeking to promote and sustain the welfare of people in the Third Age (roughly people aged 55–75). Grants under this programme should contribute to the overall objective of keeping people healthy, independent and active in mind and body. The grant programme is concerned with quality of life. It is not intended to duplicate what statutory authorities provide. We particularly welcome proposals in the areas described below.

Keeping your own front door

- Initiatives to support people wishing to remain in their own homes
- The development of housing alternatives to residential care – though we are unlikely to be able to fund significant capital developments
- Help with shopping, gardening, getting out
- Help in the home, especially where coupled with befriending

continued...

Economic independence
- Benefits take up advice, advocacy, money management advice, promotion of anti-ageism campaigns in employment

Personal safety
- Initiatives aimed at relieving the fear of crime: fitting alarm systems, neighbourhood safety schemes, visiting schemes, information and advice.

Staying active
- Projects to promote physical and mental fitness (but not medical advice or treatments)
- Creative and artistic programmes involving participation of older people
- Set up costs for University of the Third Age groups, Open College for the Arts and other less structured educational activities
- Computer and Internet classes
- Active citizenship: promotion of volunteering for older people, intergenerational work

Dealing with change
- Projects preparing people for retirement
- Bereavement counselling
- Learning to live alone, managing finances for the first time

Besides these areas we will consider any imaginative proposal which can convince us that it helps keep older people active, independent and out of residential care. We put special emphasis on combating rural isolation.

We do not support care homes, adaptations of residential care accommodation, day centres (unless they have strong user representation on the management committee) or holidays. We will not normally support the purchase or costs of transport unless they are part of a wider programme of activities and unless there are sound arrangements for the use, maintenance, sharing and replacement of the vehicle.

Grants for small organisations

What we will consider

Applications for amounts between £1,000 and £10,000, which can be used for:
- projects with a limited life-span
- core funding lasting up to four years where the total amount offered does not exceed £10,000
- capital or equipment purchase

Examples might be a single grant of £5,000 towards a project, capital or core costs; a grant of £5,000 each year for two years for a project; three instalments of £3,000 each committed over three years towards core costs; or even four instalments of say £400 per year towards core costs for a very small organisation.

What we will not help
- The Foundation will not contribute to large capital appeals. The total cost of the item or programme of capital work for which a grant is sought should not be more than £15,000
- Core or project funding will only be offered to organisations with a current annual turnover of less than £25,000

Please do not use this scheme as a regular shopping stop. It is not intended to be an open-ended or repeated source of help for any organisation.

What can these grants be used for?

This scheme is for organisations or projects that contribute towards the Foundation's primary objective. For example, we welcome organisations working for: homeless people, young people at risk – especially in crime prevention – older people, communities seeking to improve their own living environments; or organisations offering money management or debt counselling schemes or other guidance helping people to avoid or escape poverty. These are only examples and are not listed in any special order.

Applications relating to other named grant schemes will be directed to the appropriate programme.

Special considerations for applicants under this scheme

You need not be a registered charity but you must be:
- an organisation with a legal framework
- established for public benefit and
- have purposes recognised by the law as charitable

We will need to see written evidence, preferably in the form of a constitution or other legal document, which demonstrates the organisation's membership procedures and management.

If you are not yourself registered or in the process of registering with the Charity Commission you will have to ask a registered charity to receive a grant on your behalf and pass it on to you. There is no cost to the receiving charity in doing so: many Councils for Voluntary Service will help either by acting as your recipient or recommending another charity. You should ask them before you apply and tell us in your application who will accept the grant if we make one to you. You can find out where your nearest CVS is by telephoning the National Association for Councils of Voluntary Service on (0114) 278 6636.

Urban and rural regeneration

This programme is designed mainly to help charitable, voluntary organisations to contribute to the regeneration of their neighbourhoods.

Applicants must demonstrate how their proposals will bring clear public benefit to areas of social and economic deprivation.

Proposed activities may include, for example:
- relief of poverty through projects to educate, train or retrain unemployed people
- the provision of work experience to unemployed people
- assistance to unemployed people in setting up independent businesses
- improvement of the environment, e.g. reclaiming land for public benefit or in order to improve the economic prospects of the area by improving its appearance or amenities

continued...

- promotion of public safety or crime prevention in the service of regeneration
- or other activities contributing to regeneration which are agreed as charitable by the Charity Commissioners

All projects must be additional to local and national government responsibilities and activities.

Organisations should normally be registered with the Charity Commission or be in the process of registering.

Creative communities: the arts in social regeneration

This programme is intended to encourage the use of the arts and the skills of artists in helping people and communities to grow and develop.

Applications are invited from community groups, schools or other organisations working with artists.

Examples of areas likely to be considered are:

- projects combating crime and social exclusion
- projects giving confidence and skills to unemployed people
- creative work with prisoners
- artists working with youth groups, in factories or other workplaces
- arts in healthcare but not art therapy
- creative approaches to literacy teaching
- helping people on low incomes to enjoy the arts as a cultural 'right'.

All projects should aim for the highest possible quality in process and product.

Applications from arts groups will be accepted but those that are jointly made with beneficiaries are more likely to succeed.

Outside-in: a programme to combat the effects of discrimination on lesbians and gay men

Many gay men and lesbians suffer from both overt and concealed discrimination. This takes various forms from open violence to more subtle harassment. This programme is intended to help organisations that try to educate the public and which deal with the consequences of discrimination.

Projects likely to be supported include those engaged in the following activities:

- supporting vulnerable gays and lesbians in, for example, housing and homelessness
- combating violence and bullying at home, school, work and outside
- caring for older people
- prevention or treatment of alcohol and drug misuse
- promotion of safe sexual behaviour
- mental health advice
- supporting families of gay people

living in isolated villages with low employment rates need much more ...

Examples of grants in 1999

Coquet Early Years Excellence Centre, towards creating exemplary early years provision in Hadston, Northumberland – 1 year, £250,000

Scotswood Area Strategy, towards building an exemplary nursery for 0–3s in Scotswood – 1 year, £250,000

Dene Valley Community Partnership, towards 'Choices for Children', a programme of child development for the very young – 3 years, £27,000

Tik-Tok Nursery, towards producing informative and attractive marketing brochures – 1 year, £1,500

Encouraging your community – a programme for the coalfields (41 grants totalling £1,204,000. Programme now completed)

In recognition of the contribution that the coal industry had made to the prosperity of the North East, we decided to make £1,000,000 available to support local people living in the villages and towns of the coalfield communities of County Durham, Northumberland, Gateshead, Sunderland and South Tyneside.

... The history of previous regeneration activity has shown that it is vital to involve local people. They live with any problem every day of their lives and need to be part of, and take responsibility for, any suggested solutions. Top down answers have, in the past, tended to be expensive failures. The Trustees, therefore, were particularly keen to listen to the ideas of people who live and work in these communities.

We launched our programme in June 1999 and by August 1999 we had received applications for over £4,500,000. By the end of 1999, the Trustees had made awards totalling £1,204,159 to 41 projects. Grants went to organisations controlled by local people, to support projects that would provide a lasting benefit to their village or town. Grants were also made on the understanding that as much of the money as possible would be spent within that community.

Examples of grants

Lynemouth Community Trust, towards establishing a 'one-stop shop' providing employment information and training, health care, a youth club and other services including the local library, in an ex-mining community – 1 year, £100,000

Rainbow Fun Club, to contribute towards a breakfast and after school club in Trimdon in County Durham – 2 years, £10,000

Exceptional grants (13 grants totalling £1,119,000)

During the course of our first year the Trustees became aware that there were many organisations whose work was unique or perhaps so specific that they might never be able to apply under any conceivable grant programme. For example, organisations such as the Derwent Initiative (£75,000) can rarely identify grantmakers interested in their particular work. Similarly, Street UK (a micro finance initiative, £225,000) is a venture so unusual and demanding of such a large investment that most trusts would not wish to unbalance their grant programmes by supporting it. Yet these are just the sort of important initiatives that can have untold positive effects. The Trustees decided that, where they became aware of such projects, they would invite them to apply.

There are occasional substantial building projects where only a large grant will be of use. Yet giving a six-figure grant from the regular grant budget would mean squeezing out the unfortunate smaller bidders for that round of decisions. Therefore, the Trustees made a series of large capital donations from their Exceptional Grants budget. They helped, for example, St Oswald's Hospice (£250,000) to start work on its children's service and also gave smaller amounts to the other children's hospice projects in the region. Soon no child needing hospice care should have to travel hundreds of miles to find it.

When it was originally built, MEA House, where many of Newcastle's voluntary sector groups have their homes, was a state-of-the-art building. Some 30 years on, it was in serious need of refurbishment and modernisation. The Foundation's grant, together with generous gifts from local and national funders, will allow the work to begin. The Trustees saw their grant to MEA House (£150,000) as an investment in the future of 20 local voluntary organisations for the next 20 years. Considering the number and range of beneficiaries each of these has, the grant will have far-reaching consequences for many people.

Generally we prefer to look for and encourage proposals for Exceptional Grants ourselves. We will continue to seek and invite applicants in the coming year.

Developing our communities (25 grants totalling £457,000. Programme now completed)

This pilot programme, which ran for six months over 1998–9, allowed us to ' test the water' in several areas: parenting, literacy and community development. Although the programme itself has now closed, it has influenced other areas of our work. Parenting, for example, is taken up partly in our 0–7s programme. Literacy may well be a component of our new Urban and Rural Regeneration work. And Community Development itself has already appeared as a strong strand in our Coalfields programme.

Grants to small organisations (53 grants totalling £279,000)

This programme offers very small organisations, working to help disadvantaged people, the opportunity to apply to us for amounts up to £10,000. It is open to any group with charitable purpose and an annual expenditure of less than £25,000. The range of groups we have supported is very wide, stretching from projects dealing with disaffected young people to community newspapers. The programme is very flexible – applicants can ask for small capital sums, project costs or revenue. The Trustees subscribe firmly to the notion that small organisations should not be compelled to use valuable volunteer time fundraising, but should be able to get on with doing whatever the organisation was set up to do. That is why they happily provide the running costs of small, entirely voluntary operations. We are sure that more small organisations could benefit from our help and are trying to do everything in our power to encourage them. This includes distributing information about our programmes more widely – and in a format designed not to deter the unconfident.

Examples of grants in 1999

Castle Morpeth Mediation, towards establishing a permanent office base for a volunteer-run community mediation scheme, £6,000

Circle, towards a community celebration to encourage local people to explore, recognise, understand and appreciate cultural diversity, in Hartlepool, £6,000

North East Post Adoption Service, to establish an office base for a new service offering free practical help, advice and counselling support to all those whose lives have been touched by the adoption process, three years, £6,000

Respond!, to provide gap funding to ensure core services to young people are maintained whilst long term financial and organisational options are developed, £6,000

Amble Community Carnival, to contribute to the core costs, £2,000

Butterflies Children's Charity, towards the establishment of a community run café to provide a safe place to go to for children and young people in Newtown, Wigan, £2,000

Circus Zanni (Youth Circus), to provide technical equipment to assist the organisation in developing outreach performance work in the community, £2,000

Community training awards (14 grants totalling £123,000)

In 1999 we established a fund to enable us to help organisations that, for a variety of reasons, we thought were not yet ready to receive a grant. We wanted to be able to offer training to remedy skills shortages, or consultancy help to provide a new view of problems or tactics. We found the fund useful also for organisations in receipt of one of our grants but which were encountering difficulties that needed the help of an outside adviser. The small grants we have made from this allocation have helped build up organisations so that, in some cases, a larger grant can be made confidently, or a project helped to refocus its objectives or secure its financial future. The grants are made selectively; only promising organisations of potential future interest to us receive the investment. We are determined that all the inventive policy work must not be done exclusively in the South. To that end we have taken every opportunity to persuade national organisations to give the North East the benefit of their experiments and allow circumstances here to influence the outcome of research. In 1999 we offered £97,500 to the National Council for Voluntary Organisations so that it could pilot a new scheme designed to improve quality standards among voluntary organisations in the North East. NCVO will develop a structured approach towards quality assurance, improve understanding of its role in the voluntary sector and develop a series of self-assessment tools by and for organisations operating in the area. We hope that the benefits to the North East will be enormous and that their effects will be felt far beyond.

Examples of grants

Development Trusts' Association, to improve the skills and knowledge of volunteers engaged in community regeneration projects through a mentor support programme – £10,000

Newbiggin and District Village Hall, for a training programme for the management committee – £2,000

Horden Hall Residents' Association for training or exchange visits – £1,000

Exclusions

Applications for local projects outside the north east of England, Cumbria, Yorkshire and the north west of England and Scotland will not be considered, nor:

- organisations which are not registered charities or which do not have purposes recognised as charitable in British law;
- charities which trade, have substantial reserves (normally over 50% of annual running costs in unrestricted reserves) or are in serious deficit;
- national charities which do not have a regional office or other representation in the north east;
- grant-making bodies seeking to distribute grants on the foundation's behalf;
- open ended funding agreements;
- general appeals, sponsorship and marketing appeals;
- corporate applications for founder membership of a charity;
- loan or business finance;
- retrospective grants;
- endowment funds;
- replacement of statutory funding;
- activities primarily the responsibility of central or local government or health authorities;
- individuals and organisations that distribute funds to individuals;
- animal welfare;
- mainstream educational activity;
- medical research, hospitals and medical centres;
- environmental projects which do not accord with the main objectives of the foundation;
- fabric appeals for places of worship;
- promotion of religion;
- expeditions or overseas travel;
- minibuses and other vehicles;
- holidays and outings.

Applications

Applications must be made on the foundation's two page application form. This comes with full instructions and guidance. In brief, the form will have to be accompanied by:

- brief supporting statement (not more than two pages);
- current budget and recent management accounts;
- most recent annual report and accounts (or equivalent for very small organisations);
- the 'objects' and 'dissolution' parts of your constitution;
- your budget for the project, how much you are asking for and how you hope to get the rest.

The brief supporting statement needs to cover:

- your organisation and its qualifications for taking on this project;
- the need for the project, its importance, scale and urgency;
- what you plan to do and how;
- the level of user involvement at all stages;
- how you will measure its success and learn from your experience, if appropriate;
- the timetable for the project;
- how, if appropriate, you would continue when a grant expires.

Information should be accurate and comprehensive. If something essential is missing the foundation will ask you to supply it and therefore the processing of your application will be delayed.

Your application will be acknowledged and the foundation will let you know straight away if it is ineligible. If it is eligible, you will be told which staff member will assess it.

There should normally be a response within four months (for the Small Organisations scheme, two months).

'Please remember that all Foundations receive many more requests than they can help. Undoubtedly we will have to turn down many good applications.'

The Northwood Charitable Trust

Probably local causes in Dundee, health

£800,000 (1997)

Beneficial area Dundee and Tayside.

22 Meadowside, Dundee DD1 1LN

Tel. 01382 201534

Correspondent The Secretary

Trustees *B H Thomson; D B Thomson; A F Thomson; Prof. A J McDonald; A McDougall.*

Information available There was no response to a request for a copy of the charity's annual report and accounts (despite the statutory requirement to the contrary).

General

This trust is connected to the D C Thomson Charitable Trust, D C Thomson & Company and the Thomson family. It was established by Eric V Thomson in 1972 and has received additional funding from other members of the Thomson family.

In 1997, the trust had an income of £1.1 million and gave grants totalling £800,000. The grants were broken down as follows:

Local causes	66%
Cancer	19%
Medical research	9%
Paediatrics	6%

In the past grants have ranged from £500 to £100,000.

Applications

The trust's funds are fully committed and it states that no applications will be considered or acknowledged. The trust did not wish to appear in this guide and did not confirm the address above.

The Nuffield Foundation

Education, child protection, family law and justice, access to justice, mental health, ageing

£5,541,000 (to organisations, 1999)

Beneficial area UK and Commonwealth.

28 Bedford Square, London WC1B 3JS

Tel. 020 7631 0566 **Fax** 020 7323 4877

website www.nuffieldfoundation.org

Correspondent Anthony Tomei, Director

Trustees *Baroness O'Neill, Chair; Prof. Sir Tony Atkinson; Dr Peter Doyle; Dame Brenda Hale; Prof. Sir Robert May; Prof. Sir Michael Rutter; Mrs Anne Sofer.*

Information available Excellent annual report; detailed guidelines for applicants (summarised below, but all potential applicants should obtain a full copy).

Summary

'Project grants', from £5,000 to over £100,000, are made to organisations and institutions to support research, developmental or experimental projects that meet a practical or policy need. Most of the projects involve one or more of the following:

- research
- experiment
- practical development

The foundation, and its associated funds, make grants under eight programmes, as shown in the bar chart on page 234.

The trustees also currently have five areas of special interest:

- child protection, family law and justice
- education
- access to justice
- mental health
- older people and their families

There are also extensive award schemes for scientists as well as in-house projects such as the Nuffield Council on Bioethics or its new Nuffield Languages Inquiry.

Background

1999 expenditure was classified as follows:

- Grants to organisations, £6.3 million
- Individual award schemes, £1.6 million
- Directly managed projects, £1.4 million

Though the value of the endowment rose from £218 million to £247 million during the year, income was £8.6 million, or 3.6% of the mid value, in what the foundation calls a 'good year' for income. The figure of 3.6% is below what can be expected as a sustainable real return. If the foundation cannot legally operate on a 'real return' basis, it should consider seeking powers to do so, and raise its annual expenditure to nearer 5% of the value of its endowment.

General

The foundation combines its own initiatives, programmes of awards for individuals and grants for organisations. The latter are increasingly focused within the defined areas of special interest set out above, although substantial grants are also made more generally within the general fields of education and science, and social research and innovation.

The tone is academic, though grants are for projects with practical applications. The project grants are only loosely linked to the in-house programmes, the Nuffield Curriculum Projects, the Nuffield Council on Bioethics and the new Nuffield Languages Inquiry.

This entry deals only with the project grants. These are relatively few, but usually substantial, and can extend for up to three years. Although charities are often supported, most project grants go to universities, academic institutes or 'think tanks'. For example, of the 11 grants for child protection studies in 1999, only 4 went to child welfare charities, with the rest to bodies such as Cardiff Law School, the Family Policy Studies Centre or Great Ormond Street Hospital, London.

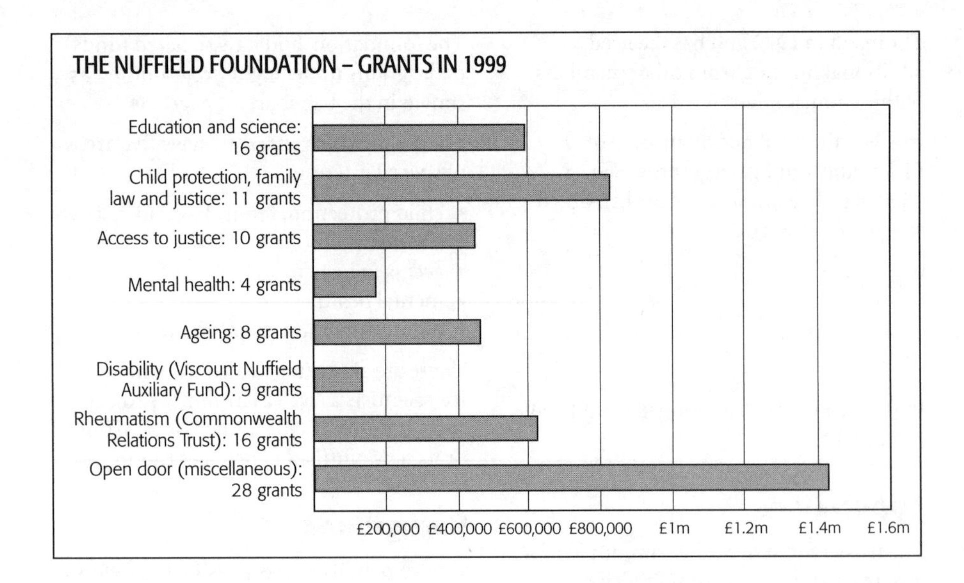

The project grants

The guide for applicants is so extensive that it cannot be reproduced here in full. Readers are referred to the website above. However, the following extracts should enable readers to decide whether or not they need the full information.

The Foundation funds self-contained practical or research projects which are:

Innovative – The Trustees are keen to fund work that has a clear element of originality. They will neither fund routine research, nor the mere repetition of existing work.

Practical – The Trustees look for outcomes that will influence practice directly or that can be translated into policy or practice in the short or medium term.

Generalisable – The Trustees will not consider proposals of purely local interest but seek to fund work that will be widely applicable.

Reflective – The Trustees look for evidence that applicants have thought carefully about how to evaluate the work undertaken and judge whether it is successful or not.

Not all projects we fund meet all these criteria, but most of them do. Applicants must be able to convince the Trustees that proposals are especially suited to the Foundation, and could not as easily be considered by a government department, Research Council or a more appropriate charity. The Trustees do not give project grants for:

- routine academic research
- projects that involve simply the doing of good works or
- the continuing provision of a service, however worthwhile.

Most of the projects supported by the Foundation involve one or more of three kinds of activity: research, experiment or practical development.

Research projects must be intended to have a practical or policy outcome in the short or medium term.

Experimental projects involve trying something new and evaluating the outcome. Such projects must be of more than local interest. They must have the potential to be widely applied, either directly or as a model which others can follow. Evaluation and dissemination must be carefully considered.

Practical development projects involve the development of some facility that will be of practical value. The range of possible projects is wide and could include, for example, written materials, a new way of providing advice or some other service, or a physical device. Again, such developments should be of general rather than local interest and the Trustees will look for evidence that applicants have carefully considered how the information can be disseminated. Some element of evaluation is also desirable. The Foundation is particularly interested in dissemination to practitioners and sees this as important activity in its own right. It is also willing to fund research reviews in any of the areas of special interest, that is synthetic exercises that bring together a body of research evidence, particularly where these draw out the implications for practice and are aimed at a defined practitioner audience ...

The Foundation also has a Commonwealth Programme under which a small number of grants are made each year to support projects in these areas of interest. This programme is currently under review.

The Trustees are interested to hear of projects of exceptional merit that lie outside [the five] areas of special interest. *The Foundation therefore keeps an 'open door' to projects that are in some way concerned with the advancement of social well-being*, our widest charitable object. Such projects must meet the criteria outlined above.

Subjects of interest include (but are not restricted to) disability, poverty and social exclusion, social welfare, and the social implications of science and medicine. Educational projects in areas not listed under our Education 'Area of Special Interest' may also be eligible. Under the 'open door' Trustees are also willing to consider applications for research that objectively examines or evaluates current or proposed statutory arrangements other than those related to our areas of special interest. A particular concern is the effect of policy or practice on disadvantaged sections of society. Trustees spend up to £750,000 per year under the Open Door.

Proposals to study health care or health services will be considered only if they are demonstrably unsuitable for consideration by the King's Fund, the Department of Health, the Medical Research Council or the Nuffield Trust for Research and Policy Studies in Health Services. Projects to study housing will be considered only if they are unsuitable for funding by the Joseph Rowntree Foundation or one of the statutory agencies concerned with housing.

The separate programmes are described as follows (with the names of relevant members of staff to contact):

Child protection, family law and justice

This programme supports work to help ensure that the legal and institutional framework is best adapted to meet the needs of children and families. Grants in this area are considered by a separate specialist Committee, whose members include academics in law, psychiatry and social work research, and practitioners in law, social work and relevant voluntary organisations. The Committee (whose annual budget is some £670,000) is interested in a broad range of topics that go beyond child protection in a narrow sense, and in practical projects as well as research.

Particular interests include (but are not limited to):

- Legal and financial aspects of divorce or separation (following marriage or cohabitation) and their aftermath. This includes studies of family finances following divorce, the new ancillary relief procedures, and pensions
- Contact following separation or divorce, including the movement of children and child abduction
- Marriage and divorce in minority ethnic communities, including expectations and practices of specific communities and changes in these over time
- Children at risk or in need, including 'looked after' children but also a much broader range of children who might benefit from support
- Placement and planning for children, including adoption, fostering and other types of care. This includes contact following adoption (special guidelines are available in this area)
- Children aged 16 or over who leave care
- Broader provision for children in need, for instance the education of looked after children (considered jointly with the Foundation's Education programme)
- The development of an integrated system of family justice, including work drawing

attention to the anomalies and obstructions in the present system
- Interdisciplinary work in family law, including other government policies with implications for families
- The roles and training needs of professionals in the system, including those that may contribute to the new family court welfare system, family mediation or support services for the family jurisdictions
- Children in the legal system, for example, child witnesses
- Policing and risk management that affects children, including the risk management of 'dangerous men'

Where a proposal is for a research study, the Committee is interested in the dispassionate examination of evidence. It notes that evidence is likely to be different in different cases, for different types of children and families, and is more likely to support work that takes this approach.

Contact Sharon Witherspoon or Theresa O'Neill.

Grants in 1999 went to:

National Council for One Parent Families, for the development of a freephone advice line for lone parents with financial problems: £76,000.

Great Ormond Street Hospital, Department of Psychological Medicine, for a follow-up study of a child care consultation team: £152,000.

London School of Economics and Political Science, Department of Law, for a study on training military and related personnel on the treatment of children in armed conflict: £80,000.

Cardiff Law School, Cardiff Family Studies Centre, for a study of the legal and child protection issues when children have sustained subdural haemorrhage: £76,000.

Institute of Education, Thomas Coram Research Unit, for a study of the effects of concurrent planning on adoption of children under nine years: £32,000.

Cardiff Law School, Cardiff University, for its Hague Abduction Convention Statistical Template Project: £34,000.

Educational research and innovation (under review at the end of 2000)

The Foundation is a major independent funder of research and innovation in education. The Trustees wish to support work of high quality which will either improve practice or inform policy making in the pre-school, school and FE sectors. Our particular areas of interest are:
- Science, mathematics and technology teaching
- Education for 16–19 year olds
- Organisation and effectiveness of the education system
- The curriculum

Contact Helen Quigley.

When this book went to press in the autumn of 2000, the foundation was reviewing the nature and content of its education programmes. Readers should consult the foundation's website for the most up-to-date information.

Grants in 1999 included:

Foyer Federation, on access of Foyer residents to higher education: £4,000.

National Foundation for Education Research, for secondary transfer and retention in key stage 3 – a longitudinal study of gypsy traveller pupils: £115,000.

Royal Holloway College, University of London, Department of Psychology, on deaf children's use of a phonological strategy in reading and writing and spelling: £59,000.

Access to justice

We have long had an interest in the area of access to justice. Our current objectives in this area are:
- to promote developments in the legal system that will improve its accessibility to all people;
- to promote wider access to legal services and advice and a better understanding of the obstacles to access to justice;
- to fund research and promote developments in alternative dispute resolution;
- to help promote a greater knowledge of the rights and duties of the individual, including those of the European citizen;
- to examine the implications of new human rights obligations on civil (not criminal) justice;
- to help promote a greater public understanding of the role of law in society and of the legal system.

Replacement of core funding of existing services (such as law centres) will not be considered. Projects on penal policy, drugs, policing, crime prevention or environmental law will not normally be supported under the 'Access to justice' area of special interest unless they fulfil one of the objectives set out above or are eligible under our 'open door' ...

This programme is administered by Sharon Witherspoon or Theresa O'Neill.

Grants in 1999 included:

University of Bristol, Department of Law, for an evaluation of internal reviews in homelessness decision-making: £52,000.

University of Manchester, Faculty of Law, for support for the Centre for Utility Consumer Law: £20,000.

Institute for Public Policy Research, to research the modernising of the magistracy: £40,000.

The AIRE Centre, to provide information and advice about the European Convention on Human Rights and the Family to legal professionals: £96,000.

University of Leicester, Faculty of Law, for an examination of the role of the Social Security and Child Support Commissioners since 1975: £46,000.

Mental health

The Trustees are interested in funding projects which aim to develop or improve the educational or social provision for those with learning disabilities or mental health problems. The annual budget is £250,000. The following areas are of particular interest:
- children and young people, particularly in the context of families and schools;
- ethical and legal issues arising from mental incapacity;
- employment, in particular transition from school to work for young people with mental disorders or disabilities (work therapy is not a priority area);
- specific language impairment, in particular implications for schooling and work. (Purely linguistic or clinical projects are excluded.)

Projects in the following areas will not in general be funded:
- community care (including normal service provision; development of new services; research; training);
- mental health and old age;
- counselling;
- clinical research into mental illness or learning disability;
- basic studies of normal or abnormal mental processes.

Contact Anthony Tomei or Patricia Lancaster.

Grants in 1999 went to:

University of Glasgow, Department of Child and Adolescent Psychiatry, for psychiatric evaluation of mental illness in young men: £22,000.

Section of Development Psychiatry, University of Cambridge, for a study of capacity to consent to admission and treatment in hospital for a 'mental disorder': £43,000.

University of Warwick, Centre for Research on Health, Medicine and Society, for a study of models of 'mental disorder' and their influence on shared decision-making in community mental healthcare; £56,000.

The Maternity Alliance, for a project to support women with postnatal depression facing a return to work after maternity leave: £52,000.

University of Glasgow, Department of Public Health, for Advance Directives in Mental Health: £64,000.

Older people and their families

The Foundation wishes to fund work that starts from the perspectives, needs and interests of the older person and his or her family, rather than those of service providers. It is interested in projects that will enhance individual autonomy and choice and that recognise variation in preferences and provision.

The Foundation is keen to support work that brings an international comparative perspective to bear, and is particularly interested in fostering work that considers European as well as other countries' perspectives.

As with all its areas of grantmaking, the Foundation is interested in a wide range of topics. Issues that might be of interest include:

- The financial circumstances of elderly people and economic planning for later life;
- Family solidarity and family obligations;
- Autonomy and decision-making in later life;
- Retirement, work and citizenship.

The Foundation will not make grants for the following:

- Theoretical or historical research with no direct bearing on policy or practice;
- Support for mainstream academic or medical training;
- Medical or biological research into ageing, disability, dementia or mental illness;
- Housing or transport unless there is direct bearing on one of the topics above.

Contact Sharon Witherspoon or Anthony Tomei.

Grants in 1999 included:

Cardiff University, Cardiff Law School and Cardiff Family Studies Research Centre, for a study of the role of grandparents in divorced families: £85,000.

Institute of Fiscal Studies, for a study of health and the labour market behaviour of older workers: £71,000.

King's College London, Age Concern Institute of Gerontology, for a study of age gaps between marital partners: £131,000.

The Chartered Institute of Taxation, for tax advice for older people – support for two pilot projects: £55,000.

Rheumatism research – the Oliver Bird Fund

This fund supports research into the basic causes and processes of rheumatism, and grants are awarded on the recommendation of an expert committee. Six grants totalling £450,000 were made in 1999, headed by £88,000 for the Rheumatology Unit at Bristol Royal Infirmary.

Commonwealth programme – the Commonwealth Relations Trust

Grants are made to support the development of service provision or policy-making in developing Commonwealth countries, focusing on projects that reflect the foundation's main areas of activity in the UK. In 1999 it was decided to move towards longer-term programme grants. Examples were the three-year support for a programme in Uganda of continuing education for medical officers and assistants, and another to enable social workers involved with child welfare to take a masters course at the University of East Anglia.

In 1999, 16 grants were made, totalling £649,000.

Open door (miscellaneous)

The trustees have maintained the option of supporting exceptional projects that fall outside either the priorities of their areas of special interest, or indeed, though less commonly, outside these areas altogether. This option has been named the 'open door'.

In 1999, within education and science, nine awards were headed by £83,000 for a website on British biodiversity from the Natural History Museum and £35,000 for a community history project at Leeds Metropolitan University.

Within Social Research and Innovation, the most striking grant was of £250,000 towards a major study of policing in London, co-funded by the Paul Hamlyn Foundation and the Esmée Fairbairn Trust. Another £121,000 was given for a study of choice and decision-making in caesarean section, to the Centre for Family Research at Cambridge; £114,000 to Warwick University for a study of child support, and £110,000 to the Hansard Society to examine the scrutiny role of parliament.

Exclusions

The trustees will not consider the following:

- general appeals;
- buildings or capital costs;
- projects which are mainly of local interest;
- research that is mainly of theoretical interest;
- day to day running costs or accommodation needs;
- the provision of health or social services;
- grants to replace statutory funding;
- healthcare (outside mental health);
- the arts, religion;
- museums, exhibitions, performances;
- sports and recreation;
- conservation, heritage or environmental projects;
- animal rights or welfare;
- attendance at conferences;
- expeditions, travel, adventure/holiday projects;
- business or job creation projects;
- academic journals;
- medical research (other than in rheumatism and arthritis research).

Grants are not made for the following purposes except when the activity is part of a project that is otherwise acceptable:

- work for degrees or other qualifications;
- production of films, videos or television programmes;
- purchase of equipment, including computers.

Applications

If you are thinking of making an application, you must first send a written outline proposal. A member of staff will then advise you whether the proposal comes within the trustees' terms of reference and whether there are any particular questions or issues you should consider. The outline should describe:

- the issue or problem you wish to address;
- the expected outcome(s);
- what will happen in the course of the project;
- (for research projects) an outline of the methods to be employed;
- an outline of the budget and the timetable.

The outline must not exceed three sides of A4, but you are welcome to include additional supporting information about yourself and your organisation.

See the four areas of special interest for contact names in these areas. Applications outside these areas will be passed to the most appropriate member of the senior staff, who will contact you directly.

Applications in the field of social research and innovation are generally dealt with by Sharon Witherspoon and those in the field of education by Helen Quigley.

If you are advised to proceed with a full application, the staff member dealing with your proposal may suggest a meeting or, if matters are straightforward, may advise you to proceed straight to a full application.

Extensive guidance on the preparation of full applications, too long to be summarised here, is available from the foundation and is published on its excellent website.

The Nuffield Trust (formerly the Nuffield Provincial Hospitals Trust)

Research and policy studies in health

See below

Beneficial area UK, except London.

59 New Cavendish Street, London W1G 7LP

Tel. 020 7631 8450 **Fax** 020 7631 8451

e-mail mail@nuffieldtrust.org.uk

website www.nuffieldtrust.org.uk

Correspondent John Wyn Owen, Secretary

Trustees *Sir Maurice Shock, Chair; Prof. John Ledingham; Prof. Sir Denis Pereira Gray; Prof. Sir Keith Peters; Dame Fiona Caldicott; Sir Christopher France; Lord Carlile; Baroness Cox; Prof. Don Detmer.*

Information available Excellent annual reports.

General

There have been major changes at this trust and it is no longer a big provider of grants, except for work to implement its own tightly focused programmes. In 1999/2000 just four grants totalling £63,000 were the result of unsolicited applications. Most of the money was spent on work commissioned to progress the trust's interests in five fields:

- health policy futures
- the changing role of the state in health policies
- public health
- quality in healthcare
- humanities in medicine

However, the trustees 'have maintained their policy of being willing to consider unsolicited applications where these are of sufficiently high quality and of particular interest to the trust'.

Exclusions

Grants are not awarded to individuals for personal studies, nor to meet the core costs of other organisations.

Applications

Potential applicants are strongly advised to obtain up-to-date guidelines for applicants before approaching the trust. These are available, in some detail, on the website listed above.

Applicants for grants are normally expected to write to the secretary initially, and well in advance of the month by which applications are required, giving a brief outline of the study for which they seek funding; if appropriate, the secretary then advises on the requirements for submitting a formal application to the trustees. The trustees meet in March, July and November.

The P F Charitable Trust

General

£1,415,000 (1998/99)

Beneficial area UK, with apparent special interests in Oxfordshire and Scotland.

25 Copthall Avenue, London EC2R 7DR

Tel. 020 7638 5858

Correspondent The Secretary

Trustees *Robert Fleming; Valentine P Fleming; Philip Fleming; R D Fleming.*

Information available Inadequate annual report. Accounts listing the 50 largest grants; basic grant information sheet.

Summary

Several hundred grants are made to registered charities across the UK. Grants average, and are typically for, £2,000, although awards of £500 or less are frequent (accounting for half of grant expenditure in 1998/99). The few large grants go as high as around £30,000. Both one-off and recurrent awards are made.

General

The trust was set up in 1951 by its settlor and namesake, the banker Philip Fleming, and is still run by family members. Its grant-making ability was enhanced considerably in 1983 when the settlor's son, Robert Fleming, made substantial donations to the trust.

In 1998/99 the trust had high investment management costs (£41,000) in relation to the low investment income (£1.5 million), and further capital losses of £1.1 million on investment assets of nearly £52 million.

Administration costs were also high, at £120,000, partly as a result of a 52% rise in staff salary costs, to £35,000 from £23,000 in the previous year.

It has previously been reported that the trust will provide both core and revenue funding, although it is not keen to support salaries of staff members of organisations. The trust may renew its commitments after the first three years are completed and occasionally makes commitments for up to five years for medical research projects.

The trust has in the past expressed its belief that charities should do more to improve the efficiency of their administration. This is particularly important when the trust makes, for example, a three-year commitment to provide a certain amount each year, because frequently it makes such commitments and after the first year receives letters asking for a repeat donation, when it has already been promised. It also frequently receives more than one letter from the same organisation requesting the same thing, but from different people, and this is something that the trust wishes to avoid.

Grants

The full grants list, referred to in previous editions of this book, is no longer available. In 1996/97, grant distribution was reported as follows:

	Amount	*%*
Welfare		
old folks	£51,000	4%
youth	£70,000	6%
rehabilitation	£86,000	7%
settlements	£2,500	<1%
housing associations	£6,000	<1%
miscellaneous	£74,000	6%
Medical research	£191,000	16%
Hospitals and associated organisations	£198,000	17%
Music, theatre, art	£148,000	12%
Conservation	£141,000	12%
Universities, schools	£76,000	6%
Blind and deaf	£48,000	4%
Youth clubs and associations	£28,000	2%
Animals	£17,000	1%
Miscellaneous	£46,000	4%
Total	£1,183,000	100%

The trust no longer gives to:

- individual hospices (but instead supports Help the Hospices);
- individual churches (but instead gives grants to the Historic Churches Preservation Trust, Scottish Churches Architectural Heritage Trust and to the Baptist Union Home Missions and Methodist Church Home Missions).

The previously expressed interest in Oxfordshire and Scotland is confirmed by the top 50 grants in 1998/99. The two largest grants were of £52,000 to the

Cancer Research Campaign, which receives major grants in most, but not every, year; and £51,000 to the Caledonian Foundation, which is reportedly part of a three-year commitment worth £170,000 intended for distribution to charities on the west coast of Scotland, where the Fleming family has strong links.

Two further grants were for more than £25,000, to the University of Dundee (£35,500) and to Oxford and District Sports and Recreation Association for the Disabled (£27,500).

Significant beneficiaries also included the Maggie Keswick Jencks Cancer Caring Centre (£25,000); British Museum (£25,000); National Portrait Gallery (£20,000), and the Multiple Sclerosis Society (£17,000).

A further 30 smaller grants in the range £5,000 to £10,000 were awarded to national charities or local organisations all across the UK but typically within London, Oxfordshire or Scotland. Examples included Royal Brompton Hospital (£10,000); East London Schools Fund (£10,000); Chipping Norton Theatre (£10,000); Soil Association (£10,000); International Spinal Research Trust (£8,000) and Cornerstone Community Care (£5,000).

Half of the trust's grant expenditure (£704,000) went on grants under £5,000, the recipients undisclosed.

Exclusions

No grants to individuals or non-registered charities. Individual churches and hospices are now excluded.

Applications

To the correspondent at any time, in writing with full information. Replies will be sent to unsuccessful applications if an sae is enclosed. Trustees meet monthly.

The Parthenon Trust

Third world, general

£4,601,000 (1998)

Saint-Nicolas 9, 2000 Neuchâtel, Switzerland

Tel. 0041 32 724 8130 **Fax** 0041 32 724 8131

Correspondent John Whittaker, Secretary

Trustees *Geraldine Whittaker, Chair; Dr Judith Darmady; Prof. Charles Hales.*

Information available Reports and accounts.

Summary

The trust makes about 60 awards each year, many of them for less than £50,000 and few of them exceeding £150,000, though one of the 1998 grants was for over £1 million. Many are given to overseas organisations. The list of beneficiaries is largely unchanging from year to year, with new recipients accounting for only about a fifth of the total awarded in a given year.

General

This is a registered UK charity, though the secretary is based in Switzerland. The trustees' interests cover the following very broad areas:

- helping children in need, refugees and famine victims;
- helping the aged, the homeless and the long-term unemployed;
- supporting longer-term development in the third world;
- supporting medical research in areas which appear to be underfunded in relation to the likelihood of achieving progress;
- supporting patient care, hospices and rehabilitation;
- helping disabled people (including the blind, the deaf and the 'mentally and physically handicapped').

Income for 1998 was more than £5 million, made up almost entirely of donations and gifts to the trust, rather than as interest or dividends from an endowment.

In 1998, £4.6 million was given out in over 60 grants. Of this, 42% went to charitable organisations providing emergency relief and/or undertaking development projects in the Third World; 23% went to medically-related purposes (mostly research); 35% was given to a wide variety of other purposes including assistance to the mentally handicapped, the physically disabled, the underprivileged and the homeless, the improvement of the administration of justice in developing countries, nutritional research and assistance to landmine victims.

The top 20 grants in 1998 made up 75% of the total donated. Three of these were to new recipients. The largest amounts went to the following (with amounts for 1997 in brackets).

Médecins sans Frontières (UK)	£1,150,000	(£1,250,000)
Save the Children	£530,000	(£180,000)
WellBeing	£175,000	(–)
Fondation ATD Quart Monde Belgique	£170,000	(£150,000)
Handicap International	£160,000	(£150,000)
Catholic University of Louvain	£140,000	(£240,000)
Cambridge University*	£127,000	(£172,000)
Euro Org. for Cancer Research/ Treatment Fdn.	£125,000	(£125,000)
British Red Cross	£100,000	(£5,000)
Les Amis de l'Institut Bordet	£100,000	(£100,000)
St Thérèse Child Development Center	£100,000	(£55,000)
Due Process of Law Foundation	£92,000	(–)

*(For the work of Professor Hales, who is also a trustee)

Other UK charities in the list of the top 20 beneficiaries were the Arthritis Research Campaign (£80,000) and Guernsey Cheshire Home Foundation (£73,000).

Exclusions

No grants for individuals or scientific/ geographical expeditions. Unsolicited applications are not normally acknowledged.

Applications

Anyone proposing to submit an application should telephone the secretary.

The Peabody Community Fund

Social welfare in London

£405,000 (to organisations, 1999/2000)

Beneficial area London.

45 Westminster Bridge Road, London SE1 7JB

Tel. 020 7928 7811 **Fax** 020 7261 9187

website www.peabody.org.uk

Correspondent Everton Counsell, Peabody Community Fund Manager

Grants Committee *Tim Cook, Chair; Dickon Robinson; Maura Santos; Sue Causton; Alvin Wade; Amanda Beswick.*

Information available Full reports and accounts available from the Peabody Trust. Application form and information pack.

Summary

The fund, part of the giant Peabody Trust, gives grants for community schemes that benefit Londoners on low incomes. They are usually for the refurbishment or improvement of premises or for items of equipment.

General

Awards in 1999/2000 were classified as follows:

	No.	*Value*
Investing in community support	37	£287,000
Overcoming handicaps	6	£71,000
Employment initiatives	6	£48,000

The largest grant was for £40,000, with six others for more than £10,000. Few grants were for less than £2,500.

Examples of grants were as follows.

Investing in community support

Field Lane Community Centre (£6,000, for refurbishment); Homerton Grove Adventure Playground (£10,000, for re-equipment); West London Action for Children (£5,000, for project costs); Mawbey Toy Library (£750, for toys and storage); The Passage (£30,000, for refurbishment).

Overcoming handicaps

Open Doors (£8,000, for wheelchairs); Interchange (£40,000, for disabled lift); Waltham Forest Mencap (£3,500, for IT equipment).

Employment initiatives

Bangladesh Welfare Association (£4,500, for equipment); Safestart (£13,000, for IT equipment).

Exclusions

No grants for the benefit of anyone other than Londoners, nor for

- political or religious purposes;
- the direct provision of housing accommodation;
- to support ordinary ongoing revenue activity;
- purposes already catered for by statutory bodies, unless the project aims to promote further action by central and local authorities, rather than to relieve them of their responsibilities;
- general appeals;
- individuals;
- the arts;
- medical charities unless projects overcome handicaps;
- intermediate bodies for redistribution to other organisations.

Applications

All applications must be made using the application form available from the trust. The trust requests that all questions are answered in as much detail as possible, and that replies such as 'see attached' are not used as far as possible. This will help it to form an idea of your organisation's ethos and ways of working, as well as finding out specific information about your project. Please ensure that the documentation asked for is provided, as an application cannot be considered until all necessary paperwork is received.

Completed forms should be returned to the Peabody Community Fund Manager. If you have any queries, please discuss them with that officer.

You will be notified of a decision made by the trust as soon as is reasonably possible. Applications will be considered three times a year (usually June, November and March).

Note: organisations seeking funds from several sources can usually enhance their success rate where they can show existing commitments from grant-making bodies. The PCF is, therefore, particularly interested in making such 'partnership' grants, where it will generate at least equivalent funding from other sources.

The Peacock Charitable Trust

Medical research, disability, general

£1,943,000 (1999/2000)

Beneficial area UK.

PO Box 902, London SW19 5WE

Correspondent Janet Gilbert

Trustees *W M Peacock; Mrs S Peacock; C H Peacock; K R Burgin.*

Information available Annual report and accounts, including a full list of grants, but without a narrative report.

Summary

The trust gives over 100 grants a year, concentrated on medical and health charities, disability and some youth work. Two thirds of the grants given out in 1999/2000 were to organisations also supported in the previous year. Although grants can be for more than £100,000, most are for amounts between £2,000 and £10,000.

This is a family trust, with a local interest in the Wimbledon/Merton area of London, where it is based, and to a lesser extent in the area around Chichester, including West Sussex and south east Hampshire.

General

Apart from the trust secretary, the trustees are assisted by Mr D Wallace, who prepares reports for them on most applications received. Administrative costs rose to £41,000 in 1999/2000. Though still a modest sum, the trust expects to reduce this figure in future by taking on directly the cash management functions previously supplied by the NatWest Bank.

The charity gave 139 grants ranging from £150 to £125,000. The 29 grants for £20,000 or more accounted for £1,086,000, or 56% of the total. Major cancer charities received large grants and some had also benefited in the previous year. They included the Cancer Research Campaign (£25,000 and £120,000) and Macmillan Cancer Relief Fund (£100,000). Marie Curie Cancer Care received £250,000 in the previous year.

Other recipients of large grants included the Mental Health Foundation (£50,000, repeated), the Royal Hospital for Neuro-disability (£81,000 in each year) and the Alzheimer Research Trust (£55,000 in each year).

Major beneficiaries outside the health field included the YMCA (£60,000 in each year) and Fairbridge (£70,000 and £60,000).

Local beneficiaries in the Wimbledon/Merton area received smaller amounts. They included Victim Support Merton (£2,500), the Kingston Boys Brigade (£1,000) and Abbeyfield Peabody South London (£2,500).

In the Chichester area beneficiaries included Cobnor Activities Centre Trust (£5,000), and the Weald and Downland Open Air Museum Trust (£5,000).

Applications

Registered charities only should apply in writing, preferably early in the year and accompanied by full accounts. Applications should include clear details of the need the intended project is designed to meet, plus any outline budget.

No donations are made to individuals and only in rare cases are additions made to charities already being supported.

To maximise the use of funds beneficially, only applications being considered will receive replies.

The Dowager Countess Eleanor Peel Trust

Medical research, general

£642,000 (1998/99)

Beneficial area UK, with an apparent interest in the Lancaster area.

Sceptre Court, 40 Tower Hill, London EC3N 4DX

Tel. 020 7423 8000 **Fax** 020 7423 8001

e-mail atwitchett@trowers.com

Correspondent Luke Valner

Trustees *J W Parkinson; R M Parkinson; R L Rothwell-Jackson; Anthony Trower; Luke Valner.*

Summary

A small number of large and often recurring grants, mainly for medical research. Over 50 grants, usually for £5,000 or less, for a wide range of causes, almost all of these previously supported by the fund.

General

The trust deed of 1951 named 31 charities, mainly benefiting older people, to be given preference in any grants awarded. It also prohibits the trustees from giving money to charitable bodies substantially under the control of central or local government or those primarily devoted to children.

The trustees' report reads as follows:

The trustees meet on at least three occasions each year. All applications for grants are vetted by the Secretary or the Chairman and the Secretary. Any applications rejected at this stage are listed in the agenda for the next trustees' meeting with the reason for rejection. Applications for consideration at the trustees' meetings are presented with a report and summary of the financial statements for the complete year.

Grant-making policy

The Trustees prefer to support specific projects rather than general operating expenses. They regret that, due to the number of applications they receive, they are not normally able to support small local charities with gross income of less than £25,000 pa. [*Most registered charities have an income of under £5,000 a year, so this excludes more than half of them. Ed.*] The Trustees scrutinise the financial position of applicants, and those with Income Accounts showing substantial surpluses are unlikely to be supported. Medical research accounts for approximately 50% of the Trustees' grants. Applications from individuals are not accepted.

Trustees are paid for their services (between £2,350 and £5,200 each) and the charity also purchases investment management and secretarial services from businesses with which two of the trustees, J W Parkinson and Luke Valner, are connected.

It is the view of these editors that experienced and competent trustees can be found for the rewarding task of giving away someone else's money, and do not normally need to be paid for this. Nor do the editors feel that it is desirable to place a charity's commercial business with bodies connected to the trustees.

Grants in 1998/99

In 1998/99, 74 grants were made, totalling £642,000. Around a third of this expenditure was spent on ongoing commitments to 10 (mainly academic or medical) institutions, of which the most significant were:

- £99,500 over three years for Lancashire & Cumbria Foundation for Medical Research;
- Research Institute for the Care of the Elderly (£35,000);
- Nottingham Trent University (£27,000);
- Institute of Orthopaedics, Oswestry (£25,000);
- Peel Studentship Trust, University of Lancaster (£20,000).

Although not listed as one of these commitments, the trust also gives large annual donations to the Peel Medical Research Trust, which has received over £1.3 million over the years (£77,000 in 1998/99).

Large grants also went to Abbeyfield Lakeland Extra Care Society (£25,000, repeat); Water Aid (£22,000) and Research into Ageing (£16,000).

Small grants

Nearly all the remaining grants were for amounts between £1,000 and £5,000, with around a quarter of the beneficiaries having been supported the year before. There was a strong special interest in the Lancaster area, accounting for perhaps a third of grants. A smaller interest was in the village of East Meon, Hampshire.

Three charities specified in the trust deed received support in the year: Ex-Services Mental Welfare Society (£5,000, repeat); Friends of the Elderly and Gentlefolk's Help (£5,000); and the 'Not Forgotten' Association (£2,000, repeat).

Less than a dozen recipients of small grants were receiving funding for the first time, including Barrow & District Disability Association; Hill Homes Development Appeal; Vision Support; Cheshire & North East Wales Society for the Blind (all £5,000 each); and Gwent Shrievalty Police Trust (£3,000).

Exclusions

No grants to children's charities, or individuals.

Applications

To the correspondent. See above.

The Pet Plan Charitable Trust

Animals

£569,000 (1998/99)

Beneficial area UK.

Great West Road, Brentford, Middlesex TW8 9EG

Tel. 020 8580 8013 **Fax** 020 8580 8186

Correspondent Roz Hayward-Butt, Administrator

Trustees *David Simpson, Chair; Clarissa Baldwin; Patsy Bloom; John Bower; Ivor Brecher; Dr Andrew Higgins; George Stratford.*

Information available Annual report and accounts on file at the Charity Commission.

General

The trust was set up in 1994 to support dogs, cats and horses through funding clinical veterinary investigation, education and welfare projects.

The trust receives income by way of donations from Pet Plan Group Ltd policyholders and the Pet Plan Group itself. In 1998/99, the trust's assets were £497,000. The income was £496,000 and management and administration costs were £70,000. Grants were made totalling £569,000.

A total of 20 new scientific grants were made, totalling £320,000. These included £110,000 to the Royal Veterinary College for a study into canine intervertebral disc herniation; £48,000 to the University of Glasgow Veterinary School for research into FIV infection, and £10,000 to Cambridge Veterinary School for a study into equine colic. Also included were 13 'starter grants' for pilot studies under £6,000. It is hoped that these grants will lead to further funding.

There was one capital grant to the Animal Health Trust, for a scintigraphy unit, of £150,000.

Welfare and educational grants totalling £99,000 were made during the year, including £11,000 for the Society for the Welfare of Horses and Ponies to provide fencing and stabling; £6,000 to Skye View Animal Shelter for an isolation unit for cats and kittens, and £5,000 to VIGIL German Shepherd Rescue for a replacement rescue vehicle. An education grant of £4,500 was awarded to Feline Advisory Bureau for a manual on feral cat rescue and management.

Exclusions

No grants to individuals or non-registered charities.

Applications

In writing to the correspondent.

Jack Petchey Foundation

Young people in east London and west Essex

About £1,500,000 (2000)

Beneficial area East London and west Essex, i.e. the boroughs/districts of Barking & Dagenham, Brentwood, Epping Forest, Hackney, Havering, Newham, Redbridge, Tower Hamlets, Thurrock, Waltham Forest, Uttlesford and Harlow.

Exchange House, 13–14 Clements Court, Clements Lane, Ilford IG1 2QY

Tel. 020 8252 8000 **Fax** 020 8252 7892

e-mail jpfoundation@aol.com

website www.jackpetcheyfoundation.org.uk

Correspondent Andrew Billington, Director

Trustees *Graham Adams; Ron Mills; Ray Rantell; Barbara Staines.*

Summary

Established in September 1999, the key objective of this trust is to help young people (aged 11 to 24) to 'find their feet' in life and build up their self-esteem. This is achieved by supporting individuals and by giving project grants (including support for running costs) to schools, youth clubs and other organisations working with young people in the area of benefit. The foundation takes the time to research and investigate projects, including liaising with other grant-making bodies.

After four months of operation the foundation had already donated £143,000 in project grants to organisations, with a view to giving away £500,000 in the following year. During 2000, organisations were also invited to apply for Millennium Awards, whereby £1 million was to be distributed to successful applicants in December that year.

The trust offers support to individuals through Achievement Awards, Leaders Awards and sponsorship for sporting events. Full details of all the foundation's programmes can be found in its report or on its website.

General

The foundation's primary objectives are set out in its first report as follows:

- To give grants through the Jack Petchey Achievement Award Scheme to individuals (mainly between 11 and 24 years of age) who have made a wholehearted contribution to their club, group or community. The monthly grant (currently £200 per person) is spent on a community project of their choice.
- To work with established youth charities and schools to promote community involvement and personal responsibility within society.
- To provide financial assistance to clubs, schools and youth groups that demonstrate that they are enabling individuals to achieve their potential, take control of their lives and contribute to society as a whole.
- To support the training of youth leaders.
- To support other projects at the discretion of the trustees.

The report goes on to describe project grants, with the amounts of specific grants awarded added by these editors:

> ... The value is normally between £500 and £50,000. ... The grants can be for capital schemes, training projects, youth development or occasionally charity running costs. The trustees require applicants to raise at least 50% of costs of a project from other sources, and evidence of this is normally requested with applications.
>
> In 1999 the Jack Petchey Foundation gave grants to many schools, clubs, and community schemes including:
>
> London Youth [£16,000] – Support for 130 clubs in East London.
>
> Community Links [£20,000] – Support for work with young people mainly in Newham.
>
> Essex Association of Boys Clubs [£41,000] – Support for clubs and Stubbers training centre in West Essex.
>
> YMCA George Williams College [£36,000] – A three year bursary for the training of Youth Leaders.

Applications

Application forms for each of the grant schemes are available from the foundation and on its website.

The Pilgrim Trust

Social welfare, art and learning, preservation of buildings

£2,865,000 (1999)

Beneficial area UK, but not the Channel Islands and the Isle of Man.

Cowley House, 9 Little College Street, London SW1P 3XS

Tel. 020 7222 4723 **Fax** 020 7976 0461

Correspondent Georgina Nayler, Director

Trustees *Mary Moore, Chair; Sir Richard Carew Pole; Neil MacGregor; Nicolas Barker; Lady Anglesey; Lord Armstrong; Lord Bingham; Dame Ruth Runciman; Eugenie Turton; Lord Cobbold.*

Information available Guidelines for applicants and excellent annual report and accounts.

Summary

The trust makes grants to specific fields within the three general areas of social

THE PILGRIM TRUST – GRANTS IN 1998/99			
	Grants 1999	*Value 1999*	*(1998)*
Social welfare	93	£1,268,000	(£1,362,000)
Art and learning	68	£704,000	(£689,000)
Preservation	48	£893,000	(£705,000)

welfare, art and learning, and preservation.

Grants can be one-off, or for up to three years, and can be for core or programme costs. Very few grants are for more than £50,000.

Grant-making policy

The trust issued new guidelines in November 2000. The main changes are under the social welfare heading, where the previous general interest in community and welfare projects has been replaced by much more focused concerns with alcohol and drug abuse, alternatives to prison, and the welfare of children 'in care'. Homelessness loses its previous priority, but the support of those with mental health problems remains.

Under 'art and learning' the previous emphasis on access has gone (perhaps in response to the excesses of government in this direction), as has the specific support for the pre-publication costs of learned works. New, and very welcome, is a preference for work outside London.

There is little change under the 'preservation' heading.

The full text of the new statement of current priorities is as follows:

Social welfare

- Projects that assist people involved in crime or in alcohol or drug misuse to change their lives and find new opportunities.
- Projects concerned with the employment, support or housing of those with mental illness.
- Projects in prisons and projects providing alternatives to custody that will give new opportunities to offenders and will so assist rehabilitation.
- Projects for young people who are looked after by local authorities in residential or in foster care and for those leaving that care, to help them into education, training and employment.
- Trustees may seek out projects concerned with the welfare and integration of refugees and asylum seekers within the UK. They have decided, however, that they themselves will identify those projects to which they wish to contribute. They will NOT consider unsolicited applications.

Art and learning

- The promotion of scholarship, academic research, cataloguing and conservation within museums, galleries, libraries and archives, particularly those outside London. Grants may not be given direct to individuals but must be made to a charitable or public organisation.
- Trustees do not exclude acquisitions for collections, but funds for this are strictly limited.

Preservation

- Preservation of particular architectural or historical features on historic buildings or the conservation of individual monuments or structures that are of importance to the surrounding environment, including buildings designed for public performance. Trustees will not normally contribute to major restorations or repairs unless a discrete element of the project can be clearly identified as appropriate for the trust to support.
- Projects that seek to give a new use to buildings that are of outstanding architectural or historic interest.
- The preparation and dissemination of architectural or historical research about buildings and designed landscapes and their importance to the community.
- Cataloguing and conservation of records associated with archaeology, marine archaeology, historic buildings and designed landscapes.

Places of worship

Fabric repairs

The trust makes annual block grants for the repair of the fabric of historic churches of any denomination to the Historic Churches Preservation Trust for Churches in England and Wales (020 7736 3054) and to the Scottish Churches Architectural Heritage Trust (0131 225 8644). Applications should be made directly to the appropriate body. Churches in Northern Ireland should apply to the trust directly.

Projects to develop new facilities within a church or their re-ordering for liturgical purposes will not be supported.

Conservation of historic contents

The trust makes an annual block grant to the Council for the Care of Churches (020 7898 1866) for the conservation of historic contents (organs, bells, glass and monuments etc.) and important structures and monuments in church yards for places of worship of all denominations. Applications should be addressed directly to the Council. Churches in Northern Ireland should apply to the trust directly.

The new 2000 guidelines also include the following general guidance:

Applications from ALL parts of the UK are welcomed.

Trustees particularly welcome collaboration between organisations to achieve their joint aims.

Grants may be offered for more than one financial year, but the trustees are reluctant to make recurring grants for more than three years.

Small grants fund

Trustees run a small grants fund and have set aside an annual sum of £200,000 for applications for £5,000 or less.

General

Though its general appearance is similar to many other funders with wide-ranging grant policies, this trust is more interesting than most. It seems to achieve more often two commonly found aspirations – to find projects where its funds 'will make a significant impact' and which would 'find it difficult to raise funds from other sources'.

These grants are described in the very full annual report, now timely as well as comprehensive. Even its design, though little changed for years, has made the jump from old-fashioned to retro-classic.

The 1999 grants came in the following range of size:

£10,000 or less	121
£10,001 to £25,000	72
£25,001 to £50,000	17
Greater than £50,000	3

The annual report suggested that the trust was becoming more receptive to core cost funding, as is reflected in the guidelines above. It also noted that the trust was suffering from situations in which applicants offered a grant did not succeed in getting the funds for other parts of the project concerned, and that a 'cut down' version, wholly funded by Pilgrim, was sometimes the result. 'We have decided to take a strong line' – recipients may now be asked to return the money in such circumstances.

Apart from the block grants referred to above, there were three grants for amounts of over £50,000, as follows:

- After Adoption, Manchester: £61,000 over three years towards the Teamwork for Children project to address the adoption and support needs of children with special needs.

- NACRO Belfast: £60,000 over three years for its 'offenders into work' project.
- Muslim Heritage Centre, London: £56,000 over three years for its advice and support service for unemployed people.

A sample of the grants for £10,000, probably the most frequently found size of grants, is as follows:

Social welfare

- Lisburn YMCA: to set up individual programmes for young people at risk.
- Tacade, Salford: for a drug education programme for parents.
- Autism Initiatives: towards furnishing a respite care home.
- Whitby Network: towards the kitchen for residential units for people with learning disabilities.

Art and learning

- Alpine Club Library: for cataloguing.
- Norton Priory Museum, Cheshire: to rehouse a giant 14th century statue.
- Orkney Natural History Society: for display cabinets.

Preservation

- Monimail Tower Trust: for conservation of the medieval palace.
- Hafod, Wales: to restore a footpath in a designed landscape.

Exclusions

No grants are made to individuals, or for projects outside the UK, or for organisations that are registered charities or have recognised charitable status.

Once a grant has been made, the trust does not usually accept another application from the same organisation for two years from the date of that decision.

Grants are not made for:

- major capital projects and major appeals, particularly where 'partnership' funding is required and where any contribution from the Pilgrim Trust would not make a significant difference;
- activities that the trustees consider to be primarily the responsibility of central or local government;
- medical research, hospices, residential homes for the elderly and for people with physical disabilities;
- projects for people with physical disabilities and schemes specifically to give access to public buildings for people with physical disabilities;
- drop-in centres (unless the specific work within the centre falls within one of the trustees' current priorities), youth and sports clubs, travel or adventure projects, community centres or children's playgroups;
- re-ordering of churches or places of worship for wider community use;
- education, assistance to individuals for degree or post degree work, school, university and college development programmes;
- trips abroad;
- one-off events such as exhibitions, festivals, seminars and theatrical and musical productions;
- commissioning of new works of art;
- general appeals.

Applications

An application form and the following supporting information is required.

Details of your organisation should include:

- its latest audited annual accounts and report (no application can be considered without accounts)
- its aims and objectives
- its track record and the support it enjoys from other organisations working in the same field

Details of the project should include:

- a full description of it, including a budget and, if relevant, a projected income and expenditure account for the organisation as a whole
- the problem you are seeking to tackle, its urgency, and how your project will solve it
- for projects involving salary costs, relevant job descriptions with the proposed salaries and the proposed management structure
- how you will monitor and evaluate the project
- a list of other organisations you have approached for funding and any offers you have received
- where you are requesting a grant of less than £5,000, two references from organisations with which you work
- for historic building repairs, details of the repair scheme with costs
- for cataloguing and conservation projects, a demonstration of how you have chosen the people who will do the work and details of their relevant expertise
- photographs, where appropriate

The Pilkington Charities Fund

General

£829,000 (1998/99)

Beneficial area Worldwide, with a preference for Merseyside.

14 Chapel Lane, Formby, Liverpool L37 4DU

Tel. 01704 834490

Correspondent Roberts Legge & Co, Chartered Accountants

Trustees *Jennifer Jones; Arnold Pilkington; Neil Pilkington.*

Information available Annual report and accounts.

Summary

The trust was originally set up for the benefit of the employees, ex-employees and their dependants, of Pilkington plc, based in St Helens. A large amount is still donated each year to the C & A Pilkington Trust Fund for this purpose. The trust's other grants remain mainly for social welfare in Merseyside, but substantial support is also given for medical research and care and overseas aid. Grants are awarded twice a year, in November and April, and frequently the original amount is repeated to the same organisation. Most range from £1,000 to £5,000, though larger grants for up to £50,000 typically go to national or international charities, apparently as part of multi-year commitments.

General

In 1998/99 total funds of £19 million generated a low income of £636,000 (3% of assets) and £829,000 was granted to about 120 organisations. Almost a third of this amount (£259,000) was for 'Specific Projects', including the usual donation to the C & A Pilkington Trust Fund (£97,000).

Other grants made under this heading went to:

- Barnardos (£45,000)
- National Meningitis Trust (£27,000)
- Bath Institute of Medical Engineering (£20,000)
- British Red Cross (Hurricane Mitch, £10,000).

A further £60,000 was provided in emergency relief for the Kosovo crisis through the Red Cross; Help the Aged (£20,000 each); Oxfam and Save the Children (£10,000 each).

The main grants programme, totalling £560,000, also included support for work overseas, to organisations such as Intermediate Technology (£30,000); Ockenden Venture (£10,000); Cambodia Trust (£5,000); UNAIS International Service (£5,000); Friends Centre (Rehabilitation of the Paralysed, Bangladesh, £3,000) and Sight Savers International (£1,000).

About two thirds of the UK beneficiaries were based in Merseyside, with a particular focus on St Helens. National charities for older people, children and disabled people were also well supported. A sample is as follows:

RUKBA (£2,000); St Helens and Knowsley Hospice (£10,000); Toxteth Community Council (£250); Victims of Violence (£2,000); Walton Youth Project (£500); Pain Relief Foundation (£2,000); NSPCC St Helens (£5,000); MENCAP (£1,000); Liverpool Citizens Advice Bureau (£500); Juvenile Diabetes Foundation (£2,500); Dove Designs (£7,000); Home-Start South Sefton (£10,000).

Exclusions

Individuals.

Applications

In writing to the correspondent.

The Porter Foundation

Education, environment, general

£467,000 (1998/99)

Beneficial area UK and Israel.

PO Box 229, Winchester SO23 7WF

e-mail theporterfoundation@btinternet.com

Correspondent Paul Williams, Director

Information available Guidelines for applicants. Annual report and accounts.

Summary

Most large grants, which can be for as much as £500,000, are given to Jewish institutions in the UK and Israel with which the foundation has long-standing connections. The main area of interest is in academic research both into the environment and Jewish culture. There is also a limited small grants programme benefiting a range of health, welfare and arts organisations.

General

The foundation was set up in 1970 by Sir Leslie Porter, former chairman and president of Tesco, and Dame Shirley Porter, a former and highly controversial leader of Westminster City Council and daughter of Sir John and Lady Sarah Cohen.

The list of major beneficiaries changes very little from year to year, as the foundation has a number of binding commitments to organisations in the UK and Israel.

The foundation's guidelines say that

> Grants can be made for capital projects or for specific programmes or activities with a measurable end result. Grants will not be made on a recurring annual basis, or to cover general running costs. There is no maximum grant. Matching funding applications are welcomed.

Assets stood at £35 million in 1998/99, a 66% increase in three years. Income was a relatively low £1.3 million, of which £467,000 was spent on grants, down from £760,000 in the previous year.

Administration costs totalling £174,000 (37% of grant expenditure) included payments of £34,000 for investment services to PFM Asset Management Ltd, in which Sir Leslie Porter, one of the trustees, had an interest, and £42,000 in salaries paid to the executive director and administrative assistant. The first arrangement is of a kind always regretted by these editors, and is one which the Charity Commission now expects not to occur unless there is 'no realistic alternative'.

The foundation's 1998/99 annual report provided the following description of its activities during the year (with figures added where relevant by these editors):

> The Porter Foundation made over 50 awards, from large capital grants to small gifts to community organisations.
>
> Major awards in the UK were made to the Royal Opera House [£50,000], the Oxford Centre for Hebrew & Jewish Studies [£40,000 for the Porter Fellowship in Yiddish Language and Literature], Templeton College, Oxford [£37,500] and the Imperial War Museum [£10,000]. Smaller community-based awards were made to a range of local organisations including the arts, welfare and young people.
>
> Much of the funding for projects in Israel continues to be towards the Porter Supercentre for the Environment and Ecology at Tel Aviv University [£120,000, annual donation over 5 years]. Multi-disciplinary research leading to practical solutions for complex environmental problems will be the major funding priority of the foundation in the coming years.

Other beneficiaries in 1998/99 included the Joint Jewish Charitable Trust – Shirene Home (£79,000; £157,000 in 1997/98); New Israel Fund – Israel Union for Environmental Defence (£24,000; £12,000 in 1997/98), and Jewish Care (£10,000, repeat).

The smaller community-based grants were led by those to the Chicken Shed Theatre and Frylands Wood Scout Camp (£1,000 each).

Over £9,000 was given in small grants of under £1,000. Unfortunately, we are unable to provide specific examples of these as the grants list only shows awards of £1,000 and over.

At the year end further major commitments to beneficiaries not already mentioned above included the following (total committed):

JPAIME – Daniel Amichai Education Centre (£552,000); Community Security Trust (£5,000 a year for four years); Friends of the Hebrew University of Jerusalem (£3,000 a year for three years).

Exclusions

The foundation makes grants only to registered charitable organisations or to organisations with charitable objects that are exempt from the requirement for charitable registration. Grants will not be made to:

- general appeals such as direct mail circulars;
- charities which redistribute funds to other charities;
- third-party organisations raising money on behalf of other charities; or to cover general running costs.

No grants are made to individuals. Individuals may benefit from scholarships established with some universities or colleges, but the organisation concerned should be applied to directly, not through the Porter Foundation.

Applications

1. An initial letter summarising your application, together with basic costings and background details on your organisation – such as the annual report and accounts – should be sent to the director. Speculative approaches containing expensive publicity material are not encouraged.

2. If your proposal falls within the foundation's current funding criteria you may be contacted for further information, including perhaps a visit from the foundation staff. There is no need to fill out an application form.

3. Applications fulfilling the criteria will be considered by the trustees, who meet three times a year, usually in March, July and November.

4. You will hear shortly after the meeting whether your application has been successful. Unfortunately, it is not possible to acknowledge all unsolicited applications (unless a stamped, addressed envelope is enclosed). If you do not hear from the foundation, you can assume that your application has been unsuccessful.

5. Due to limits on funds available, some excellent projects may have to be refused a grant. In such a case the trustees may invite the applicant to reapply in a future financial year, without giving a commitment to fund.

PPP Healthcare Medical Trust

Healthcare and public health research, training and development

£17,000,000 (anticipated for 2001)

13 Cavendish Square, London W1G 0PQ

Tel. 020 7307 2622 **Fax** 020 7307 2623

e-mail ppptrust@ppptrust.org.uk

website www.ppptrust.org.uk

Correspondent David Carrington, Chief Executive

Trustees *Mark Sheldon, Chair; Bernard Asher; Lawrence Banks; Prof. Yvonne Carter; Prof. Richard Cooke; Ram Gidoomal; Sir Anthony Grabham; Peter Lord; Prof. Mary Marshall; Dr Harry McNeilly; Sir Peter Morris; Prof. Brian Pentecost; Sir Keith Peters; Prof. Lord Renfrew; Michael Sayers; Prof. John Swales; Dr Elizabeth Vallance.*

Information available See below.

Summary

The trust makes substantial grants for research, training and the development of service delivery across the whole healthcare field. It emphasises its interest in interdisciplinary work and, although many of its initial grants were for medical research or practice, its field is much wider, covering all aspects of healthcare and public health.

Programmes described in the 1999 annual report covered:

- children and adolescents;*
- older people;*
- career development awards for healthcare professionals.

*(Grants are for specific projects, and can be for up to three years)

In July 2000 the chief executive listed seven new programmes as being prepared, all of them to be in operation by spring 2001. They included:

- a nursing research initiative;
- an annual special award, for which publicity will be sought;
- an international grants programme, worth about £800,000 a year;

and on a smaller scale:

- grants towards seminars and conferences that are intended to encourage interdisciplinary working;
- grants for the running costs of patient and service user support groups.

The last two are likely to be particularly interesting to many readers of this book.

He also announced the creation of two professorial chairs and a post-doctoral fellowship scheme.

Though the initial grants, because of the order in which new programmes have been introduced, are heavily concentrated on medicine and medical research, the trust takes a wide view of healthcare, as is shown by the range of new programmes described below.

Background

The PPP Healthcare Medical Trust was set up in 1983 and initially financed by a covenanted donation from Private Patients Plan 'to assist the development and expansion of private charitable hospital facilities'.

> Over time, ... the objectives of the Trust changed to cover support for medical education, medical research and the care of the elderly.
>
> In 1998 the Trust was subject to huge changes as a result of the acquisition of the PPP healthcare group (as Private Patients Plan had become known), by Guardian Royal Exchange. This resulted in the Trust being endowed with the proceeds of the sale of that transaction amounting to some £540 million.

The trust is now completely independent of the PPP healthcare company.

In January 1999 new grant programmes were unveiled, focusing on the mental health of children and learning disabilities among adolescents, on the health of older people, and on the career development of health sector professionals. At that time the then chairman estimated that, when the transfer of the proceeds of the sale is complete, the trust will be able to distribute about £17 million annually, making it one of the largest grant-making charities in the UK.

The previous edition of this book noted with regret that there were only two women among the 17 trustees. There have been numerous changes since then in the trustee body, but there are still only three women. There are also ten grant programme committee members who are not trustees; these include four women.

Grant-making policies

The aspirations of the trust are recorded by its chief executive in the 1999 annual report as being to help to:

- improve links between basic science, applied research and healthcare practice – the communication and implementation of the outcomes of research;
- advance research into the basis of disease processes; and into the value, impact and cost effectiveness of existing healthcare services, techniques and training programmes;
- develop and test new models of service delivery and of initiatives in public health;
- promote the integration of social care and collaboration between different parts of the health sector;
- enhance the skills and knowledge of people providing or managing healthcare;
- advance the use of information and communication technologies to improve public health and patient care;
- enable healthcare professionals to consider the future development and direction of their work by 'scanning the horizon'.

An amateur classification categorised the first 32 grants as follows

	No.	*Total*	*Average grant*
Research	19	£2,156,000	£113,000
Service development	8	£254,000	£42,000
Training	5	£239,000	£48,000

A further £1.6 million has been given to support places at medical schools to enable 80 students a year to undertake intercalated degrees.

It looks as if the research side of the foundation's work may have got off to the fastest start. The trust is therefore likely to be on the look-out for more high-class applications in the other two categories (and, indeed, for more ambitious ones). The trust has admirably broad intentions and the pattern of grantmaking seems set to become far more widely based as the trust develops.

For three programmes, grant programme committees have been established which combine trustees with other outside appointees:

- children and adolescents
- older people
- career development

As is strongly desirable for research programmes, the trust has established 'a very open peer review system ... Reviewers are asked to respond to specific questions about the quality of the application. Applicants have the opportunity to comment on the reviews before they are considered by our committees.'

There is also an admirably strong and clear policy on conflict of interest, one which could be publicly adopted with advantage by a number of trusts described in this book:

> ... a committee cannot consider applications in respect of work in which a Governor is personally and directly involved; and may only consider applications in respect of work of a Department or Institute with which a Governor or external member of a committee is connected provided that the person concerned makes a prior disclosure of the interest, does not have sight of the papers relating to the application, and absents himself from any meeting whilst the application is being discussed.

There is a two stage application process for the three initial programmes launched in 1999. Clear but detailed guidelines are available for each main programme. The annual report for 1999 notes that 533 outline applications were received, two thirds of which were deemed eligible and led to an invitation to submit a full application. 190 of these were received, 115 of which had been processed by the end of the year, leading to 32 grants (a 28% success rate for eligible applications).

In the following section the guidelines are reprinted in abbreviated form, after details of the relevant grantmaking in 1999. The text covering the first programme, Children and Adolescents, is printed more fully, but the general policies stated there apply to other programmes, with only slight modifications. Those seriously considering an application will need to obtain the full relevant text.

However, we start with a programme that is in some ways distinct from the other work of the foundation.

Governors' Discretionary Small Grants Fund

The annual report for 1999 notes the expenditure of £150,000 in 'small grants made to charitable organisations ... at the discretion of individual Governors'.

These editors support the delegation of grantmaking within defined and limited programmes, so as to concentrate and develop a trust's expertise in meeting specific objectives. However, in the absence of such conditions, they regret the practice of giving discretion over the allocation of grants to individuals, be they trustees or staff.

In this case the language above suggests a discretion within a wide range of charitable activity. Though entirely proper, given the objects of the charity, and noting that these comments can only be made because of the trust's unusually full reporting, these editors still regard such practice as unsatisfactory.

Children and adolescents programme

In 1999, 13 grants were made, totalling £1.7 million. Most of them were strictly medical, such as the largest award, of £270,000 over three years, to the Department of Medical Genetics at Manchester University. This will support the work of Professor Dian Donnai in meeting the diagnostic and genetic counselling needs of families with genetic skeletal dysplasias.

There were four grants for training or service development. £155,000 was given to the Children's Foundation in Newcastle to develop a computer network linking children with severe disabilities with their professional and community support. Youth Clubs UK received £58,000 to develop a mental health network providing training and advice for young men. Re-Solv in Staffordshire received £22,000 for an interactive training programme in adolescent solvent abuse for healthcare professionals. Roehampton Institute was given £82,000 for work on improving understanding of the emotional behavioural understanding of young people.

Guidelines for outline applications

[Note that these have been abbreviated for this book. Ed.]

Aims

This grant programme supports specific projects with defined objectives and outcomes in service development, training or research that directly address the incidence or impact of:

- mental health problems in childhood and adolescence, or
- learning disabilities in childhood and adolescence.

These could include projects about:

- the formation and evaluation of preventive and therapeutic interventions as well as
- pre-or post-natal factors that influence cognitive and behavioural development and impairment.

We do not specify an age range for 'childhood and adolescence', but expect proposals could address the programme aims from pregnancy to early adulthood.

The Trust invites proposals that directly address the aims of the programme, have defined objectives and outcomes and fall within one or more of the following categories:

- service development proposals for new projects that aim to influence wider practice in the sector and which draw on research in the area or the lessons of practitioners
- training proposals that aim to increase skills in the sector and which draw on research in the area or the lessons of practitioners
- research projects that have the potential to make a distinctive contribution to knowledge in the sector. The programme does not intend to fund proposals which provide a local service that may be new to an area, but whose benefit is known and recognised elsewhere already.

Application procedure

The PPP Healthcare Medical Trust has adopted a two-stage application process for this grant programme:

1. We use the Outline Application Form to ensure that:

- Your organisation is eligible for Trust funding.
- Your project fulfils the requirements of the programme.

Outline Applications can be sent to the Trust at any time – no deadlines are applied. However applications should be submitted at least six months before the planned starting date of the work for which funding is requested.

2. If your organisation and your project are eligible we will send you a Full Application Form. This will ask for more detailed information about how you will carry out your project, who will work on it and how much it will cost. This will be reviewed internally in the first instance, by external experts appropriate to your project, and by the Children & Adolescents Committee. This Committee considers service development, training and research applications together, with the aim of promoting exchange of knowledge between different sectors.

If your organisation or project is ineligible, we will write explaining the reasons.

By using a two-stage process we aim to save you and ourselves the effort involved in detailed applications that may not be eligible for consideration within this grant programme.

If you need further help or advice about the eligibility of your organisation or project for this programme, please telephone the Trust on 020 7307 2622.

Positive selection indicators for proposals

We particularly welcome applications for projects, which, in addition to addressing the aims of this programme, include one or more of the following features:

Crosses disciplines or professional sectors by

- establishing or extending links between basic science, applied research and healthcare practice
- improving the communication, dissemination and implementation of the outcomes of research
- promoting the integration of health and social care and collaboration between different parts of the health sector
- advancing the use of information and communication technologies to improve public health and patient care.

Develops new models of service delivery that

- encourage user engagement with healthcare delivery
- are pilot projects, initially with a local base, but which can demonstrate that they are of national significance or have the potential to be replicated nationally. Demonstrating this will generally require more than simply disseminating the results nationally. Projects which aim to introduce an existing service for the sole benefit of a local population, even though it may be a new service for that area, are not eligible for this programme.

Develops new training initiatives that

- enhance the skills and competence of people who provide, manage or administer healthcare, for example, by developing new courses or training initiatives
- enable healthcare professionals to consider the future development and direction of their work by 'scanning the horizon'
- strengthen healthcare networks and support the diffusion and exchange of knowledge, information and best practice.

Carries out research that

- advances research into the basis of disease processes
- advances research into healthcare practice
- evaluates the value, impact and cost effectiveness of existing healthcare services, techniques and training programmes or investigates inequalities in health care.

Older people

Seven grants were made, totalling £721,000, led by £207,000 for the Institute of Psychiatry at King's College, London to investigate the neurobiological basis of age-related learning disability in people with Down's Syndrome.

One of the two grants for service development was to the same institute – £98,000 for the development of a measure of life quality in old age, for use in community settings. The Department of General Practice at Queen Mary and Westfield College, also in London, got £93,000 for work on the implementation of guidelines for preventing falls in older people.

Guidelines for outline applications

[*Note that these have been severely abbreviated. Ed.*]

This grant programme supports specific projects with defined objectives and outcomes in service development, training or research that could:

- defer or prevent the onset of disabling conditions
- defer or prevent the need for long term care
- defer or prevent acute hospitalisation – among older people.

We do not specify an age range for 'older people' but most of the proposals funded in this programme are likely to directly address events occurring amongst people aged 60 and above. We recognise that many diseases that lead to disabling conditions and the need for long term care or acute hospitalisation in older people may considerably pre-date their onset. However this programme intends to address the stage at which these diseases result in an increased burden on society.

The programme invites proposals that directly address the aims of the programme, have defined objectives and outcomes and fall within one or more of the following categories:

- service development proposals for new projects that aim to influence wider practice in the sector and which draw on research in the area or the lessons of practitioners
- training proposals that aim to increase skills in the sector and which draw on research in the area or the lessons of practitioners
- research projects that have the potential to make a distinctive contribution to knowledge in the sector.

The programme does not intend to fund proposals which:

- fund the provision of long term care
- concern disability in the general population
- concern diseases such as cancer or cardiovascular disease, whose incidence increases with age, but are not specifically diseases of old age, unless the focus is clearly related to the aims of the programme stated above ...

Mid-career awards

There were 12 of these awards, totalling £421,000. Eight of them were to medical doctors or dentists, but they are just as open to other healthcare professionals, including trainers and managers. For example, Caroline Allen, through Orchard Hill College in Surrey, was awarded £39,000 for a curriculum development and training programme for professionals working with people with profound disabilities. Dr Carol Jagger was awarded £31,000 for work on the management of functional independence among older people.

Guidelines for outline applications

[*Excerpts only. Ed.*]

The aim of this programme of awards is to provide support for practitioners, teachers, managers, clinicians, researchers and other healthcare workers to devote a period of between 6 and 24 months to a training or research activity, beyond their normal professional development opportunities. This activity must be expected to enrich applicants' professional experience and enhance the contribution they will make to the quality of healthcare provision and/or teaching and research in their subsequent career.

Although the awards are intended to support proposals originating from individual applicants, the application requires the direct support of the employing organisation. The grant is formally awarded to the employing organisation, which undertakes to administer the grant and ensure that the individual applicant's time is protected to pursue the project for which the grant has been made.

The following are examples of activities that the Trust is expecting to fund, but it is by no means exclusive and we welcome other imaginative proposals for discussion:

- Support for healthcare practitioners in primary care, hospitals or public health, including those in academic positions, to research, study or train in areas where new discoveries or inventions may be impinging on their professional career, or where they see scope, at present unrealised, for the application of novel technology in their professional sphere.
- Support for teachers who want to develop new courses or investigate existing training programmes elsewhere, by providing cover for their teaching commitments and other necessary expenses.
- Support for protected time spent at the individual's own institution, or at another host institution in the UK or abroad, to investigate multidisciplinary approaches to improving healthcare, whether by engaging with different professional groups or by promoting exchange of knowledge or technology between different disciplines.

(Potential applicants should see the complete guidelines. Note that the 'Exclusions' below do not apply to this programme.)

Other charitable purposes

The trust is empowered to spend up to two per cent of its income (nearly £400,000 a year at present) on charitable activity outside its main objects. One large grant, outside the publicised programmes, was made in in 1999, but it was still within the healthcare field – £100,000 to the Disasters Emergency Committee to help UK aid agencies address the healthcare needs of Kosovan refugees.

Exclusions

Note: these exclusions apply to the Older People and Children and Adolescents programmes only (for other programmes see the specific programme details).

For the Older People and Children and Adolescents programmes the trust will not consider applications for:

- The purchase, construction, equipping or refurbishment of buildings.
- General public fundraising appeals from hospitals, hospices or other charities.
- Endowments.
- Retrospective funding – applications will not be considered for projects that have already started.
- Continuation funding for delivering existing services, whether provided by NHS facilities, local authorities or charities.
- Replacement support for reduced, terminated or time-expired funding from a statutory authority.
- Local provision of a service that may be new to an area, but whose benefit is known and recognised elsewhere already.
- Work that will be carried out outside the UK.
- The salaries of fundraisers or the cost of organising fundraising appeals.
- Administrative costs of charities acting as intermediaries for research applications.
- Overheads or indirect costs of work carried out at or by a university or NHS trust (however, general administrative and running costs directly attributable to the proposed project and incurred by a charitable organisation other than a university or NHS trust will be considered).
- Large data collection exercises either for longitudinal studies or that seek to identify groups relevant to the aims of the grant programme within larger populations. The trust will only fund projects directly addressing the aims of the grant programme. However, applications involving the analysis of existing datasets in longitudinal studies will be considered.

Applications

See above.

The Prince's Trust

Neither the Prince's Trust, nor its local committees, make any grants to organisations.

The 'small grants', 'local initiative' and 'out-of-school' learning programmes, described in the previous edition of this book, have come to an end.

The trust continues its well-known work of helping individual young people.

Mr and Mrs J A Pye's Charitable Settlement

Environment, mental health, general

£537,000 (1999/2000)

Beneficial area UK, with a special interest in the Oxford area and, to a lesser extent, in Reading, Cheltenham, Bristol and Leamington Spa.

c/o Sharp Parsons Tallon, 167 Fleet Street, London EC4A 2NB

Correspondent The Secretary

Trustees *G C Pye; J S Stubbings; David Tallon.*

Information available Good guidelines for applicants. Full accounts, but without any analysis or explanation of grants and with only a limited narrative report.

Summary

Most of the trust's funds are given to a few organisations which receive annual donations, usually up to a limit of around £35,000, but occasionally for more. However up to 250 small grants, typically for between £250 and £2,500 and sometimes repeated, are made each year for the benefit of a range of causes corresponding to those set out in the guidelines below.

Guidelines

The Charitable Settlement was created by the late Mr J A Pye, an Oxford-based builder, and his wife, Mary Pye, in 1965. The settlors had a particular interest in assisting and alleviating the consequences of aspects of mental health as well as encouraging organic solutions to environmental problems. Current assets are circa £8m and distributable income is approximately £450,000 pa.

In making grants the Trustees seek to continue the settlor's interests while expanding them to encompass other causes. The following list is by no means exhaustive and is given for guidance only:-

- Environmental – this subject particularly deals with organic farming matters, conservation generally and health related matters such as pollution research.
- Adult Health and Care – especially causes supporting the following: post-natal depression, schizophrenia, mental health generally and research into the main causes of early death.
- Children's Health and Care – for physical, mental and learning disabilities, respite breaks etc.
- Youth Organisations – particularly projects encouraging self reliance or dealing with social deprivation.
- Education – nursery, primary, secondary or higher/institutions (not individuals).
- Regional causes around Oxford, Reading, Cheltenham and Bristol – under this category the Trustees will consider academic and arts projects.

The overall policy of the Trustees is to support underfunded charities in their fields of interest in order to assist those charities to play a fuller role in the community. Unfortunately, due to the demands made it is not possible to support all applications even though they may meet the charity's criteria. However, the Trustees particularly recognise the difficulty many smaller charities experience in obtaining core funding in order to operate efficiently in today's demanding environment.

Grants in 1999/2000

Out of £537,000 given to 275 organisations, exactly £300,000 went to the top ten beneficiaries (receiving £10,000 or more), nine of which had received funding the year before.

The largest grant in both 1999/2000 and 1998/99 was for £98,000 to Elm Farm Research Centre. Two other organisations among the top ten beneficiaries had trustee connections with the trust: Music at Oxford received a £40,000 grant and a £5,000 loan, while the Children with Aids Charity was granted £14,500 and got a £4,000 loan.

It is unusual to receive from smaller grantmakers their reflections on the practical issues of their work. We are grateful to David Tallon of Mr and Mrs J A Pye's Charitable Settlement for the following.

1. There are too many charities altogether, and too many competing for the same funds, using up resources of their own, and of donor charities, unnecessarily. While I understand the compulsion of a family to set up a charity in the name of a deceased child who has died of a rare disease, there are too many such cases where there is obvious duplication, in my view. To counter-balance this remark, I should make it clear that it certainly does not only come from that kind of source. In recent weeks I have received no less than three applications from different charities dealing with the care and re-settlement of ex-offenders. I selected one to put forward to my co-trustees on the basis that it was the best presented, which was the only criterion I could use. I can be only too well aware that this may disguise the fact that it may have been the worst-run, or, more likely, that another one was doing a far better job with its resources. On the other hand I am very much aware, having some interest in the field, that there was a scandal in some Aids charities in the amount of resource being spent in the administration (which I believe has been largely rectified).

2. Secondly, it would be most helpful if there was a recognised, and not too long, categorisation of dependent charities. If I could key in a charity's number and see it drop automatically into one of our chosen areas of interest, it would be of great assistance. Further it follows from my first point above that I think that there should be greater fiscal, and other, encouragement towards creating donor charities and increasing the variety of sources available to fundraising officers of spending charities. To some extent the [March 2000] Budget has done much towards this but I have to say that I think that there are ingrained habits of thought in both the Inland Revenue and the Charity Commission which are antipathetic towards charities created by entrepreneurs. For example I thought it was short-sighted that the Wellcome Foundation felt compelled to sell off their shares in the company of the same name. There are many new entrepreneurs these days, for example in the technology field, whose main asset is the shares in their low-yielding companies who may be deterred from putting those shares into a charitable trust because the trustees may be forced to sell them off immediately and because the donor, still working for the company of course, may be treated as 'benefiting' from the charity by virtue of drawing remuneration for running the company. These Inland Revenue and Charity Commission attitudes are, in my opinion, a deterrent to the creation of grant aiding foundations.

Other organisations which have been supported in every year since at least 1996/97 included the Association for Post-Natal Illness (£32,000 in 1999/2000); Magdalen College School (£30,000); Harris Manchester College (£20,000), and the British Trust for Conservation Volunteers (£7,500).

A sample of ten recipients of £500 grants reads as follows:

Oxford Parent–Infant Project; Oxfordshire Association for the Blind; Penumbra; Population Concern; Prisoners Abroad; Psychiatry Research Trust; Raleigh Trust; Robert Owen Foundation; Royal Naval Museum; Seven Springs Playground.

The charity made interest-free loans worth £440,000 to 17 organisations, including one for £100,000 to University College for a mathematics fellowship.

A request for information from the trust in May 2000 produced the following interesting letter:

Please note that the charity, as such, has no telephone, fax, e-mail or website details to publish. Furthermore I do not wish this firm's details to be included. You may care to note, particularly, the last comment about telephone contact in the section in the Guidelines on dealing with applications. [*See 'Applications' below. Ed.*]

All applications come to me to be assessed in the first instance and I therefore get a fairly considerable amount of post each week. There are some standard responses:

a. That the application has been placed on the list for the next meeting of Trustees to consider [This probably accounts for about one in seven of all applications received].
b. That we cannot consider the application any further although it has been reviewed by a Trustee [me] on the grounds that we do not have sufficient resources to deal with all the applications we receive.

I have found that this usually stops everyone spending more time than is necessary. My original draft of this letter also mentioned that the application did not necessarily meet our Guidelines, and this only seemed to provoke one or two fundraising officers into an attempt to persuade me that their application did do so.

c. A letter indicating that we could not support individuals. We do not have the management resource to monitor individual grants and therefore hold to this line, despite meeting some fairly heart-rending stories. I find applications from students who want support for overseas expeditions, some of which seem to have very little charitable purpose, much easier to reject.
d. A letter in response to a request for our Guidelines which declines to send them on the grounds that I can see that the organisation would be wasting their time in sending them in for a variety of reasons. Again, however, I usually quote the limitation on funds as being the reason.
e. A letter which goes to the unsuccessful applicants who have been reviewed by all the Trustees in meeting, to give them the bad news.

I then start individual correspondence with successful applicants, which can get quite voluminous. The standard of feedback is, on the whole, very high. We do not demand it, and do not have to. However we do receive quite a regular supply of newsletters and annual reports acknowledging the donations. This certainly helps when those charities apply again.

Exclusions

- Organisations that are not recognised charities.
- Activities which are primarily the responsibility of government or some other responsible body.
- Activities which collect funds for subsequent re-distribution to other charities.
- Corporate affiliation or membership of charities.
- Endowment funds.
- Expeditions or overseas charities.
- Fabric appeals for places of worship, other than in geographical locations indicated above.
- Fundraising events or activities.
- Hospitals or medical centres (except for projects that are clearly additional to statutory responsibilities).
- Individuals, including students.
- Overseas appeals.
- Promotion of religion.

Applications

There are no application forms but the following information is essential:

- Registered charity number or evidence of an organisation's tax exempt status;
- Brief description of the activities of the charity;
- The names of the trustees and chief officers [NB more important than patrons];
- Details of the purpose of the application and where funds will be put to use;
- Details of the funds already raised and the proposals for how remaining funds are to be raised;
- The latest trustees report and full audited or independently examined

accounts (which must comply with Charity Commission guidelines and requirements).

Trustees meet quarterly to take decisions. Any decision can therefore take up to four months before it is finally taken. However all applicants are informed of the outcome of their applications and all applications are acknowledged. Telephone contact will usually be counter-productive.

Queen Mary's Roehampton Trust

War disabled ex-service people and their dependants

£492,000 (1999/2000)

Beneficial area UK.

13 St George's Road, Wallington, Surrey SM6 OAS

Tel. 020 8395 9980

Correspondent Alan H Baker, Clerk to the Trustees

Trustees *Major General T A Richardson, Chair; B Walmsley; J J Macnamara; Colonel S D Brewis; Major General R P Craig; Colonel A W Davis; Brigadier A K Dixon; Colonel J L Franklin; R R Holland; Brigadier J O E Moriarty; Dr E Nelson; M H Wainwright; Dr J Watkinson; R D Wilson.*

Information available Good report and accounts.

General

The trust, which has an endowment worth about £10 million, makes grants for welfare activities and for building work to a wide range of ex-service welfare charities. Its 1999/2000 grants were divided as follows:

Welfare grants	24 awards	£308,000
Building schemes	11 awards	£178,000
Other grants	4 awards	£7,000

Most recipient organisations feature regularly in the grants lists, with just two wholly new applicants supported in 1999/2000. However, the amounts awarded usually vary from year to year, and are for specific purposes rather than in the form of ongoing annual subventions.

Grants vary in size from a rare £1,000 up to, in 1999/2000, £73,000 (to the Royal Patriotic Fund's TV scheme for war widows). Other major grants were to Erskine Hospital, for rebuilding (£50,000, for the third year in succession); SSAFA (£30,000), and The Not Forgotten Association (£29,000, again for the provision of TVs).

A good number of less well-known organisations were also supported, such as Queen Victoria's Seamen's Rest (£2,500) and The Somme Nursing Home in Belfast (£5,000 for reclining chairs).

Applications

In writing to the correspondent (seven copies), to be submitted in April or September annually. Details must be given of the number of war disablement pensioners and/or war widows assisted during a recent period of 12 months. In the case of nursing/residential homes, information concerning occupancy will be required under a number of headings (complement, residents, respite holidays, waiting list). Three copies of the latest annual reports and any appeal leaflets should be enclosed.

The Joseph Rank Benevolent Trust

The Methodist Church, Christian-based social work

£2,863,000 (1999)

Beneficial area UK and Ireland.

11a Station Road West, Oxted, Surrey RH8 9EE

Tel. 01883 717919 **Fax** 01883 717411

e-mail rankchar@dircon.co.uk

Correspondent John Wheeler, Secretary

Trustees *Colin Rank, Chair; Revd David Cruise; Revd Paul Hulme; Dr Jean Moon; Ms Gay Moon; J Anthony Reddall; Revd Dr R John Tudor; Sue Warner.*

Information available Full and clear accounts and grants lists with a good annual report.

Summary

More than half of the trust's funds are given for the maintenance and improvement of Methodist churches.

Around £1 million a year is given for a variety of social causes, in grants of up to £100,000. Many are recurrent for up to five years. Perhaps less than 25 new grants are made every year, and even then rarely to beneficiaries new to the trust. Preference is given to organisations with a Christian outlook.

General

This is a Christian-based trust particularly interested in initiatives established by Christians to meet social needs. It grew out of a number of trusts initiated by Joseph Rank, founder of what is now Rank Hovis McDougall plc, and is separate to the Rank Foundation (see the next entry) although there are connections: 'The secretary to the trustees is employed by the Rank Foundation ... which is administered from the same offices. The trust is also able to call upon the expertise of other staff employed by the foundation in various areas of its work; particularly that with young people, and it makes a contribution to the Rank Foundation to cover the costs on a time involvement basis.'

The trust is responsible for two funds: the Methodist Church Fund and the General Fund. In 1999 donations worth £1,948,000 were made from the General Fund and £915,000 from the Methodist Church Fund.

The Methodist Church

Expenditure amounted to £1,443,000 (half of the total) in grants ranging from £1,000 to £60,000.

The trustees maintain valuable contacts with the Church and are able to call upon the expertise available within the Church both to identify worthy initiatives and thereafter to monitor their progress.

During the year grants were promised to 100 (1998: 112) schemes, of which 47 (1998: 68) were taken up in the year, and grants were made to a further 39 (1998: 47) schemes where promises were made in earlier years.

With regard to grantmaking for wider social needs, the trust says that:

Although the trustees do not consider themselves to be a source of on-going support for any particular organisation, some initiatives have been supported over a number of years. The increasing difficulty for organisations to secure on-going funding strengthens the view of the trustees that it is in the interests of any organisation to seek to secure as wide a financial base of support as possible which, in addition to providing stability, also provides tangible evidence of the value of the work since different aspects will have been assessed by the respective funders. With this in mind, the trustees are tending to make 'tapering' grants, with a view to gradually reducing the reliance of a recipient on the trust in the hope that funds from other sources will be available when the trust's support ends.

Youth

This represents a significant part of the trust's work.

During the year no additional projects were taken on since those currently being supported are in the third year of a five year programme.

Some of the schemes have been identified, and are monitored, by the Methodist Church whilst others have been identified by the trustees under their 'Youth or Adult?' initiative. The latter runs in conjunction with a similar initiative financed by the Rank Foundation and is monitored with help from the foundation's staff.

In 1999, £554,000 was disbursed, £304,000 for 11 'Youth or Adult?' projects and a further £138,000 on seven projects monitored by the Youth Department of the Methodist Church. Amounts paid in the year ranged from £6,000 to £38,000, being typically for over £25,000.

Another 12 grants, worth £111,000 in total, went to youth projects outside these schemes, the largest going to the Methodist Church in Ireland's Youth Department (£24,000). The remaining grants ranged from £2,500 to £15,000.

Community service (50 grants, £410,000)

The largest new grants, all part of three year commitments, were as follows (the amounts in brackets show the total commitment over the period): West London Mission (£102,000, for salary and support costs of craft/education service for vulnerable people); Who Cares? Trust (£36,000, towards increasing the post 16 education, training and employment prospects of young people leaving care); Telford Christian Council (£30,000, salaries for workers involved with vulnerable and homeless young people), and Alone in London (£30,000 for an advocacy service).

Thirty of the grants were for amounts between £750 and £5,000, still mostly to charities also supported in the previous year.

Religion – education (12 grants, £218,000)

As in the previous category, the largest amounts were given as part of three year commitments, with new grants for two organisations undertaking similar work promoting understanding between different faiths. They were the Council of Christians and Jews (£75,000) and Inter Faith Network for the UK (£60,000). The largest single year award went to Youth With A Mission (£50,000, for building renovation and development costs).

Health and healing (2 grants, £150,000)

The Dorothy Kerin Trust received £100,000 for major extension and renovation work at the Christian Medical Healing Centre, which had received funding for bursaries over the previous three years. The other grant was for £50,000 to the Harnhill Centre of Christian Healing, to upgrade and modernise its facilities.

Elderly (4 grants, £66,000)

£58,000 went on three existing commitments. The one new commitment started with a payment of £8,000 to Share and Care, providing services to elderly house bound people in Lancashire (£24,000 over three years, for manager's salary and support costs).

Disabled (4 grants, £23,000)

The largest grant went to the Agape Trust (£10,000 for equipping a home for young disabled people near Lewes). Church Action on Disability received a repeat award of £5,000.

Exclusions

No grants to individuals.

Applications

Unsolicited appeals are considered although the chance of a grant being made is small. General appeals should be addressed to the correspondent and include full details of the appeal and a copy of the most recent audited accounts.

Appeals from within Methodism should only be put forward after consultation with the relevant division of the church.

The Rank Foundation

Christian communication, youth, education, general

£8,483,000 (1999)

Beneficial area UK.

4/5 North Bar, Banbury, Oxfordshire OX16 0TB

Tel. 01295 272337 **Fax** 01295 272336

e-mail rankchar@dircon.co.uk

Correspondent Sheila Gent, Assistant Grants Administrator

Trustees *F Packard, Chair; M D Abrahams; J A Cave; A E Cowen; M E Davies; Mrs L G Fox; J R Newton; D R Peppiatt; V A Powell; Lord Shuttleworth; D R Silk; Earl St Aldwyn.*

Information available Excellent reports and accounts.

Summary

The amount donated in grants had risen to almost £8.5 million by 1999, from £7.5 million the year before. Perhaps only a quarter of this amount is available to new applicants, with large regular donations going to existing initiatives. Ten regularly supported programmes accounted for nearly half the grant total in 1999.

About one third of the money goes to the extensive range of youth programmes for which the foundation is best known, and a slightly greater proportion to a wider range of welfare organisations, especially those concerned with support for people who are elderly or disabled. Another quarter is for the promotion of Christianity, all through the associated Foundation for Christian Communication. The relatively small education programme is primarily concerned with supplementing the fees of pupils at independent schools whose families have become unable to meet all the costs involved. There is occasional support, on a relatively very modest scale for health or medical groups, and for environmental and cultural organisations.

Large grants are typically part of a three or five year commitment.

If small grants (less than £5,000) are given for two or three years consecutively, this is usually to national organisations. Local charities are unlikely to get recurrent funding or multi-year awards.

Grants in 1999 were classified as follows:

Youth	£2,884,000	(34%)
Promotion of the Christian religion	£1,955,000	(23%)
Elderly	£1,191,000	(14%)
Community service	£1,103,000	(13%)
Disabled	£807,000	(10%)
Education	£367,000	(4%)
Medicine/healthcare	£119,000	(1.5%)
Cultural	£41,000	(0.5%)
Animal conservation and welfare	£17,000	(0.2%)

General

The charity was established in 1953 by the late Lord and Lady Rank (the founders). It was one of a number established by the founders at that time and to which they gifted their controlling interest in The Rank Group plc (formerly The Rank Organisation plc). The organisation has 11 staff, including the following:

- John Wheeler, Director of Finance and Administration
- Simon Langdale, Director of Grants and Special Projects
- Charles Harris, Director of Youth Projects, England and Wales
- Christopher Dunning, Director of Youth Projects, Scotland and Northern Ireland
- Peter Attenborough, Director of Educational and Community Care projects.

The main office of the foundation is in Oxted, Surrey, but grant applications are handled through the Banbury address given above. There are four separate grant committees, no doubt each being served by one of the last four of the directors named above.

Geographically, this foundation is unusually careful to ensure that its grants reach all parts of the country. About half the money goes to programmes that are national. For the rest an unusual regional classification is used, so that full comparisons at that level cannot be made, but the figures in the table below show that the usual pro London emphasis is absent or indeed actively countered.

Grants per 1,000 people:

All UK	£0.78
Scotland	£1.74
Northern Ireland	£1.52
Wales	£1.18
England	£0.63
London	£0.40

Grant-making policy and practice

The following account of the foundation's grantmaking includes, where appropriate, the relevant comment from the foundation's 1999 annual report (with the value of the grants concerned added by the editors).

The directors continue to take an active part in all areas of the work of the Foundation, including the identification of appropriate initiatives for support and the monitoring of their progress.

This is achieved through the medium of four committees of directors:

- Appeals and Community Care
- Education
- Finance
- Youth.

The meetings of all of the committees, which in most cases are held quarterly, are attended by members of the executive staff, who are charged with implementing the policy which has been agreed by the directors and monitored by the committees.

Whilst all of the committees have certain delegated powers, full reports are made to the board and, in particular, no applications are declined before they have been considered at a meeting of the full board ...

In the course of considering unsolicited appeals, the directors see many examples of imaginative work at a local level; some of which can be greatly encouraged by modest financial help from sources outside the local community. The directors take into account the level of support which can realistically be expected from the local people and the likelihood of a small grant from the Foundation in bringing an initiative to a successful conclusion is an important factor ...

The fact that directors and staff are located around the country means that the Foundation is kept in touch with a wide variety of needs and this helps to balance the allocation of resources; both from the point of view of targeting particular areas of need and also in promoting examples of good practice.

Whilst the wider area of the Foundation's work encompasses many different types of initiative, the directors have singled out work benefiting the elderly and disabled members of society as being particularly worthy of support and have taken active steps to identify and support examples of good practice.

Youth (£2,884,000)

The directors decided that the funds available to them would be best used in firstly identifying worthy projects and then funding them on a meaningful basis over a number of years. It was also agreed that an integral part of the process should be careful monitoring and these have been the bases upon which funding has been committed.

The foundation runs four main programmes, which account for about 80% of funding under this heading. The amounts distributed in 1999 were as follows:

Youth or Adult? programme	£1,102,000
Investing in Success programme, 15 projects	£729,000
Key Workers programme, 13 posts	£320,000
Rank Volunteer (Gap) Awards	£220,000
Total	£2,371,000

Youth or Adult? ... the foundation supports projects over five years to train local youth leaders who are experienced but unqualified and where young people are involved in the design and implementation of an active programme which reflects real responsibility and commitment by them. Trainees study for a professional qualification, a Diploma in higher education, the ordinary BA Degree in informal and community education, now validated by Canterbury Christ Church University College through the YMCA George Williams College.

George Williams College had received nearly £1 million in funding by 1999 and got grants worth £181,000 during the year, mostly for students' fees. Over £900,000 was given to another 34 ongoing projects, many in Scotland, Wales and Northern Ireland, with an average of £28,000 a year. The beneficiaries included Prince's Youth Business Trust (£42,000; £212,000 to date); West Kent Voluntary Service Unit (£31,000; £157,000 to date); Northern Ireland Deaf Youth Association (£29,000; £150,000 to date); Linlithgow Young People's Project (£23,000; £74,000 to date) and the Diocese of Swansea and Brecon (£23,000; £118,000 to date).

Investing in Success ... builds upon partnerships which have been developed over the years with a number of established organisations.

Grants averaged £49,000 in the year, with the largest being as follows: People and Work Unit – £106,000 (£550,000 in total); Mobex North East, a provider of mobile training resources for young people – £76,000 (£294,000) and Young People Cornwall – £72,000 (£256,000).

Key Workers ... a number of strategic posts are supported within organisations with which the foundation has worked for some time and where qualified workers with specialist skills are often needed. This is particularly so in training up young apprentice leaders in areas such as the outdoors, enterprise and employment and in formal and informal education initiatives.

Grants ranged from £10,000 to £50,000, averaging £25,000. The largest three grants were as follows: Villages Youth Project – £50,000 (£67,500 in total); YMCA – £37,000 (£193,000); Dalston Training Initiatives – £31,000 (£92,000).

The Rank Volunteer (Gap) Award ... encourages full time volunteering in organisations with which the foundation is already working, either during the period between school and further education or during a period of unemployment.

The directors, through the careful monitoring of the projects, continue to be encouraged by the results which are being achieved by the young people who are participating in the various schemes.

The last year has seen a successful consolidation of all of the above initiatives. This investment now represents the largest co-ordinated training, qualification and development initiative in youth and community work and informal education in the United Kingdom. Overall, more than 120 full-time personnel are involved in the various projects; the vast majority of whom are training towards a professional qualification. All of the programmes are in high demand and the Gap Scheme now has a waiting list of over six months ...

General grant programme (£514,000)

As part of its more general work, the Foundation is currently supporting an educational programme in Feltham Young Offenders Institution [£25,000, 3rd of 3], an extension of that work in East Anglia [£50,000, 1st of 3] and the training of mentors with the probation service on Humberside [£20,000, 2nd of 3]. Projects involving the homeless cover a wide spectrum and include work with the very young and newly homeless with the London Connection [£20,000, 1st of 3], day centre support with the St Giles Trust in Camberwell [£7,500], the rehabilitation of families with Save the Family in Chester [£27,000, 1st of 3] and a substance misuse project with the Amber Foundation in Wiltshire [£25,000, 1st of 2].

A substantial grant of £216,000 was also made to the Sail Training Association; £200,000 for a new ship and the rest for bursaries on training voyages.

Welfare (£3,101,000)

Elderly

The Foundation has continued its support for frail and elderly people in rural areas, with additional work with Age Concern groups in Ceredigion, Leominster and Somerset; it has also made contributions to the Rural Housing Trust [£30,000] and to the Rural Resource Initiative of Help the Aged [£27,000, 1st of 3].

Support has also begun for three organisations which are trying to assist people who seek assistance on moving to residential and nursing homes.

They are Counsel and Care (£20,000, 1st of 3), Elderly Accommodation Counsel (£23,000, 1st of 3) and Relatives Association Northern Ireland ... (£10,000). Four charities, all of whom receive regular annual donations, got approximately two thirds of the funding in this category: £393,000 was given to 20 local branches of Age Concern, ranging from £1,000 in Newton-le-Willows to £59,000 in Northern Ireland; Carers' National Association, £138,000; Alzheimer's Society and Alzheimer Scotland – Action on Dementia, £100,000 each, and Crossroads Caring for Carers, £84,000.

Thirty six out of the 66 grants ranged from £500 to £10,000, with recipients including Neighbourly Care, Southall (£10,000); Bakers' Benevolent Society (£5,000); Anchor Staying Put, Hackney (£2,000); Swansea Valley Bible Church (£1,000), and Church Street Drop-in Centre, London (£500).

Disabled

A wish to increase the work of the Foundation in East Anglia, Central Wales and Cornwall led to seven of the new projects in 1999. In addition, support for core costs was provided for a further seven national organisations.

The foundation at present supports a balance between national and local work, between generic work and support for specific conditions; it helps the very young as well as the elderly, those seeking travel and holiday advice and those seeking employment. Among other things it also helps with the provision of information on the problems encountered by young people aged 16+ as they move from childhood into adulthood.

Four grants were for more than £25,000, to: PHAB Northern Ireland (£39,000, 3rd year, towards funding of a co-ordinator); MENCAP (£30,000, 2nd of 3, towards costs of a co-ordinator in east Surrey); DARE Foundation (£30,000, 1st of 3), and the Council for Disabled Children (£30,000, 1st of 3, for core costs).

About two thirds of the grants ranged from £250 to £5,000. Grants of this size are rarely repeated, but a few that were included those to Talking Newspaper Association UK (£1,000), and Stockport Cerebral Palsy Association (£500).

Organisations benefiting from a third consecutive small award in 1999 included the Motor Neurone Disease Association (£1,500); Soundaround National Magazine for the Blind (£1,000 a year); SNAPS Winchester & District Playschemes for Children (£500 a year), and the National Association of Swimming Clubs for the Disabled (£500 a year).

Community service

Nearly half of the expenditure in this category went in two grants to RASE – the Arthur Rank Fund; a £350,000 endowment for the Arthur Rank Centre and £150,000 capital costs for the Rank Training Unit, at Stoneleigh, Warwickshire.

A further £600,000 was distributed in 245 grants. About 95% ranged in size from £500 to £5,000, mostly to community centres, village halls and over 100 churches. A few recipients of small grants (less than 10%) got a repeat award, but few were for more than £1,000. These were primarily national organisations and/or children's charities such as ActionAid, Christian Aid, Save the Children, Glasgow Children's Holiday Scheme and North Plymouth Playschemes.

Promotion of the Christian religion (£1,995,000)

The directors have a substantial and continuing commitment to the Foundation for Christian Communication Limited (FCCL) which, through its Christian-based training courses and audio-visual production facilities, is involved with the promotion of Christianity.

FCCL has continued to be involved in a full schedule of productions, both on its own account and on a co-production basis with all of the major terrestrial broadcasters.

This regular donation to FCCL normally accounts for roughly a quarter of the foundation's total expenditure and was nearly £2 million in 1999.

Medicine/healthcare (£119,000)

Grants ranged from £500 for St John Ambulance, Kidderminster, to £15,000 for Erskine Hospital. Of a total of 19 grants, 14 were for either £5,000 or £10,000, including those to High Peak Hospice Care, Rainbow Family Trust – Francis House and Macmillan Nurses, Walsall (£5,000 each); Help the Hospices, King Edward VII Hospital for Officers and Marie Curie Cancer Care, Bradford (£10,000 each).

Cultural (£41,000)

Eight grants were made, the largest being a £5,000 award to the National Association of Youth Orchestras. Most of the other grants, ranging from £1,000 to £3,000, also went to youth organisations, including British Youth Opera (£1,000) and the National Youth Choir of Scotland (£1,000, repeat). Non-youth beneficiaries were the Black Dyke Band (£1,000) and the Orchestra of St John's, Smith Square (£2,000).

Animal conservation and welfare (£17,000)

Two grants accounted for more than four fifths of the new commitments (as opposed to the spending) in this category. They were £25,000 to the Animal Health Trust, for equipment used for the diagnosis and treatment of diseases, and £10,000 to the Game Conservancy Trust. Four other grants of between £500 and £2,750 were made to the Barn Owl Trust, Mare and Foal Sanctuary, Mink Eradication Scheme (Hebrides) and WWF-UK (which had received £975 in 1998).

Promotion of education (£367,000)

In interpreting this objective, the directors take a broad view and include work with young people which is designed to involve them in decisions which affect their future and to cultivate in them attitudes which will make them useful members of society.

The Foundation has continued its support in a number of independent schools of boys and girls who are thought to have leadership potential and where there is financial need which, but for the help of the Foundation, would result in a change of school at a critical time.

Candidates for these awards, who will normally be in their last two or three years at school, can only be put forward by the Heads of the schools concerned. The directors do not consider appeals which are received from parents or guardians.

Bursary payments totalling £323,000 were made to 37 independent schools in 1999. Also in this category, Churchill College Archives Extension Fund and the Millennium Library Trust Company got grants of £10,000 each. A further eight grants of between £1,000 and £5,000 were made, including ones to South London Green Badge Taxi School (£2,000) and the Royal School of Needlework (£1,000).

The editors, on the evidence available, cannot see this minor programme of the foundation as one that, in their words above, 'takes a broad view'.

Exclusions

Grants to registered charities only. Appeals from individuals or appeals from registered charities on behalf of named individuals will not be considered; neither will appeals from overseas or from UK based organisations where the object of the appeal is overseas.

In an endeavour to contain the calls made upon the foundation to a realistic level, the directors have continued with their policy of not, in general, making grants to projects involved with:

- agriculture and farming
- cathedrals and churches (except where community facilities are involved)
- culture
- university and school building and bursary funds
- medical research.

Applications

Applications should be addressed to the general appeals office at the address above in Banbury.

There is no formal application form, but for administrative purposes it is helpful if the actual appeal letter can be kept to one or two sides of A4, which can be supported by reports etc. General appeals, including unsolicited appeals relating to youth projects, should include: charity registration number, full details of project and funding sought, amount already raised, and the most recent audited set of accounts.

Preliminary enquiries are welcomed.

Unsolicited appeals are considered quarterly (see below). All appeals are acknowledged and applicants advised as to when a decision can be expected.

The trustees meet quarterly in March, June, September and December.

The Ruben and Elisabeth Rausing Trust

Human rights, self-reliance and sustainability, art and culture

£4,010,000 (1999)

39 Sloane Street, London SW1X 9LP

Tel. 020 7235 9560 **Fax** 020 7235 9580

e-mail rer@arcticnet.com

Correspondent Kirsty Wood, Administrator

Information available Policy guidelines. Annual report and accounts.

Summary

This trust has been much enlarged by a further endowment of £49 million in 1999. It does not seek unsolicited applications, and makes a relatively small number of generally large grants. Recipient organisations are mainly but not exclusively in Britain, the USA or Europe, though their work is often international.

General

Sigrid Rausing, the settlor of this trust, is a welcome addition to Britain's short list of major living philanthropists, especially as her trust has chosen fields of work that are seldom a priority for British foundations.

The trust made 48 grants in 1999, the largest for £760,000 (to Amnesty International) and all but seven for more than £10,000. It, along with two associated trusts described below, are administered on a part-time and voluntary basis. Although unsolicited applications cannot be accepted, and will not usually receive any response, the trust produces excellent guidelines, reprinted below, for those charities with whom it may work.

These editors suggest that organisations working in these fields in the very specific ways described might usefully keep the trust informed about their activities and aspirations.

Guidelines

Human rights

The category of Human Rights encompasses organisations which aim to promote and protect human rights globally. Human Rights, in this context, is defined primarily with reference to the rights which are inherent in democracies, including free expression, the right to organise and the freedom from political violence, including oppression on the grounds of race, religion, gender, level of income or sexual preference. Political violence and oppression are, however, defined as individual acts as well as the systematic violence perpetrated by states, and thus includes, for example, violence against women and racist acts.

Self-reliance and sustainability

This category refers to projects and organisations which aim to promote economic self-reliance and ecological sustainability. It incorporates organisations which work for the alleviation of poverty with due regard for the relationship to local environments and cultures. The projects chosen must be oriented towards creating self-reliance and sustainability, rather than creating a relationship of dependence and disempowerment. We appreciate careful research on the impact of aid with particular reference to gender.

This category also included projects which are primarily concerned with nature conservation and ecology.

Arts and culture

Arts and Culture incorporates projects which, broadly, promote the ethos of the trust. It includes projects which use creativity and free expression as tools in the individual and collective processes of healing and empowerment. Broadly speaking, we are interested in the power of the process of art rather than in the end product.

In addition, this category includes projects which are concerned with culture and history, preserving or documenting living culture as well as memories, documents and artefacts.

Grants in 1999

Grants are categorised by the location of the recipient organisation:

UK	26	£2,173,000
USA	14	£1,520,000
Europe	6	£240,000
Africa	2	£55,000

The largest awards were as follows:

Amnesty International	£760,000
Human Rights Watch (USA)	£550,000
NSPCC	£500,000
Oxfam	£250,000
Global Fund for Women (USA)	£200,000
Med. Fdn. for Care of Victims of Torture	£150,000
Int'l Women's Health Coalition (USA)	£150,000
UNICEF	£100,000
Ashoka (USA)	£100,000

Other recipients, selected to show the range of the trust's interests, included Global Greengrants (USA, £50,000); Mineral Policy Institute (Africa, £25,000); Women Living Under Muslim Law (Europe, £60,000); Countryside Restoration Trust (£5,000); Gaia Foundation (£25,000); the International Gay and Lesbian Human Rights Commission (USA, £75,000), and the Foundation Trust for Chinese Medicine (£7,000).

There were a number of grants to Jewish organisations working in the fields set out above, including those to The Wiener Library (£15,000) and Jewish Women's Aid (£38,000).

Comment

It has been a pleasure for these editors to find a major new trust with such clear and distinctive policies and such an apparently purposeful set of grants for their implementation.

There are two associated trusts, sharing the same (voluntary) administration, but too small for their own entries in this book – full details will be found in *A Guide to the Major Trusts, Volume 2.* They are as follows:

Kurt and Olga Koerner Charitable Trust – £90,000 in grants in 1999, supporting conservation and other causes, mainly in Scotland and Sussex.

Märit and Hans Rausing Charitable Foundation – £269,000 in grants in 1999, supporting architecture and a wide range of other interests.

Applications

May be made in writing to the correspondent, although unsolicited applications cannot normally be considered or acknowledged.

The Rayne Foundation

Arts, medicine, higher education, social welfare, general

£1,695,000 (1998/99)

33 Robert Adam Street, London W1M 5AH

Tel. 020 7935 3555

Correspondent David Lindsay-Rea

Trustees *Lord Rayne, Chair; Lady Rayne; R A Rayne; Lord Bridges; Lord Greenhill; Sir Claus Moser; Prof. Dame Margaret Turner.*

Information available Annual report and accounts available from the foundation for a fee of £10.

General

The foundation states its objectives as: 'to sponsor development in medicine, education and social welfare and the arts, and to relieve distress and to promote the welfare of the aged and young'.

The 1998/99 accounts showed net assets of over £40 million, with income at £1,867,000. Grant expenditure amounted to £1.7 million.

The foundation provided the following breakdown of all grants of £1,000 or more that were made during 1998/99 (1997/98 figures in brackets):

Arts and the environment	£421,000	(£420,000)
Medicine	£415,000	(£224,000)
Civic and sociological	£314,000	(£440,000)
Education	£228,000	(£254,000)

The largest amount, £125,000, went to the foundation's sister organisation, the Rayne Trust, which receives a large annual donation.

£100,000 grants went to new beneficiaries in the field of medicine: King's College Hospital Medical School and Guy's, King's and St Thomas' School of Medicine.

Most of the 15 recipients of awards for £25,000 to £50,000 were national cultural/arts organisations located in London, including: English Stage Company (£50,000); Royal National Theatre (£31,000); Royal Opera House (£30,000); Tate Gallery (£30,000); British Museum (£27,000); Sadler's Wells Theatre Appeal Fund (£25,000), and RADA (£25,000).

Two Jewish charities receive substantial grants every year, Norwood Ravenswood and the Jerusalem Foundation getting £26,000 and £15,000 respectively in 1998/99.

£586,000 given in grants under £10,000 was classified simply as 'other' donations, with no information about the recipients.

Exclusions

No grants to individuals.

Applications

In writing to the correspondent at any time.

The Sir James Reckitt Charity

Society of Friends, general

£602,000 (1998/99)

Beneficial area Hull and the East Riding of Yorkshire, UK and overseas.

7 Derrymore Road, Willerby, East Yorkshire HU10 6ES

Correspondent Mr J McGlashan, Joint Administrator

Trustees *Mr J Holt, Chair and 11 others, mainly descendants of the founder.*

Information available Guidelines for applicants. Report and accounts with a list of grants of £1,000 or more but lacking narrative analysis.

Summary

The charity gives grants to Quaker organisations around the UK (predominantly in England) and for local needs in Hull and East Yorkshire. Grants are typically one-off, ranging from under £1,000 to £5,000. A substantial part of the funds, however, goes in large grants of up to £40,000, mostly to regular beneficiaries. Many local organisations are regularly supported.

General

The charity was established in 1921 by Sir James Reckitt (founder of Hull-based

Reckitt and Colman plc, now Reckitt Benckiser), who was known for his philanthropy in the area. Today, the trustees continue to follow the original intentions of the settlor, and in making grants give priority to charitable work in line with Quaker beliefs. There are eight programmes of grants and within each, the variety of causes supported is broad, with the exception of the religious classification which tends to make donations only to Quaker groups.

It has been reported that approximately 60% of the trust's income is distributed in the form of annual subscriptions, providing continual support for many years. A number of independent schools, Quaker organisations and local homes for older people are among the major beneficiaries.

Grantmaking

The charity's guidelines state:

The trustees support general charitable causes, but in accordance with the wishes of the founder give priority to:

- purposes in all localities connected with the Society of Friends (Quakers);
- purposes connected with Hull and the East Riding of Yorkshire.

Other areas of support are charities, both national and regional, particularly those concerned with current social issues, and whose work extends to the Hull area.

International causes are considered in exceptional circumstances, such as major disasters, with support usually being channelled through the Society of Friends or the British Red Cross Society.

Grants are normally made only to registered charities. Support for new projects without such status, is usually channelled through an existing registered charity.

Appeals from individual Quakers need the support of their local monthly meeting. Appeals from other individuals are usually only considered from residents of Hull and the East Riding of Yorkshire.

In 1998/99, the charity's assets totalled £15,434,000, and investment income of £700,000 was generated. £602,000 was donated in grants to 251 organisations, 90% of them for amounts under £5,000. A total of 78 individuals in need were supported through the Grant Giving Trusts' Consortium, which was set up by the trustees in 1996 with the primary aim of improving co-operation between the local trusts.

Grants in 1998/99

(Figures for 1997/98 are in brackets.)

Social work	£223,000	(£170,000)
Education	£113,000	(£90,000)
Religion	£66,000	(£63,000)
Medical	£65,000	(£62,000)
Older people	£58,000	(£26,000)
Youth	£50,000	(£32,000)
Children	£22,000	(£20,000)
Environment	£5,000	(£16,000)
Total	£602,000	(£479,000)

Six main grants of £15,000 or more accounted for a quarter of the total expenditure. The recipients were as follows:

British Red Cross (for work in Central America, Kosovo and Sudan, £40,000); the Quakers' Britain Yearly Meeting (£31,000, annual grant); Pickering and Ferens Homes (£25,000); The Retreat, York (£16,000; £11,000 in 1997/98); Ackworth School (£16,000, repeat), and Dove House Hospice (£15,000).

National charities benefiting included the National Association for Gifted Children, Save the Children, NSPCC, RUKBA and the Multiple Sclerosis Society, all of which received grants of around £2,000.

Exclusions

Local organisations outside the Hull area, unless their work has regional implications.

Support is not given to causes of a political or warlike nature and trustees will not normally consider a further appeal if a grant has been paid in the previous two years.

Grants are not normally made to individuals other than Quakers and residents of Hull and the East Riding of Yorkshire.

Applications

In writing to the correspondent at any time. Urgent applications that are clearly within the charity's guidelines and require only limited funding can be dealt with rapidly.

Standard applications need to arrive a month before the trustees' meetings, in May and November, to be considered.

The Richmond Parish Lands Charity

General, in Richmond

£533,000 (to organisations, 1998/99)

Beneficial area Richmond, Kew, North Sheen, Ham and Petersham. Also, for small grants, education fund and heating vouchers, East Sheen and Palewell.

The Vestry House, 21 Paradise Road, Richmond, Surrey TW9 1SA

Tel. 020 8948 5701 **Fax** 020 8332 6792

Correspondent Penny Rkaina, Clerk

Trustees *The mayor ex-officio of Richmond; three nominated by the borough of Richmond (not necessarily councillors or officials); five nominated by local voluntary organisations; up to five co-opted.*

Information available Excellent annual report and accounts.

Summary

The charity supports a wide range of causes in Richmond-upon-Thames and selected areas nearby, as outlined above. It makes around 75 revenue grants each year, generally for between £500 and £5,000. Up to 90% of the organisations receiving revenue grants have been supported in the previous year, although the trustees prefer not to make commitments for ongoing funding. About £100,000 a year is reserved for one-off contributions to capital projects, up to a maximum of £15,000.

General

In 1998/99 the charity's assets amounted to £34.4 million, nearly £15 million held in the form of property. Income totalled £1.25 million and £755,000 was paid out in grants. Grants are made to organisations within the following fields (with totals for 1998/99):

Social and medical welfare	£111,000
Community centres and organisations	£80,000
The relief of poverty	£52,000
Mental health and learning disability	£52,000
Education	£39,000
Youth/community/sport	£33,000
Welfare of the elderly	£27,000
Physical disability	£20,000
Music and the arts	£19,000
One-off capital grants	£100,000
Total	£533,000

A further £121,000 was awarded to individuals from the charity's Education Fund; £48,000 in heating vouchers to older people through its WARM campaign, and £48,000 in small grants to individuals in need.

The revenue grants ranged from as little as £42 up to £36,000, though most were between £500 and £5,000. The larger grants included £36,000 for general support of the Citizens Advice Bureau; £35,000 to RABMIND, to subsidise the 'Vineyard Project' for people with mental health problems; £17,000 to Princess Alice Hospice, and £15,000 for voucher schemes at Richmond Adult & Community College.

£100,000 was donated in 16 one-off grants, mostly from £2,000 to £7,000; but led by £25,000 for Richmond Gymnastics Association, towards the cost of a new purpose-built gymnasium.

Exclusions

Projects and organisations located outside the benefit area, unless it can be demonstrated that a substantial number of residents from the benefit area will gain from their work.

National charities (even if based in the benefit area), except for that part of their work which caters specifically for the area.

Applications

If you would like some clarification on whether you organisation would qualify for a grant, please contact the clerk to the trustees (020 8948 5701) who will be able to give you guidance. You will also be given an application form.

When you send in your application form be sure that you have filled in all sections and that you have enclosed all the documents requested.

If your organisation or project is new, you will probably need to write a covering letter giving relevant background and explanation.

On receipt of your application the clerk to the trustees will evaluate it and may wish to ask further questions before submitting it to the trustees for their consideration. You may be assured that all eligible applications will be put before the trustees.

Trustees' meetings are held every five weeks, when eligible applications received 14 days beforehand are considered by the trustees. They may decide that they need further information before they can make a decision regarding a grant.

You will be advised by letter within 10 days of the meeting whether or not your application has been successful. If you wish to know before that you may of course telephone the clerk.

If your organisation or project is new to the charity you will be asked to sign a brief document in which the terms and conditions of the grant are set out. On receipt of the signed agreement a cheque will be sent for the appropriate amount.

The Robertson Trust

General, mainly in Scotland

£4,344,000 (1999/2000)

Beneficial area UK, especially Scotland.

PO Box 15330, Glasgow G1 2YL

Tel. 0141 352 6620 **Fax** 0141 352 6617

Correspondent Sir Lachlan Maclean, Secretary

Information available Full and clear information from the charity, including a list of grants of £10,000 and over.

Summary

Over 300 grants are made a year, most of them for amounts up to £10,000. The trust says that it receives around 1,000 requests for funding in a typical year, making the success rate about one in three. About a quarter of the money goes on a few big capital donations of up to £500,000, often (though not exclusively) for medical facilities.

A policy review in February 2000 produced the following priority areas for the trust to support:

- education
- medical
- care [*especially of older people and the young. Ed.*]
- drugs prevention and treatment

These categories accounted for 72% of the grant total in 1999/2000, but over 150 grants worth £1.2 million were made in other areas.

General

Though there is no equivalent in Scotland to the Charity Commission's SORP requirements on the disclosure of information, this charity has nevertheless decided to provide greatly increased information about its grantmaking, so this entry is an improvement on previous editions of this book. In 1999/2000 the trust received income of £5.1 million from assets of £208 million, and £4.3 million was disbursed in 355 grants. The grants list showed 99 grants of £10,000 or more. Funds were allocated within the following 12 categories (with grant figures for 1999/2000):

	No.	Amount	%
Medical	58	£1,201,000	28%
Education	13	£956,000	22%
Care	79	£746,000	17%
Community service	53	£355,000	8%
Disability	49	£263,000	6%
Drugs	44	£214,000	5%
Heritage/conservation	15	£169,000	4%
Alcoholic research	6	£151,000	3%
Arts	23	£140,000	3%
Sport	3	£62,000	1%
Animal welfare	8	£61,000	1%
Environmental issues	4	£26,000	<1%
Total	355	£4,344,000	

Details of some of the largest donations were given in the trustees' report:

In the last year, Medical donations included a donation of £250,000 to Ninewells Cancer campaign for the new facilities for Professor Lane, £250,000 to Imperial Cancer Research Fund for their new facilities at the Western General Hospital in Edinburgh and £100,000 to the Macmillan Cancer Relief Centre being built at the Borders General Hospital. A donation of £97,000 was made to the Meningitis Association Scotland to fund a new Sequencer for the laboratory at Stobhill Hospital.

In Education, the Trust donation of £500,000 to the University of Glasgow for the new Medical School was the largest single donation made by the Trust in 1999. The Trust also made a donation of £100,000 to Glasgow Central College of Commerce towards the new Library.

In Care, a donation of £75,000 was made to AgeCare Aberdeen for a development of accommodation for elderly people at Cloverfield and Kincorth. The new Dementia Services Centre at Stirling University received a donation of £73,000 and the Abbeyfield Society at Strathgryffe received £75,000 for the modernisation of its buildings at Quarriers.

The Robertson Trust's funding to the Robertson Scholarship Trust increased to £225,000. In the year under review the first students who started under the Bursary Award Scheme in 1995 graduated and another 26 new Bursary Awards were made. At the end of the year there were 78 students receiving bursaries.

The trust also continued with its support for a Drug Awareness Programme in both secondary and primary schools in Scotland, run by Calton Athletic Recovery Group. Its grant of £202,000 accounted for most of the trust's funding under the 'drugs' category. The largest beneficiaries under the other headings were as follows:

Community service: Erskine Hospital (£60,000); The Army Benevolent Fund (£26,000); Drumchapel St Andrew's Care & Comfort Minibus Fund (£19,000).

Disability: Scottish Trust for the Physically Disabled (£36,000); British Deaf Association, ENABLE (£10,500 each).

Heritage/conservation: The Waterways Trust (£30,000); St Mary's Cathedral (£25,000).

Alcohol: The Medical Council on Alcoholism (£93,500).

Arts: Edinburgh International Festival (£50,000).

Sport: Scottish Sports Aid Foundation (£60,000).

Animal welfare: Fund for the Replacement of Animals in Medical Experiments (£16,000).

Environment: The Borders Forest Trust, Marine Conservation Society (£10,000 each).

In a practice always regretted by these editors, one of the trustees is paid (£50,000 in 1999/2000) to act as the trust's secretary. If there comes to be a new regulatory body for charities in Scotland, they hope that it will share their view (which is also that of the Charity Commission in London) that the principle of unpaid trusteeship is one of the defining characteristics of the charitable sector.

Applications

In writing to the correspondent. They should include the applicant's charity number and a copy of the latest set of accounts.

Trustees meet six times a year, in January, March, May, July, September and November.

Mrs L D Rope Third Charitable Settlement

General, particularly in south east Suffolk

£618,000 (1999/2000)

Beneficial area UK and overseas, with a particular interest in south east Suffolk.

Crag Farm, Boyton, near Woodbridge, Suffolk IP12 3LH

Tel. 01473 288987 **Fax** 01473 217182

Correspondent Liz Combes, Administrator

Information available Exemplary report and accounts. Model 'Guidelines for Grant Seekers'.

Summary

Most of this trust's funds are already committed to projects it has initiated itself or to ongoing relationships. Except for charities in south east Suffolk, the amount of money available for responding to unsolicited applications is so slight as to make application here a low priority for most organisations.

General

The charity's guidelines are partly reprinted here, and partly under 'Exclusions' and 'Applications' below.

The Charity's priorities for giving … are briefly as follows:

Relief of Poverty: Support for a number of causes and individuals where the Trustees have longer term knowledge and experience. …

Support for educational projects connected with the Founder's family. Support for a proposed airship museum; support for Catholic and other schools in the general area of Ipswich; and projects relating to the interaction of mathematics and physical science with philosophy.

Support for the Roman Catholic religion and ecumenical work, both generally and for specific institutions connected historically with the families of William Oliver Jolly and his wife Alice and their descendants.

Public and other charitable purposes in the general region of south east Suffolk and in particular the parish of Kesgrave and the areas surrounding it, including Ipswich.

Distinction between charity-initiated projects and unsolicited applications

In practice, the work of the Charity may be divided into two distinct categories. Firstly it initiates, supports and pursues certain specific charitable projects selected by the Founder. Secondly, it approves grants to unsolicited applications that fall within the Founder's stated objectives and that comply with the set of grantmaking policies outlined below, specifically for this second element of its work. The Trustees devote more of the Charity's resources to self-initiated projects as compared to pure grantmaking to unsolicited requests. In terms of income distributed during the year, roughly 80% was given towards projects where the Charity had either initiated the work or where a longstanding relationship over a number of years gave rise to new or continued assistance.

Successful *unsolicited* applications to the Charity usually display a combination of the following features:

- *Size:* The Trustees very much prefer to encourage charities that work at 'grassroots' level within their community. Such charities are unlikely to have benefited greatly from grant funding from local, national (including funds from the National Lottery) or European authorities. They are also less likely to be as wealthy in comparison with other charities that attract popular support on a national basis. The charities assisted usually cannot afford to pay for the professional help other charities may use to raise funds.
- *Volunteers:* The Trustees prefer applications from charities that are able to show they have a committed and proportionately large volunteer force.
- *Administration:* The less a charity spends on paying for its own administration, particularly as far as staff salaries are concerned, the more it is likely to be considered by the Trustees.
- *Areas of interest:* Charities with the above characteristics that work in any of the following areas:
  a. Helping people who struggle to live on very little income, including the homeless.
  b. Helping people who live in deprived inner city and rural areas of the UK, particularly young people who lack the opportunities that may be available elsewhere.
  c. Helping charities in our immediate local area of south east Suffolk.
  d. Helping to support family life.
  e. Helping disabled people.
  f. Helping Roman Catholic charities and ecumenical projects.

Grants made to charities outside the primary beneficial area of south east Suffolk are usually one-off and small in scale (in the range between £100 to £750).

Grants in 1999/2000

There were 18 grants of £10,000 or more, averaging £23,500 and amounting to £424,000, or 69% of the grant total. A further 60 grants, adding up to £134,000 (22% of the funds) were in the range £1,000 to £7,500, while the remaining 185 grants were for less than £1,000 each.

The trust's major long-term projects and beneficiaries, as described in its annual report, include the following (amount donated in 1999/2000):

- Science/Human Dimension Project (£54,000) 'This project operates from Jesus College, Cambridge and is designed to improve public awareness of important philosophical and general implications of developments in science and mathematics.'
- Depaul Trust (£27,000) 'The bulk of this money constitutes the first of five instalments ... to fund a project to encourage the greater use of volunteers by the Depaul Trust itself and more generally. ...The Depaul Trust was selected because of its record in the effective use of volunteers, which our Trustees believe to be an important and neglected aspect of some charitable work.'
- Airship Museum (£25,000 to the Mrs L D Rope Fourth Charitable Settlement and £13,000 to the Airship Heritage Trust) 'This Charitable Settlement is working with the Airship Heritage Trust to establish an Airship Museum. ... additional funds were needed to move and safeguard the large quantity of exhibits already collected.'

Other major UK beneficiaries included St Mark's Roman Catholic Parish, Ipswich (£30,000); Shelter (£20,000), and the Coastal Housing Action Group (£13,000).

Exclusions

The following are the main categories of exclusion for unsolicited applications; they are spelt out in more detail in the guidelines than is possible here:

- overseas projects (the trust uses CAFOD to offer most of its overseas help);
- national charities;
- replacement of statutory funding;
- requests for core funding;
- buildings;
- medical research/healthcare;
- students, except for a few foreign postgraduate science students in the last stages of their studies;
- schools, except in the local area;
- environmental charities and animal welfare;
- the arts;
- 'matched' funding;
- individuals – repayment of debts.

Applications

Please send a concise letter (preferably one side of A4) explaining the main details of your request. Please always send your most recent accounts and a budgeted breakdown of the sum you are looking to raise. The trust will also need to know whether you have applied to other funding sources and whether you have been successful elsewhere. Your application should say who your trustees are and include a daytime telephone number.

Individuals should write a concise letter including details of household income and expenses, daytime telephone number and the name of at least one personal referee.

The Rose Foundation

Building projects for charities, general

£942,000 (1998/99)

Beneficial area UK, mainly Greater London.

28 Crawford Street, London W1H 1PL

Tel. 020 7262 1155 **Fax** 020 7724 2044

Correspondent A Quazi, Administrator

Information available Full accounts with comprehensive narrative report.

Summary

The foundation's main activity is to fund and support building projects, mainly in London or surrounding areas. Most funds are reserved for a few major projects, in which the trustees may be directly involved, such as the Crawford Street Centre, a major capital project in London which received one third of the grant total in 1998/99. A few small one-off donations are also made mainly to health/welfare charities.

The foundation is an excellent example of how the cash value of grants can be multiplied by supporting them with specialist expertise – especially when the expertise is also voluntarily donated.

(Since writing the above, these publishers have themselves been helped with valuable advice on the management of their own building's refurbishment.)

General

The foundation's assets amounted to £30 million in 1999 and its income was almost £1 million. Grantmaking totalled £942,000.

Management and administration costs of £181,000 included £72,000 in investment management fees and £65,000 for the salaries of three workers and office costs. The foundation's annual report for 1998/99 described its activities as follows.

The Trustees continued with the general aim of benefiting as large a number of people as possible, rather than providing large donations to a small specific group. In the main we provide financial assistance and, where helpful, property experience to charities requiring assistance for their building projects.

Donations policy

Notwithstanding that monetary donations are occasionally made, the main emphasis of our work is to finance building projects for other charities. A policy of seeking small self-contained projects of between £5,000 and £30,000 has now been adopted. These will usually be located in London or the Home Counties, in order that the Trustees can effectively monitor their progress. The Trustees' policy is to offer assistance where needed with the design and construction process, ensuring wherever possible that costs are minimised and that the participation of other contributing bodies can be utilised to the maximum benefit of the scheme.

Applicants are encouraged to apply for assistance for projects which meet the above criteria by the spring of each year. Where possible the Trustees prefer to commit to the following year's projects in the early summer. This enables a sufficient lead time for the details of building construction to be agreed, and if appropriate amended. Applicants are advised that the Trustees seek only to offer their guidance and experience, and that final decisions with regard to the project details remain with the benefiting charity.

In addition the trustees have offered their time and property experience to other charities.

Grants in 1998/99

Of the 58 grants, 21 were in the range £5,000 to £32,000 and 33 were for under £5,000.

Major beneficiaries

Two thirds of the funds, however, went to the following major beneficiaries and projects, which were in receipt of large grants for more than £50,000:

The Crawford Street Centre – A grant of £317,000, for both capital and revenue, helped to fund a joint project with Ability UK providing a gymnasium and therapy centre for the fully intergrated use of disabled and able-bodied people. Of the trustees, Martin Rose sits on the board of the Crawford Street Centre management.

Royal Academy of Arts – £125,000, part of a multi-year commitment providing for the restoration of Gallery IX.

New Amsterdam Charitable Foundation – £93,000, an annual donation to what could be described as the 'American branch' of the foundation, for grantmaking in the USA.

MacIntyre Care (Wingrave Manor, Buckinghamshire) – £83,000 for the construction of a new accommodation wing for students at this independent special school for teenagers with severe learning difficulties.

Other building projects

Capital grants were frequently made to help improve facilities for disabled people or children. Examples of other grant recipients included:

National Association of Toy and Leisure Libraries – £20,000 for renovation and refurbishment of the charity's headquarters in King's Cross, London.

Soho Theatre Company – £5,000 to assist with the construction of a writers' centre (unusually for the Rose Foundation, this is part of a much larger project).

St Paul's Catholic College – £10,000 for the modification of three classrooms to teach design and technology.

Small donations

Beneficiaries of grants not for building work were mainly health/welfare charities for children and disabled people and arts institutions. Examples included:

Qazi Family Foundation (£8,000); Royal National Theatre (£7,000); Children's Cancer Fund (£6,000); British Tennis Foundation (£3,000); Jewish Blind and Physically Handicapped Society (£2,000); British School of Osteopathy (£1,000).

Finally, 24 grants were for under £1,000, the recipients including Hampstead Theatre, Israel Cancer Association, Jewish Marriage Council, Kent Adventure Club for the Disabled, London Language and Literacy Unit, Merseyside and Wirral Disabled Motorists Club and Sparkle Children's Charity.

Exclusions

Income support, contributions to running expenses, and viability studies.

Applications

The foundation receives written and telephone applications. Decisions are taken by the trustees, who meet informally virtually every day and formally by regular arrangement. Commitments to small building projects (£5,000 to £30,000) to be undertaken in the following year are made in formal meetings, usually in May and October. Other meetings are concerned with the progress of existing and future (i.e. more than a year away) projects. The foundation monitors the progress of the projects to which it contributes funds and summarises this in its annual report.

The Rothschild Foundation

Heritage, Jewish charities, general

£540,000 (1998/99)

The Dairy, Queen Street, Waddesdon, Aylesbury, Buckinghamshire HP18 0JW

Tel. 01296 653235 **Fax** 01296 651142

Correspondent Julie Christmas, Secretary

Information available Annual report and accounts on file at the Charity Commission.

General

The foundation's income for 1998/99 was low, at £407,000, from assets worth £18.6 million. As for the associated Jacob Rothschild GAM Trust, grantmaking in recent years has been concentrated on the restoration of Waddesdon Manor. Of the £540,000 grant total, £481,000 went to the National Trust for this purpose in 1998/99.

The next largest grant, for £10,000, was also narrowly focused, going to Waddesdon Village Hall Committee.

A further 48 grants started at £11 (to the Family Welfare Association), with most being for amounts between £250 and £2,500. A variety of beneficiaries was supported, as shown by the following splendidly varied sample, and about a quarter were receiving repeat grants.

Age Concern, Buckinghamshire (£1,000); Bristol Cancer Clinic (£500); Calibre (£250); English Chamber Orchestra and Music Society (£2,500); Global Foundation for Humanity (£1,500); Leeds Art Collections Fund, Gilbert Fund (£500); Mentor Foundation (£1,000); Oswestry Orthopaedic Hospital (£2,500); Stepney Jewish Community Care (£150); Venetian Diamond Miners (£250); Woodland Trust, Penn Wood Appeal (£1,000).

Applications

In writing to the correspondent.

The Jacob Rothschild GAM Charitable Trust

In September 2000 the charity was 'in the course of termination, which we expect to be completed in the coming weeks'.

The Rowan Charitable Trust

Overseas aid, social welfare, general

£571,000 (1998/99)

Beneficial area UK, especially Merseyside, and overseas.

c/o PricewaterhouseCoopers, 9 Greyfriars Road, Reading RG1 1JG

Tel. 0118 959 7111 **Fax** 0118 960 7700

Correspondent The Secretary

Information available Good guidelines for applicants are available from the trust. Annual report and accounts.

Summary

The trust gives two thirds of its money to overseas projects and one third to social welfare projects in the UK. Over 100 grants are made a year, rarely for more than £25,000 and most for between £1,000 and £10,000. Larger grants usually go to charities with which the trust has an existing connection, with large annual awards upwards of £15,000 tending to go to those working in developing countries. Smaller one-off grants, sometimes repeated, go to a variety of beneficiaries, including many campaigning groups.

The trust is open to radical projects and organisations.

Guidelines

The trust gives a mix of one-off grants and recurrent ones. It has regularly given grants to a limited number of large national organisations and development agencies, but also gives smaller grants to much smaller organisations and locally based projects.

The trust will support advocacy and challenges to powerful economic forces, on behalf of the poor, the powerless or the left out, especially if they themselves are enabled to participate in articulating a vision of economic justice.

UK grants programme

The trust focuses on projects on Merseyside which will benefit disadvantaged groups and neighbourhoods in such spheres as:

- housing and homelessness
- social and community care
- education
- employment/unemployment
- after-care
- welfare rights
- community development
- environmental improvement.

The trustees are interested in projects which are concerned with self-help or advocacy as well as service provision. They also look for:

- user and community involvement in the planning and delivery of the project
- a multi-disciplinary approach
- emphasis on empowerment.

Overseas projects

The trust focuses on projects which will benefit disadvantaged groups and communities in such spheres as:

- agriculture – especially crop and livestock production and settlement schemes
- community development – especially appropriate technology and village industries
- health – especially preventative medicine, water supplies, blindness
- education – especially adult education and materials
- environmental – especially protecting and sustaining ecological systems at risk
- human rights – especially of women, children and disabled
- fair trade – especially relating to primary producers and workers.

The trustees are interested in projects which

- involve the local community in the planning and implementation
- invest in people through training and enabling
- have a holistic concern for all aspects of life ...

Grants in 1998/99

The trust made 77 grants totalling £377,000 for work overseas and 40 grants worth £194,000 to UK organisations. About three quarters of recipients in the previous year reappeared in the grants list in 1998/99.

In the overseas sector long-standing relationships continued with UNICEF (£30,000), Christian Aid and Intermediate Technology (£50,000 each). Grants for £10,000 went to the Church Mission Society, Leprosy Mission, Newick Park Initiative and Rurcon.

The remaining grants ranged from £500 to £8,000. Recipients included the Jubilee 2000 Coalition, UK Foundation for the South Pacific, Conciliation Resources, Dian Fossey Gorilla Fund, Tools for Self Reliance, Survival for Tribal Peoples, and Wales Gurkha Villages Aid Appeals Committee.

In the UK there were only four grants of £10,000 or more, all part of long-term commitments: to the Personal Service Society in Liverpool (£20,000); Barnardos (£15,000, Young Carers Project); the Children's Society (£15,000), and Liverpool Family Service Unit (£10,000).

Five further grants were for more than £5,000: to Merseyside Drugs Council (£6,000); the Prince's Trust (£6,500); the Refugee Council (£7,000); Church Action on Poverty and the Crossroads Centre (£7,500 each). The rest of the grants were on a scale from £1,000 to £5,000 for a variety of causes, as the following examples of beneficiaries show: The Big Issue in the North Trust, The Disability Law Service, Insight Arts Trust, Landlife, The Prison Video Magazine, Soil Association, Transport 2000, Western Kurdistan Association, Winged Fellowship.

Other donations with an identifiable Merseyside connection went to St Helens & Knowsley Hospice (£5,000); ChildLine North West (Merseyside Appeal, £4,500); The Weston Spirit (Knowsley, £4,000); MCVS (Merseyside Accommodation Project, £3,000); Sefton Advocacy Service (£1,500), and Mersey Volunteer Bureau (£1,000).

Exclusions

The trust does not give grants for:

- individuals
- buildings, building work or office equipment
- academic research

Applications

In writing to the correspondent. No application forms are issued.

Applications should include: a brief description (two sides of A4 paper) of, and a budget for, the work for which the grant is sought; the organisation's annual report and accounts; and an indication of the core costs of the organisation.

The applications need to provide the trustees with information about:

- the aims and objectives of the organisation
- its structure and organisational capacity
- what the funds are being requested for and how much is being requested
- how progress of the work will be monitored and evaluated

Unfortunately the volume of applications received precludes acknowledgement on receipt or notifying unsuccessful applicants. The trust is unable to make donations to applicants who are not, or do not have links with, a UK registered charity.

Trustees meet in February and August.

The Joseph Rowntree Charitable Trust

Poverty, economic and racial justice, peace, democratic process, corporate responsibility, Ireland, South Africa

£4,242,000 (1999)

Beneficial area UK, Republic of Ireland and Southern (mainly South) Africa.

The Garden House, Water End, York YO30 6WQ

Tel. 01904 627810 **Fax** 01904 651990

e-mail jrct@jrct.org.uk

website www.jrct.org.uk

Correspondent Steven Burkeman, Secretary

Trustees *Andrew Gunn, Chair; Ruth McCarthy; Margaret Bryan; Christine Davis; John Guest; Beverley Meeson; Emily Miles; Marion McNaughton; Roger Morton; Vasant Shend'ge; David Shutt; Peter Stark.*

Information available Full accounts are filed with the Charity Commission. The trust also publishes a triennial report (latest 1997/99), plus a basic guidance leaflet for applicants. In addition, detailed sheets are available on each of the programme areas. Updated information on grants' priorities are available on the JRCT website.

Summary

About 200 grants are made each year, ranging in size from a few hundred pounds to over £100,000, and from one-off to three-year grants. They cover, at present, the following areas:

- poverty and economic justice
- peace
- democratic process
- racial justice
- corporate responsibility
- religious concerns
- justice and reconciliation in South Africa and in Ireland (North and South)

Background

The JRCT was set up in 1904 by Joseph Rowntree, a Quaker businessman, who made his money from producing cocoa and chocolate.

All trustees are members of the Religious Society of Friends (Quakers). As such, they share a belief in the equal worth of all members of the human race, together with a recognition and appreciation of diversity.

The staff of the trust with whom applicants are most likely to come into contact are:

Steven Burkeman – Trust Secretary

Stephen Pittam – Deputy Trust Secretary

Juliet Prager – Assistant Trust Secretary

Maureen Grant – West Yorkshire Development Officer

General

The JRCT makes grants for projects which fit with the Trust's concerns. The Trust agrees and publishes its policies, and then invites people to apply for grants. While the success rate varies, typically about one in nine applications is successful.

The interests of the trust are set out in great detail in its briefing sheets on each of its areas of interest. These are summarised below, but those thinking of applying should first see the full texts. These are available on paper from the trust or can be seen on its comprehensive website.

The low success rate of applications seems to demonstrate the relative lack of funding available for the kind of work supported. It would be appropriate if an effort was made, based on this trust's experience, to interest more grantmakers in supporting these fields. Perhaps this could be a useful task for the Association of Charitable Foundations, which has achieved something comparable with its publication on the previously little appreciated needs of the gay and lesbian communities.

Work which the trust will consider funding

Poverty and Economic Justice Work towards a fairer society in which significant sections of the population are no longer marginalised or excluded by poverty.

Handling Conflict and Promoting Peaceful Alternatives Work which demonstrates how international, intergroup and interpersonal conflict can be handled in ways which reduces, and if possible eliminates, the use or threat of violence.

Democratic Process Work which strengthens democracy and upholds the rights of the citizen.

Racial Justice Work towards the creation of a multi- racial society, based on principles of justice and equality of opportunity. There is a special racial justice programme in West Yorkshire, covered by a separate leaflet and application procedure. The leaflet is available on request from the Trust office and can also be found at the Trust website.

Corporate Responsibility Work which encourages large organisations – public and private, commercial or not – in recognising wider responsibilities in society.

Religious Concerns Work, by Quakers or others, which supports spiritual development and reflects Quaker values.

We make grants mainly for work in Britain. Outside Britain, we make grants only for work towards peace, justice and reconciliation in South Africa and in Ireland (North and South).

Trustees try to maintain an adventurous approach to funding. Where appropriate, they are willing to take risks and fund unpopular causes which may not always fall neatly into one of the subject areas listed above.

Many JRCT funded projects share these features:

- The work is about removing problems through radical solutions, and not about making the problems easier to live with.
- There is a clear sense of objectives, and of how to achieve them.
- The work is innovative and imaginative.
- It is clear that the grant has a good chance of making a difference.

Poverty and economic justice programme (£349,000 in 1999)

The work in which the Trust is interested may be concerned with current practice, or with developing new thinking and policy. The Trust wishes to balance work which is primarily reactive to contemporary events, with work of a more visionary, radical or long-term nature. The Trust wishes to make grants which tackle the causes of poverty, rather than making poverty easier to live with.

The Trust supports legally charitable programmes in the United Kingdom through the provision of core and project funding for organisations and individuals working in the following ways:

- raising the profile of issues of poverty and economic justice on the public agenda.
- pursuing ways of increasing public commitment to a more equitable society, with less extreme differentials in income and wealth.
- work focused on influencing the policy debate. This may include setting out the intellectual case for economic justice; providing independent, authoritative and reliable data; examining the forces and processes which impoverish and exclude; developing alternative policy options; suggesting how the results of research can be translated into policy and practice.
- enabling the experience of those who live in poverty to influence public opinion, policy and practice.
- promoting contact and mutual support between different groups of people who are more liable than others to experience poverty (including women, black and ethnic minorities, the elderly and people with disabilities).
- promoting contact and mutual support between local, national and European initiatives.
- bringing test cases in order to clarify the law and publicise its consequences. Most grants will be made for work which is being done nationally, or which is of national importance. The Trust particularly wishes to support work which is innovative and which challenges current assumptions that poverty is inevitable and acceptable.

Examples of recent grants include:

- Church Action on Poverty; £60,000 over three years for core costs.
- The Fawcett Society; £20,000 for core costs.
- Friends of the Earth, Scotland: £20,000 for a Sustainable Communities project.

Peace programme (£546,000 in 1999)

The Trust believes that long-term approaches to create peace are usually more effective than short-term fixes.

We anticipate funding groups or organisations that are working to influence the behaviour and thinking of the public, and of people in powerful positions including those working in the military, national governments and international organisations.

We are particularly interested in funding organisations or individuals who are working on:

- Control or elimination of specific forms of warfare and the arms trade;
- Influencing appropriate agencies to take or promote peaceful choices to prevent violent conflict or its recurrence;
- The practicalities and improved effectiveness of peacebuilding and conflict resolution;
- The creation of a culture of peace;
- Pacifism and conscientious objection to military service.

We will not fund:

- Work on interpersonal violence, domestic violence, or violence against children;
- Work focused solely on local situations;
- Work which focuses on the immediate effect of conflict on victims;
- Research which is more theoretical than practical, or which is not aimed at making change happen;
- Work focused more exclusively on other governments' policy than on that of the UK, unless the work is on pacifism or conscientious objection to military service;
- Work which seems only to 'preach to the converted'.

We are most likely to fund individuals and organisations working in the UK and Ireland and (if the organisation is working on influencing an international institution such as the EU, NATO or the UN) the rest of Europe.

Examples of recent grants include the following:

- Trust for Research and Education on the Arms Trade: £42,000 over three years towards employing a research worker.
- Bradford University Department of Peace Studies: £4,000 towards a workshop on 'non-lethal weapons, legal and ethical dilemmas'.
- Janet Bloomfield: £3,000 towards the costs of a booklet on nuclear disarmament and proliferation since 1995.

Democratic process programme (£647,000 in 1999)

Our funding has focused on work in the following areas:

- the nuts and bolts of a new constitutional settlement, to tackle the weaknesses which result from our unwritten constitution;
- legal provision for freedom of information;
- the argument for a Human Rights Act; discussion of its content; work to raise awareness of its significance; monitoring its implementation;
- the importance of local democracy as a counter to centralisation of power;
- ways to tackle the politicisation of the civil service;
- independent scrutiny of proposed legislation;
- the right relationship between the Executive and the Judiciary;
- alternatives to the present 'first past the post' electoral system;
- the need to protect and enhance civil liberties;
- how to rectify the perception that people are subjects, rather than citizens with concomitant rights and obligations.

The Trust wishes to fund work which encourages people to take seriously their democratic rights and obligations, exercising them in ways that make them real rather than merely theoretical. This may be achieved through educational work, or other kinds of 'bottom up' initiatives.

Applications to the Trust should demonstrate clearly how the work is likely to make an impact. The Trust is unlikely to support purely academic work in this area.

Democracy committee

Margaret Bryan
Christine Davis
Vasant Shend'ge
David Shutt

Co-opted members:
Diana Scott
Trevor Smith

Examples of recent grants include:

- The Federal Trust: up to £31,500 as a contribution to a programme to monitor the progress of the intergovernmental conference considering a new European Union treaty.
- Electoral Reform Society: £16,000 towards a commission to examine the procedures used by political parties to select candidates for public elections.
- Public Law Project: £3,500 for the purchase of computer equipment.

Racial justice programme (£594,000 in 1999, including the West Yorkshire programme)

The Joseph Rowntree Charitable Trust seeks to promote, in the UK, a harmonious multi-racial and multi-cultural society based on the principles of justice and equality of opportunity.

The Trust welcomes applications from black and ethnic minority groups and from multi-racial groups, and encourages and looks for involvement of black and ethnic minority people at all levels of the projects and organisations it supports.

This [section] concerns the national programme. There is a separate [section below] covering the programme in West Yorkshire. Currently the national Racial Justice programme supports projects and individuals working to:

- promote issues of racial justice with policy shapers, decision makers and opinion formers;
- empower black and ethnic minority people to contribute to policy development on the basis of their experience in meeting needs; and to participate at planning and decision making levels;
- monitor and challenge racism and racial injustice whether relating to colour or culture;
- explore ways to eliminate racial violence and harassment;
- promote the rights of black and ethnic minority people to equal opportunities;
- promote communication and co-operation between different racial groups.

The Trust seeks to encourage work aimed at furthering its objectives in the European Union (EU). The Trust expects that work undertaken on a EU wide basis will attract funds from sources in several EU member states. In particular, the Trust has supported projects working to:

- promote awareness amongst policy makers and within the European institutions of the need to protect the human rights of minority communities, asylum seekers and migrants;
- research and disseminate information concerning current EU policies and their impact on minority communities;
- provide a forum for NGOs from all EU countries to share experiences on matters relating to race and immigration and to build alliances on shared interests;
- work for a more accountable and open process for developing EU policy in relation to race and immigration.

A small fund is available to support work on asylum and refugee issues. Grants have been made for work to:

- research and disseminate information on the impact of current policies on refugees and asylum seekers;
- research into the likely future direction of asylum policy in the UK and EU and into how this might be influenced to create a rational and humane policy;
- safeguard the rights of refugees through advice and advocacy services relating to legal protection in the north of England and in Scotland.

Racial justice committee

Ruth McCarthy
Marion McNaughton
Vasant Shend'ge

Co-opted members:
Derek Guiton
Heidi Mirza
Richmond Quarshie
Sayeeda Warsi

Examples of recent grants include:

- 1990 Trust: £175,000 for core costs and its human rights project.
- JUSTICE: £30,000 towards a project on extending protection from discrimination both in the UK and Europe.

- Scottish Gypsy/Traveller Association: £23,000 towards a salary.

West Yorkshire racial justice programme

The West Yorkshire Programme aims to promote the full participation of black and ethnic minority people in community life. The Programme will support initiatives which:

- enable black and ethnic minority communities to respond to their own needs through collective action;
- encourage black and ethnic minority groups to work together on issues of common concern;
- positively promote the black and ethnic minority communities and enable them to achieve equality in social and civil rights;
- promote communication and cooperation between all racial groups.

Two types of grants will be offered.

One-off grants up to £1,000

Examples of work for which grants might be requested are:

- a small piece of research
- seminars/workshops
- production of a report etc.

Grants up to £10,000

These grants might be for one or two years, and are likely to be for salary or running costs. They might cover such things as:

- start-up costs
- small projects
- development to help groups move forward.

Larger grants may be offered in special circumstances.

[In addition] the Trust wishes to facilitate the growth and development of the black and ethnic minority voluntary sector and will offer groups the opportunity to work with trainers/ consultants on areas of identified need. The Trust will help groups define their needs, find an appropriate consultant/trainer, and will cover reasonable costs.

Those looking for grants from this programme should contact Maureen Grant on the number above for further information. Examples of recent grants include:

- Mary Seacole Nurses Association, Leeds: £36,000 over two years towards core costs.
- Buttershaw Upper School, Bradford: £500 towards publication of a conference report on promoting anti-racist education strategies in West Yorkshire.

Corporate and financial responsibility programme (£240,000 in 1999)

The focus of this funding area is on the actions of governments, the policies of public bodies, both elected and unelected, and the actions of public companies.

We invite applications for funds to support work which is aimed at encouraging organisations to behave with integrity, transparency, and social responsibility. We will seek to fund work which:

- Identifies and demonstrates best practice and which seeks to effect changes in the law to protect the poor or powerless from the unfair actions of the wealthy and powerful.
- Attempts to influence policy makers on issues of financial responsibility and of redistribution of wealth.
- Is based in the UK, or elsewhere in the EU where the work is aimed at influencing the EU (as distinct from individual countries within it). This does not preclude occasional support for projects designed to influence global organisations, where the project is UK based.

We will not fund work based outside the EU, or work which focuses on individual EU countries other than the UK, or local (as distinct from national) projects in the UK.

Under this heading in the past, the Trust has funded work on issues such as the rights of whistle-blowers and the responsibilities of public companies to their various stake-holders – shareholders, customers, employees and the communities in which they operate.

[This] is a relatively small funding programme for the Trust.

Examples of recent grants include:

- Centre for Corporate Accountability: £350,000 over three years for core costs.
- New Economics Foundation: £145,000 over three years for core costs.

Quaker concerns (£361,000 in 1999)

The Trustees are Quakers. The Trust seeks to foster the development of what Joseph Rowntree called a 'powerful Quaker ministry', interpreted as inclusively as possible. This may include practical ways to deepen the spiritual life of Friends or developing Quaker responses to problems of our time.

Primarily, this programme area supports work designed to strengthen the Society of Friends but which is less likely to be able to attract funds from other sources. This could include support for innovative approaches to the development of Quaker life and thought.

Trustees will consider applications from Britain Yearly Meeting, from local Meetings, or from other Quaker organisations in Britain. Applications from individuals are also welcomed.

Ireland programme

Over the last twenty years a significant programme of work has been supported in Northern Ireland. After an extensive consultation process a decision was taken in 1994 to launch an experimental five year funding programme in the Republic.

Programme in Northern Ireland (£387,000 in 1999)

Currently the Trust's programme supports projects and individuals working to:

- promote new ideas to sustain the democratic process and democratic accountability;
- encourage accountability, openness and responsiveness in government, government agencies and the civil service;
- build new community structures to enable citizens to participate in the democratic process;
- protect and enhance civil liberties and human rights;
- promote dialogue, understanding and cooperation across political and religious divides;
- challenge sectarianism;
- promote nonviolence and creative ways to handle conflict;
- celebrate difference and value pluralism;
- tackle poverty, inequality and social exclusion;
- address contentious issues and develop new thinking on how to resolve these;
- explore new ideas about the future social, economic and political relationships within the island of Ireland, between Britain and Ireland, and within the European Union.

The Trust is interested in supporting work which addresses the root causes of the conflict in Northern Ireland and which is aimed at influencing policy. Much of the Trust's work has been directed towards providing infrastructure, technical assistance and support for those working at a local level. A strong focus of the Trust's programme has been on women's initiatives working in the areas outlined above. The Trust will need to be convinced that other funds such as those from statutory agencies and the European Union are not available for work which it funds.

Examples of recent grants include:

- Committee on the Administration of Justice: £96,000 over three years towards core costs.
- Upper Springfield Resource Centre: £25,000 towards the SAFFRON project.
- Enniskillen Together: £15,000 over three years towards a conflict transformation project.
- British Irish Rights Watch: £14,000 to assist with the costs of a full time observer at the Bloody Sunday Inquiry.

Programme in the Republic (£142,000 in 1999)

The Trust's programme supports projects and individuals working to:

- promote the concept of citizenship, the ability of all citizens to participate in the democratic process, and the freedom and rights of the individual;

- encourage accountability, openness and responsiveness in government, government agencies and the civil service;
- promote new ideas to sustain the democratic process;
- promote dialogue, understanding and cooperation across religious and political divides;
- explore new ideas about the future social, economic and political development of the island, north and south.

The Trust spends about UK£100,000 per annum in the Republic. Two types of grant are offered.

Strategic Grants: A small number of strategic grants are offered to encourage organisational development and to raise the effectiveness and profile of key organisations. These grants are likely to fall within a range of UK£6,000 to UK£15,000 per annum and will be offered for a maximum of three years.

Project Grants: A number of project grants are offered for work such as – action research; the dissemination of research findings; conferences, seminars, and networking events; and publications. These are one-off grants and are likely to fall within the range of UK£500 to UK£6,000.

Examples of recent grants include:

- AVP Ireland: £20,000 over three years towards the costs of employing a development worker.

South Africa programme (£393,000 in 1999)

The main thrust of current Trust funding is supporting work on conflict management and on the building of a human rights culture in the new South Africa. The Trust supports work in both urban and rural settings. In its conflict resolution work, the Trust prioritises support to projects in Kwa-Zulu/Natal. The Trust considers applications from South Africa and does not generally fund work in South Africa originating in the UK.

In recent times, Trust grants have focused on the following issues:

- conflict management in urban and rural settings;
- the use of paralegal training and legal mechanisms to empower farm-workers and other marginalised communities;
- policy research on South Africa's security and defence arrangements;
- industrial and community mediation;
- work which focuses on the Truth and Reconciliation Commission;
- the promotion of the constitutional rights of lesbians and gays;
- work to combat the abuse of women and sexual harassment.

The Trust is an Associate member of Interfund, an international donor consortium with a staffed office in Johannesburg.

While the Trust works almost exclusively in South Africa, on occasion it is willing to fund work elsewhere in Southern Africa, provided that this fits other Trust criteria.

Africa committee
Peter Stark
Andrew Gunn
Beverley Meeson

Co-opted members:
Sarah Hayward
Elaine Unterhalter
Simon Fisher

Examples of recent grants include:

- Christian Fellowship Trust: £20,000 towards the costs of preparing a history of the organisation.
- Freedom of Expression Institute: R225,000 over three years for workshops on freedom of expression and on key legislation.
- South African Centre for Public Interest Information: R405,560 over two years for core costs.

Exclusions

Generally, the trust does not make grants for:

- Work in larger, older national charities which have an established constituency of supporters.
- General appeals.
- Local work (except in Northern Ireland or parts of Yorkshire).
- Building, buying or repairing buildings.
- Providing care for elderly people, children, people with learning difficulties, people with physical disabilities, or people using mental health services.
- Work in mainstream education, including schools and academic or medical research.
- Work on housing and homelessness.
- Travel or adventure projects.
- Business development or job creation.
- Paying off debts.
- Work which should be funded by the state, or has been in the recent past.
- Work which has already been done.
- Work which tries to make a problem easier to live with, rather than getting to the root of it.
- The personal benefit of individuals in need.
- The arts, except where they are used in the context of the kinds of work which the trust does support.

The trust can only support work which is legally charitable.

Refer also to the relevant policy sheets summarised above and available in full on the trust's website, which explain more about what the trust may or may not make grants for.

Applications

The trust supplies detailed guidelines about how to apply for a grant. Those available in 1999 are summarised above but up to date versions should be obtained and read thoroughly, with the relevant policy sheet/s, before attempting to make an application. You also must complete a registration form, on which you have the task of summarising your project in 50 words.

If an application does not fit within the trust's areas of interest, a letter refusing a grant will be sent, usually within four weeks. Other applications may involve meeting the trustees, taking up references, or asking for confidential external advice. Final decisions are made at quarterly trust meetings. It can take up to six months before a final decision is reached.

Applications need to be sent at least 10 weeks before a trust meeting.

The Joseph Rowntree Foundation

Research and development in social policy

£6,964,000 (planned for 2000)

Beneficial area UK.

The Homestead, 40 Water End, York YO30 6WP

Tel. 01904 629241 **Fax** 01904 620072

website www.jrf.org.uk

Correspondent Richard Best, Director

Trustees *Sir Peter M Barclay; Dame Margaret Booth; Kenneth Dixon; Catherine Graham-Harrison; Susan V Hartshorne; Robert Maxwell; J Nigel Naish; Sir William Utting.*

Information available Full and exemplary information available from the foundation, including a pack on its research and development programme with extensive guidance notes for applicants. It also publishes *Search*, a magazine reviewing its research activities, and *Findings*, four-page summaries of the results of its projects. These are available in full on the website above, with details of current research priorities and application procedures.

Summary

This charity's work can perhaps best be seen as the commissioning and dissemination of research rather than the making of grants. However, its work is highly influential in fields of interest to many readers of this book. For information on its specific programmes and interests, readers are directed to the excellent website listed above, which is constantly developing.

The Joseph Rowntree Foundation is the largest independent funder of social science research whose resources do not derive from public funds. It allocates around £8 million a year to its research and development programme which covers the broad fields of

- housing
- social care
- social policy.

The Foundation also carries out practical innovative projects in housing and care through the Joseph Rowntree Housing Trust. We seek to ensure that these and the findings from the research programme are helpful in the development of better policies and practices across the UK.

Background

Joseph Rowntree (1836–1925) was a Quaker and a successful businessman. Contrary to his personal expectations, he became rich in later life. In 1904, he transferred a substantial part of his wealth to the three trusts which bear his name [*the other two trusts have separate entries in this book. Ed.*].

The Joseph Rowntree Foundation shares the hopes of its founder that '*to seek out the underlying causes of weakness or evil*' should contribute to '*the right measures of human advancement*' which over a period of time could 'change the face of England' (the Foundation's work now covers the UK).

General

How the research and development programme works

The Foundation does not make grants: those supported are considered partners in a common enterprise. The Foundation takes a close interest in each project from the outset, often bringing together an advisory group to give guidance on a project, and taking an active role in the dissemination of the project's findings to bring about policy and practice change. Foundation staff oversee the progress of individual projects within the Programme and act as a point of contact throughout.

As a general rule, the Foundation aims to provide full financial support rather than being one of a number of funders. However, where the involvement of another organisation would help the project achieve its aims, joint funding may be considered.

The kinds of projects supported

The Foundation is keen to fund a variety of different kinds of projects, depending on the state of knowledge about the particular topic. Thus if it is a new area of work we would expect to support more conventional research projects, which might help to define or redefine problems or issues. If these are already clear, we would expect to fund projects on the basis of 'what works'. This assessing could encompass evaluations of existing services or demonstration projects testing new ideas; such projects would be expected to incorporate a strong monitoring and evaluation component. If there is evidence, from these projects or elsewhere, of the success of particular interventions, the Foundation would wish to support work aimed at developing and extending this good practice.

Who decides what projects are approved?

Final decisions are made by the Foundation's Trustees who meet quarterly in March, June, September and December to consider proposals. They are assisted by committees covering the Foundation's priority areas. In 2000, these are: the Housing and Neighbourhoods Committee; the Work, Income and Social Policy Committee; the Social Care and Disability Committee; and the Young People and Families Committee.

Each committee includes a number of Trustees, Foundation staff and invited external members with particular knowledge of the relevant fields. Committees meet between Trustees' meetings and make recommendations about the priorities to be pursued and new programmes of work, as well as giving advice on individual proposals. Timetables differ between committees: details are given in Current Priorities (on the website).

In addition, the Trustees meet quarterly as a 'Cabinet' to consider ideas for major projects which cut across committee boundaries; these will usually be commissioned directly.

Programmes and projects

Experience has convinced us that we are more likely to have greater impact on changing policy and practice through supporting programmes of work, rather than individual, free-standing projects. The majority of the projects supported by the Foundation are part of a broader programme; we do not support many unsolicited proposals outside these programmes. The forms of the programmes vary.

- most commonly, proposals will be invited under a number of themes within which specific topics and approaches are identified. This will often be part of a competitive process; with proposals on specific topics requested by a particular date and choices made between them;
- some programmes will contain a number of themes and sub-themes covering a broad canvas within which proposals are sought over a period of time.

How the foundation informs policy and practice

The Foundation gives a high priority to dissemination and works in partnership with the projects it supports to ensure that the findings are of value to policy-makers and practitioners. We normally expect a project to produce:

- A *Findings* – a short briefing paper of around 2,000 words setting out the main findings from the project.
- An *accessible report* of about 15,000 words, usually telling the 'story' of what has been found out rather than a descriptive account of what the project has done.

In addition to the immediate dissemination of results, the Foundation's staff take an active role in identifying possible ways of persisting with the topics and issues that emerge from projects, groups of projects or programmes and of promoting change based upon them. Most of this follow-on work from projects will be initiated by the Foundation, in partnership with the projects.

Current priorities

Most of the projects funded fall into one of four committees, each one having its own priorities for any given year. To find out about a committee's priorities, and any current calls for proposals, follow the following links (on the foundation's website).

- Housing and Neighbourhood priorities
- Social Care and Disability priorities
- Work, Income and Social Policy priorities
- Young People and Families priorities.

Programmes and priorities are continually developing. [*As an illustration we print here the information available from just one of these committees – the one, in autumn 2000, with the shortest such section. Ed.*]

Social care and disability committee

The Committee supports research and development work in relation to people who are particularly excluded in society. This includes disabled people, people with learning difficulties, mental health and community care service users, psychiatric system survivors, disabled children and their families, and older people.

A core criterion in judging all proposals is the extent to which those whom projects are intending to benefit (or research) are involved in identifying the issues to be addressed, and in planning and carrying out the project. We expect all proposals to reflect Britain's multiracial and multicultural society. Within the programmes we have an additional interest in issues which affect disabled people and service users in rural areas.

THE JOSEPH ROWNTREE FOUNDATION – RESEARCH EXPENDITURE			
This has been classified as follows (in £million)			
	1997	*1998*	*1999*
Housing and neighbourhoods	2.1	1.7	1.6
Work, income and social policy	0.9	0.9	0.8
Young people and families	1.0	1.1	1.2
Social care and disability	1.1	1.1	1.1
Development overview	0.6	0.7	0.8
Charitable and voluntary sector	0.1	0.1	0.1
York	0.1	0.1	0.1
Others	2.6	1.5	1.4
Total	8.5	7.2	7.1

We also expect proposals to be located within – or to draw on – the social model of disability and related social models.

Older people's programme

During 2000 the Committee will be canvassing/ commissioning work within the Older People's Programme on

- Unmet Need (this work will now be commissioned)
- Older People from Black & Minority Ethnic Communities (this work will now be commissioned)

Exclusions

With the exception of funds for particular projects in York and the surrounding area, the foundation does not generally support:

- projects outside the topics within its current priorities;
- development projects which are not innovative;
- development projects from which no general lessons can be drawn;
- general appeals, for example from national charities;
- core or revenue funding, including grants for buildings or equipment;
- conferences and other events or publications, unless they are linked with work which the foundation is already supporting;
- grants to replace withdrawn or expired statutory funding, or to make up deficits already incurred;
- educational bursaries or sponsorship for individuals for research or further education and training courses;
- grants or sponsorship for individuals in need;
- work that falls within the responsibility of statutory bodies.

Applications

The detailed guidelines from the foundation are quoted extensively below as a general guide to good practice for these kind of applications.

Initial enquiries: The foundation's staff are happy to give advice to those uncertain about the relevance of a proposal for the foundation, or the form in which it should be presented. Proposers are advised to obtain a copy of the most recent Research and Development information before making a proposal (www.jrf.org.uk or, if no access to internet, call 01904 629241). A draft proposal or short outline covering the main headings identified below, received *early*, is welcome and usually better than a telephone call. These should be sent to:

Dr Janet Lewis, Research Director, Joseph Rowntree Foundation, The Homestead, 40 Water End, York YO30 6WP (Telephone: 0904 629241) or the relevant Committee Secretary, as follows:

Housing: Theresa McDonagh
Social Policy and Social Care:
Barbara Ballard
Disability and Community Care:
Alex O'Neill
Voluntary Action: Pat Kneen

The form of the proposal: The foundation does not have an application form for proposals but does require them to follow a standard format. You should provide two unbound copies of the proposal presented as follows:

- a succinct but clear proposal of a maximum 3,000 words;
- a summary of the proposal of not more than 600 words;
- completed copies of the foundation's project budget forms, with supporting details;
- a CV for the project proposer (and worker/s if known).

Any proposal not submitted in this way may be returned for revision and thus delayed for consideration by the relevant committee.

The required structure of proposals is the same whether you are making an unsolicited proposal or responding to a particular programme of work.

What should the proposal cover?

Title: Give the project a short, explanatory title.

Background: This section should explain the reasons for undertaking the project. You must place the proposed piece of work in the context of existing knowledge and practice, demonstrating a familiarity with the field and the relationship of your proposal to relevant recent or current work being carried out by others.

You should also explain the extent to which the new project will relate to or build upon previous work.
Demonstration projects must give details about the innovative nature of the work and the evidence that such a development is likely to be beneficial. Projects concerned to transfer good practice from one setting to another must also provide evidence that the practice is based on a sound assessment of 'what works'.
Research proposals should indicate what gaps in knowledge the proposed project seeks to fill.

Aims: You must clearly state the aims of the proposal.

Policy relevance: You must draw out the policy or practice implications of the proposed work. Be as explicit as possible about the scale and nature of the policy or practice questions your project will address and also the timeliness of the proposal.

Methods: You must state clearly the methods to be adopted and why they are appropriate. This principle applies to both practice- and research-based work. Those proposing research projects should include details of the approach to be adopted; the way in which the work would be pursued (e.g. how samples for either qualitative or quantitative work would be chosen, numbers involved, methods of analysis). Demonstration and other development projects need to provide details of the work to be carried out and show how the activities would be monitored and evaluated.

Timetable: You must provide a schedule setting out the elements of the work to be done. This should cover what activities will be carried out, when they will occur, how they relate to other activities and how long they will take. You must allow time within your schedule to complete the required outputs (usually a *Findings* and an accessible report). The foundation gives close attention to ensuring that projects are completed on time (elements of funding may be withheld in the event of delays).

Staffing: Those submitting the proposal should include a curriculum vitae detailing their qualifications, experience and any relevant publications. Similar details should be included for other key workers, where known. You should also provide information about the current and likely future commitments of staff who will be working on the project and the ways in which they would fit the additional work in with existing commitments. Any known or possible additional facilitation expenses for disabled people on the team should be included in the budget.

Dates for submissions: Dates when applications need to be received in order to be considered by the next cycle of committee and trustee meetings are shown on www.jrf.org.uk

Joseph Rowntree Reform Trust

Innovative and reforming work, ineligible for charitable status

About £750,000 (2000)

Beneficial area Mainly UK.

The Garden House, Water End, York YO30 6WQ

Tel. 01904 625744 **Fax** 01904 651502

e-mail jrrt@jrrt.org.uk

Correspondent Joy Boaden, Secretary

Trustees *Archy Kirkwood MP, Chair; Professor Lord (David) Currie; Christine Day; Pam Giddy; Christopher Greenfield; Diana Scott; Lord (David) Shutt; Professor Lord (Trevor) Smith.*

Information available An excellent leaflet including applications procedures and grant details, largely reprinted below; also a brief history of the trust entitled *Trusting in Change, A Story of Reform*, published 1998.

Summary

Grants for non-charitable political campaigning, overwhelmingly in Britain.

General

The trust was established in 1904 as the Joseph Rowntree Social Service Trust. It is one of three trusts set up by Joseph Rowntree, a Quaker businessman with a lifelong concern for the alleviation of poverty and other great social ills of his and future days. The three trusts are all entirely independent of each other and each has its own separate entry in this volume.

Though the trust is probably best known for its continuing support, in the name of political diversity, of the Liberal Democrat Party and its predecessors, it has supported liberal thought and activity in almost every political party in Britain (including, for example, paying for professional research assistance for David Trimble after his election as leader of the Ulster Unionist Party). The trust's work goes beyond parliamentary politics. It played an important part in the great development of British pressure groups in the 1970s – it was an early and major supporter of Amnesty, for example – and in recent years it has been the biggest supporter, in financial terms, of the movement for constitutional change that is now in hand. Where next? Perhaps a greater interest in local diversity (it has already given some support to the North East Convention in this area)? Or more attention to Europe wide developments in citizenship? However it is the strength of this trust in recent years that it has been willing, as well as able, to address big questions such as these without being much influenced by the immediate pressures or fashions of the day.

The trust's information leaflet explains that:

> ... it differs from almost every other trust in this book in one crucial respect; it is not a charity [*the other similar organisation is the smaller Barrow Cadbury Trust. Ed.*]. It pays tax on its income and is therefore free to give grants for political purposes; to promote political reform and constitutional change as well as the interests of social justice. It does so by funding campaigning organisations and individuals who have reform as their objective, and since it remains one of the very few sources of funds of any significance in the UK which can do this, it reserves its support for projects which are ineligible for charitable funding.
>
> From its assets, over £30 million in value (held mainly in major investment trusts and properties), the trustees allocate a potential grant budget of around £750,000 each year.

The trust's guidance notes go on to state:

> The trust's principal concern is the continuity of reform within the democratic system. It seeks to foster creative intervention by anticipating and brokering change within the body politic, and by identifying the points where the minimum amount of thrust will have the maximum effect when directed as accurately and efficiently as possible.
>
> Always aiming for good value from the projects it supports, the trust looks for those ideas whose time has come, or is about to come, and offers small amounts of money (as well as sometimes quite large amounts) at the moment when it judges that the most positive results can be achieved.
>
> The trust aims to correct imbalances of power; strengthening the hand of individuals, groups and organisations who are striving for reform. It rarely funds projects outside the UK, directing most of its resources towards campaigning activity in this country, and will not fund research or any other charitable activity.
>
> As a rule, the trust provides either funding for specific projects or seed corn grants to enable campaigns to get off the ground and attract alternative funding.

Political grants

The trust is not committed to the policies of any one political party, and has supported individual politicians or groups promoting new ideas and policies from all the major parties in the UK. Grants are not normally given towards the administrative or other costs of party organisations. Direct party support has, however, been given when trustees have judged that particular political developments should be fostered, especially those central to a healthy democratic process such as constitutional and electoral reform.

The trust's political grants aim to encourage the exchange of views and ideas among people involved in the political process, redress the balance of inequality between the parties and stimulate radical change.

Political groups which have received grants include: Labour Campaign for Electoral Reform, the Association of Liberal Democrat Councillors, Campaign for a Scottish Assembly, Charter 88, Electoral Reform Society, Tory Reform Group, Labour Co-ordinating Committee, Labour Initiative on Co-operation, the Three Hundred Group and Conservative Mainstream.

Social justice

The trust has helped a large number of non-party pressure groups and other organisations which are ineligible for charitable funding, but which need assistance for particular purposes in the short term (the trust will not normally provide long-term funding). Such groups need not be national organisations, but the national relevance of local campaigns is a crucial factor that trustees will consider.

Some examples of groups helped are Amnesty International, Friends of the Earth, Plain English Campaign, Campaign for Press and Broadcasting

Freedom, WaterWatch, Genetics Forum, and Inquest.

Personal awards

The trust occasionally gives personal awards to effective individuals.

Exclusions

The trust will not fund research or any other charitable activity. It rarely funds projects outside the UK.

Applications

The process of applying for a grant is straightforward and unbureaucratic. There are no application forms. Applicants should simply write to the trust's secretary, succinctly outlining the nature of the project and what it hopes to achieve, and enclosing a budget and any other supporting documents where appropriate.

'Proposals are judged on their merits within the prevailing social, political and economic climate, so beyond the broad aims outlined above there cannot be any advance guidance about which areas of activity the trust is likely to support, the amount of funding which might be available or for how long.'

Trust staff make an initial assessment and can reject inappropriate applications. Those which pass this first stage are considered in greater detail but may still be rejected by the trust's office. All staff rejections are reported to the trustees at their next meeting, when those applications which have survived the preliminary vetting are submitted to the trustees for decision.

The meetings take place in March, June, September and December. Applications must be submitted at least one month in advance of the meeting dates. A system of small grants, up to £3,000, also operates between quarterly meetings. Such grants must be agreed by three trustees, including the chairman, and applications can be considered at any time. In exceptional circumstances, larger grants may also be agreed at any time, but only by the unanimous postal decision of the trustees.

The J B Rubens Charitable Foundation

Mainly Jewish causes

£351,000 (1998/99)

Beneficial area UK and Israel.

Berkeley Square House, Berkeley Square, London W1X 5LE

Tel. 020 7491 3763

Correspondent Michael Phillips

Trustees *Michael Phillips; J B Rubens Charity Trustees Limited.*

Information available Annual report and accounts available on file at the Charity Commission.

General

In 1998/99 the trust had assets of £8.4 million, which generated an income of £299,000. Administrative costs of £103,000 were high considering that only two new grants were awarded in the year.

Grants totalling £351,000 were made to eight beneficiaries, nearly all of them other trusts and foundations, most being regularly supported.

The largest beneficiaries were the Ruth and Michael Phillips Charitable Trust (£115,000), the Jerusalem Foundation (£109,000) and, not supported in the previous year, the Jewish Educational Development Trust (£80,000).

Others included the Phillips Family Charitable Trust (£20,000); Simon Wiesenthal Centre (£15,000) and the Charities Aid Foundation (£10,000, probably as a vehicle for making further small donations). The only other beneficiary not in the previous year's list was the Jewish Blind and Physically Handicapped Society, which received £500.

Exclusions

No grants are made to individuals.

Applications

In writing to the correspondent.

The Rubin Foundation

Jewish charities, general

£1,293,000 (1998/99)

The Pentland Centre, Squires Lane, London N3 2QL

Tel. 020 8346 2600

Correspondent A McMillan, Secretary

Trustees *Carolyn Kubetz; Alison Mosheim; Angela Rubin; R Stephen Rubin; Andrew Rubin.*

Information available Report and accounts on file at the Charity Commission.

Summary

This appears to be a highly personal trust, with a few major donations accounting for most of its activity.

General

Endowment income runs at about £300,000 but is supplemented from time to time by further major donations, probably from the Rubin family. The foundation has recently embarked upon a new practice of making occasional £1 million grants, starting with London's Holocaust Museum in 1995, followed by a further £1 million for University College London in 1999.

The trustees' report for 1998/99 reads as follows:

> The major donation made during the year was £1 million paid to the UCL Development Fund to purchase the building for the School of Public Policy at University College. This enables the School to have a headquarters building near the college and to have proper working facilities, etc.
>
> The other major donation and commitment was for a further donation of £50,700 to Resources for Autism, to help the charity in its endeavours to locate a headquarters. This was backed up by payments to a number of Jewish charities, as has been the norm.

The 1998/99 annual report lists 27 other grants of £300 or more, and the following organisations received support in both 1997/98 and 1998/99:

Joint Jewish Charitable Trust (£51,000 in 1998/99 and £210,000 in 1997/98); Community Security Trust (£35,000 and £7,500); Board of Deputies Charitable Foundation (£20,000 and £10,000); Jewish Care (£15,000 and £6,000); L'Chaim Society Trust (£15,000 and £10,000); West London Synagogue

(£15,000 and £11,000), and World Jewish Relief (£5,000 and £15,000).

Large grants also went to the Friends of the Philharmonia (£16,000); Jewish Association for Business Ethics (£10,000), and the Holocaust Educational Trust (£6,000).

A few other non-Jewish organisations appeared at the bottom end of the list:

Hertfordshire Lawn Tennis Association (£2,500); Sue Harris Bone Marrow Trust (£600), and Arsenal FC's Community Unit (£500).

Nearly £3,000 was spent on grants of £250 or less.

'The £95,000 included in Designated Funds at the year end is expected to be utilised in the forthcoming year. The charity has pledged £50,000 to Oxford University, £25,000 to Save the Children and £20,000 has been reserved for Lancashire and Cumbria Health Authority.'

Applications

The trust has committed its funds for the next few years, and it uses the remainder for chosen charities known to members of the family, and those associated with the Pentland Group plc.

Unsolicited applications are not welcomed, and individuals should not apply.

The Rufford Foundation

Nature conservation, sustainable development, environment, general

£1,922,000 (1999/2000)

Beneficial area Developing countries, UK.

5th Floor, Babmaes House, 2 Babmaes Street, London SW1Y 6HD

Tel. 020 7925 2582 **Fax** 020 7925 2583

e-mail /taylor@rufford.org

website www.rufford.org

Correspondent Siân Taylor, Trust Administrator

Information available Annual report and accounts.

Summary

Nearly £2 million is donated every year, three quarters of which goes to charities involved in environmental conservation, usually for projects in developing countries. Larger grants, of £10,000 or more, tend to go to 'green' organisations. Charities working in other fields, such as health and social welfare, are also supported, but are more likely to receive smaller grants, typically between £500 and £5,000. The trustees tend to favour charitable organisations with a national rather than local perspective.

In 2000 the foundation said that available funds were limited due to existing commitments.

General

The foundation was established in 1982 by John Hedley Laing, a member of the wealthy Laing construction family, who is also a trustee of WWF-UK, Conservation International and the Wildlife Protection Society of India.

The foundation gives the following helpful information on its website.

Frequently asked questions

1. Are there funds available now?
There are only limited funds currently available due to our existing commitments. Only projects which meet our criteria in full are eligible, so please ensure that this is the case before you apply.

2. How long does it take for applications to be processed and responded to?
We strive to respond to all applications within 4 weeks of receipt. Please do not telephone us, we will contact you!

3. Are there any time limits or 'closing dates' for applications?
No. Applications are accepted throughout the year.

4. Is there a grant minimum?
The minimum grant awarded is £500.

5. What is the maximum grant awarded?
There is no set maximum, however, usually no gift in excess of £5,000 is granted for any non-conservation/environmental projects. Moreover, even in this sector new gifts are unlikely to be in excess of £5–10,000.

6. If a charity has been refused funding, is there an appeals procedure?
Whilst we sympathetically consider all applications which meet with our criteria, with limited funds available it is not possible to either give reasons why applications are not successful or enter into any dialogue or correspondence regarding projects which have been refused funding.

7. If our application is not successful, may we re-apply at a later date?
As long as the application meets with all our criteria, re-applications can be made a minimum of 12 months after the initial application. Applications which fail to meet our criteria are rejected and informed.

Annual report 1999/2000

The trustees' annual report for 1999/2000 reads as follows:

Donations of £1,922,246 (1999 – £1,956,871) were made during the year, with the total number of charities to which donations were being made 74 (1999 – 108).

The trustees have a strong interest in nature conservation, the environment and sustainable development with a large percentage of the foundation's funding going to these areas. The six largest gifts of £100,000 and over went to conservation charities; £364,759 to the World Wildlife Fund to fund various overseas conservation projects; £306,830 to Conservation International to fund various Aqua RAP (Rapid Assessment Programme) and Marine RAP projects; £163,500 to Royal Geographical Society (Whitley Awards); £149,300 to Peace Parks Foundation; £107,500 to TRAFFIC International and £100,000 to the EIA Charitable Trust to fund various conservation related projects.

The trustees aim to concentrate its major funding for projects in non first world countries where funds are most scarce.

Over the last twelve months the trustees have continued their policy of moving towards granting larger amounts to fewer organisations and this is reflected by the average gift increasing from £18,119 in 1998/99 to £26,136 this year.

The trustees are keen to support causes other than nature conservation, the environment and sustainable development, however, gifts will generally be in the range £500 to £5,000. …

In addition to the six-figure grants mentioned above, the grants list showed a further 31 awards ranging from £5,000 to £71,000, with 19 of the beneficiaries having received grants for a similar amount in the previous year.

Over half were conservation charities or others working overseas, such as the Wildlife Protection Society of India (£63,000); Royal Botanic Gardens, Kew (£50,000); Wildlifeline (£31,000); International Society for Ecology and Culture (£15,000), and United Mission to Nepal (£13,000).

Other beneficiaries included Abbotsholme School (£48,000); Rugby School (£12,000); the Design Museum (£45,000); Help the Aged (£20,000);

Changing Attitude Trust (£20,000); Canine Partners for Independence (£10,000); London Studio Centre (£9,000), and Charterhouse in Southwark (£7,500).

Recipients of grants for under £5,000 included African Initiatives, Sight Savers International, Link Camden, Nottinghamshire Royal Society for the Blind, National Missing Persons Helpline, Friends of Russian Children, Hampshire Autistic Society and Bognor Fun Bus. 20% of the grants in this range were repeated from the year before.

In April 2000 the trustees had already approved £2.8 million in future grant commitments.

Exclusions

The foundation cannot consider proposals for:

- building or construction projects
- non-charitable organisations
- grants to individuals

and, in addition, the trustees tend not to provide gifts to projects which seek to exclusively benefit local communities, such as playgroups, youth clubs, luncheon clubs.

The Rufford Foundation rarely accepts applications for funding salaries.

There is a definite and conscious attempt to avoid replacing statutory funding.

The foundation does not make loans.

Applications

All applications must be received by post and meet with the following criteria:

- All applicants must be charities registered in the UK.

Applications must include:

- a comprehensive plan outlining the project for which funding is being sought
- a full budget
- a covering letter with contact details
- a copy of the charity's most recent accounts
- a copy of the latest annual report (if available)

Applications are assessed monthly. Gifts over £5,000 will be considered at trustees' meetings held twice a year. Each application is assessed individually and while the trust strives to respond quickly, it only has one full-time member of staff, so please be patient. Any incomplete applications received, or applications which fail to meet with the trust's criteria, as outlined above, will immediately be rejected.

The Raymond & Beverley Sackler Foundation

Cambridge University, the British Museum

£410,000 (1999)

Beneficial area UK.

15 North Audley Street, London W1Y 1WE

Correspondent Christopher Mitchell, Solicitor

Trustees *Dr Raymond Sackler; Dr Richard Sackler; Jonathan Sackler; Christopher Mitchell; Dr Ronald Miller; Paul Manners; Raymond Smith.*

Information available Annual report and accounts.

General

The foundation's grantmaking is sustained by regular donations, of between £250,000 and £1 million a year, from Napp Laboratories Ltd, a company in which two of the trustees (Dr Richard Sackler and Jonathan Sackler) have a beneficial interest. Further grants (£100,000 in 1999) are made in support of the foundation's interests by a similarly named Canadian foundation.

In its own words, 'The practice of our foundation is to identify charitable beneficiaries with the assistance of our Trustees' and so grant applications are not accepted.

Since it was established in 1988, almost all of the foundation's grant aid has been given in large annual donations to the British Museum and Cambridge University. Grants in the three most recent years for which information was available were as follows:

	1999	*1998*	*1997*
British Museum	£80,000	£866,000	£255,000
Cambridge University	£330,000	£60,000	£283,000
Royal College of Psychiatrists	–	–	£10,000

The Institute of Astronomy was named as the recipient at Cambridge University in 1996, but it is not known whether this was the same beneficiary as in subsequent years.

Applications

Grants are not open to application.

The Alan and Babette Sainsbury Charitable Fund

General

£416,000 (1999)

See entry for the Sainsbury Family Charitable Trusts

Tel. 020 7410 0330

Correspondent Michael Pattison, Director

Trustees *Simon Sainsbury; Miss Judith Portrait.*

Information available Weak annual report and accounts, but with full grants listing.

Summary

The fund's policies are in the process of changing. In future grants are likely to go solely or mainly to specific programmes within the fields of interest set out below and to be initiated by the trustees rather than in response to unsolicited applications, as was to some extent the situation in the past. The trustees will develop programmes under the following headings:

- education
- health and social welfare
- overseas
- scientific and medical research
- the arts
- religion

The fund is ending its practice of regular support for the general funds of its beneficiaries.

General

This trust, during the lifetime of Alan Sainsbury, was not administered as part of the Sainsbury family group of trusts. This was changed by the trustees after his death in 1998 and it is now adopting the usual policies of focused grantmaking that is the standard for all the Sainsbury Family Trusts. However, the relatively modest income in relation to the large number of fields of activity being considered suggests the fund may find it hard to have very much impact.

In 1999 the trustees reviewed the capacity of the fund to continue to support all the charities which have been regular beneficiaries.

The Fund has in the past made grants towards the general funds of its beneficiaries. In the future trustees hope to provide support for a limited number of specific programmes within the chosen fields of interest. Proposals are likely to be invited by the trustees or initiated at their request. Unsolicited applications are unlikely to be successful, even if they fall within an area in which the trustees are interested.

The income of the fund in 1999 was only £468,000, so the level of new grant approvals noted below is not likely to be sustained.

The trust is staffed by Michael Pattison, Director, and Victoria Hornby, Executive.

Annual report 1998/99

Grants approved during the year were analysed as follows:

	No.	Amount
Education	4	£109,000
Health and social welfare	30	£166,000
Overseas	7	£554,000
Scientific and medical research	7	£56,000
The arts	6	£29,000
Religion	5	£61,200
Total	59	£974,000

Education

A grant of £100,000 to the Jewish Preparatory School accounted for most of the total under this heading. £10,000 was given to the Writers and Scholars Educational Trust.

Health and social welfare

There were two grants of more than £10,000 and 25 smaller awards. The major beneficiaries were as follows:

- Blessed Trinity Housing Association (£23,000 for start-up costs);
- National Self-Harm Network (£36,000 over three years for core costs).

Grants of £10,000 went to the National Children's Centre, Runnymede Trust and Willen Hospice Appeal. The smaller awards were divided mostly between campaigning organisations such as the Minority Rights Group and the Prisoners of Conscience Appeal Fund, and Jewish charities such as Nightingale House and the British Friends of Neve Shalom.

Overseas

A grant of £450,000 to Pestalozzi Children's Village Trust (to support the education of overseas students) made up much of this total. Otherwise only the grant of £79,000 for the Canon Collins Educational Trust for Southern Africa was for more than £6,000.

Scientific and medical research

Oxford's Diabetes Research Laboratories received £25,000. Other beneficiaries included the Medical Foundation for the Care of Victims of Torture and the Shaare Zadek Medical Centre.

The arts

Six modest grants, led by £6,000 each for the Anna Freud Centre and for the Young People's Theatre at English Stage.

Religion

£36,000 was given to the Holocaust Educational Trust for a three-year educational programme, and £24,000 to the Council for Christian and Jews.

Applications

See the guidance for applicants in the entry below for the Sainsbury Family Charitable Trusts. A single application will be considered for support by all the trusts in the group.

However, for this as for most of the trusts, 'proposals are likely to be invited by the Trustees or initiated at their request. Unsolicited applications are unlikely to be successful, even if they fall within an area in which the Trustees are interested.'

The Sainsbury Family Charitable Trusts

over £50,000,000 (1998/99)

See the entries for the individual trusts

9 Red Lion Court, London EC4A 3EF

Tel. 020 7410 0330 **Fax** 020 7410 0332

Correspondent Michael Pattison, Director

Information available Annual reports, with full grant lists, varying from the excellent (Gatsby) to the perfunctory. Websites, in varying degrees of development, for the Ashden, Gatsby and Woodward trusts.

Summary

These trusts, listed below, each have their own entries in this book (except for a few which are too small). They are, however, administered together and an application to one is taken as an application to all. On the whole, though, these trusts are proactive rather than reactive and responses to unsolicited applications form only a very modest part of their grantmaking.

Collectively, they make over 1,000 grants a year, valued at over £50 million in the most recent years for which information is available. Most grants are for more than £5,000 and some of them are valued in millions of pounds. They cover a very wide range of activities and interests, as can be seen from the listing in the box on page 275. Nevertheless, even when taken together, these trusts do not form a 'generalist' grant-making organisation – by and large they only fund within chosen priorities.

There has long been an interest in parenting, family welfare and child development that spreads across a number of trusts. In the summer of 2000 there was also a general interest across the trusts in self-help activities for the promotion of mental health and in small scale projects providing practical help for refugees.

The trusts each have their own policies but they have common characteristics, even though none of these are universally found. Most of the trusts say that they 'prefer to support innovative schemes that can be successfully replicated or become self-sustaining'. The Gatsby annual report could be speaking for them all when it says that its 'aim is to be original, to be pro-active, to be willing to work in unfashionable sectors, and to persist with particular programmes over a long period'. These characteristics make them among the most interesting funders in Britain.

In the past some readers of these books have been frustrated by the trusts' policy of discouraging unsolicited applications, even from those working in their specific fields of interest and in the very ways in which they say they are most interested.

Happily, the trusts have now made it clear that they do indeed like to hear about new, relevant work, and have suggested appropriate ways of bringing this to their attention: 'If you think your work really does fit the interests and approach described in one of the trust entries, send a brief letter (definitely not more than two sides of A4) to the director at the joint office. Where the staff sense the idea could strike a chord with one of the sets of trustees, they will follow it up with you.'

The trusts are also keen to handle telephone enquiries sympathetically, so that time is not wasted at either end on detailed written applications which have no hope of success. They do not want to discourage informal approaches from people trying something new but who have little experience of dealing with trusts and foundations. 'These contacts do from time to time bring forward the kinds of activity which the staff have not encountered in their usual networks.'

Like many other grantmakers, these trusts want to minimise time spent by both their small staff and by applicants on elaborately-documented proposals which will not interest trustees, or on repeated approaches by professional fundraisers. They are especially, and reasonably, unimpressed by applicants who address the same material simultaneously to several, or even most, of the 18 trusts in the group, despite the advice in successive editions of this and other guides.

In these editors' experience, all applications, solicited or not, are in fact carefully read and grants are sometimes made, even if seldom and then for small amounts. However, there is little point in approaching the trusts for help in fields outside their declared interests – it wastes the time of both parties. These interests are listed in the table on page 275, but they are often more specific than can be shown here, so the full entry for the trust concerned should be read, as well as the information below under 'Applications', which applies to all the trusts.

There are three trusts in the group which welcome unsolicited applications for small grants in their field of interest:

Woodward – on the application form provided. See that entry.

Headley – a small budget for aids for disabled people. See that entry.

Gatsby – grants of less than £2,000 to help disadvantaged children.

THE SAINSBURY FAMILY TRUSTS (FIGURES FOR MOST RECENT YEAR AVAILABLE)

	Income	*Grants*
Gatsby Charitable Foundation	£22.5 million	£32.8 million
Linbury Trust	£8.3 million	£3.4 million
Monument Trust	£5.0 million	£3.5 million
Headley Trust	£3.8 million	£6.0 million
Jerusalem Trust	£3.7 million	£3.1 million
Kay Kendall Leukaemia Fund	£2.0 million	£2.1 million
Ashden Charitable Trust	£0.8 million	£0.9 million
Staples Trust	£0.6 million	£0.9 million
Tedworth Charitable Trust	£0.6 million	£1.0 million
Glass-House Trust	£0.6 million	£0.8 million
J J Charitable Trust	£0.5 million	£0.7 million
Alan & Babette Sainsbury Charitable Fund	£0.5 million	£1.0 million
Woodward Trust	£0.5 million	£0.4 million
Three Guineas Trust	£0.6 million	£0.3 million
Elizabeth Clark Charitable Trust*	£0.1 million	£0.1 million
Mark Leonard Trust*	£0.1 million	£0.1 million
Indigo Trust*	n/a	n/a

* These trusts are too small to have separate entries in this book.

(The Monument Historic Buildings Trust, also appearing in the full list of these organisations, is not a significant grant-making body.)

General

The Sainsbury family, none of whom are now involved in managing the business of that name, have an extraordinary record of philanthropy, which is continuing. No less than £22 million was received in further donations in 1998/99, £18 million of it for the Headley and Jerusalem Trusts, both headed by Sir Timothy Sainsbury. The trusts listed in the box above, with the investment income and the value of grant approvals in the most recent year for which they are available, represent endowments from no less than three generations of the family.

Most of the trusts, though not all, continue to hold the bulk of their endowments as shares in J Sainsbury plc. Previous editions of this book have argued that the case for diversification seems overwhelming. While family members were running the business, they may reasonably have wished the benefits of their exertions to be enjoyed by the trusts they had endowed, but this no longer applies. J Sainsbury is but one of a number of competing retailers, even if it should be felt that retailing is itself the pre-eminently advantageous investment sector.

In fact, the sharp decline in the value of Sainsbury shares (though not in its dividends) has hit the asset values of the trusts – though not, yet, their incomes. However, even these incomes are at risk. If the relative profitability of the Sainsbury company were to decline, it would be too late to diversify without substantial loss.

In most cases the settlor (and often his or her wife or husband) is, as would be expected, among the trustees, who seldom number more than five and are often just three. In all except two of the larger trusts another trustee is Miss Judith Portrait, whose position in the trust world is remarkable. She is the new treasurer of the great Henry Smith's Charity (which has its own entry in this book) which gives grants of over £20 million a year and, under its new management, is introducing exciting new programmes. With the Sainsbury trusts she is involved, voluntarily or professionally, with awards of over £50 million a year. She is also, through the business of Portrait Solicitors, the solicitor for the Sainsbury Family Charitable Trusts as well as a trustee. These editors always prefer to see such arrangements avoided, although in this case the various payments involved, for legal services, are so small as to be insignificant.

The Sainsbury trusts of which Miss Portrait is a trustee hold no less than 59 trustee meetings a year, so she has a remarkable workload when this is viewed alongside her other commitments.

The administrative costs of these trusts are low, as a percentage of the value of grants, no doubt (among other considerations) because the awards overall are relatively few, but big.

The staff of the trusts

There are over 20 staff. Michael Pattison is director of all the trusts, but many of his colleagues have dual roles. They typically act as the executive for one or more trusts but they also have sectoral responsibilities for work in particular fields. The director described their job for the previous edition of this book as follows: 'The job of my staff, sometimes very much in partnership with the trustees, sometimes with delegated instructions to go and work something up, is to engage with organisations which may be able to work with trusts in the territory the trustees identify' – it sounds interesting.

The executive for each trust is named in the annual reports, but there is no publicly available information about the sectoral responsibilities. Some staff are well known in their fields, others less so. Organisations that believe they have genuine matters of common interest to discuss in one of the specialised fields of interest of the trusts may well find that a telephone call will identify the person most concerned. The trusts are not wholly unapproachable to those with common interests, and staff are courteous. On the other hand they cannot talk to all the many thousands of organisations that would welcome further funding for their work.

Unsolicited telephone calls from fundraisers are definitely unwelcome; staff are generally expert in their fields and expect to talk to their peers.

The listed staff for the different trusts, other than Mr Pattison and the finance director, Paul Stokes, are as follows:

Gatsby Charitable Foundation: Dr Yvonne Pinto; Matthew Williams; Victoria Hornby

Linbury Trust: David Brown/ Dr Patricia Morrison

Monument Trust: Matthew Williams; Victoria Hornby

Jerusalem Trust: Joanna Lunn

Headley Trust: Hester Marriott

Kay Kendall Leukaemia Fund: Elizabeth Storer

Ashden Charitable: Trust Jane Shepherd

Staples Trust: Hester Marriott

Tedworth Charitable Trust: Hester Marriott

Glass-House Trust: Hester Marriott

J J Charitable Trust: Jane Shepherd

Alan & Babette Sainsbury Charitable Fund: Victoria Hornby

Woodward Trust: Karin MacLeod

Three Guineas Trust: Joanna Lunn

Elizabeth Clark Charitable Trust: Matthew Williams

Mark Leonard Trust: Jane Shepherd

Indigo Trust: Victoria Hornby

Major grants and programmes

Major capital grants, often of many millions of pounds over the years, are given by the senior members of the family from their older, far larger trusts.

The trusts are best known for their generous support to major national arts institutions. Most famous is the elegant Sainsbury Wing of the National Gallery. And 1998/99 saw continued support for the Sainsbury Art Collection at the University of East Anglia (Gatsby), Somerset House restoration in London (Headley), and the National Theatre (Linbury). Many of the older trusts, with the exception of Gatsby, reflect a passion for opera, with a grant in 1999 of £4.5 million for the Royal Opera House, also from the Linbury Trust. The newer trusts, endowed by younger members of the family, are showing signs of going down the same route, though on an appropriately more modest scale, with the Glass-House Trust giving £210,000 to help develop the work of the Pier Trust in the field of contemporary art.

These arts grants have a higher media profile, but the major capital and core grants awarded to science and medicine are more significant in cash terms and perhaps in changing the fabric of our future lives. The Gatsby-funded Sainsbury Laboratory at the John Innes Centre in Norwich leads research into plant genetics, while the Sainsbury Centre for Mental Health and now the Cognitive Neuroscience Unit at University College London are nationally important institutions funded largely by the Gatsby Foundation. In addition, and not unsurprisingly from the trusts of former business leaders, business schools in London, Oxford and Cambridge have also been generously supported by the Gatsby, Linbury and Monument trusts. The Linbury Trust has also been a consistent and rare funder of work on Chronic Fatigue Syndrome, a condition which few other funders were willing to take seriously until very recently.

Sainsbury funding practice

Though each is distinctive, collectively these trusts, along with a very few others, such as the Carnegie UK and the Joseph Rowntree foundations, set the UK standard for active grantmaking (in the USA an active role for trusts is more common). They have a fine record of helping put new issues on the map by supporting specialised 'issue raising' charities. Large established charities, especially those with extensive fundraising structures, are seldom supported – hence the suggestion, made for a previous edition of this book, that 'where an organisation has got to the point to employ a full-time fundraiser it has probably got to the point to look for people other than us'. The grants lists support this statement.

Generally, in the health and welfare fields, which account for most of the grants, the trusts seek to achieve improvements in society, especially for its weakest or most vulnerable members. If voluntary organisations are the best way of achieving this, they will be supported, but grants are as likely to go to research organisations or to support government or quasi-government initiatives.

The trusts bring two great strengths to their task. First, they are long-term funders, sticking with issues, such as better practice in the care of those who are mentally ill or disabled, over sustained periods in a way that makes the conventional 'three-year grant and then move on' look like social tinkering.

Secondly, they bring involvement and expertise. Trustees, many of them members of three generations of the Sainsbury family, are often personally and seriously involved in the causes that they take up. And they employ expert staff. Over 20 employees have developed widely respected expertise and the trusts have developed extensive networks of advisers, some formally appointed, others consulted as the need arises.

The geographical distribution of local grants

There is a specific criticism to be made of the grants that are awarded for local activities by the group of trusts as a whole (a modest proportion of the group's total grants). They are heavily concentrated on the southern half of England and on London in particular. There may be a case, though it is one seldom heard outside London, that the major institutions based there are national rather than local assets and that, for example, the wonderful Sainsbury Wing of the National Gallery is there for the benefit of all, wherever they live. But even when such national institutions are excluded there seems to be a demonstrable bias towards London and the 'home' counties.

We looked at just the minority of grants that appeared to be for organisations doing practical work on an identifiable local basis (thereby excluding most if not all grants for national institutions, research programmes, universities, campaigning or promotional activities. We also excluded awards of over £100,000 or under £5,000, the former because a few very large grants might distort an already limited sample, the latter because even cumulatively they could have only a modest effect).

This left a sample of 133 such grants, across the whole group of trusts, and we applied it to two halves of England, of equal population, as well as to the other countries in the kingdom. This produced the following results by the number of such grants, their total value and their value per 1,000 population:

The Sainsbury Trusts: who funds what?

The trusts do not all report in exactly the same way, and some figures refer to grant payments and others to new commitments. Nevertheless the following table, taken from the 1998/99 sets of accounts, indicates the main funding areas for the group of trusts as a whole and the number of grants and scale of funding in each. The information is intended to help readers determine which of the detailed entries, and which headings within those entries, may cover the fields of work in which they are interested.

MEDICINE		
Linbury – Chronic Fatigue Syndrome research	15	£435,000
Kay Kendall – leukaemia research	17	£2.1 million
Linbury – other	6	£14,000
Elizabeth Clark – palliative care	5	£132,000
Headley	5	£184,000
HEALTH/DISABILITY/WELFARE		
Gatsby – disadvantaged children	45	£4.4 million
Gatsby – social renewal	2	£255,000
Monument – social development	31	£1.1 million
Alan & Babette Sainsbury – health/social welfare	30	£166,000
Woodward	66	£223,000
Gatsby – mental health	7	£5.2 million
Monument – health and community care	36	£440,000
Monument – AIDS	18	£404,000
Linbury – drug abuse	8	£56,000
Linbury – social welfare	37	£233,000
Staples – women's issues	9	£131,000
Ashden – homelessness	10	£85,000
Ashden – urban regeneration	6	£101,000
Tedworth – parenting, child welfare/development	12	£576,000
Headley – health and social welfare	111	£851,000
Glass-House – parenting, child welfare/ development	16	£383,000
Glass-House – social housing, urban environment	6	£113,000
EDUCATION		
Gatsby (technical education)	23	£4.6 million
Alan & Babette Sainsbury	4	£109,000
Woodward	10	£52,000
Linbury	9	£82,000
J J – literacy support	10	£271,000
Headley	19	£465,000
RESEARCH		
Gatsby (plant science)	6	£13.5 million
Gatsby (cognitive neuroscience)	6	£202,000
Gatsby (economic and social research)	8	£1.8 million
ARTS		
Linbury – art and art education	40	£601,000
Gatsby	8	£844,000
Monument	23	£1.2 million
Woodward	5	£70,000
Alan & Babette Sainsbury	6	£29,000
Ashden – community arts	13	£74,000
Glass-House	3	£270,000
ENVIRONMENT/HERITAGE UK		
Headley – arts and environment	111	£3.8 million
Monument	17	£318,000
Woodward	4	£30,000
Linbury	9	£169,000
Staples – environmental	9	£195,000
Ashden – environmental projects	36	£424,000
J J – environment	19	£344,000
OVERSEAS		
Gatsby (developing countries)	14	£1.5 million
Alan & Babette Sainsbury	7	£554,000
Woodward	2	£6,000
Linbury – education and social welfare	12	£310,000
Staples – overseas development	16	£478,000
Ashden – environmental projects	16	£152,000
J J – environment	4	£84,000
Jerusalem – Christian evangelism/relief work	27	£674,000
Headley – arts and environment	11	£294,000
Headley – developing countries	13	£425,000
RELIGION		
Alan & Babette Sainsbury	5	£61,000
Jerusalem – Christian evangelism/ social responsibility	54	£1.3 million
Jerusalem – Christian media	11	£404,000
Jerusalem – Christian education	21	£722,000
Jerusalem – Christian art	4	£11,000
GENERAL		
Gatsby	14	£456,000
Ashden	9	£42,000
Monument	1	£75,000
Staples	5	£47,000
JJ	4	£23,000
Tedworth	10	£420,000
Glass-House	4	£52,000

South of England	65	£1,825,000	74p
of which, London	*41*	*£1,140,000*	*£1.63*
North of England	19	£551,000	23p
Scotland	5	£107,000	21p
Wales	2	£90,000	31p
Northern Ireland	1	£50,000	30p

On the information available, the situation is unfair. Taxpayers throughout the country are supporting these trusts, through their tax reliefs for which the rest of us have to pay. The trusts should either justify their distribution of local grants in this respect, or change their practice, by extending their networks more widely (or just by giving London a rest for a while).

The smaller Sainsbury family trusts

Most of the trusts are big enough to justify their own entries in this book. However, there are also the following smaller trusts:

The Elizabeth Clark Charitable Trust (CC no. 265206)

Palliative care

£132,000 (1998/99)

Trustees: Judith Portrait; Dr Jane Davey; Dr Gillian Ford.

Staff: Michael Pattison, Director; Matthew Williams, Executive

At present the resources of the trust are being largely reserved for a possible major project, still being set up. The major payment to be made in 1998/99 was of £60,000 to Lifescan Healthcare NHS Trust. £22,000 was paid to the Scottish Partnership Agency for Palliative Care. There were no other grants. The work of the trust is described as follows:

> The Trustees continue to concentrate on palliative care in the community, with the aim of fostering good practice that may be adopted widely. This is achieved through a small portfolio of medium-term projects.

A pattern of grantmaking?

Writing entries for 14 Sainsbury trusts for this book has led these editors to suppose that there is an underlying pattern to much of their grantmaking, no matter how frequent the exceptions. A topic is chosen, say Christian evangelism in the media, or parenting. Then the funds are applied in three ways:

- first, there is support for a major research initiative, typically through an academic organisation (often in the form of action research);
- secondly, there is support on a smaller scale for specialised national groups promoting good practice in the field concerned;
- thirdly, there is support for a small number of service delivery organisations, typically those helping on the ground those whose difficulties are the most severe.

The support by the Glass-House Trust for work on parenting makes a good example:

The 'parenting' awards were led by £217,000 in two grants to help the London Institute of Education's Social Science Research Institute with the running and research costs of A Space.

There was support for the core costs of three national organisations: the Children's Play Council (£20,000), the Parenting Education and Support Forum (£30,000) and Parents at Work (£15,000).

There was also support for a small number of practical projects, led in this case by £46,000 in two grants for the African Caribbean Family Mediation Service for its home–school mediation work in London, but including a few smaller grants such as the £7,000 for St Ambrose Young Families Project in Salford and the £1,500 for Ipswich Youth Advice Centre's Young Parents Support Group.

The Trustees have made a commitment to a major research project, originally commissioned in 1996, for which they expect to draw on their expendable endowment. Bearing this in mind, they do not expect to make other substantial grants unless new resources become available to the Trust. They may from time to time make other small grants out of current income in accordance with the policies set out above, but the priority is to manage their resources in order to complete this major project.

There is a proactive approach to grantmaking and unsolicited applications are unlikely to succeed. 'As a rule the trustees neither support capital nor revenue appeals from hospices nor make grants to individuals.'

The Mark Leonard Trust (CC no. 1040323)

Environmental education, rehabilitation of young people

£118,000 (1998/99)

Trustees: Mark Sainsbury; Mrs Z Sainsbury; J J Sainsbury; Judith Portrait.

Staff: Ms J Shepherd, Executive.

The trust has been endowed by Mark (Leonard) Sainsbury, who donated a further £1.4 million in 1998/99, bringing assets to over £5 million. These may be expected to generate a return of over £200,000 a year in future. The investments are widely spread, and do not include any shares in the Sainsbury company.

The annual report comments on grant-making policy as follows:

Environment (£109,000)

Grants are made for environmental education, particularly supporting projects displaying practical ways of involving children and young adults. Trustees rarely support new educational materials in isolation, but are more interested in helping pupils and teachers to develop a theme over time (such as renewable energy), perhaps combining IT resources ... with exchange visits and sharing of information and ideas between schools ...

The Trustees are also interested in the potential for sustainable transport, energy efficiency and renewable energy in the wider society. In some cases trustees will consider funding research, but only where there is a clear practical application. Proposals are more likely to be considered when they are testing an idea, model or strategy in practice, such as the work being carried out by the Pedestrians Association.

Grants in 1998/99 included those to the Children's Play Council (£34,000 for an internet-based sustainable transport project), Bath Environment Centre (£16,000 towards a salary and a conference), and Forum for the Future (£7,000 for its household Carbon Calculator project).

Youth work (£50,000)

Grants are made for projects that support the rehabilitation of young people who have become marginalised and involved in anti-social or criminal activities. The trustees are also interested in extending and adding value to the existing use of school buildings and encouraging greater involvement of parents, school leavers and volunteers in extra-curricular activities.

Grants were headed by £20,000 for a detached youth work project in Islington and £10,000 for Youth at Risk. There were four 'general' grants, led by £9,000 towards emergency health work in Honduras by MERLIN.

The Indigo Trust (CC no. 1075920)

This is the latest trust to be created within the group (and probably the last, at least for the time being). It is about to start its grantmaking, but has not yet filed its first annual report.

Exclusions

Normally, no grants for individuals, whether for projects, educational fees or to join overseas expeditions. Any organisations other than registered charities or institutions that have charitable status.

Applications

Unsolicited applications are not encouraged (except for a few small and specific programmes) and the trusts warn that 'the vast majority of unsolicited applications are unsuccessful'.

Nevertheless all applications 'will receive careful consideration from all the appropriate ... trusts'. A single application will therefore cover all the trusts in the group. However if applying because of an apparent 'fit' with the work of a particular trust, it would be appropriate to mention this in the application or to address the application to that trust.

If you wish to apply please do so briefly in writing and including the following information:

- details of your charitable organisation – its aims, objectives and planned outcome
- your project proposal – its cost and detailed budget, how you propose to raise the balance of the grant sought from us, and how the project would be evaluated
- the most recent annual report and audited accounts.

It would be appreciated if you would confine your letter of application to two sides of A4 plus the additional items requested. Do not apply to more than one trust; your one application will be considered by all the relevant trusts.

The Robert and Lisa Sainsbury Trust

See below

£4,331,000 (1998/99)

c/o Horwath Clark Whitehill, 25 New Street Square, London EC4A 3LN

Tel. 0207 353 1577

Correspondent David Walker

Trustees *Sir Robert Sainsbury; Lady Lisa Sainsbury; Christopher Stone; Judith Portrait.*

Information available Accounts, with a brief report.

General

This charity is not at present making substantial grants except to closely connected institutions, primarily the University of East Anglia, its wonderful Sainsbury Centre for the Visual Arts, and its associated research units (£4 million in 1998/99 and £1.5 million the previous year).

The only two grants for more than £3,000 in the former year were to Kew Gardens (£10,000), and to Northwick Park and St Marks NHS Trust (£44,000).

This is not one of the jointly administered Sainsbury Family Charitable Trusts, though much of its funding comes from the Gatsby Foundation, which is. The trust has no significant endowment of its own, but relies on new donations for its income.

With only six grants, plus a further £3,000 in general donations, it is surprising that the annual report says that 'grants have been made to a wide range of charities'. Perhaps the phrase has been carried over on a word processor from earlier years.

Exclusions

No grants to individuals.

Applications

To the correspondent, but see above.

Basil Samuel Charitable Trust

General

£473,000 (1998/99)

c/o Great Portland Estates Plc, Knighton House, 56 Mortimer Street, London W1N 8BD

Tel. 020 7580 3040

Correspondent Mrs Coral Samuel

Trustees *Coral Samuel; Richard Peskin.*

Information available Limited annual report, with accounts.

Summary

The trust makes 'a limited number of grants of £25,000 or more to medical, socially supportive, educational and cultural charities plus a number of small donations to other charities'. The larger awards are nearly all part of ongoing annual donations, while the remainder are typically one-off awards for between £1,000 and £10,000.

General

The trust had assets worth £6.4 million in 1999 and income amounted to £456,000. In all, 34 grants, for amounts up to £50,000, totalled £473,000.

Seven grants for £25,000 or more, all but one being repeat awards, amounted to £266,000, or 56% of the total.

Of the 27 remaining grants, 11 ranged from £10,000 to £20,000, and 16 from £1,000 to £6,000. Only five were repeated from the year before.

The beneficiaries could be grouped into the following categories, with examples as follows:

Medicine/healthcare: Royal Free Hospital School of Medicine; The National Hospital for Neurology and Neurosurgery (£50,000 each); Great Ormond Street Hospital Children's Fund (£14,000); Macmillan Cancer Relief; Lord Mayor's Appeal for Leuka 2000 (£10,000 each); British Deaf Association; Global Cancer Concern; Help the Hospices (£5,000 each).

Jewish charities: Jewish Care (£50,000); Community Security Trust (£41,000); Joint Jewish Charitable Trust (£15,000); World Jewish Relief (£6,000).

Arts: Victoria and Albert Museum (£25,000); National Gallery; Royal National Theatre (£20,000 each).

Children/youth: The Prince's Youth Business Trust; Thomas Coram Foundation for Children (£25,000 each); NSPCC (£5,000).

Other: The Dauntsey's School Foundation (£15,000); Racing Welfare Charities; The Police Foundation (£10,000 each); Crimestoppers Trust (£6,000).

Exclusions

Grants to registered charities only.

Applications

In writing to the correspondent.

'The trustees meet on a formal basis annually and regularly on an informal basis to discuss proposals for individual donations.'

The Save and Prosper Charities

Education

£1,054,000 (1998/99)

Beneficial area UK, with a special interest in Islington, outer parts of east London/Essex, and a specific budget for work in Scotland.

Finsbury Dials, 20 Finsbury Street, London EC2Y 9AY

Tel. 020 7417 2332 **Fax** 020 7417 2300

Correspondent Duncan Grant, Director

Trustees *The trustee is the Save and Prosper Group Ltd, which has appointed the following Managing Committee: C J Rye, Chairman; A G Williams; M L Bassett; D Grant.*

Information available Excellent annual report and accounts. A good guidance leaflet for applicants.

Summary

The trusts make grants to educational projects, with an emphasis on helping children with special needs, particularly in disadvantaged areas. Grants range from £100 to £10,000 (a recently introduced maximum) and may be one-off, spread over two years, or on-going subject to annual review.

The charities' resources are heavily over-subscribed, with only a one in nine success rate for new applications.

General

The Save and Prosper Educational Trust was established as part of a tax-avoiding school fees planning service run by the Save and Prosper Group. Further recruitment of parents into the scheme has been stopped by the Inland Revenue and the corresponding income for this trust will diminish to zero by the year 2014.

However, another charity, the Save and Prosper Foundation, is being built up as the old one declines. This entry covers both together. In 1998/99 the trust contributed £869,000 of the grant total given above, and the foundation the balance of £185,000.

There are separate trust sub-committees for the areas of special interest of Romford and Scotland, each awarding about £30,000 of grants in 1998/99.

The charities' joint guidelines include the following:

The support from both [charities] is for UK based educational projects, with an emphasis on special needs, which generally fit into one of the following categories:

- Special needs education including youngsters disadvantaged by disability, background or lack of opportunity.
- Giving something back to the community by way of children's projects that offer education and training that widen the opportunities for youngsters, particularly those children who are in trouble or 'at risk'.
- Primary and secondary schools, universities and museums.
- Supporting school age children and students in all art forms, helping them to gain access to the arts and to better appreciate them.
- Generally, we do not give support direct to individuals but some scholarships and bursaries are made to organisations supporting educational fees and maintenance.
- New and innovative ways of advancing education in the UK.
- Save and Prosper Foundation has a modest unrestricted portion of its budget that is generally used for donations to children's charities.

Within these guidelines consideration will focus on projects dealing with

- drugs and education
- homelessness and education
- literacy and numeracy.

Applications are welcome from throughout the UK but the main focal areas are Islington and Romford. Throughout, some consideration will be given to 'core cost' funding.

The level of support provided

In recent years, we have provided educational grants which have ranged in size from £100 to £10,000. Usually we fund a project for no more than two years. This means we can support a variety of different projects and that we do not face long term commitments. In a few cases, however, we agree to review funding annually [*about 25 out of over 250 grant payments. Ed.*].

THE SAVE AND PROSPER CHARITIES – ANALYSIS OF GRANTS BY CATEGORY

	No. in 97/98	*No. in 98/99*	*Total*
Schools, universities, museums	112	71	£239,000
Community & youth 'at risk'	49	35	£230,000
Arts education	38	38	£143,000
Education and disadvantage	107	79	£442,000
Scholarships and bursaries	33	35	£92,000
New and innovative education	35	33	£240,000

Monitoring the progress of projects

We find it useful to have regular reviews of projects that we support. For example, we sometimes ask for written reports or for a questionnaire to be completed, and for larger levels of funding we arrange review visits.

Grants in 1998/99

The 1998/99 report on the awards of the trust included the following:

202 awards were agreed during the year and they totalled £965,000, although not all have been released. The total expenses of SPET grant giving was £122,000. The value of donations was £965,000; this represents an administration charge of 12%.

The 202 grants were awarded from over 1,800 applications. The success rate for grants has lowered to 1:9 which was a modest improvement as far as the applicants were concerned. This may reflect a sharper focus of the Trustee Managers during the year.

The Edinburgh SPET sub-committee, chaired by David Brown until he retired, and now chaired by Colin Wilson, awarded grants totalling £30,000 and the Romford SPET sub-committee, chaired by Karen Curtis, awarded grants of £33,000 during the year.

Grant analysis

At the start of the financial year, the committee of SPET discussed and agreed that the grant giving guidelines as set out in the applicants flyer would continue to be followed and in particular, to highlight special needs and disadvantage. Further areas of support were to include:

- Drugs related education
- Education and homelessness
- Literacy and numeracy
- Motor projects
- Museums

In view of the finite nature of SPET funds any new commitments were to be for a two year maximum and present commitments would in general be cut back to annual review.

In 1997/98 a policy of selecting specific socially deprived areas for funding was agreed and this was to continue and possibly be expanded in 1998/99.

A ... sample of the donations within the agreed support areas is shown [*in the box above – but note that about one in five grants was for £1,000 or less, a size not represented in these examples. Ed.*].

Drugs related education

Wirral Solvent Abuse, £5,000 pa x 2 years. The award supports a youth worker visiting schools and youth organisations.

Positively Women, London, £4,500. Supporting 10 speaker sessions for women with HIV and/or AIDS on reducing drug dependence and risk reduction.

Sutton Youth Awareness Programme, £5,000 pa x 2 years. Supporting a youth worker who is developing primary school work on strategies to deal with drug related situations.

Education and homelessness

Fairbridge, in Cardiff & Birmingham, £10,000 pa x 2 years. 10 youngsters, unwaged and deemed at risk, many homeless and drug dependent, funded to benefit from a full programme ranging from adventure training, through leadership, personal development, social education and education to career support.

WECAN training, Woolwich, £4,000 pa x 2 years. Funding for a support worker in the training of many homeless clients in employment advice, computer use, interview, CV's, telephone skills and practice interviews.

Housing Associations Charitable Trust (HACT), £5,000 pa x 2 years. Support for homeless youngsters training projects in Bradford and Huddersfield.

Literacy and numeracy

National Trust, Norwich, £5,000. A pilot project of activity days for parents and children at Blickling Hall in IT skills, literacy and numeracy.

Wordsworth Trust, Cumbria, £5,000 pa x 2 years. Subsidising school visits from the deprived parts of West Cumbria, Lancashire and Merseyside.

Dixons City Technology College, Bradford, £15,000. To purchase PC's and software for the literacy and numeracy development of a multi-media centre to be used by the whole community not just the school.

Motor projects

Havering Motorvations, Romford, £6,000. To seed fund the staffing and equipping of a new motor vehicle project for young people 'at risk'.

Rural and Urban Training Schemes (RUTS), Edinburgh, £3,000 pa x 2 years. To support youngsters on the 12 week programme of centre based activities including workshop skills, on and off road riding, team building, literacy, numeracy, the law and victims.

Meridian Trust Association, Portsmouth, £10,000 pa x 2 years. Funding a mechanic/ trainer for this project offering 'at risk' youngsters courses in NVQ motor mechanics, boat building and repairing as well as classes.

Museums

Museum of Scotland, Edinburgh, £10,000. To support the development of a CD-Rom of museum treasures for primary schools.

National Gallery, London, £5,000. Funding the education department for primary school work.

Verulamium Museum Trust, St Albans, £10,000. Supporting a major extension to the museum with funding for interactive displays at the entrance and called 'Virtual Verulamium'.

SPET plans for 1999/2000

Support for 1999/2000 will follow the [guidelines above] with an emphasis on 'special needs'. Within the guidelines ... consideration will also focus on projects dealing with:

- Drugs and education
- Homelessness and education
- Literacy and numeracy

and the geographical focus of:

- Islington
- Romford
- Edinburgh

It was also agreed to give some consideration to 'core cost' funding. The support for the socially deprived areas of Maidstone, Ashington and Bristol will continue and a fourth area may be developed in Harold Hill.

The annual report of the presently smaller Save and Prosper Foundation shows a roughly similar pattern of awards. However there is also a note that many of the smaller awards are co-funding staff fundraising efforts.

Exclusions

Projects that are not usually supported include:

- open appeals from national charities
- building appeals
- charity gala nights and similar events
- anniversary appeals
- appeals by individuals for study grants, travel scholarships or charity sponsorships

Applications

To apply for funding please write a brief letter (not more than two sides of A4) to Duncan Grant, the director. Please set out your reasons for applying and enclose any relevant publicity material and accounts.

Applications are always acknowledged. 'If your application is unsuccessful, we suggest you wait at least a year before reapplying.' Trustees meet in March, May, July, September and December. Applications need to arrive at least a month before the relevant meeting.

The Francis C Scott Charitable Trust

Disadvantaged people in Cumbria and Lancashire

£1,335,000 (1998/99)

Beneficial area Cumbria and Lancashire, especially the northern part.

Sand Aire House, Stramongate, Kendal, Cumbria LA9 4BE

Tel. 01539 723415 **Fax** 01539 794191

website www.fcsct.org.uk

Correspondent Donald Harding, Director

Information available Guidelines for applicants. An exemplary report analysing the past three years' activities. Full accounts with grants list.

Summary

Well over 100 grants, half of them new awards, are made each year towards capital or revenue costs. They vary from under £500 to around £100,000 and are typically for a few thousand pounds. Recipients are charities benefiting socially and economically disadvantaged people in Cumbria and Lancashire.

General

The trust was created in 1963 by Peter Scott, the then chairman of the Provincial Insurance Company. Together with other members of his family he endowed the trust with Provincial shares. It was named in honour of Francis C Scott, who was the previous chairman of the same company and son of its founder.

In 1998/99 the trust had assets of nearly £35 million, generating £1.2 million income.

This trust is exceptionally energetic and impressive. It is active in developing new initiatives, and particularly in its role in improving the performance of the local voluntary sector.

The grant distribution policy of the trust is as follows:

1. We have two areas of geographical priority:
   a) First priority – Cumbria and North Lancashire as far south as Lancaster and Heysham;
   b) Second priority – the rest of the administrative county of Lancashire.

2. Our first concern is socially and economically disadvantaged people and communities. Examples of projects include:
   - work with children and young people, family support, youth clubs, social education, child care.
   - help with special problems, e.g. disability, counselling and advice schemes involving e.g. drug or alcohol abuse.
   - self help projects to provide play facilities in deprived urban situations.
   - schemes to help housebound elderly people on low incomes.
   - services aimed at groups which are under-represented or disadvantaged in their fundraising efforts because of gender, colour, age or lack of English skills.
   - community development including community arts and theatre for e.g. 'special needs' clients.

3. Grants may be towards capital costs or revenue, and range from under £500 to £15,000. We sometimes make annual grants for up to three years for particularly worthwhile projects.

The trust's report on activities for the period 1996/97 to 1998/99 outlined the following areas of particular interest:

- family work to support children in the age range 0 to 12 years;
- youth work with young people of 12 to 20 years, including leader training;
- building the infrastructure and capacity of the voluntary sector.

In the trust's three-year review of activities it says that:

The trust welcomes and actively seeks 'funding partnerships' with other grant givers and service providers to enable the development of projects within Cumbria and Lancashire.

We aim not to provide substitute funding for services which are statutory responsibilities of local authorities, but we may look favourably on partnership funding with the public sector to provide additional services to the disadvantaged.

15% of the recipients had received funding in each of the three years under review and another 37% had received a repeat award. It appears, therefore, that around half the grants in a year are new ones.

Grants in 1998/99

'In 1998/99 we made grants to 161 organisations: 98 grants were for amounts up to £5,000, while grants of up to £25,000 accounted for about 67% of the total value of grants made.' The trust also donated over £2.75 million (£1.4 million each) to establish endowment funds for Kendal Brewery Arts Centre and the Lake District Art Gallery and Museum Trust, institutions which the trust helped to found and has consistently supported for many years. These grants were made to encourage the two charities towards financial independence.

More than 90% of the funds was distributed in the first priority area of Cumbria and north Lancashire. The rest of Lancashire got just 6% of expenditure, in 29 grants (averaging £3,000). Only two were for more than £5,000, to ChildLine North West, Manchester (£15,000, repeat) and Langley House Trust (£10,000 to fund the deficit over three years of employing a resettlement worker to run a drugs rehabilitation centre at Chatterton, Lancashire).

There were only three recipients classified as being completely outside the priority areas, as follows:

The Charities Aid Foundation (which received an annual payment of £20,000 in the three years up to 1998/99 for the 'PFS Voucher Scheme); the Association of Charitable Foundations (£1,000), and Southport Victim Support (£500).

The following major projects were described in the three-year review.

Youth work

In April 1995 we convened a meeting of the major voluntary youth service providers in Cumbria in an attempt to encourage a more co-ordinated and co-operative approach to the planning of youth service provision in Cumbria. The result was the formation of Cumbria Youth Alliance which was set up to be a voice for the voluntary youth service, a strategic planning body, and a forum to encourage good practice, appropriate quality standards, and innovative thinking in provision.

In 1998/99 a £5,000 grant from the trust helped the Cumbria Youth Alliance to produce a strategic plan entitled 'Framework for the Future'.

Example grants: Cumbria County Council, Whitehaven Breakout project [£109,000 in 1998/99, a total of £424,000 over five years]:

This expanding project is developing throughout the west coast of Cumbria, and is a joint initiative involving local schools, the Police, the Education Welfare Service, the local Council and the Careers Service. The aim is to provide young people with an educational experience which is complementary to the formal education received at school, particularly concentrating on personal and social development. Young people referred to the programme come from areas identified as having particular social disadvantage, with high unemployment, high juvenile crime rate and high number of single parent families.

Family work

We have lobbied the Cumbria statutory services to take a leading role in assisting, co-ordinating and funding the development of family support services, including those provided by the voluntary sector. We welcome the positive signs that this is happening. New Government funding sources, such as the 'Sure-Start' programme, are demanding much closer co-operation and strategic planning between service delivery agencies and local government departments. We have agreed to earmark £250,000 per year for five years to promote family support work. We believe the programmes currently in progress are, or will be, examples of distinctive good practice.

Example grants: Ewanrigg Family Support Scheme, Maryport [£60,000 in 1998/99, £299,000 over five years]:

Developed from proposals made by Howgill [Family Centre], at the invitation of the trust; focuses on families in need within one community within west Cumbria and provides a playgroup, training for parents, and general family support provided by trained volunteers. Originally managed by Howgill and now managed by Barnardos.

Building the infrastructure and capacity of the voluntary sector

We have attempted to identify strategic ways to reinforce the voluntary sector infrastructure particularly within Cumbria. We engaged in a series of consultations with the five Councils for Voluntary Service in Cumbria. We also supported the establishment of a co-ordinating body for the CVAs known as Cumbria Local Development Agencies Forum (CLDAF). CLDAF co-ordinates service developments across the county between the five CVSs and Voluntary Action Cumbria which covers the rural upland areas of the county. Another forum, Cumbria Training Forum, also works closely with CLDAF to co-ordinate the provision of training for the voluntary sector across the county. We are represented on Cumbria Training Forum which is seen as a valuable development body in its own right.

Example grants: Council for Voluntary Action South Lakeland, Training Resource for Voluntary Organisations in South Cumbria (TREVOSC) [£32,000 in 1998/99, £104,000 over three years]:

To identify training needs and implement appropriate training provision in south Cumbria; the scheme has generated an impressive volume of research into need and has increased the demand for specific training courses and events.

Other beneficiaries during the year included:

- West Cumbria Multi-Service Agency – £15,000, 3rd year, to pay the lease on the building in Whitehaven, which acts

THE FRANCIS C SCOTT CHARITABLE TRUST – VALUE AND NUMBER OF GRANTS 1998/99 AND 1997/98

	1998/99			*1997/98*		
	No.	*Amount*	*%*	*No.*	*Amount*	*%*
Youth	27	£324,000	24%	35	£326,000	29%
Families and children	16	£228,000	17%	10	£158,000	14%
Disabled people	27	£172,000	13%	23	£100,000	9%
Community development	26	£170,000	13%	12	£52,000	5%
Councils for voluntary service	6	£119,000	9%	7	£113,000	10%
Counselling	12	£91,000	7%	11	£58,000	5%
Elderly	9	£48,000	4%	6	£37,000	3%
Alcohol and drug abuse	7	£37,000	3%	2	£7,000	1%
Education and training	12	£35,000	3%	15	£16,000	1%
Projects supporting women	6	£33,000	3%	7	£42,000	4%
Homeless and unemployed	5	£28,000	2%	6	£39,000	3%
General (offenders, victims & other)	5	£27,000	2%	8	£58,000	5%
Arts and museums	2	£21,000	2%	3	£130,000	11%
Hospices and carers	2	£4,000	<1%	1	£4,000	<1%
Total	162	£1,335,000		146	£1,141,000	

as a 'one-stop shop' for helping people with a variety of problems;
- Shelter, Penrith – £15,000, 2nd of 3 awards, towards the salary of a caseworker at a new Housing Aid Centre;
- Age Concern, Barrow and District – £10,000, 3rd year, for the salary of a business development manager (five other local branches got one-off grants of between £2,000 and £10,000);
- East Cumbria Family Support Service, Carlisle and the Eden Valley – £10,000, 1st of 3 awards to match grants from the National Lottery Charities Board;
- West Lakeland Abbeyfield Project – £5,000, 1st of 3 awards, for the running costs of a day centre for the elderly at Gosforth;
- South West Burnley Community Development Trust – £3,000, 2nd of 3 awards, to fund a part-time Health and Social Care Worker post;
- West Cumbria Carers – £1,000 towards the cost of a conference;
- Horse and Bamboo Theatre, Manchester – £1,000;
- CRUSE Bereavement Care, Lancaster and Morecambe branch – £500 towards the cost of training 3 volunteer supervisors to supervise volunteer counsellors.

Exclusions

Normally only registered charities receive grants. While occasionally grants are given to national charities, these are usually only to fund a local service or appeal. The trust does not fund appeals from individuals.

The trustees are reluctant to substitute for expired or withdrawn statutory funding, although they may occasionally do so.

Church restoration, medical appeals, expeditions, scholarships and applications from schools are all excluded.

Applications

An application form is available from the correspondent and should be returned with the latest set of audited accounts. You are welcome to telephone the director or his assistant for an informal discussion prior to submitting an application.

The trustees meet three times a year, usually in March, July and November. Applications need to arrive one month before each meeting. The whole process from application to receipt of a grant may take up to four months.

Sir Samuel Scott of Yews Trust

Medical research

£667,000 (1998/99)

Beneficial area UK.

c/o Currey & Co, 21 Buckingham Gate, London SW1E 6LS

Tel. 020 7802 2700 **Fax** 020 7828 4091

Correspondent The Secretary

Information available Report and accounts, but without the required review of the trust's charitable activities.

Summary

The trust makes a large number of grants, mainly for medical research purposes and mainly to medical charities or to hospitals, but not, the charity says, for purely clinical work. In a number of cases, the grant is for the work of a named individual. Most grants are for amounts between £2,000 and £5,000 but can be for six figure sums.

General

The trust, in a welcome change that should be a model for some other trusts described in this book, has decided to spend from its capital as well as its income, rather than simply to accumulate its capital gains.

Though the trust does not use the peer review process, the trustee body is both medically and scientifically experienced.

The trust has made three very large donations, of £1 million each, two of them to cancer research bodies, the Marie Curie Research Fund and the Gray Laboratory at Mount Vernon Hospital, London. The third, in an exceptional grant outside the usual medical research interest, was to the Kathleen Trust which provides instruments for young and needy classical musicians.

There were 64 grants in 1998/99, down from 98 in the previous year. The following were for more than £20,000:

- Royal Free and University College Medical School, for Dr Wakefield at the Inflammatory Bowel Disease Study Group (£100,000);
- Marie Curie Research Wing (presumably at an unnamed institution), for Professor Denekamp (£70,000);
- Mount Vernon Hospital, two awards (£56,000);
- International Spinal Research (£50,000);
- University College London, Implanted Devices Group (£36,000);
- Institute of Cancer Research, Professor Workman (£27,000).

The smaller grants were widely spread. Examples included:

- Great Ormond Street Children's Charity (£15,000);
- Motor Neurone Disease Association (£10,000);
- British Lung Foundation (£5,000);
- Prostate Cancer Charity (£3,000);
- Migraine Trust (£2,000).

Analysis of a sample of 30 beneficiaries showed that 13 had also received grants in the previous year, but only five of them for the same amount, so it seems unlikely that many of the awards listed represented either ongoing commitments or part payments of larger awards. In the previous year the largest award, of £150,000, had been to the Gray Laboratory.

Exclusions

No core funding.

No support for purely clinical work.

No grants to individuals (although research by an individual may be funded if sponsored by a registered charity through which the application is made).

No support for research leading to higher degrees (unless the departmental head concerned certifies that the work is of real scientific importance).

No grants for medical students' elective periods.

No grants for expeditions (unless involving an element of genuine medical research).

Applications

In writing to the correspondent. Trustees hold their half-yearly meetings in April and October and applications have to be submitted two months before. There are no special forms, but applicants should give the following information:

- the nature and purpose of the research project or programme;
- the names, qualifications and present posts of the scientists involved;
- reference to any published results of their previous research;
- details of present funding;
- if possible, the budget for the next 12 months or other convenient period.

All applications are acknowledged and both successful and unsuccessful applicants are notified after each meeting of the trustees. No telephone calls.

The Samuel Sebba Charitable Trust

Jewish charities in Israel and Britain

£854,000 (1998/99)

44a New Cavendish Street, London W1M 7LG

Correspondent Clive Marks, Trustee

Trustees *Leigh Sebba; Stanley Sebba; Leslie Sebba; Victor Klein; Clive Marks.*

Information available Report and accounts with grants list and policy outline are on file at the Charity Commission.

Summary

Most grants are for £5,000, although a few regularly supported organisations get higher amounts of up to £150,000. Beneficiaries are almost exclusively Jewish organisations. The trust states that its funds are already heavily committed to certain organisations and that unsolicited applications will probably fail.

General

The trust outlines its policy as follows:

The principal aims of the Trust are to support a wide range of registered charities and to encompass many areas of the Jewish Community, particularly those involved in learning and teaching of the Jewish Faith, its history, as well as the training of Rabbis, teachers, lay-leaders and counsellors.

The trust will from time to time fund a small number of specialist consultants to advise charities on their internal structure, budgeting, staff training, as well as future planning and efficiency.

Monitoring can be carried out when recommended by a small research team who are available to attend site visits, this facility enables the trust to support efficient and effective charities, giving them the confidence for on-going support.

Future developments

The trustees will be concentrating principally on four areas:

- general communal matters including youth clubs and community centres;
- Jewish education, Jewish schools and training of future Rabbis;
- hospices and aged;
- medical aid and hospitals.

Grants in 1998/99

In 1998/99 income was a little over £1 million from assets of £18.5 million. Grant expenditure totalled £854,000, at least 90% for Jewish causes, categorised as follows:

Education	£498,000
Community	£185,000
Hospices, aged & medical projects	£101,000
Children and youth	£37,000
Arts	£32,000

The largest grants were made under the heading of 'Education and Rabbinical Training', with £200,000 going to the following four beneficiaries:

- Friends of Bar Ilan University (£150,000)
- Gateshead Talmudical College (£50,000)
- Beth Jacob Primary School (£25,000)
- Israel Institute for Talmudic Publications (£25,000)

Others included Beith Haggai Children and Youth Village (£15,500); British Council of Shaare Zedek Medical Centre (£16,000); Friends of Israel Aged (£6,000), and North London Hospice (£5,000).

Applications

Organisations applying must provide proof of need, they must forward the most recent audited accounts, a registered charity number, and most importantly a cash flow statement for the next 12 months. All applications should have an sae attached. It is also important that the actual request for funds must be concise and preferably summarised on one side of A4.

Because of ongoing support to so many organisations already known to the trust, it is likely that unsolicited applications will, for the foreseeable future, be unsuccessful.

The Ayrton Senna Foundation

Children's health and education

£345,000 (1998)

Beneficial area Worldwide, with a preference for Brazil.

74 Wimpole Street, London W1M 7DD

Tel. 020 7935 5373

Correspondent Julian Jakobi, Trustee

Trustees *Viviane Lalli, President; Milton Guerado Theodoro da Silva; Neyde Joanna Senna da Silva; Leonardo Senna da Silva; Fabio da Silva Machado; Christopher Bliss; Julian Jakobi.*

Information available Accounts up to 1998 only had been received by the Charity Commission as at July 2000.

General

The trust was established in 1994 by the father of the late Ayrton Senna, in memory of his son, the racing driver. The trust was given the whole issued share capital of Ayrton Senna Foundation Ltd, a company set up to license the continued use of the Senna trademark and copyrights. Out of a total income of £433,000 in 1998, £321,000 came from this source.

The annual report in that year noted that 'in particular, the objectives seek to provide education, healthcare and medical support for children'.

To this end, nearly all the trust's giving has been directed towards the Instituto Ayrton Senna in Brazil, which received £993,000 in 1997 and £342,000 in 1998.

The only other beneficiaries in those years were the Grand Prix Mechanics Charitable Trust (£7,000 in 1997) and Cancer Bacup (£3,000 in 1998).

Exclusions

No grants to individuals.

Applications

In writing to the correspondent.

The Archie Sherman Charitable Trust

Jewish charities, arts, welfare

£1,147,000 (1998/99)

27 Berkeley House, Hay Hill, London W1X 7LG

Tel. 020 7493 1904

Correspondent Michael Gee, Trustee

Trustees *Michael Gee; Allan Morgenthau; E Charles.*

Information available Inadequate annual report and accounts on file at the Charity Commission.

Summary

Perhaps 90% of the funds are for Jewish causes, particularly for education or welfare, which receive ongoing support, typically more than £20,000 a year each. Smaller one-off grants, mostly for £500 or £1,000, are made mainly to arts and children's charities and are frequently repeated.

General

The trust says that its policies 'are almost exclusively to benefit health and educational purposes'. It reported for the previous edition of this book that it was committed to 24 long-term projects with payments spread over as much as six years.

The 1998/99 trustees' report added that 'the Trustees review all commitments on a forward four-year basis so that new projects can be undertaken and income is made available'.

In that year a high income of £1.4 million was generated from assets worth £16.25 million and 49 grants, totalling £1,147,000, were awarded.

The five largest grants, totalling £562,000 or half of grant expenditure, went to two organisations in Israel and three charitable trusts connected with the trustees, as follows:

- Friends of the Hebrew University of Jerusalem (£196,000)
- The Jerusalem Foundation (£96,000)
- The Jacqueline and Michael Gee Charitable Trust (£90,000)
- The Diana and Allan Morgenthau Charitable Trust (£90,000)
- The Rosalyn and Nicholas Springer Charitable Trust (£90,000)

Of the remaining grants, about half were in the range £10,000 to £50,000 and half were for smaller amounts of between £100 and £5,000.

Other Jewish charities receiving substantial donations included Jewish Care (£50,000); The Home for Aged Jews (£50,000) and the Council for a Beautiful Israel (£20,000).

Also among the long-standing beneficiaries were the Imperial War Museum (£27,000); Royal Opera House (£45,000) and the Ear Foundation (£30,000).

Smaller grants similarly covered Jewish causes and the arts, as well as charities assisting children in the UK and overseas and health and welfare organisations. The recipients included Save the Children (£5,000 for the Honduras disaster); Alone in London (£1,000); Glyndebourne Festival Society (£1,000)*; Imperial Cancer Research Fund (£500); NCH Action for Children (£500)*; Jewish Women's Aid (£500)*; North West London Orchestra (£250)*; UNICEF Children's Fund (£1,000); University of Reading (£400)*, and Scopus Jewish Educational Trust (£2,000)*.

*Also supported in the previous year.

Applications

In writing to the correspondent. Trustees meet every month except August and December.

The Shetland Islands Council Charitable Trust

General, in Shetland

£7,956,000 (1998/99)

Beneficial area Shetland.

Breiwick House, 15 South Road, Lerwick, Shetland ZE1 0TD

Tel. 01595 744681 **Fax** 01595 744667

Correspondent John Barnbrook, The Finance Department

Trustees *22 trustees, being the elected Shetland councillors (acting as individuals), the Lord Lieutenant and the headteacher of the Anderson High School. Chairman: Robert Irvine Black.*

Information available Model reports and accounts, available from the trust for £2.

Summary

A wide variety of local initiatives are supported with grants or loans from £300 to about £300,000. Assistance is given, for example, to education, older people, people with disabilities, local industry, recreational facilities, the environment and the arts. The common denominator for all projects is that they benefit 'Shetland and its inhabitants'. Most grants are recurrent – the trust has committed to fund most of its present beneficiaries up until 2003.

Applications are through the appropriate Shetland Islands council department and in practice the trust operates much as a council funding programme.

General

The original trust was established in 1976 with 'disturbance receipts' from the operators of the Sullom Voe oil terminal. As a clause in the trust deed prevented it from accumulating income beyond 21 years from its inception, in 1997 most of its assets were transferred to a newly established Shetland Islands Council Charitable Trust. The new trust, identical to the old trust except for the omission of the prohibition on accumulating income, had net assets worth almost £300 million in 1998/99, and an income of more than £13.5 million.

The trust is run by the Shetland Islands council, which receives around £700,000 a year for this service. Officers from the islands' various council committees make funding recommendations to the trustees who do not consider 'applications from the general public'.

The 1998/99 annual report says:

> The Shetland Islands Charitable Trust seeks to benefit Shetland and its inhabitants. In particular the trustees set out to :
>
> - improve the quality of life for the inhabitants of Shetland, especially in the areas of:
>   - social need
>   - leisure
>   - environment
>   - education
> - build on the energy and initiatives of local self-help groups, and assist them to achieve their objectives, without destroying the independence and enterprise which brought them into being;
> - utilise the funds in order to provide large scale facilities which would be of long term benefit to the inhabitants of Shetland;
> - support traditional industries and assist in the introduction of new ones, in ways where a charity and a trust might usefully assist, particularly:
>   - agriculture

- fishing
- knitwear
- aquaculture
- maintain flexibility for the trust's funds; in order to be able to meet new situations and priorities, but to do so against the background of a published framework of plans.

Exclusions

Funds can only be used to benefit the inhabitants of Shetland.

Applications

Applications from the general public are not considered. Projects are recommended by the various committees of Shetland Islands council.

The trustees meet every six to eight weeks.

SHINE (Support and Help In Education)

Education in London and south east England

£600,000 (planned for 2000/01)

Beneficial area London and south east England.

1 Cheam Road, Ewell Village, Surrey KT17 1SP

Tel. 020 8393 1880 **Fax** 020 8394 2570

e-mail info@shinetrust.org.uk

website www.shinetrust.org.uk

Correspondent The Grants Team

General

The trust provided the following information in September 2000:

SHINE has £600,000 to fund projects in London and the South East before the end of March 2001.

The new trust focuses on education initiatives that encourage children and young people to raise their aspirations and realise their full potential. It will support projects that broaden the horizons of economically disadvantaged 7 to 18 year olds by giving them an experience they would not otherwise have.

In its first funding year, SHINE's priority is to fund projects that involve children starting from age seven to nine, innovative IT projects, projects targeting school age children who have been excluded or are at risk of exclusion, and projects tackling the problems of transition from primary to secondary school.

SHINE's aim is to build long-term relationships and partnerships. For this reason, the majority of grants will be in excess of £20,000. New start ups, pilots, development or replication of projects, and core costs will all be considered.

While educational content is the priority, we are willing to explore projects which view education in a broader social and emotional context. It is most important to us that the projects we fund are an integral part of a long-term development strategy for participants, and that they are exciting and engaging. We are particularly keen to get to groups who are working at grass roots level and would urge readers to help spread the word about SHINE beyond the mainstream voluntary sector.

As this book went to press two staff appointments were announced; of David Allanson as director and trust administrator and of Stephen Shields as director of grantmaking programmes.

Exclusions

Shine will not fund:

- individuals;
- the direct replacement of statutory funding;
- schools or other educational establishments, except where funding is for ancillary charitable activities specifically directed towards one of the agreed priority areas;
- short term programmes which have no structured link into a longer term strategy for participants.

Applications

Telephone call to the grants team, after reading the website.

Shlomo Memorial Fund

Jewish causes

£679,000 (1997/98)

Cohen Arnold & Co, 13–17 New Burlington Place, Regent Street, London W1X 2JP

Correspondent I Lopian, Secretary

Information available In August 2000 the latest accounts on file at the Charity Commission were those for 1997/98, and they had no details of grants and no narrative report.

General

This trust's income is mainly comprised of Gift Aid donations from its subsidiaries, which it utilises in making grants to Jewish charities. In 1997/98 after revaluation in investment, the trust's assets totalled £6,945,000, income was £806,000 and grants totalled £679,000.

Applications

In writing to the correspondent.

Smith's Charity

Social welfare, older people, disability, health, medical research

£22,400,000 (1999)

Beneficial area UK. Specific local programmes in East and West Sussex, Hampshire, Kent, Gloucestershire, Leicestershire, Suffolk and Surrey.

5 Chancery Lane, Clifford's Inn, London EC4A 1BU

Tel. 020 7320 6216/6277

Fax 020 7320 3842

Correspondent Miss Judith Portrait, Treasurer

Information available Long and elegant report and accounts, with good narrative reports on financial matters, but a most modest review of the charity's grant-making policies. An excellent list of grants, the purpose of each being briefly explained, but only the most limited analysis.

Summary

Following a policy review in 1999 the charity has reasserted its decision to remain primarily reactive or, as it terms it, responsive. It waits for applications to be received and funds what it finds the best, in the fields outlined above (and listed in more detail below). Grants are generally large, averaging over £60,000, and are roughly equally split between one-off grants, usually for capital purposes, and grants spread over two or three years for particular projects. These, though, may include core costs for the development of the charity as a whole.

The policy review also launched an interesting fast response small grants programme, with awards of up to £10,000 for organisations with an income of less than £250,000. There is a long-standing separate programme of small grants for the traditionally funded counties listed above.

The main exception to the reactive policy is the programme of major grants in which one field of work is chosen each year for funding, typically of £1.5 million over three years, with the aim of making 'a significant impact'. The programmes may cover a geographical area, such as the Black Country, or, as at the present, a group of beneficiaries such as older people. The policy review determined that the amount of money set aside for this programme would be increased. These editors would like to see the extra resources used to extend the funding period for these programmes.

Background

The objects of the charity, originally and famously including the ransom of captives of Turkish pirates, have been varied over the years. Grants now cover health and medical research, disability and welfare (but the charity cannot support education or art, except where they are exclusively for the benefit of disabled people).

The former two Smith charities with common trustees, the Kensington Estate Charity and the General Estates Charity, are now being combined into one, the Charity Commission willing, though without change to the objects or activities. The single name, Smith's Charity, is already in use for practical purposes.

The charity's wealth derives from the purchase by the then trustees in the seventeenth century of land 'to yield an income of at least £60 a year'. The land they chose, called the Kensington Estate, now lies in some of the most valuable parts of Belgravia. In 1995, and despite continuing ancestral connections between the estate and some of the trustees, the charity in a fine financial coup succeeded in selling the property as a whole to a single purchaser, the even larger Wellcome Trust. It was thereby enabled to diversify its investments and greatly increase the income available for annual distribution, as can be seen from the box on the right.

The target for distribution in 2000 was £23 million.

Grant-making procedure

There are two distribution committees that make decisions on grants, each meeting quarterly (and a third, new, small grants committee, with two members, Marilyn Gallyer and Mark Newton):

Distribution Committee A:
Julian Sheffield (Chairman)
Mrs A E Allen
Viscount Gage
T D Holland-Martin
Sir John James
Ms M Lowther
Ronnie Norman
Peter Smallridge

Distribution Committee B:
Julian Sheffield (Chairman)
Countess of Euston
Mrs C Godman Law
J D Hambro
Lord Hamilton
Lord Kingsdown
G E Lee-Steere
Tristan Millington-Drake

The charity's staff has an unusual structure, with an unusual job title for its 'director', Judith Portrait, who is known as the treasurer. The person responsible for the grants programme is Virginia Graham, grants administrator. Miss Portrait, a recent appointment, whose position is part time, is one of the most influential, and busiest, figures in the world of UK philanthropy. She is also a trustee of most of the massive charitable trusts established by the Sainsbury family and she appears, too, to remain an active solicitor with Portrait Solicitors, which handles some of the individual accounts arising out of the huge law practice of Denton Wilde Sapte (at whose premises Smith's Charity is located). She has been, and may still remain, the personal solicitor to David Sainsbury and a trustee of the blind trust into which his investments were placed when he became a government minister.

The charity's procedure for dealing with applications is also unusual. A summary of all applications that fall within the charity's fields of work (other than those for small grants) is sent to the members of one of the distribution committees, and may be rejected at that stage. If the project gets 'sufficient support' the applicant will then normally be visited either by one of the charity's two grants staff or, more probably, by one of the charity's team of no less than 18 voluntary 'visitors'. In specialist fields, such as medical research, further expert advice may be sought. A report is then presented to a distribution committee for decision (perhaps a different one to that whose members gave the original 'thumbs-up', which would seem the best procedure).

SMITH'S CHARITY – INCOME AVAILABLE FOR DISTRIBUTION

1994	£13.3 million
1995	£14.8 million
1996	£19.0 million
1997	£21.7 million
1998	£22.3 million
1999	£22.4 million

The charity has recently said that 15% of all applications and 29% of eligible applications – that is, those within the charity's powers and policies – get to the 'visitor' stage. This is a low number and suggests that in practice the real decision making occurs at the first stage – when only a summary, without any supporting information, is seen by trustees. It may be that the summary is accompanied by a recommendation from the charity's staff; if not, a great deal of weight rests on these documents on their own. Applicants are asked to include a half page summary with their applications, and probably this is text on which the vital preliminary decisions are usually made (an improvement on the earlier situation when the then treasurer said that each application was summarised 'in a few lines' and decisions taken based on that).

Grant-making policies

The charity gives good information for applicants, mostly reprinted in this entry, but charity staff are happy to give preliminary advice to potential applicants, especially small organisations, over the telephone.

Special and general grants

The charity both funds one-off appeals (generally the Special List, in the charity's terminology) and supports projects for a fixed period, usually three years (usually in the General List), with a very roughly similar amount attributed to each – £8.7 million and £9.7 million in 1999.

The average size of the grants in these two main programmes is very high. An analysis of a sample of 80, covering a total of £2.6 million, gave an average of £58,000 for capital grants and £68,000 for project grants. Few grants are for less than £10,000, though smaller awards are possible.

The development of Smith's Charity

This book occasionally criticises trusts that it describes, taking the view that these are public institutions, accountable to us all, which need to justify their massive tax subsidies. Henry Smith's Charity has been a regular target.

The first edition of this book in 1985 complained about the charity's apparently unchanging list of grant recipients; its concentration on the south of England; its corresponding neglect, for a supposedly national charity, of Scotland, Wales and Northern Ireland; its policy of confining its small grants to a few prosperous counties traditionally supported (referring to the seventeenth century) which contained the country residences of many of its trustees; an overall lack of information, and a distant relationship with the organisations and people it supported. Subsequent editions discovered and questioned the composition of the trustee body, which was found to mix aristocracy and banking, but apparently little else.

Overall, the face presented by the charity was extraordinarily dated. We suggested that, with only a few years to go, the charity was at risk of failing even to enter the twentieth century.

In the last year of that century, however, almost all of these issues were being addressed, though the process is often hard to see behind the charity's still forbidding facade – applicants, even successful ones, can still be upset by the style in which the charity presents itself.

First, excellent grants are generally being made, and this has now been the case for a number of years. By its present concentration on either capital grants, which represent a permanent investment for the beneficiary group concerned, or on project funding, within which it is willing to consider core costs, when that is what is needed, the charity has avoided forcing its applicants down the damaging road of artificial 'projects'.

The relatively new 'major grants' programme, a little unfocused in its first years, is a welcome attempt by a grant-making trust to try to identify and attack specific needs on a significant scale, and to seek informed and expert help in doing so.

Secondly, the problem of geographical fairness is rapidly reducing. The disproportionate funding of the south as against the north of England has come down to a ratio of two to one – better than the average for supposedly 'national' trusts as a whole. Scotland, Wales and Northern Ireland seem to be receiving more grants than ever before, even if these are still less than their population and their needs would suggest appropriate. In 1998, the only year for which any figures have come from the charity, the value of Henry Smith grants per head of population was £0.13 in Scotland, against £0.38 in England; but in 1985 we had said that grants outside England were scarcely visible in the grants lists at all.

On the same issue, even the stoutly defended small grants scheme for the 'traditional' and very prosperous 'Henry Smith' counties is being diluted with an enterprising small grants scheme to cover other areas.

Finally, the trustee body itself is being reformed. In a strange statutory arrangement, the trustees are appointed on the nomination of the Archbishop of Canterbury and the Lord Chancellor. Early on, we asked this oddly chosen pair to tell us about the criteria they employed in making their nominations, but they would not. They were probably just accepting the suggestions of the existing trustees themselves, thus explaining the strong element of family continuity in the group.

Now, new trustees are being appointed to the trust who have a lifetime of personal knowledge and experience in fields in which the charity works. They include Peter Smallridge, formerly the director of Kent Social Services (one of the most energetic departments of its type in the country), and Tristan Millington-Drake, director of the Chemical Dependency Centre. Equally welcome, there are now 5 women on the 20-strong body, as against none at all 12 years ago, so another start has been made.

These editors would still like to see more emphasis on active policies, and a more sympathetic approach to applicants who have trouble, no matter how excellent their charitable activities, in rising to the standards of funding application they feel to be expected of them. Nevertheless the twenty-first century will start with this charity as a generally effective and energetic support for the many people in Britain still suffering avoidable hardship.

The charity's information for applicants says of the trustees:

> Where possible, they like to make grants to moderate sized projects to get them off the ground or to allocate a grant specifically towards a particular item within the budget of a larger project which they decide to support (eg. towards the cost of the construction of a particular facility or the payment of a particular project worker's salary for a specific period).

All grants are for a fixed period, after which a new application has to be made. The format of the annual reports does not make it easy to see whether many grants are in fact a response to such a request for, effectively, renewal – until 1999 the grant recipients were listed in neither alphabetical order nor by the size of the award. Nevertheless this editor believes he would have noticed any general tendency towards ongoing funding, and a check of just four organisations whose grants had expired did not show any successful reapplications. Nor were any of the six major beneficiaries in 1993 prominent in the 1999 awards.

For many years consecutive editions of this book have criticised the apparently excessive concentration of this national charity's grants on the home counties of England (though not, for once, in London). There are now substantial and very welcome sums being spent in Scotland and Wales. For England, a sample of 50 new larger awards (for £25,000 or more) was examined. After dividing the country into northern and southern halves of equal population, it was found that 34 of these grants, worth £1.8 million, were in the southern half and 16, worth £0.8 million, were in the northern half. This appears to show a marked improvement over the situation two years previously when the south was getting three times as much per head as the north; now it is little more than double. And the change from 1993, when four out of five such grants were in the south, is remarkable.

Also confirmed in the report is the decision to retain the charity's responsive role, 'thus providing a substantial resource for the numerous applications put forward by the charity world', which seems a wholly respectable policy if followed with energy and enterprise, and '... with so many of the other grantmakers becoming proactive'. This second suggestion, though, is a curious one, as it seems to these editors that the opposite has been happening. The arrival of the huge and primarily reactive funding programmes of the National Lottery Charities Board and the Bridge House

Estates, Lloyds TSB, Northern Rock and PPP Healthcare foundations has meant a surge in this type of funding unprecedented in sixteen years of writing about such grantmaking. The moves by a few funders (such as Tudor, the unhappily reduced Baring Foundation or the City Parochial) towards a more proactive approach, usually with only a small part of their grants, do not amount to a tenth of the money moving in the other direction.

Medical research

At about £2 million a year, the charity has one of the country's larger funding programmes for medical research.

The guidance supplied to potential applicants notes that 'the trustees seek advice from experts when making grants in areas such as medical research or treatment where they feel that specialist advice is required'. Their applications are also subject to the process of peer review.

The actual grants are of similar duration and size to those in other fields, but it is generally beyond the capacity of these editors to offer any critical commentary here. About 10 awards are made a year. Most go to universities or hospitals or to independent charities for their work in such institutions. A grant of a kind too seldom seen was the £70,000 for the British Brain and Spine Foundation 'towards the shortfall on approved research projects'.

Small grants

There are also long-standing small grants programmes for amounts up to £10,000 in the counties named in the paragraph below – totalling £1.3 million in 1999. These have now been joined by a pilot programme for the rest of the country, of grants up to £10,000 for organisations with an income of less than £250,000. A most interesting feature of the programme is that applications are being processed fortnightly, which shows an uncommon understanding of the needs of the smaller applicant. (See under 'Applications' below for the procedures involved.) Only a modest amount, perhaps £250,000, has been allocated initially for this programme, which has not been publicised. If expanded and advertised, its fast turnaround could make it a most valuable and appreciated part of the charity's activity.

The grants must be spent within six months, thus ruling out support for ongoing running costs. The charity suggests that the programme will be 'ideal for organisations needing equipment or help with the costs of transport, training, information packs, or for volunteer expenses'.

Small county grants

The pilot scheme augments the charity's traditional support for grassroots organisations in the eight counties where the founder had estates – Gloucestershire, Hampshire, Kent, Leicestershire, Suffolk, Surrey, East Sussex and West Sussex. This ancient geographical link is further maintained through the high proportion of trustees (at least 12) with homes in these counties. Applications for up to £10,000 (most beneficiaries receive between £1,000 and £3,000), which must fall within the areas of interest noted above, are made through the offices of the charity. One trustee in each county has the initial specific responsibility for these grants. These county programmes received about six per cent of the charity's total funding in 1998.

Previous editions of this book have criticised the charity for this regrettable emphasis on the most prosperous shires in England – based on history rather than on any assessment of present day need. The charity believes it is honouring the wishes of Henry Smith (although these particular ones no longer appear as part of the charity's objects, any more than do the unfortunate captives of the Turks). These editors prefer to suppose that, if Henry Smith were in a position to see what today's trustees are doing, he would wish them to give priority to areas where his help is most needed. However, the charity points out, correctly, that there are areas of deprivation in all the counties concerned and that the trustees are seeking to give these some priority.

The major grants

'The trustees select in each year a special area which will be the subject of a Major Grant consisting of a programme of grants paid over a period of three years, with the aim of making a significant impact in the chosen field.' This is the major proactive activity of the charity. Organisations may well wish to suggest interesting new topics for these awards, but there is no application process and the charity develops its own ideas.

The topics chosen since the programme began in 1992 are listed below. Three of the first five were centred on geographical areas previously little supported by the charity – the north east, the Glamorgan valleys and the Black Country (in two cases working in partnership with the local community foundation). In practice this has also led to continued funding for applicants from these areas. The 'significant impact' is not clear. So far as these editors are aware, few evaluations have been published or reported, and the sums involved were small in relation to the size and needs of the areas concerned – for example, the current EU funding programme for social regeneration in South Yorkshire is worth £200 million. A far narrower geographical focus, or a tight concentration on one kind of need within a wider area, would seem to be needed.

More recent topics, such as Abbeyfield's establishment of demonstration projects of good practice in integrated care, and the efforts of the Bishop of London to get schoolchildren to address ethical issues, seem better suited to this funding approach. But for either kind of funding greater concentration on evaluation and dissemination seems to be needed – and in many cases three years may come to be seen as an improbably short time scale to achieve permanent results.

- The Bishop of London's Paternoster Centre 2001, 2002, 2003
  £1.5 million for a centre to help users, especially children at key stages 2 and 3, to meet a wide range of current ethical dilemmas. This marks the trustees' wish to commemorate the Christian aspect of the millennium, given Henry Smith's concern for '... Godly Preachers and the better furtherance of knowledge and religion'.
- Older people – Abbeyfield Integrated Care Project 2000, 2001, 2002
  Funding of £1.5 million for three community-based model schemes, in rural Scotland, Ilkley and central Bristol, intended to set new quality standards across all types of Abbeyfield's care provision.
- South Yorkshire Initiative – 1999, 2000 and 2001
  There is an emphasis on projects for older people. A local consultant/assessor, Jennie Woodley, is based within the South Yorkshire Community Foundation office. Expenditure: £1,500,000 over three years.
- Black Country Initiative – 1998, 1999 and 2000
  An independent consultant, Maureen Stallard, has 'sought out and assessed' projects. Expenditure: £490,000 (1998). Total allocation: £1.8 million over three years.
- Persistent young offenders – 1997, 1998 and 1999
  Two projects are being funded with Surrey Springboard and Asset, South London. The Home Office is evaluating the effectiveness of the projects. Expenditure: £500,000 (1997 and 1998).

- The valleys of Mid Glamorgan – 1996, 1997 and 1998
  This programme to combat social deprivation was assembled with the help of South East Wales Community Foundation and an advisory committee from the voluntary, private and public sector in the area. By its third year, six employment and welfare projects had been supported. Expenditure: £425,000 (1998).
- Older homeless people – 1994, 1995 and 1996
  A pilot project in London with St Mungo's, to assess the needs of older homeless people with mental health problems and to discover why they are not gaining access to permanent housing. Expenditure: £360,000 (1998).
- The North East of England – 1992, 1993 and 1994
  This programme has continued in co-operation with the former Tyne and Wear Foundation (now the Community Foundation), which in 1998 disbursed £880,000 in 30 grants between £5,000 and £80,000. Almost all (23) were multi-year awards for £20,000 or more.

Grants in 1999

The charity made over 300 new awards in 1999 from its main programmes and perhaps a further 600 small grants.

Payments were classified as follows:

	1999	1998
Special List (one-off grants)	£8,693,000	£9,996,000
General List (period grants)	£9,668,000	£9,836,000
Small grants	£1,336,000	£1,231,000

The charity also has two programmes outside the scope of this book:

	1999	1998
Poor Kindred	£235,000	£250,000
Poor Clergy	£780,000	£855,000

The annual report also breaks down the grants by field of work, for special and general grants, as shown in the chart on the right.

MAJOR GRANTS

For older homeless people	–	£359,877
For young offenders project	£500,000	£500,000
For arthritis & rheumatism	–	£15,750
In the valleys of Mid Glamorgan	–	£424,709
In the Black Country	£650,500	£490,500
In South Yorkshire	£366,761	–

£400,000 was also allocated to a wide range of housing projects for older people through the Housing Associations Charitable Trust (HACT).

Special and general grants

The capital grants were very often for round amounts, say of £100,000, suggesting that the charity was seldom likely to be the sole funder but was one contributor to a larger appeal. A typical such grant was the £50,000 for Broadreach House (Devon) 'towards the provision of new rooms and the cost of updating bathroom facilities', or the £15,000 for Deaf Connections (Scotland) 'towards the upgrading of the kitchen at Craigholm Eventide Home'. But not all one-off grants were for capital works. For example, £35,000 was given to Deafblind UK 'towards the cost of training interpreters/volunteers ...'.

The project grants were for a wide range of activities. Many were for specific projects, such as the £60,000 to enable Comeback (London) to set up a new project to enable prisoners to access employment/training during their sentences. However, many grants were for more general needs, such as the £75,000 three-year grant for the salary of a head of finance at ARCH (North Staffordshire), or the same amount to the Centre for Complementary Care in Cumbria for its core costs and general work (maintaining a minor but long-standing interest of the charity in complementary medicine). Other grants were for the straightforward delivery of services, such as the £210,000 for the salaries of school/home support workers in the Isle of Dogs for the East London Schools Fund.

There is a striking scarcity of the major national charities in the grants lists. If they appear at all, it is usually for one of their specific local projects, such as £69,000 over three years for the Children's Society City Outreach Team in Manchester.

The largest new awards in the year included the following:

- Bethshan Nursing Home (Wales): £200,000 for building costs.
- Scottish Council on Alcohol: £117,000 over three years for a telephone support service.
- The Haven Trust (London): £200,000 towards a Breast Cancer Help Centre.
- Marie Curie Cancer Care: £150,000 for a hospice in Bradford.
- Rural Housing Trust: £150,000 over three years for core costs.
- Queen Charlotte's Hospital (London): £150,000 'towards Professor Fisk's new laboratory'.
- Mulberry Bush School (Oxfordshire): £200,000 for building work to create a therapeutic environment.
- King's Cross Furniture Project (London): £96,000 over three years for salaries.
- Foundation Training Company (East Anglia): £150,000 over three years to expand a service for young offenders.

Exclusions

The charity cannot make grants for education, for the arts or for the care or

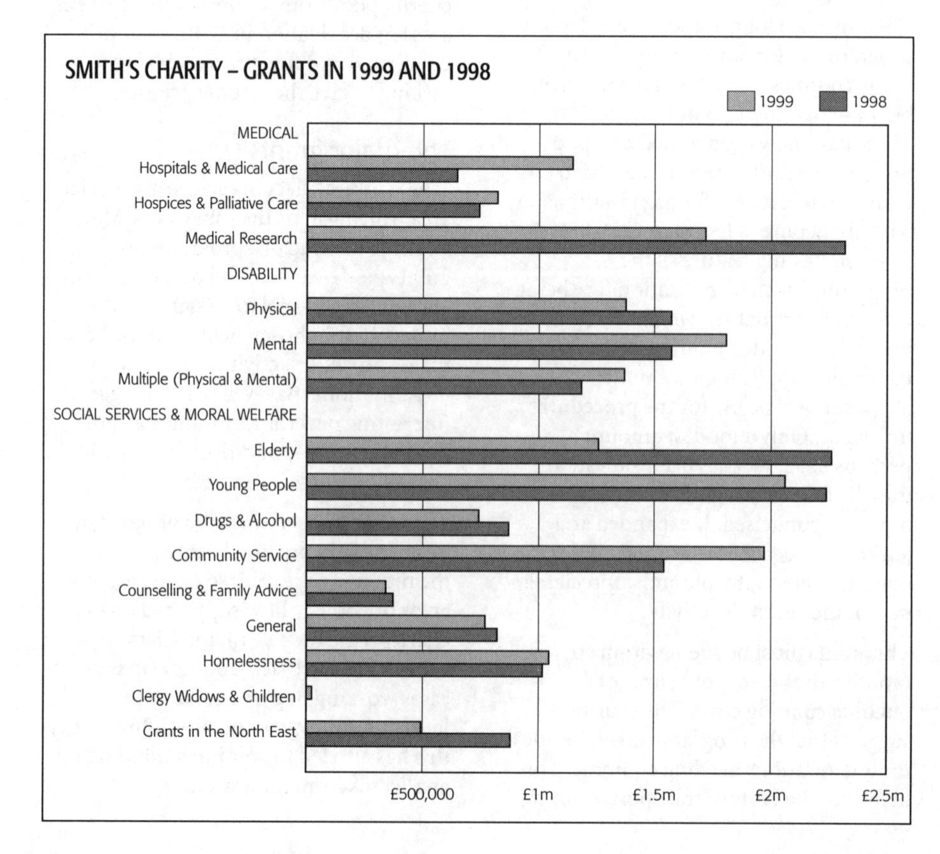

restoration of buildings, or for individuals. Grants for the latter, except in the case of Henry Smith's 'poor kindred', are made through local parish charities only, as detailed in DSC's companion volume *A Guide to Grants for Individuals in Need.*

Generally speaking, the charity avoids making grants to other grant-making organisations.

Applications

In writing to the correspondent. The charity does not use application forms but offers the following guidelines to applicants.

Main grants programmes

1. Applications should be no longer than four A4 sides (plus budget and accounts) and should incorporate a short (half page) summary.

2. Applications should:

a) State clearly who the applicant is, what it does and whom it seeks to help.
b) Give the applicant's status (e.g. registered charity).
c) Describe the project for which a grant is sought clearly and succinctly; explain the need for it; say what practical results it is expected to produce; state the number of people who will benefit from it; show how it will be cost effective and say what stage the project has so far reached.
d) Enclose a detailed budget for the project together with a copy of the applicant's most recent audited accounts. (If those accounts show a significant surplus or deficit of income, please explain how this has arisen and explain the charity's reserves policy.)
e) Name the applicant's trustees/patrons and describe the people who will actually be in charge of the project, giving details of their qualifications for the job.
f) Describe the applicant's track record and, where possible, give the names and addresses of two independent referees to whom Henry Smith's Charity may apply for a recommendation if it wishes to do so.
g) State what funds have already been raised for the project and name any other sources of funding to whom the applicant has applied.
h) Explain where the ongoing funding (if required) will be obtained when the charity's grant has been used.
i) State what plans have been made to monitor the project and wherever possible to evaluate it and, where appropriate, to make its results known to others.
j) Ask, where possible, for a specific amount.

3. Please keep the application as simple as possible and avoid the use of technical terms and jargon.

Trustees meet in March, June, September and December, and applications must be received at least two months before the relevant meeting.

Small grants programme

- The programme is available to organisations with an annual income of under £250,000. Applications may be made for grants under £10,000.
- The organisations must be based within the UK but outside Smith's Charity's traditional counties, which have their own Small Grants Programme. These are Gloucestershire, Hampshire, Kent, Leicestershire, Suffolk, Surrey, East and West Sussex. [*Applicants within these counties who are unaware of their local programme should be able to get information from a local umbrella body such as the Council for Voluntary Service or Rural Community Council. Ed.*]
- Grants can be for capital or for one-off revenue purposes, but not for running costs. For example, the programme may be ideal for organisations needing equipment or help with the costs of transport, training, information packs, or for volunteer expenses. However, ongoing running costs will not be supported, as grants need to be spent within a six-month period.
- Applications are considered at any time throughout the year and will be processed fortnightly. When applying, please enclose your most recent annual report/audited accounts.
- Applications should be to the treasurer and should be no longer than two A4 sides. Please keep the application as simple as possible and avoid the use of technical terms and jargon.

The Sobell Foundation

Jewish charities, health and welfare

£3,672,000 (1998/99)

Beneficial area England, Wales and Israel.

PO Box 2137, Shepton Mallet, Somerset BA4 6YA

Tel. 01749 813135 **Fax** 01749 813136

Correspondent Mrs P J Newton

Information available Brief annual report, full accounts.

Summary

A few very large grants are made in most years, for welfare or health causes (other than research), specifically for:

- children
- sick people
- older people
- people in need
- people with disabilities

About half the grants by value are to Jewish organisations, mainly in Britain but also in Israel. There is an extensive further grant-making programme, involving a large number of one-off grants, many of them small.

Note that no grants are made in Scotland or Northern Ireland.

General

By April 1999 the foundation had assets of nearly £50 million, generating a rather low £1.6 million in income. However, the trustees decided in principle to distribute a further £1 million a year from gains on their capital account. Nevertheless, without further receipts from the estate of the settlor, the late Michael Sobell, it is possible that the 1997/98 donations figure, of £2.9 million, will be a better guide to the future grant-making capacity of the foundation than the £3.7 million of 1998/99. Indeed, the trust has said that 'due to heavy charitable commitments during 2000–2002, applications for funding for major building projects are unlikely to be considered'.

Sir Michael Sobell 'was interested in causes benefiting children, the sick, elderly, needy and disabled'. In following these interests, the trustees aim to achieve a balance between Jewish charities (in the UK and Israel) and non-Jewish charities in England and Wales. In the last two years there has been roughly equal funding in the two fields.

'Most grants are in the region of £1,000 to £10,000, although larger grants are given. In exceptional cases grants of between £500,000 and £1 million have been made.'

The foundation makes some major commitments with payments spread over a number of years. Probably less than half the grant total is available for new awards in any one year. In April 1999 there were the following big commitments (in each case there had also been similar payments in the previous year):

- Countess Mountbatten Hospital (£500,000);
- St Mary's Hospital, London (£300,000);
- Haven Trust (£100,000);
- Bethlem and Maudsley NHS Trust, London (£500,000);
- Nightingale House Home for Aged Jews (£250,000).

There was no less than £1.7 million in undisclosed future commitments, but these appear to be part payments of agreed totals rather than ongoing annual support.

Few organisations supported in 1994/95 were still receiving similar grants in 1998/99; the trust says that 'where charities have received a grant they may not reapply within a year of a grant being made'. There is little information at all about the purposes of the grants, but the pattern of giving seems to be more consistent with the support of capital programmes, or endowments, rather than for revenue projects. The only specific advice is that 'although the trustees will support specific projects for hospices, they will not give grants towards running costs'.

Other than those listed above, major payments (perhaps one of a number over consecutive years) in 1998/99 were as follows: Joint Jewish Charitable Trust (£173,000); Jerusalem Foundation (£129,000); Bidwell Brook Foundation (£90,000); Disability Challenge (£80,000); Kepplewray Trust (£75,000); Bobath Centre for Children with Cerebral Palsy (£50,000); Tel Aviv Foundation (£50,000), and Norwood Ravenswood (£50,000).

The £10,000 grants included the following wide-ranging selection of charities: Global Cancer Concern; St Martin in the Fields Social Care Unit; Friends of Ohr Someach; Psychiatry Research Trust; High Peak Hospice Care, and Speech, Language and Hearing Centre.

The foundation probably has an extensive small grants scheme. The 1998/99 accounts only list the 74 largest donations. These account for about £3.2 million out of the total £3.7 million. The balance of about £500,000 might, on the precedent of the previous year, have been distributed in over 250 grants of £10,000 or less, many of them for £250 or £500. In 1998/99 the annual report says that the trustees had supported a high proportion of the applications that fall under the headings given in the 'Summary' section above, so it is likely that some of these small grants were given in response to appeals for larger amounts.

Most were then for national or specialist charities, with few grants for local organisations belonging to national networks. Beneficiaries such as Elderly Accommodation Counsel (£250) or the National Playing Fields Association (£500) were much more typical than Aylesbury Women's Aid (£500).

Unfortunately the grants of below £10,000 are not listed in the 1998/99 accounts, and none of the above paragraph can be confirmed. The administrator of the foundation said in summer 2000 that at present most grants are for £1,000 or more, so it is possible that the policy has been changed. In cases where large numbers of small grants are not disclosed, the charity concerned should at least report on the existence and number of such grants, as well as their general nature and purposes.

Exclusions

No grants to individuals. Only registered charities or organisations registered with the Inland Revenue should apply.

Applications

In writing to the correspondent. The application should be simple and concise, indicating clearly the aims of the charity, stating for what purpose funding is required and what sum is requested. Where possible a copy of the latest accounts should be enclosed.

Applications are considered by the trustees on a monthly basis, in between their full meetings. Some applications, generally where a larger grant is being considered, will be held back for consideration at a full meeting. These are held irregularly, at about three to four month intervals.

The Souter Foundation

Social welfare; Christianity, especially in Scotland; third world

£1,626,000 (1999)

Beneficial area UK, but with a strong preference for Scotland; overseas.

PO Box 7142, Perth PH1 1WH

Tel. 01738 634745 **Fax** 01738 440275

Correspondent Linda Scott, Secretary

Information available Accounts, without a narrative report, available for a fee from the correspondent.

Summary

This growing foundation made 378 grants in 1999. 82% of the money was disbursed in 19 donations for amounts of £10,000 or more, leaving an average of under £1,000 for the remaining 359 awards. Of the organisations getting the 19 largest grants, 11 had also been supported in the previous year. Grants are said to be usually for revenue costs.

General

The foundation was established in 1991 with an endowment from Brian Souter, a creator of the Stagecoach Company, who continues to make substantial donations. Mr Souter has been prominent in Scotland for his vociferous attacks on the proposed repeal of 'Section 28', the law banning the promotion of homosexuality in schools.

In 1999 the value of the foundation's investments, whose nature is not disclosed, declined from £10 million to £7 million and generated only £130,000 in dividends. However, further donations of £1.2 million were received during the year, presumably from Mr Souter, enabling the grant programme to be increased. In April 2000 the University of Glasgow announced the gift of £1 million from Mr Souter for a heart scanner for research purposes. It was not clear whether the gift was from Mr Souter directly or via this foundation.

The foundation does not say why grants are given, where the beneficiaries are based, or what they do. From the 19 disclosed recipients it appears that more than half of the money may go to Scottish causes, a substantial proportion of them with Christian connections. If so, it is good to see Scottish money, newly made in the country, being put to good use locally. There are many London-based foundations described in this book at least part of whose wealth derives from the prosperous days of Scottish industry which has now been brought south.

The nature of one major beneficiary, Strathclyde House Development Trust, has not been disclosed. It accounted for over a third of the grant total (£715,000) in 1999 and had also been strongly supported in some but not all previous years. This charity is registered with the Inland Revenue in Scotland, with its address given as that of a firm of Glasgow solicitors, Holmes McKillop. The other major beneficiary over time has been the

Church of the Nazarene (£133,000 in 1999 and £174,000 in 1998).

The other major grants in 1999 (and 1998) were as follows:

Scottish Business Awards Trust	£60,000	(£20,000)
Children's hospices, Scotland	£50,000	(£38,000)
Fanfare for a New Generation	£50,000	(–)
Save the Children	£50,000	(£100,000)
The Christian Institute	£50,000	(£63,000)
Bethany Christian Trust	£40,000	(£38,000)
Perth Festival 1999	£33,000	(–)
Scripture Union	£30,000	(£23,000)
Oasis Trust	£20,000	(£10,000)
Princess Royal Trust for Carers	£20,000	(£24,000)
Scottish Crusaders	£15,000	(£15,000)
JC2000	£12,000	(–)
New Hope Trust	£12,000	(–)
Scottish Offenders Project	£11,000	(–)
Glasgow City Mission	£10,000	(–)
National Bible Society of Scotland	£10,000	(£10,000)
Ninewells Cancer Campaign	£10,000	(–)

There is a small programme of grants for individuals, worth nearly £10,000 in 1999.

The foundation's information sheet, provided in 1998, may no longer be current but, in the absence of other information from the charity, is reproduced below:

In the year ended 31 December 1997, charitable donations totalled £761,000 and ranged from £50,000 to an organisation working with the homeless to £200 to a local youth club.

Most of the grants we make are in the region of £200–£500 (204 out of 285 in 1997). Our stated policy is to assist 'projects engaged in the relief of human suffering in the UK or overseas, particularly those with a Christian emphasis". We tend not to get involved with research or capital funding, but would be more likely to assist with revenue costs of a project, for example, supporting a community worker. There is inevitably also a certain bias towards Scotland.

The largest grants of 1997 were awarded to Church of the Nazarene (£125,000) and Strathclyde House Development Trust (£114,000; £171,000 in 1996). The third largest grant, for £50,000, was to Turning Point – perhaps the 'organisation working with the homeless' mentioned in the foundation's information sheet. Also 46 individuals received donations totalling £6,000 (average: £130).

Exclusions

Building projects, personal education grants, expeditions.

Applications

Applicants should apply in writing, setting out a brief outline of the project for which funding is sought. Trustees meet every two months or so, and all applications will be acknowledged in due course, whether or not they are successful.

Subsequent applications should be made no more frequently than annually.

South Yorkshire Community Foundation

General, in South Yorkshire

£712,000 (1999/2000)

Beneficial area South Yorkshire.

Round House, Heritage Park, 55 Albert Terrace Road, Sheffield S6 3BR

Tel. 0114 273 1765 **Fax** 0114 278 0730

e-mail admin@sycf.org.uk

website www.sycf.org

Correspondent Anthony Blackett, Administrator

Information available Application form and guidelines. Annual review and accounts.

Summary

This community foundation, launched in 1986, supports the voluntary sector in South Yorkshire. As well as running its own programme, it makes grants on behalf of its donors, and, through funds such as the South Yorkshire Key Fund, channels statutory funding to local groups. Under the main programme, grants are normally for up to £1,000, while Key Fund grants can be for as much as £25,000.

General

The foundation describes its work thus:

What work does the foundation support?

The Foundation supports voluntary groups anywhere in South Yorkshire and focuses on:

- Neighbourhood based community development initiatives
- The education and training needs of voluntary sector community groups
- Voluntary sector housing and homelessness initiatives
- Community information and advice services
- Community based self help health projects
- Local community environmental projects

Who can apply?

- Voluntary organisations
- Community groups
- Small charities

Priority is given to small and medium sized groups which find it hard to raise money elsewhere.

How much is available?

Grants are normally for amounts of up to £1,000 in any one year, but Key Fund grants are larger [up to £25,000].

Grants in 1999/2000

Key Fund Grants totalling £662,000 were made to 54 organisations, most in the range £10,000–£25,000.

There were 12 beneficiaries of over £20,000, including Relate Rotherham, Armthorpe Community Enterprise, Doncaster Women's Aid, Hoyland and District Credit Union, Friends of the General Cemetery and Pakistan Community and Advice Centre (both in Sheffield).

Smaller grants, in the range £1,000–£3,000, went to 20 organisations, including Sheffield Independent Film Company, Grimethorpe and District Band, Hillsborough One Parent Group, Spring Vale Pre-School Playgroup and the Special Educational Garden Experience.

Under the main grants programme, grants totalling £60,000 went to over 150 local groups.

Exclusions

- party political and religious activities
- medical charities (except self help groups)
- individuals
- branches of national charities (unless with independent bank accounts, committees and constitution)

Applications

Applications are made by completing a simple form, available with the grant closing dates, from the foundation. Initial enquiries can be made using the internet, telephone or fax.

The main foundation grants have three closing dates per year – the end of February, August and November.

There is a separate application form and contact number for the South Yorkshire Key Fund. Groups should ring 0845 140 1400. There are no fixed closing dates.

The applications received that fit the grant priorities are then sent out to the grant assessors of the district advisory committees for each local authority area, or the Key Fund Advisory Committee. The assessors visit the group and then meet as the advisory committee to make their recommendations to the trustees on the grants to be made and the sums given.

The Southover Manor General Education Trust

Education, youth, in Sussex

£496,000 (1998/99)

Beneficial area Sussex.

Old Vicarage Cottage, Newhaven Road, Iford, Lewes, East Sussex BN7 3PL

Correspondent Secretary

Information available Inadequate annual report and accounts, without any information about grants.

General

Established in 1988, with initial funding coming from the sale proceeds of Southover Manor School in Sussex, the trust's principal object is the 'education of boys and girls under 25 by providing books and equipment, supporting provision of recreational and educational facilities, scholarships and awards'. Grants are given to 'schools and individuals in Sussex'.

In 1998/99 the trust's income was £155,000 – around a third of grant expenditure. Nevertheless, due to unrealised gains in investments, its assets still increased slightly to a total of £3,220,000. Grantmaking totalled £496,000 to schools and individuals.

As usual, there was no grants list for the year on file at the Charity Commission and the report and accounts gave no information about grants at all (beyond their total). It is deplorable that the Commission allows such a situation to continue year after year.

This entry must therefore resort to information going back to 1995/96 when the report and accounts were more revealing. In that year, the trust made 55 grants ranging from £100 to £50,000 (£277,000 in total). Four, accounting for a tiny percentage of total grants expenditure, were repeated from the previous year. The largest seven grants accounted for about 60% of the total. Most beneficiaries were state schools, but funds also went to private schools, individuals (amounts between £100 and £5,000), and other youth organisations (scouts, guides, the YMCA).

Exclusions

Those over 25 years of age. Organisations and individuals outside Sussex.

Applications

In writing to the correspondent.

The Spitalfields Market Community Trust

Education, employment, welfare in Tower Hamlets

£1,130,000 (1999/2000)

Beneficial area The London Borough of Tower Hamlets.

Attlee House, 28 Commercial Street, London E1 6LR

Tel. 020 7247 6689 **Fax** 020 7247 8748

e-mail smct.org@virgin.net

Correspondent Sandra Davidson, Grants Administrator

Information available Guidelines for applicants. Excellent report and accounts.

Summary

Around 100 grants a year are awarded to organisations benefiting the Tower Hamlets community in a variety of ways. Roughly two thirds of the money is given for revenue costs and a third for capital projects. Most grants range from £1,000 to £10,000, but recently the trust has funded a few major projects with grants of up to £500,000, contributing to a grant total of £1,130,000 in 1999/2000.

These payments have had a significant impact on the trust's grant-making ability. Its priorities were to be reviewed at a strategy meeting in March 2000, and to be discussed was 'the depletion of trust funds and future of the trust itself'.

General

Founded in 1991 as a limited company (then called Startaid Ltd), the trust was established as part of the 'planning gain' arrangements accompanying the development of what had been Spitalfields fruit and vegetable market. The trust received £3.75 million from Spitalfields Development Ltd (the developers of the site) and £1.25 million from the City of London Corporation (freeholders of the site). All directors of the trust have local connections.

The Trust was established with the aim of benefiting the inhabitants of the London Borough of Tower Hamlets with particular emphasis on Bethnal Green. Its objects cover a broad charitable base including the relief of poverty, the advancement of education and other purposes of benefit to the community. The Directors of the Trust are willing to consider applications for funding from organisations whose work might fall within the Trust's general objects or any of the following specific areas:

- research into job opportunities
- job training centres and schemes
- workshops and light industrial facilities
- environment improvement
- gardens and open spaces
- sheltered housing facilities

Criteria

Priority will be given to projects which demonstrate the following:

- impact
- leverage
- partnership
- sustainability
- track record
- equal opportunities.

Particular attention will be given to projects incorporating consortia bids and matching funding. The Grants Administrator will be happy to discuss bids before an initial application is made … All applicants will be informed in writing of the outcome of their initial bid and may be invited to complete a detailed application for our consideration.

Each year charitable expenditure exceeds income, so grant-making capacity is diminishing, though apparently not as rapidly as was previously thought. The trust said in 1998 that it expected to make fewer donations each year, soon ceasing to make grants altogether, and that it would work in an advisory role only, giving information on fundraising and other charity matters. In fact, grants worth £759,000 were made during 1998/99 and the trust's assets still stood at £4.27 million by the end of the year.

Grants in 1998/99

Breakdown of projects supported, 1998/99:

Type	*No.*	*Amount*
Education	22	£184,000
Youth	10	£155,000
Training	9	£110,000
Social welfare	16	£100,000
Housing	3	£55,000
Advice and information	9	£47,000
Art and culture	16	£47,000
Community development	9	£41,000
Environmental	2	£20,000
Total	96	£759,000

Major projects

Grants to Cityside Regeneration:

- Rich Mix Centre (£500,000)
  Part of a £7 million project to establish a centre in Bethnal Green celebrating 'the contributions which London's communities have made to its economic, social and cultural life and to promote London's significance as a major world city'.
- Graduate Programme – Qualify for Employment (£275,000)
  The programme provides diagnostic assessment, screening, matching and job preparation for local graduates to match their career aspirations.
- Kobi Nazrul Centre (Bengali Cultural and Education Centre) – £60,000 towards major refurbishment work.

Other major projects included:

- Tower Hamlets Youth Counselling Service – £118,000 towards the purchase and refurbishment of premises for a Youth Advice Centre.
- Tower Hamlets College – £300,000 matched funding for the Hardship Fund.

Main grants programme

Other recipients of grants for £10,000 or more included: Providence Row Housing Association (£50,000); Keen Students School (£40,000); Collective of Bangladeshi School Governors (£22,000); the Environment Trust (£18,000); Spitalfields Festival (£13,000), and Jagonari Women's Educational Resource Centre (£10,000).

A further 79 grants ranged from £1,000 to £8,750 and almost £3,000 was awarded in grants of less than £1,000.

Exclusions

The trust does not fund:

- individuals
- political parties
- religious activities
- grants which do not benefit people living in Tower Hamlets and Bethnal Green in particular

Applications

To the grants administrator. Prior to submitting a detailed application, you are requested to send in an outline application. All applicants are required to provide the following basic details:

- your legal status and aims;
- a statement about your organisation: brief history, staffing and management committee details, current activities and reference to any previous grants from SMCT;
- a precise outline of the *current* financial position of your organisation, listing the main sources of income;
- a statement on the particular need for which funding is being sought and who will benefit;
- full costing of your project proposal;
- precise details of other funding sources for the project.

The outline application should be accompanied by:

- a job description, if the application concerns a post;
- a list of the names and addresses of the office holders of your management body.

The application must not exceed two sides of A4 plus necessary appendices.

The directors of the trust usually meet monthly, except in August and December.

Foundation for Sport and the Arts

Sport, the arts

£8,242,000 (1999)

Beneficial area UK.

PO Box 20, Liverpool L13 1HB

Tel. 0151 259 5505 **Fax** 0151 230 0664

Correspondent Grattan Endicott, Secretary

Information available Full information from the foundation. Monthly grants lists, containing a short informative note on the purposes of each grant. An application pack is available.

Summary

The foundation's income, derived mainly from the football pools companies, now looks set to stabilise at £10 million to £11 million a year. It usually gives one-off grants for buildings and equipment, but there is some two or three-year funding and there can be interest-free loans. The maximum grant is £75,000, although most grants are between £1,000 and £5,000. The foundation's aim has always been to support 'a lot with a little'; it looks to encourage wide participation in sport and the arts rather than elite performers and the development of excellence.

The money is divided two thirds for sport and one third for art.

The foundation generally makes relatively rapid decisions, but even if provisionally agreed a grant may not be paid until the foundation has sufficient funds available. (See under 'Applications' below.)

General

The foundation is not a charity but an independent discretionary trust founded by and funded by way of the football pools companies. The foundation is driven by a desire to put money back into those areas and communities where pools punters can see and enjoy the benefits. Grassroots activities with community benefit are the priority for the trustees.

The foundation gives a third of its funding to the arts, with the remainder given to sports. The bulk of the sporting commitments are for 'athletic' activities. There is a smaller allowance for 'non-athletic sports' or recreational pursuits which nevertheless enhance or promote physical fitness.

Income is entirely responsive to the fortunes of the football pools. There have been dramatic changes over the last four years, and regular readers of this guide will note the marked reduction from the £52 million reported in 1995/96. In its infancy after its creation in 1991, the foundation was giving away large grants, sometimes up to the giddy heights of £2 million for a single project. Grant totals peaked at around £70 million, with income of £1.4 million arriving weekly at the foundation. This situation was indeed too good to last.

The decline is almost entirely the result of the arrival of the National Lottery in 1994 which had a dramatic effect on levels of other forms of gambling. However, fiscal concessions for the pools were made in 1999 and income may settle at something more than £10 million a year. This means that the foundation should remain a major funder in each of its two fields.

In 1999 grants were categorised as follows:

	No.	*Amount*
Sport	1,288	£4.8 million
Non-athletic sports	102	£0.3 million
Arts	423	£3.1 million

The grants: sports

The foundation has continued with its policy of giving awards mainly for capital and equipment. The desire to give pools customers something to see for their money informs trustees' decisions in every area of the foundation, including the ongoing debate over revenue funding (see below). Modest grants are occasionally given for individuals' expenses, but usually where competitors face disadvantage or have a disability. A few grants are given to support team costs (travel and participation, but no longer for those going abroad) and events, or sports programme development.

Most awards are for small voluntary sports clubs representing an impressive array of sporting activity and taking in a large number of small communities throughout the country. Over 130 different sports have been supported, from aikido to yachting. A tiny handful of sports are not supported by the foundation. These are: angling, croquet, fishing, horse racing and motorised sport. Shooting applications are considered on a case by case basis.

The FSA is keen to support all geographical areas, and is generally successful in this. The enterprise is Liverpool based, and uses local advisers throughout the country. There seems to be no noticeable bias towards London and the south east of England. The distribution, however, is totally in response to applications. The foundation does not have programmes of its own to fund.

Capital grants

Capital funding is the main element of the FSA's support. The FSA prefers projects where it is the lead funder, but will in some selected cases be involved in partnership funding where the Lottery is also supporting. 'In particular the foundation may be prepared to take on the principal funding of a discrete segment of a project where this can be distinguished as a significant, self-contained "foundation" exercise.'

Though a very occasional grant can be for as much as £75,000, most grants are for less than £5,000.

Loans

In December 1996, the foundation announced that it was considering making interest-free loans where appropriate. The potential borrower would have to show how the lease or purchase of land or property would make enough income available to repay the loan.

Revenue funding

The FSA has always supported capital costs. In 1996 revenue funding was added:

> In the past we have avoided commitments to core funding and, in general, to payment of wages. Where we can deal with cases on a two-year or three-year basis with no prospect of further funding subsequently, we have now made exceptions. Trustees are now prepared to look with interest at further applications coming forward.
>
> It is expected that a Business Plan will be required with closely detailed assessments of the revenue expenditure envisaged. Specify staff to be employed and why. The application should incorporate a plan in outline showing key figures or alternatively the full plan accompanied by a summary of key proposals.

and

> Trustees should be given details of the other revenue funding anticipated with information as to the extent to which it has been structured. Bodies that should evidently contribute to be designated and their position statements attached to the plan. (Local authorities in particular please note.)

At that time, trustees indicated that revenue funding bids should be for schemes with a duration of not more than three years.

Major beneficiaries in the first half of 2000 included Barnstaple Cricket Club (£39,000 to improve pitches), Ravenscroft Tennis Club, London (£50,000 towards a clubhouse), The Marsh Sports Ground in Weymouth (£42,000) and St Benedict's Sports College in Cheltenham (£50,000).

The grants: arts

The FSA supports both amateur and professional activities and gives grants to most art forms. Grants are not currently given for uniforms or instruments for brass, silver or marching bands.

Grant categories include music (including opera); museums and galleries; festivals; theatres; drama; visual arts (including sculpture); film and television; dance; crafts.

Grants are made for capital projects, for artistic productions, and to support individual students.

An analysis of the grants for the first six months of 2000 showed the following totals:

Music (inc. opera)	£276,000
Theatres	£130,000
Drama	£92,000
Multi-disciplinary	£87,000
Dance	£80,000
Film/TV	£71,000
Museums	£64,000
Visual arts	£39,000
Literature	£35,000
Festivals	£34,000
Crafts	£30,000

Major beneficiaries had included the Plaza Community Cinema, Liverpool (£35,000 for projection equipment), the British Library (£20,000 towards buying the Olivier Archive), Kent Music School (£20,000 for a rehearsal room) and the Almeida Theatre, London (£50,000 for a production).

Exclusions

No grants outside the foundation's chosen fields, as described above.

Applications

Full application packs are available from the telephone number above. Grants are considered on a rolling basis.

Where applicants are considering revenue funding or interest-free loans, they also should read the notes above.

The following information should be included in the application:

- The latest financial statements of the enterprise to be assisted.
- A description of the purpose for which a grant is sought. Where applicable this should be backed up with the reports of consultants and professional advisers.
- The total cost of the project. The amount of the grant desired from the foundation.
- A statement of the way in which it is proposed to fund the project, with information on other money which will, or may, be committed alongside that of the foundation.
- A special point should be made of telling the FSA (where applicable) such information as:
  – How many people will benefit from the proposal?
  – What numbers of people can be accommodated in the auditorium or spectator accommodation?
  – The precise nature of the ownership of the club, society, premises, trustees, members' committee or the like.
- Information as to the persons who will be involved in the realisation of the plan. Where available and applicable, facts as to suppliers and contractors who will be invited to give effect to the proposals.
- A completed questionnaire. This is important: cases are delayed if there is no completed questionnaire.
- In the case of a club or organisation a potted history of its founding, development and future aims.

'The trustees would prefer that a detailed application should be accompanied by a synopsis of the key elements set out on a single sheet of A4 size paper. Videos and books are not encouraged. A photograph or two may be helpful in some cases.'

When assessing an application, the trustees have two main considerations:

(i) The project should benefit the general community: 'The money comes out of the pockets of pools punters: we would like to plough it back largely into things that the general community will experience and enjoy.'

(ii) Therefore, the foundation is particularly keen to support the 'little clubs' – ie. regional and particularly local clubs.

In recent years, the FSA has looked for how much self-help the application contains. It is keen to see other fundraising initiatives as well as other supporters involved in the project.

Owing to the way the foundation is funded, there may be time-lags between agreeing a grant and the cheque being sent. The FSA empties the funding barrel whenever pools income is received. Successful applications have therefore to wait their turn. This can be four to six months or more, depending on the size of the application. 'When a case is approved and put in the queue of potential grant offers waiting funds, the foundation sends to the applicant a letter of intent. This is carefully worded so that it does not commit the trustees to a grant and the applicant is warned not to go too far in acting upon the content of the letter for this reason. Until a letter of intent is issued it remains the case that the final decision may be to refuse the application. No applicant should make an assumption that prolonged consideration implies an eventual decision to offer a grant.'

Pam Bennett leads the Sports Team; Carla Roberts, the Arts.

Applicants are asked not to send applications direct to trustees. The only effect is to slow the process down, and no special attention will be given.

The Spring Harvest Charitable Trust

The promotion of Christianity

£361,000 (1997/98)

Beneficial area Overseas.

14 Horsted Square, Uckfield, East Sussex TN22 1QL

Tel. 01825 769111

Correspondent J C Yeomans

Information available Annual report and accounts.

General

This is a charity for the promotion of Christianity, most of whose revenue comes from the annual Spring Harvest bible teaching event. Grants are made to projects overseas, both for evangelical activity and for Christian-based community work.

In 1997/98, 48 grants were made, 30 of them for amounts between £3,000 and £5,000. Few of these were repeat awards. The largest grants were as follows (with the figure for the preceding year in brackets):

Evangelical Alliance	£35,000	(£35,000)
Jubilee 2000 Africa Project	£34,000	–
Saltmine	£26,000	(£31,000)
Youth for Christ (Millennium)	£15,000	(£20,000)
World Relief	£13,000	–
Care for the Family	£11,000	–

Applications

In writing to the correspondent.

The Staples Trust

Development, environment, women's issues

£862,000 (approved, 1998/99)

See the entry for the Sainsbury Family Charitable Trusts

Tel. 020 7410 0330 **Fax** 020 7410 0332

Correspondent Michael Pattison, Director

Information available Good annual report and accounts.

Summary

This is one of the Sainsbury Family Charitable Trusts which share a joint administration. It gives most of its support to development/environmental work overseas. It also supports UK-based environmental activities. It is rare among trusts in having women's issues as a particular concern.

General

The trust was endowed by Jessica Sainsbury and its trustees include her husband and her two brothers who lead the Tedworth and Glass-House trusts (see separate entries).

Its staff include Michael Pattison, who is director of each of the Sainsbury Family Trusts, and Hester Marriott, executive.

In 1998/99 the trust had an income of £631,000 and made grant payments totalling £664,000. New grant approvals were categorised as follows (readers should note that grants were also made for work overseas under headings other than 'development'):

	No.	Value
Overseas development	16	£478,000
Environmental	9	£195,000
Women's issues	9	£131,000
General	5	£47,000

The trust says that 'proposals are generally invited by the trustees or initiated at their request' and that 'unsolicited applications are discouraged and are unlikely to be successful'. The staff, and in some cases individual trustees, already have a relationship with many established organisations in the relevant fields. These organisations feel free to approach the trust with their ideas. Those outside this circle should not be deterred from doing likewise.

The rest of this entry is taken from the 1998/99 annual report, but with added examples of individual grants.

Overseas development – £478,000 approved

Support tends to be focused in East and South Africa, South and South East Asia and South America, although projects from other areas are considered on their merits.

Trustees are interested in supporting projects which contribute to the empowerment of women, the rights of indigenous people, improved shelter and housing, income generation in disadvantaged communities and sustainable agriculture and forestry.

Trustees are particularly interested to support development projects which take account of environmental sustainability and, in many cases, the environmental and developmental benefits of the project are of equal importance.

The 16 grants were led by four grants between £60,000 and £70,000, as follows:

- Akina Mama wa Afrika (for a women's leadership small grant scheme)
- Homeless International (towards community infrastructures in Mumbai)
- Survival International (over three years, for its Urgent Action bulletins)
- Womankind Worldwide (for core costs over three years)

The remaining grants were for amounts from £500 to £50,000; about half of them were for projects specifically associated with the empowerment of women.

Environment – £195,000 approved

Projects are supported in developing countries, Central and Eastern Europe and the UK. Grants are approved for renewable energy technology, training and skills upgrading and, occasionally, research.

In Central and Eastern Europe, trustees are interested in providing training opportunities for community/business leaders and policy makers and in contributing to the process of skill-sharing and information exchange. In the UK, trustees aim to help communities protect, maintain and improve areas of land and to support work aimed at informing rural conservation policy.

The eight grants in 1998/99 were led by £45,000 for Charity Know How, to help with the development of environmental organisations in Central and Eastern Europe. £33,000 was given to four environmental organisations in Romania and £22,000 to the Regional Environmental Centre in Hungary. The largest UK grant was to Sustrans (£22,000) and there was also support for Friends of the Earth and the Trust for Education and Development.

Women's issues – £131,000 approved

Trustees remain interested in domestic violence issues. Although their priority is innovative strategic programmes of support with a national focus (particularly interagency work and work to tackle domestic violence from the male perpetrator perspective), they also provide smaller grants to assist local refuge services and women's self-help groups.

Two large grants accounted for most of the expenditure. £75,000 was given to the Trinity Centre's Tryangle Project and £28,000 to the Islington Women's Counselling Centre. There were seven smaller grants, all for less than £8,000, with well spread beneficiaries including Women's Aid organisations in Chester, Stirling, Falkirk, Hartlepool, Margate and West Lancashire.

General – £47,000 approved

Grants of £16,000 each were made to the Headley and Jerusalem Trusts (see separate entries), as two among numerous transfers between the various Sainsbury family trusts.

Applications

See the guidance for applicants in the entry for the Sainsbury Family Charitable Trusts. A single application will be considered for support by all the trusts in the group.

However, for this as for many of the trusts, 'proposals are generally invited by the Trustees or initiated at their request. Unsolicited applications are discouraged and are unlikely to be successful, even if they fall within an area in which the Trustees are interested.'

See also the text above.

The Steel Charitable Trust

Social welfare, health, medical research, general

£950,000 (1999/2000)

Beneficial area UK, with a local interest in the Luton area.

Bullimores Chartered Accountants, 3 Boutport Street, Barnstaple, Devon EX31 1RH

Correspondent The Secretary

Information available Annual report and accounts on file at the Charity Commission.

Summary

A large number of grants, typically one-off and from £500 to £5,000, go to a wide range of mainly national charities. However larger amounts tend to go to regularly supported charities, with grants for more than £20,000 often given to those benefiting the Luton area.

General

Following the death of the settlor, Mrs M M Steel, in 1999 the residue of her estate was transferred to the trust, raising its incoming resources to an exceptional £1.6 million for the year to 31 January 2000. £950,000 was disbursed in 190 grants, as shown in the box opposite.

The trust now provides a full grants list with some short descriptions of grants. Examples of the larger ones are reprinted here, with the accompanying brief description, unless it was listed as being simply for the 'general' purposes of the charity.

The Luton and South Bedfordshire Hospice, which comprises the Pasque Hospice and Keech Cottage children's hospice and typically receives annual donations of between £50,000 and £100,000, benefited from the largest grants in the year.

These were headed by an exceptional 'memorial' grant from the late settlor's estate of £150,000 to the Pasque Hospice, towards the cost of its building extension, while a further £50,000 went to the Keech Cottage Hospice.

Large new grants went to the following beneficiaries:

- Luton Churches Education Trust (£22,000, 'Safe & Sound Project')

THE STEEL CHARITABLE TRUST – GRANTS IN 1998/99 AND 1999/2000

	1999/2000		1998/99	
Social services	£397,000	(42%)	£365,000	(46%)
Health	£263,000	(27%)	£141,500	(18%)
Environment & preservation	£113,000	(12%)	£106,000	(13%)
Culture & recreation	£84,000	(9%)	£57,000	(7%)
Medical research	£71,000	(8%)	£110,500	(14%)
International aid & activity	£22,000	(2%)	£20,000	(2%)
Total	£950,000	(100%)	£800,000	(100%)

- Action on Addiction (£20,000)
- Fairbridge (£20,000)
- Royal Academy of Music (£20,000 towards a 'Masterclass Programme')
- National Trust (£20,000 to restore Arlington Lake, Devon)

Seven of eight charities given priority for support in the original Deed of Settlement received grants of £20,000, as follows:

- Imperial Cancer Research Fund (for equipment and ongoing support)
- The Salvation Army
- National Deaf Children's Society (third and final grant towards the funding of training and conference officer)
- The Donkey Sanctuary
- PDSA (for a Pet Aid Scheme in Luton)
- International League for the Protection of Horses
- Friends of St Mary's Church, Luton (for building maintenance)

'Social services' recipients were diverse, as shown by the following sample of grants for £1,000 made under that heading (none of these beneficiaries had received support in the previous year): Bradford Cathedral ('National Millennium Faith Experience' project); Clwyd Cornerstone Trust; Deafblind UK (to fund a volunteer in Bedfordshire); Friends of Harold Magnay School (purchase of 'Genie' for computer equipment); Gurkha Welfare Trust; Ipswich & District Crossroads; MENCAP; Northamptonshire Association of Youth Clubs; One Parent Families Scotland.

Exclusions

Individuals, students, expeditions.

Applications

In writing to the correspondent, including:

- statement of purpose for which the grant is required;
- full latest accounts showing all other sources of funding;
- statement of existing funding for the grant application.

Applications are not acknowledged.

Stevenson Family's Charitable Trust

Museums, health, general

£865,000 (1998/99)

33 St Mary Axe, London EC3A 8LL

Tel. 020 7342 2630

Correspondent H A Stevenson

Information available Full accounts are on file at the Charity Commission.

General

This trust appears to be primarily the vehicle for the philanthropic activities of Mr Stevenson and of his family. Hugh Stevenson was formerly the chairman of Mercury Asset Management, one of London's largest investment management companies. As is common for trusts of this kind, 'no unsolicited applications can be considered' and the trust may best be seen as simply a tax effective vehicle for personal philanthropy.

The annual reports are purely formal, and do not include the review of charitable activities required by law, but they do include details of all grant payments. Following the donation of almost £8 million to the trust in 1997/98, grants in the following year nearly doubled to £865,000. This was more than twice the trust's investment income.

The grants list for 1998/99 shows 44 awards, but only 12 were for more than £2,000, and just six of them accounted for 90% of the total. These beneficiaries were as follows:

The British Museum (£200,000, as in 1997/98); St Hilda's and University Colleges, Oxford (£200,000 each), and the Tate Gallery and the Institute of Child Health, of which Mr Stevenson is a trustee (£100,000 each).

A further £2.6 million of commitments had been entered into during the year.

Applications

As the charity's funds are required to support purposes chosen by the trustees, no unsolicited applications can be considered.

The Sir Halley Stewart Trust

Medical, social and religious research

£834,000 (1999/2000)

Beneficial area Unrestricted, but mainly UK and south and west Africa in practice.

22 Earith Road, Willingham, Cambridge CB4 5LS

Tel. 01954 260707 **Fax** 01954 260707

website www.sirhalleystewart.org

Correspondent Mrs Sue West, Administrator

Information available Leaflet – 'Notes for those seeking grants'. Excellent five-year review with full grants list for the period. Report and accounts. Website updated regularly with latest policy.

Summary

This is a Christian-based organisation whose grantmaking is divided into three areas – medical, social and educational, and religious – each with a separate grants committee and approximately equal grant expenditure. Of nearly £750,000 worth of grants during 1998/99, £700,000 went in awards of at least £5,000 each. However, a third of the grants were for less than £1,000 each.

General

Income is typically about £1 million, but was nearly £2.5 million in 1999, largely due to a legacy gift of over £1.5 million.

The three grants committees are not mutually exclusive. For example, the social trustees are anxious to fund projects which address the social aspects of the problems which the medical trustees consider to be important.

The former administrator has written that:

The Sir Halley Stewart Trust is somewhat unusual in the trust world, firstly because its main role is to fund salaries, and secondly because its wide terms of reference give the trustees the freedom to operate in almost any field they wish. It is not a 'medical', 'social' or 'religious' trust. Our main role is to give support at the start of a project, when funding is particularly hard to come by, in the hope and expectation that the recipient will then be able to get more extensive support from one of the larger funding bodies.

Guidelines for applicants

The following information is reprinted from the trust's 'Notes for those seeking grants':

Origin and management of the trust

The trust was established in 1924 by Sir Halley Stewart with a capital sum and over subsequent years he established guidelines governing awards. Continuity with the founder is maintained by trustees drawn from the Stewart family. Other trustees provide expertise in special areas of interest.

Objects of the trust

The trust has a Christian basis and is concerned with the development of body, mind and spirit, a just environment, and international goodwill. To this end it supports projects in religious, social, educational and medical fields. The trust aims to promote and assist innovative research activities or developments with a view to making such work self-supporting. It emphasises prevention rather than alleviation of human suffering.

It is desirable that grants should be on a diminishing scale; when the grantee's work has justified itself other means will be found of carrying it on, and when it has not justified itself the trust grants should not be continued.

Types of grant given

Grants are usually in the form of a salary, and the trustees prefer to support innovative and imaginative people – often promising young researchers – with whom they can develop a direct relationship. Sometimes a contribution towards the expenses of a project are given. Grants are normally limited to two or three years, but are sometimes extended. Small individual grants are sometimes given. In general, the trustees do not favour grant-giving to enable the completion of a project initiated by other bodies.

Current priority areas

The trustees have selected certain areas of special interest which are currently treated as priorities. Each priority may be reflected in the social, religious and medical fields.

Religious

The trust is committed to advancing Christian religion. The trustees' particular interests are :

- Theological training in cases where there is special and specific need (e.g. in Africa or Eastern Europe).
- Teaching in the UK about Christianity, outside the formal education system.
- Encouragement of specific groups of people (e.g. the elderly, people with disability, students in higher education, those from ethnically mixed communities ...) to explore their spiritual needs and strengths.

Anyone contemplating approaching the Trust for support in this field is strongly advised to make a preliminary enquiry before submitting an application.

Social and educational

Applications are welcomed for research and development projects which will have a direct impact on the conditions of a particular group of people, as well as having wider implications. The trustees are particularly interested in:

- Projects which attempt to prevent and resolve conflicts and increase understanding within families and across racial, cultural, class, religious and professional divides.
- Projects which involve conflict resolution and reconciliation.
- Projects which attempt to help people to 'move beyond disadvantage' – and its consequences, e.g. youth unemployment, rehabilitation of offenders, homelessness, prevention of the downward spiral of youth criminality, race relations.
- Projects which address the needs of people, especially the young and elderly, which are not met by statutory services but are nevertheless serious.
- Small-scale projects overseas, particularly in Africa, which are aimed at community development.

Medical

Projects should be simple, not molecular, and capable of clinical application within 5 to 10 years, and they may include a social or ethical element. Non-medical Trustees should be able to understand the application and appreciate the value of the work. Projects may be of a type unlikely to receive support from Research Councils or large research-funding charities.

The trustees particularly welcome applications concerned with:

- Problems associated with the elderly such as Alzheimer's Disease, nutrition, osteoporosis and incontinence.
- The prevention of disease and disability in children.
- The prevention, diagnosis and treatment of tropical infectious and parasitic diseases.
- Innovative projects, involving any discipline, which are likely to improve health care.
- Ethical problems arising from advances in medical practice.

Main grants programme 1998/99

There are about 50 new grants a year, typically for 1 or 2 salaries over 3 years, and averaging perhaps a total of £27,000 over this period. In most years, over 50% of funds has gone into medical research. The trustees are now aiming for a better balance between the three areas of grantmaking. In the year to April 1999, the share was as follows:

Medical grants	£355,000	(47%)
Social grants	£266,000	(36%)
Religious grants	£126,000	(17%)
Total	£747,000	

Size of grants	*Paid*	*No.*
Under £1,000	£9,000	27
£1,000–£4,999	£38,000	23
£5,000 and over	£700,000	35

The following examples of both long-term funding and one-off grants are taken from the trust's five-year review:

Religious

World's End Community Church, London – £48,000 (1997–2000), salary for the manager of Community Computer Training Centre.

University of Cambridge, Margaret Beaufort Institute of Theology – £40,000 (1998-2000), to enable two students from Zambia and Kenya to take a two-year MA course.

The Magdalene Group, Norwich – £40,000 (1999–2000), salary for the project manager of this organisation, which offers support and refuge for young prostitutes.

Time and Space, Birkenhead, Wirral – £30,000 (1998–2000), salary for the assistant director of this Christian organisation designed to train facilitators in spiritual exploration.

Methodist Homes for the Aged – £36,000 (1995–99), to facilitate the setting up, and follow-up study, of an Age Awareness Project, the main purpose of which is to increase understanding of the spiritual needs of older people.

One-off grants in 1998/99 included:

The Living with Dying Trust – £18,000, salary for researcher to review work providing psychological, emotional and spiritual counsel and care to people who are facing death.

St Margaret's Church, Thornbury, Avon – £12,000, to pay for a Christian multi-faith worker from South Asia to spend three years in Thornbury as a 'mission partner' to help build relationships between religious communities.

St James's University Hospital, Leeds – £750, contribution to a study trip to the USA looking into Christian Healing and Hospital Chaplaincy.

Social and educational

Dementia Voice: Dementia Services Development for the South West – £66,000 (1997–2000), salary for the director and a part-time member of staff.

University of Sheffield, Dept of Healthcare for Elderly People – £57,000 (1996–2000), to support work investigating the causes of homelessness in elderly people.

The Warrington Project – £54,000 (1997–2000), salary for the co-ordinator of this project to promote mutual understanding between the people of Northern Ireland, the Republic of Ireland and England.

Highway Hospice Association, Natal, South Africa – £48,000 (1996–2000), for the salary and costs of a nursing sister to help to start one of 27 satellite hospices in the greater Durban area.

Lifeline Network International – £15,000 (1999–2000), for the 'Nehemiah Project' to promote rehabilitation of war traumatised children in Sierra Leone.

Other grants, awarded only in 1998/99, included:

Plan International UK, Genital Mutilation Project Burkina Faso – £10,000, for the training of animators who then pass on their training to local community volunteers.

York Health Services Research Unit – £5,000, contribution to a project aiming to help staff in care homes for the elderly to recognise and manage clinical depression in their clients.

HM Prison, Lindholme – £2,000, contribution to a project developing an electronic Braille station to help blind and deaf people to access information on television.

Medical

Medical Research Council Laboratories, Fajara, The Gambia – £51,000 (1997–2000), to employ a research assistant to work on the project 'Who Gets Tuberculosis?'.

The following grants in 1998/99 were for research:

London School of Hygiene and Tropical Medicine, Dept of Medical Parasitology – £45,000;

University of Edinburgh, Dept of Biological Sciences – £44,000;

University of Nottingham, Dept of Life Sciences – £41,000;

Sheffield Children's Hospital, Division of Child Health – £31,000;

University College Hospital, London, Dept of Paediatrics – £28,000.

Personal grants

'Each year the trustees are entitled to £1,000 each to donate to charitable causes of their choice.' Between 1994 and 1999 these included The Mouth & Foot Painting Artists Organisation, The Fan Museum, Rosehill Theatre Trust, Harefield Hospital Scanner Appeal, and Medical & Scientific Aid for Vietnam, Laos and Cambodia.

Exclusions

- general appeals of any kind;
- personal education, fees for courses;
- educational and travel projects for young people;
- the purchase, erection or conversion of buildings, or other capital costs;
- running costs of established organisations;
- university overhead charges.

Applications

The application should come, in the first instance, from the individual concerned, rather than the 'host' organisation. Applications can be received throughout the year and will be considered for the next available meeting. Assessment can take several weeks, so applicants should allow for this when submitting their proposals.

The following is reprinted from the trust's own material:

How to apply to us for a grant

First make sure that your project falls within the trust's current areas of interest. If you are in doubt, a quick telephone call to the Trust Office is welcomed.

There is no formal application form. Applicants should write to the administrator with a short description of the proposed work. We need to know exactly what you plan to do with the grant, where you will be doing the work, how much money you will need and approximately how long the work should take. You need to state what you believe will be the benefit of your work, within what time frame and how the findings will be disseminated. We also require a brief CV. Development projects should indicate where they hope to obtain future funding after the Trust's support has ended.

If we cannot help you we will let you know. It is worth pointing out that we receive many applications for support, and although your work may fit the objects of the trust, we may not necessarily be able to help you.

If it is decided to take your application further, it will be seen by those trustees who are most interested in that particular field. Please note that this process may take several weeks. You may be asked for more details at this stage. These trustees may then recommend that the application be considered at a full trustees' meeting at which final decisions are made.

Full trustees' meetings are held three times a year, in February, June & October.

Other advice

The following guidance for trustees should also be helpful for applicants:

The trust should seek to fund the unfashionable and unpopular.

Points to be borne in mind when assessing an application:

- Does it fit with the objects of the trust and fall within one of the current priority areas?
- How much funding is requested?
- What exactly will the money be used for?
- Where will the work be done?
- How long will it take?
- What will be the benefit of the work?
- Within what time frame?
- How will the findings be disseminated?

The Stobart Newlands Charitable Trust

Christian causes

£744,000 (1998)

Mill Croft, Hesket Newmarket, Wigton, Cumbria CA7 8HP

Tel. 01697 478261

Correspondent Mrs Margaret Stobart, Trustee

Information available Annual report and accounts.

Summary

Up to 50 grants a year, nearly all made on a recurring basis to Christian religious and missionary bodies. The trust wishes to emphasise that unsolicited applications are most unlikely to succeed.

General

The trustees are directors and shareholders of J Stobart and Sons Ltd, which gives the trust around £500,000 a year, forming the major part of its income. The total income in 1998 was £843,000, and its assets were a little over £3 million.

The grants list for that year showed 30 organisations in receipt of grants over £1,000, 25 of which had appeared in the equivalent list for 1997.

The major beneficiaries in both years were as follows:

	1998	*1997*
Operation Mobilisation	£150,000	£101,000
World Vision	£105,000	£60,000
Mission Aviation Fellowship	£80,000	£51,000
Keswick Convention	£118,000	£7,000

In 1998 these made up 61% of the year's total grant aid. A further nine grants to previously supported organisations were for between £10,000 and £26,000 and accounted for a further 22% of the total. The largest went to Way to Life, Tear Fund, London City Mission, Open Air Mission and Every Home Crusade (each receiving £20,000 or more).

The five new beneficiaries were Manchester City Mission (£30,000); Evangelical Alliance (£10,000); Trans World Radio (£5,000); 'SASRA' (£2,500) and Leprosy Mission (£2,000). Just under £8,000 was disbursed in grants of £1,000 or less.

Exclusions

No grants for individuals.

Applications

Unsolicited applications are most unlikely to be successful.

The W O Street Charitable Foundation

Education, disability, young people, welfare

£394,000 (1998)

Beneficial area UK, with local interests in the north west of England and Jersey.

c/o Barclays Bank Trust Company Ltd, Osborne Court, Gadbrook Park, Rudheath, Northwich CW9 7UE

Tel. 01606 313213 **Fax** 01606 313005/6

Correspondent Miss M Bertenshaw, Administrator

Information available In July 2000 the latest annual report and accounts received by the Charity Commission were those for 1998.

Summary

Grants, of which there are about 70 a year, do not normally exceed £20,000, and most are for £5,000 or less. Most support is given for educational purposes, followed by one-off grants, rarely repeated, mainly for local branches of national welfare and disability charities. A separate trust is used to distribute funds in Jersey.

General

In 1998 the foundation's income amounted to £656,000, from net assets of £17.5 million. Management fees from Barclays, already high at £164,000 in 1997 (as reported in the previous edition of this book), increased further to £188,000, which represents 29% of income or 48p for each £1 donated. The Charity Commission should not allow such costs to go unexplained by the foundation.

The annual report reads as follows:

> In considering grants the trustees pay close regard to the wishes of the late Mr Street who had particular interests in education, relief of poverty, the relief of persons with financial difficulties (particularly the aged, blind and disabled) and the relief of ill health or sickness and social welfare generally. Special support is given to the North West of England and to Jersey. £50,550 was paid to the W O Street Jersey Charitable Trust – the trustees of which apply the income (and where appropriate the capital) for charitable purposes within Jersey. £72,000 was spent on education bursaries and a further £271,250 in grants for charitable purposes.
>
> The trustees have selected a limited number of educational projects to which significant grants are being given over a shortish period (usually no more than three years) to enable the projects to find their feet. The trustees are keeping this policy under review but it is likely that a programme of supporting projects of this nature will be sustained (at least for the foreseeable future). As a result the trustees will not be able to devote so much of their resources as they have in the past to smaller 'one-off' grants.

Two of the largest grants in 1998 were repeat awards, presumably for the kind of educational projects mentioned above. These went to Life Education Centres (£20,000; £12,000 in 1997) and the Education 2000 Trust (£12,000; £38,000 in 1997).

Two other large grants were for new beneficiaries apparently under the same heading, to Tameside Education Business Partnership (£10,000) and the 21st Century Learning Initiative (£8,000).

The largest amounts over the two years, however, went to Home Start UK (£20,000 in 1998; £40,000 in 1997).

The remaining 70 grants listed were nearly all for either £2,500 or £5,000. Less than 10 of these beneficiaries had been supported the year before.

Of the following recipients clearly located in the north west of England, a couple confirm a previously stated interest in Bury:

Royal School for the Deaf, Manchester; Merseyside Youth Association; Manchester Grammar School Foundation Appeal (£5,000 each); Bury Church of England High School (£1,000); Bury United Reformed Churches (£500).

Other recipients included African-Caribbean Network Science and Technology; Rehab UK (£5,000 each); Victim Support Northern Ireland; Hampshire Autistic Society; YMCA Exeter (£2,500 each).

Applications

In writing to the correspondent.

The Bernard Sunley Charitable Foundation

General

£3,205,000 (1998/99)

Beneficial area Unrestricted, but overwhelmingly London and the south east of England in practice. Strong local interests in Kent (especially east Kent) and Northamptonshire (especially near Guilsborough).

53 Grosvenor Street, London W1X 9FH

Tel. 020 7409 1199 **Fax** 020 7409 7373

Correspondent Dr Brian Martin, Director

Trustees *John B Sunley; Bella Sunley; Joan Tice; Sir Donald Gosling.*

Information available Report and accounts, but without the required narrative report on policies and activities. List of grants paid, but with no indication of their nature or purpose other than for the 19 largest.

Summary

This old-style, reactive and lightly staffed foundation makes about 300 grants a year, mostly one-off, almost all for capital purposes and ranging from a few hundred pounds to several hundred thousand. The geographical spread is narrow, with most of the money, and the grants, going for work in London, Hertfordshire, Kent or Northamptonshire.

Background

The value of grantmaking by the foundation has been in relative decline. In 1984 it made awards of over £3 million, making it the ninth largest grantmaker in the country. By 1998, awarding a similar amount, it ranked 59th. It is exceptional for an endowed charity at this level to have seen its grantmaking actually reduced, in real terms, over this period. Most of the other foundations that might be regarded as its peers are now giving far more than they were fifteen years ago, even taking inflation into account.

This is in no way to the discredit of the foundation; indeed the opposite is as likely to be the case. The trust has preferred to do good now, rather than accumulate funds to do good later: and Britain is a far richer country now than it was ten or twenty years ago.

The figures are interesting, as they suggest that the US experience may also apply in the UK: that by and large a trust can afford to invest for an income of over five per cent of its net worth a year and still maintain its value in real terms – but over six per cent is not so easy.

Year	*Assets £million*	*Income*	*%*
1998/99	£68.2	£3.4	5.0%
1997/98	£64.5	£3.6	5.6%
1996/97	£55.0	£3.3	6.0%
1995/96	£57.8	£3.3	5.7%
1994/95	£51.6	£3.0	5.8%
1993/94	£53.2	£3.2	6.0%
1992/93	£48.6	£3.3	6.8%
1991/92	£42.8	£3.6	8.4%
1990/91	£46.9	£3.8	8.0%
1989/90	£45.1	£4.0	8.9%

It is noticeable that the trust has not tried to sustain the high levels of income of the early 1990s, in relation to its net worth, and it may now be seeking to maintain its present position even at the cost of reduced grantmaking in real terms.

This record may help to account for a note in the 1998/99 annual report of costs of £251,000 – a remarkably high figure – 'incurred in reviewing our investment management arrangements and, in particular, replacing one of the foundation's investment managers' (apparently Independent Investment Managers Ltd, replaced by Morgan Grenfell).

The foundation is still receiving donations from the founding family. In 1998/99, £804,000 was received from the estate of the late Mrs Eva Sunley, apparently in the remarkable form of specie (that is coin, presumably gold, as opposed to bullion).

Grantmaking

The grant-making pattern of the foundation has been little changed for many years. Most large grants are for buildings or their refurbishment, or for medical or research equipment. An occasional big exception has been support for university endowments.

The largest grants are mostly in one of four fields:

- Schools (usually independent), colleges and universities.
- Medicine, for research facilities, staff accommodation and general buildings and equipment.
- Youth, mainly for local building projects but often through national youth organisations.
- Community welfare, covering most forms of disability or need, though few

An old-style trust?

The Bernard Sunley Foundation, apparently unchanged in many ways since this series of books first appeared fifteen years ago, is something of a reminder of earlier times when many trusts admitted to no explicit policies, had a generally static trustee body and few if any staff, and offered no funding of salaries or 'projects'. Donations were gifts, and the recipient charities were generally left to get on with the job of putting the money to good use. Some such trusts were excellent, with knowledgeable trustees carefully seeking out the best homes for their money; others were dreadful, with grants being given largely to whoever the trustees happened to know or meet socially, or just going to the same unchanging list of recipients as repeated annual doles. Good or bad, they have been a disappearing species, and Sunley is now something of a reminder of an earlier age.

The Sunley trustee body is an exceptionally unchanging group (some members of which, unusually, do not live in Britain). The first edition of this book named six trustees in the year 1984. In 1999 there were just four trustees, all of them survivors from the original list. Though it is no criticism, a previous director, some while back, noted that the trustees were, even then, generally old.

Typically of the old-style trusts, the foundation does not fund core or revenue costs; by and large it sticks to buildings or endowments. At one time such grants made up almost half of all trust funding, but most trusts now have a wider repertoire.

There is with Sunley, as was once general practice, very little guidance for applicants on what the foundation is looking for in the applications it receives. They are all 'considered on their merits', as merit may be seen by the trustees, whose views on this significant issue can only be deduced from the grants that they make.

Finally, the foundation has recently said, as is now seldom admitted, that it has no formal grant monitoring procedures, 'relying largely on the grant recipient keeping the foundation informed' (though a 'close eye' is kept on larger grants).

child welfare organisations appear to be supported.

These main areas are said to account, typically, for about 80% of the value of the grants, in approximately equal proportions over time. There is also, in most years, a substantial value of grants for art and museum projects, for churches and for wildlife and conservation. The relatively small total of grants for work overseas usually includes a few awards for specifically Spanish activities; there are no comparable grants for work in other European countries.

For 1998/99 and 1997/98 the grants were summarised as follows, in a categorisation apparently going back to the founding of the foundation 40 years ago:

	1998/99	*1997/98*
Universities, colleges and schools	£1,036,000	£380,000
The arts, museums, etc.	£440,000	£105,000
Community aid and recreation	£424,000	£774,000
Youth and sport	£289,000	£238,000
Churches and chapels	£128,000	£106,000
Professional and public bodies, miscellaneous	£55,000	£62,000
Hospitals, medical schools, research inst's	£340,000	£385,000
General medicine	£118,000	£106,000
Provision for the elderly, including housing	£137,000	£278,000
Service charities	£58,000	£78,000
Wildlife and the environment	£92,000	£82,000
Overseas	£88,000	£178,000

Though payments may be spread out over a number of years, there is little if any funding of the costs of ongoing activity. The purposes of the smaller grants (less than £50,000 at present), which make up about half of the foundation's grant total, have never been disclosed, but anecdote suggests that they follow the same pattern as for big awards. Although the same organisations appear frequently over the years, they do not normally receive regular annual subventions, but appear to receive fresh individual grants each time. For example, SSAFA Forces Help received nothing in 1996/97, £10,000 in 1997/98 and £1,250 in 1998/99. The range of recipients is wider than for major grants, from hospices to racing welfare charities, and includes an extensive selection of uniformed youth groups such as scouts or sea cadets.

Many of the beneficiaries of the larger awards fall into one of three general groups:

- Major national institutions such as the National Gallery or London teaching hospitals.
- Institutions with a specifically 'free market' focus, such as Buckingham University, London Business School or the Thatcher Foundation.
- Independent schools with personal or local connections with the Sunley family or individual trustees, probably including places such as Northampton Grammar School, Elstree School or the Purcell School in Bushey.

Smaller grants are much more widely distributed, both geographically and in the kind of organisations supported, but there are marked local preferences. The most striking of these, commented on over many editions of this book and remaining unchanged in 1998/99, is the concentration of the charity's activities on the south of England, and particularly on London and the home counties. A necessarily approximate analysis of the 1998/99 grants showed 142 awards whose work could be geographically located:

South of England	120
North of England	18
Scotland	2
Wales	2
Northern Ireland	0

In the south of England group the preference for London, Kent and Northamptonshire continued to be marked. We have compared those two counties with the roughly similarly placed Suffolk and Leicester (together with London):

London	39
Kent	25
Northants	19
Suffolk	2
Leicestershire	0

The grants in Kent are spread throughout the county (though with a concentration in or near Sandwich). Those in Northants are closely clustered in villages within about 10 miles of Guilsborough, in the north west of the county. The previously reported interest in Hanwell, London, where Bernard Sunley lived as a child, is not apparent in recent grants lists, but this may be due to a lack of applications from this restricted area.

Within London generally, in contrast to a number of other grantmakers described in this book, there is no apparent concentration on areas of particular need, but there seems to be special interest in north west London and adjacent areas, such as Bushey and Elstree.

In the past, the foundation has defended the concentration of its grants on some of the most prosperous parts of the country. They are given in places that trustees either live in or know well, and where they are therefore said to be best informed about local needs. Editors of this series of books have long taken the view that this is an inadequate justification and that the foundation should give greater attention to putting its local grant money where it will be of most use, and that if existing trustees are not suited to achieving this, new trustees should be appointed who are.

Methods of working have been described as follows:

> The foundation has only three full time members of staff, and so cannot actively seek projects to support, having to rely on unsolicited applications or upon trustee-originated intelligence. ... The accounts of organisations which send in applications are very closely examined and are viewed more favourably if they are up to date.

Major grants in 1998/99

Universities, colleges and schools. Total £1,036,000 including

Elstree School, Berkshire: £100,000 towards anniversary appeal for cultural and sporting facilities.

London Business School: £100,000 (2nd of two) towards a new building.

Netherhall Educational Association, London: £100,000 (3rd of three) to increase accommodation for overseas students.

Northamptonshire Grammar School: £220,000 towards a science and technology block.

The Purcell School: £100,000 (3rd of three) for school relocation from Harrow to Bushey.

Sir Roger Manwood's School, Sandwich: £200,000 for a sports hall.

Thatcher Foundation: £100,000 (1st of three) to endow a Chair of Enterprise Studies at Cambridge University.

The arts, museums, etc. Total £440,000 including

Dulwich Picture Gallery, London: £200,000 (1st of three), for renovation.

The National Gallery, London: £60,000 (one of several) for exhibitions in the Bernard and Mary Sunley room.

The Natural History Museum, London: £50,000 (1st of two) for conserving the Sloane botanical collection.

Community aid and recreation. Total £424,000 including

The Enham Trust, Hampshire: £50,000 (3rd of three) for building development.

St John Ambulance, Northampton: £50,000 towards a new HQ building.

Youth clubs, youth training and sports organisations. Total £289,000 including

British Racing School Charitable Trust, Newmarket: £100,000 for building development and refurbishment.

Merseyside Youth Association (Starting Point Appeal): £50,000 (2nd of two) for building conversion.

Churches and chapels. Total £128,000 including

Falklands Islands Memorial Chapel, Pangbourne, Reading: £50,000 (1st of two) for chapel.

Hospitals, medical schools, research institutions. Total £340,000 including

King Edward VII Hospital for Officers, London: £50,000 (1st of two) for nurses' accommodation.

National Hospital for Neurology, London: £50,000 (3rd of five) for relocation of in-patient unit.

The National Heart and Lung Institute: £50,000 (2nd of two) for research microscope.

Provision for the elderly, including housing. Total £137,000 including

Extra Care Charitable Trust, Coventry: £100,000 (2nd of two) for housing schemes for frail elderly people in Kettering and Wellingborough.

Exclusions

No grants for individuals.

We would reiterate that we do not make grants to individuals; we still receive several such applications each week. This bar on individuals applies equally to those people taking part in a project sponsored by a charity such as VSO, Duke of Edinburgh Award Scheme, Trekforce, Scouts and Girl Guides, etc., or in the case of the latter two to specific units of these youth movements.

Applications

In writing to the director. The letter should include clear succinct details as to:

- What project the grant is required for.
- How much will it cost? Also sources of expected funding and how much has been raised or pledged to date.
- If it is for a building, some back-up is required, i.e. costings and drawings.
- The last set of audited or independently examined accounts (as the case may be) should be enclosed, plus any annual report or review prepared by the charity.
- Any appeal documentation.

Trustees normally meet in January, May and October.

The Sutton Coldfield Municipal Charities

Relief of need, education and general in Sutton Coldfield

£1,668,000 (to organisations, 1998/99)

Beneficial area The former borough of Sutton Coldfield, comprising three electoral wards: New Hall, Vesey and Four Oaks.

Lingard House, Fox Hollies Road, Sutton Coldfield, West Midlands B76 8RJ

Tel. 0121 351 2262 **Fax** 0121 313 0651

Correspondent Andrew MacFarlane, Clerk to the Trustees

Trustees *John Gray, Chair; Sue Bailey; Dr Nigel Cooper; Brian Fitton; Cllr John Jordan; Col. Anthony Fender; Cllr Suzanna McCorry; Jean Millington; Alfred David Owen; Cllr David Roy; John Slater; Cllr James Whorwood.*

Information available Full accounts are on file at the Charity Commission. Annual report with plenty of information including a full grants list showing the purposes of the awards. These are available at local libraries, or sold by the charity.

Summary

About 60 grants a year, almost all for capital costs, to schools and other organisations in Sutton Coldfield working within the charities' objectives, set out below. Grants start at hundreds of pounds, but roughly a quarter are for larger amounts over £50,000.

In addition to grants to organisations, a small amount (5% of the grant total in 1999/2000) is given in grants for individuals.

General

The charity, which is one of the largest and oldest local trusts in the country, was set up by Royal Charter in 1528. In 1999 it held assets of £26.5 million from which £1,287,000 in income was generated. Sixty-three organisations benefited from grants totalling £1,668,000.

The objectives of the charity are:

- to help the aged, the sick, those with disabilities, and the poor;
- to support facilities for recreation and leisure occupations;
- to promote the arts and advance religion;
- the repair of historic buildings;
- the advancement of education through grants to schools, and individuals for fees, maintenance, clothing and equipment.

Relevant parts of the excellent annual report are reprinted here.

Making the grants

Applications are received from individuals and organisations, and total in excess of 200 per year. Except for those which cannot be considered because the applicants are from outside the area of benefit, each request is investigated thoroughly by the staff who then present a case to the Grants Committee which meets eight or nine times a year. After considering each application in detail, the committee decides whether an award should be made and if so how much money should be granted. …

If the proposed grant exceeds £20,000 it is referred to the full board for a final decision. Staff keep detailed records and monitor decisions so that trustees have up to date information and comparisons with other grants made. No reasons are given to applicants for decisions taken by the trustees.

Normally, payments are made directly to the suppliers or contractors and not to the applicants. In the few cases where this is not appropriate applicants receive a cheque, but proof of payment or, in the case of students, academic reports are required.

Grants to groups

The largest grants made each year are to local groups and organisations representing a wide variety of interests. Some are charities which aim to meet the needs of people with medical, social and other problems. Others are groups providing for young people or those with disabilities or the elderly. Grants are also made to sports clubs, churches, drama and music groups and schools.

Anyone considering making an application on behalf of an organisation is invited to telephone the office to seek informal advice. There are no forms but an information sheet sets out the requirements. One of the officers usually meets the applicant representative, often on site, before the application is finalised in order to discuss the nature of the project and the content and timing of the application.

Grants in 1998/99

£1,333,000 (80% of the total donated to organisations) was spent on 13 grants in excess of £50,000. The largest grant was for £220,000 to Sutton Coldfield College (for the renovation of Moat House) and others included £171,000 to the Carpenter's Arms (Sutton Central Churches Trust, repairs and extensions); £94,000 to Emmanuel Church, Wylde Green (refurbishment of organ); £88,500 to the 1st Sutton Coldfield Sea Scouts (refurbishment of premises), and £58,000 to Royal Sutton Athletic Club (fencing and lighting). Five schools also benefited from grants in this range.

A further 14 grants were for over £10,000, the recipients mostly primary or infants' schools, but also, for example, Sutton Coldfield Fellowship of the Handicapped (£21,000); Boldmere St Michael's Bowling Club, and Sutton Coldfield YMCA (£20,000 each).

Exclusions

No awards are given to individuals or organisations based outside the area of benefit.

Applications

In writing to the correspondent. The following applies to applications from groups and organisations.

There are no forms, so applicants may provide information in a format which is most convenient for them but they must include the following:

- A brief description of the organisation, its objects and its history.
- The number of members/users, their age range and any membership fees paid.
- A full account of the purpose of the project for which a grant is requested.
- Accurate costs, including VAT if payable. No additional sums will be granted if estimates prove to be inaccurate.
- 12 copies of the latest audited accounts or, for very small organisations, copies of bank statements. Notes of explanation may be included; for example, if accounts show a balance set aside for a particular project applicants may wish to point this out.

The clerk will be happy to discuss applications informally at an early stage and to comment on draft submissions. In some cases a visit is helpful.

Receipt of applications is not normally acknowledged unless a stamped addressed envelope is sent with the application.

(There are application forms for individuals, who must obtain them from the charity.)

The grants committee meets eight or nine times a year. Requests for grants over £20,000 must be approved by the trustees, who meet four times a year. Staff will advise applicants about the dates by which requests must be received.

The Sutton Trust

Education

£2,000,000 (planned for 2000)

Beneficial area UK.

Heritage House, 21 Inner Park Road, London SW19 6ED

Tel. 020 8788 3223 **Fax** 020 8788 3993

e-mail sutton@suttontrust.com

website www.suttontrust.com

Correspondent The Administrator

Information available Annual report and accounts. Comprehensive website.

Summary

The trust funds:

1. Educational opportunities for young people in the state sector, with particular emphasis on meeting the needs of academically able young people from non-privileged backgrounds. To this end, it will support projects that are concerned with raising their aspirations and developing their potential within a formal education setting.

2. Projects which address the issue of widening access to universities.

3. Experimental schemes addressed to problems of early learning in the under-three age group and including the involvement of parents in stimulating their children's early mental development.

'To avoid wasting your time, before making a formal application to the Sutton Trust please write a brief outline or make an exploratory telephone call to discuss your project.' Grants are not normally made in response to unsolicited applications.

General

This developing trust exemplifies the power of a grant-making trust to influence policy and practice when the application of the money is associated with clear and specific objectives which are driven forward by energetic trustees, and backed by relevant research and evaluation.

In this case, Peter Lampl has, as a result of the work of this trust, been appointed to lead the government's drive towards more open access to higher education, thus multiplying many times over the resources available for the work in hand.

Some of the methods used to achieve the wholly desirable objectives of the trust are controversial, if only in the sense of raising doubts in the minds of these editors. But it is precisely the ability of trusts to ignore the opinions of others and to innovate in their own way that best justifies their legal and tax privileges. It is therefore a pleasure to report rather fully on the work of this trust, largely in its own words, and with the hope that it may encourage other trusts or putative philanthropists to take a similarly energetic approach.

Peter Lampl, chairman and founder of the Sutton Trust, is a graduate of Oxford University and London Business School. Before establishing the Sutton Trust in 1997, Peter Lampl was a successful entrepreneur as founder and Chairman of the Sutton Company, an Investment and Private Equity firm that made investments both in the United States and Europe. [He writes as follows:]

My initial motivation was sparked when I returned to this country after many years abroad and discovered that the grammar school which I had attended was now private, charging £6,000 per year, and that my old university (Oxford) had significantly fewer students from the state sector than it had had when I was there, and that all my friends who could afford it were sending their children to private schools despite the fact that they were mostly state educated themselves.

Entry to Oxbridge for students from State Funded Schools fell from 64% in 1978 to 42% by 1985 and is only a little higher today. Shocking as these statistics are, the actual situation is far worse. Many of the entrants to Oxbridge and other leading universities are from selective state schools such as the remaining grammar and church schools which tend to be largely middle class. Estimates of entrants from unselective comprehensives, which account for over 85% of schools, are as low as 20% of the total. This contrasts sharply with the 7 per cent of children at private schools who account for 47 per cent of Oxbridge places. The chances of getting into Oxbridge is about 30 times greater from a private school than from a comprehensive.

The result is that in such areas as the legal profession, the judiciary, the City, the Armed Forces and medicine, private schools are over represented relative to the normal talents of our young people. The polarisation continues and the career advantages of a private education look like increasing. The situation makes a mockery of any notion of equality of opportunity. It requires urgent action.

Living in the US, I became familiar with the summer schools offered by Ivy League universities. In 1997, we approached Oxford University with the offer to fund a pilot summer school for comprehensive school pupils. The offer was taken up enthusiastically. Of the 64 sixth form students who attended the first summer school, 25 per cent are now undergraduates at Oxford. Of course, some might have got in anyway, although it should be noted that Oxford selected people from schools with little or no previous record of putting pupils forward. Encouraged by this success, [other] schools were set up at Cambridge, Bristol and Nottingham, as well as a summer school for comprehensive teachers, aiming to encourage them to put forward their brightest children.

The under representation of the state sector at leading universities is not just a question of lack of ambition: there is also a serious under-performance by pupils in the state sector. In order to address this issue, the Sutton Trust (independently and in conjunction with the government) has funded longer term projects which involve both the state and independent sectors of education working together to share experience and resources. Some 60 projects involving c.15,000 pupils have so far been funded.

But even these latter initiatives do not address the fundamental issue: pupils from non-privileged backgrounds do not have access to the top academic schools which are almost exclusively private. We have looked at the practicalities of providing open access to one or more top independent day schools. We have established with the Girls Public Day School Trust an open access scheme at Belvedere School in Liverpool, which we hope will provide an example for wider implementation.

Current programmes are as follows:

University projects

- Student summer schools
- INSET summer school (for teachers)
- Other university access projects

Independent/state school partnerships

- DfEE Independent/State School Partnership Fund 1999-00
- Other Independent/State School Partnerships

Projects for able children

Gifted & Talented Summer Schools 1999. Each project was delivered by schools working with local partners such as museums, galleries, local businesses or universities. Examples include:

- Newham EAZ working with BBC's *Newsround*, giving the children the opportunity to learn about television broadcasting;
- Monkseaton Community High School in Tyne and Wear worked with Granada Learning to develop a website that all the summer schools can use to showcase their achievements.
- National Primary Trust. Among its initiatives is the Advanced Maths Centre (AMC), which has been successfully piloted at Grove School in Birmingham since 1996.

Specialist schools

The trust has committed to funding the conversion of at least two secondary schools to specialist school status. The Technology Colleges Trust acts as the central co-ordinating body for the specialist schools programme.

Open access

The principle of 'Open Access' is that independent schools should be allowed to take any pupil based on merit, irrespective of their ability to pay. If accepted, it will be the right of that child to go to the school. There is no limit on funded places, which avoids the charity aspect of the Assisted Places Scheme (APS). The first example is the Belvedere School in Liverpool.

The trust has funded an outreach officer who promotes the open access scheme to all the local maintained primary schools.

Early years

In 1998, the trustees of the Sutton Trust started to consider funding projects that are focused on early learning in the under three-year-old age group, through the involvement of parents in stimulating their children's involvement. This was motivated by the interest of Karen Lampl (a trustee), which developed from her experience of projects in the United States and research indicating that a wide and growing difference in educational attainment between advantaged and disadvantaged children can be evident as early as 22 months.

To date six projects have been funded with grants totalling £40,300, including:

- Camden Pre-School Learning Alliance. Parenting skills workshops covering a range of topics including: managing children's behaviour, introduction to child development, play activities in the home, diet and nutrition and childhood illnesses.
- Mothers' Union. A training course for the facilitators of parenting support groups. The aim is to train volunteers so that they can go back into the local community and facilitate parenting workshops.

Research

The trust is planning to fund research projects in areas related to able children who are educationally disadvantaged. These include provision for able children, the development of aptitude testing for entrance to higher education and the destinations of high-achieving candidates at 'A'-level.

In April 2000, the Sutton Trust published a report, 'Entry to Leading Universities', which analyses access to the top 13 universities. The benchmark statistics, provided by the Higher Education Funding Council, demonstrate that students from non-privileged backgrounds who are achieving high scores at GCSE and A-level are not gaining access to our top universities in sufficient numbers.

The trust has the following advisers:
– Dr Eric Anderson
– Michael Oakley
– George Walden
– Sir David Winkley

Exclusions

- individuals;
- scholarships;
- assisted places replacement schemes;
- sports and arts projects;
- capital projects and general appeals.

Applications

To avoid applicants wasting their time, they are encouraged to understand that unsolicited applications are not generally considered. However they are welcome to write in with a brief outline of a project or to make an exploratory call to discuss their project.

The Sutton Trust does not have a standard application form, 'as we believe that it can be too restrictive. However there is some basic information that we would be grateful if you could provide.' Applications must be no more than two pages.

Background

- What sort of organisation are you (legal status)?

- What are the organisation's general aims and objectives?
- If the organisation is part of a larger or national organisation, what is its name?

Project

- An outline of the proposed project
- Its specific aims and objectives
- How the project is to be organised and by whom
- Where the project is to take place
- What problems you anticipate in setting up and operating the project
- When it will start and how long it will take
- Whom it is intended to benefit and how many people

Finance

- How much money do you need and for what purposes, i.e. salaries, rent, administration?
- How much are you asking the Sutton Trust for and when?
- Which other funders have you approached and with what success?
- If you will need funding beyond the period of the grant where is it to come from?

Evaluation

- How will you know whether the project has succeeded?
- What are the measurable specific objectives?
- How will you publicise the outcome of the project to other interested parties?
- Please provide the name and telephone number of two independent referees

Attachments

Please also include:

- The most recent set of annual accounts
- Annual report
- A detailed budget for the project

The Talbot Village Trust

General, in east Dorset

£598,000 (1999)

Beneficial area The boroughs of Bournemouth, Christchurch and Poole; the districts of East Dorset and Purbeck.

Dickinson Manser, 5 Parkstone Road, Poole, Dorset BH15 2NL

Tel. 01202 673071

Correspondent G Cox, Clerk

Trustees *Sir Thomas Lees, Chair; Henry Plunkett-Ernle-Erle-Drax; Sir George Meyrick; Sir Thomas Salt; James Fleming; Christopher Lees.*

Information available Annual report and accounts on file at the Charity Commission, or available from the trust for an excessive charge of £25.

General

This is a large local charity which owns and manages land and property at Talbot Village, Bournemouth, including almshouses which it maintains through an associated trust. The trust had an income of £1.37 million in 1999, half of which came from rents, and had assets worth almost £22 million.

A total of 43 grants were authorised in 1999, many to organisations such as schools, churches, youth clubs and playgroups, with grants being given mainly for equipment and capital costs. Examples of the larger grants included £100,000 to the Shaftesbury Society (for new buildings and a day centre) and five grants of £50,000 each for the refurbishment of Dorset Christian Activity Centre, improvements to the Retired Nurses National Home and for three schools.

Other grant recipients included Bournemouth Heart Club (£20,000 for a gymnasium and enlarged rest area); South Wessex Addiction Centre (£9,000 for refurbishment), and Project Christchurch (£2,500 to purchase electric wheelchairs and a portable loop). The smallest payment was £350 to Bournemouth Churches Housing Association, to equip a creche.

The trust had interest free loan commitments worth over £1 million to various churches, parishes and community groups, most ranging from £20,000 to £50,000, with the largest being for £200,000 to Wessex Autistic Society.

Exclusions

No grants for individuals.

Applications

In writing to the correspondent.

The Tedworth Trust

Parenting, child welfare and development, general

£996,000 (approved, 1998/99)

Beneficial area Unrestricted, but UK in practice.

See entry for the Sainsbury Family Charitable Trusts

Tel. 020 7410 0330

Correspondent Michael Pattison, Director

Trustees *T J Sainsbury; Mrs M Sainsbury; A J Sainsbury; Jessica Sainsbury; Miss Judith Portrait.*

Information available Annual report and accounts, with good information on grants but none on grantmaking policy.

Summary

This trust is one of the Sainsbury Family Charitable Trusts which share a joint administration. Its main concern is with child development, both practical and from the research point of view, though in 1998/99 this was coupled with generous support for the endowment of Worcester College, Oxford.

General

The settlor of this trust is (Timothy) James Sainsbury. Staff include Michael Pattison, director of all the Sainsbury trusts, and Hester Marriott, executive. Its concentration on child development is timely in a field where the former consensus has been set alight by new debate about the nature of parental influence.

As only a very small number of grants is made each year (less than five for each meeting of the trustees) it is likely that the usual Sainsbury statement discouraging unsolicited applications is more than usually justified.

The only statement of policy by the trustees is the usual 'Sainsbury' formulation that they 'prefer to support innovative schemes that can be successfully replicated or become self-sustaining'.

Grants approved in 1998/99 were classified as follows:

	No.	Amount
Parenting, family welfare and child development	12	£576,000
General	10	£420,000
Total	22	£996,000

Parenting, family welfare and child development

Major grants included the following:

Winnicott Research Unit (University of Reading): £250,000. A five-year grant towards the continuing core costs of the Winnicott Research Unit, which is looking at the development of infants and children in order to determine how environmental influences and interpersonal relationships influence individual characteristics and personality, and vulnerability to physical and psychiatric disorder throughout childhood, adolescence and adult life.

Home-Start: £221,000 to support the charity's development strategy. Home-Start has been generously supported by the trust for at least three years.

Open University (Department of Biology): £43,000 for the research study 'The Origin of Complex Human Behaviours: a review of twin and adoption studies'.

Parenting Education and Support Forum: £30,000 towards core costs.

General

Worcester College, Oxford: £250,000. A five-year grant towards the Endowment Appeal.

Common Ground: £30,000 towards the costs of the 'Confluence' and 'Community Orchards' projects.

DEMOS: £60,000 for the research study 'Fishes and Loaves – the spatial configuration of British food poverty'.

Friends of the Earth: £19,000 towards the salary of a web producer post.

Exclusions

Grants are not normally made to individuals.

Applications

See the guidance for applicants in the entry for the Sainsbury Family Charitable Trusts. A single application will be considered for support by all the trusts in the group.

However, for this as for many of the trusts, 'proposals are generally invited by the Trustees or initiated at their request. Unsolicited applications are discouraged and are unlikely to be successful, even if they fall within an area in which the Trustees are interested.'

The Sir Jules Thorn Charitable Trust

Medical research, medicine, welfare

£3,209,000 (1999)

Beneficial area UK.

24 Manchester Square, London W1U 3TH

Tel. 020 7487 5851 **Fax** 020 7224 3976

e-mail julesthorntrust@compuserve.com

website www.julesthorntrust.org.uk

Correspondent David Richings, Director

Trustees *Ann Rylands, Chair; Prof. J Richard Batchelor; Prof. Frederick Flynn; Sir Bruce McPhail; Christopher Sporborg; Nicholas Wilson.*

Information available Guidelines for applicants. Good annual report and accounts.

Summary

Most grants are for medical research or medically related projects, for up to three years. One or two 'special' grants of as much as £400,000 are made each year to beneficiaries working in a particular field sought out by the trustees.

A Small Donations Fund, giving amounts of up to £2,000 to over 500 organisations a year, is open to charities providing relief to sick or disabled people and other disadvantaged groups.

There was, in 1999, a lengthy 'waiting list' for new applications for medical research grants.

General

The trust says: 'The policy of the Trust is to direct its main funding to medicine generally, with the emphasis on medical research, but some other funds are allocated to humanitarian purposes.'

Project grants for medical research

The trust's criteria include the following points:

- Applications for projects which could reasonably be expected to be submitted to disease-specific charitable funders (e.g. British Heart Foundation, Arthritis Research Campaign, British Diabetic Association, Multiple Sclerosis Society) will not be accepted without an acceptable explanation.
- The applicant(s) must be able to make an unequivocal statement that there is a very reasonable prospect of the research providing clinical benefit within 5 years. The peer review committee will need to be convinced by the justification given for this opinion.
- No other external funder to be involved.

Further restrictions are listed under 'Exclusions' below.

Small Donations Fund

This fund is described as follows:

The Trust receives appeals from a very wide range of humanitarian causes, many more than it can support with a grant. It treats each case on its merits and can only offer relatively small donations because of its policy of spreading its support as widely as possible. Appeals can be considered only if they are submitted by registered charities. The Trust will consider requests for contributions towards core funding, specific appeals.

Grantmaking was categorised as follows:

	1999	*1998*
Medical research projects	£1,827,000	£1,951,000
Medically related projects	£300,000	£326,000
Special projects	£800,000	£516,000
Non-medical projects	–	£75,000
Single donations	£282,000	£281,000
Total	£3,209,000	£3,148,000

Annual report 1999

Medical research grants and medically related projects

Demand for grants and donations was sustained at a high level throughout the year, and the Trust had continually to manage a lengthy waiting list. A total of 78 new preliminary applications was considered, and 41 applications reached the final stage of the assessment process. This resulted in the award of 20 new research grants and two extensions to previous projects, a total commitment of £1,904,192. At the end of the year there were 86 projects in various stages of progress with the aid of funding from the Trust.

The Trust's primary interest is in supporting research which will lead to patient benefit in the reasonably short term [*up to five years. Ed.*]. All projects are reviewed by the Medical Advisory Committee, which recommends to the Trustees only those applications which they judge to be of a high standard, and to meet best the Trust's criteria. Project grants are awarded for periods of up to three years but, where outstanding results are achieved, the Trust is prepared to consider additional funding if resources permit in order to enable a programme of work to be extended.

Conditions receiving substantial research funding included epilepsy, asthma, diabetes, peripheral nerve injury, diarrhoeal disease, brain haemorrhage and skin disease (each for amounts around £125,000). Examples included:

- Southampton University MRC Environmental Epidemiology Unit (£139,000): 'The influence of antioxidant vitamins on cerebrovascular disease and cognitive decline in elderly people.'
- University of Manchester, Manchester Visualisation Centre (£125,000): 'Development of a computer augmented magnetic resonance angiogram guidance system for interventional cerebral angiography.'
- Edinburgh Royal Infirmary Liver Research Laboratory (£69,000): 'Liver cell transplantation: isolation, characterisation and culture of hepatic stem cells for therapeutic use.'

The largest grant for a ' medically related project' was for £300,000, to the National Society for Epilepsy, for a new assessment and treatment centre at its headquarters in Chalfont St Peter, Buckinghamshire.

Special charitable projects

It is the Trustees' practice to identify, each year, one special charitable project to receive a major allocation of funding. In 1999 the initiative focused on hospice and respite care. Two projects received awards:

Katherine House Hospice, Stafford

The Trust's donation of £400,000 has enabled the Hospice to reach its fundraising target for the creation of a ten bed in-patient unit to augment the existing Day Care and Hospice at Home facilities. When the unit opens in June 2000, free palliative care will be provided for patients with life-limiting illnesses. This will fill an important gap in the care provision available currently in the local area.

Children's Respite Home and Hydrotherapy Unit, Malvern

A grant of £400,000 to the Development Trust (for the Mentally Handicapped) is enabling the provision of the first dedicated respite/short stay facility for mentally handicapped children in South Worcestershire. When completed in summer 2000, the unit will meet the needs of children who are multiply and/or profoundly handicapped, involving a mix of both physical and mental handicaps. A hydrotherapy pool will be an important feature of the facilities.

Charitable appeals

During the year, the Trustees approved over 600 donations of amounts of up to £2,000 each in response to charitable appeals. Most were contributions to core funding to support continuing operations but some were for capital-raising projects.

The Trust focuses its support particularly on appeals which relate to the care of those in society who are sick, vulnerable and less fortunate. This policy derives from the humanitarian ethos established by Sir Jules Thorn. During the course of the year, charities supported by the Trust included those working with the visually handicapped, the hearing impaired, those with learning disabilities, the disabled, the elderly, the homeless, disadvantaged children and youth, the sick in hospices, and others, including carers, who seek to alleviate the suffering from illnesses which are either life-threatening or which reduce severely the quality of life of those affected.

These small donations totalled £282,000, most being for £500, but starting at under £100. Four of the six grants of £1,000 or more were to support hospices, as follows: Help the Hospices (£2,000); St Barnabas Hospice Trust (£1,500); High Peak Hospice Care; Royal School for the Blind, Liverpool; Royal School for the Deaf, Manchester; St Luke's Hospice, Plymouth (£1,000 each).

Exclusions

Medically related grants to UK universities and hospitals

Funds are not allocated to:

- research which is unlikely to result in therapeutic benefit to patients within five years;
- cancer or AIDS research, for the sole reason that these fields are relatively well funded elsewhere;
- individuals, except in the context of a project undertaken by an approved institution;
- third parties who themselves fund research;
- to complete projects previously supported by another external funder, unless these were pilot studies, or work to obtain preliminary data;
- joint projects with other organisations or 'top up' funding for ongoing projects;
- projects or data collection overseas.

Small Donations Fund

It is not possible for the trust to make donations in the following categories:

- to overseas organisations or organisations based in the UK who use their funds for charitable purposes overseas;
- to denominational beneficiaries;
- to organisations undertaking research;
- for the purchase of raffle tickets;
- for church restoration/repairs;
- where support has been given within the previous 12 months or for several consecutive years.

Applications

Applicants for support for medical research should consult the trust's website or liaise with the director to ascertain whether the project falls within the trust's areas of interests and its funding ability. A waiting list may apply before guidelines and a preliminary application form can be sent. Briefly, the preliminary application calls for not more than two sides of A4, covering:

1. Some tabulated information covering title, objective and clinical relevance.
2. Project outline, including background and methodology.
3. Direction, approval and supervision. Has ethical approval and/or a Home Office licence (if relevant) been sought or granted?
4. Duration and approximate cost, preferably showing the likely split between salaries, consumables and equipment.
5. Other sources of funding for this project either received or expected.

Successful preliminary applicants are invited to send fully detailed applications. Applicants for funding for purposes other than medical research should submit brief applications to the correspondent in the normal way.

Trustees meet normally in April and November. All applications for medical research are subject to peer review by a medical advisory committee, which meets four times annually, usually in January, April, June and November, and makes recommendations to the trustees. Following receipt, applications are considered on the first available agenda of the medical advisory committee. The director will advise likely timescales.

Small Donations Fund

There is no special application form. Applicants should submit their appeal to the director and ensure that they cover the following briefly:

a) nature and objectives of the charity;
b) the reason for the appeal;
c) how much is being raised in total and from what sources, including the charities' own resources, fundraising and funding from local authorities/ statutory bodies;
d) the gap to be bridged;
e) a short financial budget (one side) plus a copy of the last audited accounts.

Items (a) through (d) in total should not extend to more than two sides of A4 paper. A brochure about the charity may be included.

The Three Guineas Trust

Autism, women's issues, poverty/homelessness

£284,000 (approved 1998/99)

Beneficial area UK.

See the entry for the Sainsbury Charitable Trusts

Tel. 020 7410 0330 **Fax** 020 7410 0332

Correspondent Michael Pattison, Director

Trustees *Clare Sainsbury; Miss Judith Portrait; Christopher Stone.*

Information available Annual report and accounts.

General

Though created in 1996, this trust is just getting under way as a grant-making organisation. Although only £89,000 was paid in grants in 1998/99, a total of £284,000 was committed. This will account for nearly half of the present expendable endowment of the trust, itself deriving from a donation by Miss Sainsbury of £600,000 in that year, and 'trustees intend to broaden their grantmaking activities in the future'.

In a welcome exception to usual Sainsbury practice, the trust has said that it is interested in hearing from those in its specialist field with whom it may not already be in contact, instead of such approaches being 'discouraged'.

Grantmaking was described as follows in the 1998/99 annual report:

> Trustees have been actively developing their strategy ... They have identified three areas of interest
> - autism and Asperger's Syndrome
> - women's issues
> - relief of poverty and homelessness.
>
> The trustees ... do not at present wish to invite applications, except in the fields of autism and Asperger's Syndrome, where they will examine unsolicited proposals alongside those that result from their own research and contacts with expert individuals and organisations working in this field...

The major grant approvals in 1998/99 were for two awards to the National Autistic Society: £90,000 over three years for a support project in Northamptonshire and £53,000 towards the dissemination of a diagnostic interview system. £10,000 was also given to Refuge, to support its women's National Crisis Line.

The executive working for this trust is Miss J Lunn.

Exclusions

Grants are not normally made to individuals.

Applications

See above, but note also the guidance for applicants in the entry for the Sainsbury Family Charitable Trusts.

The Tompkins Foundation

Health, welfare

£525,000 (1997/98)

Beneficial area UK.

31 St John's Square, London EC1M 4DN

Tel. 020 7608 1369

Correspondent The Secretary

Trustees *Elizabeth Tompkins, Patron; John Sharp; Colin Warburton.*

Information available In July 2000 the latest accounts on file at the Charity Commission were those for 1997/98.

Summary

The trust is managed by its unpaid trustees, makes a substantial proportion of its grants to organisations previously supported, and does not seek further applications.

General

The foundation was established in 1980, based on Green Shield stamp money, by the late Granville Tompkins and his wife Elizabeth. The objects of the foundation are as follows:

- The advancement of education, learning and religion.
- The provision of facilities for recreation and other purposes beneficial to the community in the parishes of Hampstead Norreys in Berkshire and of West Grinstead in Sussex, and any other parishes with which the patron may have a connection with from time to time.

Major beneficiaries are mostly well-known national or local London charities. Of the 30 grants in 1997/98, 20 fitted into a standard range of grants given in £10,000 jumps, from £10,000 up to £60,000. Six recipients got under £1,000.

Five beneficiaries at the top end of the grants scale took half of the funds, with the largest amount of £60,000 going to an apparently new beneficiary, the Order of Malta Volunteers. Four £50,000 grants went to the Order of St John, St Mary's Hospital, the Foundation of Nursing Studies and the Variety Club of Great Britain, all of which had received substantial support in the previous year.

Other recipients included the Anna Freud Centre (£40,000); the Police Foundation (£30,000); the Chicken Shed Theatre (£20,000); City of London Migraine Clinic (£10,000); Gayfields Home and Rest (£5,000), and the Foundation for Children with Leukaemia (£650). All had previously been funded by the foundation.

The trust does not encourage applications and has written: 'As a small private Foundation ... our funds are fully committed for the foreseeable future and in these circumstances we would much prefer that our name is not publicly recorded as it is obviously time-consuming in having to reply to prospective applicants and of course equally disappointing to them that we are unable to assist with funds'.

However, it is the policy of these editors to include entries for all relevant grant-making charities, so that as complete a picture as possible can be given of the sector as a whole.

Applications

Applications are not sought. See above.

The Triangle Trust

Carers, elderly, homeless, disabled, regeneration

£536,000 (1999/2000)

Beneficial area UK.

Glaxo Wellcome House, Berkeley Avenue, Greenford, Middlesex UB6 0NN

Tel. 020 8966 8285 **Fax** 020 8966 8330

e-mail triang@triangletrust.org

Correspondent The Secretary

Trustees *J Charles Maisey, Chair; Mrs M Burfitt; Michael Pearce; M Powell; Jane Turner; Revd David Urquhart; Dr Marjorie Walker; Diane Ware.*

Information available Annual report and accounts with grants list. Guidelines with good explanation of policies and priorities.

Summary

This interesting trust seeks out its own projects to support. The list of resulting beneficiaries is both catholic and impressive.

General

Founded by a former chairman, this trust is still based in the offices of the Glaxo Wellcome Company (presently merging with Smith Kline Beecham). It is, however, completely independent from the company (and from the huge Wellcome Trust).

The trust is unusual among those described in this book in that it both gives some grants itself to individuals in need (£54,000 in 1998/99, mostly to former employees of the pharmaceutical industry or their dependants) and also gives grants to other 'relief of need' charities who in turn pass on the money to individuals (perhaps a further £75,000). This is pleasant to record, as even indirectly given help for individuals in distress seldom features in the activities of many trusts.

The trust makes about 50 grants a year to organisations, mostly for amounts between £1,000 and £5,000, but it also supports a small number of causes with larger amounts. The trust states firmly that it approaches its potential beneficiaries and does not respond to unsolicited applications. Nevertheless the selected charities must have made themselves known in some way for the trust to be able to approach them in the first place, even if an 'application' may not be the best way of doing this.

In the following description of some of the trust's grants for organisations, reprinted from its guidelines of the summer of 2000, the amount given in 1998/99 has been added in brackets:

Applications will be considered when made by organisations that are approached by the trust. Trustees do not respond to unsolicited applications. Current criteria, which may change from time to time ... are:

- support for carers' organisations
- projects helping elderly, homeless and disabled people
- regeneration.

Over the past three years the trust has supported a number of short and long term projects. ... Details of some of these are as follows:

Long term grants

AbilityNet Financial aid for disabled people to purchase specially adapted computer equipment [£5,000].

Action on Elder Abuse Three year award towards the development of a Practitioner Support Network [£5,000].

Alzheimer's Disease Society, Penrith Three year contribution to befriending service [£2,000].

Care and Repair West Leicestershire Two year contribution in support of a Handyperson scheme, part of a 'staying put' project for elderly people [£5,000].

Deafblind UK Three year revenue grant in support of a new training and rehabilitation centre. [£5,000].

Dundee City Council Quarterly hardship fund administered by senior debt training officer [£20,000].

Edinburgh Sitters Three year grant to fund volunteer recruitment, training and ongoing support [£3,500].

Housing Associations Charitable Trust Ongoing support for various housing and homelessness projects throughout the UK [£20,000].

Leicester Charity Organisation Society Quarterly hardship fund ... [£20,000].

London University Eight two-year post graduate studentships over four years in medicine and business administration [£31,000].

Southampton City Mission Expenses of delivery vehicle of this furniture and clothing redistribution scheme [£3,000].

Trafford Women's Aid Three year grant for employment of refuge worker ... [£15,000].

Examples of short term grants

The Befriending Network ... rural Oxfordshire [£2,000]. National Youth Orchestra Contribution to bursary fund (£3,000).

Queen's Nursing Institute Grant to cover admin costs of pilot project ... for sexually abused men in prison [£4,000].

Exclusions

- environmental, wildlife or heritage appeals
- medical electives
- grants for further study in relation to employment
- private medicine or education
- the promotion of religion
- loans
- holidays or educational trips
- nursing, convalescent or residential home fees.

Applications

Organisations: In writing to the correspondent (but see below).

The trust's guidelines state 'applications will be considered when made by organisations that are approached by the trust. Trustees do not normally respond to unsolicited applications'.

Individuals, in the pharmaceutical industry only: By application form, available from the secretary. Applications on behalf of individuals for one-off grants are considered when submitted by social workers, CAB officers, health visitors, GPs, probation officers, employers etc., or (for educational grants) teachers.

The Trust for London

See entry for the City Parochial Foundation.

The Trusthouse Charitable Foundation

General

Probably about £2,000,000

SG Hambro's Trust Co. Ltd., 41 Tower Hill, London EC3N 4SG

Tel. 020 7480 5000

Correspondent Derek Harris, Administrator

Trustees *Lord Peyton, Chair; Lord Alex Bernstein; Lord Callaghan; Sir Richard Carew Pole; Baroness Cox; the Earl of Gainsborough; the Duke of Marlborough; Olga Polizzi; Sir Hugh Rossi; Sir Paul Wright.*

Information available Grant application form with a general guidance note for applicants. No annual reports or accounts had been filed at the Charity Commission by October 2000.

Summary

For the entry in the previous edition of this guide we wrote that 'As a newly formed charity, no report and accounts had been produced at the time of going to press'. Two years later, the situation was no different, so the following information is mostly reprinted from the previous edition.

The foundation will be giving one-off grants for specific purposes, to headquarters organisations and not normally to local branches of national charities, and it will have the following six priority areas for its funding:

- relief of hardship and disability
- education
- environment
- heritage
- the arts
- sporting activities

General

The foundation derives from a tranche of Trusthouse Hotels shares, which were held for the public benefit (though not for causes that were necessarily charitable). Trusthouse became a part of the Forte group, and the income from the shares was then distributed by the council of Forte. When the Forte companies in their turn were taken over by the Granada group, the shares were realised for £50 million, and placed as permanent endowment in this new, charitable and welcome foundation.

In 1998 the foundation said that it was working towards the production of new policies and the outcome is the information given under the 'Summary' heading above. One of these headings is unusual: sport is not in itself a charitable activity, and grants will need to be for educational or welfare activities, with a sporting connection.

We said then that these very general policies would need to be developed further. This still seems to be the case.

The foundation produces a 'General Guidance Note to Applicants' with its application form, in which it says:

> Above all the Trustees wish to know the answer to four simple but important questions:
> - Who are you?
> - What do you do?
> - How much do you want and for what?
> - Who will benefit?

Further information given in the note is reprinted under 'Exclusions' and 'Applications' below.

Exclusions

The foundation will not normally support:

- small local charities;
- applications from individuals;
- foreign charities, except those which are based in the UK and are operating overseas.

Appeals received directly from local branches of national charities will not normally be considered (see below). The foundation does not give grants to other grant-giving bodies.

Applications

On brief application forms available from the correspondent (one side of an A4 sheet). Applicants are invited, if necessary, to supply such supporting documentation as is required.

The accompanying guidance note says (in addition to the section quoted in the main text):

- The foundation does not normally commit itself to give grants for more than one year.
- Local branches of national charities are encouraged to channel appeals through their headquarters, giving details, where appropriate, of particular projects and their costs.
- It would be helpful to the trustees if applicants could indicate a specific sum required when applying for a grant.

The trustees meet quarterly.

The Tudor Trust

Social welfare, general

£24,851,000 (approved in 1999/2000)

7 Ladbroke Grove, London W11 3BD

Tel. 020 7727 8522 **Fax** 020 7221 8522

website www.tudortrust.org.uk

Correspondent The Grants Administrator

Trustees *Grove Charity Management Ltd, of which the directors are: Mary Graves**; *Helen Dunwell**; *Dr Desmond Graves**; *Penelope Buckler; Christopher Graves** *(the present director of the trust); Ray Anstice; Sir James Swaffield; Catherine Antcliff; Louise Collins; Elizabeth Crawshaw; Matt Dunwell**; *James Long**; *Ben Dunwell. (Asterisks show membership of the grant-making trustee committee)*

Information available Good annual report and guidelines for applicants (reprinted below) are available from the trust.

Summary

The grants of this trust are increasingly focused. It has adopted five priority areas for funding, and applications within these are more likely to be funded. They cover support for charitable organisations working to help people:

- with mental health problems or head injuries
- who are substance misusers
- who are homeless
- who are offenders or ex-offenders
- who are at risk, such as those leaving care

The trust also funds more widely, in the following fields:

- accommodation
- education
- health

and, to a lesser extent,

- recreation
- relationships
- resources

Extensive examples of fundable activities within these fields are given in the guidelines. However, much is also specifically excluded (see 'Exclusions' below). In particular, the trust is 'unlikely to fund' organisations working on behalf of people with

- learning disabilities
- physical disabilities
- physical illnesses

Grants in response to applications are typically for amounts between £3,000 and £100,000, though there are exceptions at both extremes. They can be one-off, or spread over a period of up to three years.

Much larger grants can be made, but these are more likely to be the result of proactive work by the trust, for example through one of its three 'Targeted Funding Committees' composed of both trustees and members of staff. These, which accounted for about 10% of the value of grants in 1999/2000, cover addiction, community development and 'retracking' for young people at risk.

Grants for work outside the UK are made by the Overseas Committee, working proactively. It made 19 grants in 1999/2000, totalling £390,000, mainly to projects promoting sustainable agriculture in Africa. Note that this was only 1.5% of the value of grants awarded.

General

This trust continues to enjoy widespread respect. Applicants, successful and unsuccessful alike, speak highly of the knowledge and understanding of the trust's staff (and of its trustees). All are impressed by the speed with which the trust is able to come to its decisions and by the prompt response when unable to give an application detailed consideration. This is felt to show a respect for the interests and concerns of applicants which is too often found lacking.

The fact that the grant-making trustee committee, overseeing most grant decisions, meets every fortnight is another example of good practice that could be taken up with advantage by other trusts.

The staff who deal with grants include:

Christopher Graves, Director
Roger Northcott, Trust secretary
Jill Powell, Grants administrator
Anne Lane, Grants officer
Catriona Slorach, Grants officer
Philippa Watts, Grants officer
Eryl Foulkes, Grants officer
Claire Kimbell, Secretary to the overseas committee.

It is worth noting that the director, Christopher Graves, is also a trustee (and a grandson of Godfrey Mitchell, who endowed the trust in the first place).

The 1999/2000 annual report was less comprehensive than in previous years because the trust was planning to produce a separate review of its grantmaking, after this book had gone to press. One issue on which it would be useful to have more information concerns the chances of success of individual applications. Overall, the percentage of applicants who were promised grants (though not necessarily for the full amount requested) increased to 29% from the 23% reported in the previous edition of this book from two years earlier.

The actual number of applications has been reducing since a peak in 1997/98.

1993/94	4,500
1994/95	4,350
1995/96	4,220
1996/97	4,725
1997/98	5,050
1998/99	4,600
1999/2000	4,150

It would be interesting to know how far the chances of success for an individual application may vary. For example, how far is it still worth applying for work outside the chosen priority areas? Or, how often does the trust give grants for less than the full amount requested? The authors of the recent QUEST report (see the Introduction), after talking to over 160 applicants and running focus groups on application issues, identified information on this kind of issue as what they most often looked for.

The pattern of the grants lists suggests that the trust often gives a round sum as a donation towards the work for which support is requested.

Grants can be for capital or revenue purposes, or can combine both types of funding. The figures for 1999/2000 were as follows:

Revenue	£17.1 million
Capital	£4.9 million
Both	£2.9 million

The guidelines reprinted here are followed by brief excerpts from the 1999/2000 annual report and by details of grantmaking in that year.

The largest grant payment recorded in the 1999/2000 annual report was of £900,000 to the Onward Trust, representing the total of a series of payments towards a 1998/99 commitment. Tudor set up the Onward Trust as an independent charity responsible for the development of a new prison visitors' centre at Edinburgh prison. This is the fourth major grant by Tudor towards the setting up of such centres in prisons across the UK, and is an example of the kind of proactive initiative by a trust that these editors see as often making the most constructive use of trust resources.

Guidelines for applicants 2000–03

The Tudor Trust makes grants to charities and organisations with charitable objectives. Support is given both for capital and revenue costs. … Priorities in grantmaking are constantly evolving and a full policy review is undertaken every three years.

The Trust is fairly selective in what it supports within relatively broad areas of activity. These guidelines give an overview of the Trust's current interests. This is not a comprehensive list; however, it offers applicants a firm indication of the Trust's priorities and indicates which organisations and activities are unlikely to receive a grant. Demand for funding greatly exceeds available resources and not all applications meeting the current criteria will be successful.

The Tudor Trust is keen to support organisations and groups which help people to fulfil their potential and make a positive contribution to the communities in which they live. The Trust will focus its funding where there is significant need in both rural and urban communities. Schemes addressing rural isolation will receive special consideration. Projects which offer accessible, integrated and sustained support to people who are vulnerable or only just managing are of particular interest. The Trust will target projects working alongside *young people (9–18 year olds), families and older people* living in disadvantaged or marginalised communities.

Before making an application please check the list [under ' Exclusions' at the end of this entry] of organisations and areas of work which the Trust is unable to fund.

Organisations whose main focus of work incorporates at least one of the following areas of work can be considered for funding:

- Accommodation
  including rent deposit schemes, supported accommodation and floating support, housing for young people (including self build), schemes offering integrated care for older people.
- Education
  including basic skills for young people, supplementary schools teaching core curriculum, home/school links, school exclusion, literacy and IT schemes involving the family, support for people with specific educational problems, detached youth work.
- Health
  including promotion of good mental health, support for families under stress, older people, particularly those who are frail or have dementia, work with carers.
- Recreation
  including projects which help people and their communities to flourish, projects which offer new experiences and fun learning opportunities, places and events which encourage social interaction, green spaces in urban settings.
- Relationships
  including work with careleavers, young parents, befriending, support for families in difficulties, relationship counselling, family and school mediation, contact centres, counselling and confidence building for young people, work with fathers/young men, intergenerational work and parenting.
- Resources
  including advice for young people, centres and community buildings offering resources for the whole community, support workers, charitable/not for profit schemes stimulating the local economy, voluntary sector offices.

Some members of society require more intensive support. The Trust particularly wants to fund projects developing services with:

- People with mental health problems, head injuries
  Self help groups, centres, clubhouses, respite and safe places, crisis services, new types of accommodation (particularly for dementia sufferers), employment and training schemes, schemes addressing mental illness in children and young people, arts and educational projects.
- People who are substance misusers
  Residential and community based rehabilitation, arrest referral schemes, work with women and families, parent groups, training for workers, complementary therapies.
- People who are homeless
  Outreach work, day facilities, shelters, hostels, resettlement and training, accommodation for older street homeless, projects run by homeless people themselves, integration of service provision, preventive work among young people, arts and educational projects, complementary therapies.
- Offenders/ex-offenders, people at risk of re-offending (and their families)
  Alternatives to custody, pre- and post-release education and training, employment schemes, work with mentally disordered

offenders, those with personality disorders and perpetrators of domestic violence, support for families of offenders, arts and educational projects.

- People at risk
  Troubled young people in residential care (therapeutic communities), young people coming out of care, refuges, people at risk of exclusion from services, people who are isolated.

As a result of the need to target funding the Trust is unlikely to fund organisations working on behalf of:

- People with learning disabilities
- People with physical disabilities
- People with physical illnesses

The targeted funding committees

These are (with their 1999/2000 grant totals)

- Addictions Committee (£527,000)
- Community Committee (£660,000)
- Retracking Committee (£980,000)
- Overseas Committee (£390,000)

Their work is described in the following excerpts from the annual report.

Annual report 1999/2000

Applications for funding are administered by staff of the Tudor Trust. Each application falling within the guidelines is considered by Trustees. Recommendations are submitted for decision to committees of the Board. The Trustee Committee meets fortnightly. The full Board meets three times a year when grant decisions are ratified, large commitments discussed and policy decisions made.

During the year 1999/2000 the Trust received just over 4,000 applications for funding and anticipated making 1,150 future grant payments with a total value of £24,851,000. The average grant awarded has risen again to £21,652 (£19,584 in 1998/99 and £19,155 in 1997/98). We continued to make small grants and 38% of grants in the year did not exceed £10,000.

The Targeted Funding Committees continue to complement the general work of the Trust.

During the year the *Addictions Committee*, which is chiefly concerned with treatment and support for people with drug and alcohol problems and their families, made 15 grants, a total of £526,580.

The *Community Committee* continued to look for imaginative ways of reinforcing a sense of community, evaluating the fundamental aspects of community life and encouraging capacity-building within the local community. It made 24 grants, a total of £659,600.

The *Retracking Committee's* main focus has been on home/school liaison work around the time children move from primary to secondary school, when intervention may prevent later alienation, and it made 15 grants, a total of £980,000.

The *Overseas Committee*, working proactively, has made 19 grants totalling £390,200 mainly to projects promoting sustainable agriculture in Africa.

Investment income for the year was £14.6 million, compared with £13.8 million in the previous year ... Grant payments amounted to £21.4 million, an increase of £3.1 million compared with the previous year.

Management and administration costs amounted to £674,000, an increase of £19,000 over the previous year. ... Management and administration costs represent 2.7% of grant commitments made during the year.

The Tudor Trust offers people working in the voluntary sector an accessible and responsive source of charitable funding. The Trustees are aware of the value to applicants of funding that is unencumbered and administered in a straightforward manner. We will continue to target resources in this way.

Grant payments in 1999/2000

1999/2000 grant payments were categorised as follows:

	1999/2000	*1998/99*
Welfare	£10,878,000	£8,278,000
Health	£3,390,000	£2,863,000
Accommodation	£2,986,000	£3,639,000
Crime prevention	£1,866,000	£989,000
Education	£1,083,000	£1,065,000
Overseas	£729,000	£631,000
Employment & training	£269,000	£413,000
Environment	£126,000	£180,000
Arts	£37,000	£8,000
Leisure	£25,000	£218,000
Total	£21,389,000	£18,284,000

The largest donations (paid, as opposed to awarded) were noted in the annual report. They included:

WELFARE

Albion Trust	£527,000
Changemakers	£95,000
Eric Liddell Centre	£76,000
Promoting Effective Parenting	£70,000
Health National Clubhouse Association	£90,000
Winsford Trust	£78,000

ACCOMMODATION

Bethshan Nursing Homes & Housing Project	£150,000
National Homeless Alliance	£143,000

CRIME PREVENTION

Onward Trust	£900,000
Howard League for Penal Reform	£75,000

OVERSEAS

Jubilee 2000	£105,000
Interminds	£70,000

EDUCATION

Harmeny Educational Trust	£100,000
JC 2000	£75,000
Walthamstow Home-School Support Project	£65,000

EMPLOYMENT

Apex Charitable Trust Ltd	£50,000

ENVIRONMENT

(8 payments totalling £126,000)

ARTS

(4 payments totalling £37,000)

LEISURE

(2 payments totalling £25,000)

Exclusions

Unless specifically mentioned (in the guidelines above) the following organisations and areas of work are outside the current guidelines and cannot be considered for funding. (NB Eligibility for funding is generally assessed by the main purpose/function of the organisation applying. The trust does not fund individuals.)

- Activity centres
- Homework clubs
- Advice
- Hospitals & hospices
- Advocacy
- Illness (physical)
- After-school clubs
- Individuals
- Animal charities
- Large national charities enjoying widespread support
- Arts
- Leisure clubs
- Breakfast clubs
- Medical care
- Bursaries and scholarships
- Medical research
- Capacity building and technical support
- Minibuses
- Church and hall fabric appeals
- Mother tongue classes/cultural activities
- Colleges
- Museums/places of entertainment
- Commercial organisations
- Neighbourhood mediation
- Community foundations
- Nurseries, creches, pre-school childcare
- Community transport
- Playschemes and groups, parent & toddler
- Conferences/seminars
- Playgrounds
- Conservation of buildings, flora & fauna
- Research
- Councils of Voluntary Service
- Religion
- Counselling

- Schools
- Disabilities (mental and physical)
- Scouts, guides and other uniformed youth groups
- Endowment appeals
- Sponsorship and marketing appeals
- Expeditions/overseas travel
- Sports
- Fabric
- Training and employment schemes
- Fundraising events/salaries of fundraisers
- Universities
- Halls & church centres
- Victims (of crime, domestic and sexual abuse, trauma, war)
- Healthy living centres
- Volunteer centres
- Helplines
- Women's centres
- Holidays/holiday centres

Applications

Applications can only be made in writing and cannot be accepted by fax or e-mail. The trust does not use an application form. Information needed includes:

- A summary of the current work of the organisation, with the latest annual report.
- A description of the project/proposals/ area of work for which funding is requested.
- An indication of the numbers of people involved/likely to be involved and how they will benefit.
- A breakdown of costs (for capital works, these might be building costs, VAT; fees, furniture and equipment; for revenue they might be salaries, premises, training, publicity, expenses, etc). Retrospective grants are not available.
- Details of funding raised or committed to date and steps being taken to raise the balance other than the approach to the Tudor Trust.
- Any other relevant information such as catchment area served, numbers attending existing activities per month or per annum, how revenue implications of capital proposals will be met. For new buildings or major refurbishment schemes, drawings/plans and possibly a photo are helpful.
- The latest annual accounts (or a copy of a recent financial/bank statement if the organisation is too new to have annual accounts).

Grants are given for amounts from £500 upwards. Loans are offered occasionally. Applications may be sent at any time to the grants administrator, Mrs Jill Powell.

Each application will be assessed taking account of how the main purpose/ function of the organisation fits with current priorities and the funding available. Some applicants will be told almost immediately that the trust cannot help. For the remainder, there is a continuous process of assessment, and applicants will usually be told the outcome eight weeks after all the information has been received by the trust. Please do not telephone for news of progress during this period.

A letter will be sent giving the trustees' decision. If a grant has been approved, conditions relating to the release of the grant will be included in the letter. A visit may be made to the project; but this will be initiated by the trust and will not necessarily result in a grant being approved. Organisations are requested not to approach the trust again for at least 12 months after a grant has been paid or notification of an unsuccessful application has been given.

The Underwood Trust

General

£564,000 (1998/99)

Beneficial area UK, with apparent local interests in London, Scotland and Wiltshire.

32 Haymarket, London SW1Y 4TP

Correspondent Antony Cox, Manager

Information available Report and accounts with categorised grants list are on file at the Charity Commission or available from the trust for an expensive fee of £11.

Summary

The trust supports mainly well established national charities. Up to half of the funding is for academic or medical research. Other beneficiaries are based mainly in London, Wiltshire or Scotland. Grants are typically recurring and are made to a broad range of organisations within the categories shown below. Many are for the curious figure of £5,650, and most of the others are for either £1,000 or £10,000. The few grants for £20,000 or more tend to focus on education and research.

General

In 1998/99 income, from shares in Taylor Clark plc and other investments, amounted to £536,000. Grants totalling £564,000 were distributed as follows (1997/98 figures in brackets):

	No.	*Amount*	*(1997/98)*
Medicine and health	23	£223,000	(£228,000)
Welfare	26	£150,000	(£135,000)
Education, sciences, humanities, religion	9	£129,000	(£61,000)
Environmental resources	10	£62,000	(£35,000)
Total	68	£564,000	(£459,000)

Substantial donations went to the Robert Clark Centre for Technological Education at the University of Glasgow, named after one of the trust's founders (£72,500), the Thames Salmon Trust (£1,000), and the environmentally radical Henry Doubleday Research Association (£25,000).

The other recipients not supported in the previous year were as follows: British Museum Development Trust (£20,000); The Children's Society (£10,000); Winged Fellowship (£5,000), and Halo Trust (£1,000).

Most grants, however, were given to organisations that had been supported for a number of years, the major ones including Frenchay Hospital Speech Therapy Research Unit (£100,000); National Eye Research Centre (£25,000); Listening Books (£5,650); Centrepoint (£25,000), and Wiltshire Community Foundation (£10,000).

Further examples of beneficiaries can be grouped into the following categories (all received £5,650 unless stated otherwise):

Social welfare

Royal Star and Garter Home; Crime Concern; Scottish Council on Alcohol; RAF Benevolent Fund; Royal Naval Benevolent Trust; Samaritans.

Arts/culture

Scottish Opera; National Museums of Scotland (£5,000); London Philharmonic Orchestra.

Environment

Wiltshire Wildlife Trust; National Trust for Scotland; Friends of the Earth; Wiltshire and Berkshire Canal Amenity Group (£1,000).

Exclusions

No grants to individuals, including students, under any circumstances. Grants are not made for expeditions, nor to overseas projects.

Applications

'The trust's income is committed to long term projects, therefore new applications are very unlikely to be considered.' Applications are not normally acknowledged unless accompanied by an sae.

Trustees normally meet quarterly.

John and Lucille van Geest Foundation

Medical research, healthcare, general

£841,000 (1998/99)

Beneficial area UK and overseas, with a special interest in south Lincolnshire and adjoining areas.

42 Pinchbeck Road, Spalding, Lincolnshire PE11 1QF

Tel. 01775 723170

Correspondent Stuart Reid Coltman, Secretary

Information available Accounts with a thin report which does not analyse or explain the year's grants.

Summary

The foundation sets aside three quarters of its disposable income, and typically the largest awards, for medical research funding. The rest is mainly for charities providing care for many of the same diseases and disabilities. A few grants are given to charities working in the region around Spalding. A little over 30 grants are awarded every year, with about a quarter being repeated from the year before. Grants are normally for between £10,000 and £50,000, and rarely for less than £5,000.

General

In 1998/99 the foundation had assets of £27 million. Income, at £819,000, was exceeded by grants expenditure. Administration costs were low, running at less than two per cent of spending on grants. The annual report contained the following information on policy:

Trustees' policy

The charity's funds available for making grants will normally be applied by the trustees:-

In providing financial support to charitable bodies concerned with the following areas of medical research:-

- Brain damage (Alzheimer's Disease, Huntingdon's Disease, Parkinson's Disease, Strokes, etc.);
- Cancer;
- Heart disease;
- Lung disease;
- Sight and/or hearing loss with broadly 75% of the charity's annual income being applied this way.

In providing financial support:-

to charitable bodies concerned with the welfare of people in need through illness, infirmity or social circumstances, in particular the welfare of older people and of children who reside in South Lincolnshire and adjoining areas and who:-

- Suffer from brain damage/mental illness;
- Suffer from cancer;
- Suffer from heart disease;
- Suffer from lung disease;
- Suffer from sight and/or hearing loss;
- Suffer from disfigurement through injury;
- Are physically disabled;
- Are bedridden;
- Are terminally ill;
- Are at risk.

to charitable bodies concerned with the welfare of victims of natural disasters and man-made disasters;

with broadly 25% of the charity's annual income being applied for such welfare purposes.

Grants in 1998/99

Reflecting the policy statement, 24 out of 33 grants, accounting for more than 90% of the funds, were disbursed to organisations coming under the category of 'health', which includes health care and medical research. The foundation occasionally makes three-year funding commitments in this area, typically for research projects. During the year these included awards to Nottingham Trent University (final grant of £50,000 for cancer research), and the Orchid Cancer Appeal (first award of £50,000 for research).

Four further grants of £50,000 or more were awarded to the Cancer Research Campaign (£250,000); The Foundation for the Prevention of Blindness (£100,000; £62,000 in 1997/98); SENSE (£50,000; £60,000 in 1997/98), and British Red Cross (£50,000).

Other recipients included the Rett Syndrome Association (£25,000); Muscular Dystrophy Group (£20,000); Whizz Kidz (£16,000, repeat); the Cot Death Society (£5,000) and The Hospital for St Vincent and the Grenadines (£2,000).

Another £40,500 was disbursed in six grants under the heading of 'Social Care and Development (Community Facilities; Community Services)'.

The average grant was nearly £7,000, ranging from £12,000 to the Lincolnshire and Nottinghamshire Air Ambulance to £1,500 for British Blind Sport (3rd year). Boston and South Holland Blind Society also got a repeated grant of £7,000, again part of a three-year commitment. Another local grant was £10,000 to the Spalding branch of the British heart Foundation.

Two grants were for 'Conservation and Environment': £10,000 to Rockingham Forest Trust and £5,000 to SRTA.

Finally, one grant was made under the heading of 'Education and Training', to Reactivate (£3,000).

Exclusions

Individuals.

Applications

To the correspondent in writing, but only if they are from other charities engaged in areas of work to which the trustees' policy extends. Telephone calls are not welcome.

The trustees meet three to four times a year to consider applications, but there are no set dates. Every applicant will receive a reply.

Bernard Van Leer Foundation (UK) Trust

Childhood development

£395,000 in the UK (1996/97)

Beneficial area International.

The Royal Bank of Scotland plc, Private Trust and Taxation, 2 Festival Square, Edinburgh EH3 9SU

Tel. 0131 523 2648 **Fax** 0131 228 9889

Correspondent David Macdonald

Information available Report and accounts.

Summary

This is the UK branch of a Netherlands-based foundation. Support, usually through multiple grants, is given to governmental and non-governmental projects seeking to improve the lives and opportunities of young children. In summer 2000, no grants had been made in the UK in the preceding two or three years. However, this was not a policy change and UK charities seemed likely to benefit from grants in the near future.

Grants have previously ranged from £1,000 to £75,000.

General

The foundation's guidelines, unchanged since the previous edition of this book, say:

Our mission is to enhance opportunities for children 0–7 years, growing up in circumstances of social and economic disadvantage, with the objective of developing their innate potential to the greatest extent possible. We concentrate on children from zero to seven years because scientific findings have demonstrated that interventions in the early years of childhood are most effective in yielding lasting benefits to children and society.

We accomplish this through two interconnected strategies:

1) a grant making programme in 40 countries aimed at developing contextually appropriate approaches to early childhood and development; and
2) the sharing of knowledge and know-how in the domain of early childhood development that primarily draws on the experiences generated by the projects that the foundation supports, with the aim of informing and influencing policy and practice.

We make grants to about 140 major projects at any one time and these operate in a variety of contexts:

- some are in developing countries, others in industrialised countries;
- they may be situated in urban slums, shanty towns and remote rural areas;
- they may focus on children living in violent settings, children of ethnic and cultural minorities, children of single or teenage parents, children of refugees and migrants;
- they often work to improve quality in daycare centres, pre-schools, health or other services;
- they may develop community based services;
- they may improve the quality of home environment by working with parents and other family members and caregivers.

The foundation:

- is concerned with young children's overall development and therefore promotes a holistic approach including education, health and nutrition;
- believes that children's development is the primary responsibility of parents and therefore actively promotes the enhancement of parents' capacity to support their children's development;
- attaches great importance to the involvement of the community as a major factor in children's development and therefore promotes a development strategy that is rooted in the community and is culturally, socially and economically appropriate;
- has adopted a contextual approach which builds on people's strengths as a guiding principle and therefore encourages building of local capacity, local ownership and working in partnership.

As well as our major focus, grantmaking is guided by thematic and programmatic priorities, geographic criteria, and budget limitations. Grants are made to governmental and non-governmental organisations.

We encourage projects to document their experiences, and we collect and systemise materials, publications and videos that they produce. We also support projects in producing their own publications and videos for their principal audiences.

The foundation's publications are available free of charge in single copies to organisations and individuals working in the area of early childhood development and related fields anywhere in the world. A list is available on request.

The foundation rarely considers unsolicited proposals. The vast majority of the projects supported result from a process of consultation with organisations that have been identified by the foundation itself.

Exclusions

Grants are not made to individuals, nor for the general support of organisations. The foundation does not provide study, research or travel grants. No grants are made in response to general appeals.

Applications

Applications can only be made in writing. The trust does not use an application form. Information that you should include is as follows:

- charity title or a description of your organisation's activities;
- registered charity number or evidence of tax-exempt status;
- list of the charity's key people;
- a contact name, address and telephone number;
- summary of the current work of the organisation – with latest annual report;
- description of the project/proposals/ area of work for which funding is requested, including costs, funds raised in relation to the target and details of any promised;
- indication of the numbers of beneficiaries likely to benefit and how they will benefit;
- how you intend to monitor and evaluate the project.

The foundation gives preference to countries in which the Van Leer group of companies is established.

The trust will acknowledge receipt of your application and may contact you for further information prior to consideration. There is a continuous process of assessment and you will be advised of any decision and, if successful, of any conditions attached to it.

For further information on the trust please either write to the correspondent or you are welcome to call direct on the above number.

The Vardy Foundation

Christian, education in the north east of England, general

£2,200,000 (1997/98)

Beneficial area UK.

c/o Reg Vardy plc, Houghton House, Wessington Way, Sunderland, Tyne & Wear SR5 3RJ

Tel. 0191 516 3636

Correspondent P Vardy, Trustee

Information available Full accounts on file at the Charity Commission.

General

The trust was set up in 1989 with general charitable objectives. In 1997/98 it had an income of £356,000, including £154,000 in donations. The trust's grant-making capacity of £2.2 million, way in excess of its income, appears to have come from funds transferred from its assets, which decreased by £2.2 million in the year to £5.2 million.

A total of 44 grants over £1,000 were listed by the trust, 16 of them to recipients supported in the previous year. Grants were in the range of £1,000 to £50,000, but were mainly for smaller amounts. At least 15 were made to individuals. By far the largest donations were £1.3 million to

Bethany Church and £542,000 to Emmanuel College in Gateshead, a regular beneficiary.

Other larger grants included Crusaders in the North (£50,000); Christian Action Research and Education Trust and the County Durham Foundation (£25,000 each); Kepplewray Project (£18,000); Christian Institute and Youth for Christ (£10,000 each).

Other smaller grants, ranging from £2,000 to £5,000, included those to Bible Mission International, Caring for Life, NSPCC, Project SEED, The Red Cross and Save the Children Fund.

Unlisted grants to other charitable causes totalled £8,500, with 'other' individuals receiving £7,000.

Applications

In writing to the correspondent.

The Variety Club of Great Britain

Children's charities, 'Sunshine Coaches'

£4,476,000 (to institutions, 15 months, 1998/99)

Beneficial area UK.

Variety Club House, 93 Bayham Street, London NW1 0AG

Tel. 020 7428 8100 **Fax** 020 7428 8111

e-mail info@varietyclub.org.uk

website www.varietyclub.org.uk

Correspondent Jim Whittell, Appeals Chairman

Trustees *Hugo Amaya-Torres; Jarvis Astaire; Hedy-Joy Babini; Lloyd Barr; Philip Burley; Stephen Crown; Raymond Curtis; Tony Frame; Richard Freeman; Anthony Harris; Tony Hatch; Gloria Huniford; Teddy Langton; Paul Lawrence; Eric Morley; Julia Morley; Charles Murray; Ronnie Nathan; Rod Natkiel; John Ratcliff; Angela Rippon; Neil Sinclair; Pamela Sinclair; John Webber; Jim Whittell.*

Information available Annual review and accounts.

Summary

This is an international children's charity originally established in the 1920s in the USA. Its members, who come from the worlds of entertainment, sport and business, help to raise considerable amounts each year through fundraising events. In 1999 the Variety Club of Great Britain celebrated its 50th anniversary.

It helps sick, disabled or disadvantaged children, mainly through the provision of Sunshine Coaches and grants to schools, hospitals, children's homes and young people's charities. Of the several hundred grants awarded each year, over 90% are for under £5,000, averaging about £1,000. These are nearly all one-off donations, though a very few major beneficiaries attract commitments to be paid over a number of years.

General

The charity's total incoming resources over the 15-month period to the end of 1999 were £11.8 million. Most of this money came from the fundraising activities of its trading subsidiary, Variety Club Events (£5 million), and from donations and legacies (£4.3 million). Of this, £1.2 million was spent on fundraising and publicity and £583,000 on administration (25 employees). Grant expenditure of £5,165,000 consisted of the following:

	No.	Value	%
Sunshine Coaches	171	£3,444,000	67%
Grants to institutions	386	£1,031,000	20%
Wheelchairs for individuals	213	£411,000	8%
Grants to individuals	249	£247,000	5%

The 50 largest grants to institutions listed with the accounts, starting at £3,000, amounted to £640,000, leaving nearly £400,000 donated to 336 recipients undisclosed – an undesirable proportion.

Nine organisations in receipt of grants for £20,000 or more accounted for a third of the total. For the following four beneficiaries, these grants were apparently part of long-term commitments, all having been supported in previous years: Army Benevolent Fund (£70,000); Royal Hospital for Sick Children, Bristol (£50,000); London Federation of Clubs for Young People (£42,000); Outward Bound Trust (£35,000).

The other large grants went to London Youth (£46,000); Browning House (£37,000); The Mulberry Bush (£25,000); The League of Friends of Middlesex Hospital (£25,000) and the Children's Hospital Appeal for Wales (£20,000).

A further 21 grants over £5,000 represented 20% of the total, the beneficiaries including: Alaris (£16,000); Central Manchester Healthcare Trust (£13,000); Wyken Adventure Centre (£8,000), and SeeAbility (£8,000).

Major future commitments totalling £2,772,000 at the end of 1999 included:

- £1,130,000 for Sunshine Coaches;
- £575,000 for Variety Club Children's Hospital at King's College;
- £150,000 for the Royal Hospital for Sick Children, Bristol;
- £75,000 for Leuka 2000;
- £70,000 for the Army Benevolent Fund.

Exclusions

No grants are made towards administration costs.

Applications

In writing at any time to the head of appeals.

Sir Siegmund Warburg's Voluntary Settlement

Medicine and education

£531,000 (1998/99)

Beneficial area UK, especially London.

c/o Ernst & Young, Broadwalk House, Southernhay West, Exeter EX1 1LF

Tel. 020 7567 8000

Correspondent Robin Jessel

Trustees *Doris Wasserman; Hugh Stevenson; Dr Michael Harding; Christopher Purvis.*

Information available Annual report and accounts.

Summary

The largest grants, sometimes for well over £100,000, are reserved for a few organisations regularly supported by the trust. Less than ten new grants are awarded in most years, for anything between £1,000 and £50,000. They generally cover a three year period.

General

The trust had net assets worth £15.1 million in 1998/99, which produced an income of £419,000. Administration costs continued to be high, considering the small number of grants to administer, at £96,216, or 18% of grant expenditure. These costs included over £64,000 paid to investment managers.

In 1999 it was reported that 'there has been a recent change in priorities to allow greater focus upon projects that encourage communication, both within the organisation supported and between the organisation and people outside of the project'. No changes were foreseen in the main area of funding, that of medical research.

In 1998/99 two thirds of the funds went to two organisations that have received substantial donations over a number of years. These donations were of £220,000 to the Institute of Child Health, and £134,000 to the University of Birmingham.

One of the trustees, Hugh Stevenson, is the chairman of the Institute of Child Health (he also appears in this book as a trustee of the Stevenson Family's Charitable Trust).

A further five grants went to the following beneficiaries, which had also been supported in the previous year: University of Bristol (£39,000); Lewisham Hospital (£25,000); Queen Mary & Westfield College (£18,000); British Scoliosis Research Foundation (£10,000), and St Paul's Girls School (£1,000).

The remaining grants went to UMDS (£36,000); King's College (£16,000); Royal Brompton & Harefield NHS Trust (£15,000); British School of Osteopathy (£10,000), and the Wishbone Trust (£8,000).

Applications

In writing to the correspondent, but see above.

The Waterside Trust

Christian causes, welfare

£2,121,000 (1999)

56 Palmerston Place, Edinburgh
EH12 5AY

Tel. 0131 225 6366 **Fax** 0131 220 1041

Correspondent Robert Clark

Trustees *Irvine Bay Trustee Company.*

Information available Annual report and accounts.

General

There is little information to be gleaned from the annual report of this charity, but further information has been supplied by the correspondent.

The trust supports Christian causes in the UK and overseas. Grants are made to organisations which 'provide adult Christian formation and pastoral care of the young, offer educational and recreational activities for disadvantaged young people, and provide care and support for the elderly, the unemployed and deprived families, especially those with young children. The trust supports projects in the areas of community development, the homeless, the mentally ill, ex-offenders, refugees and those with a history of substance abuse.' Support for this latter category is now minimal. This is a pretty comprehensive list from the which the most notable absentee is help for the sick.

The major beneficiary in 1998 and 1999, to the extent of £1 million and £850,000 respectively, was Rathbone Jersey Ltd (formerly Curzon Secretaries and Trustees Ltd). Also supported in 1998 were the Kulika Trust (£235,000), a Brenninkmeyer family foundation working primarily in East Africa, and Home Concern for the Elderly (£157,000).

There were small programmes of unspecified 'general, religious and charitable grants' in each year, of less than £30,000. In 1999 there was then an extensive list of overseas donations, worth about £1 million and covering much of the globe, but most of them were to Catholic organisations.

The largest grants were as follows: Duchenne Muscular Dystrophy Research Centre, USA (£169,000); St Stephen's Priory, Israel (£156,000); Catholic Research Centre, Malaysia (£93,000); Pontificia Universidade Catholica, Brazil (£78,000).

The annual report notes that 278 applications were received in 1999.

Exclusions

No grants to individuals, environmental projects, arts organisations, conservation groups, endowment appeals or major research projects.

Applications

In writing to the correspondent for consideration on an ongoing basis.

The Wates Foundation

Social welfare, especially in south London

£1,586,000 (1999/2000)

Beneficial area Unrestricted, but mainly London.

1260 London Road, Norbury, London SW16 4EG

Tel. 020 8764 5000

Correspondent Brian Wheelwright, Director

Trustees *John Wates, Chair; Ann Ritchie; Michael Wates; David Wates; Jane Wates; Revd Jonathan Edwards.*

Information available Exemplary reports and accounts, including guidance for applicants.

Summary

Grants are for amounts up to £25,000, and for up to three years, and they are almost exclusively for work in London, especially south London. Even so, only one in six applications can be accepted.

The trust concentrates its grants on

- homelessness
- unemployment
- substance abuse and offending

General

The chairman of this trust, John Wates, is highly active in the voluntary sector and the trust at board level appears unusually close to the issues which its funds are addressing.

The trust is regarded as friendly but demanding from the applicants' point of view. There is a referee system, so the probable quality of the work proposed is likely to be expertly reviewed. In the 1999/2000 annual report the chairman, who sometimes likes to be provocative, notes: 'I would imagine that the time is not far off when only charities with some outside accreditation like PQASSO or Investors in People will get grants from the Wates Foundation.'

The trust's special interest in addiction and criminality was due for a six-year review at the end of 2000. These editors hope that it will be renewed, as the expertise and authority that have been built up would not be easily replaced.

Unlike many trusts in this book that are criticised for spending a disproportionate amount of their money in London, Wates does this as a result of conscious decision rather than from a failure to seek applications from elsewhere. Its concentration on south London is welcome, as that half of the city is relatively under-resourced by local trusts compared to many areas north of the river.

Applicants from local charities outside London are unlikely to be funded.

Guidance for fundseekers

The foundation publishes the following excellent information.

Origin

In 1966 three brothers, Norman, Ronald and Allan Wates (directors of the building firm), set up the Foundation in order to amalgamate their three personal charitable trusts into a single entity. The Foundation is quite separate from the commercial interests of the Wates Group and has its own capital endowment which at present yields an annual income of about £1.6m.

The six [trustees] are all members of the Wates family. A Grants Committee, composed of around a dozen members of the family, meets three times a year, in Spring, Summer and Winter.

Funding priorities

The Foundation's primary aims are the alleviation of distress and the improvement of the quality of life. In line with its origin, the Foundation has always had an interest in the built environment and its impact on society. There is emphasis on the physical, mental and spiritual welfare of the young and disadvantaged aged 8–25. Grants are largely concentrated on projects in the Greater London area with a preference for South London.

The Foundation does not run programmes as such but puts emphasis on the following areas:

- homelessness,
- unemployment,
- substance abuse and offending.

There is support for post school education and training, particularly in good citizenship. Also, help for a wide range of community projects and activities. Since 1994 an area of special focus has been the field of addiction and criminality. Racial equality is stressed throughout.

Range and type of grant

Normal range up to £25,000. Maximum length of support 3 years, frequently 'tapered'. Once a grant has been made, we usually insist on a gap of two or three years before we can consider a renewed application.

Applications are invited from registered charities only. N.B. No grants to individuals.

THE WATES FOUNDATION – GRANTS PAID 1999/2000

	No.	*Value*
Education and science	11	£100,000
Health	8	£58,000
Community projects and the disadvantaged	138	£821,000
Church and religious	4	£49,000
Arts	25	£112,000
Overseas	10	£63,000
Heritage, conservation and the environment	9	£71,000
Area of special focus (addiction and criminality)	26	£262,000
Northern Ireland	4	£26,000
Miscellaneous	4	£25,000

Typical grants

The following examples under the main headings of its work are given by the foundation and can be taken as representing the kind of projects that it is most likely to support.

Community projects and the disadvantaged (approx. 55% of total grants)

Divert Trust – for a mentoring project at the Abeng Centre in Brixton which takes pupils who have dropped out from local secondary schools, over 3 years: £10,000, £7,500 & then £5,000

Emmaus – to go towards the re-opening of the Emmaus Greenwich Centre, using pioneering techniques to help and rehabilitate the homeless: £15,000.

Area of special focus – presently addiction and criminality (approx. 18% of total grants)

CARE (Christian Action Research & Education) – a high profile education resource against drugs, including a video and teacher's pack, for primary schools: £20,000.

Arts (approx. 7% of total grants)

Irene Taylor Trust – for a performance of Julius Caesar, with music, at Bullingdon Prison: £10,000.

Education and science (usually around 5% of total grants)

Institute for Citizenship Studies – towards the salary of an Information Officer to develop local contacts and liaise with local government: £10,000 pa x 3 years.

Church and religious projects (approx. 3% of total grants)

Inter Faith Network – core funding for the promotion of good inter-faith relations through its information service etc. over 3 years: £15,000, £10,000 & then £5,000.

Other (lesser) headings include health, heritage conservation and the environment, and miscellaneous.

Monitoring arrangements

One-off grants are paid soon after the Grants Committee meeting concerned. A follow- up report at the end of the period covered is requested. Grants made over a 2/3 year period are usually paid twice a year. The first instalment comes soon after the meeting concerned and the second is payable six months later once an Interim Report form (copy attached where appropriate) has been completed satisfactorily. In some instances, evaluation of an interesting project is agreed with the recipient.

Finally ...

We have a small staff but we like people to ring us up as this often saves correspondence. Please therefore telephone if you are in doubt about whether you fall within our guidelines or need help over completing your application.

Grants paid 1999/2000

The average size of a single grant was £6,637. Grants were categorised as shown in the box above.

Annual report 1999/2000

The reports of the foundation are among the best in the sector. Space allows only a few excerpts.

[Trustees'] desire to become more pro-active and to make fewer but larger grants will continue to lead to an increase in the rejection of 'unsolicited' appeals.

This year [we] received Professor Mike Hough's Report on the impact of the work of the Inner London Probation Services with drug offenders, which we part funded. This showed that non-custodial community sentences could have a major impact in reducing drug addiction and the offending behaviour associated with it.

The Irene Taylor Trust produced a very good Report, [with], perhaps for the first time, impartial evidence that an arts project in a prison setting can make a real contribution to prisoners' lives and reduce offending during their time in prison and, hopefully, beyond. [Outcomes] included a 94% reduction in offending during the course of the project itself and a 58% decrease in the offence rates of participants in the following 6 months. We very much hope that other Trusts and Foundations approached by arts organisations for similar projects will support them confident that they are likely to have real benefits.

In a new departure for the Foundation, we signed up in support of a Croydon Partnership bid for governmental Single Regeneration bid money. This will help us to take a strategic and pro-active role.

The Foundation tries to take a helpful and supportive role in encouraging charities to raise standards. ... I would imagine that the time is not far off when only charities with some outside accreditation like PQASSO or Investors in People will get grants from the Wates Foundation.

Director's report

In 1999/2000 we received 1,431 applications and made a total of 239 grants. Total applications have once more diminished (by 140). This is probably because of the way we encourage people to telephone to investigate our guidelines, instead of firing off their letters to us in ignorance. The main category of inappropriate applications continues to be those which are geographically wrong (in view of our focus on the Greater London area), but there is also a raft of applications from individuals (102).

I wanted to allude to the Single Application Form. After playing a small part in knocking this into shape at the draft stage, we bravely went ahead in sending it out to applicants. We had qualms about this; but the new form contained most of the vital elements and it seemed to us eminently worthwhile for us to help to pilot this potentially useful project (something similar is widely accepted in America).

Exclusions

- individuals
- large well established or national charities
- umbrella organisations
- large building projects
- other grant-making bodies
- medical appeals
- sporting, social or other fundraising events
- foreign travel including expeditions
- conferences
- repair of churches and church appeals
- overseas projects, except for a few which have been funded over the years
- projects outside the Greater London area

Applications

Applications at any time by completing the application form (the standardised single application form of the London Funders Group). A brief covering letter to the director conveying the flavour and key points of the project should also be sent.

With the completed application form, the following documents should please be sent:

- most recent annual accounts and annual report
- job description for any post for which funding is sought
- a business plan/work plan where appropriate

The following additional information will be useful:

- staffing details
- composition of the management committee
- the name, address and telephone number of a suitable referee

The Weinstock Fund

General

£569,000 (1998/99)

PO Box 17734, London SW18 3ZQ

Tel. 020 7493 8484

Correspondent Jacqueline Elstone

Trustees *Susan Lacroix; Laura Weinstock; John R Wood.*

Information available Accounts are filed at the Charity Commission but without a narrative report.

Summary

About 200 grants a year, normally one-off for amounts between £500 and £5,000, for a wide range of causes.

General

The charity's total funds amounted to over £10 million in 1998/99, while grants totalling £569,000 outstripped income (£292,000). Of this, £227,500, or 40% of the total, was given in seven grants to the following major beneficiaries (the last two having been supported in the previous year):

Marie Curie Cancer Care (£51,000); The Maclaren Trust (£50,000); Leuka 2000 (£31,500); The Royal Society (£25,000); University of Cambridge (£25,000); St Mary's School, Calne (£25,000; £5,000 in 1997/98), and Friends of the Ravenna Festival (£20,000, repeat).

The remaining grants, ranging from £250 to £11,500, were similarly widely spread, with between a quarter and a third repeated from the year before. Jewish organisations were less prominent among the beneficiaries than in previous years.

Examples of beneficiaries can be grouped under the following headings:

Medical/disability

Royal National Institute for the Blind (£11,500); National Society for Epilepsy (£7,000); Brain Research Trust (£5,000); Royal Free Hospital (£1,000); Prostate Cancer Charity (£1,000); Disability Law Service (£1,000).

Arts/heritage

London Bach Society (£10,000); Glyndebourne Arts Trust (£6,000); Royal Naval Museum (£2,500); English National Ballet (£1,000).

Overseas

WWF (£5,000); Ockenden Venture (£1,000); VSO (£500); Central Italy Earthquake Appeal (£250).

Jewish/general

St John's Wood Synagogue (£5,000); Jerusalem Foundation (£1,000); British Racing School (£5,000); Home Warmth for the Aged (£1,000); Teachers' Benevolent Fund (£1,000).

Exclusions

No grants to individuals or unregistered organisations.

Applications

In writing to the correspondent. There are no printed details or applications forms. 'Where nationwide charities are concerned, the trustees prefer to make donations centrally.' Donations can only be made to registered charities, and details of the registration number are required before any payment can be made.

The Wellcome Trust

Biomedical research, history of medicine, biomedical ethics, public engagement with science

£392,000,000 (1998/99)

Wellcome Building, 183 Euston Road, London NW1 2BE

Tel. 020 7611 7215 **Fax** 020 7611 8700

e-mail r.christou@wellcome.ac.uk

website www.wellcome.ac.uk

Correspondent Rebecca Christou, Grants Information Officer

Trustees *Sir Dominic Cadbury, Chair; Prof. Sir Michael Rutter; Prof. Martin Bobrow; Prof. Julian B Jack; Prof. C R W Edwards; Prof. Sir John Gurdon; Prof. Sir David Weatherall.*

Information available A grants booklet and extensive further information are available from the Marketing Department and are accessible through the foundation's website.

Summary

With an asset base of £13 billion and an estimated expenditure in 1999/2000 of some £600 million, the Wellcome Trust is the world's largest medical research charity.

Its programmes are too extensive and too specialised to be summarised or reviewed in this entry, but potential applicants should note that the trust is concerned primarily with medical science, at the highest levels, and is not normally a funder of service-delivering or campaigning charities even in the fields of health and medicine.

General

The trust classified its grants in 1998/99 and 1997/98 as follows:

	1998/99 £m	1997/98 £m
Career support	76.9	37.9
Genetics	45.0	17.2
Neurosciences	43.9	26.7
Building grants	37.3	20.0
Infection and immunity	33.2	23.8
Molecular and cell biology	29.8	26.8
Physiology/pharmacology	22.4	16.6
International	22.1	19.4
University Challenge Fund	18.0	–
Joint Infrastructure Fund	17.5	–
Equipment grants	15.8	8.0
Tropical medicine and infectious diseases	11.2	4.7
Population studies	7.1	5.0
History of medicine	4.9	5.4
Veterinary	3.9	1.5
Public understanding of science	3.5	1.2
Cardiovascular	1.2	3.1
Other schemes	7.3	5.6

Although grants are generally awarded in support of particular individuals the award is normally made to the host institution. Small grants may be awarded directly to individuals for the purpose of travel and for developing the public understanding of science. Grants awarded during the year are analysed by recipient as follows:

	1998/99 £m	1997/98 £m
University of Oxford	46.2	22.3
University College London	42.5	17.3
University of Cambridge	25.9	16.9
University of Manchester	21.1	4.1
Imperial College of Science, Technology and Medicine	20.6	20.0
University of Edinburgh	19.8	11.0
King's College London	13.5	11.0
University of Glasgow	10.1	5.0
University of Newcastle upon Tyne	9.7	3.8
University of Bristol	7.8	5.4
University of Dundee	7.3	7.8
University of Birmingham	7.3	2.4
University of Southampton	6.4	2.5
University of Wales College, Cardiff	5.6	1.5
The SNP Consortium Limited	5.5	–
University of Sheffield	5.2	1.3
University of Leicester	4.9	4.1
University of Liverpool	4.9	3.4
University of Aberdeen	3.6	0.7
University of Leeds	3.2	2.5
National University of Singapore	3.2	–
Bristol 2000 Limited	3.1	–
Science Centre, Glasgow	3.0	–
University of Nottingham	2.8	1.9
British Association for the Advancement of Science	2.8	–
St George's Hospital Medical School	2.7	1.5
Birmingham Museum and Art Gallery	2.7	–
University of Strathclyde	2.7	0.7
University of Bath	2.4	1.6
London School of Hygiene and Tropical Medicine	2.3	2.5
University of Manchester Institute of Science and Technology	2.2	0.4
Queen's University of Belfast	2.2	0.1
University of Natal	2.2	1.1
University of Sussex	2.2	0.5
Queen Mary & Westfield College	1.8	0.6
Science Centre, Dundee	1.8	–
University of Dublin	1.7	0.6
Kennedy Institute of Rheumatology	1.4	–
Science Museum	1.3	3.0
University of York	1.2	0.7
University of Kent	1.1	0.1
Medical Research Council	1.0	0.6
University of Reading	1.0	0.2
University of Portsmouth	1.0	0.1
City University	0.9	–
University of St Andrews	0.8	3.1
University of California	0.8	0.5
Royal Holloway & Bedford New College	0.8	–
India Institute of Medical Science	0.8	–
University of Aston	0.8	–

Exclusions

The trust does not normally consider support for the extension of professional education or experience, the care of patients or clinical trials. Contributions are not made towards overheads and not normally towards office expenses. The trust does not supplement support provided by other funding bodies, nor does it donate funds for other charities to use, nor does it respond to general appeals. For policy on funding cancer research (and other funding policies) please refer to 'Research Funding Policies' on the website (www.wellcome.ac.uk/en/1/biopolcan.html).

Applications

Applicants are advised, in the first instance, to contact the Grants Section by telephone for further relevant information or to make a preliminary application in writing.

A preliminary application should include brief details of the proposed research (one A4 page maximum); a note of existing funding from all sources, including the source of the applicant's salary funding; a brief CV; a list of relevant publications and an approximate costing. The quality of the proposed research is not judged at this stage.

If applicants are eligible to apply, they are sent a full application form. A preliminary application can be submitted at any time, other than those for special schemes and initiatives with advertised closing dates.

For UK-based project or programme grants a preliminary application is not necessary and an application form can be obtained via the trust's website.

The trust has many funding schemes and therefore potential applicants are advised to refer to the website for information on meeting dates and application deadlines.

The Welton Foundation

Medical research, music, general

£491,000 (1998/99)

Beneficial area UK.

33 St Mary Axe, London EC3A 8LL

Tel. 020 7280 2800

Correspondent Robin Jessel, Secretary

Information available Accounts, but without the required narrative review of the charity's activities.

Summary

Around 40 grants are made each year for sums in the range of £2,500 to £100,000. About two thirds of the total value of donations is given to hospitals and medical research establishments. Other interests include music.

General

The charity is administered by an independent consultant, R R Jessel.

Management and administration costs remain little changed, at £62,000, or about £1,800 per grant and 12% of charitable expenditure (up from the 8% reported in the previous edition of this book). There were only 15 grants of £10,000 or more and 6 of these were to institutions also funded in the previous year, and for which much information was presumably already to hand. It is possible that there are other activities as well as the straight-forward allocation and monitoring of grants which could fully justify these levels of costs. But if they exist, they are not reported as they should be.

A little over 40 grants were made in all. Though six of the major beneficiaries had also been supported in the previous years, the amounts were all changed, so it is likely that grants are one-off, with new projects being supported each time.

There is no information on the purposes of the grants given, but of those for £10,000 or more that were probably for medical research, the largest awards went to the Gastroenterology and Nutritional Trust (£47,000); Help the Hospices (£45,000); the National Backpain Association (£43,000), and the Royal Postgraduate Medical School (£32,000).

Music grants included the £22,000 to the Young Concert Artists Trust; £25,000 for the Rugby School Chapel Organ Appeal; £20,000 to the Drake Music Project; £4,000 for the Dartington Summer School, and £2,500 for British Youth Opera. Large but unclassifiable awards were given to the Advisory Centre for Education (£25,000) and the University of Cape Town (£37,000).

The smaller grants, those for less than £10,000, are even more widely spread. Recipients included the Royal Horticultural Society (£2,000); the Academy of St Mary's Wimbledon (£2,000); Africa Vision Fund (£5,000); Camphill Village Trust (£4,000), and Victim Support, Esher (£5,000).

Overall, the impression received tends to be one of an individual philanthropist, of wide sympathies, using the vehicle of a charitable trust.

Exclusions

Grants only to registered charities, and not in response to general appeals.

Applications

In writing to the secretary, stating:

- what the charity does;
- what specific project the money is needed for, giving as much detail as possible;
- how much money is needed;
- the source of any other funding.

Due to the number of appeals received, the foundation only replies to those that are successful.

The Westminster Foundation

General

£1,172,000 (1999)

Beneficial area UK, with local interests in central London (SW1 and W1 and immediate environs) and the north west of England, especially rural Lancashire and the Chester area.

70 Grosvenor Street, London W1X 9DB

Tel. 01252 722557

Correspondent J E Hok, Secretary

Information available Full annual report and accounts.

Summary

Nearly 200 grants a year, most for £2,000 or less but the largest for £60,000, are disbursed widely (about half are repeated). Many small grants, and the occasional large one, go to local charities in the areas specified above. The main areas of interest are social welfare and conservation, chiefly rural. A significant number of the beneficiaries have military connections.

'It is usual that the Trustees have knowledge of, or connection with, those charities which are successful applicants.'

'The Trustees tend to support caring causes and not research.' (Though note that grants of £1,000 to Leukaemia Research and £5,000 to the Habitat Research Trust are listed in the 1999 report.)

General

The trust's assets of £41.5 million produced an unusually low income of £1.3 million. The grants are influenced by the Grosvenor family's landownings, in the form of the Grosvenor Estate in Knightsbridge, London, and of property interests in north west England.

The trust's review of the year provided the following commentary on its major grants:

> ... The most significant grant was £60,000 to the Carline Project. The Royal United Services for Defence Studies received £55,000 as part of a three year commitment. Other grants of £50,000 and above were made to: The Game Conservancy Trust, The Royal Hospital, Friends of Kirov Opera and RNIB. A total of £100,000 towards the alleviation of homelessness was shared between Cardinal Hume Centre, Centrepoint Soho, The Passage Centre, Chester Aid to the Homeless, and CRISIS. [*The same amount was allocated to the same beneficiaries in 1997/98. Ed.*]
>
> The Trustees anticipate fewer but larger grants in the future. However, they will still assist the smaller charities of local interest to them, specifically in rural Lancashire, Chester and its surrounding area and central London. The Trustees are concerned to address some of the areas of need which are currently emerging in rural areas.

Grants in 1999

Social and welfare

Large grants went to the charities benefiting the homeless and the RNIB, as mentioned in the report, above. Additional large grants were made to:

- Local Initiative Support (Muncaster Conference, £30,000)

THE WESTMINSTER FOUNDATION – GRANTS IN 1998 AND 1999

	1999		*1998*	
Social and welfare	£473,000	41%	£532,000	54%
Conservation	£252,000	22%	£114,000	12%
Education	£157,000	13%	£121,000	12%
Youth	£132,000	11%	£64,000	6%
Arts	£71,000	6%	£94,000	10%
Medical	£57,000	5%	£38,000	4%
Church	£29,000	2%	£17,000	2%
Total	£1,172,000	100%	£981,000	100%

- University of Liverpool (£27,000)
- Northern Ireland Council for Voluntary Action (£25,000, repeat)
- Royal Agricultural Society of the Commonwealth (£20,000)
- Arthritis Care (£18,000)

A sample of the smaller grants is as follows: Gamekeepers' Welfare Trust (£1,000); Gurkha Welfare Trust (£5,000); Home Farm Trust (£2,000); Ibero-American Benevolent Society (£250); King George's Fund for Sailors (£1,000); Kosovo in Cheshire Appeal (£5,000); Lancashire & Morecambe Agricultural Society (£1,000).

Conservation

More than half the expenditure went to the following three beneficiaries:

- The Royal Hospital (£51,000)
- Game Conservancy Trust (£50,000)
- Sustainability North West (£35,000, repeat)

Of the 21 beneficiaries, 10 had also been funded in the previous year, including West Sutherland Fisheries Trust (£5,000); The Grosvenor Museum (£2,000), and Lancashire Farming and Wildlife Advisory Group (£600).

Education

After the £55,000 grant to the Royal United Services mentioned in the report, the next largest was to The Royal Armouries (£15,000). Some of the 23 other beneficiaries were the Chester C}ivic Trust (£10,000); Pembroke College Cambridge (£8,000), and Common Purpose UK (£6,000).

Youth

The trust says: 'Youth is supported via Youth Sport Trust, Chester Boys Club, and to those Scouts and Guides where the Foundation has close connections.'

Three grants of over £15,000 went to the Carline Project (£60,000, as mentioned above); the National Playing Fields Association (£16,000) and Chester Boys' Club (£15,500). Another 15 grants were in the range £1,000 to £5,000, recipients including Farms for City Children and the London Federation of Boys' Clubs (both repeat grants of £5,000).

The 14 remaining grants ranged from £60, to the Prince's Trust, to £844, to the NSPCC.

Arts

Two grants to the Friends of the Kirov Opera and the Northern Ballet Theatre (£10,000) accounted for the bulk of the arts expenditure. Three other beneficiaries had been funded the year before: the Young Concert Artists Trust (£5,000), Chester Summer Music Festival (£1,000) and the Northlands Festival (£1,000).

Medical

The largest grants went to Hospice of the Good Shepherd (£25,000), British Kidney Patients Association (£11,000) and Christie Hospital (£10,000).

Church

The largest grants went to the Church of the Holy Ascension Parochial Church Council (£10,000) and Eccleston and Pulford (£4,000). And 10 out of 11 other churches got repeat grants of between £500 and £2,500, including St George's Memorial Church, Ypres.

Exclusions

Only registered charities will be considered; charitable status applied for, or pending, is not sufficient. No grants to individuals, 'holiday' charities, student expeditions, or research projects. The arts and education budgets are fully committed until at least 2004, and homeless and related support until 2005.

Applications

In writing to the secretary, enclosing an up to date set of accounts, together with a brief history of the project to date, and the current need.

The Westminster Foundation for Democracy

Strengthening democracy overseas

£4,000,000 (2000/01)

Beneficial area Outside the UK.

2nd Floor, 125 Pall Mall, London SW1Y 5EA

Tel. 020 7930 0408 **Fax** 020 7930 0449

e-mail wfd@wfd.org

website www.wfd.org

Correspondent The Chief Executive

Trustees *Ernie Ross MP, Chair; Georgina Ashworth; Frances D'Souza; Nicola Duckworth; Tim Garton Ash; Nik Gowing; Mary Kaldor; Archie Kirkwood MP; Gillian Merron MP; Elizabeth Smith; Richard Spring MP; Gary Streeter MP; Ieuan Wyn Jones MP.*

Information available Annual report and accounts, information leaflets and details of projects supported are available from the foundation.

Summary

The foundation gives grants, seldom for more than £30,000 and more than two thirds for less than £10,000, for projects to support democracy anywhere in the world, but its work is concentrated in Central and Eastern Europe, in the former Soviet Union and in anglophone Africa.

General

The foundation receives almost all its money from the government (which has increased its annual income from £3 million to £4 million a year), but it makes its own decisions about the projects to be supported. It describes its policies as follows:

The ... Foundation may support any project which is aimed at building pluralist democratic institutions abroad. These may include:

- election systems or administration
- parliaments or other representative institutions
- political parties
- independent media
- legal reform
- trades unions
- human rights groups
- women's organisations
- other political non-governmental institutions

It will give preference to projects which contain clear action plans, designed to achieve concrete results; those whose effects will be lasting; and to building up organisations which can be self-sustaining, rather than encouraging continuing dependence on outside assistance.

The foundation concentrates its funding on three priority areas:

- Central and Eastern Europe,
- the former Soviet Union and
- anglophone Africa.

It will consider sympathetically applications for projects elsewhere in the world.

The foundation seeks to avoid duplication of effort with other governmental and non-governmental agencies and to reinforce their commitment to enhancing participatory democracy. Where possible, it will carry out projects in cooperation with other organisation and foundations.

Support for individual political parties is provided through that part of the foundation's budget which is channelled through the UK political parties [*50%. Ed.*]. Individual parties from overseas seeking ... funding for their programmes must therefore apply to the individual UK party with which they have links.

Alternatively, the foundation may carry out cross-party projects, where a range of political parties from a country are involved, and these projects are funded directly from the foundation's general resources.

The foundation does not seek to foster any particular model of democracy. It seeks to keep administrative costs to a minimum, and will not support the administrative costs of its recipients beyond what is absolutely necessary, nor provide equipment beyond reasonable need.

Grants in 1999/2000

In 1999/2000 331 projects were approved, from 444 proposals. The main areas of work were as follows:

	No. of projects	*Value*
Political party training and strengthening	135	£1,531,000
Building civil society	73	£718,000
Strengthening the media	31	£331,000
Human rights	30	£297,000
Women's political and civil involvement	27	£215,000
Parliament	16	£147,000
Legal organisations and reform	11	£105,000
Trades unions	3	£17,000
Cross party	1	£6,000

The value of the projects by area was as follows:

Central and Eastern Europe (EU accession countries)	£183,000
Central and Eastern Europe (other countries)	£1,497,000
CIS and Mongolia	£588,000
Anglophone Africa	£662,000
Other countries	£497,000

Five projects had a budget of more than £40,000, three being for work in former Yugoslavia: £80,000 funding for the Conservative Party to continue work within its West Balkan Initiative; and two projects funded through the Labour Party to assist the Social Democratic Party of Bosnia Herzegovina – £64,000 to help purchase necessary equipment and £51,000 to produce materials for the April 2000 municipal elections. The other large awards were for various East European party leaders to attend the Conservative Party conference (£44,000), and £48,000 to support a meeting of the Democratic Union of Africa alliance in Ghana, through the Conservative Party.

Other projects included £18,000 funding for the Labour Party to assist political awareness training for the Sandinista Front for National Liberation in Nicaragua; £15,000 for a training programme to provide civic education to women in rural Kenya; £10,000 core funding of Deca Press Information Agency in Moldova; £9,000 support for Human Rights in China's website; £6,000 to fund Association Obnovlenie, providing legal advice and support to Romany people in Bulgaria; and £5,000 to help the Democratic Left in Slovakia organise a media training workshop.

Exclusions

The foundation does not fund conferences, research, educational scholarships, cultural, health or social projects.

Applications

In writing to the correspondent. Applicants are advised first to obtain the trust's pamphlet 'Overview', which includes some guidelines for applications. Project evaluations are part of the conditions of assistance from the foundation. Trustees normally meet in January, April, July and October.

The Garfield Weston Foundation

Arts, education, health, general

£31,550,000 (1998/99)

Beneficial area UK.

Weston Centre, Bowater House, 68 Knightsbridge, London SW1X 7LQ

Tel. 020 7589 6363 **Fax** 020 7584 5921

Correspondent Fiona Foster, Administrator

Trustees *Guy Weston, Chair; Miriam Burnett; Nancy Baron; Camilla Dalglish; Anna C Hobhouse; Jana R Khayat; Sophia Mason; Barbara Mitchell; Galen Weston; George G Weston.*

Information available Excellent annual report and accounts with narrative report, grants analysis and a full list of grants. There is a separate very brief sheet outlining grant-making practice.

Summary

The foundation makes more than 1,000 awards a year from a usual minimum of £1,000 to a present maximum of £10 million. All grants are one-off. The same organisation is only occasionally supported in consecutive years. The fields covered are categorised as follows:

- education
- health
- the arts
- welfare
- environment
- religion (including church buildings)
- youth
- community
- mental health
- other (including heritage)

The 44% success rate for applications (though not necessarily always for the full amount requested) is very high, made possible no doubt by the rapid rise in the income of the charity in recent years.

So far as is known the foundation is about as 'policy free' as it is possible to get. Only the general absence of radical or controversial causes or organisations is unusual (and even here, there was substantial support in 1998/99 for Amnesty International). The high success rate is probably an indication that the trustees are as yet seldom forced to choose between a number of equally good applications. When this changes, new policies will have to be introduced.

For most of its grants, except perhaps the largest, the foundation is probably solely reactive. There is one administrator who, with two assistants, has responsibility for the initial qualitative examination of applications. All applications are also seen by at least one trustee and all grants are ratified at trustees' meetings. However, some individual trustees have been active in meeting applicants and visiting projects.

The money from the foundation goes overwhelmingly to national organisations or to London-based charities. Although the smaller grants are spread widely through the country, they do not account for a substantial part of the foundation's expenditure.

There are no detailed guidelines for applicants. The simple requirements are set out under the 'Applications' heading below. However, the excellent annual reports are a good guide to the thinking of the trustees; the bulk of this entry consists of the text of the 1998/99 report, after some initial analysis of grantmaking as a whole.

The finances of the foundation are interesting as well as enormous, and are discussed in the box below.

General

Although a large number of grants is made, one tenth of the awards, all for £20,000 or more, accounted for £28 million of the 1998/99 total, while the remaining 1,000 smaller grants totalled just £4 million. The five largest grants, detailed below, accounted for about half the total expenditure. Nevertheless the £4 million of smaller grants still makes this foundation one of the largest sources of such funding in the country.

In October 2000, Garfield H Weston retired as chairman and was replaced by his eldest son, Guy Weston. His daughter Sophia Mason, who acted as administrator of the trust for a period until she moved temporarily to the USA a few years ago, has also become a trustee. Of the ten trustees, five are based in North America: the board meets as a whole once a year. The trustees living in Britain meet monthly. They are the chairman, Guy Weston, and four of his bothers and sisters, George Weston, Jana Khayat, Anna Hobhouse and Sophia Mason. However, other trustees can also be actively involved in UK voluntary activity; this editor has met Galen Weston, for example, at an interfaith presentation in London.

Unusually, the secretary to the trustees is a solicitor 'in practice', Janette Cattell. With Judith Portrait, who fulfils a similar function for the Smith Charity and is also a trustee of most of the Sainsbury family trusts, these two lawyers are concerned with a remarkably high proportion of all foundation wealth.

Because the figures for any one year can be dominated by one or two exceptionally large grants, the table on page 326 covers both 1998/99 and 1997/98, and gives totals for both the number of grants and their value (in £ million).

In 1998/99 the grants were led by £10 million towards the cost of roofing and enclosing the Great Court of the British Museum (whose portico has recently been found to have been rebuilt in the 'wrong' stone, though one which this editor finds striking and attractive). This was the second grant of this size from the foundation for the same purpose, making a total contribution comparable to that by other foundations for the Sainsbury wing of the National Gallery.

Other £1 million plus grants were made to Hammersmith Hospital Medical School (£2.5 million), the Technology Colleges Trust, the London Science Museum and Christie's Hospital in Manchester (£1 million each).

In the previous year Cambridge University had received £2.5 million, while £3 million was given to the Royal Shakespeare Company and £2 million to the Wales Millennium Centre. New

The endowment of the Weston Foundation

The assets of this foundation were valued at over £2.5 billion in April 1999. An unrestricted endowment of this size might generate an income of about five per cent of that sum, or about £125 million a year, while still maintaining its full value in real terms. However the foundation regards its 'normal' income as being about £26 million, an absurdly small amount in the circumstances.

The main asset of the foundation is its unexpendable endowment, in the form of an 80% holding in a company, Wittington Investments, which in turn owns half the shares in Associated British Foods and around 90% of the shares in Fortnum and Mason. The Wittington shares may not be sold except by a unanimous vote of all the trustees. At present there is no intention to make such a divestment, nor does it seem likely in the future. All the trustees are descendants of W Garfield Weston and would probably be reluctant to sell the company so remarkably created by their family.

The income of the charity depends on the profits of the Wittington company, but also on what proportion of these profits the directors (a majority of whom are also trustees of the foundation), decide to pay out as dividends. The company made profits for the foundation of £374 million, £148 million and £108 million in the three years to 1998/99. However, the normal dividend income of the foundation in those years was just £24 million, £37 million and £39 million.

In 1998/99 the trustees asked Wittington (that is, largely themselves) to pay a one-off extra dividend. This led to additional payments of no less than around £90 million – perhaps more after tax recovery. This was primarily a response to the phasing out of tax credits on dividend income. It was not, the foundation says, because retention of profits on this scale could be seen as approaching 'accumulation' rather than 'use' of the charity's resources – the assumption initially made by these editors. Such accumulation would not, in general, be permitted; it is indeed this issue which has led to the requirement on most foundations in the USA to expend five per cent of their net worth each year on actual charitable activities.

The trust says, rather, that its normal level of dividends is the maximum that should be reasonably and prudently sustained, given the need for the company to retain proper reserves. If so, the Wittington investment is offering very poor returns. Were the holdings to be sold and the endowment conventionally invested, there would be much more money available for charitable purposes.

There is also inherent danger in a lack of diversification of investments. The examples of the once huge Ronson trusts, or of the Nuffield Foundation's investments in its founder's car companies, come to mind, as does the exposed position at present of many of the Sainsbury family trusts.

The foundation has reasonably asked the Charity Commission to be allowed to spend its extra £90 million of unplanned income over a period of time, on the grounds that such a huge amount could not be sensibly spent in a single year. It is also seeking permission to re-invest some of this income rather than to spend it for charitable purposes. Given the already high value of the foundation's capital compared to its low levels of income, this seems inappropriate.

THE GARFIELD WESTON FOUNDATION – GRANTS IN 1998/99 AND 1997/98
(number and value in £ million)

	1998/99		*1997/98*		*Total*	
Education	142	£15.0	127	£8.2	269	£23.2
Health	100	£6.0	88	£4.8	188	£10.8
The arts	58	£1.5	68	£6.7	126	£8.2
Welfare	212	£2.4	220	£2.5	432	£4.9
Environment	41	£0.8	33	£1.4	74	£2.2
Religion (inc. church buildings)	284	£1.2	180	£1.0	464	£2.2
Youth	178	£2.4	175	£0.5	353	£2.9
Community	158	£0.6	136	£0.6	294	£1.2
Mental health	33	£0.8	31	£0.1	64	£0.9
Other (including heritage)	36	£0.5	34	£0.2	70	£0.7
Total	1,136	£31.5	1,003	£26.1	2,139	£57.6

College, Oxford, the National Gallery, the Royal Opera House, the National Botanic Garden of Wales, Marie Curie Cancer Care and the National Playing Fields Association each received £1 million. There is no precedent for nine separate organisations receiving million pound gifts from one foundation in a single year.

The geographical distribution of grants

The text of the 1998/99 annual report describes 20 of the larger grants where the work, worth £18 million, is geographically identifiable:

South of England	16 grants	£16.4 million
of which, London	11 grants	£15.5 million
North of England	3 grants	£1.3 million
Scotland	nil	nil
Wales	1 grant	£0.1 million
Northern Ireland	nil	nil

This foundation is now so big that the element of tax subsidy, contributed by people throughout the country to support the spending decisions of these trustees, represents a significant transfer of their money to London from the rest of the country. The decision to do this should, at the least, be explained and defended by the trustees.

The smaller grants, though they represent an altogether smaller amount of money, are distributed quite differently. A sample of 153 grants of £5,000 (all that could readily be placed geographically) gave the following results:

South of England	68 grants
of which, London	*20 grants*
North of England	35 grants
Scotland	20 grants
Wales	9 grants
Northern Ireland	1 grant

Given the generally supposed propensity of southern Englanders to submit more applications than anyone else except the Scots, this distribution may well approximate to the applications received. Is it unreasonable, in the absence of further information, to guess that these smaller applications are processed pretty automatically, while the larger awards represent the personal and active decisions of trustees?

Annual report 1998/99

Overview

As in previous years, the trustees have supported a wide range of charitable activity and have in this financial year made grants totalling in excess of £31.5 million. This represents an increase of 21% over the total value of grants in 1997/98 (just over £26 million). A total of 1,242 appeals were supported, of which six were of £1 million or more and another 50 were between £100,000 and £1 million. A total of 1,536 appeals were not supported.

The Foundation continues to accept appeals from UK registered charities only. No applications from individuals are considered. In accordance with its policy of making one-off cash donations, all donations approved were paid during the year and at 5 April 1999 the Foundation had no material forward commitments. Trustees meet on a regular basis to review and approve grant applications and aim to deal with each application within ten weeks of it being received. Whenever it is considered necessary or desirable, visits are made by trustees and the Foundation's administrator in order to gain a better understanding of applicants' requirements. Regular contact is also maintained with recipients of grants for monitoring purposes.

Special mention should be made in relation to the further grant of £10 million to the British Museum Great Court project. The trustees provided an initial major donation to the project in 1996/97 and indicated then that they would be taking a continuing interest in the project as it moved forward. The donation this year has assisted the Museum in reaching its funding target for this project which is vital to the future of our National Museum. The new exhibition space, catering facilities, retail outlets and Centre for Education which are being developed on this two acre site will be one of the leading tourist attractions for the Millennium and many years to come. The trustees regard their support for this project as their main contribution to the nation's charitable Millennium activities.

The trustees have continued their commitment to making a large number of small grants to local community projects. Although in terms of value the largest grants were made in the fields of health and education (the latter category including the grant to the British Museum), the trustees are still committed to funding other main areas of charitable activity, including the arts, community projects, environment, mental health, religion, welfare and youth projects. …

The arts – £1,479,000 distributed in 58 grants

Reference to the Foundation's annual report two years ago will reveal grants of £500,000 to the Royal National Theatre and £150,000 to Sadler's Wells Theatre for restoration, modernisation and refurbishment of their respective premises. The trustees have agreed to provide the same amounts again to both establishments, to help them complete their upgrade programmes.

The Royal Academy of Arts and Welsh National Opera continue to receive support, with donations in this financial year of £200,000 and £100,000 respectively. One-off capital grants of £100,000 have been provided to the Royal Court Theatre for its rebuilding programme and to the East Anglia Art Foundation towards the major refurbishment of the 900 year old Norwich Castle.

The geographic spread is further illustrated by grants to the Aldeburgh Festival, Scottish Opera, the Lake District Art Gallery and Museum, Mobex North East, the Aberystwyth Arts Centre, the Northern Chamber Orchestra and the Theatre Royal Bath Youth Theatre.

Community – £688,000 distributed in 158 grants

A £100,000 grant to the Salvation Army will help to extend and refurbish an outdated community centre in London's East End. The upgraded premises will offer full day centre activities, extended lunch club, drop in coffee lounge, disabled access, facilities for chiropodist and hairdresser and homework station and will double the numbers served to over one thousand.

A similar amount to the Notting Dale Partnership is supporting the major refurbishment of the Harrow Club W10 premises, which provide youth facilities, a sports hall, arts and drama, computer related training and residential accommodation for homeless young people in a densely populated area in North Kensington.

Of the 158 successful applicants in this category, 147 are for less than £10,000. Many are for improving village halls and reordering church premises for community use in rural areas.

Education – £15,136,000 distributed in 142 grants

The donation of £10,000,000 to the British Museum has been covered earlier in this report.

£1,030,000 is provided to the Technology Colleges Trust, making the total contributed by the Foundation in the last six years almost £4,000,000. The progress made by the secondary schools which have successfully achieved technology status since this programme was first introduced by the Government in 1993 has encouraged the trustees to maintain their sponsorship.

A £1,000,000 donation to the Science Museum is allocated to the Wellcome Wing development. This will be the world's leading centre for the presentation of contemporary science and technology to the public and will increase the Museum's space by one third. It will include a state of the art IMAX 3D film theatre and exhibitions specifically targeted at very young visitors.

The Horniman Museum in Forest Hill has received a further £400,000 following an initial grant of £100,000 last year. Frederick Horniman, tea merchant, politician and philanthropist, gave his collections, the building and adjoining 16.5 acres of gardens to the people of London for their 'recreation, instruction and enjoyment'. Exhibits include a fine Musical Instruments collection with 6,000 specimens, a Natural History display with a Living Waters aquarium and an Ethnography section. A recently built, ecologically designed centre focuses on Understanding the Environment. The development plan will provide a new main entrance with facilities for the disabled, new lifts to all levels, new space for the educational activities, extra display space to enable more of the collections to be exhibited and a new temporary exhibition gallery.

The grant of £250,000 to the British Council is contributing towards a short term, merit based scholarship scheme for Asian students in the UK, following the turmoil in the Asian financial markets.

Nursery, primary and secondary schools, universities, colleges of further education, adult education centres, training schemes and museums all benefited in this category.

Environment – £858,000 distributed in 41 grants

A wide range of activities has been supported this year.

The largest grant, £250,000, was donated to the Lindley Library development at the Royal Horticultural Society. This is the most comprehensive horticultural library in Europe and probably in the world, with unique and irreplaceable collections dating from the 16th century to the present day. It will be relocated in larger, environmentally controlled and more accessible space on the same site and will include digital cataloguing and sophisticated IT hardware and software.

The trustees have agreed to provide continued support to the Royal Botanic Gardens in Kew. The £250,000 grant this year will be used for research into Chinese herbal medicines.

Brogdale Horticultural Trust, home of the National Fruit Collections, received a grant of £50,000 towards restructuring the organisation and developing the research activities. £25,000 has been provided to the Marine Stewardship Council for promoting responsible, environmentally appropriate, socially beneficial and economically viable fishery practices, whilst maintaining the biodiversity, productivity and ecological processes of the marine environment.

Organisations working for the protection and conservation of waterways, woodlands, birds and wildlife are all represented on the list.

Health – £6,040,000 distributed in 100 grants

This category received the second highest amount of funding after Education.

The Royal Postgraduate Medical School at Hammersmith Hospital received a grant of £2,500,000 towards rebuilding the Institute of Obstetrics and Gynaecology adjacent to the new Queen Charlotte's Hospital. Cancer charities have again benefited, with £1,000,000 to the Christie's Hospital Appeal in Manchester; £500,000 to Imperial Cancer Research Campaign and £100,000 to Leuka 2000. The British Liver Trust, which provides information and support as well as funding for research, received £200,000 and the Liver Group, a research programme currently based at Hammersmith Hospital, £100,000.

Significant funding was provided for neurological research, treatment and care, with grants to the Royal Hospital for Neurodisability, the British Brain and Spine Foundation, the Brain Research Trust, the National Society of Epilepsy and the British Neurological Research Trust.

The trustees continue to support children's hospitals, the largest donation being £250,000 to the Alder Hey Children's Hospital in the North West for a new Oncology Unit and Outpatients Department.

More than thirty hospices throughout the UK also received funding.

Mental health – £792,000 distributed in 33 grants

The trustees responded to an appeal from Maudsley Hospital, a leading provider of psychiatric facilities and expertise, with a grant of £500,000 for the redevelopment of the 1920s building housing the Centre for Children and Young People.

The Mental Health Foundation was awarded £125,000 for its programme on dementia. This will include a nationwide homecare support service for families suffering with dementia, dementia research and funding of studentships.

The third significant grant in this category was £100,000 for the Home Farm Trust's national capital development plan for adults with learning disability and mental handicap. This will include both major improvements to current schemes to provide residents with more appropriate conditions and new developments to cater for geographic areas not currently covered.

Other – £520,000 distributed in 36 grants

For the third year in succession the Foundation has supported the Vivat Trust in its work to acquire and preserve listed buildings of historical and architectural interest, which are subsequently turned into holiday homes. A grant of £250,000 has also been provided to the Phoenix Trust for acquiring, restoring and converting larger historic but redundant buildings for the benefit of communities and the public at large. The intention is to create places where people live and work rather than museums or show buildings. Buildings identified include former military establishments, hospitals, mills and warehouses which are falling into disrepair.

The trustees' concern for the built environment is also demonstrated by grants to the Civic Trust, to the Ancoats Buildings Preservation Trust in Manchester; to the Trades Hall of Glasgow Trust and to the Rural Building Preservation Trust. Funding has also been allocated to Sulgrave Manor in Towcester; Beckford Tower in Bath and the Historylinks Building Appeal in Dornoch.

HMS Trincomalee Trust in Hartlepool and the SS Great Britain project in Bristol were given renewed assistance with the restoration of the vessels and the creation of educational and visitor facilities.

Religion – £1,237,000 distributed in 284 grants

This year has seen a steep increase in the number of grants allocated in this category, up from 180 in the previous year. This is mainly due to the number of parishes aiming to achieve completion of fabric repairs in time for the Millennium. The list includes a number of churches applying for help with the restoration of bells.

In addition to cathedral and church restoration, with which the trustees have always been sympathetic, a number of religious educational projects were approved this year. These include the Divinity Faculty at the University of Cambridge; EducareM, which aims to advance and promote the spiritual, moral, social and cultural development of children and young people and the development of family life values through an education programme with schools; and JC2000, a Millennium drama/ arts festival inspired by the life of Christ in which all schools throughout the country are being encouraged to participate.

Welfare – £2,385,000 in 212 grants

As always, a significant number of grants are allocated to the welfare category, demonstrating the trustees' commitment to assisting disadvantaged people and communities.

Amnesty International's aim of creating the first Human Rights Centre in the world to coincide with the 50th anniversary of the UN declaration on human rights has been supported with a grant of £250,000. The same amount has been donated to Abbeyfield Development Trust for creating new supported and sheltered housing for elderly people. Various other organisations working with the elderly have also been provided with funding.

A further £200,000 to the Enham Trust in Hampshire brings the total provided by the Foundation in the last five years to £600,000. This large capital development programme is in the process of transforming what was an institutional home for disabled people into independent housing, where every resident will have a self contained flat with modest living room, bedroom, kitchen and bathroom.

£100,000 has been allocated to Toynbee Hall for upgrading the premises for its work with disadvantaged people in the East End of London. Emmaus UK and Riverpoint were each awarded £100,000 and the Passage £50,000 for their work with the homeless. £50,000 has also been provided to Carr-Gomm towards additional housing for vulnerable people who would otherwise be inappropriately housed or homeless. A £50,000 grant to Shelter will help to fund a new national 24 hour telephone service, Shelterline, offering help and advice to any person who is homeless or who has housing problems anywhere in England, Scotland or Wales.

The 999 Club's need to upgrade its premises in Deptford for its work with vulnerable people was recognised with a donation of £50,000. The redevelopment will provide temporary housing for the homeless, training, literacy classes, all forms of support and day centre/ community facilities.

Youth – £2,415,000 in 178 grants

The largest grant in this category, £1,000,000 to the National Playing Fields Association, is responding to a need to reverse the loss of recreation land and is enabling the Association to set up a Field's Fighting Fund. This aims to save playing fields from building development, to protect new fields, to campaign for the retention of school playing fields, to challenge the local planning process, to provide information and support to local communities and to ensure the Government has play, sport and recreation facilities high on its agenda.

The trustees' commitment to encouraging sport is also demonstrated by another grant to the Youth Sport Trust. A similar scheme to the Technology Colleges Trust initiative, this partnership between the government and the private sector ensures that qualifying schools can develop and implement quality sports programmes.

A £250,000 grant to the YMCA is contributing to the refurbishment of its forty bed housing project in Southampton. This brings the total provided to the YMCA in the last six years to £2,250,000 and demonstrates the trustees' support of this organisation's important work with disadvantaged young people. £250,000 is also donated to the Caldecott Foundation, which provides year round education and care for severely emotionally disturbed and disruptive children, plus aftercare for ex residents and specialist training for people working with children and young people.

Lodge Hill, formerly a Sussex County Council owned and run residential centre and camp site for schools, voluntary groups and community organisations, was at risk of closure when the Council put it on the market to raise capital for its school building programme. The Foundation contributed £200,000 to the newly formed Lodge Hill Trust and these facilities have now been rescued for continued use by young people in the area.

£50,000 has been donated to Merseyside Youth Association for acquiring and refurbishing a large disused building in central Liverpool as a centre for young people. This will provide a resource centre offering lifeskills training, information and advice, counselling, a health project, art, drama and music facilities.

As in previous years, a large number of small grants have been provided to various youth organisations and church groups throughout the UK who are working to eliminate disaffection and lack of motivation in young people.

Exclusions

The following excerpt is taken from the foundation's grant-making policy:

Support cannot be considered for organisations or groups which are not UK registered charities. Applications from individuals or for individual research or study or from organisations outside the UK cannot be considered. Animal welfare charities are also excluded.

Charities are asked not to apply within a 12-month period of an appeal to the foundation, whether or not they have received a grant.

Applications

To the administrator, including the following information:

1. The charity's registration number.
2. A copy of the most recent report and audited accounts.
3. An outline description of the charity's activities.
4. A synopsis of the project requiring funding, with details of who will benefit.
5. A financial plan.
6. Details of current and proposed fundraising.

All applications are considered on an individual basis by a committee of trustees. From time to time, more information about a charity or a visit to the project might be requested. There is no deadline for applications, which are normally processed within three months of receipt. All applicants will be notified of the outcome by letter.

Sir Richard Whittington's Charity

See entry for the Mercers' Company

The Will Charitable Trust

Environment/ conservation, cancer care, blindness, mental handicap

£967,000 (1998/99)

c/o Farrer & Co, 66 Lincoln's Inn Fields, London WC2A 3LH

Tel. 020 7242 2022

Correspondent Vanessa Reburn

Information available Annual report and accounts on file at the Charity Commission.

Summary

Support is provided for charities caring for people with cancer, blindness or having learning disabilities, and for environmental conservation. Most grants, in the charity's words, 'are made to substantial organisations having proven records of successful work in their fields of operation', namely to large national charities, and are typically in the form of regular annual subventions of £20,000 or more. One-off grants, usually for lesser amounts, more often go to local or county-wide organisations.

General

The trust describes its policy as to:

support organisations whose activities fall within the following categories:

a) Conservation of the countryside in Britain, including its flora and fauna
b) Care of blind people and the prevention and cure of blindness
c) Care of and services for people suffering from cancer and their families
d) The provision of residential care for mentally handicapped people in communities making a lifelong commitment to provide a family environment and the maximum choice of activities and lifestyles.

A proportion of the charity's income is devoted to assistance in other fields, but this is reserved for causes which have come to the attention of individual trustees and which the trustees regard as deserving. It is only in exceptional circumstances that the trustees will respond favourably to requests from organisations whose activities fall outside the categories listed above.

It is unlikely that applications relating to academic or research projects will be successful. The trustees recognise the importance of research, but lack the resources and expertise required to judge its relevance and value.

The charity's general administration and accountancy are carried out by a firm of accountants in which one of the trustees (Mr McDonald) is a partner, and which charged the sum of £27,738 for its services in 1998/99. A further £31,499 was paid to Farrer and Co. solicitors, from which the trust's chairman had recently retired as a consultant.

These editors always regret such arrangements, believing that it is both possible and preferable to find trustees and providers of services who have no connection with each other.

Following a £6 million legacy gift from the founder, grantmaking peaked at nearly £1.5 million in 1996/97. In the following year a £9 million capital grant was made to the associated Will Woodlands Trust, reducing the trust's assets to £22.8 million for 1998/99. By then grant expenditure was approaching a more natural level, from income of £952,000. Most of the 49 grants, totalling £967,000, went to regularly supported charities.

The following examples of grant recipients confirm the trust's statement that mainly 'substantial' organisations are supported, many of them being among the best known charities operating in their respective fields.

Woodland and other conservation (14 grants, £252,500)

The main beneficiaries were the Council for the Protection of Rural England (£40,000) and the Woodland Trust (£37,000). Grants for £25,000 were made to the British Trust for Conservation Volunteers, Lincolnshire Trust for Nature Conservation and Peterborough Cathedral Development and Preservation Trust.

Care of the blind, prevention of, or cure of blindness (13 grants, £235,000)

The largest grants went to the Royal National College for the Blind (£30,000); Royal National Institute for the Blind (£25,000) and the Royal Commonwealth Society for the Blind (£25,000).

Other beneficiaries not supported in the previous year included Fight for Sight (£15,000) and Worcestershire Association for the Blind (£15,000).

Sight Savers International, reportedly the only charity working overseas that the trust supports, received grants of £25,000 in each of the two previous years.

Care of mentally handicapped people (11 grants, £234,000)

The largest grant was for £35,000, to L'Arche. Three grants were for £25,000, to Camphill Village Trust, Care Fund and Home Farm Trust, and four went to organisations not supported in the previous year: Elizabeth Fitzroy Homes (£20,000); Lincolnshire House Association (£20,000); Robert Owen Foundation (£15,000), and Wirral Autistic Society (£9,000).

Care of cancer patients (8 grants, £200,000)

The main beneficiaries were Marie Curie Cancer Care (£50,000); Macmillan Cancer Relief (£40,000), and the British Association of Cancer United Patients and their Family and Friends (£25,000). The others included four hospices, only one having received a grant in the previous year.

Grants for other causes (3 grants, £45,000)

All were to regularly supported charities: Royal United Kingdom Beneficient Association (£30,000); National Association of Almshouses (£10,000), and King George's Fund for Sailors (£5,000).

Exclusions

See above. Grants are only given to registered charities.

Applications

In writing to the correspondent. If it is necessary to contact the grant office in Sunbury (which had a temporary address when this book went to press), ring 01932 724148.

There are no application forms. The trust normally distributes income twice yearly. Grants are made in March to organisations whose activities fall within categories (b) and (d) above and applications should be received by 31st January at the latest. Grants are made in October to organisations operating within categories (a) and (c) and applications should be received by 31st August at the latest.

The H D H Wills 1965 Charitable Trust

General (particularly preservation of wildlife, 2001–03)

£691,000 (1998/99)

Beneficial area UK and Ireland.

Henley Knapp Barn, Fulwell, Chipping Norton, Oxfordshire OX7 4EN

Tel. 01608 678051 **Fax** 01608 678052

e-mail willsct@ukonline.co.uk

Correspondent Wendy Cooper, Secretary

Information available Accounts on file at the Charity Commission. Further information was provided by the trust for this entry.

Summary

The trust runs three separate funds with a combined income of around £1 million. About £900,000 a year is disbursed in grants but in some years about 85% of this money must be donated to certain named charities. Unrestricted grants start at £100, are usually under £1,000 and peak at around £125,000. However, most of the large grants are to charities with a strong family connection.

General

The trust has been endowed by the family of Sir David Wills and had assets of more than £29 million in 1998/99. The three funds it operates are the Martin Wills Fund (partially restricted), the General Fund (unrestricted), and the Knockando Church Fund (restricted solely for the upkeep of this church in Morayshire and amounting to just £3,800 in 1998/99).

Donations from the General Fund are made for general charitable purposes, which have recently included substantial amounts to the Ditchley Foundation and the Sandford St Martin Trust, the latter having been formed by Sir David Wills to promote high standards in Christian religious broadcasting. Some 90% of grants made from this fund are for amounts of £500 or less, but most of the money is given in only one or two repeated large awards.

The income of the Martin Wills Fund is donated to the following institutions in seven-year cycles (starting April 1999):

1st year: Magdalen College, Oxford (1999/2000), a college at which many family members have been educated.

2nd year: Rendcomb College, Gloucestershire (2000/01), set up by Sir David Wills' father, Noel Hamilton Wills, in 1920 as a college for underprivileged Gloucestershire boys.

3rd and 4th years: Any registered charity dedicated or primarily dedicated to the preservation of wildlife (2001/02 and 2002/03), which was of particular interest to the late Martin Wills.

5th year: Ditchley Foundation (2003/04), which was set up by Sir David Wills in 1965 as a conference centre to discuss topics of mutual Anglo/American interest.

6th and 7th years: Charities at the trustees' discretion, being charities which reflect the trustees' particular interests (2004/05 and 2005/06).

Grants in 1998/99

Donations from the Martin Wills Fund totalled £600,000 and were made to:

Oxford University (Dr Jacoby's Project, £250,000); Ethox (£250,000); Martin Wills Memorial Fund (£50,000); St Martin's Benefice Trust (£20,000); Maidwell Hall School (£10,000); Care International (£10,000), and Marshall Sherfield Fellowship (£10,000).

Donations from the General Fund amounted to just £87,000, a low figure in relation to previous years (£108,000 in 1997/98; £360,000 in 1995/96). More than half of this went to the Central Board of Finance of the Church of England, in a grant of £50,000. Only three other beneficiaries got more than £1,000: Rendcomb College (£6,000 for students' fees); The Spey Research Trust (£5,000) and the University of Glasgow (Sir Fitzroy Maclean Scholarship Fund, £2,500).

Smaller grants went to 45 diverse beneficiaries, about a third having been previously supported, and ranged from £100 (for Fivemiletown Age Concern and St Francis Church Centre Play Group) to £1,000 (The Elgin Museum, Emergency Relief for Thoroughbreds and Sandford St Martin Parish Church Council Organ Fund).

Most grants were for £500, the beneficiaries including Crossroads Caring for Carers, Dream Holidays, English Chamber Orchestra and Music, The Family Nurturing Network, Farm Africa, GAP Activity Projects and the Guideposts Trust.

Exclusions

Individuals, national charities.

Grants to registered or 'recognised' charities only.

Applications

In writing to the correspondent. The trust considers small appeals monthly and large ones bi-annually from the Martin Wills Fund. Only one application from a given charity will be considered in any one 18 month period.

The Charles Wolfson Charitable Trust

Medical research, health, education, Jewish charities, general

£6,588,000 (1998/99)

Beneficial area UK, Israel.

c/o 129 Battenhall Road, Worcester
WR5 2BU

Correspondent Mrs Cynthia Margaret Crawford

Information available Report and accounts with full grants list but limited analysis and explanation of grants.

Summary

Around 40 payments are made a year for amounts from a few thousand pounds upwards. A single project may receive several million pounds spread over a number of years. A wide range of causes is supported, with the focus on medicine, education and general welfare. Somewhere around 20% of funds are allocated to Jewish charities. The trust says that it only makes annually recurrent grants for medically related research projects and does not fund running costs.

As only a small number of grants is made, it is likely that most projects will enjoy the personal interest of the trustees, and probably only a few are the result of unsolicited applications.

Background

The trust was set up by the late Charles Wolfson and his son (now Lord Wolfson of Sunningdale) jointly in 1960 with an endowment of shares in the family business, the Great Universal Stores.

Later, it was decided to invest most of the funds in commercial property, handled through the trust's associated charity Benesco Charity Ltd.

This charity says that it seeks to expend its income while preserving the value of its assets in real terms (though in practice the latter have grown greatly). The 1998/99 annual report includes an interesting paragraph on the charity's reasons for focusing on property investment as means of achieving these ends:

> After allowing for annual running costs and renewals and refurbishment the rental income over the years tends to keep pace with inflation, so long as the portfolio is well spread ... Also ... property income is received gross, unlike dividends from share portfolios which cause complications so far as administration and cash flow are concerned. Furthermore, repayment to charities of tax credits on dividends is in any case to be progressively phased out over the five years from April 1999.

These arguments seem strong and they are supported by dramatic long-term growth in the value of the endowment. However, the detail given, and the slightly defensive tone, suggests that there may have been some pressure on the charity from the Charity Commission, perhaps because of the extent of capital accumulation on which previous editions of these books have commented. In our 1989 edition, this charity appears as only 143rd in order of size of the major trusts! On the other hand the Commission sometimes appears unhappy with unconventional practices, no matter how successful, while often seeming less concerned about merely poor, but conventional, financial performance.

One of the trustees, John Franks, is a consultant with Chethams Solicitors, who were paid £294,000 in fees (at commercial rates) by the charity in 1998/99. These editors always regret payments to organisations with which trustees are connected, unless there are unusual and specific reasons, spelt out in the annual report, that make alternative arrangements unsuitable.

Grants policy

Grants are made in the following areas, usually for capital or fixed-term projects and with 'particular but not exclusive regard to the needs of the Jewish community':

- Medical research and facilities.
- Education, including grants for buildings and for short-term assistance with facilities for special needs.
- Welfare, including grants for both buildings and research.
- Ecology, including grants for research.

Though the trust makes interest-free loans and offers rent-free premises to some (unnamed) beneficiaries, 'direct grants of money constitute the major part' of its charitable activities.

'In the year to 5 April 1999, £6.6 million has been distributed by way of direct grants to operative charities. Major ongoing projects again included grants to King's Lynn and Wisbech Hospitals for building a day surgery centre (£2.1 million in the year), and to Royal West Sussex NHS Trust for the HS2000 Ward Information Project (£1.3 million).' The trust notes its commitment to the latter enterprising project, which went live in 1998 and was expected to need another £500,000 to reach completion. No reason is given for the support of the day surgery building at Wisbech. As it stands, this is an activity that would normally be seen as part of normal NHS investment.

Grants for identifiably Jewish causes accounted for about one sixth of the grants by value.

Looking at grants for the last two years together, almost all of the 25 grants with a readily identifiable location were in the south of England, usually London (the exceptions were £11,000 for the Edinburgh Hillel Committee and £5,000 for Age Concern Warwickshire).

The interest in ecology is limited, but in 1998/99 the sum of £55,000 was given to Kew Gardens.

The major grants in 1998/99, other than those reported above, were as follows (with 1997/98 figures in brackets):

MEDICAL RESEARCH AND FACILITIES (12 GRANTS)		
King's College Hospital (leukaemia research)	£268,000	(–)
Ben Gurion University	£121,000	(£119,000)
Worthing Hospital (ward information)	£94,000	(£344,000)
St Mary's Hospital (scanner)	£55,000	(–)
EDUCATION (17 GRANTS)		
Huntingdon Foundation	£550,000	(£780,000)
Oxford Centre for Hebrew Studies	£300,000	(£5,000)
Beth Jacob Teachers Seminary	£130,000	(–)
British Council	£100,000	(–)
Massoret Teacher Training College	£100,000	(–)
WELFARE (14 GRANTS)		
Jewish Blind Society	£250,000	(–)
Hillel Foundation	£62,000	(–)
Community Security trust	£25,000	(£25,000)
ECOLOGY (1 GRANT)		
British Friends for a Beautiful Israel	£5,000	(£5,000)

Exclusions

It is not the policy of the trust to make grants to individuals or to charities for running costs.

Applications

In writing to the correspondent. Grants are made in response to applications, and while all applications will be considered, the trustees cannot undertake to notify all unsuccessful applicants, because of the volume of appeals received.

The Wolfson Family Charitable Trust

Jewish charities

£3,062,000 (income, 1998/99)

Beneficial area Israel and UK.

8 Queen Anne Street, London W1M 9LD

Tel. 020 7323 5730 **Fax** 020 7323 3241

Correspondent Dr Victoria Harrison

Trustees *Lord Wolfson of Marylebone; Lady Wolfson; Janet Wolfson de Botton; Laura Wolfson Townsley; Martin Paisner; Sir Martin Gilbert; Prof. Barrie Jay; Prof. Sir Eric Ash; Sir Bernard Rix.*

Information available Annual reports and accounts.

Summary

This trust gives a relatively small number of often very large grants. Most of the money goes to organisations based in Israel. A high proportion of the trust's future income is already committed.

The trust shares offices and administration with the Wolfson Foundation, and an application to one may be considered by the other.

General

The trust reported its 1998/99 grantmaking under the following headings:

- Health and welfare
  - Hospitals
  - People with special needs
- Science and medical research
- Arts and humanities
- Education

Although over £8 million was committed in new grants in 1998/99, income was £3 million and this figure is a better guide to the resources of the charity. Because of the very large size of individual grants, actual levels of payment vary greatly from year to year.

Grantmaking in 1998/99 was described as follows:

Health and welfare (hospitals)

The trustees provided £1,885,000 over two years, with matched funding, for medical equipment for hospitals in Israel. The grants included £375,000 to 'the Hassadeh Medical Organisation to enlarge the Bone Marrow Transplantation Department, £450,000 to the Chaim Sheba Medical Centre to upgrade the magnetic resonance imaging system, £250,000 to the Rabin Medical Centre for operating theatres in the Department of Obstetrics and Gynaecology, £230,000 to the Edith Wolfson Medical Centre's Neonatal Intensive Care Department and £200,000 to the Shaare Zedek Medical Centre towards an operating theatre in the Woman and Infant Centre.

Health and welfare (people with special needs)

The Trustees continued their support for children with mental handicap by a grant of £150,000 for the modernisation programme of Ravenswood Village in Berkshire.

Science and medical research

Trustees contributed £1,750,000 (over four years) towards a new Centre for Computer and Software Engineering at Tel Aviv University. Further grants for laboratory refurbishment and equipment totalling £1,475,000 over four years were made to the Hebrew University of Jerusalem, Technion, Ben Gurion University and the Weizmann Institute.

Arts and humanities

The Trustees continued their support for the Israel Museum with a grant of £200,000 (over two years) towards the renovation of the European Art Galleries. A grant of £80,000 was made to the Council for a Beautiful Israel towards a garden in the city of Akko.

Education

A grant of £200,000 was made to the Hasmonean High School for Girls, London, for a new science and technology building. A grant of £1,500,000 (over four years) was made for an Information and Technology Program for university libraries in Israel.

Exclusions

Grants are not made to individuals.

Applications

The trust shares its application procedure with the Wolfson Foundation. A brief explanatory letter, with organisation and project details, including costs and current shortfalls, will cause an up to date set of guidelines to be sent, if the charity is able to consider the project concerned.

The Wolfson Foundation

Medical and scientific research, education, health and welfare, heritage, arts

£36,480,000 (1998/99)

Beneficial area Mainly UK.

8 Queen Anne Street, London W1G 9LD

Tel. 020 7323 5730 **Fax** 020 7323 3241

Correspondent Dr Victoria Harrison, Executive Secretary

Trustees *Lord Wolfson of Marylebone, Chair; Lady Wolfson; Mrs Janet Wolfson de Botton; Mrs Laura Wolfson Townsley; Prof. Sir Eric Ash; Lord McColl; Lord Quinton; Lord Quirk; Sir Derek Roberts; Prof. Lord Turnberg; Prof. Sir David Weatherall.*

Information available Basic annual report and accounts. Guidelines for applicants available after an initial outline submission of the project concerned.

Summary

Grants for buildings and equipment in three major areas:

- Medical and healthcare, especially the prevention of disease and the care and treatment of sick, disadvantaged and disabled people.
- Science, technology and education, particularly where the benefits may accrue to the development of industry, commerce and teaching in the UK.
- Arts and the humanities, including libraries, museums, galleries, the visual arts and historic buildings.

Grants can be very large; few are for amounts of less than £5,000.

Background

With assets of £600 million and an income in 1998/99 of £40 million, this is one of the largest trusts in Britain. It derives its endowment from the fortune created by Sir Isaac Wolfson through the wonderfully named Great Universal Stores. It has long been known for major projects in universities and medical schools, though its grants have always been spread more widely than this. The foundation shares its very lean administration with the Wolfson Family Charitable Trust, with which it 'has shared objectives' (see separate entry). Little is publicly known about how the foundation's programmes and policies are determined.

There are two separate strands to the foundation's work.

The largest strand is concerned with scientific and medical research and education. The other strand has interests in health and welfare, heritage and the arts.

Overall, the information available about the work of this big institution, though it meets and even, on occasion exceeds, legal requirements, falls short of what may be reasonably expected from public charities of its size, not least in making itself accountable for the perhaps £5 million a year or so of public subsidy that it receives through its charitable tax reliefs. In particular, though it may exist, there is little visible sign of the level of policy development that would be expected in order to meet the needs of the fast changing environment in which it operates.

General

The foundation is unusual in that it generally makes grants for buildings and equipment, and does not normally support the widely funded 'projects' let alone regular salaries or running costs.

The following account of its policies and practices is from the 1998/99 annual report:

The Wolfson Foundation is a charitable foundation set up in 1955, whose aims were stated by the founder trustees to be the advancement of health, education, the arts and the humanities. These remain the aims of the trustees today. As a general policy, grants are given to act as a catalyst, to back excellence and talent and to provide support for promising future projects which may currently be underfunded, particularly for renovation and equipment. There is a continued emphasis on science and technology, research, education, health and the arts. Trustees meet twice a year and are advised by panels comprising trustees and specialists which meet before the main board meetings.

Priorities, which are described in this report [*apparently a reference to the list of grants. Ed.*] include the renovation of historic buildings, libraries, support for preventive medicine, programmes for people with special needs, and education. Grants are made to universities for student accommodation, equipment for scientific research, new buildings and renovations. Awards for university research are normally made under the umbrella of designated programmes in which vice-chancellors and principals are invited to participate.

THE WOLFSON FOUNDATION – GRANTS IN 1997/98 AND 1998/99 (COMBINED VALUE)		
Research and technology	£27.6 million	50%
Health and welfare	£12.3 million	23%
Arts and humanities	£12 million	22%
Education	£2.5 million	5%

The combined value of grants for the two years 1997/98 and 1998/99 is shown in the box above.

Though still unequally distributed, by the standards of other 'national' trusts grants are relatively well spread throughout England. In 1998/99 there were 176 geographically identifiable grants. If England is divided into two halves of equal population, 107 of these fell in the southern half and 69 in the northern half. There were a substantial number of grants to Scottish organisations, but, as usual, Wales and Northern Ireland seem seriously under-represented.

Specific grant programmes

As referred to above, the foundation has a number of specific grant programmes (though not just in the research field). These probably account for between a quarter and a third of the grant total.

Information about the individual programmes is said to be available to university vice-chancellors and other organisations such as museums, public libraries or the hospice movement. It is not available to the public (who are in part paying for these programmes), either through the Charity Commission files or on direct request. This is, so far as these editors are aware, the only major trust described in this book where such information is withheld from the public view.

Identified programmes include the following:

- Laboratory refurbishment programme (with the Royal Society).
  This programme will be worth £10 million over four years from 1998/99. There will apparently be different subject areas each year, starting in 1998/99 with information technology applied to medicine and biotechnology. A total of 17 university laboratories were supported, but the amounts were not disclosed. In the previous year there had been an even more extensive series of laboratory grants, apparently outside the Royal Society partnered programme, with 69 grants worth £7 million. Most of these awards, whose value was disclosed, were for amounts between £100,000 and £150,000.
- Wolfson – Dorothy Hodgkin Fellowships (with the Royal Society).
  Fellowships for three post-doctoral scientists, for three years from 1998/99.
- University library programme.
  'The trustees decided to establish Wolfson Technology Resource Centres attached to the libraries of selected universities. Nine grants were made totalling £450,000 to facilitate students' access to databases for science, technology and medicine.' It is not clear whether this programme continues.
- Public library programme (a 'challenge fund' with the Department of Culture, Media and Sport).
  In 1998/99 this programme was extended 'for another two years'.
- Medical education programme, for intercalated training. There were 18 grants to universities and medical schools, worth £161,000, under this apparently ongoing programme, each for between £3,000 and £25,000.
- Heritage programme.
  The Heritage Lottery Fund said, in the summer of 1999, that this programme was now coming to an end. The 1998/99 annual report noted: 'The foundation maintained its partnership with the Heritage Lottery Fund under which applicants might apply to both bodies with a shared assessment process.' Projects supported appear to be all for capital expenditures. There were nine awards totalling £3,725,000 in 1998/99, including £2 million to the Victoria and Albert Museum towards the refurbishment of its British Galleries (1500–1900) and £1.3 million to the Tate Gallery.

Other beneficiaries included the Black Country Living Museum in Dudley (£150,000 for refurbishment), the Fleet Air Arm Museum (£75,000) and the Tooley Boatyard Museum in Banbury (£50,000).

In the previous year the major beneficiaries had been the National Portrait Gallery in London (£500,000) and the Bodleian Library in Oxford (£300,000).

- Secondary schools building programme.
  Only one grant in 1998/99 (£50,000 for the library at King's School, Ely), and three grants the previous year, headed by £25,000 for Liverpool College.
- Secondary schools equipment programme.
  This is either mainly or entirely for the provision of IT equipment, with £1.28 million being given in 1998/99 to 47 secondary schools in amounts ranging from £10,000 to £40,000.

Grants outside specific programmes (1998/99)

These are listed and categorised in the annual report, and account for between two thirds and three quarters of the value of grants. There is normally no information given about the purposes of the individual grants, nor of the policies that lie behind them, nor about their geographical distribution, nor about the numbers of applications received.

However, information has been made available about assessment procedures. There are three panels which meet on a regular basis to cover:

- science and medicine
- arts and humanities
- education

The panels include trustees (the majority) and individuals with relevant expertise. They make recommendations to the trustees as a whole. References are always taken up and applications for all projects are subject to peer review or other expert assessment.

There are two trustee meetings a year, at each of which about 50 grant 'non-programme' decisions are made, from an unknown number of applications (apart from the other business of the foundation). The foundation only employs four staff and part time advisers, a remarkably small number, so it is impressive that more than one recipient has remarked on the thoroughness with which the detail of their building project was addressed.

Health and welfare

Preventive medicine and clinical research: Six grants amounted to £6,925,000. Of this, £6,000,000 went to the associated Wolfson Centre for Age-related Diseases at King's College, London. Other awards were to St Mary's Hospital, London (£250,000 for a paediatric accident and emergency project), and to the Wolfson Laboratory at the Centre for Urological Cancers at the Institute for Cancer Research in London (£250,000).

Hospices: A total of £353,000 went to 12 hospices, with £50,000 each for hospices in Birmingham, Southampton and Harrow.

People with special needs: 24 organisations benefited from awards amounting to £786,000. Much the largest was to Manchester's Jewish Home for the Aged (£190,000). Other major beneficiaries included St Mary's Convent, Chiswick and the Coram Foundation, London (£50,000 each); Bromley Autistic Trust (£40,000); Cornwall Blind Association (£23,000); Wilberforce Home, York (£20,000), and Berkshire Multiple Sclerosis Therapy Centre (£13,000). The smallest grant was for £5,000, to Support for People with Alzheimers, Bath.

Arts and humanities

National Art Collections Fund: £300,000 over three years, for acquisitions.

Performing arts: £10,000 for two vans for English National Ballet.

Historic buildings: 20 grants totalling £107,000. All but three were to cathedrals and churches. Two of the former, St Albans and Peterborough, received £25,000 each. None of the churches got more than £5,000.

Archives and related research: Three grants totalling £20,000, led by £10,000 for the Wiener Library in London to modernise its photographic archive.

Literary award for history: Last year the two awards of £10,000 each went to John Brewer for his The Pleasures of the Imagination and to Patricia Hollis for her life of Jennie Lee.

Education

Higher education: Three grants totalled £125,000, led by £100,000 for the London Business School to refurbish seminar rooms.

Student accommodation: There were three grants totalling £656,000, led by £500,000 to refurbish the Wolfson Hall of Residence at Glasgow University.

Learned societies: £80,000 was paid out in awards to two Royal Colleges.

Music: £84,000 was disbursed in seven donations, four of them for instruments to colleges of music and three to other bodies: the Prince's Youth Business Trust (£30,000); the Lakelands School, Ellesmere, and the Scout Association (£15,000 each).

Exclusions

Grants are not made to individuals.

The trustees do not make grants for:

- Overheads, running or administrative costs, VAT or professional fees.
- Non-specific appeals (including circulars), endowment funds or conduit organisations.
- Costs of meetings, exhibitions, concerts, expeditions, etc.
- The purchase of land.
- Research involving live animals.
- Films or video production.

Applications

Prospective applicants should ascertain their project's eligibility by submitting in writing a brief outline of the project with one copy of the organisation's most recent audited accounts for the previous two years.

If appropriate, they will then be informed of what further information is needed.

The Woodward Charitable Trust

General

£660,000 (approved, 1999)

See the entry for the Sainsbury Charitable Trusts

Tel. 020 7410 0330 **Fax** 020 7410 0332

website www.woodwardcharitabletrust.org.uk

Correspondent Michael Pattison, Director

Trustees *Camilla Woodward; Shaun Woodward MP; Miss Judith Portrait.*

Information available Annual report, with full listing of grants.

Summary

This is one of the Sainsbury Family Charitable Trusts which share a joint administration. Unusually for a trust in this group, it gives a large number of small grants under £10,000 to organisations working in a wide range of activities, but most frequently for social welfare causes.

This element of the trust's work may, though, be decreasing in importance. Unusually, there is an open application form available from the correspondent. As such applications are only considered twice a year, a response may take some time.

Each year a small number of larger, often capital, grants are made, but these are for causes of which the trustees have personal knowledge (and in the working of which they may, in this editor's experience, take a continuing personal interest).

General

This is the trust of Camilla, née Sainsbury, and of her husband, Shaun Woodward, at the time of writing the newly-Labour MP for Witney in Oxfordshire. The charity became part of the Sainsbury Family Charitable Trust joint administration in 1997, before which it was directly managed by the trustees.

Uncharacteristically for one of the newer Sainsbury foundations, the largest single grant, of £174,000, was to the Royal Opera House, a favoured cause of some of the older trusts in the group.

There appears to be a minor local interest in Oxfordshire, where the Woodwards live and of part of which Shaun Woodward is the MP, with grants for Oxfordshire Motor Project, the Oxfordshire County History, the Dragon School Trust, Mulberry Bush School and perhaps the All Saints Millennium Project in Churchill (there are similarly named villages elsewhere).

The trust had a net income in 1998/99 of £566,000, deriving almost entirely from its holding of shares in J Sainsbury plc. Divestment of about 1% of this holding in 1997/98 was not repeated the following year.

A total of 117 grants was approved in 1998/99, totalling £660,000. Grants paid (as opposed to approved) during the year were analysed as shown in the box below.

The trustees described their policies as follows in the 1998/99 annual report:

THE WOODWARD CHARITABLE TRUST – GRANTS PAID IN 1998/99

	1998/99		1997/98	
	Value	No.	Value	No.
Arts	£199,000	10	£70,000	5
Disability and health	£148,000	45	£48,000	21
Community and social welfare	£135,000	47	£175,000	45
Education	£69,000	13	£52,000	10
Environment	£30,000	10	£30,000	4
Overseas	nil	–	£6,000	2
Total	£582,000	125	£382,000	87

The trustees give priority to a few charitable causes of which they have personal knowledge. In addition they make a limited number of small grants in response to selected appeals in their fields of interest. These grants are usually of £1,000 or less in each case and rarely more than £5,000. The trustees prefer to make one-off grants for specified purposes and they are generally unable to provide any form of recurrent core funding. They will, however, consider subsequent appeals from previous beneficiaries for further specific purposes.

Unsolicited applications within the trustees' selected categories and not covered by the exclusions (below) will be considered with care, but there are limited funds for such appeals. The trustees expect to make around 100 grants each year but receive many times this number of applications.

Trustees strongly favour smaller-scale, locally based initiatives.

Trustees will only consider applications made on the Trust's own form and returned with the latest annual report and audited accounts. Potential applicants are encouraged to telephone to discuss their work if they think it might meet the trustees' criteria.

Application forms will be sent where the Trust's staff believe the trustees will be able to consider a proposal, but the trustees are keen to spare charities the wasted time involved in applying when there is no prospect of success. Trustees review applications twice a year, usually in January and July.

Grants in 1998/99

Arts

Seven grants, dominated by £174,000 for the Royal Opera House. No other grant was larger than the £7,000 for Bath Festivals Trust.

Disability and health

There were 30 grants for more than £1,000, led by £25,000 for the Mulberry Bush School (a special school in Witney, Oxfordshire, and one of the year's major fundraising successes), £20,000 for the National Autistic Society (also supported by other trusts in the Sainsbury group) and £10,000 for Sense. There were 14 grants for smaller amounts.

Community and social welfare

There were 29 grants for amounts over £1,000 and 14 for lesser amounts. The major beneficiaries were Noah's Ark Children's Venture (£28,000), Youth Sport Trust, Edinburgh Family Service Unit and the International Centre for Missing and Exploited Children (£10,000 each).

Education

There were 10 grants, led by £25,000 for the Dragon School Trust (a fee-paying school in Oxford) and £15,000 for the Trialogue Educational Trust.

Environment

Three grants, including £10,000 for All Saints Millennium Project, Churchill, and £8,000 for the Marine Stewardship Council (also supported in the previous year).

Exclusions

- Standard appeals.
- General appeals from large national charities.
- Requests for small contributions to large appeals.
- Medical research.
- Individuals.
- Student support.
- Course fees.
- Expedition costs.

Applications

On application forms available from the trust, when trust staff consider an application may be appropriate. Potential applicants are invited to telephone Karin MacLeod in advance to discuss the advisability of making an application.

The Zochonis Charitable Trust

General, especially Greater Manchester

£1,007,000 (1997/98)

Beneficial area UK, particularly Greater Manchester, and overseas, particularly Africa.

Cussons House, Bird Hall Lane, Stockport SK3 0XN

Correspondent The Secretary

Trustees *John Zochonis, Richard B James; Alan Whittaker.*

Information available Report and accounts.

Summary

Grants are typically one-off and range from £500 to £150,000, but are most often for around £5,000. They go to a range of national charities or local beneficiaries in Manchester. About half of the grants, but most of those over £20,000 (and therefore most of the money) go to local organisations, particularly educational or arts institutions.

Organisations working in developing countries are also supported.

General

The trust's assets amounted to £21 million in 1997/98, producing an income of £983,000. The trust made 75 grants totalling over £1 million, with a third going to the following three beneficiaries in Manchester:

- Withington Girls' School (£150,000)
- Manchester University (£100,000)
- Cheetham's School of Music (£100,000)

Other local beneficiaries receiving substantial awards included: Greater Manchester Shrievalty Trust (£50,000; £25,000 in 1996/97); Trafford Park Institute (£30,000); Manchester Grammar School (£30,000), and Manchester YMCA (£22,500).

Arts beneficiaries included Opera North (£5,000) and Patrons of Manchester City Art Gallery (£2,500).

Other recipients included the Trust Fund for the Greek Orthodox Church (£30,000) and health and welfare charities mainly assisting children and sick or disabled people, including Adventure Farm Trust (£25,000); Macmillan Cancer Research (£25,000); Princess Royal Trust for Carers (£15,000; £20,000 in 1996/97); Motability North West (£5,000); Sue Ryder Foundation (£5,000); Barnardos (£5,000); Delamere Toys and Tapes Library (£5,000); SSAFA Forces Help (£2,500); Liverpool Voluntary Society for the Blind (£1,500).

A significant number of grants were for assistance to developing countries, especially in Africa, as follows:

VSO (£40,000; £70,000 in 1996/97); Africa Centres (£15,000); Royal African Society (£5,000); Rhodes Foundation Scholarship Trust (£5,000); Sight Savers International (£5,000, repeat); Liverpool School of Tropical Medicine (£5,000).

Exclusions

No grants for individuals.

Applications

In writing to the secretary by registered charities only.

Subject index

The following subject index begins with a list of the categories used. The categories are very wide-ranging to keep the index as simple as possible. *The Grant-making Trusts CD-ROM* has a much more detailed search facility on the categories. There may be considerable overlap between some of these categories – for example, children and education, or older people and social/moral welfare.

The list of categories is followed by the index itself. Before using the index, please note the following.

How the index was compiled

1. The index aims to reflect the most recently recorded grant-making practice. It is therefore based on our interpretation of what each trust has actually given to, rather than what its policy statement says or its charitable objects allow it to do in principle. For example, where a trust states it has general charitable purposes, but its grants list shows a strong preference for welfare, we index it under welfare.
2. We have tried to ensure that each trust has given significantly in the areas where it is indexed (usually at least £15,000). Thus small, apparently untypical grants have been ignored for index purposes.
3. The index has been compiled from the latest information available to us.

Limitations

1. Policies may change.
2. Sometimes there will be a geographical restriction on a trust's grantgiving which is not shown up in this index, or a trust may not give for the specific purposes you require under that heading. It is important to read each entry carefully. You will need to check:

(a) The trust gives in your geographical area of operation.

(b) The trust gives for the specific purposes you require.

(c) There is no other reason to prevent you making an application to this trust.

3. We have omitted the General category as the number of trusts included would make it unusable. It is also worth noting that some of the categories, such as social/moral welfare, list over half the trusts included in this guide.

Under no circumstances should the index be used as a simple mailing list. Remember that each trust is different and that often the policies or interests of a particular trust do not fit easily into the given categories. Each entry must be read individually and carefully before you send off an application. Indiscriminate applications are usually unsuccessful. They waste time and money and greatly annoy trusts.

The categories are as follows:

Agriculture *page 338*

Arts and culture *page 338*

A very wide category including performing, written and visual arts, theatres, museums and galleries.

Children *page 339*

Mainly for welfare and welfare-related activities. (See below for young people.)

Disadvantaged people *page 339*

This includes people who are:

- socially excluded
- socially and economically disadvantaged
- unemployed
- homeless
- offenders
- educationally disadvantaged
- victims of social/natural occcurences, including refugees and asylum seekers

Economics, commerce, business *page 340*

This includes:

- enterprise, regeneration
- labour, employment, unemployment
- finance

Education and training *page 340*

Environment and animals *page 341*

This includes:

- education and research
- natural resources and ecology
- regeneration and development
- access to the countryside
- preservation of the environment, including buildings
- heritage

Geography and foreign links *page 341*

This includes:

- travel expeditions and exploration
- life/language of other countries
- industrial/economic links with other countries.

Ill or disabled people *page 341*

This includes people who are ill, or who have physical or mental disabilities, or learning difficulties, or mental health problems.

Manufacturing industry and services *page 342*

Medicine and health *page 342*

This excludes medical research, which is listed separately.

Medical research page 343

Older people ***page 344***

Philosophy ***page 344***

This includes concern about values and attitudes, spiritual/personal growth and philosophies of particular individuals.

Political and policy issues ***page 344***

This includes:

- government and policy issues
- world policy issues, including third world development
- conflict resolution
- rights, justice and equality
- legal matters

Religion general ***page 344***

Mainly ecumenical or inter-faith work, or where a trust gives grants to more than one faith.

Christianity page 344

This includes grants to churches, for Christian work and causes and for missionary work in the UK and overseas.

Judaism page 345

Masons page 345

Science ***page 345***

Social and moral welfare ***page 345***

This is a very broad category, including:

- counselling and advice
- community organisations and development
- community care
- accommodation
- human relationships
- crime and punishment

Sport and recreation ***page 346***

Technology, including engineering ***page 346***

This includes intermediate and alternative technologies, communications and information technology.

Voluntary sector management and development ***page 346***

Young people ***page 347***

Agriculture

Childwick Trust 47
Ernest Cook Trust 70
Fishmongers' Company's Charitable Trust 98
Gatsby Charitable Foundation 100
Headley Trust 134
J J Charitable Trust 146
MacRobert Trusts 208
Mr and Mrs J A Pye's Charitable Settlement 248
Rowan Charitable Trust 260

Arts and culture

29th May 1961 Charitable Trust 1
Arbib Foundation 6
Lord Ashdown Charitable Settlement 9
Band Trust 12
Baring Foundation 14
Audrey & Stanley Burton Charitable Trust 32
William Adlington Cadbury Charitable Trust 33
Carnegie United Kingdom Trust 39
Charities Advisory Trust 43
CHK Charities Limited 48
Clore and Duffield Foundations 56
Clothworkers' Foundation 59
Ernest Cook Trust 70
Cripplegate Foundation 71
D'Oyly Carte Charitable Trust 74
Djanogly Foundation 80
Drapers' Company Charities 80
John Ellerman Foundation 88
Eranda Foundation 92
Esmée Fairbairn Charitable Trust 93
Hugh Fraser Foundation 99
Gannochy Trust 100
Gatsby Charitable Foundation 100
Robert Gavron Charitable Trust 104
J Paul Getty Jr Charitable Trust 105
Glass-House Trust 108
Goldsmiths' Company's Charities 110
Great Britain Sasakawa Foundation 113
Gulbenkian Foundation 118
Paul Hamlyn Foundation 125
Charles Hayward Foundation 131
Headley Trust 134
Horne Foundation 143
Jerwood Charitable Foundation 149
Graham Kirkham Foundation 162
Sir James Knott Trust 163
Kreitman Foundation 165
Kirby Laing Foundation 168
Laing's Charitable Trust 172
Lankelly Foundation 178
Leathersellers' Company Charitable Fund 182
Lord Leverhulme's Charitable Trust 187
Linbury Trust 188
Lloyds TSB Foundation for England and Wales 191
John Lyon's Charity 205
Mackintosh Foundation 207
MacRobert Trusts 208
Manifold Trust 209
Mercers' Company Charities 212
Monument Trust 215
Henry Moore Foundation 216
Peter Moores Foundation 219
National Art Collections Fund 220
National Lottery 221
Network Foundation 223
P F Charitable Trust 237
Pilgrim Trust 241
Porter Foundation 244
Mr and Mrs J A Pye's Charitable Settlement 248
Ruben and Elisabeth Rausing Trust 254
Rayne Foundation 255
Robertson Trust 257
Rose Foundation 259
Raymond & Beverley Sackler Foundation 271
Alan and Babette Sainsbury Charitable Fund 271
Robert and Lisa Sainsbury Trust 277
Basil Samuel Charitable Trust 277
Save and Prosper Charities 277
Francis C Scott Charitable Trust 279
Archie Sherman Charitable Trust 283
Spitalfields Market Community Trust 292
Foundation for Sport and the Arts 294
Steel Charitable Trust 296
Stevenson Family's Charitable Trust 297
Bernard Sunley Charitable Foundation 301
Trusthouse Charitable Foundation 310
Wates Foundation 318
Weinstock Fund 320
Welton Foundation 322
Westminster Foundation 322
Garfield Weston Foundation 324
Charles Wolfson Charitable Trust 330
Wolfson Family Charitable Trust 331
Wolfson Foundation 332
Woodward Charitable Trust 334

Children

29th May 1961 Charitable Trust 1
Al Fayed Charitable Foundation 3
H B Allen Charitable Trust 4
Lord Ashdown Charitable Settlement 9
Band Trust 12
David and Frederick Barclay Foundation 13
BBC Children in Need Appeal 19
John Beckwith Charitable Settlement 22
Bedford Charity 22
Camelia Botnar Foundation 25
Bridge House Estates Trust Fund 26
William Adlington Cadbury Charitable Trust 33
Church Urban Fund 49
Clore and Duffield Foundations 56
Clothworkers' Foundation 59
Community Foundation Network 67
Cripplegate Foundation 71
D'Oyly Carte Charitable Trust 74
Baron Davenport's Charity 76
10th Duke of Devonshire's Charitable Trust 77
Diana, Princess of Wales Memorial Fund 77
E B M Charitable Trust 86
Maud Elkington Charitable Trust 87
John Ellerman Foundation 88
Equitable Charitable Trust 91
Eveson Charitable Trust 92
Donald Forrester Trust 99
Gatsby Charitable Foundation 100
Robert Gavron Charitable Trust 104
Gosling Foundation 111
Greggs Trust 116
Gulbenkian Foundation 118
Peter Harrison Foundation 129
Charles Hayward Foundation 131
Headley Trust 134
Help a London Child 136
Alan Edward Higgs Charity 139
Reta Lila Howard Foundation 144
Albert Hunt Trust 144
Kirby Laing Foundation 168
Maurice Laing Foundation 169
Beatrice Laing Trust 170
J W Laing Trust 171
Leathersellers' Company Charitable Fund 182
Levy Foundation 187
George John Livanos Charitable Trust 191
Lloyds TSB Foundation for England and Wales 191
John Lyon's Charity 205
Mackintosh Foundation 207
Jim Marshall Charitable Trust 210
Northern Rock Foundation 226
Nuffield Foundation 233
Parthenon Trust 238
Pilkington Charities Fund 243
PPP Healthcare Medical Trust 245
Mr and Mrs J A Pye's Charitable Settlement 248
Rank Foundation 251
Rayne Foundation 255
Rose Foundation 259
Basil Samuel Charitable Trust 277
Ayrton Senna Foundation 282
SHINE (Support and Help In Education) 284
Smith's Charity 284
Sobell Foundation 289
South Yorkshire Community Foundation 291
Tedworth Trust 306
John and Lucille van Geest Foundation 315
Bernard Van Leer Foundation (UK) Trust 315
Variety Club of Great Britain 317
Weinstock Fund 320
Woodward Charitable Trust 334
Zochonis Charitable Trust 335

Disadvantaged people

29th May 1961 Charitable Trust 1
AIM Foundation 2
Alchemy Foundation 3
H B Allen Charitable Trust 4
Ashden Charitable Trust 7
Baring Foundation 14
Bedford Charity 22
William Adlington Cadbury Charitable Trust 33
Edward Cadbury Charitable Trust 34
Barrow Cadbury Trust 34
Sir John Cass's Foundation 41
Charities Advisory Trust 43
Charities Aid Foundation 43
Church Urban Fund 49
City Parochial Foundation 51
Clothworkers' Foundation 59
Richard Cloudesley's Charity 62
Sir James Colyer-Fergusson's Charitable Trust 63
Comic Relief 64
Community Foundation (Tyne & Wear and Northumberland) 68
Ernest Cook Trust 70
Diana, Princess of Wales Memorial Fund 77
Drapers' Company Charities 80
John Ellerman Foundation 88
Eveson Charitable Trust 92
Esmée Fairbairn Charitable Trust 93
Fishmongers' Company's Charitable Trust 98
Hugh Fraser Foundation 99
Gatsby Charitable Foundation 100
J Paul Getty Jr Charitable Trust 105
Goldsmiths' Company's Charities 110
Grand Charity of Freemasons 112
Greater Bristol Foundation 114
Constance Green Foundation 115
Greggs Trust 116
H C D Memorial Fund 122
Hact (The Housing Associations Charitable Trust) 123
Hadley Trust 124
Paul Hamlyn Foundation 125
Hampton Fuel Allotment Charity 127
Peter Harrison Foundation 129
Charles Hayward Foundation 131
Help a London Child 136
Hilden Charitable Fund 139
Jane Hodge Foundation 142
Horne Foundation 143
J J Charitable Trust 146
King's Fund 157
Laing Family Foundations 167
Allen Lane Foundation 176
Lankelly Foundation 178
Law Society Charity 182
Leathersellers' Company Charitable Fund 182
William Leech Charity 183
Enid Linder Foundation 191
Lloyds TSB Foundation for England and Wales 191
Lloyds TSB Foundation for Northern Ireland 199
Lloyds TSB Foundation for Scotland 200
Mackintosh Foundation 207
Mercers' Company Charities 212
John Moores Foundation 217
National Lottery Charities Board 221
Network Foundation 223
North British Hotel Trust 224
Northern Ireland Voluntary Trust 225
Nuffield Foundation 233
Parthenon Trust 238
Peabody Community Fund 238
Pilgrim Trust 241
Pilkington Charities Fund 243
Sir James Reckitt Charity 255
Mrs L D Rope Third Charitable Settlement 258
Rowan Charitable Trust 260
Joseph Rowntree Charitable Trust 261
Save and Prosper Charities 277
Francis C Scott Charitable Trust 279
Smith's Charity 284

South Yorkshire Community Foundation 291
Sir Halley Stewart Trust 297
W O Street Charitable Foundation 300
Three Guineas Trust 309
Triangle Trust 309
Tudor Trust 311
Waterside Trust 318
Wates Foundation 318

Economics, commerce, business

Charities Aid Foundation 43
CHK Charities Limited 48
Church Urban Fund 49
Cleveland Community Foundation 56
Community Foundation (Tyne & Wear and Northumberland) 68
Dulverton Trust 81
Gatsby Charitable Foundation 100
J Paul Getty Jr Charitable Trust 105
Isle of Dogs Community Foundation 146
Lloyds TSB Foundation for England and Wales 191
Northern Ireland Voluntary Trust 225
Northern Rock Foundation 226
Rowan Charitable Trust 260
Joseph Rowntree Charitable Trust 261
Spitalfields Market Community Trust 292
Tudor Trust 311
Wates Foundation 318
Wolfson Foundation 332

Education and training

29th May 1961 Charitable Trust 1
Lord Ashdown Charitable Settlement 9
Band Trust 12
Baring Foundation 14
John Beckwith Charitable Settlement 22
Bedford Charity 22
Boltons Trust 24
Booth Charities 25
Camelia Botnar Foundation 25
Audrey & Stanley Burton Charitable Trust 32
William Adlington Cadbury Charitable Trust 33
Edward Cadbury Charitable Trust 34
Campden Charities 38
Sir John Cass's Foundation 41
Childwick Trust 47
CHK Charities Limited 48
Church Urban Fund 49
City Parochial Foundation 51
Cleveland Community Foundation 56
Clore and Duffield Foundations 56
Clothworkers' Foundation 59
Ernest Cook Trust 70
Cripplegate Foundation 71
Cripps Foundation 73
D'Oyly Carte Charitable Trust 74
Roald Dahl Foundation 75
10th Duke of Devonshire's Charitable Trust 77
Djanogly Foundation 80
Drapers' Company Charities 80
Dulverton Trust 81
Sir John Eastwood Foundation 86
Equitable Charitable Trust 91
Eranda Foundation 92
Esmée Fairbairn Charitable Trust 93
Fishmongers' Company's Charitable Trust 98
Hugh Fraser Foundation 99
Gannochy Trust 100
Gatsby Charitable Foundation 100
G C Gibson Charitable Trust 107
Goldsmiths' Company's Charities 110
Grand Charity of Freemasons 112
Greater Bristol Foundation 114
Greggs Trust 116
Gulbenkian Foundation 118
H C D Memorial Fund 122
Paul Hamlyn Foundation 125
Hampton Fuel Allotment Charity 127
Philip and Pauline Harris Charitable Trust 129
Maurice Hatter Foundation 131
Charles Hayward Foundation 131
Headley Trust 134
Hedley Foundation 136
Help a London Child 136
Jane Hodge Foundation 142
Horne Foundation 143
Reta Lila Howard Foundation 144
J J Charitable Trust 146
John James Bristol Foundation 147
Jerwood Charitable Foundation 149
Ian Karten Charitable Trust 155
Graham Kirkham Foundation 162
Sir James Knott Trust 163
Kreitman Foundation 165
Laing Family Foundations 167
J W Laing Trust 171
Laing's Charitable Trust 172
Lambeth Endowed Charities 172
Allen Lane Foundation 176
Lankelly Foundation 178
Leathersellers' Company Charitable Fund 182
Leverhulme Trust 186
Lord Leverhulme's Charitable Trust 187
Lewis Family Charitable Trust 188
Linbury Trust 188
Lloyds TSB Foundation for England and Wales 191
Lloyds TSB Foundation for Northern Ireland 199
Lloyds TSB Foundation for Scotland 200
John Lyon's Charity 205
Mackintosh Foundation 207
MacRobert Trusts 208
Medlock Charitable Trust 211
Mercers' Company Charities 212
John Moores Foundation 217
Peter Moores Foundation 219
Nuffield Foundation 233
P F Charitable Trust 237
Parthenon Trust 238
Dowager Countess Eleanor Peel Trust 240
Pilgrim Trust 241
Porter Foundation 244
Mr and Mrs J A Pye's Charitable Settlement 248
Rank Foundation 251
Rayne Foundation 255
Sir James Reckitt Charity 255
Robertson Trust 257
Rose Foundation 259
Rowan Charitable Trust 260
Alan and Babette Sainsbury Charitable Fund 271
Robert and Lisa Sainsbury Trust 277
Basil Samuel Charitable Trust 277
Save and Prosper Charities 277
Francis C Scott Charitable Trust 279
Ayrton Senna Foundation 282
SHINE (Support and Help In Education) 284
South Yorkshire Community Foundation 291
Southover Manor General Education Trust 292
Spitalfields Market Community Trust 292
W O Street Charitable Foundation 300
Bernard Sunley Charitable Foundation 301
Sutton Coldfield Municipal Charities 303
Sutton Trust 304
Tompkins Foundation 309
Trusthouse Charitable Foundation 310
Tudor Trust 311
Underwood Trust 314
Vardy Foundation 316

Sir Siegmund Warburg's Voluntary Settlement 317
Wates Foundation 318
Weinstock Fund 320
Westminster Foundation 322
Garfield Weston Foundation 324
Charles Wolfson Charitable Trust 330
Wolfson Foundation 332
Zochonis Charitable Trust 335

Environment and animals

29th May 1961 Charitable Trust 1
AIM Foundation 2
Allchurches Trust 4
Arbib Foundation 6
Architectural Heritage Fund 6
Ashden Charitable Trust 7
Bridge House Estates Trust Fund 26
William Adlington Cadbury Charitable Trust 33
Carnegie United Kingdom Trust 39
Childwick Trust 47
CHK Charities Limited 48
Church Urban Fund 49
Clore and Duffield Foundations 56
Clothworkers' Foundation 59
Sir James Colyer-Fergusson's Charitable Trust 63
Community Foundation Network 67
Ernest Cook Trust 70
Cripps Foundation 73
D'Oyly Carte Charitable Trust 74
10th Duke of Devonshire's Charitable Trust 77
Dulverton Trust 81
E B M Charitable Trust 86
John Ellerman Foundation 88
Esmée Fairbairn Charitable Trust 93
Fishmongers' Company's Charitable Trust 98
Donald Forrester Trust 99
Gannochy Trust 100
Gatsby Charitable Foundation 100
Robert Gavron Charitable Trust 104
J Paul Getty Jr Charitable Trust 105
G C Gibson Charitable Trust 107
Glass-House Trust 108
Gloucestershire Environmental Trust Company 109
Goldsmiths' Company's Charities 110
Gosling Foundation 111
Greater Bristol Foundation 114
Charles Hayward Foundation 131
Headley Trust 134
Historic Churches Preservation Trust 141
J J Charitable Trust 146
Jerwood Charitable Foundation 149
Jordan Charitable Foundation 154
King George's Fund for Sailors 156
Graham Kirkham Foundation 162
Ernest Kleinwort Charitable Trust 163
Sir James Knott Trust 163
Maurice Laing Foundation 169
J W Laing Trust 171
Laing's Charitable Trust 172
Landfill Tax Credit Scheme and ENTRUST 174
Leathersellers' Company Charitable Fund 182
Lord Leverhulme's Charitable Trust 187
Linbury Trust 188
Lloyds TSB Foundation for England and Wales 191
Mackintosh Foundation 207
Manifold Trust 209
Mercers' Company Charities 212
Monument Trust 215
Peter Moores Foundation 219
National Lottery 221
Network Foundation 223
Northern Ireland Voluntary Trust 225
Northern Rock Foundation 226
P F Charitable Trust 237
Peabody Community Fund 238
Peacock Charitable Trust 239
Pet Plan Charitable Trust 240
Pilgrim Trust 241
Porter Foundation 244
Mr and Mrs J A Pye's Charitable Settlement 248
Rank Foundation 251
Ruben and Elisabeth Rausing Trust 254
Rayne Foundation 255
Sir James Reckitt Charity 255
Robertson Trust 257
Mrs L D Rope Third Charitable Settlement 258
Rothschild Foundation 260
Rowan Charitable Trust 260
Rufford Foundation 270
Alan and Babette Sainsbury Charitable Fund 271
Spitalfields Market Community Trust 292
Foundation for Sport and the Arts 294
Staples Trust 295
Steel Charitable Trust 296
Bernard Sunley Charitable Foundation 301
Tedworth Trust 306
Triangle Trust 309
Trusthouse Charitable Foundation 310
Tudor Trust 311
Underwood Trust 314
Wates Foundation 318
Weinstock Fund 320
Westminster Foundation 322
Garfield Weston Foundation 324
Will Charitable Trust 328
H D H Wills 1965 Charitable Trust 329
Charles Wolfson Charitable Trust 330
Wolfson Foundation 332

Geography and foreign links

Charity Know How *(Eastern Europe)* *46*
Great Britain Sasakawa Foundation *(Japan)*
Gulbenkian Foundation *(Portugal, Ireland) 118*

Ill or disabled people

29th May 1961 Charitable Trust 1
Alchemy Foundation 3
H B Allen Charitable Trust 4
Baily Thomas Charitable Fund 10
Band Trust 12
David and Frederick Barclay Foundation 13
Barnwood House Trust 17
Percy Bilton Charity 23
Camelia Botnar Foundation 25
Bradbury Foundation 26
Bridge House Estates Trust Fund 26
William Adlington Cadbury Charitable Trust 33
Edward Cadbury Charitable Trust 34
Campden Charities 38
Childwick Trust 47
City Parochial Foundation 51
Clore and Duffield Foundations 56
Richard Cloudesley's Charity 62
Sir James Colyer-Fergusson's Charitable Trust 63
Comic Relief 64
Community Foundation (Tyne & Wear and Northumberland) 68
Ernest Cook Trust 70
Cripplegate Foundation 71
D'Oyly Carte Charitable Trust 74
Roald Dahl Foundation 75
Diana, Princess of Wales Memorial Fund 77
Drapers' Company Charities 80
E B M Charitable Trust 86
Sir John Eastwood Foundation 86
Maud Elkington Charitable Trust 87

John Ellerman Foundation 88
Eveson Charitable Trust 92
Esmée Fairbairn Charitable Trust 93
Fishmongers' Company's Charitable Trust 98
Donald Forrester Trust 99
Hugh Fraser Foundation 99
Gatsby Charitable Foundation 100
Robert Gavron Charitable Trust 104
J Paul Getty Jr Charitable Trust 105
G C Gibson Charitable Trust 107
Glencore Foundation for Education & Welfare 109
Goldsmiths' Company's Charities 110
Gosling Foundation 111
Grand Charity of Freemasons 112
Greater Bristol Foundation 114
Constance Green Foundation 115
Greggs Trust 116
H C D Memorial Fund 122
Hadley Trust 124
Hampton Fuel Allotment Charity 127
Peter Harrison Foundation 129
Headley Trust 134
Hedley Foundation 136
Jane Hodge Foundation 142
Albert Hunt Trust 144
J J Charitable Trust 146
Elton John AIDS Foundation 152
Jordan Charitable Foundation 154
Ian Karten Charitable Trust 155
King's Fund 157
Ernest Kleinwort Charitable Trust 163
Laing Family Foundations 167
Laing's Charitable Trust 172
Allen Lane Foundation 176
Lankelly Foundation 178
Leeds Hospital Fund Charitable Trust 185
Levy Foundation 187
Linbury Trust 188
Enid Linder Foundation 191
George John Livanos Charitable Trust
Lloyds TSB Foundation for England and Wales 191
Lloyds TSB Foundation for Northern Ireland 199
Lloyds TSB Foundation for Scotland 200
Lord's Taverners 204
John Lyon's Charity 205
Mackintosh Foundation 207
MacRobert Trusts 209
Jim Marshall Charitable Trust 210
Mental Health Foundation 212
Mercers' Company Charities 212
Metropolitan Hospital–Sunday Fund 214
John Moores Foundation 217
North British Hotel Trust 224
Northern Rock Foundation 226
Nuffield Foundation 233
Nuffield Trust 237
P F Charitable Trust 237
Parthenon Trust 238
Peacock Charitable Trust 239
Dowager Countess Eleanor Peel Trust 240
Pilgrim Trust 241
Pilkington Charities Fund 243
PPP Healthcare Medical Trust 245
Queen Mary's Roehampton Trust 250
Joseph Rank Benevolent Trust 250
Rank Foundation 251
Robertson Trust 257
Mrs L D Rope Third Charitable Settlement 258
Rose Foundation 259
Rowan Charitable Trust 260
Save and Prosper Charities 277
Francis C Scott Charitable Trust 279
Smith's Charity 284
Sobell Foundation 289
South Yorkshire Community Foundation 291
Spitalfields Market Community Trust 292
Steel Charitable Trust 296
Sir Halley Stewart Trust 297
W O Street Charitable Foundation 300
Bernard Sunley Charitable Foundation 301
Triangle Trust 309
Trusthouse Charitable Foundation 310
Tudor Trust 311
Waterside Trust 318
Wates Foundation 318
Weinstock Fund 320
Garfield Weston Foundation 324
Sir Richard Whittington's Charity 328
Will Charitable Trust 328
Wolfson Foundation 332
Woodward Charitable Trust 334
Zochonis Charitable Trust 335

Manufacturing industry and services

Clothworkers' Foundation 59
Drapers' Company Charities 80
Leathersellers' Company Charitable Fund 182

Medicine and health

29th May 1961 Charitable Trust 1
AIM Foundation 2
Al Fayed Charitable Foundation 3
Allchurches Trust 4
H B Allen Charitable Trust 4
Artemis Charitable Trust 7
Lord Ashdown Charitable Settlement 9
Baily Thomas Charitable Fund 10
Band Trust 12
David and Frederick Barclay Foundation 13
Barnwood House Trust 17
Percy Bilton Charity 23
Boltons Trust 24
Booth Charities 25
Bradbury Foundation 26
Burdens Charitable Foundation 31
Audrey & Stanley Burton Charitable Trust 32
William Adlington Cadbury Charitable Trust 33
Charities Advisory Trust 43
Childwick Trust 47
CHK Charities Limited 48
Church Urban Fund 49
Clore and Duffield Foundations 56
Clothworkers' Foundation 59
Richard Cloudesley's Charity 62
Sir James Colyer-Fergusson's Charitable Trust 63
Community Foundation (Tyne & Wear and Northumberland) 68
Cripplegate Foundation 71
D'Oyly Carte Charitable Trust 74
Roald Dahl Foundation 75
Baron Davenport's Charity 76
10th Duke of Devonshire's Charitable Trust 77
Diana, Princess of Wales Memorial Fund 77
Djanogly Foundation 80
Dunhill Medical Trust 84
E B M Charitable Trust 86
Sir John Eastwood Foundation 86
John Ellerman Foundation 88
Eranda Foundation 92
Eveson Charitable Trust 92
Donald Forrester Trust 99
Hugh Fraser Foundation 99
Gannochy Trust 100
Gatsby Charitable Foundation 100
Robert Gavron Charitable Trust 104
J Paul Getty Jr Charitable Trust 105
G C Gibson Charitable Trust 107
Grand Charity of Freemasons 112
Constance Green Foundation 115

H C D Memorial Fund 122
Paul Hamlyn Foundation 125
Maurice Hatter Foundation 131
Charles Hayward Foundation 131
Headley Trust 134
Hedley Foundation 136
Help the Aged 138
Jane Hodge Foundation 142
Hospital Saving Association Charitable Trust 143
Albert Hunt Trust 144
Jerwood Charitable Foundation 149
Elton John AIDS Foundation 152
Jordan Charitable Foundation 154
Ian Karten Charitable Trust 155
Kay Kendall Leukaemia Fund 155
King's Fund 157
Mary Kinross Charitable Trust 161
Graham Kirkham Foundation 162
Ernest Kleinwort Charitable Trust 163
Sir James Knott Trust 163
Kreitman Foundation 165
Maurice and Hilda Laing Charitable Trust 165
Kirby Laing Foundation 168
Maurice Laing Foundation 169
Beatrice Laing Trust 170
Laing's Charitable Trust 172
Leathersellers' Company Charitable Fund 182
Leeds Hospital Fund Charitable Trust 185
Levy Foundation 187
Lewis Family Charitable Trust 188
Linbury Trust 188
Enid Linder Foundation 191
George John Livanos Charitable Trust 191
Lloyds TSB Foundation for England and Wales 191
Lloyds TSB Foundation for Northern Ireland 199
Mackintosh Foundation 207
MacRobert Trusts 208
Medlock Charitable Trust 211
Mental Health Foundation 212
Mercers' Company Charities 212
Metropolitan Hospital–Sunday Fund 214
Monument Trust 215
Peter Moores Foundation 219
Frances and Augustus Newman Foundation 223
North British Hotel Trust 224
Northern Ireland Voluntary Trust 225
Northwood Charitable Trust 233
Nuffield Foundation 233
Nuffield Trust 237
P F Charitable Trust 237
Peacock Charitable Trust 239
Dowager Countess Eleanor Peel Trust 240
Porter Foundation 244
PPP Healthcare Medical Trust 245
Mr and Mrs J A Pye's Charitable Settlement 248
Joseph Rank Benevolent Trust 250
Rayne Foundation 255
Sir James Reckitt Charity 255
Robertson Trust 257
Rose Foundation 259
Rothschild Foundation 260
Rowan Charitable Trust 260
Rufford Foundation 270
Alan and Babette Sainsbury Charitable Fund 271
Basil Samuel Charitable Trust 277
Ayrton Senna Foundation 282
Archie Sherman Charitable Trust 283
Smith's Charity 284
Sobell Foundation 289
South Yorkshire Community Foundation 291
Steel Charitable Trust 296
Sir Halley Stewart Trust 297
Stevenson Family's Charitable Trust 297
Bernard Sunley Charitable Foundation 301
Sir Jules Thorn Charitable Trust 307
Three Guineas Trust 309
Tompkins Foundation 309
Triangle Trust 309
Underwood Trust 314
John and Lucille van Geest Foundation 315
Sir Siegmund Warburg's Voluntary Settlement 317
Waterside Trust 318
Wates Foundation 318
Weinstock Fund 320
Wellcome Trust 321
Welton Foundation 322
Westminster Foundation 322
Garfield Weston Foundation 324
Will Charitable Trust 328
Charles Wolfson Charitable Trust 330
Wolfson Family Charitable Trust 331
Wolfson Foundation 332
Woodward Charitable Trust 334
Zochonis Charitable Trust 335

Medical research

Arbib Foundation 6
Baily Thomas Charitable Fund 10
Band Trust 12
David and Frederick Barclay Foundation 13
Barnwood House Trust 17
William Adlington Cadbury Charitable Trust 33
Charities Advisory Trust 43
Childwick Trust 47
Drapers' Company Charities 80
Dunhill Medical Trust 84
E B M Charitable Trust 86
John Ellerman Foundation 88
Eranda Foundation 92
Eveson Charitable Trust 92
Hugh Fraser Foundation 99
G C Gibson Charitable Trust 107
Grand Charity of Freemasons 112
Philip and Pauline Harris Charitable Trust 129
Charles Hayward Foundation 131
Hedley Foundation 136
Jane Hodge Foundation 142
Jones 1986 Charitable Trust 153
Kay Kendall Leukaemia Fund 155
Mary Kinross Charitable Trust 161
Ernest Kleinwort Charitable Trust 163
Kreitman Foundation 165
William Leech Charity 183
Kennedy Leigh Charitable Trust 185
Levy Foundation 187
Lewis Family Charitable Trust 188
Linbury Trust 188
Enid Linder Foundation 191
George John Livanos Charitable Trust 191
Lloyds TSB Foundation for Northern Ireland 199
Lloyds TSB Foundation for Scotland 200
Frances and Augustus Newman Foundation 223
NiKeNo Trust 224
Northwood Charitable Trust 233
Nuffield Foundation 233
P F Charitable Trust 237
Parthenon Trust 238
Peacock Charitable Trust 239
Dowager Countess Eleanor Peel Trust 240
Pilkington Charities Fund 243
PPP Healthcare Medical Trust 245
Mr and Mrs J A Pye's Charitable Settlement 248
Robertson Trust 257
Raymond & Beverley Sackler Foundation 271
Alan and Babette Sainsbury Charitable Fund 271
Sir Samuel Scott of Yews Trust 281
Smith's Charity 284
Steel Charitable Trust 296
Sir Halley Stewart Trust 297
Bernard Sunley Charitable Foundation 301

Sir Jules Thorn Charitable Trust 307
John and Lucille van Geest Foundation 315
Sir Siegmund Warburg's Voluntary Settlement 317
Wellcome Trust 321
Welton Foundation 322
Garfield Weston Foundation 324
Charles Wolfson Charitable Trust 330
Wolfson Family Charitable Trust 331
Wolfson Foundation 332

Older people

29th May 1961 Charitable Trust 1
Alchemy Foundation 3
Allchurches Trust 4
H B Allen Charitable Trust 4
Lord Ashdown Charitable Settlement 9
Band Trust 12
David and Frederick Barclay Foundation 13
Barnwood House Trust 17
Percy Bilton Charity 23
Boltons Trust 24
Booth Charities 25
Bradbury Foundation 26
Bridge House Estates Trust Fund 26
William Adlington Cadbury Charitable Trust 33
Carnegie United Kingdom Trust 39
Childwick Trust 47
Clore and Duffield Foundations 56
Comic Relief 64
Community Foundation 67
Cripplegate Foundation 71
10th Duke of Devonshire's Charitable Trust 77
Djanogly Foundation 80
Dulverton Trust 81
Dunhill Medical Trust 84
Sir John Eastwood Foundation 86
Maud Elkington Charitable Trust 87
Eveson Charitable Trust 92
Esmée Fairbairn Charitable Trust 93
Donald Forrester Trust 99
Hugh Fraser Foundation 99
G C Gibson Charitable Trust 107
Gosling Foundation 111
Grand Charity of Freemasons 112
Greggs Trust 116
Charles Hayward Foundation 131
Headley Trust 134
Help the Aged 138
Albert Hunt Trust 144
King's Fund 157
Ernest Kleinwort Charitable Trust 163
Maurice Laing Foundation 169
Beatrice Laing Trust 170
Lankelly Foundation 178
Linbury Trust 188
Lloyds TSB Foundation for England and Wales 191
Peter Moores Foundation 219
North British Hotel Trust 224
Northern Rock Foundation 226
Nuffield Foundation 233
Nuffield Trust 237
P F Charitable Trust 237
Dowager Countess Eleanor Peel Trust 240
Pilkington Charities Fund 243
PPP Healthcare Medical Trust 245
Queen Mary's Roehampton Trust 250
Joseph Rank Benevolent Trust 250
Rank Foundation 251
Rayne Foundation 255
Sir James Reckitt Charity 255
Robertson Trust 257
Francis C Scott Charitable Trust 279
Smith's Charity 284
Sobell Foundation 289
South Yorkshire Community Foundation 291
Spitalfields Market Community Trust 292
Bernard Sunley Charitable Foundation 301
Talbot Village Trust 306
Triangle Trust 309
Tudor Trust 311
John and Lucille van Geest Foundation 315
Waterside Trust 318
Weinstock Fund 320
Garfield Weston Foundation 324

Philosophy

Mrs L D Rope Third Charitable Settlement 258
Joseph Rowntree Charitable Trust 261
Sir Halley Stewart Trust 297

Political and policy issues

Alchemy Foundation 3
H B Allen Charitable Trust 4
Lord Ashdown Charitable Settlement 9
Boltons Trust 24
Bridge House Estates Trust Fund 26
William Adlington Cadbury Charitable Trust 33
Edward Cadbury Charitable Trust 34
Barrow Cadbury Trust 34
Charities Advisory Trust 43
Charity Know How 46
Church Urban Fund 49
City Parochial Foundation 51
Comic Relief 64
Diana, Princess of Wales Memorial Fund 77
Dulverton Trust 81
Esmée Fairbairn Charitable Trust 93
Donald Forrester Trust 99
Gatsby Charitable Foundation 100
Robert Gavron Charitable Trust 104
Gulbenkian Foundation 118
H C D Memorial Fund 122
Hilden Charitable Fund 139
J G Joffe Charitable Trust 152
King's Fund 157
Allen Lane Foundation 176
Law Society Charity 182
Leverhulme Trust 186
Linbury Trust 188
Lloyds TSB Foundation for England and Wales 191
Lloyds TSB Foundation for Scotland 200
John Moores Foundation 217
Peter Moores Foundation 219
Network Foundation 223
Northern Ireland Voluntary Trust 225
Nuffield Foundation 233
Parthenon Trust 238
Peabody Community Fund 238
Ruben and Elisabeth Rausing Trust 254
Rowan Charitable Trust 260
Joseph Rowntree Charitable Trust 261
Joseph Rowntree Foundation 265
Joseph Rowntree Reform Trust 268
Alan and Babette Sainsbury Charitable Fund 271
Staples Trust 295
Sir Halley Stewart Trust 297
Three Guineas Trust 309
Tudor Trust 311
Westminster Foundation for Democracy 323

Religion general

Alan and Babette Sainsbury Charitable Fund 271
Underwood Trust 314

Christianity

Allchurches Trust 4
Burdens Charitable Foundation 31
William Adlington Cadbury Charitable Trust 33
Edward Cadbury Charitable Trust 34
Church Urban Fund 49
Clothworkers' Foundation 59

Richard Cloudesley's Charity 62
Sir James Colyer-Fergusson's Charitable Trust 63
Dulverton Trust 81
G C Gibson Charitable Trust 107
Hedley Foundation 136
Jane Hodge Foundation 142
Jerusalem Trust 148
Kennedy Charitable Foundation 156
J W Laing Biblical Scholarship Trust 165
Laing Family Foundations 167
J W Laing Trust 171
John and Rosemary Lancaster Charitable Foundation 173
Leathersellers' Company Charitable Fund 182
William Leech Charity 183
Mercers' Company Charities 212
Peter Moores Foundation 219
Joseph Rank Benevolent Trust 250
Rank Foundation 251
Sir James Reckitt Charity 255
Mrs L D Rope Third Charitable Settlement 258
Joseph Rowntree Charitable Trust 261
Souter Foundation 290
Spring Harvest Charitable Trust 295
Sir Halley Stewart Trust 297
Stobart Newlands Charitable Trust 299
Tompkins Foundation 309
Vardy Foundation 316
Waterside Trust 318
Westminster Foundation 322
Garfield Weston Foundation 324

Judaism

A W Charitable Trust 1
Achisomoch Aid Company 1
Alglen Ltd 3
Lord Ashdown Charitable Settlement 9
Balint Family Charitable Trusts 12
Boltons Trust 24
Audrey & Stanley Burton Charitable Trust 32
Charitworth Limited 45
Charity Association Manchester Ltd 46
Childwick Trust 47
Clore and Duffield Foundations 56
Itzchok Meyer Cymerman Trust Ltd 74
Djanogly Foundation 80
Entindale Ltd 91
Glencore Foundation for Education & Welfare 109
M & R Gross Charities 118
Gur Trust 122
Maurice Hatter Foundation 131
Huntingdon Foundation 145
Kreitman Foundation 165
Kennedy Leigh Charitable Trust 185
Levy Foundation 187
Lewis Family Charitable Trust 188
Lolev Charitable Trust 204
M K Charitable Trust 206
Mayfair Charities 211
Rayne Foundation 255
Rothschild Foundation 260
J B Rubens Charitable Foundation 269
Rubin Foundation 269
Basil Samuel Charitable Trust 277
Samuel Sebba Charitable Trust 282
Archie Sherman Charitable Trust 283
Shlomo Memorial Fund 284
Sobell Foundation 289
Weinstock Fund 320
Charles Wolfson Charitable Trust 330
Wolfson Family Charitable Trust 331

Masons

Grand Charity of Freemasons 112

Science

Clothworkers' Foundation 59
Gatsby Charitable Foundation 100
Jerwood Charitable Foundation 149
Leathersellers' Company Charitable Fund 182
MacRobert Trusts 208
Nuffield Foundation 233
Mrs L D Rope Third Charitable Settlement 258
Raymond & Beverley Sackler Foundation 271
Alan and Babette Sainsbury Charitable Fund 271
Underwood Trust 314
Wellcome Trust 321
Wolfson Family Charitable Trust 331
Wolfson Foundation 332

Social and moral welfare

29th May 1961 Charitable Trust 1
AIM Foundation 2
Alchemy Foundation 3
Allchurches Trust 4
Anglian Water Trust Fund 5
Arbib Foundation 6
Artemis Charitable Trust 7
Ashden Charitable Trust 7
Lord Ashdown Charitable Settlement 9
Band Trust 12
David and Frederick Barclay Foundation 13
Baring Foundation 14
Barnwood House Trust 17
Bedford Charity 22
Percy Bilton Charity 23
Booth Charities 25
Camelia Botnar Foundation 25
Bradbury Foundation 26
Burdens Charitable Foundation 31
Audrey & Stanley Burton Charitable Trust 32
William Adlington Cadbury Charitable Trust 33
Edward Cadbury Charitable Trust 34
Barrow Cadbury Trust 34
Campden Charities 38
Carnegie United Kingdom Trust 39
CHK Charities Limited 48
Church Urban Fund 49
City Parochial Foundation 51
Clore and Duffield Foundations 56
Clothworkers' Foundation 59
Richard Cloudesley's Charity 62
Sir James Colyer-Fergusson's Charitable Trust 63
Comic Relief 64
Community Foundation (Tyne & Wear and Northumberland) 68
Cripplegate Foundation 71
D'Oyly Carte Charitable Trust 74
Baron Davenport's Charity 76
10th Duke of Devonshire's Charitable Trust 77
Diana, Princess of Wales Memorial Fund 77
Djanogly Foundation 80
Drapers' Company Charities 80
Dulverton Trust 81
E B M Charitable Trust 86
Sir John Eastwood Foundation 86
Maud Elkington Charitable Trust 87
John Ellerman Foundation 88
Eranda Foundation 92
Esmée Fairbairn Charitable Trust 93
Fishmongers' Company's Charitable Trust 98
Donald Forrester Trust 99
Hugh Fraser Foundation 99
Gannochy Trust 100
Gatsby Charitable Foundation 100
Robert Gavron Charitable Trust 104
J Paul Getty Jr Charitable Trust 105
G C Gibson Charitable Trust 107
Glass-House Trust 108
Goldsmiths' Company's Charities 110
Gosling Foundation 111
Grand Charity of Freemasons 112
Greater Bristol Foundation 114
Constance Green Foundation 115
Greggs Trust 116
Gulbenkian Foundation 118
H C D Memorial Fund 122

Hact (The Housing Associations Charitable Trust) 123
Hadley Trust 124
Hampton Fuel Allotment Charity 127
Charles Hayward Foundation 131
Headley Trust 134
Hedley Foundation 136
Help a London Child 136
Help the Aged 138
Hilden Charitable Fund 139
Albert Hunt Trust 144
Isle of Dogs Community Foundation 146
J J Charitable Trust 146
John James Bristol Foundation 147
King's Fund 157
Mary Kinross Charitable Trust 161
Graham Kirkham Foundation 162
Ernest Kleinwort Charitable Trust 163
Sir James Knott Trust 163
Laing Family Foundations 167
Laing's Charitable Trust 172
Lambeth Endowed Charities 172
Allen Lane Foundation 176
Lankelly Foundation 178
Leathersellers' Company Charitable Fund 182
William Leech Charity 183
Leeds Hospital Fund Charitable Trust 185
Lord Leverhulme's Charitable Trust 187
Levy Foundation 187
Linbury Trust 188
Lloyds TSB Foundation for England and Wales 191
Lloyds TSB Foundation for Northern Ireland 199
Lloyds TSB Foundation for Scotland 200
John Lyon's Charity 205
MacRobert Trusts 208
Manifold Trust 209
Medlock Charitable Trust 211
Mercers' Company Charities 212
Metropolitan Hospital–Sunday Fund 214
Monument Trust 215
John Moores Foundation 217
National Lottery 221
National Lottery Charities Board 221
Northern Ireland Voluntary Trust 225
Northern Rock Foundation 226
Nuffield Foundation 233
Nuffield Trust 237
P F Charitable Trust 237
Parthenon Trust 238
Peabody Community Fund 238
Peacock Charitable Trust 239
Jack Petchey Foundation 241
Pilgrim Trust 241
Pilkington Charities Fund 243
Porter Foundation 244
Queen Mary's Roehampton Trust 250
Joseph Rank Benevolent Trust 250
Rank Foundation 251
Ruben and Elisabeth Rausing Trust 254
Rayne Foundation 255
Sir James Reckitt Charity 255
Robertson Trust 257
Mrs L D Rope Third Charitable Settlement 258
Rowan Charitable Trust 260
Joseph Rowntree Charitable Trust 261
Rufford Foundation 270
Alan and Babette Sainsbury Charitable Fund 271
Basil Samuel Charitable Trust 277
Francis C Scott Charitable Trust 279
Smith's Charity 284
Souter Foundation 290
South Yorkshire Community Foundation 291
Spitalfields Market Community Trust 292
Foundation for Sport and the Arts 294
Steel Charitable Trust 296
W O Street Charitable Foundation 300
Bernard Sunley Charitable Foundation 301
Sutton Coldfield Municipal Charities 303
Tedworth Trust 306
Sir Jules Thorn Charitable Trust 307
Tompkins Foundation 309
Triangle Trust 309
Trusthouse Charitable Foundation 310
Tudor Trust 311
Underwood Trust 314
Bernard Van Leer Foundation (UK) Trust 315
Waterside Trust 318
Wates Foundation 318
Weinstock Fund 320
Welton Foundation 322
Westminster Foundation 322
Garfield Weston Foundation 324
Sir Richard Whittington's Charity 328
Woodward Charitable Trust 334
Zochonis Charitable Trust 335

Sport and recreation

John Beckwith Charitable Settlement 22
Bedford Charity 22
Childwick Trust 47
Gannochy Trust 100
Gloucestershire Environmental Trust Company 109
Peter Harrison Foundation 129
Charles Hayward Foundation 131
George John Livanos Charitable Trust 191
Lord's Taverners 204
John Lyon's Charity 205
National Lottery (and Awards for All) 221
Robertson Trust 257
Francis C Scott Charitable Trust 279
Foundation for Sport and the Arts 294
Bernard Sunley Charitable Foundation 301
Tompkins Foundation 309
Trusthouse Charitable Foundation 310
Tudor Trust 311
Woodward Charitable Trust 334

Technology

Ernest Cook Trust 70
Esmée Fairbairn Charitable Trust 93
Paul Hamlyn Foundation 125
Jerwood Charitable Foundation 149
MacRobert Trusts 208
Wolfson Family Charitable Trust 331
Wolfson Foundation 332

Voluntary sector

Baring Foundation 14
Bridge House Estates Trust Fund 26
Edward Cadbury Charitable Trust 34
Carnegie United Kingdom Trust 39
Charities Advisory Trust 43
Charities Aid Foundation 43
Charity Know How 46
City Parochial Foundation 51
Community Foundation (Tyne & Wear and Northumberland) 68
Paul Hamlyn Foundation 125
Lankelly Foundation 178
William Leech Charity 183
Lloyds TSB Foundation for England and Wales 191
Lloyds TSB Foundation for Scotland 200
Medlock Charitable Trust 211
John Moores Foundation 217
National Lottery Charities Board 221
Northern Ireland Voluntary Trust 225
Mrs L D Rope Third Charitable Settlement 258
South Yorkshire Community Foundation 291
Westminster Foundation for Democracy 323

Young people

29th May 1961 Charitable Trust 1
AIM Foundation 2
Alchemy Foundation 3
Allchurches Trust 4
Lord Ashdown Charitable Settlement 9
Balcraig Foundation 11
Band Trust 12
BBC Children in Need Appeal 19
John Beckwith Charitable Settlement 22
Bedford Charity 22
Boltons Trust 24
Booth Charities 25
Bridge House Estates Trust Fund 26
William Adlington Cadbury Charitable Trust 33
Edward Cadbury Charitable Trust 34
Carnegie United Kingdom Trust 39
CHK Charities Limited 48
Church Urban Fund 49
City Parochial Foundation 51
Clore and Duffield Foundations 56
Clothworkers' Foundation 59
Comic Relief 64
Community Foundation Network 67
Ernest Cook Trust 70
Cripplegate Foundation 71
D'Oyly Carte Charitable Trust 74
Baron Davenport's Charity 76
10th Duke of Devonshire's Charitable Trust 77
Diana, Princess of Wales Memorial Fund 77
Djanogly Foundation 80
Drapers' Company Charities 80
Dulverton Trust 81
E B M Charitable Trust 86
Sir John Eastwood Foundation 86
John Ellerman Foundation 88
Esmée Fairbairn Charitable Trust 93
Donald Forrester Trust 99
Gannochy Trust 100
Gatsby Charitable Foundation 100
J Paul Getty Jr Charitable Trust 105
G C Gibson Charitable Trust 107
Glass-House Trust 108
Goldsmiths' Company's Charities 110
Grand Charity of Freemasons 112
Greggs Trust 116
Gulbenkian Foundation 118
Hampton Fuel Allotment Charity 127
Peter Harrison Foundation 129
Headley Trust 134
Hedley Foundation 136
Help a London Child 136
Alan Edward Higgs Charity 139
Horne Foundation 143
Reta Lila Howard Foundation 144
Jerwood Charitable Foundation 149
Mary Kinross Charitable Trust 161
Ernest Kleinwort Charitable Trust 163
Laing Family Foundations 167
J W Laing Trust 171
Laing's Charitable Trust 172
Lankelly Foundation 178
Leathersellers' Company Charitable Fund 182
Levy Foundation 187
Enid Linder Foundation 191
George John Livanos Charitable Trust 191
Lloyds TSB Foundation for England and Wales 191
Lloyds TSB Foundation for Northern Ireland 199
Lloyds TSB Foundation for Scotland 200
John Lyon's Charity 205
MacRobert Trusts 208
Jim Marshall Charitable Trust 210
Mercers' Company Charities 212
Peter Moores Foundation 219
Northern Ireland Voluntary Trust 225
P F Charitable Trust 237
Peacock Charitable Trust 239
Jack Petchey Foundation 241
PPP Healthcare Medical Trust 245
Prince's Trust 248
Mr and Mrs J A Pye's Charitable Settlement 248
Joseph Rank Benevolent Trust 250
Rank Foundation 251
Rayne Foundation 255
Sir James Reckitt Charity 255
Robertson Trust 257
Mrs L D Rope Third Charitable Settlement 258
Basil Samuel Charitable Trust 277
Francis C Scott Charitable Trust 279
SHINE (Support and Help In Education) 284
Smith's Charity 284
South Yorkshire Community Foundation 291
Southover Manor General Education Trust 292
Spitalfields Market Community Trust 292
W O Street Charitable Foundation 300
Bernard Sunley Charitable Foundation 301
Talbot Village Trust 306
Tudor Trust 311
John and Lucille van Geest Foundation 315
Variety Club of Great Britain 317
Waterside Trust 318
Wates Foundation 318
Westminster Foundation 322
Garfield Weston Foundation 324

Geographical index

The following geographical index aims to highlight when a trust gives preference for, or has a special interest in, a particular area: county, region, city, town or London borough. Please note the following:

1. Before using this index please read the following and the introduction to the subject index on page ***. We must emphasise that this index:

   (a) should not be used as a simple mailing list, and

   (b) is not a substitute for detailed research.

   When you have identified trusts, using this index, please read each entry carefully before making an application. Simply because a trust gives in your geographical area does not mean that it gives to your type of work.

2. Most trusts in this list are not restricted to one area. Usually the geographical index indicates that the trust gives some priority to an area or areas.
3. Trusts which give throughout England, Northern Ireland, Scotland and Wales have been excluded as have those which give throughout the UK, unless they have a particular interest in one or more locality.
4. Each section is ordered alphabetically according to the name of the trust.

The categories for the overseas and UK indices are as follows:

England

We have divided England into the following six categories:

North East *page 350*
North West *page 350*
Midlands *page 350*
South West *page 350*
South East *page 351*
London *page 351*

The trusts are listed as follows:

(a) Trusts giving throughout a whole region or in several counties within it (or throughout London).

(b) Trusts giving in a particular county (or a particular borough in London).

(c) Trusts giving to a particular town or city within that county.

A trust may be listed under (b) or (c) as well as (a), if it has a particular interest in a town or county within a region where it also gives more widely.

Channel Islands *page 351*

Wales *page 351*

The trusts are listed as follows:

(a) Trusts giving throughout the whole of Wales or a substantial part of it.

(b) Trusts giving in a particular region.

Scotland *page 351*

The trusts listed as follows:

(a) Trusts giving throughout the whole of Scotland or a substantial part of it.

(b) Trusts giving in a particular region.

Northern Ireland *page 352*

Overseas categories

Trusts giving overseas are listed in the following order:

Overseas general page 352

Trusts which (a) give to at least two continents in the world and (b) do not limit their giving to the third world.

Third world/developing world page 352

This includes trusts which support missionary organisations when they are also interested in social and economic development.

Individual continents pages 352–3

These are listed in alphabetical order of continent. Trusts giving in that continent are ordered as follows:

(a) Trusts giving throughout the whole continent or a substantial part of it.

(b) Trusts giving in a particular region which covers more than one country (e.g. East Africa).

(c) Trusts giving to a particular country within that region.

The Middle East has been listed separately. Please note that most of the trusts listed are primarily for the benefit of Jewish people and the advancement of the Jewish religion.

North East

Greggs Trust 116
M K Charitable Trust 206
Northern Rock Foundation 226

Cleveland

Cleveland Community Foundation 56

Hartlepool

Anglian Water Trust Fund 5

Durham

Sir James Knott Trust 163
William Leech Charity 183

East Yorkshire

Sir James Reckitt Charity 255

Northumberland

Community Foundation 68
Sir James Knott Trust 163
William Leech Charity 183

South Yorkshire

South Yorkshire Community Foundation 291

Tyne & Wear

Community Foundation 68
Sir James Knott Trust 163
William Leech Charity 183

Yorkshire general

Audrey & Stanley Burton Charitable Trust 32
Constance Green Foundation 115
Leeds Hospital Fund Charitable Trust 185

North West

Burdens Charitable Foundation 31
Northern Rock Foundation 226
W O Street Charitable Foundation 300
Westminster Foundation 322

Cheshire

Lord Leverhulme's Charitable Trust 187

Ellesmere Port

John Moores Foundation 217

Halton

John Moores Foundation 217

Cumbria

Francis C Scott Charitable Trust 279

Greater Manchester

Zochonis Charitable Trust 335

Salford

Booth Charities 25

Lancashire

Francis C Scott Charitable Trust 279

Clitheroe

John and Rosemary Lancaster Charitable Foundation 173

Lancaster

Dowager Countess Eleanor Peel Trust 240

Skelmersdale

John Moores Foundation 217

Merseyside

Baring Foundation 14
Lord Leverhulme's Charitable Trust 187
John Moores Foundation 217
Pilkington Charities Fund 243
Rowan Charitable Trust 260

Midlands

Burdens Charitable Foundation 31
Alan Edward Higgs Charity 139

Derbyshire

10th Duke of Devonshire's Charitable Trust 77

Herefordshire

Eveson Charitable Trust 92
Jordan Charitable Foundation 154

Leicestershire

Anglian Water Trust Fund 5
Ernest Cook Trust 70
Maud Elkington Charitable Trust 87
Smith's Charity 284

Lincolnshire

Anglian Water Trust Fund 5
John and Lucille van Geest Foundation 315

Boston

Medlock Charitable Trust 211

Northamptonshire

Anglian Water Trust Fund 5
Cripps Foundation 73
Maud Elkington Charitable Trust 87
Horne Foundation 143
Bernard Sunley Charitable Foundation 301

Nottinghamshire

Djanogly Foundation 80
Sir John Eastwood Foundation 86
Jones 1986 Charitable Trust 153

Rutland

Anglian Water Trust Fund 5

Warwickshire

29th May 1961 Charitable Trust 1

Leamington Spa

Mr and Mrs J A Pye's Charitable Settlement 248

West Midlands

William Adlington Cadbury Charitable Trust 33
Edward Cadbury Charitable Trust 34
Baron Davenport's Charity 76
Eveson Charitable Trust 92

Birmingham

29th May 1961 Charitable Trust 1

Coventry

29th May 1961 Charitable Trust 1

Sutton Coldfield

Sutton Coldfield Municipal Charities 303

Worcestershire

Eveson Charitable Trust 92

South West

Mercers' Company Charities 212

Avon

Bath

Medlock Charitable Trust 211

Bristol

Burdens Charitable Foundation 31
Greater Bristol Foundation 114
John James Bristol Foundation 147
Mr and Mrs J A Pye's Charitable Settlement 248

Cornwall

Baring Foundation 14

Devon

Baring Foundation 14

Dorset

Ernest Cook Trust 70
Talbot Village Trust 306

Gloucestershire

Barnwood House Trust 17
CHK Charities Limited 48
Ernest Cook Trust 70
Gloucestershire Environmental Trust Company 109
Smith's Charity 284

Cheltenham

Mr and Mrs J A Pye's Charitable Settlement 248

Wiltshire

Underwood Trust 314

South East

Childwick Trust 47
Peter Harrison Foundation 129
Mercers' Company Charities 212
SHINE (Support and Help in Education) 284
Bernard Sunley Charitable Foundation 301

Bedfordshire

Anglian Water Trust Fund 5
Bedford Charity 22
Steel Charitable Trust 296

Berkshire

Reading

Mr and Mrs J A Pye's Charitable Settlement 248

Buckinghamshire

Anglian Water Trust Fund 5
Ernest Cook Trust 70

Cambridgeshire

Anglian Water Trust Fund 5

East Anglia

Anglian Water Trust Fund 5
G C Gibson Charitable Trust 107

Essex

AIM Foundation 2
Anglian Water Trust Fund 5
Jack Petchey Foundation 241
Save and Prosper Charities 277

Hampshire

Smith's Charity 284

Kent

Sir James Colyer-Fergusson's Charitable Trust 63
Smith's Charity 284
Bernard Sunley Charitable Foundation 301

Oxfordshire

Arbib Foundation 6
CHK Charities Limited 48
P F Charitable Trust 237
Mr and Mrs J A Pye's Charitable Settlement 248

Suffolk

Sir James Colyer-Fergusson's Charitable Trust 63
Mrs L D Rope Third Charitable Settlement 258
Smith's Charity 284

Surrey

Ian Karten Charitable Trust 155
Smith's Charity 284

Sussex

Ernest Kleinwort Charitable Trust 163
NiKeNo Trust 224
Smith's Charity 284
Southover Manor Education Trust 292

West Sussex

Dunhill Medical Trust 84

London

Baring Foundation 14
Bridge House Estates Trust Fund 26
Sir John Cass's Foundation 41
City Parochial Foundation 51
Clore and Duffield Foundations 56
Drapers' Company Charities 80
Fishmongers' Company's Charitable Trust 98
Goldsmiths' Company's Charities 110
Help a London Child 136
Hilden Charitable Fund 139
Ian Karten Charitable Trust 155
King's Fund 157
Leathersellers' Company Charitable Fund 182
John Lyon's Charity 205
Mercers' Company Charities 212
Metropolitan Hospital–Sunday Fund 214
Peabody Community Fund 238
Jack Petchey Foundation 241
Richmond Parish Lands Charity 256
Rose Foundation 259
Save and Prosper Charities 277
SHINE (Support and Help in Education) 284
Bernard Sunley Charitable Foundation 301
Underwood Trust 314
Sir Siegmund Warburg's Voluntary Settlement 317
Wates Foundation 318
Westminster Foundation 322

City of London

Cripplegate Foundation 71
Drapers' Company Charities 80
Fishmongers' Company's Charitiable Trust 98

Islington

Richard Cloudsley's Charity 62
Cripplegate Foundation 71
Save and Prosper Charities 277

Lambeth

Lambeth Endowed Charities 172

Richmond-upon-Thames

Hampton Fuel Allotment Charity 256

Tower Hamlets

Isle of Dogs Community Foundation 146
Spitalfields Market Community Trust 292

Channel Islands

Jersey

W O Street Charitable Foundation 300

Wales

G C Gibson Charitable Trust 107
Grand Charity of Freemasons 112
Historic Churches Preservation Trust 141
Jane Hodge Foundation 142
Lloyds TSB Foundation for England and Wales 191
Sobell Foundation 289

Isle of Anglesey

Isle of Anglesey Charitable Trust 145

Powys

Burdens Charitable Foundation 31

Scotland

Balcraig Foundation 11
Hugh Fraser Foundation 99
Gannochy Trust 100
G C Gibson Charitable Trust 107

Jordan Charitable Foundation 154
Lloyds TSB Foundation for Scotland 200
MacRobert Trusts 208
North British Hotel Trust 224
Northern Rock Foundation 226
P F Charitable Trust 237
Robertson Trust 257
Save and Prosper Charities 277
Souter Foundation 290
Underwood Trust 314

Perth

Gannochy Trust 100

Shetland Islands

Shetland Islands Council Charitable Trust 283

Tayside

Northwood Charitable Trust 233

West of Scotland

Mackintosh Foundation 207

Northern Ireland

William Adlington Cadbury Charitable Trust 33
Lloyds TSB Foundation for Northern Ireland 199
John Moores Foundation 217
Northern Ireland Voluntary Trust 225

Overseas general

A W Charitable Trust 1
Achisomoch Aid Company 1
AIM Foundation 2
Al Fayed Charitable Foundation 3
Alglen Ltd 3
Arbib Foundation 6
John Beckwith Charitable Settlement 22
Boltons Trust 24
Barrow Cadbury Trust 34
Charities Aid Foundation 43
Itzchok Meyer Cymerman Trust Ltd 74
John Ellerman Foundation 88
Donald Forrester Trust 99
Glencore Foundation for Education & Welfare 109
Constance Green Foundation 115
M & R Gross Charities 118
Gur Trust 122
Maurice Hatter Foundation 131
Charles Hayward Foundation 131
Jane Hodge Foundation 142
J J Charitable Trust 146
Jerusalem Trust 148
Elton John AIDS Foundation 152
King George's Fund for Sailors 156
Ernest Kleinwort Charitable Trust 163
J W Laing Biblical Scholarship Trust 165
Maurice and Hilda Laing Charitable Trust 165
Maurice Laing Foundation 169
J W Laing Trust 171
Law Society Charity 182
Leverhulme Trust 186
Lewis Family Charitable Trust 187
Lolev Charitable Trust 204
Network Foundation 223
Frances and Augustus Newman Foundation 223
NiKeNo Trust 224
Nuffield Foundation 233
PPP Healthcare Medical Trust 245
Ruben and Elisabeth Rausing Trust 254
Rayne Foundation 255
Sir James Reckitt Charity 255
Rubin Foundation 269
Basil Samuel Charitable Trust 277
Archie Sherman Charitable Trust 283
Shlomo Memorial Fund 284
Stevenson Family's Charitable Trust 297
Bernard Sunley Charitable Foundation 301
Trusthouse Charitable Foundation 310
Tudor Trust 311
John and Lucille van Geest Foundation 315
Bernard Van Leer Foundation (UK) Trust 315
Waterside Trust 318
Wates Foundation 318
Weinstock Fund 320
Wellcome Trust 321
Westminster Foundation for Democracy 323
Will Charitable Trust 328
Woodward Charitable Trust 334

Third world/ developing world

Alchemy Foundation 3
Baring Foundation 14
Burdens Charitable Foundation 31
Audrey & Stanley Burton Charitable Trust 32
William Adlington Cadbury Charitable Trust 33
Edward Cadbury Charitable Trust 34
Charities Advisory Trust 43
Clothworkers' Foundation 59
Diana, Princess of Wales Memorial Fund 77
H C D Memorial Fund 122
Headley Trust 134
Hilden Charitable Fund 139
J G Joffe Charitable Trust 152
Kirby Laing Foundation 168
Beatrice Laing Trust 170
William Leech Charity 183
Leverhulme Trust 186
Linbury Trust 188
Enid Linder Foundation 191
National Lottery Charities Board 221
Parthenon Trust 238
Rowan Charitable Trust 260
Rufford Foundation 270
Alan and Babette Sainsbury Charitable Fund 271
Souter Foundation 290
Spring Harvest Charitable Trust 295
Staples Trust 295

Africa

Ashden Charitable Trust 7
Balcraig Foundation 11
Comic Relief 64
Dulverton Trust 81
Gatsby Charitable Foundation 100
Ruben and Elisabeth Rausing Trust 254
Sir Halley Stewart Trust 297
Zochonis Charitable Trust 335

South Africa

Childwick Trust 47
John Moores Foundation 217
Joseph Rowntree Charitable Trust 261

Americas

Central America

Barbados

Peter Moores Foundation 219

North America

Jordan Charitable Foundation 154
Mayfair Charities Ltd 211
Ruben and Elisabeth Rausing Trust 254

South America

Brazil

Ayrton Senna Foundation 282

Asia

India

Paul Hamlyn Foundation 125

Hong Kong

Bradbury Foundation 26

Japan

Great Britain Sasakawa Foundation 113

Nepal

Jerwood Charitable Foundation 149

South East Asia

Mackintosh Foundation 207

Europe

Henry Moore Foundation 216

Eastern Europe

Charity Know How 46
Headley Trust 134

Ireland

Carnegie United Kingdom Trust 39
Gulbenkian Foundation 118
Rita Lila Howard Foundation 144
Kennedy Charitable Foundation 156
Graham Kirkham Foundation 162
Allen Lane Foundation 176
Northern Ireland Voluntary Trust 225
Joseph Rank Benevolent Trust 250
Joseph Rowntree Charitable Trust 261
H D H Wills 1965 Charitable Trust 329

Portugal

Gulbenkian Foundation 118

Spain

Bernard Sunley Charitable Foundation 301

Middle East

Israel

Balint Family Charitable Trusts 12
Charity Association Manchester Ltd 46
Djanogly Foundation 80
Glencore Foundation for Education & Welfare 109
Ian Karten Charitable Trust 155
Kreitman Foundation 165
Kennedy Leigh Charitable Trust 185
Levy Foundation 187
Mayfair Charities Ltd 211
Porter Foundation 244
Rothschild Foundation 260
J B Rubens Charitable Foundation 269
Samuel Sebba Charitable Trust 282
Sobell Foundation 289
Charles Wolfson Charitable Trust 330
Wolfson Family Charitable Trust 331

Alphabetical index

29th May: The 29th May 1961 Charitable Trust 1

A W: The A W Charitable Trust 1
Achisomoch: Achisomoch Aid Company 1
AIM: The AIM Foundation 2
Al Fayed: The Al Fayed Charitable Foundation 3
Alchemy: The Alchemy Foundation 3
Alglen: Alglen Ltd 3
Allchurches: Allchurches Trust 4
Allen: The H B Allen Charitable Trust 4
Anglian: The Anglian Water Trust Fund 5
Arbib: The Arbib Foundation 6
Architectural: The Architectural Heritage Fund 6
The Art Fund: *see* The National Art Collections Fund (The Art Fund) 220
Artemis: The Artemis Charitable Trust 7
Ashden: The Ashden Charitable Trust 7
Ashdown: The Lord Ashdown Charitable Settlement 9
Awards for All: Awards for All small grants 10
see also The National Lottery (and Awards for All) 221

Baily Thomas: The Baily Thomas Charitable Fund 10
Balcraig: The Balcraig Foundation 11
Balint:
The George Balint Charitable Trust 12
The Andrew Balint Charitable Trust 12
The Balint Family Charitable Trusts 12
Band: The Band Trust 12
Barclay: David and Frederick Barclay Foundation 13
Baring: The Baring Foundation 14
Barnwood: The Barnwood House Trust 17
Baron: Baron Davenport's Charity 76
Barrow Cadbury: *see* Cadbury
BBC: The BBC Children in Need Appeal 19
Beckwith: The John Beckwith Charitable Settlement 22
Bedford: The Bedford Charity 22
Benesco: Benesco Charity Limited 23
Bilton: The Percy Bilton Charity 23
Boltons: The Boltons Trust 24
Booth: The Booth Charities 25
Botnar: The Camelia Botnar Foundation 25
Bradbury: The Bradbury Foundation 26
Bridge House: The Bridge House Estates Trust Fund 26
Burdens: Burdens Charitable Foundation 31
Burton: The Audrey & Stanley Burton Charitable Trust 32

Cadbury:
The William Adlington Cadbury Charitable Trust 33
The Edward Cadbury Charitable Trust 34
The Barrow Cadbury Trust and the Barrow Cadbury Fund 34
CAF: *see* The Charities Aid Foundation 43
Campden: The Campden Charities 38
Carnegie: The Carnegie United Kingdom Trust 39
Cass: Sir John Cass's Foundation 41
Charities:
The Charities Advisory Trust 43
The Charities Aid Foundation 43
Charitworth: Charitworth Limited 45
Charity:
Charity Association Manchester Ltd 46
Charity Know How 46
Charity Projects *see* Comic Relief 64
Children in Need: The BBC Children in Need Appeal 19
Childwick: The Childwick Trust 47
CHK: CHK Charities Limited 48
Church: The Church Urban Fund 49
City: The City Parochial Foundation and the Trust for London 51
Cleveland: Cleveland Community Foundation 56
Clore: The Clore and Duffield Foundations 56
Clothworkers: The Clothworkers' Foundation 59
Cloudesley: Richard Cloudesley's Charity 62
Cohen: The John S Cohen Foundation 63
Colyer-Fergusson: Sir James Colyer-Fergusson's Charitable Trust 63
Comic: Comic Relief 64
Community:
Community Foundation Network 67
The Community Foundation (serving Tyne & Wear and Northumberland) 68
Cook: The Ernest Cook Trust 70
Cripplegate: The Cripplegate Foundation 71
Cripps: The Cripps Foundation 73
Cymerman: Itzchok Meyer Cymerman Trust Ltd 74

D'Oyly Carte: The D'Oyly Carte Charitable Trust 74
Dahl: The Roald Dahl Foundation 75
Davenport: Baron Davenport's Charity 76
Devonshire: The 10th Duke of Devonshire's Charitable Trust 77
Diana: The Diana Princess of Wales Memorial Fund 77
Djanogly: The Djanogly Foundation 80
Drapers: The Drapers' Company Charities 80
Duffield: *see* The Clore and Duffield Foundations 56
Duke: *see* The 10th Duke of Devonshire's Charitable Trust 77
Dulverton: The Dulverton Trust 81
Dunhill: The Dunhill Medical Trust 84

E B M: The E B M Charitable Trust 86
Eastwood: The Sir John Eastwood Foundation 86
Elkington: The Maud Elkington Charitable Trust 87
Ellerman: The John Ellerman Foundation 88
Entindale: Entindale Ltd 91
ENTRUST: *see* Landfill Tax Credit Scheme and ENTRUST 174
Equitable: The Equitable Charitable Trust 91
Eranda: The Eranda Foundation 92
Eveson: The Eveson Charitable Trust 92

Fairbairn: The Esmée Fairbairn Charitable Trust 93
Fishmongers: The Fishmongers' Company's Charitable Trust 98
Forrester: The Donald Forrester Trust 99
Fraser: The Hugh Fraser Foundation 99

Gannochy: The Gannochy Trust 100
Gatsby: The Gatsby Charitable Foundation 100
Gavron: The Robert Gavron Charitable Trust 104
General Estates Charity: *see* Smith's Charity 284
Getty: J Paul Getty Jr Charitable Trust 105
Gibson: The G C Gibson Charitable Trust 107
Glass-House: The Glass-House Trust 108
Glencore: The Glencore Foundation for Education & Welfare 109
Gloucestershire: The Gloucestershire Environmental Trust Company 109
Goldsmiths: The Goldsmiths' Company's Charities 110
Gosling: The Gosling Foundation 111
Grand: The Grand Charity of Freemasons 112
Great: The Great Britain Sasakawa Foundation 113
Greater: Greater Bristol Foundation 114
Green: The Constance Green Foundation 115
Greggs: Greggs Trust 116
Gross: The M & R Gross Charities 118
Gulbenkian: The Gulbenkian Foundation 118
Gur: The Gur Trust 122

H C D: H C D Memorial Fund 122
Hact: Hact (The Housing Associations Charitable Trust) 123
Hadley: The Hadley Trust 124
Hamlyn: The Paul Hamlyn Foundation 125
Hampton: The Hampton Fuel Allotment Charity 127
Harpur Trust: *see* The Bedford Charity 22
Harris: The Philip and Pauline Harris Charitable Trust 129
Harrison: Peter Harrison Foundation 129
Hatter: The Maurice Hatter Foundation 131
Hayward:
The Charles Hayward Foundation 131
The Hayward Foundation 133
The Charles Hayward Trust 134
Headley: The Headley Trust 134
Hedley: The Hedley Foundation 136
Help:
Help a London Child 136
Help the Aged 138
Higgs: Alan Edward Higgs Charity 139
Hilden: The Hilden Charitable Fund 139
Historic: Historic Churches Preservation Trust 141
Hodge: The Jane Hodge Foundation 142
Horne: The Horne Foundation 143
Hospital: The Hospital Saving Association Charitable Trust 143
Housing Associations Charitable Trust: *see* Hact 123
Howard: The Reta Lila Howard Foundation 144
Hunt: The Albert Hunt Trust 144
Huntingdon: The Huntingdon Foundation 145

Isle:
The Isle of Anglesey Charitable Trust 145
Isle of Dogs Community Foundation 146

J J: The J J Charitable Trust 146
James:
John James Bristol Foundation 147
The Dawn James Charitable Foundation 148
Jerusalem: The Jerusalem Trust 148
Jerwood: The Jerwood Charitable Foundation and the Jerwood Foundation 149
Joffe: J G Joffe Charitable Trust 152
John: The Elton John AIDS Foundation 152
Jones: The Jones 1986 Charitable Trust 153
Jordan: The Jordan Charitable Foundation 154

Karten: The Ian Karten Charitable Trust 155
Kendall: The Kay Kendall Leukaemia Fund 155
Kennedy: The Kennedy Charitable Foundation 156
Kensington Estate Charity: *see* Smith's Charity 284
King George: King George's Fund for Sailors 156
King's Fund: The King's Fund (King Edward's Hospital Fund for London) 157
Kinross: The Mary Kinross Charitable Trust 161
Kirkham: The Graham Kirkham Foundation 162
Kleinwort: Ernest Kleinwort Charitable Trust 163
Knott: The Sir James Knott Trust 163
Kreitman: The Kreitman Foundation 165

Laing:
The J W Laing Biblical Scholarship Trust 165
Hilda Laing Charitable Trust *see* Maurice and Hilda Laing Charitable Trust 165
Maurice and Hilda Laing Charitable Trust 165
The Laing Family Foundations 167
The Kirby Laing Foundation 168
The Maurice Laing Foundation 169
The Beatrice Laing Trust 170
The J W Laing Trust 171
Laing's Charitable Trust 172
Lambeth: Lambeth Endowed Charities 172
Lancaster: The John and Rosemary Lancaster Charitable Foundation 173
Landfill: Landfill Tax Credit Scheme and ENTRUST 174
Lane: The Allen Lane Foundation 176
Lankelly: The Lankelly Foundation 178
Law: The Law Society Charity 182
Leathersellers: The Leathersellers' Company Charitable Fund 182
Leech: The William Leech Charity 183
Leeds: The Leeds Hospital Fund Charitable Trust 185
Leigh: The Kennedy Leigh Charitable Trust 185

Leverhulme:
The Leverhulme Trade Charities Trust 186
The Leverhulme Trust 186
Lord Leverhulme's Charitable Trust 187
Levy: The Levy Foundation (formerly the Joseph Levy Charitable Foundation) 187
Lewis: Lewis Family Charitable Trust 188
Linbury: The Linbury Trust 188
Linder: Enid Linder Foundation 191
Livanos: The George John Livanos Charitable Trust 191
Lloyds:
Lloyds TSB Foundation for England and Wales 191
Lloyds TSB Foundation for Northern Ireland 199
Lloyds TSB Foundation for Scotland 200
Lolev: The Lolev Charitable Trust 204
Lord's: The Lord's Taverners 204
Lottery:
see The National Lottery (and Awards for All) 221
The National Lottery Charities Board 221
Lyon: John Lyon's Charity 205

M K: The M K Charitable Trust 206
Mackintosh: The Mackintosh Foundation 207
MacRobert: The MacRobert Trusts 208
Manifold: The Manifold Trust 209
Marshall: The Jim Marshall Charitable Trust 210
Mayfair: Mayfair Charities 211
Medlock: The Medlock Charitable Trust 211
Mental Health: The Mental Health Foundation 212
Mercers: The Mercers' Company Charities 212
Metropolitan: The Metropolitan Hospital–Sunday Fund 214
Monument: The Monument Trust 215
Moore: The Henry Moore Foundation 216
Moores:
The Moores Family Charity Foundation 217
John Moores Foundation 217
The Peter Moores Foundation 219

National Art: The National Art Collections Fund (The Art Fund) 220
National Lottery:
The National Lottery (and Awards for All) 221
(*see also* Awards for All small grants 10)
The National Lottery Charities Board 221
Network: The Network Foundation 223
Newman: The Frances and Augustus Newman Foundation 223
NiKeNo: NiKeNo Trust 224
North: The North British Hotel Trust 224
Northern:
The Northern Ireland Voluntary Trust 225
The Northern Rock Foundation 226
Northwood: The Northwood Charitable Trust 233
Nuffield:
The Nuffield Foundation 233
The Nuffield Trust (formerly the Nuffield Provincial Hospitals Trust) 237

P F: The P F Charitable Trust 237
Parthenon: The Parthenon Trust 238
Peabody: The Peabody Community Fund 238
Peacock: The Peacock Charitable Trust 239
Peel: The Dowager Countess Eleanor Peel Trust 240
Pet Plan: The Pet Plan Charitable Trust 240
Petchey: Jack Petchey Foundation 241
Pilgrim: The Pilgrim Trust 241
Pilkington: The Pilkington Charities Fund 243
Porter: The Porter Foundation 244
PPP: PPP Healthcare Medical Trust 245
Prince: The Prince's Trust 248
Princess of Wales: *see* The Diana Princess of Wales Memorial Fund 77
Pye: Mr and Mrs J A Pye's Charitable Settlement 248

Queen Mary: Queen Mary's Roehampton Trust 250

Rank:
The Joseph Rank Benevolent Trust 250
The Rank Foundation 251
Rausing: The Ruben and Elisabeth Rausing Trust 254
Rayne: The Rayne Foundation 255
Reckitt: The Sir James Reckitt Charity 255
Richmond: The Richmond Parish Lands Charity 256
Robertson: The Robertson Trust 257
Rope: Mrs L D Rope Third Charitable Settlement 258
Rose: The Rose Foundation 259
Rothschild:
The Rothschild Foundation 260
The Jacob Rothschild GAM Charitable Trust 260
Rowan: The Rowan Charitable Trust 260
Rowntree:
The Joseph Rowntree Charitable Trust 261
The Joseph Rowntree Foundation 265
Joseph Rowntree Reform Trust 268
Rubens: The J B Rubens Charitable Foundation 269
Rubin: The Rubin Foundation 269
Rufford: The Rufford Foundation 270

Sackler: The Raymond & Beverley Sackler Foundation 271
Sainsbury:
The Alan and Babette Sainsbury Charitable Fund 271
The Sainsbury Family Charitable Trusts 272
The Robert and Lisa Sainsbury Trust 277
Samuel: Basil Samuel Charitable Trust 277
Save: The Save and Prosper Charities 277
Scott:
The Francis C Scott Charitable Trust 279
Sir Samuel Scott of Yews Trust 281
Sebba: The Samuel Sebba Charitable Trust 282
Senna: The Ayrton Senna Foundation 282
Sherman: The Archie Sherman Charitable Trust 283
Shetland: The Shetland Islands Council Charitable Trust 283
SHINE: Support and Help In Education 284
Shlomo: Shlomo Memorial Fund 284
Smith: Smith's Charity 284
Sobell: The Sobell Foundation 289
Souter: The Souter Foundation 290
South Yorkshire: South Yorkshire Community Foundation 291
Southover: The Southover Manor General Education Trust 292
Spitalfields: The Spitalfields Market Community Trust 292

Sport: Foundation for Sport and the Arts 294
Spring: The Spring Harvest Charitable Trust 295
Staples: The Staples Trust 295
Steel: The Steel Charitable Trust 296
Stevenson: Stevenson Family's Charitable Trust 297
Stewart: The Sir Halley Stewart Trust 297
Stobart: The Stobart Newlands Charitable Trust 299
Street: The W O Street Charitable Foundation 300
Sunley: The Bernard Sunley Charitable Foundation 301
Support and Help In Education: *see* SHINE 284
Sutton:
The Sutton Coldfield Municipal Charities 303
The Sutton Trust 304

Talbot: The Talbot Village Trust 306
Tedworth: The Tedworth Trust 306
Thorn: The Sir Jules Thorn Charitable Trust 307
Three: The Three Guineas Trust 309
Tompkins: The Tompkins Foundation 309
Triangle: The Triangle Trust 309
Trust for London: *see* The City Parochial Foundation and the Trust for London 51
Trusthouse: The Trusthouse Charitable Foundation 310
Tudor: The Tudor Trust 311

Underwood: The Underwood Trust 314

van Geest: John and Lucille van Geest Foundation 315
Van Leer: Bernard Van Leer Foundation (UK) Trust 315
Vardy: The Vardy Foundation 316
Variety: The Variety Club of Great Britain 317

Warburg: Sir Siegmund Warburg's Voluntary Settlement 317
Waterside: The Waterside Trust 318
Wates: The Wates Foundation 318
Weinstock: The Weinstock Fund 320
Wellcome: The Wellcome Trust 321
Welton: The Welton Foundation 322
Westminster:
The Westminster Foundation 322
The Westminster Foundation for Democracy 323
Weston: The Garfield Weston Foundation 324
Whittington: Sir Richard Whittington's Charity 328
Will: The Will Charitable Trust 328
Wills: The H D H Wills 1965 Charitable Trust 329
Wolfson:
The Charles Wolfson Charitable Trust 330
The Wolfson Family Charitable Trust 331
The Wolfson Foundation 332
Woodward: The Woodward Charitable Trust 334

Zochonis: The Zochonis Charitable Trust 335